D1266053

MARINE GEOLOGY OF THE GULF OF CALIFORNIA

Published with the aid of funds furnished jointly by the American Petroleum Institute and The American Association of Petroleum Geologists, the latter fund having been established by the New York committee for the mid-year meeting of the Association, November 1926

Memoir 3

a symposium

Marine Geology of the Gulf of California

Edited by TJEERD H. VAN ANDEL and GEORGE G. SHOR, JR.
Scripps Institution of Oceanography, University of California

Published by The American Association of Petroleum Geologists, Tulsa, Oklahoma, U.S.A., 1964

Published September 1964
Library of Congress Catalog Card No. 64-24367

Composed, Printed, and Bound by The Collegiate Press
GEORGE BANTA COMPANY, INC.
Menasha, Wisconsin

CONTENTS

PREFACE. By *Tjeerd H. van Andel and George G. Shor, Jr.* 1
GEOLOGY OF AREAS BORDERING GULF OF CALIFORNIA. By *Edwin C. Allison* 3
OCEANOGRAPHIC ASPECTS OF GULF OF CALIFORNIA. By *Gunnar I. Roden* 30
BATHYMETRY AND FAULTS OF GULF OF CALIFORNIA. By *Gene A. Rusnak, Robert L. Fisher and Francis P. Shepard* 59
GRAVITY ANOMALIES IN GULF OF CALIFORNIA. By *J.C. Harrison and S.P. Mathur* ... 76
SEISMIC REFRACTION STUDIES IN GULF OF CALIFORNIA. By *Richard P. Phillips* 90
MAGNETIC PROFILES ACROSS GULF OF CALIFORNIA. By *Thomas W.C. Hilde* 122
GEOPHYSICAL FRAMEWORK OF NORTHERN END OF GULF OF CALIFORNIA STRUCTURAL PROVINCE. By *Shawn Biehler, Robert L. Kovach and Clarence R. Allen* 126
STRUCTURAL HISTORY AND EVOLUTION OF GULF OF CALIFORNIA. By *Gene A. Rusnak and Robert L. Fisher* 144
SEA-FLOOR VALLEYS OF GULF OF CALIFORNIA. By *Francis P. Shepard* 157
PLEISTOCENE DELTAIC PROGRADATION OF CONTINENTAL TERRACE, COSTA DE NAYARIT, MEXICO. By *Joseph R. Curray and David G. Moore* 193
RECENT MARINE SEDIMENTS OF GULF OF CALIFORNIA. By *Tjeerd H. van Andel* 216
FACTORS AFFECTING DISTRIBUTION OF LAMINATED DIATOMACEOUS SEDIMENTS IN GULF OF CALIFORNIA. By *Stephen E. Calvert* 311
ZOOGEOGRAPHY AND ECOLOGY OF MACRO-INVERTEBRATES, GULF OF CALIFORNIA AND CONTINENTAL SLOPE OF WESTERN MEXICO. By *Robert H. Parker* 331
PATTERNS OF LIVING BENTHONIC FORAMINIFERA. By *Fred B Phleger* 377
OSTRACODA FROM GULF OF CALIFORNIA. By *F.M. Swain, P.L. Miller, and E.C. Mandelbaum* 395
PRELIMINARY REPORT ON RADIOLARIA IN RECENT SEDIMENTS OF GULF OF CALIFORNIA. By *Richard N. Benson* 398
INDEX 401

CHARTS *In pocket*

SUBMARINE TOPOGRAPHY OF GULF OF CALIFORNIA, By *Rusnak, Fisher, and Shepard.*
SIMPLE BOUGUER ANOMALY MAP OF SALTON TROUGH. By *Biehler, Kovach, and Allen.*
SUBMARINE CANYONS AND TROUGHS AROUND SOUTHERN END OF BAJA CALIFORNIA. By *Shepard.*

PREFACE[1]

TJEERD H. VAN ANDEL[2] AND GEORGE G. SHOR, JR.[2]
La Jolla, California

The Gulf of California, one of the first areas of North America to be explored,[3] has been largely ignored by modern geologists and oceanographers. This neglect, due largely to its inaccessibility by land, is remarkable in view of the great interest of many of its features, and its nearness to centers of geologic research. The structure and origin of long deep basins bordered by continental masses such as this one are not well understood; they are important for the interpretation of many major ancient tectonic features and of the present structure of continents and oceans. The large variations in many factors controlling sedimentation, such as climate, water depth, and type of sediment supply, plus the Gulf's nearly landlocked character and well-defined water circulation, make it a natural laboratory for the study of many aspects of sedimentology and oceanography in which the effects of various factors can ultimately be isolated.

The principal work on the land geology of the Baja California side of the Gulf was published by Beal (1948); the results of two oceanographic expeditions in 1939 and 1940 were summarized in Memoir 43 of the Geological Society of America (Anderson and others, 1950). Since that time only a few papers containing new observations have appeared.

In 1957 a group of marine geologists at Scripps Institution of Oceanography who had been intimately associated with studies of recent sediments in the Gulf of Mexico under the auspices of the American Petroleum Institute turned to the Gulf of California to continue their investigations. At the same time, another group at Scripps and at the Institute of Geophysics of the University of California, who had been studying the structure of the Pacific margin by bathymetric and geophysical means (supported by contracts with the Office of Naval Research), were ready to extend their investigations into the Gulf. A combined program for study of the Gulf of California by all available methods was proposed, and met with considerable enthusiasm from many staff members of Scripps Institution, while a few investigators elsewhere also promised their participation. At approximately the same time, and quite independently, a group from the Seismological Laboratory of the California Institute of Technology commenced geophysical studies of the Salton depression to the north—work which has been extended until the two projects joined. Because of this combination of efforts, the present volume contains far greater emphasis on geophysics and structure than did the earlier volume reporting the results of studies carried out in the Gulf of Mexico under American Petroleum Institute Project 51 (Shepard and others, 1960).

Field work began in 1958, and most of the observations and samples were collected during the *Vermilion Sea Expedition* in the spring of 1959. Since that time additional trips by land and sea have added more data. It was realized early in the planning that existing knowledge of the Gulf was inadequate for the design of many detailed studies, and that regional reconnaissance would have to come first. This volume presents the results of that reconnaissance. Several more detailed studies based on information gained in this work are in progress and will be published elsewhere, including studies by S.E. Calvert on the genesis of laminated diatomites, R.W. Thompson on the tidal flats of the Colorado estuary, R.A. Berner on the sulfur cycle in marine sediments, D.L. Inman and W.R. Gayman on the nearshore dynamics, A.T. Cross on the palynology of marine deposits, and J.R. Curray on portions of the continental shelf and coastal plain.

Nearly all papers in this volume contain the

[1] Manuscript received, June 25, 1963.

[2] Scripps Institution of Oceanography, University of California.

[3] The Gulf of California was circumnavigated in 1539 by Francisco de Ulloa, who named it *Mar Bermejo*, the Vermilion Sea, because of the reddish color of the muddy waters of the Colorado estuary, not, as is often assumed, because of the red plankton blooms of the central region.

results of original and previously unpublished work. Two papers have been written upon request of the editors to provide a general background of regional geology and physical oceanography needed to set the stage for several of the other contributions. The editors owe a considerable debt of gratitude to E.C. Allison and G.I. Roden for their willingness to undertake these tasks.

The investigations have received much benefit from the generous cooperation of Mexican scientists, institutions and authorities; in fact, the studies would have been impossible without it. Among the many, the assistance of Ing. Guillermo P. Salas, Dr. Ricardo Monges Lopes, and Dr. Julian Adem may be mentioned especially. To them and all others, the participants in the investigations express their considerable gratitude.

The primary financial support for the investigations was received from the Office of Naval Research; funds to aid specific projects were provided by the American Petroleum Institute and the National Science Foundation. Specific acknowledgments are made in the individual papers, but the role of the American Petroleum Institute Project 51 deserves special mention, because its interest and encouragement stimulated so strongly the original planning, and its support and advice have been of major influence in many of the investigations. The A.P.I. Project 51 Coordinating Committee, under its chairmen, Hugh A. Bernard, R. Dana Russell, and Howard R. Gould, has provided considerable assistance, and its wholehearted and fruitful cooperation is gratefully acknowledged. The A.P.I.-supported portion of the program was administered by the Institute of Marine Resources, University of California; the O.N.R.-supported part through the Marine Physical Laboratory of the Scripps Institution of Oceanography and the Institute of Geophysics. Tj.H. van Andel directed the operations of Project 51, and served as an informal coordinator of the entire program.

The editorial work on this publication, involving many authors and the need to gather at one specific time the results of many independent studies, was a difficult and sometimes frustrating task. The editors and authors are deeply indebted to Fred B Phleger, who aided with the paleontological papers, to Miss Janet Witte, editorial assistant, who took admirable care of a major portion of the editorial work, and to Robert H. Dott and Miss Norma Ridley, of the headquarters staff of The American Association of Petroleum Geologists, who prepared the index and carried the book through to publication.

The Gulf of California is a rich and varied region and its problems are both interesting and numerous. The studies presented here have answered a few of the questions asked at the outset and raised many more. Comparison of individual papers will show that large areas of insufficient evidence and some of substantial disagreement still exist. Perhaps we may compare the mood of this book to the geological surveys of the American West in the 1870's; authors and editors alike can only hope that it will be of similar consequence.

La Jolla, California
July 1, 1963

REFERENCES

Anderson, C.A., Durham, J.W., Shepard, F.P., Natland, M.L., and Revelle, R.R., 1950, The 1940 E. W. Scripps Cruise to the Gulf of California: Geol. Soc. America Mem. 43.

Beal, C.H., 1948, Reconnaissance of the geology and oil possibilities of Baja California, Mexico: Geol. Soc. America Mem. 31.

Shepard, F.P., Phleger, F.B, and van Andel, Tj.H., editors, 1960, Recent sediments, northwest Gulf of Mexico: Am. Assoc. Petroleum Geologists, Tulsa, Okla.

GEOLOGY OF AREAS BORDERING GULF OF CALIFORNIA[1]

EDWIN C. ALLISON[2]
San Diego, California

ABSTRACT

The Gulf of California is an integral part of the North American Cordilleran segment located between lat 18° and 35° N.—the trans-Mexico volcanic belt of central Mexico and the Transverse Ranges of Southern California, respectively. Distributions of gross rock types and of major structures within these limits exhibit a characteristically Cordilleran north-northwest structural grain. That structural grain appears to have persisted since the Paleozoic Era, although the evidence is obscured by the effects of intense late Mesozoic orogenic disturbances. The Transverse Ranges structural trend, which terminates the Cordilleran segment that includes the Gulf, also appears to have had an ancient geologic history.

The demonstrable history of the Gulf of California begins with the Miocene, although redeposited older marine fossils and Eocene outcrops at the head of the trough in which the Gulf is situated suggest a possible earlier origin as one of the possible explanations for their anomalous occurrences.

Geological information available at present does not permit a definitive choice between several hypotheses for the origin of the Gulf, although recent geophysical work has ruled out the earlier widely accepted graben theory.

INTRODUCTION

The Gulf of California and the adjacent areas which provide a geological context for its discussion represent an unique segment of the North American Cordillera. That descriptive term, Cordillera, was first applied by the Spaniards to the mountain chains along the western margin of South America, but later was expanded by Alexander von Humboldt to include similar features along almost the entire Pacific margin of the New World. Von Humboldt's use of the term Cordillera suggests the broad physiographic unity, a superficial manifestation of the gross geological continuity which links the Gulf of California area with such remote areas as the South American Andes and the Alaska Ranges. Structural instability is its dominant theme. Historically, it is expressed in records of volcanic and seismic activity; geologically, it is revealed in deformed sequences of coarsely clastic sedimentary rocks and in masses of extrusive and intrusive igneous rocks. Geological episodes responsible for these scenes have occurred repeatedly along most of the Cordillera, at least since the early part of the Paleozoic Era.

Principal rock provinces of diverse geological ages occur as bands oriented approximately parallel to the western continental margin of North America. Thin eastern Cordilleran stratigraphic sections, characteristically dominanted by carbonate rocks, blend laterally into much thicker, more coarsely clastic and commonly volcanic western Cordilleran sections of comparable ages. The deformation of western Cordilleran rocks and their disruption by great masses of granitic rocks further emphasize the continued tectonic instability of their sites of deposition. Gross tectonic relationships and general orientations of this principal Cordilleran structural trend appear to have persisted since an early part of the Paleozoic Era.

Secondary structural trends are oriented transversely or obliquely to the gross north-northwestern, or Cordilleran, trend of western North America. These are the "transverse trends" of this discussion. The transverse structures appear to represent relatively ephemeral episodes of faulting and folding which, in the area under discus-

[1] Manuscript received, June 25, 1963.

Discussions of geological problems concerning the Gulf of California with many colleagues have been a rich source of information and inspiration for this paper. The individuals who contributed are too numerous to cite individually. Gordon Gastil of San Diego State College, J. Wyatt Durham of the University of California at Berkeley, and Tjeerd H. van Andel of the Scripps Institution of Oceanography have provided especially valuable assistance in critically reading the manuscript in its various stages of preparation. Miss Janet M. Witte of the Scripps Institution of Oceanography not only has provided most valuable secretarial assistance, but also has assisted in editing and rewriting the manuscript. J.R. Moriarty prepared the final illustrations.

[2] Department of Geology, San Diego State College.

sion, have not imposed decisive changes on the primary Cordilleran trend which they cross. Two such transverse structural trends, one of which appears to have had a long history, delimit the somewhat arbitrarily defined Gulf of California area considered in this summary.

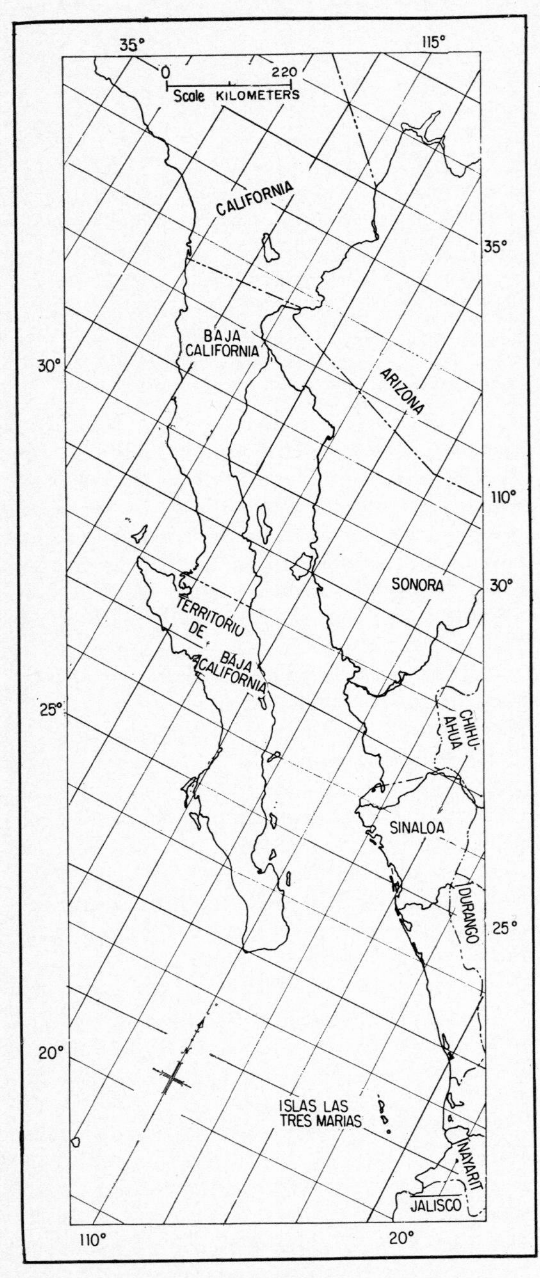

Fig. 1.—Political divisions of northwestern Mexico and Southwestern U.S.A.

The geological history of the elongate, southward-opening trough which is almost completely occupied by the Gulf of California must be related to the history of bordering Cordilleran features. It is in these adjacent areas that geological information can be sought to serve as a basis for an understanding of that uniquely significant feature—a slender oceanic salient, at a continental margin, crossing more than nine degrees of latitude at the present northern boundary of tropical climates and warm seas. Further field work, some of which is reported for the first time in this volume, will contribute a firmer and more provocative basis for geological discussions of the Gulf of California and its history than is attempted through the following pages (Rusnak and Fisher, this volume).

Parts of two states of the United States of America and parts of seven states and one territory of Mexico provide pertinent geological data which must be considered in a discussion of the Gulf of California (Fig. 1). The Gulf is bordered immediately by the Territory and the State of Baja California and by the states of Sonora, Sinaloa, and Nayarit. Adjacent states of Chihuahua, Durango, and Jalisco, south of the International Border, and of California and Arizona north of the Border, provide the additional required geological context.

The submarine geology of the Gulf of California and of adjacent areas of the eastern Pacific Ocean is known mostly from the indirect evidence of bottom topography and geophysical phenomena.

Published results of areal geological investigations around the Gulf of California vary widely in comprehensiveness and refinement. The Gulf is considered especially in Memoir 43 of the Geological Society of America (Anderson and others, 1950). Southern California, Arizona, and New Mexico have been subjected to more intensive and comprehensive study than most adjacent parts of Mexico, but extensive areas and diverse geological topics remain scarcely touched, even on the north side of the Border. Bulletin 170 of the California Division of Mines (Jahns, 1954) provides a modern and thorough treatment of the geology of Southern California, which includes areas bordering the northern and northwestern edges of the Gulf of California trough. The recently prepared geological map of Arizona (Wilson, 1960; Wilson, Moore, and O'Haire, 1960; Arizona Bureau of Mines, 1959; Wilson and Moore, 1958; Wilson and Moore, 1959) and a general summary discussion (Wilson, 1962) with numerous individual reports, contribute richly to the geological knowledge of southern Arizona. Baja California geology is summarized in several works, mostly based on reconnaissance field studies (Beal, 1948; Mina, 1957; Durham and Allison, 1960). Parts of Mexico bordering the east side of the Gulf of California are most inadequately known. This is due in part to the paucity of general field work in these areas and in part to the masking of the older geology by Tertiary volcanic rocks and alluvium. Geological papers of limited scope (Böse and Cavins, 1927; Burckhardt, 1930; R.E. King, 1939), and maps (Mejorada, 1956; Z. de Cserna, 1961) are important. An excellent general summary of North American Cordilleran structure and history is provided by P.B. King (1959). An index chart to formation names is presented in Table I.

GEOLOGICAL SETTING

The segment of the Cordillera which includes the Gulf of California encompasses a number of physiographic provinces (Fig. 2). These provinces exhibit distinct meteorologic and biogeographic characteristics, and generally coincide with areas of well-defined geological characteristics.

Transverse structural trends which delimit this Cordilleran segment include the Transverse Ranges of Southern California and the trans-Mexico volcanic belt, between latitudes 33°–35° N. and 18°–22° N., respectively.

Between these two limits six physiographic provinces (Fig. 2) are to be considered in the discussion of the Gulf of California. They are, from east to west—the Sierra Madre Occidental province and Sonoran Desert-Pacific Coastal Plain province on the east side of the Gulf of California trough, and the Peninsular Ranges province, and Continental Borderland province on the west side of the Gulf of California trough. The Colorado Desert is considered to be a northern, at present emerged, part of the Gulf of California trough.

TABLE I. RELATIONS OF NAMED FORMATIONS AND GROUP

		Transverse Ranges	*Peninsular Ranges*	*Gulf Trough*	*Pacific Coastal Plain Sonoran Desert*
CENOZOIC	NEOGENE	Rincon	San Diego Comondú, Tortugas Isidro, San Gregorio	Truckhaven Rhyolite Imperial	
	PALEOGENE	Vaqueros Sespe Alegria Sierra Blanca Martinez, Anita	Sespe Poway	Maniobra	
MESOZOIC	CRETACEOUS	Jalama	Rosario Valle Salitral ?Eugenia, San Hipólito Alisitos, San Fernando, Santiago Peak Volcanics		
		—Honda, Espada—	—Black Mountain Volcanics—		
	JURASSIC	Franciscan Santa Monica Slates	Bedford Canyon		
	TRIASSIC				Barranca
PALEOZOIC					
PRECAMBRIAN					Apache

TRANSVERSE RANGES STRUCTURAL TREND

The Transverse Ranges are part of an almost continuous band of continental structures and geological discontinuities which interrupt the general north-northwest grain of the middle North American Cordillera. A similarly aligned band of distinctive sea-floor topography and interrupted magnetic anomalies, the Murray fracture zone, is believed to be a westward, oceanic extension of the same structural trend. An east-southeast band of faults and anomalous geology in western Texas has been considered to be an eastern continuation of the same structural trend, called the Texas lineament (Albritton and Smith, 1957). The Transverse Ranges structural trend also delimited distinct provinces during earlier episodes of its geological history.

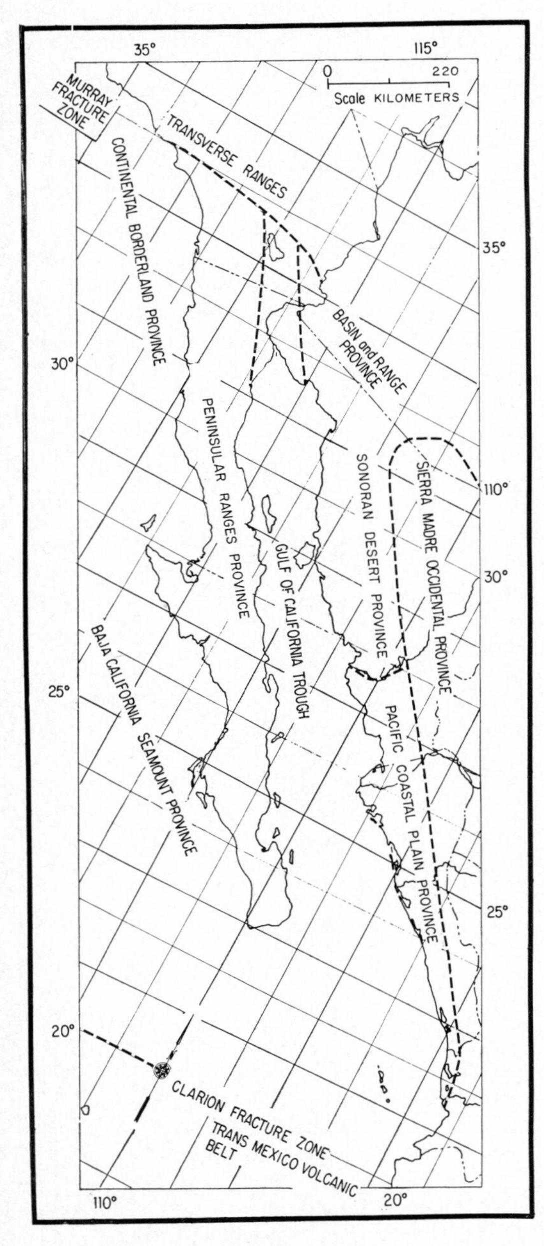

FIG. 2.—Physiographic divisions of areas bordering the Gulf of California.

MURRAY FRACTURE ZONE

Narrow, west-trending submarine ridges and depressions in the Pacific Ocean appear to mark the western sea-floor extent of the structural trend along which the Transverse Ranges lie. This is the Murray fracture zone (Menard, 1955). South of this narrow band of parallel topographic features, the general elevation of the sea floor is about 400 meters higher than the elevation of the sea floor to the north. The two sides of the Murray fracture zone also exhibit contrasting topographic textures—relatively flat and monotonous on the lower north side, irregular and broken by many seamounts on the higher south side. Irregular submarine topography off the Southern California and northwestern Mexico continental margin and south of the Murray fracture zone characterizes the Baja California Seamount province (Menard, 1955).

Patterns of magnetic anomalies, the origins of which are not understood, are disrupted along the Murray fracture zone. Generally north-trending bands of equal magnetic intensity are abruptly terminated along a line coincident with the sea floor topographic expression of that feature (Mason and Raff, 1961). That the Murray fracture zone represents a great fault system cannot be doubted. Vertical separation of several hundred meters along most of the recognized length is indicated by the persistence of higher sea-floor elevations on the south side of the feature. Its extended linearity is comparable to that exhibited by major faults on land, although not necessarily with lateral displacements of great magnitude.

The precise nature, magnitude, and time (or times) of displacement of the two sides of the Murray fracture zone are difficult to assess. Comparisons of linear north-south patterns of magnetic intensity across the feature suggest right-lateral separations of approximately 600 kilometers along its western extent and 150 kilometers along its eastern extent (Raff, 1962). Temporal limits of the displacement, whatever it is, are even more difficult to determine. The ages of the involved rocks are unknown. Erben Guyot (Carsola and Dietz, 1952; Bandy, 1952; Bandy, 1963), a submerged volcanic peak in the Murray fracture zone, with a truncated summit at 410 meters depth and a broad flanking terrace at about 720 meters depth, existed during an early part of the Miocene Epoch. It may owe its origin and subsidence to structural instability along that transverse trend, and therefore indicate an origin for the Murray fracture zone which cannot be younger than early Miocene.

The characteristic topography and patterns of magnetic anomalies of the Murray fracture zone and adjacent sea floor areas are lost in or under features of the Southern California continental margin, but a structural continuity with the similarly aligned Transverse Ranges appears certain. Whether or not the offshore and adjacent California (oceanic and continental) segments of the Transverse Range structural trend have undergone identical and simultaneous movements, however, cannot be proved at this time. Cenozoic movements on major faults of the Transverse Ranges, revealed by predominantly left-lateral separations, would be opposite those postulated for the Murray fracture zone.

Several major features paralleling the edge of the continent are terminated or interrupted in the anomalous strip between the Murray fracture zone and the Transverse Ranges. The block-faulted continental borderland (Emery, 1960, p. 62–96), with its north-northwest-trending topography, which parallels the Southern California and northern Baja California Pacific coast, ends at the Transverse Ranges, and cannot be recognized off the California coast farther north. A relatively steep slope which separates the continental borderland from the sea floor to the west (the Patton Escarpment) is interrupted opposite the Transverse Ranges, but can be recognized to the north (the Santa Lucia Escarpment).

WESTERN TRANSVERSE RANGES

The Transverse Ranges at the western end of this major band of transverse structures have been carefully studied and are the principal topics of abundant geological literature. A summary of Transverse Range geology is published in *Geology of Southern California* (Bailey and Jahns, 1954).

Traceable limits of the Transverse Ranges and of the Garlock fault, a major structure which follows a slightly divergent, yet similarly transverse trend, extend across California from the Channel Islands and Point Conception almost to the Colorado River. A great variety of rock types is encompassed by this band of structures. Late Mesozoic and Cenozoic layered rocks, mostly marine in origin, crop out through most of the western ranges, where they are variously faulted and folded in transverse structures. Older crystalline rocks which dominate outcrops of the eastern ranges are faulted in response to deformational forces similar to the forces which produced western structures.

Major faults in the Transverse Ranges, such as the Garlock fault, exhibit abundant evidence of a left-lateral strike separation, possibly of great magnitude (Dibblee, 1950, p. 54–58; Hill, 1954, Fig. 1; Smith, 1962). This is contrary to the right-lateral strike-slip relationship, postulated for the Murray fracture zone to the west (Mason and Raff, 1961).

A part of the late Mesozoic and Cenozoic structural history of the Transverse Ranges is summarized by Dibblee in his account of their northwestern part (Dibblee, 1954, p. 60–65). The distribution and thinning of Paleogene detrital sedimentary rock units, with their inferred origins and environments of deposition, suggest that the area was bordered on the north by a high area, the San Rafael uplift. At least an early Paleogene origin for the transverse structures is suggested by these relationships. The San Rafael uplift was disrupted and submerged during the Miocene Epoch by clearly identifiable movement on faults of the modern Transverse Ranges. Paleogene erosional-depositional relationships across the Garlock fault, to the east of the area under consideration, suggest a similarly early origin for vertical movement (Smith, 1962, p. 87). Major elevation of a southern block, however, has characterized movement on the Garlock fault, whereas a northern block, the San Rafael uplift, stood higher during Paleogene episodes of the northwestern Transverse Ranges.

Precambrian.—An anorthosite-norite complex in the western San Gabriel Mountains, of probable Precambrian age (Woodford, 1960, p. 401–403), is one of the oldest rock units recognized in the western ranges. Zircon from the norite has yielded a radiometric age of 930 ± 90 million years (Neuerburg and Gottfried, 1954). Gneiss, in which the anorthosite-norite mass is emplaced, must be older. Some of the other diverse crystalline rocks, including metamorphosed units of unidentified origin, are undoubtedly younger.

Jurassic-Early Cretaceous.—The oldest sedimentary rocks known are disturbed sequences of detrital sedimentary rocks, some with interbedded radiolarian cherts and pillow basalts, for which the formational names Honda, Espada, Franciscan (Dibblee, 1950, p. 21–23), and Santa Monica Slates (Woodford and others, 1954) are used locally. The total stratigraphic thickness of rocks represented in these units must be many thousands of meters, but the intricacy of structural complications and the limitations of outcrops prohibit a clear stratigraphic analysis.

Fossils in these older rocks are few, poorly preserved, and scarcely known. Species of the late Mesozoic pelecypod *Buchia* ("*Aucella*" of older literature) are recognized in the Santa Ynez Mountains, where *B. crassicollis* (Keyserling) and *B. piochii* (Gabb) have been reported (Page, Marks, and Walker, 1951, p. 1739; Dibblee, 1954, p. 23). *B. crassicollis* is indicative of the Valanginian Stage of the Lower Cretaceous, and *B. piochii* is indicative of the Portlandian Stage of the Upper Jurassic (Imlay, 1959). Poorly preserved specimens of a slightly older Upper Jurassic *Buchia* species have been recognized in the Santa Monica Mountains (Silberling and others, 1961, p. 1746; Imlay, 1963); that species is compared by Imlay to *B. concentrica* (Sowerby), of late Oxfordian to middle Kimmeridgian age.

The environment of deposition of the *Buchia*-bearing rocks is disputed. A hard substratum in shallow, agitated water has been postulated as a preferred environment (Imlay, 1959, p. 156), but the general lack of other larger invertebrate fossils with *Buchia*, or even in rocks near those in which that genus is abundantly represented, suggests that other factors were effective. Rapid deposition of clastic sediments, possibly in an oxygen-impoverished water mass, also might have provided the environment to which *Buchia* was almost alone adapted. Such an environment can occur at various oceanic depths, depending on local geologic-oceanologic-meteorologic conditions.

Late Cretaceous.—Oldest recognized rocks overlying *Buchia*-bearing strata of the western Transverse Ranges are late Cretaceous in age, but great thicknesses of poorly known intervening strata scarcely demonstrate that a record of depositional continuity is lacking (Page, Marks, and Walker, 1951, p. 1732–1744). *Metaplacenticeras pacificum* (Smith) and *Inoceramus subundatus* (Meek), of the Santa Monica Mountains, are well-known northeastern Pacific representatives of the Campanian Stage (Matsumoto, 1960, p. 68). Adequately known fossils, such as "*Meekia*" *navis* Gabb (Saul and Popenoe, 1962), of the Jalama Formation in the Santa Ynez Range, are probably younger.

Paleogene.—At least 2,500 meters of clastic sedimentary rocks of marine origin compose Paleogene sections of the western Transverse Ranges. Contemporary sections eastward are less predominantly marine (Durham, Jahns, and Savage, 1954; Bailey and Jahns, 1954). Transgressive basal beds of the Paleogene sections characteristically include coarsely detrital rocks, with the distinctive western California and Baja California Paleocene ("Martinez") fauna dominated by *Turritella pachecoensis* Stanton and *Turritella infragranulata* Gabb. The Sierra Blanca Limestone occurs elsewhere directly over the pre-Paleogene rocks (Keenan, 1932). It is commonly a clastic limestone with abundant coralline algae (Howe, 1934) and large Foraminifera (Cole, 1958).

The oldest post-Cretaceous (post-Maestrichtian) Foraminifera now recognized in the Transverse Ranges are of the Ynezian Stage of the California Coast Ranges Tertiary foraminiferal succession (Mallory, 1959, p. 22–29). They occur at the base of the Anita Formation at the western end of the Santa Ynez Range. A rich planktonic assemblage of those same rocks includes *"Globorotalia" pseudomenardii* Bolli (*Globorotalia membranacea auct.*) and other species which are separated by several zones (the Danian Stage equivalents) from highest Cretaceous rocks elsewhere (Bolli, 1957; Berggren, 1960).

Neogene.—A mid-Cenozoic episode of general coastal emergence is recognized in the stratigraphic record as hiatuses, and in the westward attenuation of a widely distributed and locally massive nonmarine detrital sedimentary unit, the Sespe Formation. That formation makes up a decreasingly significant part of the total Cenozoic section toward the western end of the Santa Ynez Range. It is almost entirely replaced by marine deposits west of Gaviota Pass. At its most attenuated extent, the Sespe Formation occupies a stratigraphical position between the Alegria Formation below and the Vaqueros and Rincon Formations above. Benthonic Foraminifera in the upper part of the Alegria Formation (LSJU locality No. 1436 of Kleinpell, 1938) are assigned to the Zemorrian Stage and, according to E.D. Milow (oral communication, January 1963), are accompanied by planktonic Foraminifera considered to be Oligocene in the sense of Eames, Banner, Blow, and Clark (1962). Overlying rocks of the Rincon Formation, separated stratigraphically from the Alegria Formation and the attenuated Sespe Formation by the intervening Vaqueros Formation, contain the widely distributed and distinctive benthonic Foraminifera, *Siphogenerina transversa* Cushman (Kleinpell, 1938, p. 112–113). That species occurs in numerous Central and South American localities with earliest Miocene planktonic Foraminifera—those of the Aquitanian and Burdigalian Stages as defined in the Mediterranean area by Blow (1959), and by Eames and others (1962).

The western Transverse Range sites of deposition for Cenozoic sedimentary rocks with their enclosed fossils appear to have been highly variable, with steep-sided basins contributing to the intricate, stratigraphically and laterally varying pattern of lithologies and faunules. Some basins appear to have persisted for a major part of the Cenozoic Era, whereas others were decidedly ephemeral. Orogenic movements which produced deep coastal basins have occurred almost to the present time, being manifested in such phenomena as the steeply tilted Pleistocene rocks of the Ventura Basin (Bailey and Jahns, 1954, p. 92–93). Cenozoic volcanism was important only during the Miocene Epoch when basic extrusive igneous rocks accumulated over a wide area, including offshore sites. The deposition of marine diatomite, a prominent aspect of Neogene sections on the North American west coast, also took place primarily during the Miocene.

EASTERN TRANSVERSE RANGES

Eastward in the Transverse Ranges, as throughout most of the Cordilleran segment of which the Gulf of California is a part, the effects of a major geological event interrupt the continuity of the late Mesozoic geological record. That is the mid-Jurassic to mid-Cretaceous western Cordilleran (Nevadan) orogeny. The possibility that two distinct events are represented—one Jurassic and the other Cretaceous—must be further explored. Older rocks and earlier geological events are obscured by volcanism, deformation, and emplacement of great batholiths, the results of which now dominate the landscape. Subsequent patterns of faulting, drainage, and sedimentation commonly appear to have been decisively influenced by rocks and structures of that late Mesozoic origin.

A few fossils and radiometric age analyses provide a sparse context within which the ancient geological history of the Transverse Ranges can be considered (Woodford, 1960). Most of the information is derived from areas adjacent to the eastern part of this trend.

Radiometric determinations of granitic rocks indicate Precambrian and late Mesozoic ages of crystallization (Larsen and others, 1958; Woodford, 1960; Silver and McKinney, 1962; Hsu and others, 1963).

Fossils of late Paleozoic age occur in thick carbonate sections of the San Bernardino Mountains (Woodford and Harriss, 1928, p. 270; Guillou, 1953; Merriam, 1954, p. 13–14; Woodford, 1960, p. 403–404). Information concerning Paleozoic and early Mesozoic deposition to the east is so sparse that discussion is scarcely meaningful. Fossiliferous float in the Colorado Desert, at the head of the Gulf of California, may indicate the presence there of not yet demonstrated, eroded remnants of Paleozoic formations. Metamorphosed carbonate and detrital rocks of northeastern Riverside County are identified as Paleozoic deposits of platform environments (Hamilton, 1963).

The relationships of Transverse Range and more southern Paleozoic outcrops with the fairly well-defined rock provinces farther north (McKee, 1951; McKee and others, 1956, 1959; P.B. King, 1959; Eardley, 1962; Dickinson, 1962) cannot be clearly outlined. A transitional band linking relatively stable eastern areas of the Cordillera (characterized by thin carbonate sections) with orogenically active western areas (characterized by thick stratigraphic sections including important clastic and andesitic volcanic units) appears to have extended northeastward and northward from central California. Apparent westward thickenings of Carboniferous sections across Southern California (Hewett, 1954; McKee, 1951) are compatible with, though not necessarily indicative of, a continuous relationship with the similar trend which can be demonstrated farther northward.

Major faults of the eastern Transverse Ranges exhibit left-lateral separation, as do those in the western ranges (Hill, 1954, p. 10).

The Garlock fault, which forms an easterly and slightly northerly divergent continuation of the northern Transverse Range structures, exhibits both left-lateral and vertical separation of great magnitude. A present distribution of distinctive swarms of steeply dipping dikes near its easternmost known traces is believed to indicate about 65 kilometers of left-lateral strike-slip displacement (Smith, 1962). Locally, the south side of the Garlock fault is elevated thousands of meters above adjacent parts of the north side (Hewett, 1954; Jahns and Wright, 1960), and has been subjected to deep erosion. Discrepant appearances of the geology on opposite sides of the fault can be explained, at least in part, by deeper erosion of the elevated block. An almost continuous succession of Paleozoic and early Mesozoic marine deposits is preserved immediately to the north in the Basin and Range province of eastern California and Nevada. Only sparsely distributed fragments of that record remain in the eroded southern, or Mohave Desert, block.

Initial movement along the Garlock fault probably took place no later than during the Paleocene Epoch, as patterns of clastic deposition suggest that an elevated southern block was then already shedding coarse detritus northward. A similarity of pre-batholithic (late Mesozoic) fold trends across the fault is presumed by Hewett (1954, p. 15) to be evidence that the fault had a post-batholithic origin. Movement has continued intermittently almost to the present time.

EASTERN CORDILLERAN TRANSVERSE FEATURES OF ARIZONA, NEW MEXICO, AND TEXAS

Paleozoic rocks of southern Arizona, southern New Mexico, western Texas, and adjacent areas of northern Mexico consist principally of thin carbonate sequences of shallow marine origin. Rare, inadequately studied areas of Paleozoic outcrops in northern Sonora suggest a possible southward thickening, but general conclusions are elusive.

Lower Mesozoic rocks of the same area, along the International Border, are principally of nonmarine origin, thickening westward toward the thick marine sedimentary-volcanic sections of California (McKee and others, 1956, 1959).

A major episode in the geological history of the more easterly areas of the North American Cordillera—the eastern Cordilleran (Laramide) orogeny—appears to have been initiated later than the comparable (Nevadan) event of the western Cordillera. Principal igneous rock masses of southeastern Arizona, New Mexico, and adjacent areas of Mexico are latest Cretaceous and Paleogene in age. Their origin is therefore contemporary to waning stages of the great western Cordilleran (Nevadan) orogeny which, during the Jurassic and Cretaceous Periods, produced similar rocks in southwestern Arizona, California, and other areas along the western continental margin.

A linear and, by inference, a structural relationship of the California Transverse Ranges and/or Garlock fault trend with comparable structures of trans-Pecos Texas has intrigued geologists for more than 50 years (Albritton and Smith, 1957). At the eastern end of this hypothetical structural band, the Texas lineament, discrepant geological scenes are brought into juxtaposition along a series of faults oriented in approximately a west-northwest direction. Left-lateral separation is exhibited by some of those faults.

The continuity of transverse features between California and Texas is insufficient to demonstrate the persistence of a continuous band of structures, but discordant relationships of Cordilleran rocks and structures across the intervening area imply an ancient history for at least parts of that postulated transverse trend. Distributions of Mesozoic rocks, the apparent sources of their clastic detritus, and their probable environments of deposition indicate recurrent activity along such a transverse structural trend since the Triassic Period. A topographically high area appears to have existed south of this trend during the early part of the Mesozoic Period (McKee, 1951; McKee and others, 1956, 1959). Later, an extensive mid-Cretaceous Mexican sea spread northward to approximately the same limit (Imlay, 1944; Stoyanow, 1949), apparently reversing the relative positions of positive and depressed areas.

TRANS-MEXICO VOLCANIC BELT

The trans-Mexico volcanic belt of south-central Mexico, with its westward continuation in the Clarion fracture zone of the eastern Pacific Ocean, forms a southern, somewhat arbitrary limit of the Cordilleran segment which includes the Gulf of California. Its principal expression is in a transverse arrangement of Neogene volcanoes, some of which are active. An aligned and contiguous band of distinctively irregular topography, including the Revilla Gigedo Islands and seamounts of similar volcanic origin, marks the seaward continuation of the trans-Mexico volcanic belt (Menard, 1955, p. 1166–1170; Menard and Fisher, 1958, p. 249; Maldonado-Koerdell, 1958; Richards, 1960).

This transverse structural trend appears to be of less fundamental geological significance than is the approximately parallel Transverse Range trend which forms the northern limit of the area considered here. Volcanism associated with the trans-Mexico belt, characteristically basaltic in nature, is believed to be of Pliocene or later origin (Z. de Cserna, 1961). Older Cordilleran structural trends crossed by this transverse trend, such as those evident in middle Cretaceous rocks, are not significantly disturbed or interrrupted. In contrast, major, geologically persistent differences are exhibited in close proximity on opposite sides of the Transverse Range trend, a feature which appears to have had a prolonged and widely significant geological history.

BAJA CALIFORNIA SEAMOUNT PROVINCE

The eastern Pacific sea floor beyond the continental limits of Southern California and northern Mexico—the Baja California Seamount province (Menard, 1955, p. 1158–1162)—is characterized by an irregular topography. Two of the many seamounts of the province stand above sea level. They are the volcanic Alijos Rocks and Guadalupe Island (Richards, 1958; Johnson, 1953). Others appear to be submerged, as are Fieberling Seamount and Erben Guyot to the north within the bordering Murray fracture zone. Henderson Seamount, with a 400-meter-deep summit, is capped by rounded basaltic debris considered to have been eroded at or near sea level (Menard, 1955).

Cores from a Mohole test site east of Guadalupe Island provide some information about the geology of the Baja California Seamount province. Basalt was encountered beneath 170 meters of Miocene and younger rocks, including dolomitized calcareous ooze (Riedel and others, 1961). Patterns of geomagnetic anomalies in the area are similar to those mapped near the Murray fracture zone—they are oriented approximately parallel to the adjacent continental margin (Krause, 1961).

CONTINENTAL BORDERLAND PROVINCE

The geology of the continental borderland off Southern California is described in a recently published book by Emery (1960). Its southward continuation along the Pacific coast of northern Baja California is treated by Krause (1961).

A distinctive bottom topography of ridges and troughs, elongate approximately parallel to the continental margin except at the northern limit, where the Transverse Range trend is evident, characterizes the sea floor along the coast of Southern California and northern Baja California. This is the Continental Borderland province. The basins are variously filled, depending on their ages and on local rates of sedimentation; their buried equivalents can be recognized slightly inland from the modern coasts of Southern California and northern Baja California.

The Continental Borderland province stands several thousands of meters above the level of the adjacent sea floor of the Baja California Seamount province. Northward, the two provinces are separated by a distinct slope, the Patton Escarpment. Southward, that escarpment is bordered at its base by a trough.

Latitudinal limits of the Continental Borderland province fall at the southern edge of the Transverse Ranges off Southern California (about lat 34° N.) and in the Sebastián Vizcaíno Peninsula area of west-central Baja California (about lat 28° N.). It cannot be recognized farther southward where the continental margin descends directly to the Baja California Seamount province.

The most prominent features of the modern continental borderland appear to have been developed by faulting and folding during the Miocene Epoch (Emery, 1960, p. 88–96). Miocene volcanic rocks are as abundantly evident offshore as they are in adjacent parts of Southern California and Baja California. More recent structural modifications are apparent in such anomalously elevated marine Pliocene and Pleistocene deposits as occur on San Clemente Island and in the Palos Verdes Hills of Southern California.

Pre-Miocene records of deep basins along the continental margin, similar to those which characterize the Continental Borderland province at present, are obscure. Brief lateral extents of detrital sedimentary rock units, with the relative water-depth implications provided by their enclosed fossils and accompanying sedimentary structures suggestive of steep depositional slopes, are uncertain evidence of Upper Cretaceous and Paleogene coastal basins similar to those which now distinguish the province. The geometry and history of those probable older basins are generally unknown.

PENINSULAR RANGES PROVINCE

Baja California, the 1,300-kilometer-long peninsula which forms almost the entire Peninsular Ranges province, is a physiographic, oceanographic, and geologic barrier separating the Gulf of California from the eastern Pacific. Its origin and history are of greatest significance in a discussion of the Gulf. Northward, the Peninsular Ranges extend beyond the northern latitude of the Gulf of California, although not beyond the structural trough in which the Gulf lies. Both the Gulf of California trough and the Peninsular Ranges are abruptly truncated against the Transverse Ranges in Southern California.

Late Mesozoic granitic rocks, collectively termed the Peninsular Range batholith (Jahns, 1954), and variously metamorphosed older rocks form principal elevations of the northern part of the Peninsular Ranges province. Similar granitic rocks at the southern end of the Baja California Peninsula, in the Sierra Victoria, and at Cape San Lucas, are considered to be closely related (Hammond, 1954, p. 66; Wisser, 1954, p. 50). Radiometric determinations of the Peninsular Range plutons indicate ages comparable to those of plutons of other North American western Cordillera areas—the range is from about 92 to 115 million years old, depending on the rock sampled and the analytical method exploited (Larsen and others, 1958; Curtis and others, 1958).

The effects of the emplacement of the plutons and of the immediately preceding massive volcanism generally obscure the pre-batholithic geological history of the Peninsular Ranges province. Geological studies of a few exposures of older rocks provide sparse evidence for parts of that history.

Precambrian and Paleozoic.—Oldest rocks are recognized by scattered bits of information derived from work in northern parts of the province. Precambrian detrital zircons have been recovered from Mesozoic and possibly older rocks (Bushee, 1962), but their derivation is unknown. Diverse metamorphic rocks which occur widely, particularly at higher elevations, may be of any age older than the late Mesozoic time of emplacement of associated plutons. Poorly preserved and scarcely diagnostic fossils in erratics suggest the erosion, somewhere, of rocks of Paleozoic marine origin.

Early Mesozoic.—Triassic rocks are tentatively identified in one area. An impression of an ammonoid cephalopod collected from the Julian Schist of central San Diego County was considered by J.P. Smith to represent a Triassic form (Hudson, 1922, p. 190). No other fossils have been collected in that area.

Fossiliferous Jurassic rocks are recognized in two southwestern California areas—the Santa Ana Mountains and western San Diego County. Marine invertebrate fossils appear to occur through a thick stratigraphic section, having been found at localities representative of Middle and Upper Jurassic stages. Brachiopods from one part of the heterogeneous Bedford Canyon Formation of the Santa Ana Mountains were determined by D.V. Ager to be of an undescribed genus intermediate in form between known Upper Triassic and Lower Cretaceous genera (Silberling and others, 1961, p. 1748). Other fossils from the same nominal formation are Jurassic in age, but the rocks from which they were collected are so intricately deformed and inadequately exposed that general stratigraphic relationships through the formation cannot be determined now. According to an unpublished U. S. Geological Survey report by R.W. Imlay, dated April 13, 1961, the fossils include a Bajocian ammonoid. Callovian ammonoids and pelecypods are recognized in fossil collections from another locality in the same area (Imlay, 1963) which was once thought to provide evidence for the frequently cited Triassic age for the entire Bedford Canyon Formation.

Belemnoid cephalopods and bivalves of the genus *Buchia* occur at several localities in western San Diego County (Milow, 1961, p. 40).

Lithologies of these demonstrably Jurassic rocks are varied. Middle Jurassic rocks and a large part of the Bedford Canyon Formation of the Santa Ana Mountains, are dominantly argillaceous siltstones, in part thinly laminated, with interbedded graywacke sandstones and sparse, dark, fossiliferous limestones (Woodford, 1960, p. 405; Gray, 1961, p. 11–12). Upper Jurassic rocks of western San Diego County are in part more coarsely clastic, with massive breccia and conglomerate units. Their source is unknown.

Early Cretaceous.—Youngest rocks intruded by the Peninsular Range batholith are Aptian and possibly younger. No post-Jurassic and pre-Aptian rocks are recognized, although possible areas of outcrop can scarcely be considered as geologically explored. An abundantly fossiliferous section of Lower Cretaceous pre-batholithic rocks, the Alisitos Formation, occurs in the northwestern part of Baja California (Santillán and Berrera, 1930; Allison, 1955; Allen and others, 1961). It consists of more than 5,000 meters, possibly twice that thickness, of predominantly andesitic pyroclastic rocks and immediately derived sedimentary rocks. The lower part of the section is commonly siliceous, finely clastic, and thinly bedded, with Aptian ammonoids and other invertebrates representative of sand- to mud-bottom communities. Higher parts of the section are generally more coarsely pyroclastic and epiclastic, apparently derived from a near volcanic source. Fossils from the upper part of the section are much more abundant and diverse, and include a rich representation of Aptian pantropical hermatypic coral and pachydontid bivalve reef ("Urgonian") faunas. Species known from California and more northern areas of outcropping Aptian and Albian rocks are scarce in Alisitos faunas. Uppermost strata of the Alisitos Formation in its type area, with a rich Ostracoda fauna of uncertain temporal significance, are of nonmarine origin. A specimen of the ammonoid *Douvilleiceras*, identified by J.B. Reeside, Jr. as close to *D. mammillatum* (Schlotheim), has been collected in the same general area of northwestern Baja California (Larsen and others, 1958, p. 46) and is indicative of Alisitos rocks slightly younger (Albian) than those of the type area of the formation. The regional mapping and stratigraphic studies which will reveal the temporal extent and characteristics of pre-batholithic rocks in the Peninsular Ranges have not progressed beyond initial stages.

Rocks similar to those just described can be traced southward to almost the center of the Baja California Peninsula. Briefly studied exposures have been recognized for many years near the site of the old Dominican Mission of San Fernando, about 325 kilometers south of the northern boundary of Baja California. That is the type locality for the San Fernando Formation (Anon., 1924; Beal, 1948). The distinct lithological and paleontological similarities of the San Fernando and Alisitos Formations, in their type areas, with the almost continuous outcrop of comparable rocks in intervening areas, require that the earlier but repeatedly preoccupied name, "San Fernando," be dropped in favor of Santillán and Berrera's incontrovertible name, Alisitos.

Similar, probably equivalent units of Southern California, apparently with identical structural-stratigraphical relationships, are the Santiago Peak Volcanics of the Santa Ana Mountains (Larsen, 1948, p. 22–30; Woodford, 1960, p. 406–407) and part of the Black Mountain Volcanics of San Diego County (M.A. Hanna, 1926, p. 199–204; Larsen, 1948, p. 20–32; Milow, 1961). No significant fossils have been found, however, in these rocks of the northernmost Peninsular Ranges.

Metamorphic rocks exposed locally along the eastern side of the Peninsular Ranges are probably of various origins. They are at least in part Early Cretaceous and possibly originally comparable to the Alisitos Formation along the western slope. Radiometric determinations of zircons from gneiss on the eastern slope of the northernmost Peninsular Ranges indicate ages of 105–110 million years (Bushee and others, 1963).

Late Mesozoic of southern Baja California.—Oldest identified rocks south of the widely distributed and approximately contiguous Alisitos Formation outcrops of northwestern Baja California occur in the Sebastián Vizcaíno Peninsula-Cedros Island area of west-central Baja California, immediately south of the political boundary between the State and Territory of Baja California. Middle Cretaceous and Upper Cretaceous ammonoids occur there with other mollusks, Foraminifera, and Radiolaria, in thick but structurally isolated sequences of argillaceous siltstones, sandstones, and conglomerates. Other units of probable Jurassic and Cretaceous ages, possibly in part equivalent to those identified by paleontological evidence, occur in the same general Baja California area. A system of great northwest-trending faults so divides the area into discontinuous strips (McIntyre and Shelton, 1957) that the total stratigraphic sequence cannot be defined, nor can the relationships of the diverse rock units be determined. The total thickness of the Mesozoic section of the Sebastián Vizcaíno Peninsula area is probably many thousands of meters.

All of the identified Cretaceous fossils, including silicified logs, come from rocks mapped as the Valle Salitral Formation by Mina (1956, p. 17–18; 1957, p. 159–162). They include the uppermost Albian or lowermost Cenomanian ammonoids *Mariella* (Allison, 1957) and *Graysonites* (Matsumoto, 1959a, p. 69–70) with Foraminifera of comparable temporal significance, and the Campanian ammonoid *Submortoniceras* (Mina, 1957, p. 162). Younger Upper Cretaceous rocks are suggested by the identification of the planktonic Foraminifera *Pseudotextularia* in Valle Salitral Formation outcrops (Mina, 1957, p. 162). No Paleogene rocks are known. Marine deposition in this area thus appears to have persisted for at least part of the interval represented by the unconformity separating Lower Cretaceous and uppermost Cretaceous rocks of the principal Peninsular Ranges.

Two other marine units described by Mina (1957, p. 154–159) in west-central Baja California are the San Hipólito Formation and the Eugenia Formation. Neither has produced definitive fossils, but both appear to be late Mesozoic on the basis of their structural relationships to the Valle Salitral Formation and lithologic similarities to rocks of the westernmost Cordillera of North America which are known to be Jurassic and Cretaceous in age. The San Hipólito Formation is characterized by chert and pillow basalt, which give to it a distinctly Franciscan-like aspect.

Crystalline rocks of the west-central Baja California, other than the basalts just noted, are predominantly ultramafic and widely serpentinized (Beal, 1948, p. 36–37; Mina, 1957). They are distinctly different from crystalline rocks of the major Peninsular Range batholith.

The association of ultramafic crystalline rocks, serpentines, and Franciscan-like sedimentary-volcanic rocks of the Sebastián Vizcaíno Peninsula area is reported in several other locations along the westernmost margin of Baja California and on offshore islands. From north to south, they are—San Geronimo Island at about lat 30° N. (G.D. Hanna, 1927), San Benito Islands (Condie and others, 1963), Cedros Island (G.D. Hanna, 1925, p. 268), San Roque and Asuncion Islands (G.D. Hanna, 1927), and the western border of Bahia Magdalena (Hirschi and De Quervain,

1933). This distribution, with the occurrence of similar rocks farther north in the western Transverse Ranges, suggests an upper Mesozoic, Franciscan-like rock province bordering the area under consideration. Detritus from this rock province occurs locally east of its known limits (Woodford, 1925).

Crystalline rocks of the southern tip of Baja California, of the Sierra de Victoria, are similar and almost certainly closely related to those of the more northern Peninsular Ranges. A more or less continuous distribution of granitic rocks can be recognized by sparse outcrops and in subsurface data in the intermediate area of the eastern part of the southern Baja California Territory and in the western Gulf of California (Mina, 1957). The nature of the pre-batholithic rocks in that area, however, is poorly known. Some of the rocks in which the batholith appears to have have been emplaced are only weakly metamorphosed. Near Todos Santos they have been reported by Robert Dietz (oral communication, April 1963) to be "eugeosynclinal" in aspect and to consist of thinly bedded detrital sedimentary rocks with chert. Neither Dietz nor Wisser (1954, p. 50) has recognized volcanic rocks or their metamorphosed equivalents among these older rocks of southernmost Baja California.

Major structural trends in pre-batholithic rocks are indistinctly related to the north-northwest Cordilleran trend of the Peninsular Ranges. This is the general trend of the Peninsula of Baja California and its foundation, the Peninsular Range batholith. Older structural trends can be recognized locally which appear to have been cut obliquely by the irregular western margin of the batholith. One such area is located in the northwestern part of Baja California, where great folds, involving thousands of meters of Alisitos strata, have axes oriented approximately in a northwesterly direction. The Agua Blanca fault follows the same general northwesterly trend across the Peninsular Ranges (Allen and others, 1960) and may derive its orientation, at least in its western sectors, from pre-batholithic structures. Oblique and transverse trends of older rocks are suggested also by structures in other northern Peninsular Range areas which are less adequately known.

The complex fault pattern of the Sebastián Vizcaíno Peninsula area and of related offshore areas follows a similarly oblique northwest trend, but the antiquity of movement along those faults is unknown. Miocene or earlier movement can be recognized, but not defined, by what is now known of the geology of that area.

A great hiatus interrupts the Cretaceous stratigraphic record in the northwestern parts of the Peninsular Range province. The major deformation of the Alisitos and comparable Lower Cretaceous rock units, and the emplacement of principal plutons of the Peninsular Range batholith took place during the interval represented by that break in the record. Oldest Cretaceous rocks overlying the unconformity are those of the Santa Monica and Santa Ana Mountains which carry Turonian ammonoids (Popenoe and others, 1960, p. 1511–1519). Structurally less disturbed Upper Cretaceous rocks exposed along the Pacific coast of northern Baja California—the Rosario Formation—appear to be no older than Campanian (Durham and Allison, 1960, p. 48–51; Kilmer, 1961) and locally are as young as Maestrichtian (Milow, 1961, p. 35).

Late Cretaceous.—The coastal topography over and against which detrital materials of the Rosario Formation were deposited appears to have been remarkably similar to the modern topography. That coincidence is the result of preservation which is believed to be attributable partly to late Cretaceous burial and late Cenozoic exhumation, and partly to weakness of erosive forces in an arid climate affecting a stable and persistently emergent coastal area. Minor headlands on the Pacific shore of northern Baja California, such as Punta China (Allison, 1955; Allen and others, 1961 p. 62–64) existed during the late Cretaceous, when they exercised an influence on the nature of Rosario deposits comparable to that observable in modern sediments adjacent to the same coastal irregularities. Major limestone units of the Alisitos Formation stood as prominent topographic features near the late Cretaceous coastline as they do today—a phenomenon which is explained only with great difficulty unless continuously arid Cretaceous to Recent local climates can be assumed. Stratigraphically and topographically highest undisturbed beds of the Rosario Formation locally trail eastward, as scarcely lithified sandstone-conglomerate veneers, over eroded edges of steeply dipping Alisitos strata and across major coastal terraces. Those terraces may have been modified through the Cenozoic Era, but must have been eroded initially during the Cretaceous Period. A lack of evidence for significant post-Cretaceous submersion of the apparently stable coastal segments where these older features are evident suggests that the present great width of the terraces may be a result of pedimentation acting on a feature initially cut at sea level.

Late Cretaceous environments of deposition represented within the northern Peninsular Range area of Campanian-Maestrichtian outcrops were as variable as the modern environments which can be studied now along the same coastal area. The stratigraphic alternation and lateral transition of marine and nonmarine clastic units near El Rosario (Kilmer, 1961), the northwestern Baja California town from which the Rosario Formation takes its name, is evidence of fluctuating shorelines. Lateral and vertical successions of marine faunules culminate locally, in other coastal areas of Baja California, in probable bathyal associations of Foraminifera and mollusks. Nearshore accumulations of coarsely clastic late Cretaceous detritus grade laterally into more finely clastic deposits, apparently representative of more sheltered sites of deposition. Hermatypic corals and other invertebrates of comparable climatic (tropical) and bathymetric (depth less than 90 meters) implications are common locally.

Upper Cretaceous rocks are not exposed at the surface of Baja California south of the Vizcaíno Peninsula area, but are reported in exploratory oil wells. Foraminifera from two central Baja California wells, the San Angel No. 1 and the Pozo Iray No. 2 (Mina, 1957, p. 243–261), suggest a distribution of late Cretaceous seas across most of the southern half of the Peninsula. At the southernmost extreme, the Cape San Lucas area was probably emergent during the late Cretaceous, as it was during most of the Cenozoic Era. No Upper Cretaceous rocks are known there.

Paleogene.—The distribution of Paleogene rocks is generally similar to the distribution of the Upper Cretaceous Rosario Formation along the west margin of northern Baja California. Rapid deposition in a similar diversity of environments also is evident. Characteristic Paleogene sequences include post-Danian Paleocene clastic marine deposits overlying (commonly with only slight angular discordance) Maestrichtian or older Cretaceous rocks. Nowhere is an uninterrupted depositional continuity demonstrated between known Cretaceous and Paleogene sections.

Paleocene rocks of the northern Peninsular Ranges are commonly overlain by at least as widely distributed lower and middle Eocene rocks. Youngest recognized Paleogene marine deposits, those of the Poway Formation of the San Diego area, contain Foraminifera indicative of the Narizian Stage, considered to represent the upper Eocene in the California chronology (Mallory, 1959). Planktonic species from the same rocks suggest a synchronization with the faunas designated as middle Eocene in the Gulf of Mexico-Caribbean region (Milow, 1961, p. 30–32).

Paleogene rocks of southern Baja California (Durham and Allison, 1960, p. 52) are sparsely represented in surface exposures but are widely recognized in exploratory holes (Mina, 1957, p. 162–165, 184–188). Their apparent distribution across the southern part of the Baja California Peninsula indicates general submergence during at least Paleocene and early Eocene Epochs. Lithologies and microfossils of these rocks commonly suggest relatively slow rates of deposition in moderately shallow and broadly continuous marine environments, isolated from major sources of coarse clastic debris. Characteristic rocks include mudstones in which planktonic Foraminifera are exceedingly abundant. The general aspect of slow deposition of these southern Paleocene and Eocene rocks provides a marked contrast to the appearance of contemporary coarsely detrital rocks exposed along the Pacific coast of northern Baja California and Southern California.

An anomalous northern occurrence of characteristic southern Baja California Paleogene rocks on the eastern shore of Sebastián Vizcaíno Bay is probably a result of strike-slip faulting, possibly of a major relative displacement of the western block northward. Richly fossiliferous lower Eocene mudstone occurs there, in Santa

Rosalía Bay, in exposures of severely disrupted strata immediately adjacent to (west of) a large area covered by flat-lying, coarsely clastic, Paleocene and Pliocene rocks of nearshore origin. The juxtaposition of such temporally, lithologically, and environmentally discrepant Cenozoic sections appears to lack more satisfactory explanations.

No marine record of the Oligocene Epoch (in the sense of Eames and others, 1962) is recognized in the province, although nonmarine deposits (including those of the Sespe Formation in Southern California) may represent at least part of that interval.

Neogene.—Oldest Neogene rocks (lowest Miocene or Aquitanian equivalents) of the Peninsular Range province include sandstone with remains of the distinctive and important marine mammal *Cornwallius* (Vanderhoof, 1942; Durham, 1950a, p. 34–36; Reinhart, 1959, p. 98–99) which crops out on the eastern shore of Baja California, about 125 kilometers north of La Paz (Anderson, 1950, p. 14, Fig. 3). Argillaceous rocks with interbedded dark chert, stratigraphically overlying the *Cornwallius*-bearing sandstone, are comparable to those of the San Gregorio Formation (Anon., 1924, p. 43), stratigraphically the lowest Neogene unit recognized elsewhere on the Baja California Peninsula. The San Gregorio Formation in its type locality near the village of La Purisima, which is located near the center of the Peninsula, southwest of Bahía de la Concepción, is overlain by abundantly fossiliferous sandstone that carries gastropods of the family Turritellidae with chronologic implications similar to those of *Cornwallius* (Durham and Allison, 1960, p. 56). That fossiliferous unit represents at least part of Heim's Isidro Formation (Heim, 1922, p. 539–541; Beal, 1948, p. 56–74).

The relationships of these formations with other, generally younger, Miocene rocks of Baja California are rarely demonstrable. The large number of formational terms evident in the relatively sparse descriptive literature reflects this situation (Durham and Allison, 1960, p. 56–58, Table 3). The San Gregorio, Isidro, and other Miocene formations of marine origin recognized in southern Baja California are generally covered by massive volcanic and related rocks of the Comondú Formation (Heim, 1922, p. 542–543; Beal, 1948, p. 74–77, 113–114; Wilson and Rocha, 1955, p. 54; Mina, 1957, p. 177–178, 203–206). They are exposed generally in the bottoms of the deepest arroyos which have been cut through the resistant Comondú volcanics. Elsewhere, the pre-Comondú Miocene rocks are known in structurally complicated areas and from submarine outcrops.

Outcrops of Miocene rocks in the Cedros Island-Sebastián Vizcaíno Peninsula area of west-central Baja California are fragmented and isolated by the northwest-trending faults noted previously (Mina, 1957, p. 175–177; Durham and Allison, 1960, p. 58). The Tortugas Formation there, like the San Gregorio Formation exposed to the southeast, is characterized by cherts and diatomaceous rocks comparable to those of the well-known Monterey Formation of California. Their age, like that of most of the type Monterey, is middle Miocene (Luisian, by the California "Middle Tertiary" chronology of Kleinpell, 1938). Tortugas Formation materials appear to have been deposited in relatively shallow basins formed by faults off the Miocene shore of Baja California and possibly bounded by islands. Nothing in the abundant microfossil assemblages of the formation suggests that depositional environments were comparable in depths to those of modern and past continental borderland basins of northern Baja California and Southern California. Biogeographical implications of the megafossils of the Tortugas Formation indicate conditions that were less tropical and less like those in the Gulf of California than is suggested by the inadequately known megafossil assemblages of the Isidro Formation and other units of inland Baja California areas.

Monterey-like diatomaceous rocks occur also on the Tres Marías Islands, southeast of Baja California, near the coast of Nayarit (G.D. Hanna, 1926b, p. 66–76; Hertlein and Emerson, 1959, p. 3–4).

Northward, off the Pacific coasts of northern Baja California and southernmost California, the Miocene shore appears to have been located west of the modern shore. Miocene rocks, mostly representative of the Luisian and Mohnian Stages, crop out on coastal islands and on the sea floor at the edge of the continent (Walton, 1955, p. 999;

Emery and others, 1952; Emery, 1960, p. 67–68, Fig. 62).

Thick and widely distributed volcanic and related rocks of the Comondú Formation (Heim, 1922) form one of the most widespread and prominent lithogenetic elements of the geology of the Peninsular Ranges. The formation consists largely of andesitic volcanic, pyroclastic, and related epiclastic rocks. Over the southern part of the Baja California Peninsula, where these rocks dominate the landscape and mask most older rocks, the volcanism appears to have taken place on land or in marginal marine environments adjacent to a generally emerging peninsula. Along both Pacific and Gulf of California coasts of northern Baja California and Southern California, persistently elevated since at least the mid-Cretaceous, volcanic sequences similar to those of the Comondú Formation were deposited above sea level, beyond the limits of contemporary shorelines (Hertlein and Allison, 1959, p. 17–19).

Temporal limits of such volcanic suites do not necessarily coincide through their entire distribution, although volcanism was a characteristic part of the Miocene history of the Cordilleran segment of which the Gulf of California is a part. Evidence for earlier Cenozoic volcanism is sparse. Post-Miocene volcanism can be demonstrated in scattered Pliocene-Pleistocene ash deposits, notably in the northwesternmost part of the Peninsular Range province, but significant eruptions appear to have been restricted to a few spots, such as east-central Baja California. There, the Tres Virgenes volcano has remained active into historic times (Ives, 1962). The areal extent and duration of at least partly contemporary and related volcanism of the continental borderland are poorly understood.

Sources for the principal masses of Comondú volcanics appear to have been located along the western margin of the Baja California Peninsula (Anderson, 1950, p. 47–48; Wilson and Rocha, 1955, p. 21). Similar rocks, probably with similar ages, in the northern part of the province must have originated from widely scattered sources on both sides of the Peninsula. Western (offshore) and eastern (Mexican mainland) volcanics, which are compared lithologically and chronologically with the Comondú volcanics, are not contiguous to southern Baja California rocks and appear to have distantly separated sources.

The presence of rocks and fossils corresponding to the interval upper Miocene through lower Pliocene is not clearly demonstrated in Baja California. Such transitional rocks have been identified in the extreme northwestern part of the Peninsular Range province, but their sites of deposition were probably more characteristic of the continental borderland than of the Peninsular Ranges. Middle Miocene rocks (the Topanga Formation of Kew, 1923) of the area adjacent to the Los Angeles basin are representative of shallow-marine environments of deposition (Loel and Corey, 1932, p. 51–61). Fossil assemblages of stratigraphically higher rocks suggest associations which lived in deeper water, outlining a history of gradually deepening (subsiding) basins which culminated during the early part of the Pliocene Epoch (Natland and Rothwell, 1954; White, 1956). Later Pliocene deposition in that area took place in shallowing (filling) sedimentary basins.

Post-Miocene detrital rocks of shallow marine origin occur generally, though not continuously, along both Pacific and Gulf of California coasts of the Peninsular Range province. The Gulf of California, during at least part of that interval, extended northward to the latitude of the Transverse Ranges, in the vicinity of San Gorgonio Pass (Allen, 1957, p. 327–328).

The distribution of shallow-water faunules in these post-Miocene deposits outlines gross patterns of shifting cooler-water (Californian) to warmer-water (Panamanian) biogeographical gradients of varying magnitudes (Valentine, 1955, 1961). Miocene and older distributions are obscured by a scarcity of data but could not be expected to show comparable biogeographical distinctions, as the entire province was more nearly tropical due to more northward locations of critical isotherms (Durham, 1950b).

Complicating minor distributional patterns of post-Miocene faunules are caused by an unusually decisive combination of physical factors, which are—coastal configuration, nearshore bottom topography, meteorology, and oceanic currents. Their effects are especially manifested in modern, and presumably past, nearshore water temperatures which exhibit discontinuous patches of anomalously warm water in protected bays and anomalously cool (upwelling) water on the lee sides of exposed headlands. That contrast is clearly revealed along the Pacific coast of southern Baja California. Water sufficiently warm to support an impoverished Panamanian molluskan fauna occurs within Laguna Ojo de Liebre, adjoining Bahia de Sebastían Vizcaíno (Phleger and Ewing, 1962). Farther south, in Bahia de San Cristóbal, surface water temperatures are more nearly related to those of Southern California than those of much nearer Baja California areas (Emery and others, 1957).

The precise correlation of non-contiguous post-Miocene rocks and fossil assemblages on the two sides of the Peninsular Ranges province is at present difficult. The transitional faunas of intervening areas, particularly those of southwestern Baja California, have not been adequately investigated. Extraordinary occurrences of certain relatively well-known fossil groups, however, provide a means of tentatively synchronizing faunal successions of southwestern California with those of southeastern Baja California and of areas at the head of the Gulf of California. Specimens of the warm-water echinoid, *Encope tenuis* Kew, in the San Diego Formation of Southern California (Hertlein and Grant, 1960, p. 125–127), a standard unit for the Pliocene of the California marine invertebrate chronology, suggest an equivalency of that formation with the Imperial Formation in the northern Gulf trough. A correlation of at least a major part of the Imperial Formation with the lowest units of the tripartite divisions of southeastern Baja California "Pliocene" sections (Durham, 1950a; Wilson and Rocha, 1955, p. 33–39) is suggested by Durham (1950a, p. 23–25). Major evaporite deposits occur within or at the bases of the lower units of these sections.

Controversy concerning the Pliocene-Pleistocene boundary in the California-Baja California area may involve all of these units conventionally referred to as Pliocene. If that boundary is to be drawn at the base of the Mediterranean Calabrian (marine)-Villafranchian (nonmarine) strata, as was decided by vote of the 1948 International Geological Congress (Woodring, 1962; Durham and others, 1954, p. 69; Valentine, 1961, p. 422–428), the standard San Diego Formation is more likely Pleistocene than Pliocene. A tooth of a horse from a relatively low stratigraphic position in that formation belongs to the genus *Equus* s. l., which is characteristic of the Blancan in the North American terrestrial vertebrate chronology. Remains of comparable horses of western European sections occur in rocks which, by I.G.C. decree, belong to the post-Pliocene Series.

Implications of water temperature of San Diego Formation invertebrate assemblages vary widely, suggesting surface temperatures both cooler and warmer than those indicated by local undisputed Pleistocene and Holocene assemblages of otherwise similar ecological requirements. Coolest water assemblages occur low within San Diego Formation sections and suggest an early cooling of marine climates. At least part of the San Diego Formation thus may be Pleistocene, on the basis of paleoclimatologic criteria.

Marine invertebrates from rocks overlying the San Diego Formation, or from those believed to be of an equivalent age, occur in numerous coastal areas of the Peninsular Ranges province. They are considered in summary discussions by Valentine (1961) and by Durham (1950b).

GULF OF CALIFORNIA TROUGH

The geology of the elongate trough which contains the Gulf of California is sparsely revealed in rock outcrops of immediate relevance. Waters of the Gulf and deltaic deposits of the Colorado River, and other drainage systems cover most emergent parts of this feature. Most of what can be said at present about the Gulf of California trough must be implied from the evidence of bottom topography and geophysical investigations within the Gulf, or must be deduced from what can be determined about the geology of adjacent areas. In this volume, conclusions based on submarine features are presented by Rusnak, Fisher, and Shepard; those of a geophysical nature by Phillips, by Harrison and Mathur, and by Biehler, Kovach, and Allen. Only those limited aspects of the geology which have been subjected to direct investigation on land will be considered here. Discussions of the Gulf of California, involving its geology and numerous other aspects, have been presented by C.A. Anderson and others (1950) and by Byrne and Emery (1960).

Pre-Cenozoic geology.—Pre-Cenozoic rocks occur widely around the head of the Gulf of California and are revealed in fault splinters exposed above the alluvium at the northern end of the trough (Dibblee, 1954; Kovach and others, 1962). All of the known pre-Cenozoic outcrops are older than the Peninsular Range batholith (early Cretaceous or older), but discontinuous exposures and generally severe metamorphism obscure their relationships. Great thicknesses of limestone and mica schist, such as are found immediately north of the International Border in the Coyote Mountains, would appear to be Triassic or older on the basis of regional relationships of thick carbonate sections of the western Cordillera. A poorly preserved fossil from float collected in the Coyote Mountains area, which might represent part of a a straight Paleozoic cephalopod, offers only little support for this interpretation.

Cenozoic geology.—Exploratory drill holes and geophysical investigations at the north end of the Gulf of California trough reveal an irregular and northward-shallowing basement which, near the International Border, lies at a depth of about 6,400 meters (Biehler and others, this volume). The bulk of overlying sedimentary rocks appears to be late Cenozoic in age and to represent deposits of the Colorado River, though the evidence of older rocks and the possibility of an earlier history of the Gulf trough cannot be ignored. The Colorado River is believed to have entered the Gulf trough for the first time during the Miocene (Lovejoy, 1963) or Pliocene (Longwell, 1954) Epoch.

Paleogene.—Oldest known post-Mesozoic sediments were deposited on an irregular topography of crystalline rocks in an Eocene sublittoral marine environment. The evidence for this Eocene deposition is in the isolated exposures of the Maniobra Formation (Cole, 1958; Crowell and Susuki, 1959). That formation is recognized only in the Orocopia Mountains, near the northeast corner of the Gulf of California trough, and in boulders collected from basal beds of the Imperial Formation about 16 kilometers to the west (Dibblee, 1954, p. 24). Marine invertebrate faunules from the Maniobra Formation are comparable to those known along most of the Pacific coast of North America. The site of deposition may have been in a basin which was an integral part of an otherwise undemonstrated pre-Miocene Gulf of California (Durham and Allison, 1960, p. 52), or in an Eocene embayment opening westward directly to the Pacific but since then disrupted by a controversial, major (260-kilometer) right-lateral slip along a fault system related to the San Andreas (Crowell, 1962, p. 41–42). Neither biogeographical nor geological evidence permits a clear choice between these hypotheses.

Neogene.—Post-Eocene marine deposits, which, without doubt, represent ancestral aspects of the Gulf of California, are widely recognized within the Gulf trough, but are not yet adequately described. Northernmost outcrops in the vicinity of San Gorgonio Pass (Allen, 1957, p. 327–328) are assigned to the Imperial Formation of G.D. Hanna (1926a). Their fossils indicate a tropical sea which had almost completely flooded the trough. A similar, though not necessarily contemporary, northward flooding by the Gulf is apparent eastward near the Colorado River, where planktonic Foraminifera and other marine invertebrates occur in strata underlying the dry Danby and Cadiz Lakes (Bassett, Kupfer, and Barstow, 1959, p. 106–109; Durham and Allison, 1960, p. 61).

Various volcanic rocks underlying post-Eocene marine deposits within the Imperial Valley area, at the northern extent of the Gulf of California trough, have been compared with those of the Comondú Formation of southern Baja California (Durham, 1950a, p. 24; Dibblee, 1954, p. 22). Nowhere, however, can these northern volcanics be observed resting on paleontologically determined Miocene rocks. Their upper limits are similarly indefinite. Certain northern Gulf-trough Neogene volcanics, notably the Truckhaven Rhyolite (Dibblee, 1954), clearly are younger than volcanics which are undeniably part of the Comondú Formation.

Volcanic units, including pyroclastic and immediately derived epiclastic rocks believed to be of the same general Neogene origin and recognized by similar suites of rocks throughout the entire area, crop out along the margins of the northern Gulf of California and on the higher islands within the Gulf (Anderson, 1950). Consag Rock appears to be part of such a volcanic suite (andesitic; van Andel, personal communication).

Plutonic rocks related to those of the Peninsular Range batholith, and to those of similar and at least in part contemporary batholiths of the Mexico mainland, also appear on islands of the northern Gulf.

Correlation of marine Neogene faunules of the northern part of the Gulf trough with Neogene faunal successions elsewhere has inspired controversy. Some of the problems involving best-known fossil assemblages of the Imperial Formation are outlined by Durham (1950a, p. 28–34). The uncertain duration of deposition represented by the Imperial Formation and the local occurrences of apparently temporally restricted species such as *Encope tenuis* Kew, both in the Imperial Formation and in the Pliocene and/or Pleistocene San Diego Formation, pose additional problems. Age uncertainty also obscures the significance of fossiliferous strata of the subjacent Split Mountain Formation of Tarbet and Holman (1944) in the Imperial Valley (Durham and Allison, 1961).

Coarse detrital sedimentary rocks with Neogene Panamanian fossil assemblages composed of shallow marine invertebrates, commonly accompanied by hermatypic corals (Vaughan, 1917; Squires, 1959, p. 397–398), are labeled "Imperial Formation" wherever found in low stratigraphic positions at the north end of the Gulf of California trough. Faunas with such an aspect probably occupied the Gulf of California throughout its entire Neogene history, whatever the antiquity of its origin. The equivalency in age of isolated Imperial Formation fossil outcrops therefore must be demonstrated by stratigraphic-paleontologic studies before being accepted without qualification. Oldest assemblages now recognized appear to be most nearly comparable in age to those of the San Diego Formation, which, in turn, must be analyzed with respect to the controversial Pliocene-Pleistocene boundary. Youngest marine strata within the Imperial Valley, those of the Palm Springs Formation, with a marginal marine *Ostrea-Anomia* fauna (Downs and Woodward, 1961), are considered to be middle Pleistocene (Irvingtonian) in age on the basis of associated terrestrial mammalian fossils.

Undoubted Pleistocene fossil deposits along the western Gulf of California shore occur locally at elevations of up to at least 340 meters. They emphasize the long, persistent, structural instability which characterizes the geology along that margin of the Gulf trough (Anderson, 1950; Wilson and Rocha, 1955). Pleistocene rocks of marine origin on the opposite side of the Gulf, as at Puerto Peñasco (Hertlein and Emerson, 1956), occur on land at low elevations, in a province generally manifesting a far greater structural stability.

Structures involving Neogene rocks.—Western Gulf trough faults, along the west side of which fossiliferous Pleistocene rocks are elevated, are of unknown antiquity. At the north end of the Gulf, these faults exhibit linear trends comparable to those of the Elsinore, San Jacinto, Imperial, Banning-Mission Creek, and other faults of the San Andreas fault system (Kovach and others, 1962), none of which is truly parallel to the adjacent Gulf axis. Kovach and others suggest that the San Andreas system enters the north end of the Gulf of California as a series of great *en echelon* breaks, rather than as a single curving fracture.

The history and significance of the San Andreas fault, the major element of the San Andreas system north of the Transverse Ranges of Southern California, is actively debated. Crowell (1962) recently has with great care summarized and evaluated numerous published discussions of this feature. Important most recent displacements have shown the modern San Andreas fault to be a right-lateral slip fault, as are many great faults of the North American western Cordillera. Its origin in the Transverse Ranges appears to be no earlier than Miocene. Farther north, earlier movements have been suggested, but their verification is difficult (Crowell, 1962).

Right slip of approximately 270 kilometers along the San Andreas system in central and Southern California is suggested by evidence accepted by Crowell to be most sound. Extreme, and at least in part invalid, speculative restorations of pre-Cenozoic geological scenes on opposite sides of the fault, requiring accumulative right-slip movements in excess of 500 kilometers, have been discussed by several geologists (Hill and Dibblee, 1953; Crowell, 1962). An analysis of bedrock geology in southwestern California has led Woodford to the contrasting conclusion that a total right-slip movement of no more than 50 kilometers has occurred along the San Andreas fault system (Woodford, 1960).

Implications which can be drawn from these and other views concerning movement on the San Andreas and related faults are of fundamental importance in the interpretation of the geological history of the Gulf of California. These implications are discussed in the final section of this paper.

SONORAN DESERT AND PACIFIC COASTAL PLAIN PROVINCES

The north-northwestward-widening strip of land which separates the Gulf of California trough from the steep western slopes of the Sierra Madre Occidental of the northwestern Mexican mainland is referred to generally as the Sonoran Desert and Pacific Coastal Plain provinces (Ordoñez, 1936; R.E. King 1939; Z. de Cserna and Kent, 1961). An indefinite boundary between the two provinces can be drawn near the Rio Yaqui, at a latitude of about 28° N. Aridity and desert landscapes characterize the more northern, or Sonoran Desert, part of this strip. Greater precipitation and alluvial plains related to the debouchment of several major rivers give to the more southern, or Pacific Coastal Plain, area a distinctly different appearance.

An intermediate province of parallel ranges and valleys (R.E. King, 1939, p. 1635–1638) locally is recognized between the two provinces bordering the Gulf of California and the Sierra Madre Occidental province to the east. It is considered here as part of the more generally treated Sonoran Desert and Coastal Plain provinces.

Deeply eroded blocks of diverse rocks, elevated along numerous north-northwest-trending dip-slip faults, provide the Sonoran Desert province with a general geological aspect which is clearly comparable to that of the Basin and Range province in the southwestern United States. The movement on these faults generally is shown to be normal (R.E. King, 1939, Pl. 9). The Cenozoic age of most of the normal faults and the Neogene age of associated thrust faults enhance the comparison. A narrower, deeply alluviated southward continuation in the Pacific Coastal Plain province is less evidently related. Great thicknesses of Cenozoic volcanic and immediately derived sedimentary rocks of the Sierra Madre Occidental province, affected by a similar north-northwest structural grain, form the high area bordering the east side of the Sonoran Desert and Pacific Coastal provinces.

Pre-Cenozoic rocks and structural trends, evident in elevated and eroded fault blocks which characterize the modern topography of the Sonoran Desert and Pacific Coastal Plain provinces, are not well known. A lack of continuity of exposures and a limited scope of published geological investigations, especially in western Sonora, impose serious obstacles on the geological analysis of such rocks.

Precambrian geology.—Oldest Precambrian rocks, described by Anderson (1951), are widely recognized by their geological relationships to younger Precambrian and Paleozoic rocks in southern Sonora and adjacent parts of California, Sonora, and New Mexico. Variously metamorphosed sedimentary and volcanic rocks of the stratigraphically thick sections, labeled older Precambrian, are folded into predominantly northeastward-trending structures and cut by 1,200- to 1,550-million-year-old plutonic rocks (Giletti and Damon, 1961). The orogenic episode (Mazatzal) which produced this most ancient recognized structural grain appears to have culminated in the emplacement of these plutons (Wilson, 1962).

Rocks considered to be younger Precambrian, including those of the Apache Group of Arizona, exhibit structural trends and radiometric age relationships comparable to older Precambrian rocks. They are cut by diabase sills which probably are 1,200 million years old, or older (Silver, 1960). Calcareous algae are recognized in these rocks in several areas, both north and south of the International Border.

Paleozoic geology.—A major northeastward-oriented paleogeographical trend is evident in the Paleozoic geology of the northern part of the Sonoran Desert province. Generally emergent land areas during the Paleozoic included Mazatzal Land and the Defiance Positive area, which extended northeastward across Arizona and eastward through northern New Mexico and adjacent states (McKee, 1951; Wilson, 1962), following structural trends of the Precambrian. Paleozoic seas appear to have been distributed generally southward and westward through southernmost New Mexico, Arizona, and adjacent parts of California, and across large parts of Sonora and adjacent states of Mexico. Beyond the limits of Arizona, New Mexico, and northern Sonora, the evidence for these extensive epicontinental seas is restricted to a few isolated outcrops and to widespread occurrences of fossiliferous limestone debris (R.E. King, 1939, p. 1641–1645; Hazzard, 1954; Bowen, 1954, p. 41–43; Grose, 1959). Thickest Paleozoic sections and evidence for a most continuous history or marine deposition occur near the Arizona-Sonora Boundary and west of the area of immediate consideration. Paleozoic volcanic rocks are recognized only in westernmost outcrops near the present continental margin. Paleozoic plutonic rocks are totally unknown.

Structural trends of the Paleozoic sedimentary rocks, as of the Mesozoic rocks, differ widely from the predominant north-northwestern trend of faults and folds in the overlying Cenozoic rocks (R.E. King, 1939, Pl. 1; Fig. 7). The older rocks appear to strike toward the Gulf of California in a westerly or northwesterly direction in most outcrops.

Mesozoic rocks and fossils of the Sonoran Desert and Pacific Coastal Plain provinces reveal paleogeography unlike that which can be interpreted from Paleozoic data. A widespread Permian-Triassic unconformity and a hiatus which is of major significance locally are manifestations of the structural disturbances which brought about part of that change.

Triassic-Jurassic.—Relatively thin stratigraphic sections of Triassic and Jurassic detrital rocks, mostly representing nonmarine and marginal marine environments of deposition, cover great areas of the Colorado Plateau province and areas bordering the northern limit of the present Sonoran Desert province (Wilson, 1962). In ascending order with major recognized thicknesses, the principal lithogenetic units are—Moenkopi Formation (2,560 meters), Glen Canyon Group (6,150 meters), San Rafael Group (2,180 meters), and Morrison Formation (1,160 meters). A Triassic-Jurassic boundary is recognized within the Glen Canyon Group.

An eroded highland which contributed most of the detritus of these units was located across southern Arizona, southern New Mexico, and adjacent parts of western Texas and southeastern California (McKee, 1956; Erben, 1957; McKee, 1959; G.A. de Cserna, 1961). Traces of this early Mesozoic positive area form a band which is approximately aligned with the modern trend of the Transverse Ranges and related structures of Southern California. This band remains as a Cordilleran area of discrepant structural trends (Wilson, 1962).

Adjacent areas of northern Mexico appear to have been emergent during most of the Triassic Period and during the early part of the Jurassic Period. Outcrops and fossils of the Barranca Group (Upper Triassic and Lower Jurassic of Sonora) suggest that the western margin of the north Mexican land mass was situated near the present eastern Gulf of California margin. A deep embayment, the Sonora embayment (Erben, 1957) or the Paleobahía del Antimonio (G.A. de Cserna, 1961), allowed seas to spread temporarily eastward across the northwestern corner of Sonora. The sea bordering Sonora may have communicated directly with contemporary seas of California, but a lack of outcrops in intervening areas permits only speculation about such paleogeographical details.

Later Jurassic (Callovian) ammonoids from the Santa Ana Mountains of southwestern California appear to have their closest affinities southward rather than with ammonoids of comparable age found in more northern West Coast outcrops (Imlay, 1963), but the Mexican areas immediately bordering the Gulf of California are without marine deposits of that age. The southern course of faunal communications suggested by the Santa Ana Mountain fossils may have been indirect.

Marine deposits of Late Jurassic age are recognized in the northern Peninsular Ranges and adjacent Peninsular Ranges of Southern California, but not in the Sonoran Desert and Pacific Coastal provinces nor in immediately adjacent areas. Late Jurassic seas covered a much more extensive area of central and eastern Mexico than did earlier seas. The area of marine communication with the Pacific can be outlined in the southern Mexico area of the Guerrero embayment (Erben, 1957).

Early Cretaceous.—The general distributions and configurations of early Cretaceous seas, which ultimately covered most of Mexico, were determined essentially by the paleogeography which developed during the late Jurassic (Imlay, 1944). During the most widely transgressive episode (Aptian-Albian) of the Early Cretaceous, shallow, tropical seas flooded northern Mexico and an adjacent strip of southern Arizona and southern New Mexico. The northern limit of this Aptian-Albian sea appears to have been on an east-west line, approximately corresponding in position to the line which separated inversely related earlier Mesozoic land and depositional areas (Imlay, 1939, 1944).

The eastward extent is represented by widespread carbonate sequences, mostly of shallow marine origin (Böse and Cavins, 1927), which cover central and northeastern Mexico as well as adjacent areas of the United States. Aptian-Albian carbonate rocks give way westward to thick sequences of andesitic volcanics of similar age (R.E. King, 1939, p. 1659–1678), which are lithologically and paleontologically comparable to the Alisitos Formation of northwestern Baja California (Durham and Allison, 1960). Neither this lithologic continuity nor the biogeographic implications of the fossils require an unbroken seaway directly linking the Gulf of Mexico with the eastern Pacific Ocean across northern Mexico. Less marked similarities of later Cretaceous fossils on opposite sides of Mexico suggest a provincialism, however, which developed as relatively direct Aptian-Albian transcontinental marine communications became more remote.

The contact between the two Aptian-Albian rock provinces, carbonate toward the east and volcanic toward the west, is largely obscured by the massive Tertiary cover of the intervening Sierra Madre Occidental province. It would appear to fall along a general northward- or north-northwestward-trending line extending from southeastern Arizona to a point west of Tepic, southwestern Nayarit (Z. de Cserna, 1961). A western margin of the volcanic province would fall beyond the westernmost exposure of the Alisitos Formation and probably east of the exposures of Franciscan lithologies of the western Transverse Ranges, Sebastián Vizcaíno Peninsula, and west of Magdalena Bay.

Granitic rocks of the Sonoran Desert and Pacific Coastal Plain provinces, as well as of adjacent physiographic provinces of western Mexico, are generally late Cretaceous in age where they have been analyzed by radiometric or stratigraphic-paleontologic means (Larsen and others, 1958; Giletti and Damon, 1961). They were emplaced west of the principal volcanic-carbonate rock province boundary across the Sonoran Desert, but may have intruded areas of Aptian-Albian carbonate deposition south of Mazatlán. One hundred-million-year-old granite is known to intrude Albian limestone south of the trans-Mexico volcanic belt in Guerrero (Larsen and others, 1958, p. 46).

Structures of the Aptian-Albian rocks, like those of the underlying Paleozoic rocks, are locally oriented predominantly in western to northwestern directions (R.E. King, 1939, Pl. 1; Imlay, 1939). These structural trends are comparable to those affecting rocks of the same age in northwestern Baja California. Younger structural trends in the physiographic provinces bordering the eastern margin of the Gulf of California are characteristic of the modern Cordillera—north-northwest in orientation.

Post-Cretaceous geology.—So little is known of rocks younger than Cretaceous that conclusions concerning the late geological history of land areas bordering the eastern side of the Gulf of California are hardly meaningful. The area appears to have remained generally emergent, with the exception of coastal fossiliferous Pleistocene deposits at low elevations (Hertlein and Emerson, 1956).

CONCLUSIONS

The origin of the Gulf of California cannot be clearly defined from the array of geological data now available from studies of adjacent land areas. Various hypotheses that might be and have been reasonably entertained are as follows.

1. Downfaulting of an elongate block which once joined Baja California directly with the Mexican mainland;
2. Emergence of the peninsula of Baja California at some distance from what was at one time the continental margin, leaving the Gulf as an oceanic area in between;
3. Strike-slip movement of great magnitude along one or more fault systems, such as the San Andreas, to produce a sliver of land almost completely separated from the mainland;
4. Cross-strike movement of Baja California from the Mexican mainland and flooding of the resulting gap;

or combination of these (*see* Rusnak and Fisher, this volume).

The oldest and simplest explanation, presenting the Gulf of California as a graben or half-graben, now must be rejected on the basis of geophysical evidence presented by Phillips, and by Harrison and Mathur (this volume).

The second hypothesis, a possible emergence of Baja California offshore from the continent, lacks support in the geological history. The hypothesis probably would require an early Cretaceous or older origin for the Gulf, because of the occurrence of Aptian-Albian fresh-water deposits in the northern Peninsula.

Strike-slip movement along western Cordilleran faults would be reflected beyond the limits of the Gulf proper, if it were of sufficient magnitude to explain the Gulf-Peninsula system. The evidence for lateral continuity and temporal persistence of the Transverse Ranges structure would appear to preclude a formation of the Gulf by strike-slip movement later than the earliest Mesozoic.

Lateral separation of Baja California from the Mexican mainland should be reflected in the disruption of previously continuous geological structures. This type of cross-strike displacement is part of the hypothesis for the origin of the Gulf presented by Hamilton (1961), who cited the distribution of late Mesozoic granitic rocks on both sides of the Gulf to support his argument. The pre-batholithic rocks, however, appear to be dissimilar across the Gulf. Those of the late Lower and earliest Upper Cretaceous appear to be distributed as three major rock provinces with boundaries which follow a general Cordilleran trend. They are—a western continental margin province of Franciscan-like rocks (possibly including some rocks intruded by the granites of southernmost Baja California); a middle trans-Gulf province dominated by thick sequences of andesitic eruptive rocks (the Alisitos Formation of the nothern Peninsular Ranges and similar rocks in Sonora); and an eastern ("Gulf Coast") province of relatively thin sections of carbonate rocks, intruded by at least some of the Cretaceous plutons along the Pacific coast of central Mexico.

The problems presented by the Gulf of California ultimately will be solved by a variety of geological and geophysical methods. For the time being, there appears to be a pressing need for better geological maps and more stratigraphic information. Scarcely any of the many problems outlined in earlier paragraphs are exempt from possible solution when the geology of the lands bordering the Gulf of California is known more comprehensively.

REFERENCES

Albritton, C.C., Jr., and Smith, J.F., Jr., 1957, The Texas lineament: Internat. Geol. Cong., 20th, Mexico, D.F., 1956, v. 2, sec. 5, p. 501–518.

Allen, C.R., 1957, San Andreas fault zone in San Gorgonio Pass, Southern California: Geol. Soc. America Bull., v. 68, no. 3, p. 315–350.

——— Silver, L.T., and Stehli, F.G., 1960, Agua Blanca fault—a major transverse structure of northern Baja California, Mexico: Geol. Soc. America Bull., v. 71, no. 4, p. 457–482.

——— Allison, E.C., Roberts, E.R., and Silver, L.T., 1961, Geology of northwestern Baja California, Mexico, *in* Guidebook for field trips, 57th ann. mtg. of Cordilleran section, Geol. Soc. America: p. 56–65.

Allison, E.C., 1955, Middle Cretaceous Gastropoda from Punta China, Baja California, Mexico: Jour. Paleontology, v. 29, no. 3, p. 400–432.

——— 1957, A Cretaceous faunule from Bahia Tortugas, territoria sur de Baja California, Mexico [abs.]: Geol. Soc. America Bull., v. 68, no. 12, p. 1817.

Anderson, C.A., 1950, Geology of islands and neighboring land areas, pt. 1 *of* The 1940 E.W. Scripps Cruise to the Gulf of California: Geol. Soc. America Mem. 43, p. 1–53.

——— 1951, Older Precambrian structure in Arizona: Geol. Soc. America Bull., v. 62, no. 11, p. 1331–1346.

——— Durham, J.W., Shepard, F.P., Natland, M.L., and Revelle, R.R., 1950, The 1940 E.W. Scripps Cruise to the Gulf of California: Geol. Soc. America Mem. 43, 362 p.

Anonymous, 1924, Informe sobre la exploracion geologica de la Baja California, por la Marland Oil

Company de Mexico: Petrol. Bol., v. 17, no. 6, p. 417–453; v. 18, no. 1, p. 14–53.
Arizona Bureau of Mines, 1959, Geological map of Cochise County, Arizona: Univ. of Arizona, Tucson.
Bailey, T.L., and Jahns, R.H., 1954, Geology of the Transverse Range province, Southern California: Calif. Dept. Nat. Res., Div. Mines Bull. 170, ch. 2, p. 83–106.
Bandy, O.L., 1952, Miocene Foraminifera from Erben Bank: Cushman Found. Foram. Res. Contr., v. 3, pt. 1, p. 18–19.
——— 1963, Aquitanian planktonic Foraminifera from Erben Guyot: Science, v. 140, p. 1402–1403.
Bassett, A.M., Kupfer, D.H., and Barstow, F.C., 1959, Core logs from Bristol, Cadiz, and Damby dry lakes, San Bernardino County, California: U.S. Geol. Survey Bull. 1045-D, p. 97–138.
Beal, C.H., 1948, Reconnaissance of the geology and oil possibilities of Baja California, Mexico: Geol. Soc. America Mem. 31, 138 p.
Berggren, W.A., 1960, Paleogene biostratigraphy and planktonic Foraminifera of SW Soviet Union: Stockholm Contr. Geol., v. 6, p. 63–125.
Blow, W.H., 1959, Age, correlation, and biostratigraphy of the upper Tocuyo (San Lorenzo) and Pozón Formations, eastern Falcón, Venezuela: Am. Paleont. Bull., v. 39, no. 178, p. 67–235.
Bolli, Hans, M., 1957, The genera *Globigerina* and *Globorotalia* in the Paleocene-lower Eocene Lizard Springs formation of Trinidad, B.W.I.: U.S. Natl. Mus. Bull. 215, p. 61–81.
Böse, E., and Cavins, O.A., 1927, The Cretaceous and Tertiary of southern Texas and northern Mexico: Univ. Texas Bull. 2748, p. 1–142.
Bowen, O.E., 1954, Geology and mineral deposits of Barstow quadrangle, San Bernardino County, California: Calif. Dept. Nat. Res., Div. Mines Bull. 165, p. 1–185.
Burckhardt, C., 1930, Étude synthétique sur le Mésozöique Méxicain: Soc. Paléont. Suisse Mém., vs. 49, 50, 280 p.
Bushee, J., 1962, Lead alpha ages for zircons from batholithic and prebatholithic rocks, *in* Abstracts for 1962: Geol. Soc. America Spec. Paper 73, p. 29.
——— Holden, J., Geyer, B., and Gastil, G., 1963, Lead-alpha dates for some basement rocks of southwestern California: Geol. Soc. America Bull., v. 74, no. 6, p. 803–806.
Byrne, J.V., and Emery, K.O., 1960, Sediments of the Gulf of California: Geol. Soc. America Bull., v. 71, no. 7, p. 983–1010.
Carsola, A.J., and Dietz, R.S., 1952, Submarine geology of two flat-topped northeast Pacific seamounts: Am. Jour. Sci., v. 250, no. 7, p. 481–497.
Cole, W.S., 1958, Names of and variation in certain American larger Foraminifera, particularly the discocyclinids, No. 3: Am. Paleontology Bull., v. 38, no. 176, p. 411–429.
Condie, K. C., and others, 1963, Petrology and structure of the San Benito Islands, Baja California, Mexico [abs.]: Program, 59th ann. mtg. of Cordilleran section, Geol. Soc. America, Berkeley, Calif., p. 28.
Crowell, J.C., 1962, Displacement along the San Andreas fault, California: Geol. Soc. America Spec. Paper 71, p. 1–61.
——— and Susuki, T., 1959, Eocene stratigraphy and paleontology, Orocopia Mountains, southeastern California: Geol. Soc. America Bull., v. 70, no. 5, p. 581–592.
Curtis, G.H., Evernden, J.F., and Lipson, J., 1958, Age determination of some granitic rocks in California by the potassium-argon method: Calif. Dept. Nat. Res., Div. Mines Special Rept. 54, p. 1–16.
de Cserna, G.A., 1961, Estratigrafía del Triasico Superiór de la parte central del Estado de Sonora: Paleontologia Mexicana, no. 11, pt. 1, p. 1–8.
de Cserna, Zoltan, 1961, Tectonic map of Mexico: Geol. Soc. America.
——— and Kent, B.H., 1961, Mapa geológica de reconocimiento y secciones estructurales de la región de San Blas y El Fuerte, Estados de Sinaloa y Sonora: Univ. Nac. Aut. Mexico, Inst. Geol. y Min. no. 4.
Dibblee, T.W., 1950, Geology of southwestern Santa Barbara County, California: Calif. Dept. Nat. Res., Div. Mines Bull. 150, p. 1–95.
——— 1954, Geology of the Imperial Valley region, California, *in* Geology of Southern California: Calif. Dept. Nat. Res., Div. Mines Bull. 170, pt. 2, ch. 2, p. 21–28.
Dickinson, W.R., 1962, Petrogenetic significance of geosynclinal andesitic volcanism along the Pacific margin of North America: Geol. Soc. America Bull., v. 73, no. 10, p. 1241–1256.
Downs, T., and Woodward, G.D., 1961, Middle Pleistocene extension of the Gulf of California into the Imperial Valley, *in* Abstracts for 1961: Geol. Soc. America Spec. Paper 68, p. 21.
Durham, J.W., 1950a, Megascopic paleontology and marine stratigraphy, pt. 2 *of* The 1940 E.W. Scripps Cruise to the Gulf of California: Geol. Soc. America Mem. 43, 216 p.
——— 1950b, Cenozoic marine climates of the Pacific coast: Geol. Soc. America Bull., v. 61, no. 11, p. 1243–1264.
——— 1954, The marine Cenozoic of Southern California, *in* Geology of Southern California: Calif. Dept. Nat. Res., Div. Mines Bull. 170, pt. 4, ch. 3, p. 23–31.
——— and Allison, E.C., 1960, The geologic history of Baja California and its marine faunas: Systematic Zoology, v. 9, p. 47–91.
——— 1961, Stratigraphic position of the Fish Creek gypsum at Split Mountain Gorge, Imperial County, California, *in* Abstracts for 1961: Geol. Soc. America Spec. Paper 68, p. 22.
——— Jahns, R.H., and Savage, D.E., 1954, Marine-nonmarine relationships in the Cenozoic section of California, *in* Geology of Southern California: Calif. Dept. Nat. Res., Div. Mines Bull. 170, pt. 7, ch. 3, p. 59–71.
Eames, F.E., Banner, F.T., Blow, W.H., and Clarke, W.J., 1962, Fundamentals of mid-Tertiary stratigraphical correlation: Cambridge Univ. Press, 151 p.
Eardley, A.J., 1962, Structural geology of North America: Harper & Row, New York and Evanston, 2nd ed., p. I–XV, 743 p.
Emery, K.O., 1960, The sea of Southern California: John Wiley & Sons, Inc., New York and London, 366 p.
——— Butcher, W.S., Gould, H.R., and Shepard, F.P., 1952, Submarine geology off San Diego, California: Jour. Geology, v. 60, no. 6, p. 511–548.
——— Gorsline, D.S., Uchupi, E., and Terry, R.D.,

1957, Sediments of three bays of Baja California—Sebastian Viscaino, San Cristobal, and Todos Santos: Jour. Sed. Petrology, v. 27, no. 2, p. 95–115.

Erben, H.K., 1957, Paleogeographic reconstructions for the Lower and Middle Jurassic and for the Callovian of Mexico: Internat. Geol. Cong., 20th, Mexico, D.F., Sec. 2, p. 35–42.

Gardner, D.L., 1940, Geology of the Newberry and Ord Mountains, San Bernardino County, California: Calif. Jour. Mines and Geol., v. 36, no. 3, p. 257–292.

Giletti, B.J., and Damon, P.E., 1961, Rubidium-strontium ages of some basement rocks from Arizona and northwestern Mexico: Geol. Soc. America Bull., v. 72, no. 4, p. 639–644.

Gray, C.H., Jr., 1961, Geology of the Corona south quadrangle and the Santa Ana Narrows area; Riverside, Orange, and San Bernardino Counties, California: Calif. Dept. Nat. Res., Div. Mines Bull. 178, p. 1–58.

Grose, L.T., 1959, Structure and petrology of the northeast part of the Soda Mountains, San Bernardino County, California: Geol. Soc. America Bull., v. 70, no. 12, p. 1509–1548.

Guillou, R.B., 1953, Geology of the Johnston Grade area, San Bernardino County, California: Calif. Dept. Nat. Res., Div. Mines Spec. Rept. 31, p. 1–18.

Hamilton, Warren, 1961, Origin of the Gulf of California: Geol. Soc. America Bull., v. 72, no. 9, p. 1307–1318.

——— 1963, Nappes in southeastern California: Program, Rocky Mtn. Section, 16th ann. mtg., Geol. Soc. America, p. 27.

Hammond, E.H., 1954, A geomorphic study of the Cape region of Baja California: Univ. Calif. Pub. Geography, v. 10, no. 2, p. 46–112.

Hanna, G.D., 1925, Expedition to Guadalupe Island, Mexico, in 1922: Calif. Acad. Sci. Proc., 4th ser., v. 14, no. 12, p. 217–275.

——— 1926a, Paleontology of Coyote Mountain, Imperial County, California: Calif. Acad. Sci. Proc., 4th ser., v. 14, no. 18, p. 427–503.

——— 1926b, General report, pt. 1 *of* Expedition to the Revillagigedo Islands, Mexico, in 1925: Calif. Acad. Sci. Proc., 4th ser., v. 15, p. 1–113.

——— 1927, Geology of the west Mexican islands: Pan-American Geologist, v. 48, p. 1–24.

Hanna, M.A., 1926, Geology of the La Jolla quadrangle, California: Univ. Calif. Dept. Geol. Sci. Bull., v. 16, no. 7, p. 187–246.

Hazzard, J.C., 1954, Rocks and structures of the northern Providence Mountains, San Bernardino County, California: Calif. Dept. Nat. Res., Div. Mines Bull. 170, ch. 4, p. 27–35.

Heim, Arnold, 1922, Notes on the Tertiary of southern Lower California: Geol. Mag., v. 59, p. 529–547.

Hertlein, L.G., and Allison, E.C., 1959, Pliocene marine deposits in northwestern Baja California, Mexico, with the description of a new species of *Acanthina* (Gastropoda): Southern Calif. Acad. Sci. Bull., v. 58, pt. 1, p. 17–26.

——— and Emerson, W.K., 1956, Marine Pleistocene invertebrates from near Puerto Peñasco, Sonora, Mexico: San Diego Soc. Nat. History Trans., v. 12, no. 8, p. 154–176.

——— 1959, Pliocene and Pleistocene megafossils from the Tres Marias Islands: Am. Mus. Novitates, no. 1940, p. 1–15.

——— and Grant, U.S., IV, 1960, The geology and paleontology of the marine Pliocene of San Diego, California, pt. 2a: San Diego Soc. Nat. History Mem., v. 2, p. 73–133, pls. 19–26, table 1.

Hewett, D.F., 1954, General geology of the Mojave Desert region, California: Calif. Dept. Nat. Res., Div. Mines Bull. 170, ch. 2, p. 5–20.

Hill, M.L., 1954, Tectonics of faulting in Southern California: Calif. Dept. Nat. Res., Div. Mines Bull. 170, ch. 4, p. 5–13.

——— and Dibblee, T.W., Jr., 1953, San Andreas, Garlock, and Big Pine faults, California: Geol. Soc. America Bull., v. 64, p. 443–450.

Hirschi, H., and De Quervain, F., 1933, Beiträge zur Petrographie von Baja California: Schweiz. Miner. u. Petrog. Mitt., v. 13, p. 232–277.

Howe, M.A., 1934, Eocene marine algae (Lithothamnieae) from the Sierra Blanca limestone: Geol. Soc. America Bull., v. 45, no. 3, p. 507–518.

Hsu, K.J., Edwards, G., and McLaughlin, W.A., 1963, Age of the intrusive rocks of the southeastern San Gabriel Mountains, California: Geol. Soc. America Bull., v. 74, no. 4, p. 507–512.

Hudson, F.S., 1922, Geology of the Cuyamaca region of California, with special reference to the origin of the nickeliferous pyrrhotite: Univ. Calif. Dept. Geol. Sci. Bull., v. 13, no. 6, p. 175–252.

Imlay, R.W., 1939, Paleogeographic studies in northeastern Sonora: Geol. Soc. America Bull., v. 50, no. 11, p. 1723–1744.

——— 1944, Cretaceous formations of Central America and Mexico: Am. Assoc. Petroleum Geologists Bull., v. 28, no. 8, p. 1077–1195.

——— 1959, Succession and speciation of the pelecypod *Aucella:* U.S. Geol. Survey Prof. Paper 314-G, p. 155–169.

——— 1963, Jurassic fossils from Southern California: Jour. Paleontology, v. 37, no. 1, p. 97–107.

Ives, R.L., 1962, Dating of the 1746 eruption of Tres Virgenes volcano, Baja California del sur, Mexico: Geol. Soc. America Bull., v. 73, no. 5, p. 647–648.

Jahns, R.H., editor, 1954, Geology of Southern California: Calif. Dept. Nat. Res., Div. Mines Bull. 170, pt. 1, ch. 2, p. 29–52.

——— and Wright, L.A., 1960, Garlock and Death Valley fault zones in the Avawatz Mountains, California [abs.]: Geol. Soc. America Bull., v. 71, no. 12, p. 2063–2064.

Johnson, C.W., 1953, Notes on the geology of Guadalupe Island, Mexico: Am. Jour. Sci., v. 251, no. 3, p. 231–236.

Keenan, M.F., 1932, The Eocene Sierra Blanca limestone at the type locality in Santa Barbara County, California: San Diego Soc. Nat. History Trans., v. 7, no. 8, p. 53–84.

Kew, W.S.W., 1923, Geologic formations of a part of Southern California and their correlation: Am. Assoc. Petroleum Geologists Bull., v. 7, no. 4, p. 411–420.

Kilmer, F.H., 1961, Stratigraphy and paleontology of the Late Cretaceous, El Rosario area, Baja California, Mexico: unpub. abs. of paper read before graduate symposium of Univ. of Calif., L.A., May 13, 1961.

King, P.B., 1959, The evolution of North America: Princeton Univ. Press, 190 p.

King, R.E., 1939, Geological reconnaissance in northern Sierra Madre Occidental of Mexico: Geol. Soc. America Bull., v. 50, no. 11, p. 1625–1722.

Kleinpell, R.M., 1938, Miocene stratigraphy of California: Am. Assoc. Petroleum Geologists, Tulsa, Okla., 450 p.
——— and Weaver, D.W., 1963, Oligocene biostratigraphy of the Santa Barbara embayment, California: Univ. Calif. Geol. Sci. Pub., v. 43.
Kovach, R.L., Allen, C.R., and Press, F., 1962, Geophysical investigations in the Colorado Delta region: Jour. Geophys. Research, v. 67, p. 2845–2871.
Krause, D.C., 1961, Geology of the sea floor east of Guadalupe Island: Deep-Sea Research, v. 8, no. 1, p. 30–40.
Larsen, E.S., Jr., 1948, Batholith and associated rocks of Corona, Elsinore, and San Luis Rey quadrangles, Southern California: Geol. Soc. America Mem. 29, p. 1–182.
——— Gottfried, D., Jaffe, H.W., and Waring, C.L., 1958, Lead-alpha ages of the Mesozoic batholiths of western North America: U.S. Geol. Survey Bull. 1070-B, p. 35–62.
Loel, W., and Corey, W.H., 1932, Paleontology, pt. 1 *of* The Vaqueros formation, lower Miocene of California: Univ. Calif. Dept. Geol. Bull., v. 22, p. 31–410.
Longwell, C.R., 1954, History of the lower Colorado River and the Imperial depression: Calif. Dept. Nat. Res., Div. Mines Bull. 170, ch. 7, p. 53–56.
Lovejoy, E.M.P., 1963, Age of the Colorado River in the Colorado plateau: Program, Rocky Mtn. Section, 16th ann. mtg., Geol. Soc. America, p. 33.
Maldonado-Koerdell, M., 1958, El volcán Bárcena en la Isla San Benedicto, Archipiélago de los Revillagigedo (Mexico): Ciencia, v. 18, nos. 7–8, p. 114–123.
Mallory, V.S., 1959, Lower Tertiary biostratigraphy of the California coast ranges: Am. Assoc. Petroleum Geologists, Tulsa, Okla., 416 p.
Mason, R.G., and Raff, A.D., 1961, Magnetic survey off the west coast of North America, 32° N. latitude to 42° N. latitude: Geol. Soc. America Bull., v. 72, no. 8, p. 1259–1266.
Matsumoto, T., 1959a, Upper Cretaceous ammonites of California; Pt. II: Kyushu Univ. Faculty Sci. Mem., Ser. D, Geology, spec. v. 1, 172 p.
——— 1959b, Upper Cretaceous ammonites of California; Pt. I: Kyushu Univ. Faculty Sci. Mem., Ser. D, Geology, v. 3, no. 4, p. 91–171.
——— 1960, Upper Cretaceous ammonites of California; Pt. III: Kyushu Univ. Faculty Sci. Mem., Ser. D, Geology, spec. v. 2, 204 p.
McIntyre, D.B., and Shelton, J.S., 1957, Preliminary report on tectonic history of Vizcaino Peninsula and San Benito Islands, Baja California, Mexico [abs.]: Am. Assoc. Petroleum Geologists Bull., v. 41, no. 2, p. 352–353.
McKee, E.D., 1951, Sedimentary basins of Arizona and adjoining areas: Geol. Soc. America Bull., v. 62, no. 5, p. 481–506.
——— 1956, Paleotectonic maps of the Jurassic System: U.S. Geol. Survey Misc. Geol. Inv. Map I-175, p. 1–6.
——— 1959, Paleotectonic maps of the Triassic System: U.S. Geol. Survey Misc. Geol. Inv. Map I-300, p. 1–33.
Mejorado, S.H.S., compiler, 1956, Carta geologica de la Republica Mexicana; escala 1:2,000,000: Internat. Geol. Cong., 20th, Mexico, D.F., 1956.
Menard, H.W., Jr., 1955, Deformation of the northeastern Pacific basin and the west coast of North America: Geol. Soc. America Bull., v. 66, no. 9, p. 1149–1198.
——— and Fisher, R.L., 1958, Clipperton fracture zone in the northeastern equatorial Pacific: Jour. Geology, v. 66, no. 3, p. 239–253.
Merriam, C.W., 1954, Rocks of Paleozoic age in Southern California: Calif. Dept. Nat. Res., Div. Mines Bull. 170, pt. 1, ch. 3, p. 7–14.
Milow, E.D., 1961, Guide to geologic field trip of southwestern San Diego County, *in* Guidebook for field trips, 57th ann. mtg. of Cordilleran Section, Geol. Soc. America: p. 23–43.
Mina, U.F., 1956, Bosquejo geológico de la parte sur de la Península de Baja California: Internat. Geol. Cong., 20th, Mexico, D.F., Excursion A-7, p. 1–79.
——— 1957, Bosquejo geológico del territoria sur de la Baja California: Assoc. Mexicana Geól. Petroleros Bol., v. 9, nos. 3–4, p. 141–269.
Natland, M.L., and Rothwell, W.T., Jr., 1954, Fossil Foraminifera of the Los Angeles and Ventura regions, California: Calif. Dept. Nat. Res., Div. Mines Bull. 170, pt. 5, ch. 3, p. 33–42.
Neuerburg, G.J., and Gottfried, D., 1954, Age determinations of the San Gabriel anorthosite massif, California: Geol. Soc. America Bull., v. 65, no. 5, p. 465.
Ordoñez, E., 1936, Principal physiographic provinces of Mexico: Am. Assoc. Petroleum Geologists Bull., v. 20, no. 10, p. 1277–1307.
Page, B.M., Marks, J.G., and Walker, G.W., 1951, Stratigraphy and structure of mountains northeast of Santa Barbara, California: Am. Assoc. Petroleum Geologists Bull., v. 35, no. 8, p. 1727–1780.
Phleger, F.B, and Ewing, G.C., 1962, Sedimentology and oceanography of coastal lagoons in Baja California, Mexico: Geol. Soc. America Bull., v. 73, no. 2, p. 145–182.
Popenoe, W.P., 1954, Mesozoic formations and faunas, Southern California and northern Baja California: Calif. Dept. Nat. Res., Div. Mines Bull. 170, pt. 3, ch. 3, p. 15–21.
——— Imlay, R.W., and Murphy, M.A., 1960, Correlation of the Cretaceous formations of the Pacific coast (U.S. and northwestern Mexico): Geol. Soc. America Bull., v. 71, no. 10, p. 1491–1540.
Raff, A.D., 1962, Further magnetic measurements along the Murray fault: Jour. Geophys. Research, v. 67, p. 417–418.
Reinhart, R.H., 1959, A review of the Sirenia and Desmostylia: Univ. Calif. Geol. Sci. Pub., v. 36, no. 1, p. 1–146.
Richards, A.F., 1958, Petrographic notes on two eastern Pacific oceanic islands and a seamount [abs.]: Geol. Soc. America Bull., v. 69, no. 12, p. 1634.
——— 1960, Rates of marine erosion of tephra and lava at Isla San Benedicto, Mexico: Internat. Geol. Cong., 21st, Copenhagen, Pt. 10 (Submarine geology), p. 59–64.
Riedel, W.R., Ladd, H.S., Tracey, J.I., Jr., and Bramlette, M.N., 1961, Summary of coring operations, pt. 2 *of* Preliminary drilling phase of Mohole project: Am. Assoc. Petroleum Geologists Bull., v. 45, no. 11, p. 1793–1798.
Santillán, M., and Barrera, T., 1930, Las posibilidades petrolíferas en la costa occidental de la Baja California, entre los paralelos 30° y 32° de latitud norte: Inst. Géol. Mexico Anales, v. 5, p. 1–37.

Saul, L.R., and Popenoe, W.P., 1962, *Meekia*, enigmatic Cretaceous pelecypod genus: Univ. Calif. Pub. Geol. Sci., v. 40, p. 289–344.

Silberling, N.J., Schoellhamer, J.E., Gray, C.H., Jr., and Imlay, R.W., 1961, Upper Jurassic fossils from Bedford Canyon formation, Southern California: Am. Assoc. Petroleum Geologists Bull., v. 45, no. 10, p. 1746–1748.

Silver, L.T., 1960, Age determinations on Precambrian diabase differentiates in the Sierra Ancha, Gila County, Arizona [abs.]: Geol. Soc. America Bull., v. 71, no. 12, p. 1973–1974.

——— and McKinney, C.R., 1962, U-Pb isotopic age studies in a Precambrian granite, Marble Mountains, San Bernardino County, California: Geol. Soc. America Spec. Paper 73, p. 65.

Smith, G.I., 1962, Large lateral displacement on Garlock fault, California, as measured from offset dike swarm: Am. Assoc. Petroleum Geologists Bull., v. 46, no. 1, p. 85–104.

Squires, D.F., 1959, Corals and coral reefs in the Gulf of California: Am. Mus. Nat. History Bull., v. 118, art. 7, p. 371–431.

Stoyanow, A.A., 1949, Lower Cretaceous stratigraphy of southeastern Arizona: Geol. Soc. America Mem. 38, 196 p.

Tarbet, L.A., and Holman, W.H., 1944, Stratigraphy and micropaleontology of the west side of Imperial Valley, California [abs.]: Am. Assoc. Petroleum Geologists Bull., v. 28, no. 12, p. 1781–1782.

Valentine, J.W., 1955, Upwelling and thermally anomalous Pacific coast Pleistocene molluscan faunas: Am. Jour. Sci., v. 253, no. 8, p. 462–474.

——— 1961, Paleoecologic molluscan geography of the California Pleistocene: Univ. Calif. Geol. Sci. Pub., v. 34, p. 309–442.

Vanderhoof, V.L., 1942, An occurrence of the Tertiary marine mammal *Cornwallius* in Lower California: Am. Jour. Sci., v. 240, no. 4, p. 298–301.

Vaughan, T.W., 1917, The reef-coral fauna of Carrizo Creek, Imperial County, California, and its significance: U.S. Geol. Survey Prof. Paper 98-T, p. 355–376.

Walton, W.R., 1955, Ecology of living benthonic Foraminifera, Todos Santos Bay, Baja California: Jour. Paleontology, v. 29, no. 6, p. 952–1018.

White, W.R., 1956, Pliocene and Miocene Foraminifera from the Capistrano formation, Orange County, California: Jour. Paleontology, v. 30, no. 2, p. 237–260.

Wilson, E.D., 1960, Geologic map of Yuma County, Arizona: Arizona Bur. Mines, Univ. Arizona, Tucson.

——— 1962, A resumé of the geology of Arizona: Arizona Bur. Mines Bull. 171, p. i–ix, 1–140.

——— and Moore, R.T., 1958, Geologic map of Graham and Greenlee Counties, Arizona: Arizona Bur. Mines.

——— 1959, Geologic map of Pinal County, Arizona: Arizona Bur. Mines.

——— Moore, R.T., and O'Haire, R.T., 1960, Geologic map of Pima and Santa Cruz Counties, Arizona: Arizona Bur. Mines.

Wilson, I.F., and Rocha, V.S., 1955, Geology and mineral deposits of the Boleo copper district, Baja California, Mexico: U.S. Geol. Survey Prof. Paper 273, p. 1–134.

Wisser, E., 1954, Geology and ore deposits of Baja California, Mexico: Econ. Geol., v. 49, no. 1, p. 44–76.

Woodford, A.O., 1925, The San Onofre breccia; its nature and origin: Univ. Calif. Dept. Geol. Sci. Pub., v. 15, p. 159–280.

——— 1960, Bedrock patterns and strike-slip faulting in southwestern California: Am. Jour. Sci., v. 258-A, p. 400–417.

——— and Harriss, T.F., 1928, Geology of Blackhawk Canyon, San Bernardino Mountains, California: Univ. Calif. Dept. Geol. Sci. Pub., v. 17, p. 265–304.

——— 1938, Geological reconnaissance across Sierra San Pedro Mártir, Baja California: Geol. Soc. America Bull., v. 49, no. 9, p. 1297–1336.

——— Schoellhamer, J.E., Vedder, J.G., and Yerkes, R.F., 1954, Geology of the Los Angeles basin: Calif. Dept. Nat. Res., Div. Mines Bull. 170, pt. 5, ch. 2, p. 65–81.

Woodring, W.P., 1938, Distribution and age of the marine Tertiary deposits of the Colorado Desert: Carnegie Inst. Washington Pub. 418, p. 1–25.

——— 1952, Pliocene-Pleistocene boundary in California coast ranges: Am. Jour. Sci., v. 250, no. 6, p. 401–410.

OCEANOGRAPHIC ASPECTS OF GULF OF CALIFORNIA[1]

GUNNAR I. RODEN[2]
La Jolla, California

ABSTRACT

The Gulf of California comprises a large evaporation basin which, at its southern end, is in open communication with the Pacific Ocean. Surface temperatures range between 14°C and 21°C in February, and between 28°C and 31°C in August. Surface salinities fluctuate mostly between 35.0‰ and 35.8‰ and change little with season. The amplitude of the mean annual sea-level oscillation observed at tide gage stations is about 15 cm, and agrees closely with that of the steric sea-level oscillation above 500 m. The mean tidal range increases from about 1 m at the Gulf entrance, to 7 m near the mouth of the Colorado River. This river, which is rich in sulfate, sodium, and calcium, has a mean annual discharge rate of 120 m^3/sec. Northwesterly winds in winter drive the surface water southward and cause extensive upwelling along the east coast and in the lee of Isla Tiburón; southeasterly winds in summer move the surface water northwestward and give rise to some upwelling along the Baja California coast. The order of magnitude of the upwelling speed is 3 m per day. In the northern part of the Gulf, winter cooling may lead to convective overturn near the coast that may extend downward to about 100 m. The subsurface circulation in the Gulf is rather complicated. The salinity distribution suggests that there is inflow of low-salinity water along the east coast and outflow of high-salinity water along the west coast, at depths between 50 m and 100 m. Below the bottom of the thermocline, the water in the Gulf is essentially the same as elsewhere off southern Mexico; it is characterized by a salinity minimum of less than 34.60‰ between 400 m and 800 m, and by an oxygen minimum of less than 0.2 ml/L between 200 m and 800 m. In some instances, the amount of dissolved oxygen was below the titration accuracy (0.05 ml/L). At depths between 2,500 and 3,000 m there is a temperature minimum of slightly less than 1.85°C; from there to the bottom, the temperature increases again, mainly as a result of adiabatic compression. Unusual hydrographic conditions, not found elsewhere in the eastern Pacific, are encountered in Ballenas Channel, which is completely isolated from the rest of the Gulf below 250 m. Here the bottom (1,500 m) temperatures are about 11°C, or about 8°C higher than at comparable depths outside the channel.

INTRODUCTION

The Gulf of California occupies an oceanographically unique position among the marginal seas of the Pacific Ocean. Lying as it does between the arid peninsula of Baja California in the west, and the equally arid states of Sonora and Sinaloa in the east, it comprises a large evaporation basin, which, at its southern end, is in open communication with the Pacific. The moderation effect of this ocean upon the climate of the Gulf is greatly reduced by an almost uninterrupted chain of mountains, 1 km to 3 km high in Baja California. The climate of the Gulf of California is therefore more continental than oceanic, a fact which contributes to the large annual and diurnal temperature ranges observed there (Hernandez, 1923). Topographically, the Gulf can be divided into a series of basins and trenches, separated from each other by transverse ridges (Shepard, 1950). Most of the basins are deep and in open communication with the ocean, although Ballenas Channel, between Isla Angel de la Guarda, Isla San Lorenzo, and Punta San Gabriel, has no connection with the latter.

The first hydrographic cruise into the Gulf was made in 1889 by the U.S. Fish Commission steamer, *Albatross* (Townsend, 1901). This was followed (Table I) fifty years later, by the E.W. Scripps cruise (Sverdrup, 1941; Roden, 1958). In 1940, rather detailed geological investigations were made in the Gulf (Anderson and others, 1950) and

[1] Manuscript received, September 1, 1962. Contribution from Scripps Institution of Oceanography.

The author is indebted to M. Blackburn, J.D. Isaacs, J.L. Reid, and Tj.H. van Andel for suggestions. Sea-level records for the Pacific coast of Mexico were kindly furnished by H. Cepeda. The illustrations were patiently done by Mrs. Terry Garate.

This paper was written on request of Tj.H. van Andel. The research reported herein was supported by the Marine Life Research and by the Scripps Tuna Oceanography Research Programs of the University of California, La Jolla, Calif. Funds for the latter program were provided by the U.S. Bureau of Commercial Fisheries under Contract No. 14-17-007-1, originally made available under the Act 1, 1954 (*68* Stat. 376), commonly known as the Saltonstall-Kennedy Act.

[2] Scripps Institution of Oceanography, University of California.

TABLE I. CHRONOLOGICAL LIST OF HYDROGRAPHIC CRUISES INTO GULF OF CALIFORNIA

Date	Ship	*Hydrographic Casts*		Properties Observed	Area Covered
		No.	*To Depth*		
11 Mar.–7 Apr. 1889	*Albatross*	28	bottom	temperature, salinity	Cabo San Lucas northward to Colorado River
13 Feb.–19 Mar. 1939	*E.W. Scripps*	53	bottom	temperature, salinity, oxygen, calcium	Cabo San Lucas northward to Colorado River
6 Feb.–17 Feb. 1956	*Black Douglas*	22	1,200 m	temperature, salinity, oxygen	Cabo San Lucas northward to Isla Tiburón
7 Apr.–23 Apr. 1956	*Black Douglas*	40	600 m	temperature, salinity, oxygen	Cabo San Lucas northward to Colorado River
26 Nov.–16 Dec. 1956	*Horizon*	59	bottom	temperature, salinity, oxygen	Cabo San Lucas southward to Isla Socorro and Cabo Corrientes
8 Feb.–23 Feb. 1957	*Horizon*	59	bottom	temperature, salinity, oxygen	Cabo San Lucas northward to Isla Tiburón
7 Apr.–23 Apr. 1957	*Black Douglas*	37	600 m	temperature, salinity, oxygen	Cabo San Lucas northward to Colorado River
7 Jun.–23 Jun. 1957	*Stranger*	57	600 m	temperature, salinity, oxygen	Cabo San Lucas northward to Colorado River
9 Aug.–26 Aug. 1957	*Stranger*	57	600 m	temperature, salinity, oxygen	Cabo San Lucas northward to Colorado River
16 Apr.–24 May 1959	*S.F. Baird*	47	bottom	temperature, salinity, oxygen	Cabo Corrientes to Colorado River
16 Jan.–4 Feb. 1960	*Alaska*	—	—	bathythermograph temperature to 250 m.	Isla Tiburón northward to Colorado River
20 Oct.–11 Nov. 1961	*H.M. Smith*	41	bottom	temperature, salinity, oxygen	Cabo San Lucas northward to Isla Tiburón

in 1943 the Mexican government conducted a few studies for the purpose of establishing a guano industry there (Osorio-Tafall, 1943). During the years 1956 and 1957, six hydrographic expeditions were sent to the Gulf by the U.S. Fish and Wildlife Service in cooperation with the California Fisheries Investigations; the aim was, among other things, to investigate the seasonal changes (Roden and Groves, 1959). Since then, hydrographic casts have been taken during the *Vermilion Sea Expedition* in 1959, and during the geological investigations in 1961. The stations occupied during the 1956–1961 cruises are shown in Figure 1.

METEOROLOGICAL ASPECTS

Air temperature and precipitation.—Figure 2, modified from Page (1930), and Ward and Brooks (1936), summarizes the areal distribution of air temperature and rainfall in the Gulf of California and adjacent regions. It is seen that in winter, the air temperatures decrease toward the interior of the Gulf, and that the temperature differences between the east and west coasts of Baja California are small. Over the adjacent land areas, temperatures depend mainly upon altitude; winter frosts are not uncommon at higher elevations and may occasionally occur near the coast in the northern regions. In summer, the air temperature increases toward the interior of the Gulf and the temperature differences between the east and west coasts of Baja California are large, sometimes exceeding 10°C.

Precipitation in the Gulf is more plentiful on the east than on the west side. The northern half of the Gulf is dry, desert-like, with annual rainfall amounts of less than 10 cm. In the southeastern part, rainfall along the coast increases to about 100 cm per year; here extensive swamps are common. Most of the rain in the Gulf falls between June and October, though winter rainfall is to be expected in the northern third. Over the adjacent land areas, rainfall increases with altitude. Thus, the mountains of Baja California have an average annual rainfall of 25–75 cm; whereas, on either coast of the central peninsula, it is less than 10 cm. The year-to-year variation of rainfall is large and the amounts shown in Figure 2 may differ by a factor of seven in any particular year.

The month-to-month variation of air temperature and rainfall for a few representative coastal stations is given in Table II. It is seen that the mean annual temperature range increases from about 6°C at Cabo Corrientes to 18°C near the mouth of the Colorado River. The number of rainy days per year decreases from about 60 at Cabo Corrientes to about 5 along the central Baja California coast.

Evaporation.—Direct measurements from evaporation pans at coastal stations indicate that the mean annual evaporation ranges between 200 cm and 250 cm per year (Servicio Meteorológico Mexicano, 1928–1941). The minima occur in winter, and the maxima in summer. Though pan evaporation may be indicative of conditions in the immediate vicinity of the coast, it does not neces-

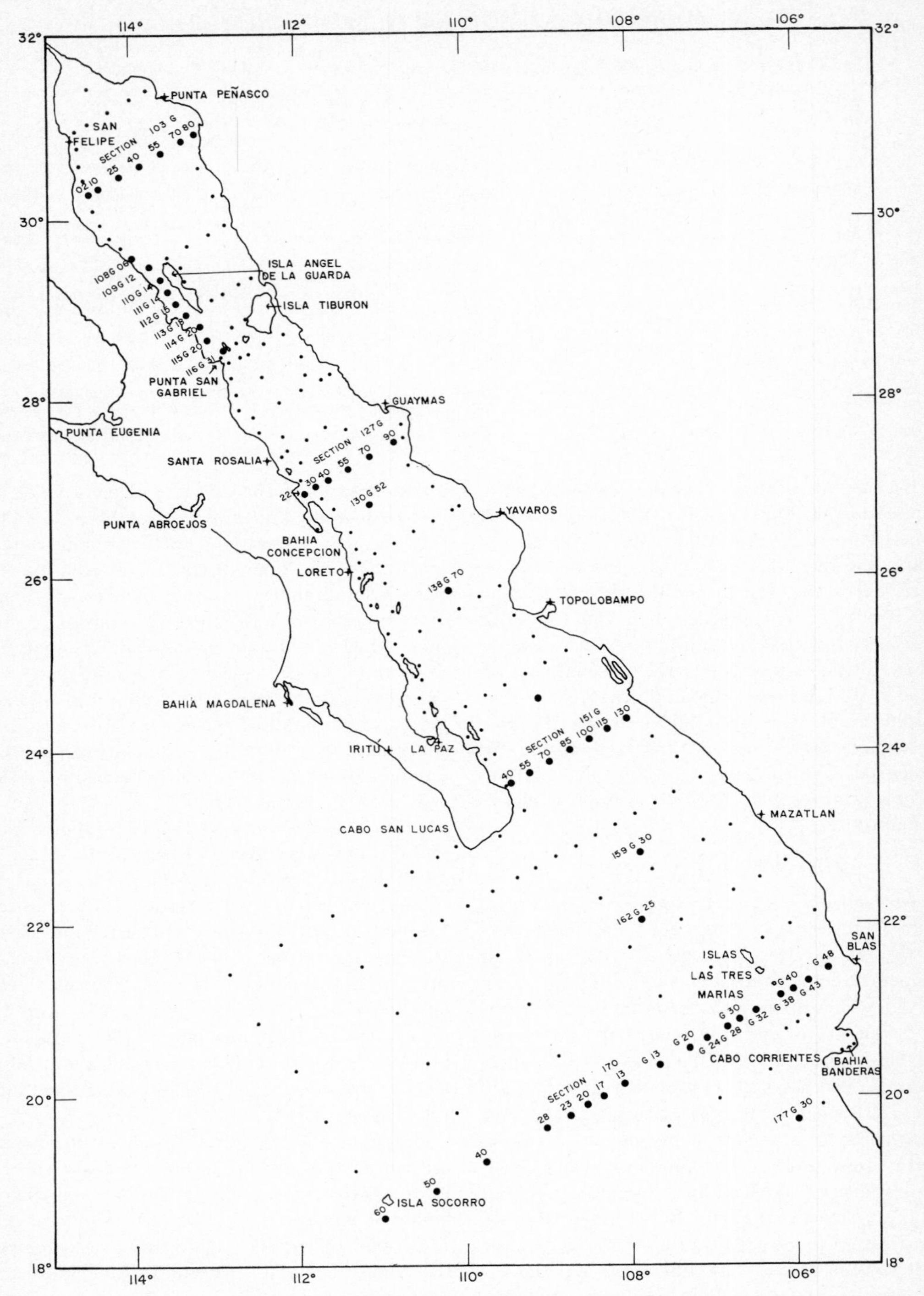

FIG. 1.—Stations occupied during the 1956–1961 hydrographic cruises. Sections and stations used in this investigation are numbered and shown by filled circles.

TABLE II. AIR TEMPERATURE (T) AND PRECIPITATION (P) AT COASTAL STATIONS
(After Servicio Meteorológico Mexicano, 1928–1941)

	I	*II*	*III*	*IV*	*V*	*VI*	*VII*	*VIII*	*IX*	*X*	*XI*	*XII*	*Year*
[1] San Luis, Río Colorado, Son. 32°38′N 114°50′W													
T mean (°C)	11.9	14.7	18.3	21.5	25.4	29.7	34.4	34.0	30.2	23.8	16.8	12.4	22.7
P (mm)	7.1	9.6	4.2	2.6	1.0	0.0	9.5	12.0	5.7	8.0	2.8	14.0	76.5
P (days)	2	2	1	<1	<1	0	<1	2	<1	<1	<1	1	12
Guaymas, Son. 27°55′N 110°53′W													
T mean (°C)	17.6	19.0	21.0	23.3	26.4	29.1	30.8	30.8	30.2	27.2	22.5	19.5	24.8
T mean max. (°C)	22.6	24.2	26.6	29.1	32.1	34.1	35.2	35.2	34.9	32.3	28.2	24.5	29.9
T mean min. (°C)	12.7	14.1	15.8	17.9	20.9	24.7	27.1	26.9	26.0	22.4	18.2	15.0	20.1
P (mm)	7.9	6.3	4.6	3.0	2.8	0.7	46.7	75.5	54.4	9.5	11.1	28.9	251.4
P (days)	1	2	<1	<1	<1	<1	5	7	4	1	1	3	28
Mulegé, B.C. 26°53′N 112°00′W													
T mean (°C)	14.0	16.0	17.8	20.1	22.9	27.2	30.5	30.4	29.0	24.6	19.5	14.9	22.2
P (mm)	2.6	3.4	0.1	0.2	0.1	0.0	6.1	16.8	40.4	5.4	6.8	19.2	101.1
P (days)	<1	<1	<1	<1	<1	0	<1	2	1	<1	<1	2	5
Topolobampo, Sin. 25°36′N 109°03′W													
T mean (°C)	18.6	19.7	20.1	22.2	25.0	29.1	29.8	29.7	29.7	27.8	24.0	19.7	24.6
P (mm)	6.4	6.6	6.4	0.0	1.8	5.3	39.9	100.6	55.9	73.7	7.0	55.3	358.9
P (days)	<1	<1	1	0	<1	<1	4	4	4	3	<1	4	24
La Paz, B.C. 24°10′N 110°18′W													
T Mean (°C)	18.4	18.9	21.2	23.2	25.6	27.0	30.2	30.1	28.9	27.1	23.5	20.5	24.6
T mean max. (°C)	21.4	22.5	25.2	27.6	30.6	32.0	34.3	33.3	31.9	30.7	26.6	23.3	28.3
T mean min. (°C)	15.7	15.8	17.5	18.8	21.2	22.7	27.0	27.1	26.4	23.9	20.6	17.8	21.2
P (mm)	3.2	11.4	0.8	0.2	0.0	0.2	6.3	41.7	51.9	9.6	13.4	34.5	173.0
P (days)	<1	2	<1	<1	0	<1	1	3	4	1	1	4	16
Mazatlán, Sin. 23°11′N 106°25′W													
T mean (°C)	19.4	19.3	20.2	21.9	24.2	26.7	27.6	27.8	27.6	26.9	23.9	21.3	23.9
T mean max. (°C)	21.7	21.7	22.7	24.4	26.4	28.6	29.7	29.9	29.5	29.0	26.3	23.5	26.1
T mean min. (°C)	16.6	16.5	17.1	18.7	21.2	24.5	25.1	24.9	25.0	24.4	21.2	18.3	21.1
P (mm)	11.0	9.7	3.4	0.1	1.8	29.2	166.9	241.8	268.6	61.6	11.7	44.4	850.2
P (days)	1	1	<1	<1	<1	4	14	15	14	4	1	4	61
Isla María Madre, Nay. 21°35′W 106°30′W													
T mean (°C)	21.1	20.0	20.6	22.6	25.0	27.0	27.8	27.7	27.8	25.2	24.0	21.5	24.2
T mean max. (°C)	26.1	25.7	26.6	28.9	31.0	32.5	32.7	32.8	32.8	31.2	28.8	26.4	29.6
T mean min. (°C)	16.5	14.8	14.0	15.1	18.0	21.6	23.4	23.6	23.8	22.0	19.9	16.4	19.1
P (mm)	10.8	20.0	0.5	0.0	0.1	37.5	89.1	118.3	210.0	75.1	28.0	77.6	667.6
P (days)	<1	3	<1	<1	<1	2	9	11	4	4	1	4	46
Cabo Corrientes, Jal. 20°24′N 105°43′W													
T mean (°C)	23.2	22.9	22.7	23.9	25.4	26.7	28.1	27.9	27.5	27.8	26.1	23.8	25.5
P (mm)	19.5	29.6	1.3	0.0	2.3	57.3	145.0	272.1	307.0	91.0	15.2	13.5	953.8
P (days)	1	1	<1	0	<1	9	12	14	15	6	1	2	61

[1] Station San Luis, Rio Colorado, Sonora, is inland. It has been used here to illustrate conditions for the upper Gulf, for which no other data are available.

sarily reflect those over the open Gulf. To estimate evaporation from the sea surface, an equation of the type

$$E = K \Delta e W \quad (1)$$

is frequently applied (Sverdrup, 1951). Here E is evaporation (cm/day), Δe is the vapor pressure difference between the sea surface and the air above it (in millibars), and W is the wind speed (m/sec). The proportionality factor K depends upon both the height of observation and the wind speed; for a height of 10 m and wind speeds between 4 m/sec and 8 m/sec, its magnitude is 0.011 (Roden, 1959). The above equation is valid only when the stratification of the air is neutral, and when horizontal moisture gradients can be neglected. It is obviously not applicable in the coastal regions, where large horizontal humidity gradients occur, nor in the northern third of the Gulf where advection of dry desert air is considerable. For the southern two-thirds of the Gulf, the mean annual vapor pressure difference, when determined from sea and air temperature entries in the ship's meteorological journals, is about 8 millibars. With a mean annual wind speed of about 4 m/sec, the evaporation rate is estimated from equation (1) as 128 cm/year. This value is only 60 per cent of the pan evaporation at coastal stations. Inasmuch as neither method is very accurate, the discrepancy is not surprising.

Winds and hurricanes.—Winds in the Gulf of

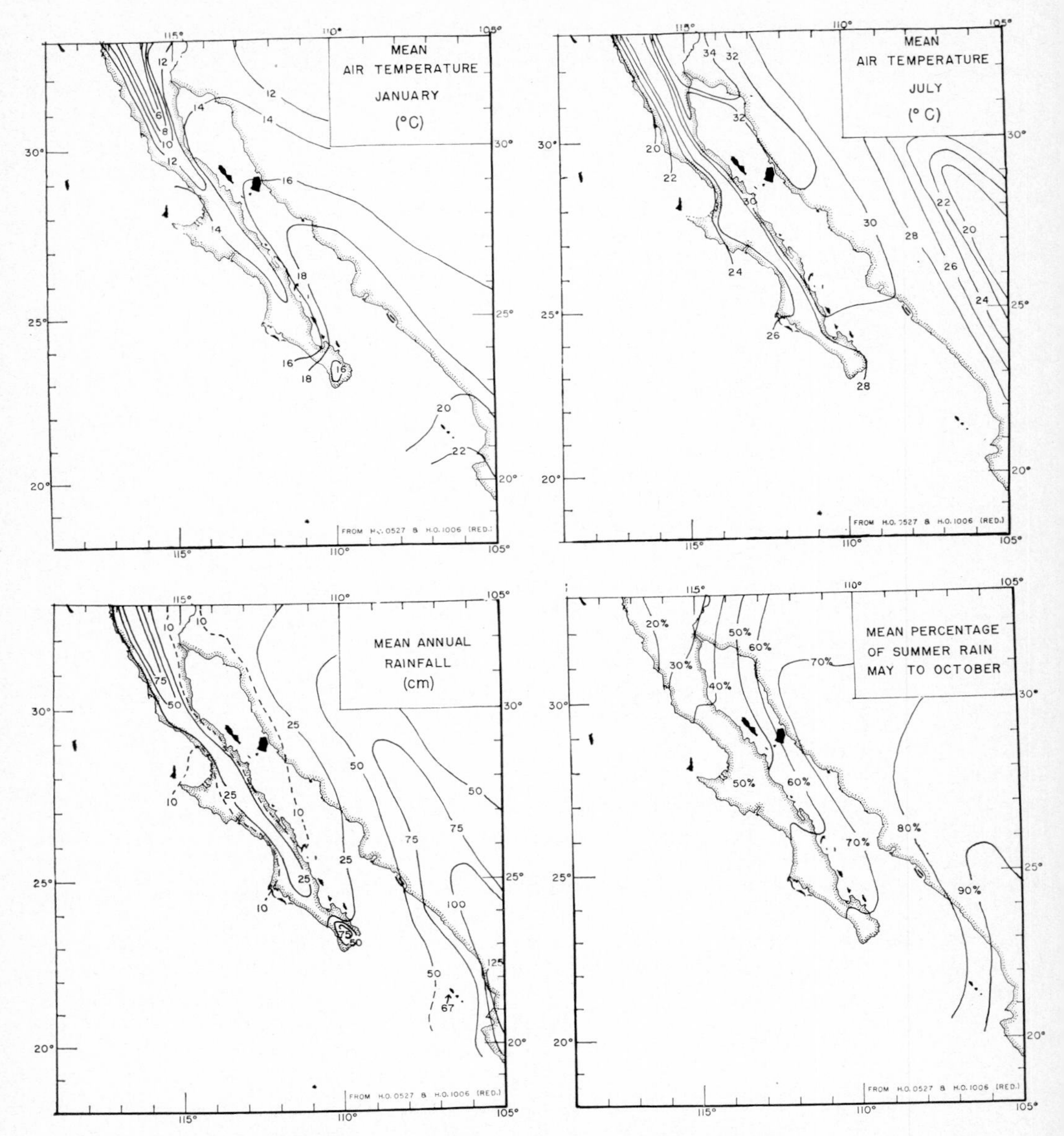

FIG. 2.—Mean air temperature and mean precipitation in the Gulf of California and adjacent regions (after Page, 1930; and Ward and Brooks, 1936).

California are extremely variable. Near the coast, the land and sea breeze system prevails and the diurnal wind changes are usually larger than the annual ones (Table III). The sea breeze reaches its highest speeds, 5 m/sec to 7 m/sec, in the early afternoon and calms down after sunset. The land breeze is very much weaker and rarely attains speeds in excess of 2 m/sec. Near the mountainous coast of Baja California, mountain and valley winds may locally predominate. In the more offshore regions of the Gulf, northwesterly winds prevail from November to May, and

TABLE III. MEAN MONTHLY AND MEAN MONTHLY MAXIMUM WIND SPEED AT FIRST ORDER METEOROLOGICAL STATIONS (After Servicio Meteorológico Mexicano, 1928–1941)

	I	*II*	*III*	*IV*	*V*	*VI*	*VII*	*VIII*	*IX*	*X*	*XI*	*XII*	*Mean*	*Years of Record*
					Mean wind speed (m/sec).									
Guaymas	5.2	5.9	6.2	6.7	5.2	4.6	3.9	3.5	5.4	5.6	5.6	5.3	5.3	10
La Paz	2.5	2.2	2.3	2.4	2.0	2.4	2.0	2.0	1.6	1.9	2.3	2.2	2.2	6
Mazatlán	6.0	6.1	5.9	5.6	4.9	5.0	4.4	4.7	5.0	5.2	4.5	5.2	5.2	12
Isla María Madre	2.3	2.7	2.8	2.7	2.8	2.6	2.0	2.1	2.3	2.2	1.9	2.2	2.4	3
					Mean maximum wind speed (m/sec).									
Guaymas	22.5	21.3	21.8	22.0	18.2	17.6	23.7	29.5	28.4	20.2	21.3	23.2	22.5	10
La Paz	12.8	11.7	11.5	12.4	11.4	10.8	13.0	13.9	20.7	10.4	11.6	11.4	12.6	6
Mazatlán	15.8	17.3	15.5	15.3	15.4	17.8	22.6	24.6	28.8	18.1	13.8	16.1	18.4	12
Isla María Madre	8.1	9.6	11.0	10.4	10.3	16.4	8.0	15.9	14.5	14.3	8.1	9.5	11.3	3

southeasterly ones during the rest of the year. Moderate northwest gales that last two or three days at a time are frequently experienced in the upper Gulf between December and February. These winds are particularly strong in Ballenas Channel between the montainous Baja California coast and the equally high island of Angel de la Guarda; they may on occasion raise such a heavy sea that navigation becomes impossible (U.S. Hydrographic Office, 1951). During summer, gusty and hot desert winds are encountered frequently in the northern third of the Gulf. In the southern part of the Gulf, violent storms of relatively short duration, called *chubascos*, occur during the rainy season—from June to October. These gales may last from two to four days, and may blow from any quarter with speeds ranging between 12 m/sec and 19 m/sec (Beaufort, 6–8).

Hurricanes may strike the coastal areas of the Gulf of California any time between late May and early November. They are, however, much more common in September and October than during any other time of year. These hurricanes originate off the southern coast of Mexico or Central America, and proceed toward the west or northwest with speeds averaging between 180 and 360 nautical miles per day (Fig. 3). Upon reaching Cabo Corrientes, they may continue on a westward course (May to August), or they may curve to the north or northeast, either crossing the southern part of Baja California, or proceeding directly into the Gulf. Most hurricanes are dissipated before they reach the islands of Tiburón and Angel de la Guarda. In Table IV are shown pertinent hurricane data for recent years. It is seen that maximum wind speeds of 77 m/sec (150 kn) may be expected, and that the atmospheric pressure at the surface may drop to 958 millibars. Heavy loss of life and damage to ships may occur, as is amply illustrated by the October 1959 hurricane, which claimed about 1,000 lives and sank seven ships.

TABLE IV. RECENT HURRICANES AFFECTING THE GULF OF CALIFORNIA AND VICINITY (After U.S. Weather Bureau, 1954–1961)

Year	*Date*	*First Reported*	*Coastline Crossed*	*Highest Observed Wind Speed*	*Lowest Atmos. Press.*	*Place of Dissipation*	*Remarks*
1954	12–17 Jul.	14°N 95°W	Near Bahía Ballenas	39 m/s	991 mb	near Isla Tiburón	—
1955	15–16 Oct.	16°N 104°W	north of Manzanillo	33 m/s	999 mb	north of Manzanillo	—
1956	——	——	——	——	——	——	No hurricane affected the Gulf.
1957	1–5 Oct.	18°N 118°W	Bahía Magdalena	46 m/s	996 mb	south of Guaymas	Ship damage in Bahía Magdalena.
	17–20 Oct.	13°N 103°W	none	41 m/s	986 mb	south of Mazatlán	—
	20–21 Oct.	16°N 113°W	near Mazatlán	67 m/s	959 mb	near Mazatlán	Extensive damage to ships and structures in Mazatlán area.
1958	29 Sept.–4 Oct.	16°N 100°W	tip of Baja California	46 m/s	960 mb	north of Guaymas	Town of San José del Cabo, Baja California virtually wiped out.
1959	3–11 Sept.	13°N 93°W	Baja California	39 m/s	987 mb	31°N 116°W	—
	22–27 Oct.	13°N 96°W	near Manzanillo	77 m/s	958 mb	northeast of Manzanillo	1,000 lives lost in Manzanillo Minatitlán, and nearby communities. Seven ships sunk.
1960	21–23 Oct.	18°N 104°W	north of Mazatlán	32 m/s	989 mb	north of Mazatlán	—

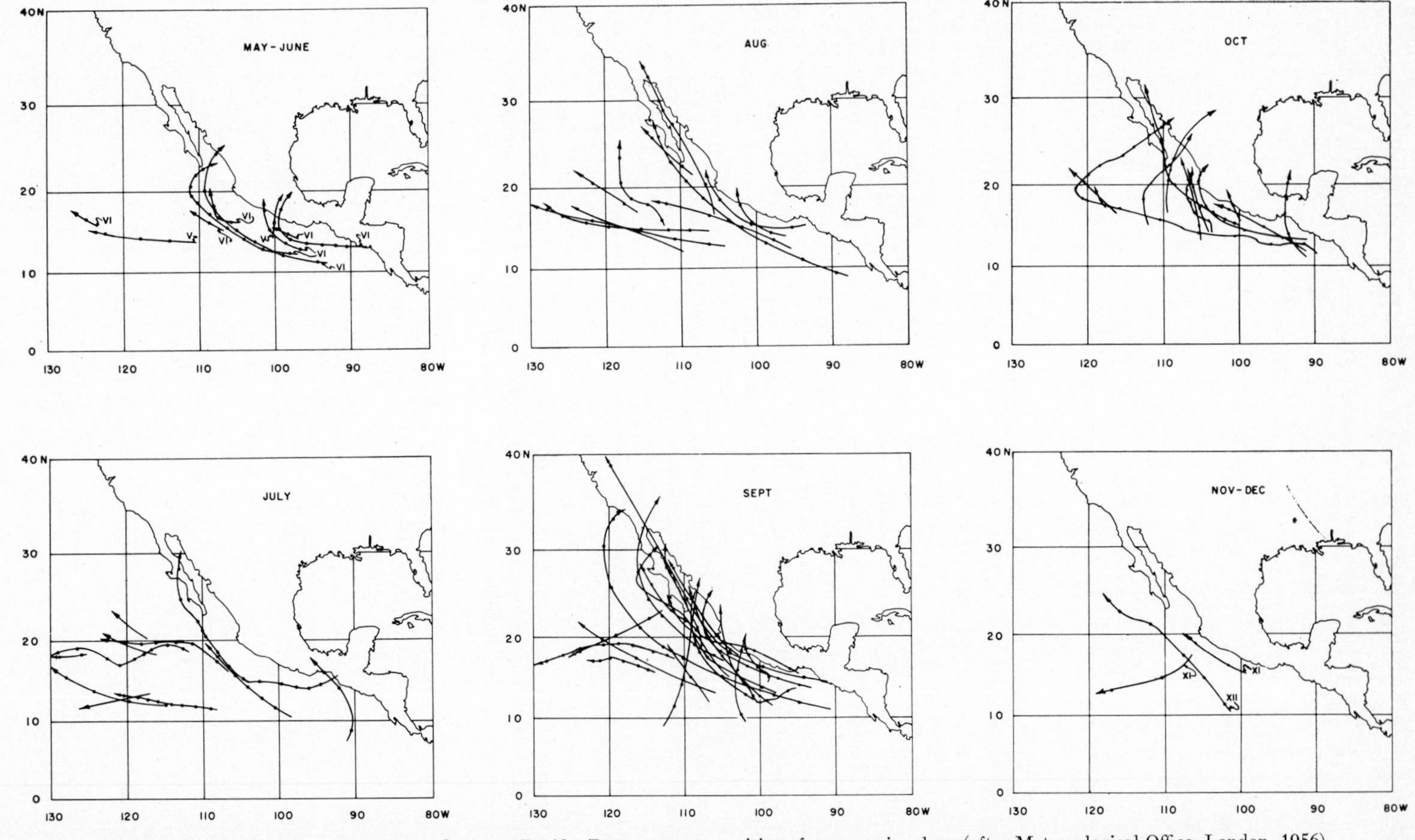

FIG. 3.—Paths of hurricanes in the northeastern Pacific. Dots represent positions for successive days (after Meteorological Office, London, 1956).

DISCHARGE AND CHEMICAL COMPOSITION OF RIVERS

The chief source of stream-borne sediments, at least until the Hoover Dam was completed in 1935, was the Colorado River; it is estimated that this river contributed about 50 per cent of the total amount of sediment brought annually into the Gulf (Byrne and Emery, 1960). The mean annual discharge of the Colorado River at Yuma, Arizona, was about 600 m^3/sec prior to the construction of the Hoover Dam (U.S. Geological Survey, 1954); since then it has decreased to about 120 m^3/sec. The year-to-year variation of the discharge is large, and so is the seasonal variation. During the recent five-year period 1955–1959, the discharge ranged from a minimum of 11 m^3/sec in October 1956 to a maximum of 260 m^3/sec in January 1958. Very little water is likely to reach the Gulf in the summer and early fall months.

The chemical composition of the Colorado River at Yuma is given in Table V. The concentrations are expressed in equivalents per million of cations and anions, except for silica and boron which may be present in a colloidal state and which are expressed in parts per million. It is seen that the most abundant ions are sulfate, sodium, and calcium, followed by bicarbonate, chloride, and magnesium. The average annual concentrations given in Table V may differ by a factor of two for any particular month.

Along the southeastern coast, several large rivers enter the Gulf, the most important ones being, from north to south—Río Yaqui, Río Fuerte, Río Piaxtla, Río Presidio, Río Baluarte, and, particularly, Río Grande de Santiago. These rivers differ from the Colorado River by the fact that they carry more water during the summer and fall than during the winter and spring.

TIDES AND SEA LEVEL

Tide observations have been recorded from very few locations. In Table VI are shown eight of the more important tidal constituents at Bahia Magdalena on the west side of Baja California, Mazatlán near the Gulf entrance, and Guaymas in the central part of the Gulf. No station was available for the northern part. It is seen that the tides at Bahía Magdalena and Mazatlán are of a mixed type, with the semidiurnal components M_2 and S_2 being slightly larger than the diurnal components K_1 and O_1. At Guaymas, however, the diurnal components dominate over the semidiurnal ones. The composite tidal range

TABLE V. CHEMICAL ANALYSIS OF COLORADO RIVER WATER AT YUMA, ARIZONA

Values Represent Averages of Daily Observations Made from October 1956 to September 1957
(After U.S. Geological Survey Water-Supply Paper 1524 (1960)

	Mean	*Monthly Range*	*Unit*
SiO_2[1]	13	8–17	parts per million
Ca	5.49	5.09–6.69	equivalents per million
Mg	2.80	2.38–3.37	equivalents per million
Na	5.70	4.61–6.74	equivalents per million
K	0.14	0.12–0.15	equivalents per million
HCO_3	2.87	2.75–3.08	equivalents per million
SO_4	7.62	6.60–8.29	equivalents per million
Cl	3.58	2.99–4.17	equivalents per million
F	0.02	0.02–0.03	equivalents per million
NO_3	0.02	0.00–0.03	equivalents per million
B	0.24	0.20–0.24	parts per million
dissolved solids[2]	889	791–1,000	parts per million
per cent sodium[3]	40	32–43	per cent
sodium absorption ratio	2.8	2.1–3.2	—
specific conductance	1,340	1,270–1,470	micro-ohms at 25°C
pH	—	7.7–8.2	—
discharge	28	11–60	m^3/sec

[1] Colloidal state.
[2] Residues after evaporation at 180°C.
[3] Calculated from $\frac{100\ Na}{Na+K+Ca+Mg}$.

TABLE VI. TIDAL CONSTANTS IN AND OUTSIDE GULF OF CALIFORNIA
(H) Refers to Amplitude of each component; (K) to the epoch
(After U.S. Coast and Geodetic Survey Measurements *in*: Hydrographic Department, London, 1961)

Component	K_1	O_1	P_1	Q_1	M_2	S_2	N_2	K_2	*Record Length*
Period (hours)	*23.93*	*25.82*	*24.07*	*26.87*	*12.42*	*12.00*	*12.66*	*11.97*	
Bahía Magdalena, B.C. 24°38′N 112°09′W (outside Gulf)									
H (cm)	24	17	8	—	49	31	12	8	30 days
K (deg)	071	077	071	—	244	253	246	253	
Mazatlán, Sin. 23°11′N 106°27′W (Gulf entrance)									
H (cm)	20	14	8	—	33	23	7	7	369 days
K (deg)	072	075	069	—	265	254	254	248	
Guaymas, Son. 27°55′N 110°54′W (central Gulf)									
H (cm)	27	19	9	4	14	11	4	3	221 days
K (deg)	071	058	070	049	295	276	305	271	

(Fig. 4) increases gradually from the Gulf entrance to Isla Tiburón, and then rapidly to the mouth of the Colorado. At the latter, the spring tidal range is about 10 m, the average range 7 m, and the neap range 2 m. The tidal wave continues into the Colorado River in the form of a tidal bore. Marigram records of the bore at a station about 25 km upstream (Valenzuela, personal communication) show that the front of the bore is an almost vertical wall of water, 1.5 m–3 m high, and that after the passage of the front, the water level decreases gradually with time, until the front of the next bore appears, almost 12 hours later.

The time of high or low water gets progressively later up the Gulf, the time difference between the Gulf entrance and the vicinity of the Colorado River being approximately 5.5 hours for high water and 6 hours for low water. Thus one observes the interesting feature that when there is low water at one end of the Gulf, there is high water at the other. Whether the tidal wave is a progressive or a standing one cannot be decided from the meager data available (Roden and Groves, 1959).

Tidal currents in the narrows between the islands and the coast, and in the vicinity of the delta of the Colorado River are strong, sometimes causing heavy rip tides. Strong tidal currents may also be expected in narrow passages connecting semienclosed lagoons with the open Gulf. The speed of these currents is variable, depending upon the stage of the moon and the prevailing winds. Velocities up to 3 m/sec (6 kn) at full and change of the moon have been reported locally (U.S. Hydrographic Office, 1951).

Sea-level records from tide gage stations in the Gulf (Instituto de Geofísica, Univ. Nac. Aut., Mexico D.F., unpublished) show that the amplitude of the mean annual oscillation increases from 13 cm at Mazatlán to 17 cm at Guaymas (Table VII). The lowest sea levels occur from February to April and the highest from July to September. The amplitude of the annual sea-level change due to heating and salinity effects in the upper 500 m is about 16 cm, which suggests that most of the observed annual sea-level changes are due to changes in heat and salt content. A similar result was obtained by Pattullo, Munk, Revelle, and Strong (1955). The nonseasonal sea-level oscillations in the Gulf of California and adjacent regions are shown in Figure 5. The seasonal variation was eliminated by taking differences between the monthly means and the long-term means for the respective months. Although the details of the resulting anomaly records vary, several common features stand out—(a) the mean amplitude of the nonseasonal sea-level oscillation appears to be close to 7 cm, or to about half the mean annual oscillation; (b) sea-level oscillations in the Gulf are of the same type as elsewhere along the southern coast of Mexico; (c) the average duration of the sea-level anomalies appears to be of the order of several months. A spectral analysis of the nonseasonal sea-level variations

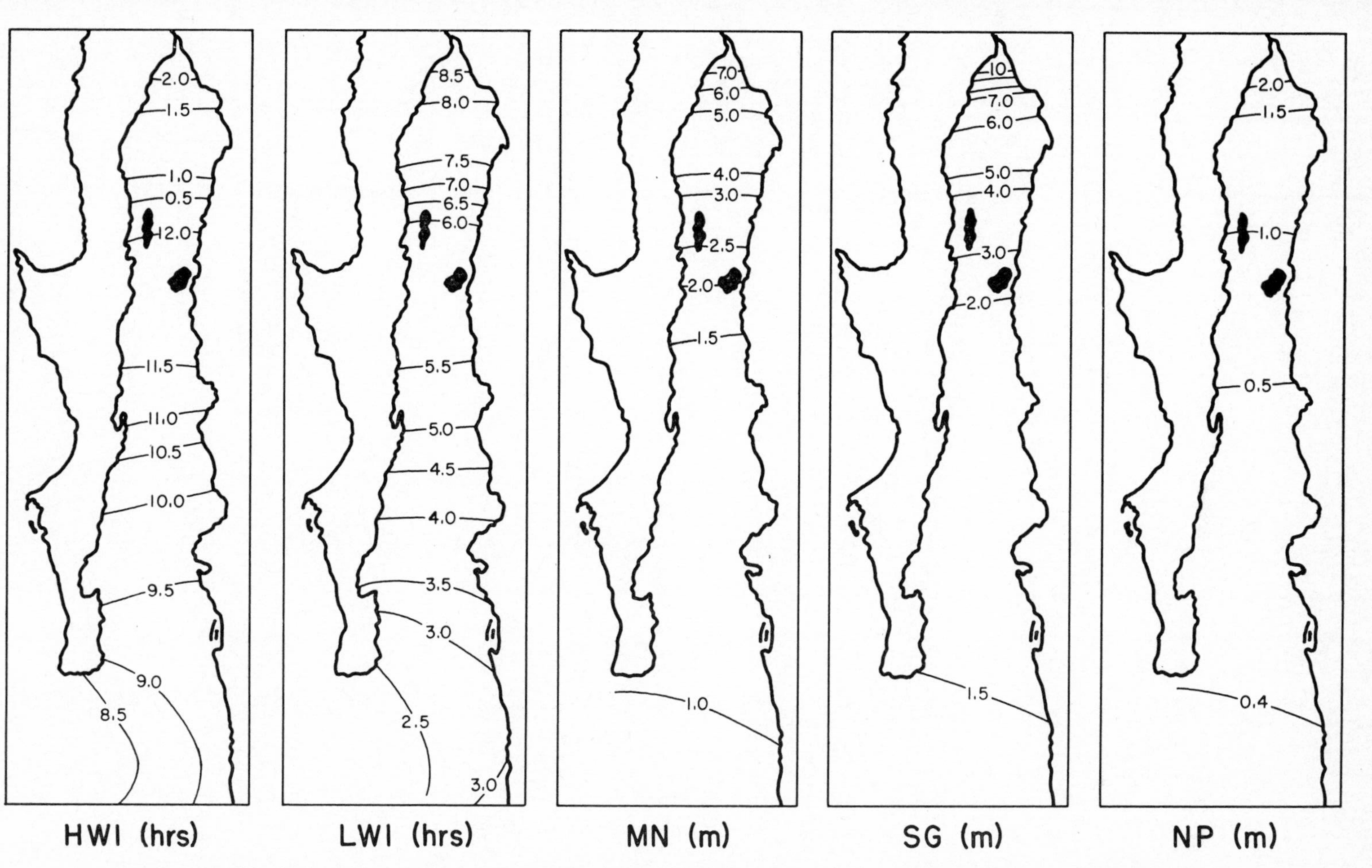

FIG. 4.—Tides in the Gulf of California. HWI and LWI refer to high and low water interval in hours. MN, SG, and NP denote the mean, spring, and neap tidal ranges in meters.

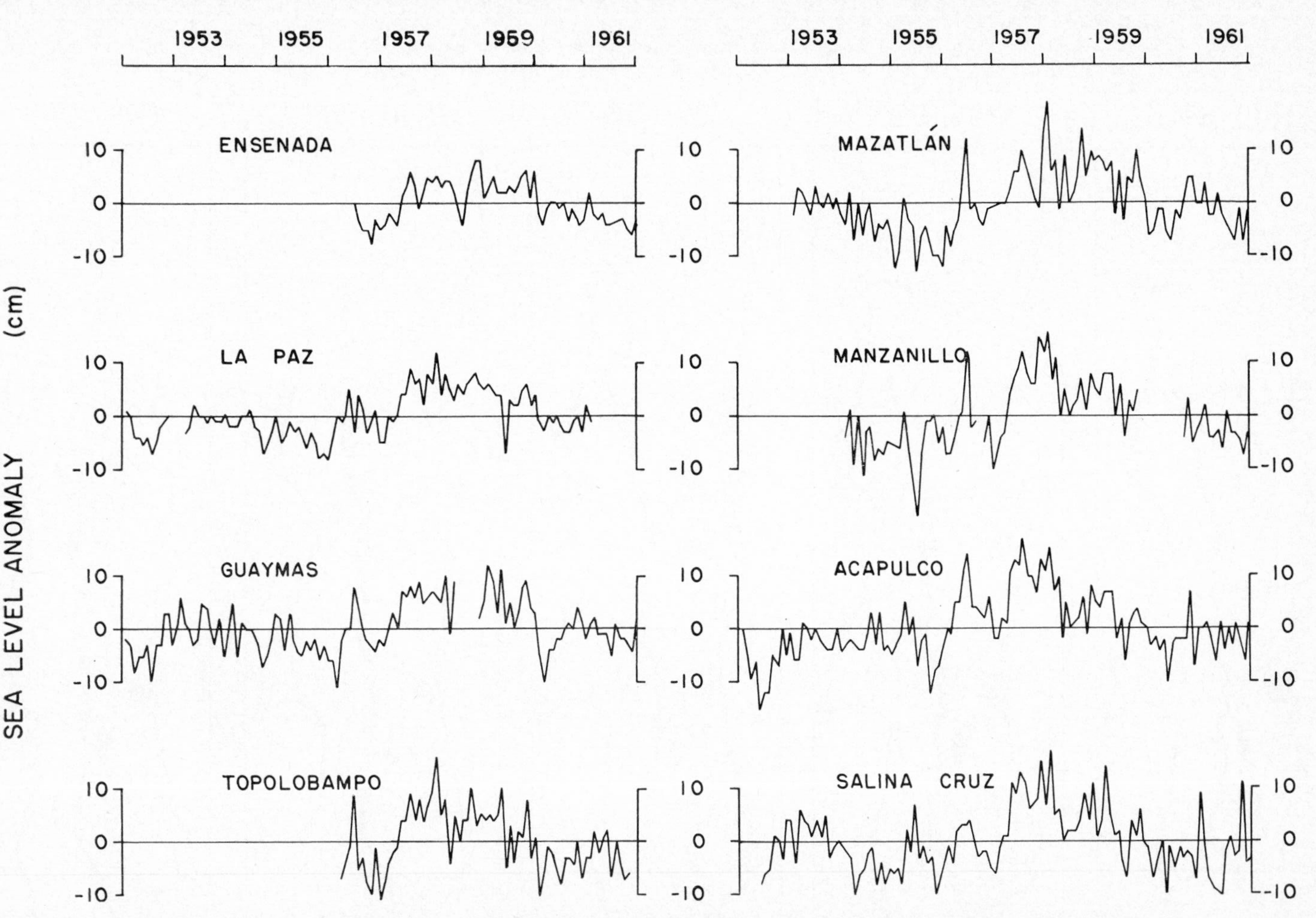

FIG. 5.—Sea level anomalies from the long-term monthly means along the Pacific coast of Mexico. The stations La Paz, Guaymas, Topolobampo, and Mazatlán are in the Gulf of California.

TABLE VII. SEA LEVEL AND SEA SURFACE TEMPERATURE OBSERVATIONS AT TIDE GAGE STATIONS IN THE GULF OF CALIFORNIA

	I	II	III	IV	V	VI	VII	VIII	IX	X	XI	XII	Annual Record			
													Mean	*Range*	*Length*	*Source*
Sea level (cm)																
Guaymas	−14.1	−14.7	−14.0	− 9.3	−0.8	+12.6	+18.8	+17.6	+18.3	+ 6.8	−9.5	−11.7	0	33.5	11	IG-UNAM
Topolobampo	− 9.7	−13.3	−14.9	−12.7	−2.8	+11.4	+16.6	+15.4	+18.2	+ 7.2	−4.9	−10.5	0	33.1	6	IG-UNAM
La Paz	− 6.9	− 8.9	−11.4	−10.5	−7.5	− 1.9	+ 6.0	+11.5	+14.4	+11.0	+6.0	− 1.7	0	25.8	11	IG-UNAM
Mazatlán	− 4.7	− 9.3	−12.2	−11.1	−3.4	+ 7.0	+13.8	+12.7	+12.9	+ 5.0	−5.1	− 5.6	0	25.1	10	IG-UNAM
Isla Socorro[1]	− 0.9	− 2.2	− 0.2	+ 0.4	+2.4	+ 1.8	− 1.5	− 1.4	+ 2.5	+ 1.0	−0.5	− 1.4	0	4.7	1	IG-UNAM
Mean sea surface temperature (°C)																
Puerto Peñasco	14.9	15.8	17.8	20.6	23.8	26.3	29.7	31.2	31.0	28.4	22.0	17.1	23.2	16.3	4	USCGS
Bahía de los Angeles	16.0	15.8	15.6	17.1	18.0	21.0	25.1	27.1	25.1	23.6	19.0	16.0	20.0	11.5	1	SIO
Guaymas	17.4	18.3	19.2	22.3	25.2	29.5	31.6	31.6	31.2	28.1	22.7	18.2	24.6	14.2	8	USCGS
Topolobampo	19.0	20.0	21.0	23.6	26.3	29.7	31.1	31.5	31.3	28.9	23.1	19.5	25.4	12.5	6	USCGS
La Paz	20.3	20.3	21.6	22.7	24.3	25.2	27.5	29.1	29.7	28.2	25.2	21.8	24.7	9.4	11	USCGS
Mazatlán	22.2	21.1	21.3	22.5	24.9	28.2	29.6	30.0	30.1	28.8	25.2	22.9	25.6	9.0	9	USCGS
Cabo San Lucas	20.8	20.5	—	20.6	23.1	23.6	25.9	28.2	29.0	—	26.2	24.4	24.2	(8.5)	1	SIO
Isla Socorro[1]	24.6	24.3	25.0	—	—	—	28.3	27.3	28.6	—	—	—	—	(4.3)	1	USCGS
Mean minimum sea surface temperature (°C)																
Puerto Peñasco	12.8	14.4	15.8	17.8	21.0	23.0	27.5	30.0	29.2	25.8	19.2	13.8	20.9	17.2	4	USCGS
Bahía de los Angeles	—	—	—	15.8	16.0	18.6	21.8	22.5	22.5	19.4	17.5	15.0	—	—	1	SIO
Guaymas	15.6	15.9	15.3	18.1	19.8	26.4	29.1	27.7	28.9	25.8	19.9	14.3	21.4	14.8	3	USCGS
La Paz	17.7	17.3	19.3	20.4	21.9	21.9	24.2	27.0	27.3	26.4	23.1	19.8	22.2	10.0	6	USCGS
Mazatlán	18.5	18.3	18.2	19.1	20.8	24.9	28.2	28.8	26.7	26.1	22.2	17.8	22.5	10.0	3	USCGS
Mean maximum sea surface temperature (°C)																
Puerto Peñasco	17.6	17.8	20.2	23.3	26.0	28.9	32.0	32.2	32.2	30.6	25.7	19.7	25.5	14.6	4	USCGS
Bahía de los Angeles	16.6	16.2	16.0	19.1	19.9	24.0	27.0	28.5	27.6	25.0	23.0	18.0	21.7	12.5	1	SIO
Guaymas	22.2	20.3	21.7	23.3	29.2	32.8	33.0	33.8	33.9	31.5	27.4	22.7	27.7	13.6	3	USCGS
La Paz	21.5	21.7	24.3	25.7	27.2	27.7	29.8	31.3	31.3	30.3	27.7	24.3	26.9	9.8	6	USCGS
Mazatlán	22.7	22.7	23.8	24.9	26.0	30.0	30.8	31.1	31.3	29.4	27.8	23.8	27.0	8.6	3	USCGS

[1] Isla Socorro is outside the Gulf and has been added for comparison.

showed that most of them are related to variations in temperature at low frequencies, and that there is very little relation between sea level and atmospheric pressure relations (Roden, 1960).

SURFACE CURRENTS

Direct current measurements in the interior regions of the Gulf are nonexistent. The few currents determined from the drift of ships indicate that the flow is predominantly southeasterly in winter and spring and northwesterly in summer and fall (Fig. 6). North of Isla Tiburón, and in the narrows between the islands and the coast, tidal currents predominate. These may reach speeds between 1 m/sec and 3 m/sec, and they are frequently accompanied by strong rips and impressive eddies (U.S. Hydrographic Office, 1951). Across the Gulf entrance, between Cabo San Lucas and Cabo Corrientes, the surface currents are variable (Table VIII). Southeasterly set with speeds ranging between 10 cm/sec and 15 cm/sec is commonly observed from February to May. Between June and September, the set is generally toward the northwest with maximum speeds of about 10 cm/sec. During the remaining months of the year, the currents are weak and set mostly toward a westerly or southwesterly direction.

SOME HYDRODYNAMIC ASPECTS OF CURRENTS

We shall here consider only a linear and stationary model. Assuming that the total pressure, p, is equal to the sum of the hydrostatic pressure, p_o, and the atmospheric pressure, p_a, the equations of motion and continuity take the following form

$$(1)\quad \mathbf{k}\times \mathbf{V}_H = -\frac{\alpha}{f}\nabla_H p_o - \frac{\alpha}{f}\nabla_H p_a + \frac{\alpha}{f}\frac{\delta \boldsymbol{\tau}_H}{\delta z}$$

$$(2)\quad 0 = -\alpha\frac{\partial p}{\partial z} - g$$

$$(3)\quad \frac{\partial \rho w}{\partial z} = -\nabla_H\cdot\rho \mathbf{V}_H.$$

Here $\mathbf{v}_H$ is the horizontal (vector) velocity, w is the vertical velocity, $\boldsymbol{\tau}_H$ is the horizontal (vector) stress due to vertical shear, $\nabla_H p_o$ is the horizontal (hydrostatic) pressure gradient in the ocean, $\nabla_H p_a$ is the horizontal pressure gradient in the atmosphere, f is the Coriolis parameter, g is gravity, ρ is density, $\alpha = 1/\rho$ is the specific volume, and $\mathbf{k}$ is a unit vector. The first term of the right hand side of the equation (1) denotes the geostrophic part of the current, the second term, the part due to the atmospheric pressure gradient, and the third term, the part due to the vertical gradient of the stress. The geostrophic term can be evaluated from temperature and salinity observations at different depths. The term containing the atmospheric pressure can be obtained from the weather map. The evaluation of the vertical gradient of stress, however, presents some difficulties. At the sea surface the stress must equal that of the wind. A rough estimate of the latter can be obtained from the well known expression $\tau = k'\rho_a W^2$ (Sverdrup, Johnson, and Fleming, 1946) where ρ_a is the density of air (1.2×10^{-3} g/cm^3) and W is the wind speed near the sea surface (cm/sec). The proportionality factor is $k' = 2.6\times10^{-3}$, approximately. At the sea surface, the gradient $\partial\bar{\tau}_H/\partial z$ can be approximated by $-\boldsymbol{\tau}_{Ho}/H$ where H (to be taken as a negative value) is the depth to the bottom of the upper mixed layer, where the wind stress is supposed to vanish (Yoshida, 1955).

The magnitude of the terms on the right hand side of equation (1) is as follows *at the surface of the Gulf*

$$\text{February:}\quad -\frac{\alpha}{f}\nabla_H p_0 = -4 \text{ cm/sec};$$

$$-\frac{\alpha}{f}\nabla_H p_a = -1 \text{ cm/sec};$$

$$\frac{\alpha}{f}\frac{\partial\bar{\tau}_{Ho}}{\partial z} = -5 \text{ cm/sec}.$$

$$\text{August:}\quad -\frac{\alpha}{f}\nabla_H p_0 = +13 \text{ cm/sec};$$

$$-\frac{\alpha}{f}\nabla_H p_a = +2 \text{ cm/sec};$$

$$\frac{\alpha}{f}\frac{\partial\bar{\tau}_{H0}}{\partial z} = +6 \text{ cm/sec}.$$

Here, the positive sign is taken to denote inflow, and the negative one, outflow. The net surface current across the Gulf entrance is thus -10 cm/sec in February and $+21$ cm/sec in August. The above values are in reasonable agreement with the observed ship drifts (U.S. Hydrographic Office, 1947). It is of interest to note that the contribution to the net current of the term containing the horizontal gradient of atmospheric

Table VIII. Speed and Direction of Surface Currents in the Vicinity of the Gulf of California
(After U.S. Hydrographic Office, 1947)

	I	*II*	*III*	*IV*	*V*	*VI*	*VII*	*VIII*	*IX*	*X*	*XI*	*XII*	*Notes*
						18–19 N	104–105 W						
V (cm/sec)	12.8	12.5	15.3	2.1	5.5	13.2	11.3	9.8	4.6	2.1	7.6	12.4	Off Manzanillo
degrees	300	230	230	190	280	300	290	300	290	230	300	310	
						19–20 N	106–107 W						
V (cm/sec)	8.7	10.3	10.6	8.0	4.0	8.8	10.7	5.1	3.0	7.6	8.8	8.4	Off Cabo Corrientes
degrees	220	190	180	190	190	300	300	270	300	190	230	220	
						20–21 N	107–108 W						
V (cm/sec)	8.7	10.3	10.6	8.0	4.0	8.8	7.6	5.1	2.1	3.6	6.6	8.8	Entrance to Gulf of California
degrees	230	180	180	190	190	300	290	300	340	270	240	210	
						21–22 N	108–109 W						
V (cm/sec)	6.4	9.2	9.1	6.3	5.1	2.1	4.0	3.5	2.1	6.2	4.0	6.6	
degrees	230	160	180	160	160	190	310	340	020	300	250	230	
						22–23 N	110–111 W						
V (cm/sec)	4.0	10.7	12.4	15.0	11.3	5.5	4.0	4.6	4.0	6.3	7.5	4.0	Off Cabo San Lucas
degrees	230	170	150	160	170	180	230	280	250	240	270	210	
						23–24 N	111–112 W						
V (cm/sec)	5.1	9.8	14.3	17.0	15.4	10.3	4.0	2.1	3.6	4.6	7.5	2.6	
degrees	220	150	150	160	160	170	200	250	260	260	300	220	
						24–25 N	112–113 W						
V (cm/sec)	4.5	12.8	11.8	15.0	16.5	11.3	7.2	16.7	3.6	4.6	4.6	3.0	Off Bahía Magdalena
degrees	170	170	150	140	160	160	180	220	280	290	290	220	
						25–26 N	113–114 W						
V (cm/sec)	3.6	7.6	11.8	13.2	15.0	11.8	7.7	3.0	3.0	4.0	3.0	2.1	
degrees	180	160	180	150	160	140	170	180	230	290	300	240	

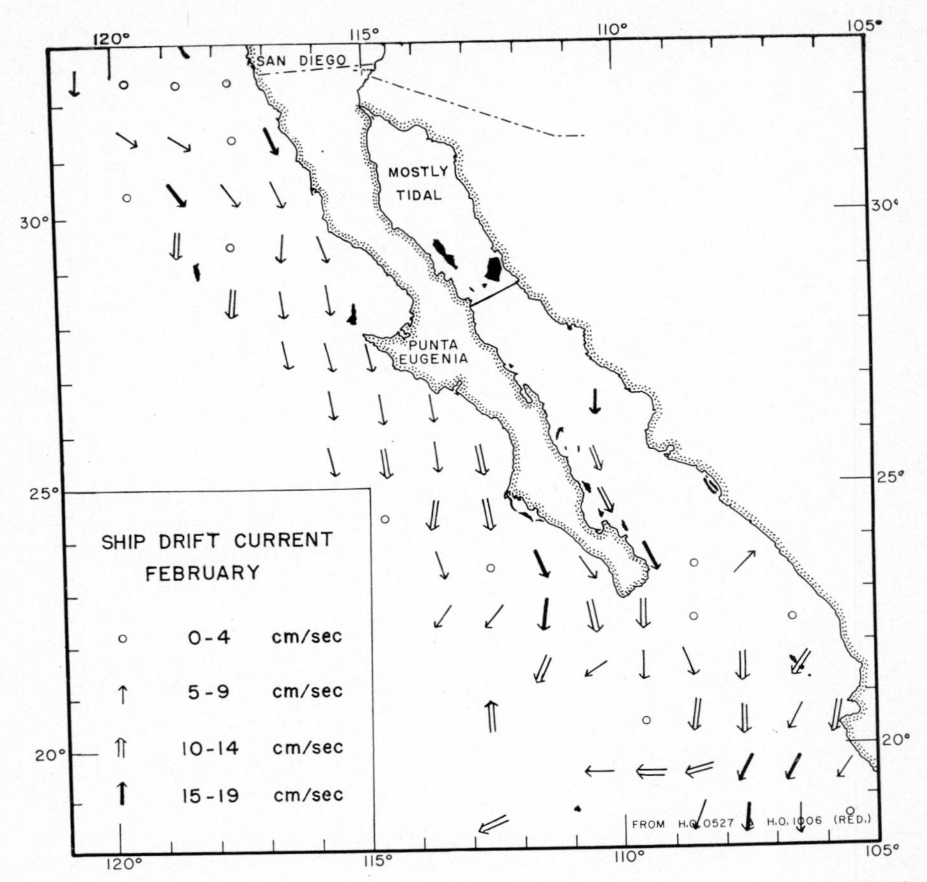

FIG. 6.—Ship drift currents in the Gulf of California and

pressure is not negligible in comparison to the other terms. At depths, where the geostrophic currents are weak, this term may be of considerable importance.

It is obvious that inflow and outflow must compensate each other closely in the Gulf of California; if this were not so, the sea-level changes in the Gulf would be unreasonably large. Whether compensation takes place by opposite flow at different levels, or by opposite flow along the shores of the Gulf, or both, cannot be decided with accuracy from the available data.

A rough estimate of the vertical velocity, w, can be obtained by integrating the equations of motion and continuity with respect to z and taking the integration limits between H, the depth where the wind stress is supposed to vanish (such as the bottom of the upper mixed layer), and η, the sea surface. After some calculations, one obtains

$$(4)\quad W_H = \frac{\beta}{f^2\bar{\rho}}\left[H\frac{\partial pa}{\partial x} + \bar{\rho}hH\frac{\partial \eta}{\partial x} + \tau_{xo}\right] + \frac{\nabla_{H}\times\tau_o}{\bar{\rho}f}.$$

Here w_H is the vertical velocity at the bottom of the upper mixed layer, H, here assumed constant; $\bar{\rho}$ is the mean density of the upper mixed layer, β, the change of the Coriolis parameter with latitude, τ_{x0}, the wind stress component toward the east at the sea surface, and $\nabla_H\times\boldsymbol{\tau}_o$ the vertical component of the curl of the wind stress at the sea surface.

The terms on the right hand side of equation (4) can be roughly evaluated from a knowledge

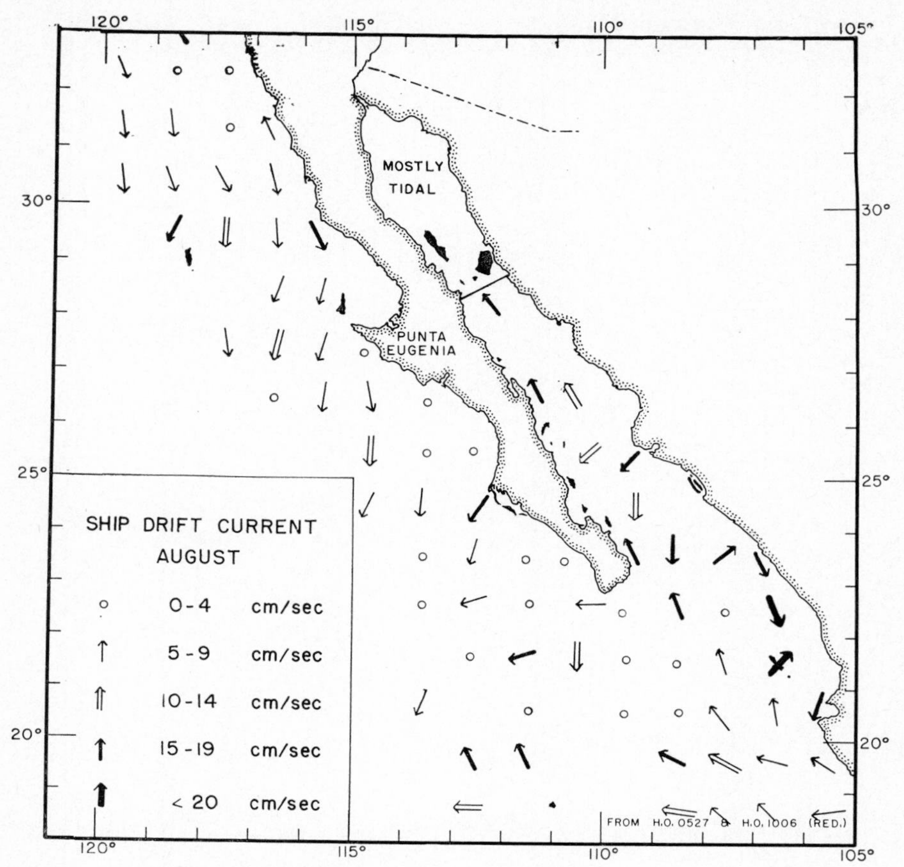

adjacent regions (after U.S. Hydrographic Office, 1947).

of the atmospheric pressure and wind distribution at the sea surface, and from hydrographic observations at different depths. Making use of the data collected by the February 1957 cruise into the Gulf, the following results are obtained for the central region (Section 127 G of Fig. 1)

East coast—

$$\frac{\beta}{\bar{\rho} f^2} H \frac{\partial p_a}{\partial x} = 0.5 \times 10^{-5} \text{ cm/sec};$$

$$\beta/f^2 gH \frac{\partial \eta}{\partial x} = 1.8 \times 10^{-4} \text{ cm/sec}$$

$$\frac{\beta}{\bar{\rho} f^2} \tau_{xo} = 2.8 \times 10^{-5} \text{ cm/sec};$$

$$\frac{\nabla_H \times \tau_o}{\bar{\rho} f} = 3.6 \times 10^{-3} \text{ cm/sec}.$$

West coast—

$$\frac{\beta}{\bar{\rho} f^2} H \frac{\partial p_a}{\partial x} = 1.3 \times 10^{-5} \text{ cm/sec};$$

$$\frac{\beta}{f^2} gH \frac{\partial \eta}{\partial x} = -0.9 \times 10^{-4} \text{ cm/sec}$$

$$\frac{\beta}{\bar{\rho} f^2} \tau_{xo} = 2.2 \times 10^{-5} \text{ cm/sec};$$

$$\frac{\nabla \times \tau}{f \bar{\rho}} = -2.7 \times 10^{-3} \text{ cm/sec}.$$

It is seen that the dominant term is that involving the vertical component of the curl of the wind stress; it is positive along the Mexican mainland coast and negative along the Baja California coast. Upwelling can therefore be expected to occur at the former and downwelling at the

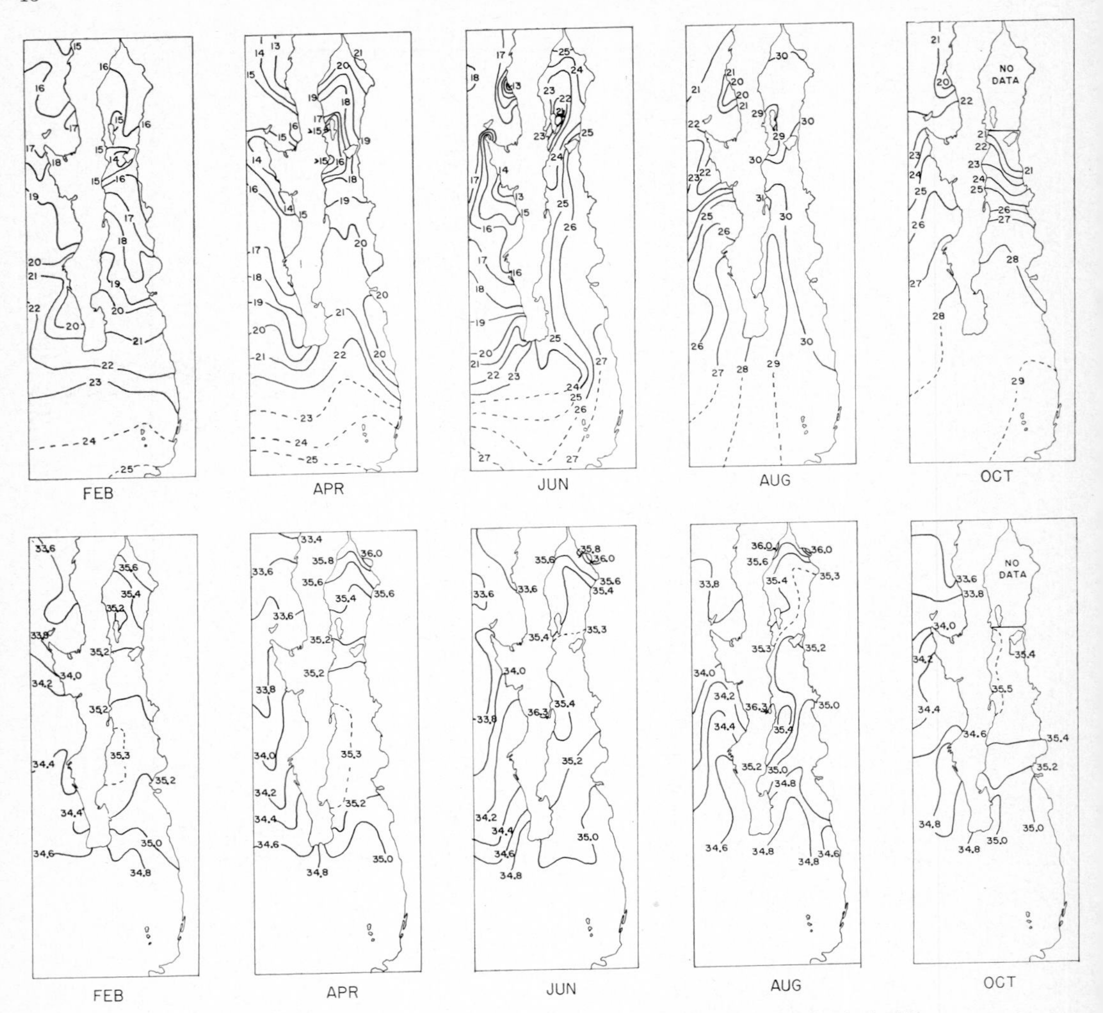

FIG. 7.—Temperature (top) and salinity (bottom) at a depth of 10 m. The dashed lines are extrapolations based on merchant ship observations.

latter. An inspection of the surface temperatures in Figure 7 shows that this is actually the case. The net upwelling speed along the east coast is about 3.8×10^{-3} cm/sec, or roughly 3.2 m per day.

DISTRIBUTION OF PROPERTIES

TEMPERATURE AND SALINITY IN SURFACE LAYERS

The distribution of temperature and salinity at the 10 m level is shown in Figure 7. This level, rather than the sea surface, was chosen in order to eliminate diurnal effects. Compared to temperatures in the neighboring Pacific, those in the Gulf are warmer from April to September and about equal during the remaining months of the year. The annual range is large and increases from about 9°C near Cabo Corrientes, to roughly 15°C near the mouth of the Colorado River. The lowest temperatures do not occur in the upper shallow Gulf, but, instead, are found in the vicinity of Isla Angel de la Guarda, where tidal mixing is strong. The low temperatures along the east coast

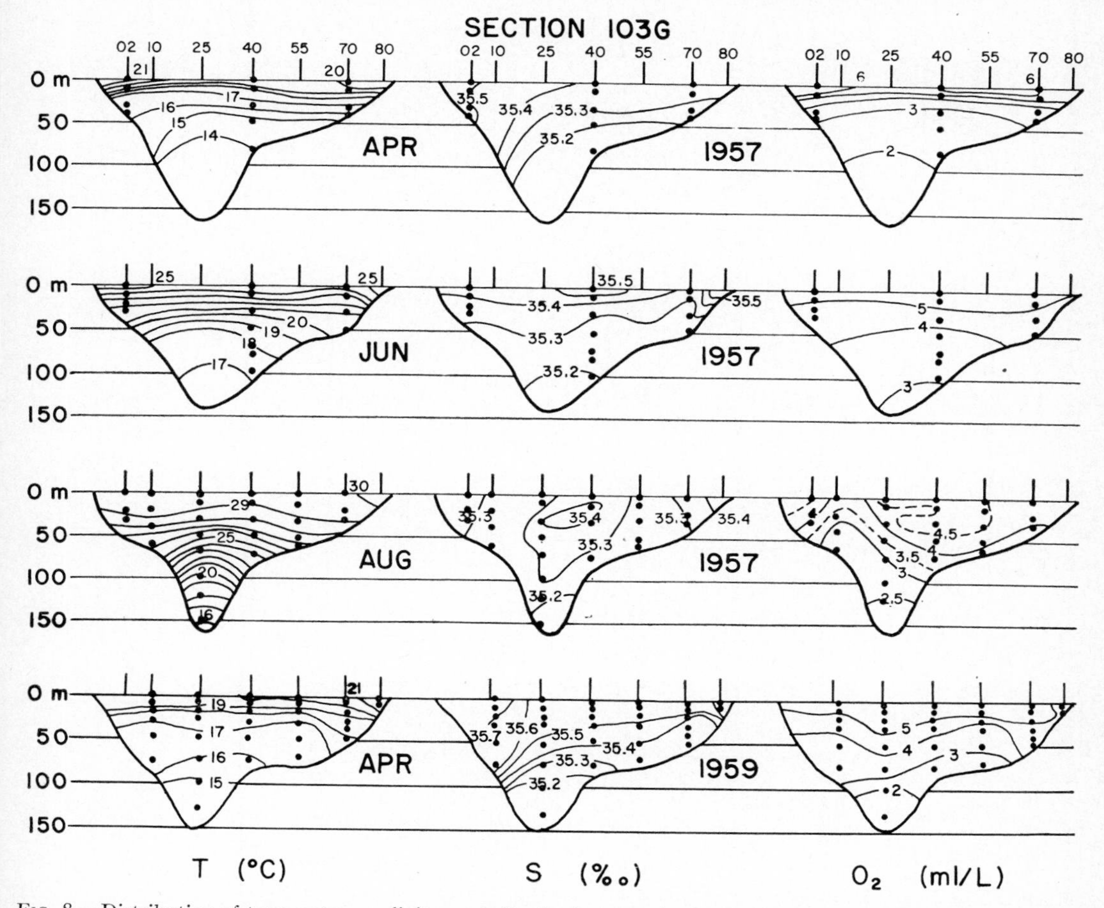

FIG. 8.—Distribution of temperature, salinity, and dissolved oxygen in the upper Gulf (Section 103 G of Fig. 1).

and in lee of Isla Tiburón in winter, are related to upwelling, caused by the prevailing northwesterly winds. In summer, southeasterly winds lead to upwelling and cooler temperatures along the Baja California coast.

Salinities in the northern two-thirds of the Gulf range mostly between 35.0°/₀₀ and 35.8°/₀₀ and are 1°/₀₀–2°/₀₀ higher than those at comparable latitudes outside the Gulf. Salinities higher than 36°/₀₀ are only encountered locally in semienclosed and shallow bays in the northern region and along the east coast of Baja California; the largest of these are Bahía Concepción, Bahía Adaír, and Bahía San Jorge. In the southern third of the Gulf, between Cabo San Lucas, Cabo Corrientes, and the mainland, offshore salinities range mostly between 34.6°/₀₀ and 35.0°/₀₀. In coastal waters the salinity may be considerably less than 34.6°/₀₀ during the rainy season, June to October.

VERTICAL DISTRIBUTION OF PROPERTIES

Northern Gulf (*Fig. 8*).—This region, between the Colorado River and Isla Tiburón is characterized by large seasonal and year-to-year changes of temperature and salinity in the upper 150 m. During winter, the water is almost isothermal in the shallow northern part, judging from the few bathythermograph observations by the R/V *Alaska* (unpublished). During late

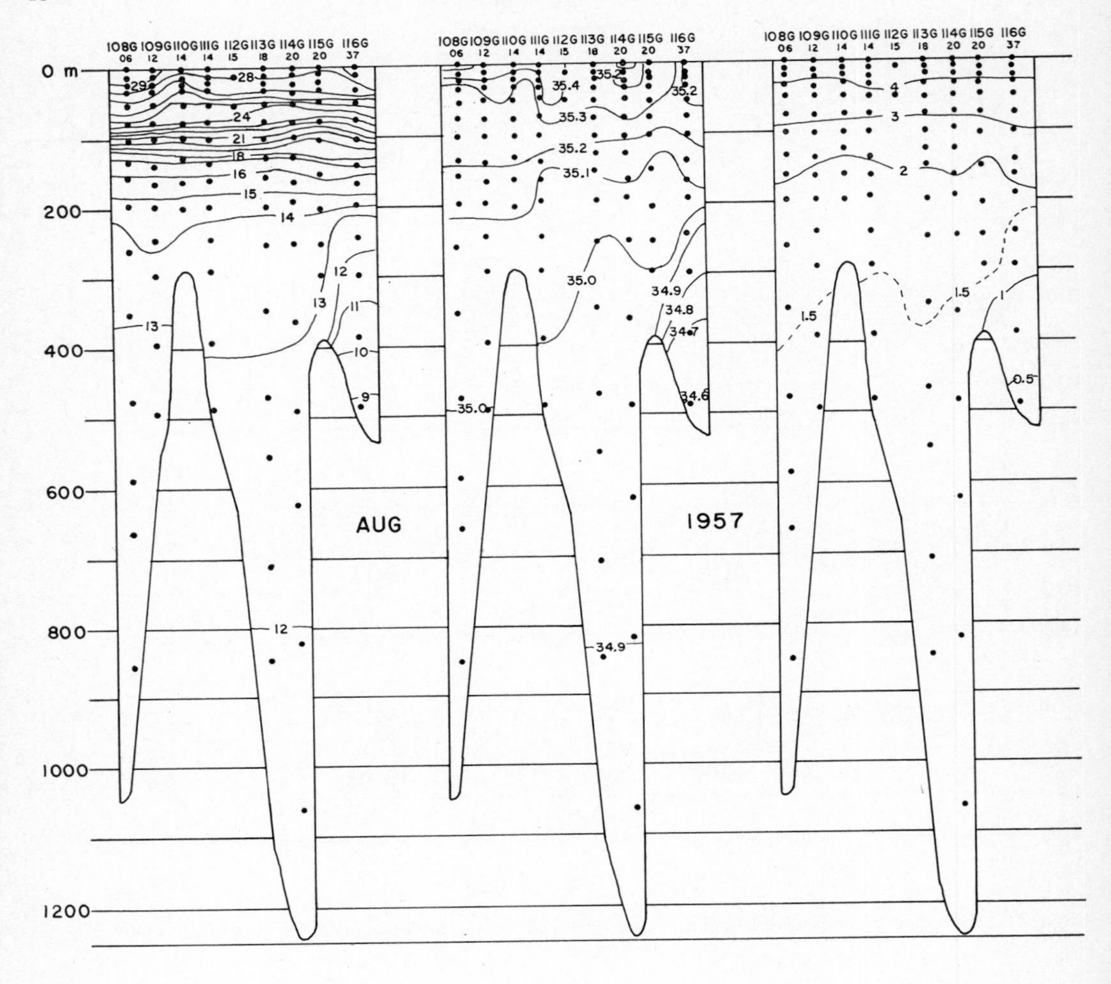

FIG. 9.—Distribution of temperature, salinity, and dissolved

summer, the thermocline is strong and the temperature difference between the surface and 150 m amounts to almost 14°C. In spring, salinities tend to be higher along the Baja California than along the Sonoran coast, whereas in summer the highest salinities appear in the more central parts of the Gulf. The amount of dissolved oxygen at the surface decreases from about 5.5 ml/L in April, to about 4.5 ml/L in August, the decrease being mostly due to the increase in temperature. At the bottom (150 m), however, there is a slight increase in dissolved oxygen content from spring to summer, despite a temperature increase and a strongly developed thermocline.

It is of interest to know whether winter cooling can lead to convective overturn in the northern part of the Gulf, and where, if at all, this is likely to occur. The requirement for the process to take place is that the surface density exceed the density of the subsurface layers. Because the density increases with decreasing temperature and increasing salinity, and because the lowest temperatures and the highest salinities occur near the coast, the most likely places for convective overturn are the coastal regions. The mean minimum temperature in coastal regions is about 13°C

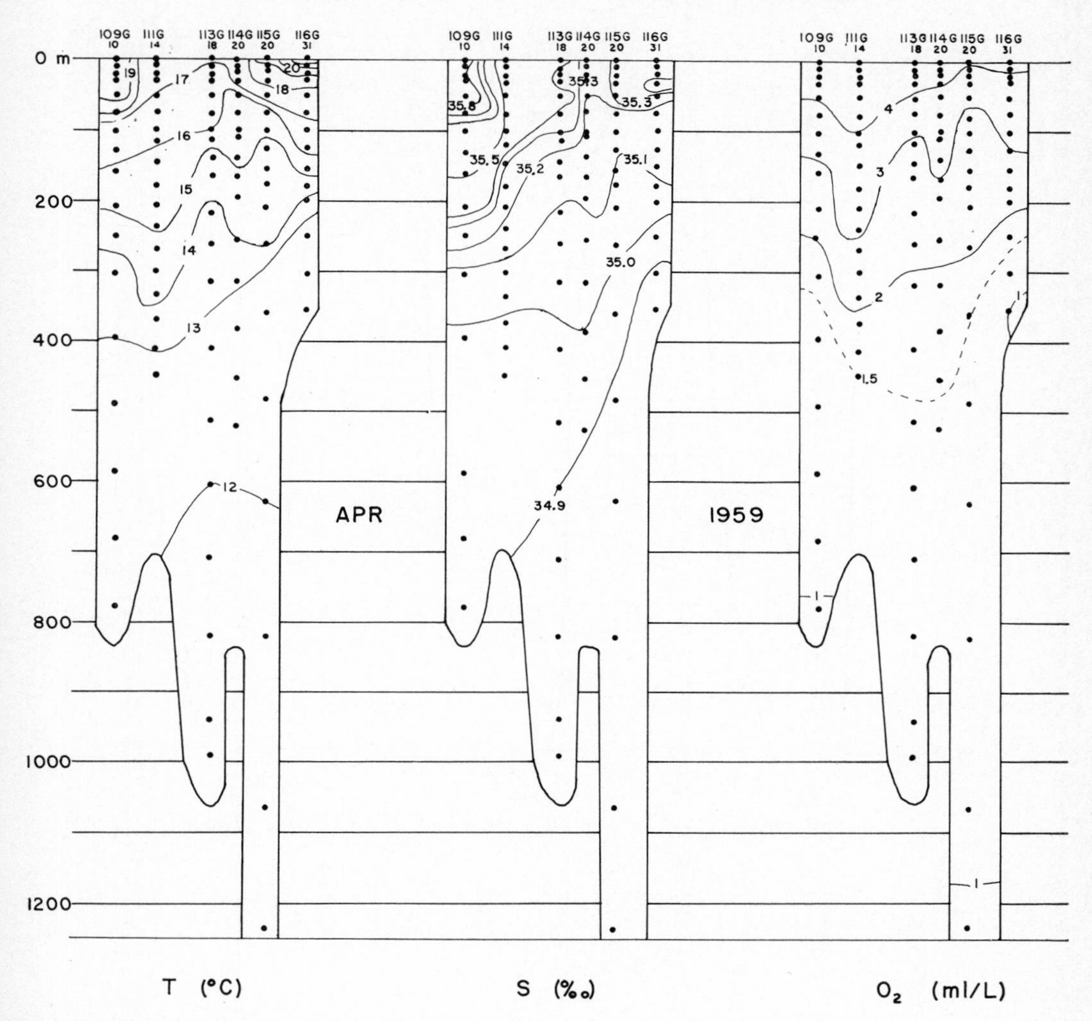

oxygen in Ballenas Channel (for location, see Fig. 1).

(Table VII), whereas the salinities are generally in excess of 35.5°/₀₀. For a temperature of 13°C and a salinity of 35.5°/₀₀, the density at the surface is 1.02680 g cm^{-3}. The same density (*in situ*) is found at a depth of about 100 m, where the temperature is 14°C and the salinity is 35.2°/₀₀. Convective overturn due to winter cooling can therefore be expected to reach to roughly 100 m near the coast. In the more offshore parts of the Gulf, surface temperatures do not drop much below 15°C, whereas the salinities average about 35.4°/₀₀. With these conditions, convection is insignificant.

Ballenas Channel (*Fig. 9*).—The Ballenas Channel, which lies between Isla Angel de la Guarda, Isla San Lorenzo, and Baja California, is completely isolated from the southern part of the Gulf by a submarine ridge connecting Isla Angel de la Guarda with Punta San Gabriel. The sill depth of this ridge is about 250 m. The topography of the channel is very irregular with maximum depths exceeding 1,500 m. The outstanding hydrographic features of the channel are the high temperatures, salinities, and oxygen concentrations at great depths. Compared to conditions elsewhere in the Gulf, the difference in tempera-

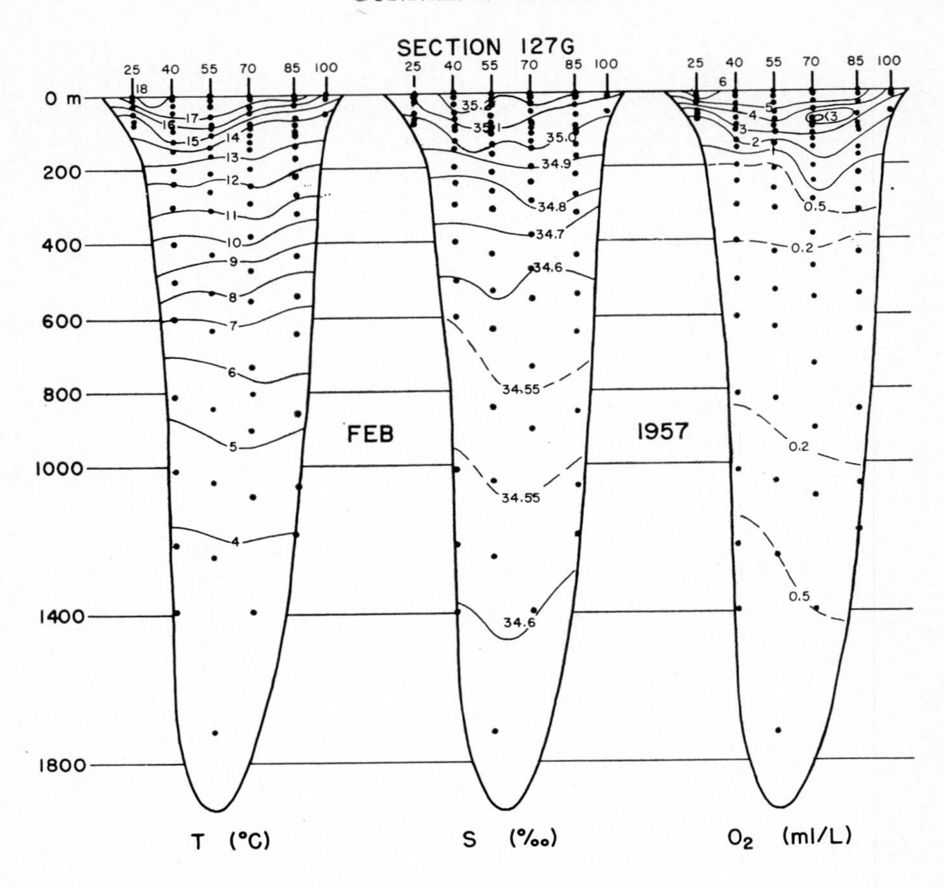

FIG. 10.—Distribution of temperature, salinity, and dissolved oxygen in the

ture at 1,000 m is 6°C, in salinity 0.4°/₀₀, and in dissolved oxygen content 1 ml/L. The deep salinity and oxygen minima, characteristic of the southern half of the Gulf, do not occur here. Instead, most of the deep water in the channel has the same features as that at the sill depth (250 m). In view of the strong tidal currents observed in the narrows, it is quite likely that the rather uniform temperatures, salinities, and oxygen concentrations below about 250 m are caused by tidal mixing. Above 250 m, the exchange of water between the northern and southern parts of the Gulf is unrestricted and the temperatures and salinities in the trench differ little from those outside. During winter months, the stability in the upper layers is weak and limited convection of cold and high salinity water from the bays is likely; the 35.8‰ salinity in the upper 75 m in April 1959 is probably a remnant of this. During the summer, the thermocline in Ballenas Channel is well developed, as elsewhere in the Gulf.

Central Gulf (*Figs. 10 and 11*).—Here, the

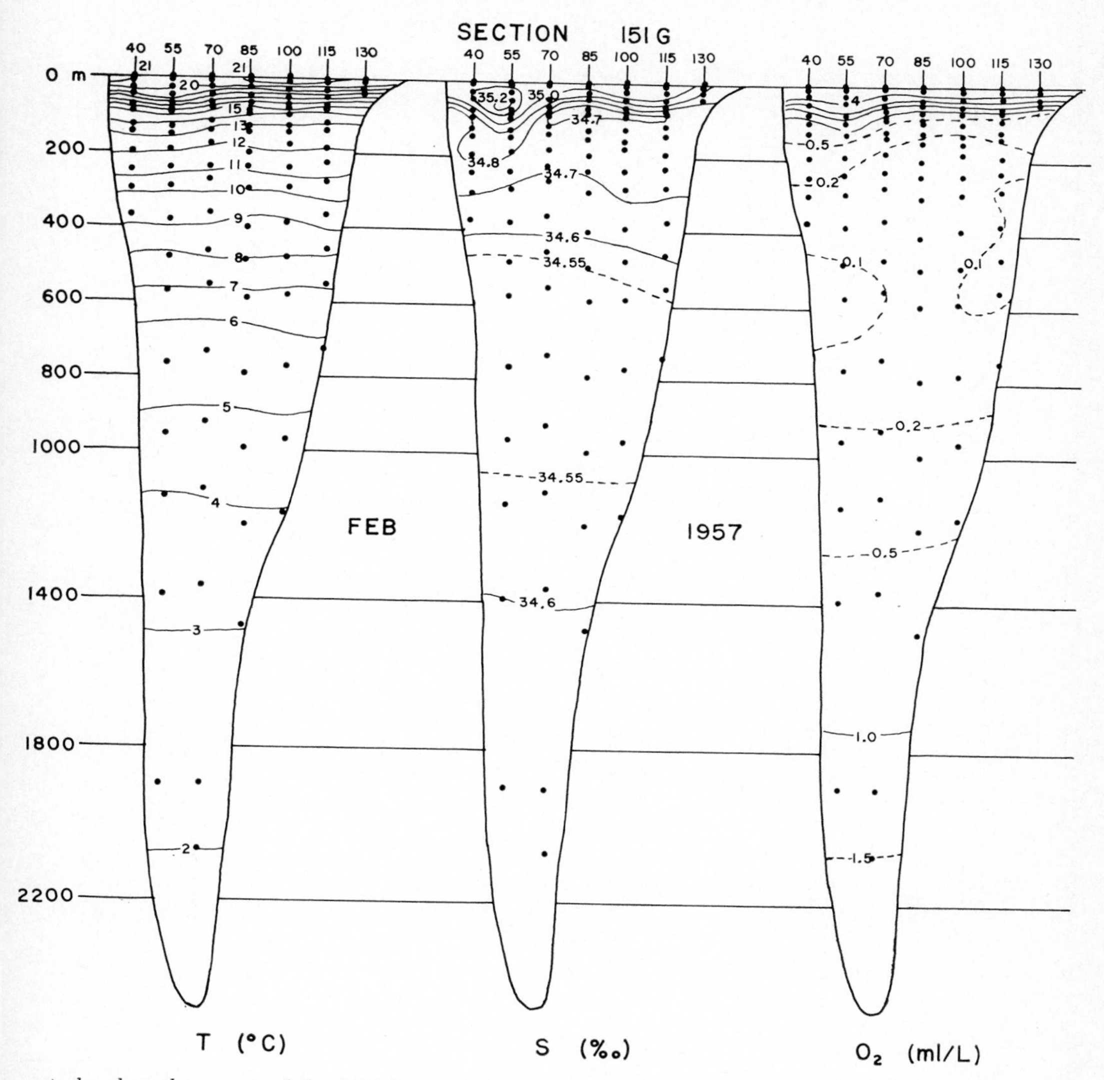

central and southern parts of the Gulf (Sections 127 G and 151 G of Fig. 1).

depths are great and the water is in open communication with the Pacific Ocean to the southeast. In February, the isotherms, isohalines, and the lines of equal oxygen concentration in the upper layers rise toward the eastern coast. This is probably due to upwelling induced by the northwesterly winds, which prevail during this time of the year. Between April and October, the thermocline is well developed; it reaches its maximum strength in August, when the temperature gradient between the surface and 150 m reaches 16°C. In August, the salinity distribution in the upper layers is characterized by a minimum between 25 m and 75 m in the eastern half of the Gulf, and by a maximum off the Baja California coast. Since the only source of low salinity water is from the southeast, the salinity minimum probably indicates the presence of a northwestward-setting current between the above-mentioned depths. With regard to the salinity maximum along the western shore, this could either indicate the influence of Bahía Concepción, the salinity of which

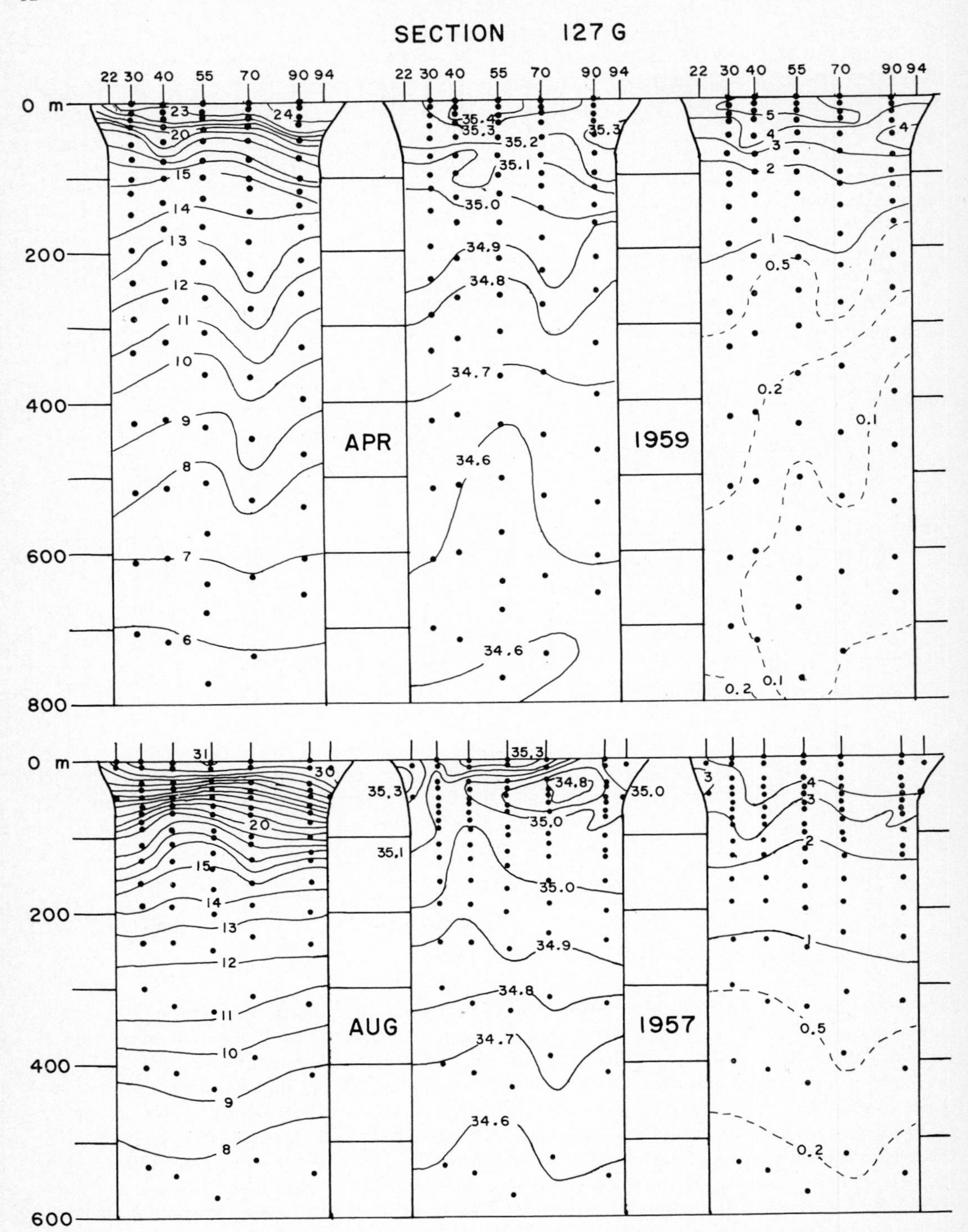

FIG. 11.—Distribution of temperature, salinity, and dissolved oxygen

is very high (36.3°/oo), or it could represent the southward movement of high-salinity water from the northern regions of the Gulf. The available data are too incomplete to decide between the two alternatives.

Below the thermocline, the water is essentially the same as in the equatorial Pacific (Sverdrup, 1941). The outstanding hydrographic features are the salinity minimum of slightly less than 34.55°/oo between 600 m and 1,000 m and the oxygen minimum of less than 0.2 ml/L between 400 m and 800 m. The low concentrations of dissolved oxygen, occasionally undetectable by ordinary techniques (Winkler method), are characteristic of the Gulf and the regions off the southern coast of Mexico (Sverdrup, Johnson, and Fleming, 1946).

Southern Gulf (*Figs. 10 and 12*).—The region of the Gulf is characterized by a well developed thermocline throughout the year, and by numerous salinity maxima and minima in the upper layers. During February and April, the isotherms and isohalines ascend toward the Mexican mainland coast, suggesting upwelling by northwesterly winds. In winter and spring, a core of high salinity water occurs near the Baja California coast at a depth of 50 m; whereas in the central parts there is a salinity minimum of less than 34.7°/oo at about 100 m. The former probably represents southeasterly flow from the interior regions of the Gulf, and the latter, northwesterly flow from more southerly latitudes. During June and August, the upper salinity minimum extends from coast to coast, and is found between roughly 50 m and 100 m; the minimum values are mostly between 34.5°/oo and 34.7°/oo.

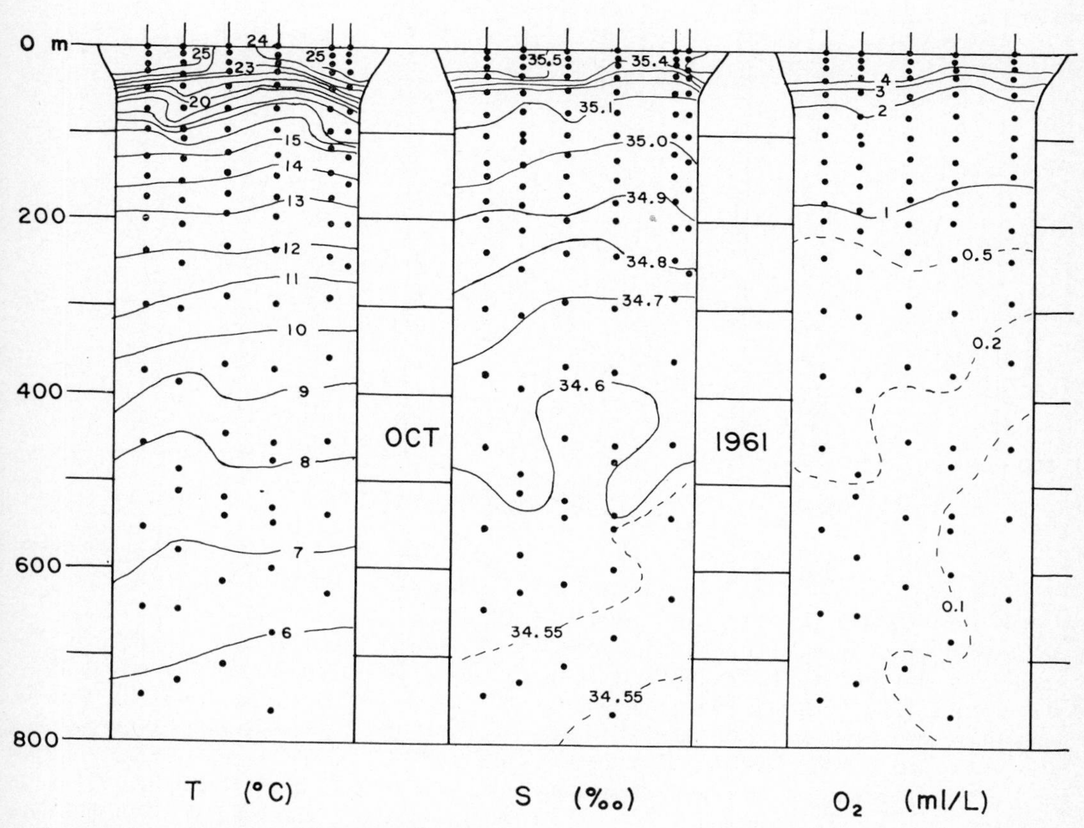

in the central part of the Gulf (Section 127 G of Fig. 1).

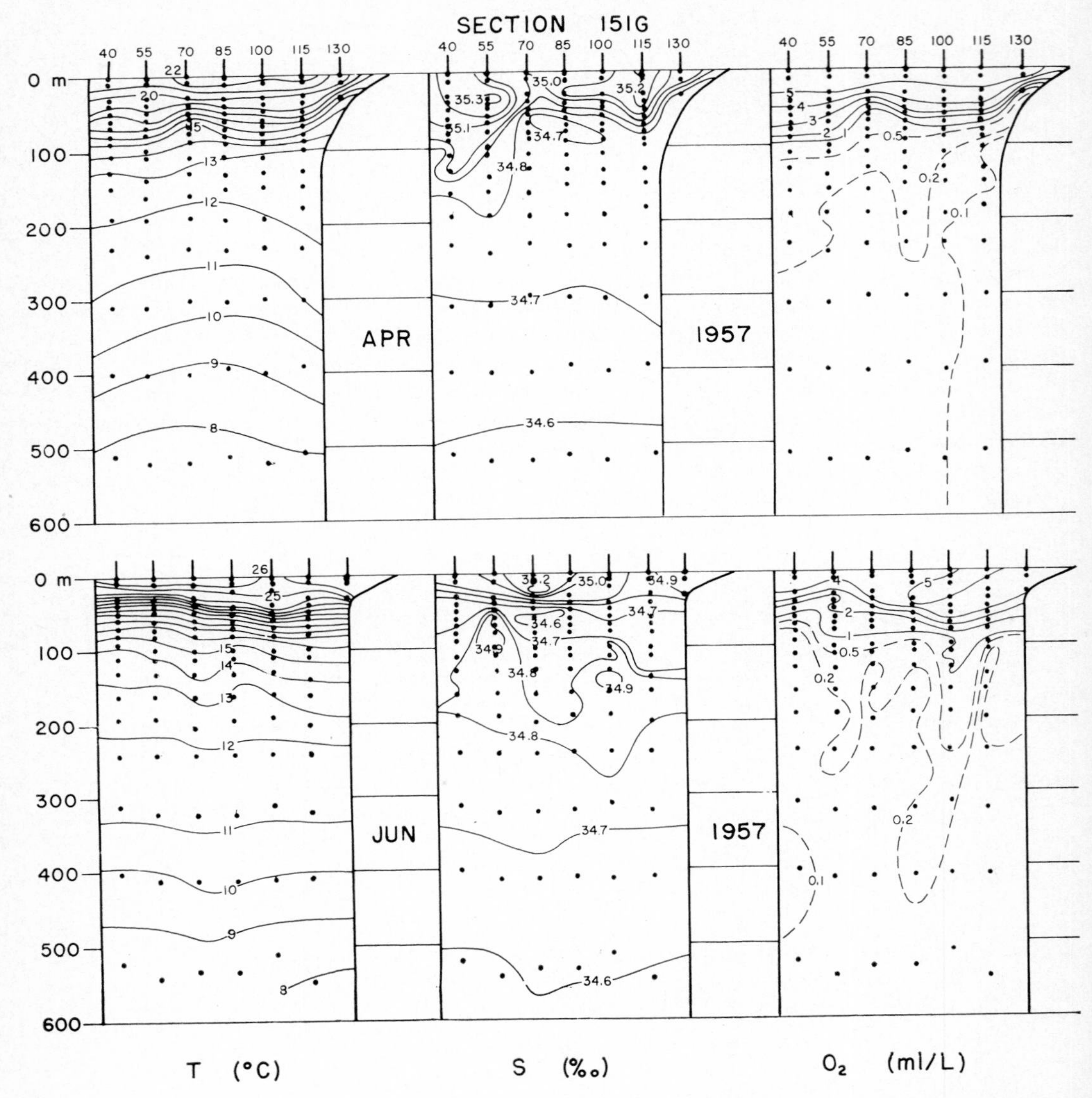

FIG. 12.—Distribution of temperature, salinity, and dissolved

Below about 200 m, the temperature, salinity, and oxygen distributions differ only slightly from those in the central Gulf. The main difference is the oxygen minimum, which is more pronounced, and which covers a larger depth interval. Here dissolved oxygen concentrations of less than 0.1 ml/L are common between 200 m and 600 m, and may occur on either side of the Gulf.

The region between *Islas Tres Marías and Isla Socorro* (*Fig. 13*) is tropical and oceanic. The annual surface temperature range is only 4°C—25°C–29°C. The thermocline lies mostly between 40 m and 100 m, the temperature decrease being about 12°C. The upper salinity minimum is pronounced and lies in the 50–100 m depth range in most of the region. Near Isla Socorro, the influence

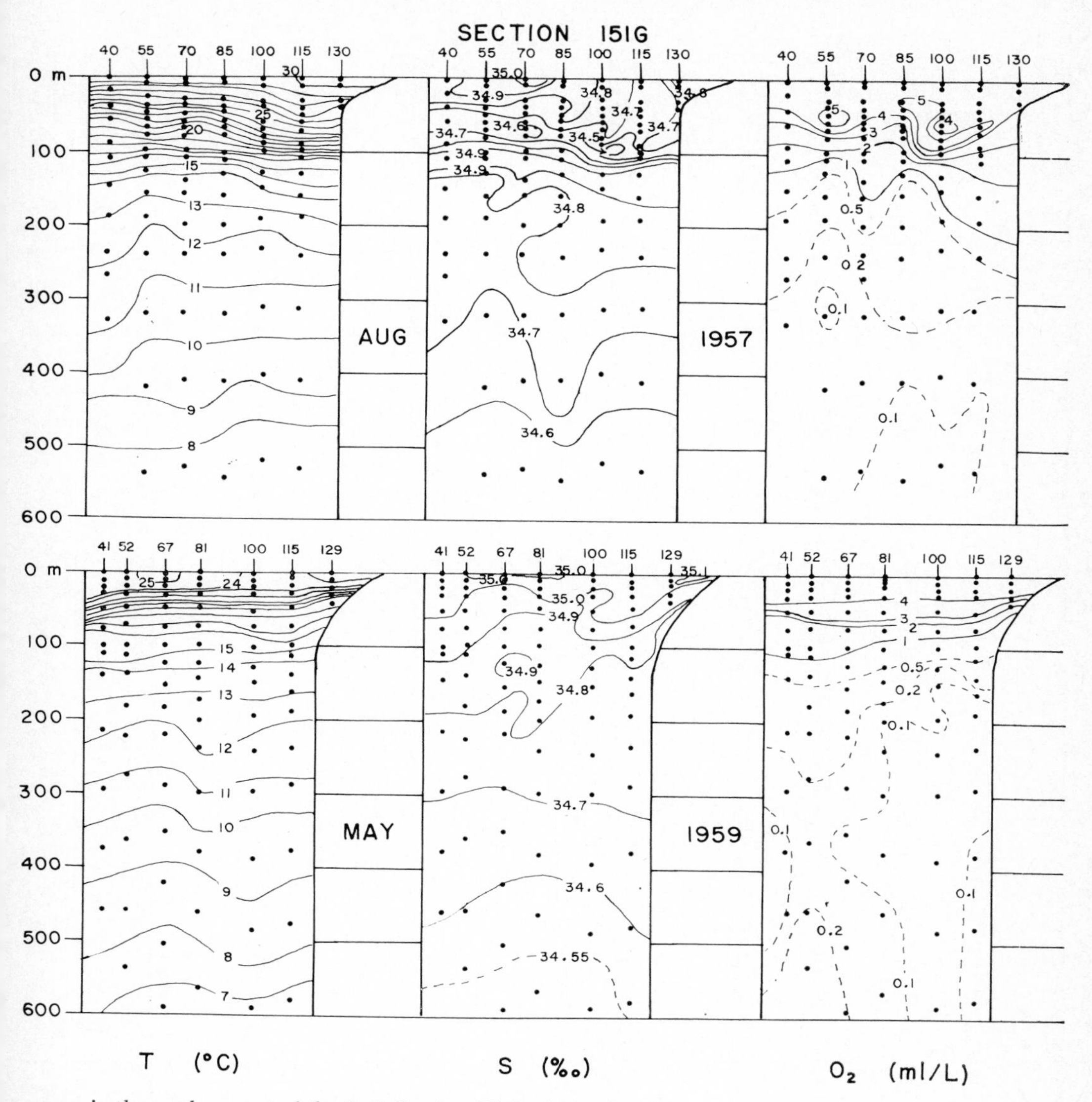

oxygen in the southern part of the Gulf (Section 151 G of Fig. 1).

of the California Current is indicated by the low surface salinities of less than 34.0°/₀₀. Low salinities in the upper layers are also likely to be found between Islas Tres Marías and the mainland owing to heavy rainfall and runoff from May to October. Between 100 m and 300 m there is a salinity maximum with values ranging mostly from 34.7°/₀₀ to 34.8°/₀₀. Below 300 m, the salinity distribution is the same as elsewhere in the tropical Pacific. The amount of dissolved oxygen decreases rapidly from 50 m to 100 m. In May 1959 the 0.1 ml/L isoline of dissolved oxygen occurred at 125 m and extended downward, in the eastern part, to about 500 m; in December 1956, the oxygen concentrations did not fall to 0.1 ml/L. These rather remarkable differences at

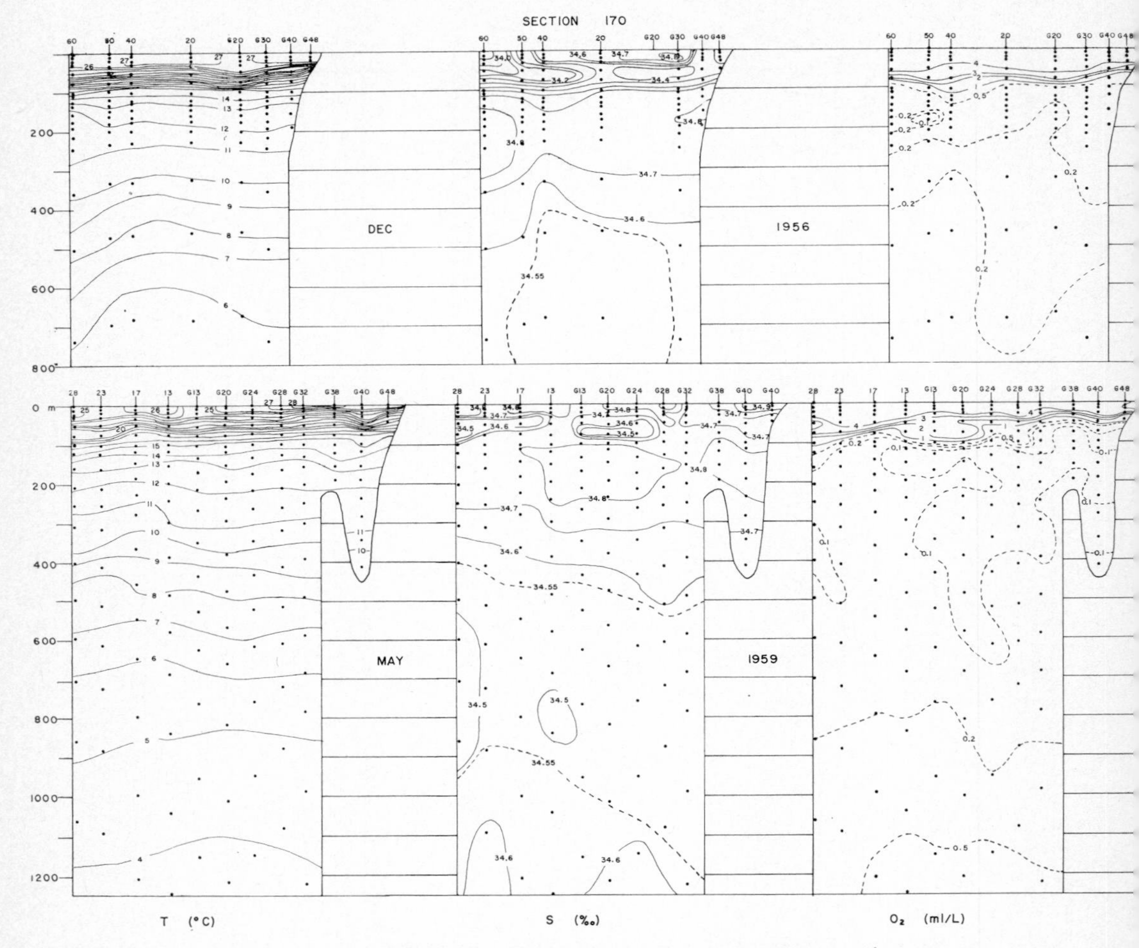

FIG. 13.—Distribution of temperature, salinity, and dissolved oxygen in a section extending from Islas Tres Marías to Isla Socorro (Section 170 G of Fig. 1).

depths shown by the two surveys indicate that temporal changes in dissolved oxygen between 100 m and 500 m may be appreciable. It is of interest to note that along the southern shore of Bahía Banderas (near Cabo Corrientes) no oxygen was found between 75 m and 500 m in May 1959.

Hydrographic conditions at great depths (*Fig. 14*). —Hydrographic conditions at depths below 1,000 m are illustrated in a longitudinal section running from Guaymas Basin to Cabo Corrientes. It is seen that there is a temperature minimum of slightly less than 1.85°C between 2,500 m and 3,000 m. From 3,000 m to the bottom, the temperature increases again at a rate of approximately 0.1°C per 1,000 m. The adiabatic temperature increase between two depths is given by Defant (1961)

$$\Delta\theta = \int_{h_1}^{h_2} \frac{Tg}{Jc_p} \frac{1}{\alpha} \frac{\partial\alpha}{\partial T} dp$$

where $\Delta\theta$ is the temperature increase, T, the absolute temperature of the water, α, the specific volume, c_p, the specific heat at constant pressure, g, gravity, J, the mechanical equivalent of heat ($J = 4.1863 \times 10^7$ erg/cal), and dp, the pressure (depth) interval. If the pertinent values (Fofonoff

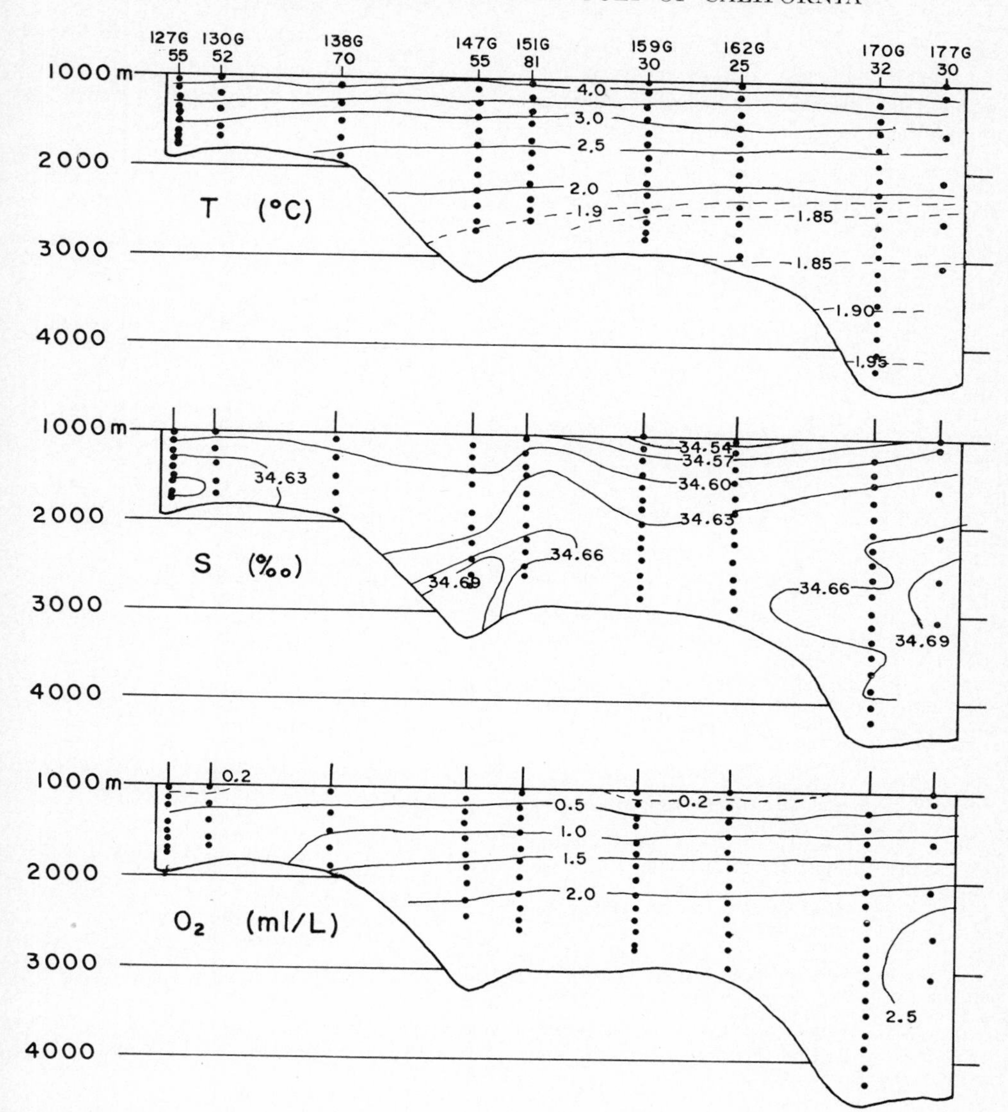

FIG. 14.—Distribution of temperature, salinity, and oxygen at depths below 1,000 m along a section extending from Guaymas Basin (left) to Acapulco Trench (right). For station positions, see Fig. 1.

and Froese, 1958) are inserted, it is found that the observed temperature increase between 3,000 m and 4,000 m agrees closely with the adiabatic increase calculated from the above equation.

The salinity distribution between 1,000 m and the bottom is surprisingly complex. The contour interval of 0.03°/₀₀ chosen here approaches the titration accuracy, and the validity of the details is not obvious. Nevertheless, there is a general tendency for the salinity to increase from 1,000 m toward the bottom.

The distribution of dissolved oxygen content shows that concentrations increase from about 0.2 ml/L at 1,000 m to about 2.4 ml/L at 4,000

m. It is noteworthy, however, that in the central part of the Gulf, oxygen concentrations at the bottom are much lower than at comparable depths (2,000 m) outside.

REFERENCES

Anderson, C.A., and others, 1950, The 1940 E.W. Scripps cruise to the Gulf of California: Geol. Soc. America Mem. 43.

Byrne, J.V., and Emery, K.O., 1960, Sediments of the Gulf of California: Geol. Soc. America Bull., v. 71, no. 7, p. 983–1010.

Defant, A., 1961, Physical Oceanography, I: Pergamon Press, New York, 729 p.

Fofonoff, N.P., and Froese, C., 1958, Tables of physical properties of sea water: Canada Fish. Res. Board, Ms. Rept. Series, v. 24, 35 p.

Hernandez, J., 1923, The temperature of Mexico: Monthly Weather Rev. Supp. 23, 24 p.

Hydrographic Department, London, U.K., 1961, Admiralty tide tables for 1962, v. 2; Pacific Ocean and adjacent areas (including tidal stream tables), 620 p.

Instituto de Geofisca, Univ. Nac. Autonama de Mexico, unpublished, Sea-level records for tide gauge stations along the Pacific coast: Mexico, D.F.

Meteorological Office, London, U.K., 1956, Monthly meteorological charts of the eastern Pacific Ocean: Meteorol. Office Pub. 518.

Osorio-Tafall, B.F., 1943, El Mar de Cortés y la productividad fitoplanctónica de sus aguas: Escuela Nac. Cienc. Biológicas Anales, v. 3, nos. 1–2, p. 78–118.

Page, J.L., 1930, Climate of Mexico: Monthly Weather Rev. Supp. 33, 33 p.

Pattullo, J., Munk, W.H., Revelle, R.R., and Strong, E., 1955, The seasonal variation in sea level: Marine Res. Jour., v. 14, no. 1, p. 10–35.

Roden, G.I., 1958, Oceanographic and meteorological aspects of the Gulf of California: Pacific Sci., v. 12, no. 1, p. 21–45.

——— 1959, On the heat and salt balance of the California current: Marine Res. Jour., v. 18, no. 1, p. 36–41.

——— 1960, On non-seasonal variations of sea level along the west coast of North America: Geophys. Res. Jour., v. 65, no. 9, p. 2809–2826.

——— and Groves, G.W., 1959, Recent oceanographic investigations in the Gulf of California: Marine Res. Jour., v. 18, no. 1, p. 10–35.

Servicio Meterológico Mexicano, 1928–1941, Boletin Anual: Tacubaya, D.F.

Shepard, F.P., 1950, Submarine topography of the Gulf of California, pt. 3 *of* The 1940 E.W. Scripps cruise to the Gulf of California: Geol. Soc. America Mem. 43, 32 p.

Sverdrup, H.U., 1941, The Gulf of California; preliminary discussion on the cruise of the E.W. Scripps in February and March 1939: 6th Pacific Sci. Cong. Proc., v. 3, p. 161–166.

——— 1951, Evaporation from the oceans, *in* Compendium of meteorology: Am. Meteorol. Soc., p. 1071–1081.

——— Johnson, M.W., and Fleming, R.H., 1946, The oceans—their physics, chemistry, and general biology: Prentice-Hall Inc., New York, 1087 p.

Townsend, C.H., 1901, Dredging and other records of the U.S. Fish Commission steamer Albatross with bibliography relative to the work of the vessel: U.S. Fish Comm. Rept. for 1900, p. 387–562.

U.S. Coast and Geodetic Survey, 1916, Tide tables for the year 1917: Washington 25, D.C.

——— 1956, Surface water temperatures at tide stations, Pacific coast of North and South America: Spec. Pub. 280, Washington 25, D.C., 74 p.

——— 1957, Density of water at tide stations, Pacific coast of North and South America: Spec. Pub. 31-4, Washington 25, D.C., 79 p.

U.S. Geological Survey, 1954, Compilation of records of surface waters of the United States through September 1950: Water-Supply Paper 1313, Washington 25, D.C.

——— 1960, Quality of surface waters for irrigation, western United States, 1957: Water-Supply Paper 1524, Washington 25, D.C.

U.S. Hydrographic Office, 1947, Atlas of surface currents for the northeastern Pacific Ocean: Pub. 570, Washington 25, D.C., 750 p.

——— 1951, Sailing directions for the west coast of Mexico and Central America: Pub. 84, Washington 25, D.C., 308 p.

U.S. Weather Bureau, 1945–1961, Climatological data: Natl. Summary 1954 to 1961, Washington 25, D.C.

Ward, R. DeC., and Brooks, C.F., 1936, The climates of North America, I (Mexico, United States, Alaska): Handb. Klimatol. II (j), Gebr. Borntraeger Verlag, Berlin, 327 p.

Yoshida, K., 1955, Coastal upwelling off the California coast: Records Oceanogr. Works Japan, v. 2, no. 2, p. 8–20.

BATHYMETRY AND FAULTS OF GULF OF CALIFORNIA[1]

GENE A. RUSNAK,[2] ROBERT L. FISHER,[3] AND FRANCIS P. SHEPARD[3]
Miami, Florida and La Jolla, California

ABSTRACT

The numerous cruises of Scripps Institution vessels to the Gulf of California between 1957 and 1963 have provided thousands of miles of new sounding lines that have made possible an extensive revision of the earlier bathymetric charts. The fault scarps suggested by earlier soundings are now well confirmed, and also the indications of right-lateral movement with resulting tensional fractures. Several newly discovered northeast-trending deeps have been discovered. *En echelon* faults diagonal to the general trend of the Gulf are apparently a southward extension of the San Andreas system. Displacements of the order of 160 miles appear to have taken place between the two sides of the Gulf, with a break in the crust forming the central Gulf with its near-oceanic depths. The end of the Baja California Peninsula is thought to have been located originally in the vicinity of Banderas Bay on the mainland.

Two types of elevations occur in the Gulf, (1) those forming islands and banks along the western margin and consisting largely of "granite," and (2) central highs, most of which do not reach the surface and contain basic volcanics. The continental shelves are very narrow or nonexistent on the west side of the Gulf but fairly broad on the east, especially to the south of Mazatlán. The eastern shelves appear to be of a depositional character.

INTRODUCTION

The Gulf of California is a structurally complex trough reaching nearly oceanic depths though bounded by the mountainous Peninsula of Baja California on the west and the mainland of Mexico on the east. From Cape San Lucas to the Colorado Delta it is 600 miles long; throughout this length it averages less than 100 miles in width. Interest in the peculiar structural character of the Gulf led the Scripps Institution of Oceanography's staff to conduct two early scientific cruises there aboard the *E.W. Scripps* during the spring of 1939 and the fall of 1940. An expedition report was published (Anderson and others, 1950) on the geologic history, paleontology, and submarine morphology. Shepard (1950) at that time presented a general topographic chart of the area and considered the Gulf of California to be a steeply faulted and sheared depression which resembled the Red Sea and Persian Gulf in shape. Although this conclusion was based only on morphological similarities, later work in these regions suggests that the Red Sea, at least, may have many structural similarities (Carey, 1958; Drake, personal communication; Drake and others, 1959; Girdler, 1958, 1962; Swartz and Arden, 1960—compare with Harrison and Mathur, and with Phillips, this volume).

During 1957–1962, a series of Scripps Institution of Oceanography geological-geophysical cruises to the Gulf of California provided more than 23,000 miles of precise sounding tracks from which Shepard's early chart could be refined and extended. In particular, coverage was enlarged to include the region between Cape San Lucas and the Mexican mainland extending southward from lat 25° N. to Banderas Bay, where the Gulf debouches into the Pacific Basin near the north

[1] Manuscript received, June 25, 1963. Contribution No. 497 from the Marine Laboratory, University of Miami. Contribution from Scripps Institution of Oceanography, University of California.

All members of the scientific parties on each of the several 1957–1962 cruises participated in the collection of bathymetric data; their help is gratefully acknowledged. Officers and crew of the research vessels *Horizon*, *Spencer F. Baird*, *Orca*, and *Argo* efficiently carried out the demanding maneuvering and navigational operations required for such studies in the Gulf of California. Thomas W.C. Hilde and Franz Emmel aided in reducing bathymetric data. Donna Snyder, James Moriarty, Richard Marra, Don Heuer, David Crouch, and Bonnie Swope drafted the illustrations.

The authors are especially grateful to George G. Shor, Jr., Richard P. Von Herzen, Tj.H. van Andel, J.C. Harrison, and Richard Phillips, whose previously unpublished results have been considered in the following presentation. George G. Shor, Jr., Tj. H. van Andel, Dale Krause, and P.B. King read and made suggestions in the manuscript.

Financial support for this study was provided by the Office of Naval Research, National Science Foundation, and the American Petroleum Institute's Project 51.

[2] Marine Laboratory, University of Miami.

[3] Scripps Institution of Oceanography, University of California.

end of the Middle America Trench (Fisher, 1961). Several thousand miles of track were added in the upper Gulf north of lat 29° N.; there the present chart is based almost entirely on these new lines. Along the western side of the Gulf between lats 24° N. and 28° N., little additional work was done around the islands. The contours and interpretation for this region, therefore, are taken almost entirely from Shepard's 1950 report. The present paper presents a more comprehensive bathymetric and structural interpretation from these recent off-shore sounding data (Chart I, in pocket) and provides a morphological framework to which other geological and geophysical investigations can be related.

BATHYMETRY

Preparation of Chart I.—The individual and collective ship's tracks (Chart I, in pocket) of recent Scripps Institution of Oceanography (SIO) expeditions to the Gulf of California provided a large number of precise soundings from which the bathymetric charts could be compiled. In all these cruises the base sheets used aboard ship consisted of updated copies of U.S. Hydrographic Office (now U.S. Oceanographic Office) Charts 619, 620, 621, and 622. Because these standard nautical charts are based largely on coastal surveys conducted during the late 1800's and have not been corrected throughout by triangulation and aerial photography, some of the landmarks are charted with questionable accuracy. Specific discrepancies were noted during SIO surveys in the vicinity of Tiburón and Angel de la Guarda Islands, where charted shoreline features differed as much as 1½ to 2 miles from their positions relative to the finally accepted ships' tracks. In general, therefore, the position control available throughout the Gulf is taken as accurate only to within 1 mile.[4] Sun lines obtained at frequent intervals supplemented the usual meridian altitude and morning and evening star sights. Only celestial navigation furnished the control beyond moderate distances offshore. In coastal areas visual bearings and radar ranges on known points were obtained every few minutes. Some near-shore surveys, as those off southern Baja California, were controlled by horizontal sextant angles on well-located shore points. All ships' tracks between fixes were corrected for drift and speed variations where these were known. In the over-all compilation, older or less well-controlled tracks were adjusted in position until their soundings made good crossings with the accepted lines; doubtful lines were used in part, only, or not at all. Small gaps or offsets in the sounding tracks occur at sampling stations and signify on-station drift.

For the 1957–62 explorations each ship was equipped with a Precision Depth Recorder or PDR (Luskin and others, 1953) having a reading precision of better than one fathom in 3,000 under all conditions when a recordable bottom echo is detected. The relatively precise values recorded are subject to the usual difficulties of interpretation of echo-sounding—side-echo effects, slope corrections, and sweeping of the sound cone as the ship rolls. In the present instance such corrections have not been made.[5] Soundings were recorded in fathoms, assuming a nominal sounding velocity of 4,800 ft/sec; the nominal soundings have not been corrected for local temperature-salinity-pressure conditions.[6]

Soundings were taken at 1-second intervals but, except in areas of rapidly changing depth, they were logged only every six minutes. With a ship's speed of 10–12 knots, this gives approximately one sounding notation per mile of track. In steeper regions, soundings were logged at 1 to 3 minute intervals, and so plotted along the corrected tracks. Such spacings are believed sufficiently detailed for good topographic representation throughout the Gulf generally. Canyon surveys off southern Baja California and east of Farallón Basin, reported by Shepard (this volume), were

[4] Exceptions are found around the southern end of Baja California where much greater survey accuracy was possible through visual control on the high peaks of the mainland.

[5] The reader is directed to Krause (1962) for details and magnitude of such corrections.

[6] With the temperature-salinity-pressure conditions prevailing at depth in the Gulf, the true sounding velocity ranges from 4,872 to 4,896 ft/sec. Recorded soundings from which charts were constructed thus are 1½ to 2 per cent too shoal. As the increase in sounding velocity with depth is about 1 per cent per 1,500 fathoms (in the deeper parts of the Gulf), values determined for bottom slopes within any one basin, for example, are relatively accurate.

conducted in much greater detail; for these areas the contours drawn on Chart I are abstracted from large-scale plots. In areas of very rough topography, reference to the original continuous PDR sounding traces often was necessary to resolve depth differences at track intersections. Some of this bottom irregularity is implicit in the finer details of the contouring, but the 100-fathom contour interval accepted does not allow expression for any but the larger of these irregularities. In the shallow northern Gulf a 20-fathom contour interval was required to depict significant topographic features; elsewhere the shelves deepen nearly continuously seaward from the shoreline. A 50-fathom interval was adopted locally in the Guaymas Basin and west of the northern part of Angel de la Guarda Island.

Lastly, the representation of land topography on Chart I is schematic, intended to show only the approximated distribution and general elevation of hills, mountains, and coastal plains.

General bathymetric features.—The most obvious characteristic of the Gulf of California is its linearity expressed by features of various scales. These appear as steep escarpments and as narrow-to-broad linear troughs and ridges suggestive of thin "sliver-fault ridges" with intervening troughs and *V*-shaped basins. The Gulf's axial-basin depths range from near oceanic (1,600–2,000 fathoms) in the lower Gulf, to continental shelf depths (about 100 fathoms or less) in the upper reaches. The Gulf is bounded on both sides by steep escarpments and ridges with slopes up to 38°, although most are less than 15°. Steep slopes appear to be most common on the western side. On the eastern side, the broad Sinaloan and Sonoran deltaic plains have spilled down into the basin, blanketing many slopes and many of the irregular structural features. Long, narrow ridges rise above the sea surface or above the deltaic plain to form islands. Linear islands are largely confined to the western margin of the Gulf, but similar features appear also along the eastern margin in the subsurface of the alluvial plain.

Steeply dipping scarps are everywhere evident where they have not been too much modified by sediment fill and consequent slope reduction. Bathymetric cross sections clearly demonstrate

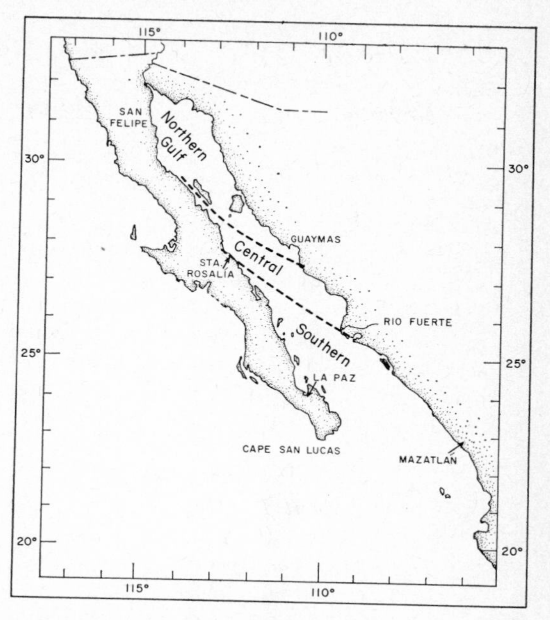

FIG. 1.—Topographic provinces of the Gulf of California as defined in this paper.

these features, but blanketed irregularities are divulged only in sub-bottom acoustic profiles such as were occasionally evident on echo traces. For purposes of relating sediment distribution patterns to the slopes, van Andel (this volume, Table II) has grouped the slopes into three categories (1) those greater than 30°, (2) those between 5° and 30°, and (3) those less than 5°. No genetic significance appears to be attached to this grouping, however. The most spectacular single scarp observed occurs on the east side of the Ballenas Channel, between San Lorenzo and the Peninsula of Baja California. Here, the scarp has a slope of 38°. Another scarp of equal steepness is found associated with the eastern margin of the Gulf at the Tres Marías Islands. Arguments for the fault origin of these and related steep escarpments and the criteria applying to their recognition were presented earlier by Shepard (1950). The earlier conclusions favoring a fault origin for the escarpments and for most of the Gulf's major morphological features now seem inescapable. The features are best discussed in terms of specific morphologic provinces.

On morphological grounds, the Gulf of Cali-

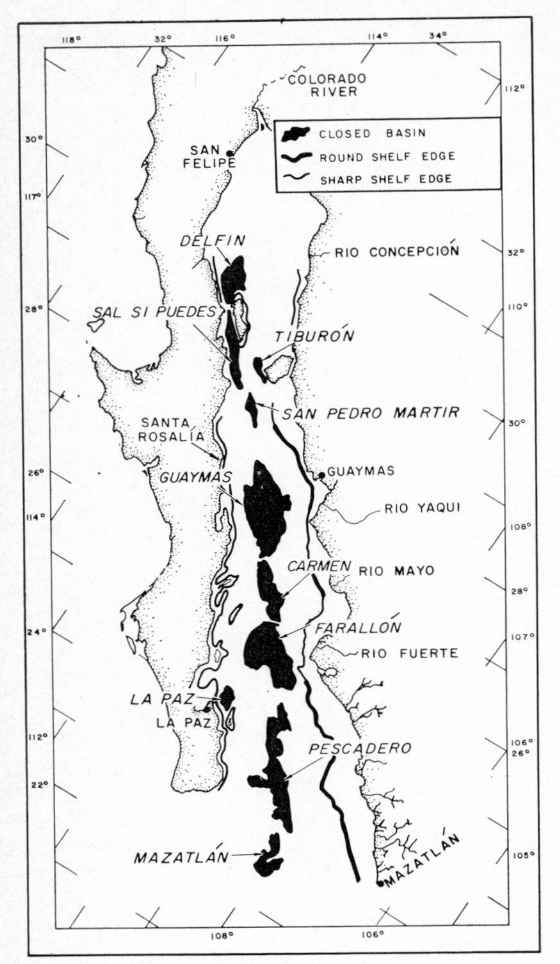

FIG. 2.—Basins and shelves in the Gulf of California.

fornia can be subdivided into three regions (Fig. 1) as (1) north, (2) central, and (3) southern. The head of the Gulf, between the Colorado River Delta and the islands of Tiburón and Angel de la Guarda, does not exhibit fault features as strongly as elsewhere; here the bedrock structure has been masked by sediment. This segment of the Gulf appears similar to the broad Imperial Valley trough and is similarly filled by thick alluvial deposits supplied by the Colorado River and local streams (Kovach and others, 1962; Biehler and others, this volume; Phillips, this volume). Except for a northward extension of the Sal si Puedes Basin and several smaller depressions suggesting a channel off the Colorado mouth, the Gulf bottom north of Angel de la Guarda and Tiburón Islands is smooth and bowl shaped. This smooth character extends southward on the eastern Gulf margin to the vicinity of Guaymas.

In the southern and central portions of the Gulf, four major elongated basins trend subparallel to the Gulf axis. The deepest parts of these basins are approximately normal to their over-all trend, however. From south to north, these basins are Pescadero, Farallón, Carmen, and Guaymas (Fig. 2). Pescadero Basin, irregular in outline, is known from recent work to include several deeps previously charted separately. Mazatlán Basin, a smaller depression lying on the deep-sea floor off the mouth of the Gulf, is made irregular in outline by ridges extending into it from the northeast and northwest; no obvious basin trend is apparent. To the north, another narrow but deep depression, the Sal si Puedes Basin, mentioned previously, is elongated parallel to the Gulf and lies between the peninsula and the chain of islands including Angel de la Guarda, bounding Ballenas Channel. A relatively large, smooth-floored basin has been delineated just north of Angel de la Guarda; it is here named the "Delfin Basin." In addition to San Pedro Mártir and Tiburón Basins, several smaller depressions also have been outlined to the north; these have not been given separate names because of their limited size. The "Ceralbo Basin" of older maps of the southern Gulf is now shown to be an unsilled trough rather than a closed basin. Ceralbo Trough, La Paz, Sal si Puedes, and Delfin Basins are on the flank of the Baja California Peninsula; the other large basins are axial depressions.

Well-developed shelves or terraces are confined largely to the eastern margin of the central and southern Gulf. The western border has practically no shelf development except for narrow terraces and the small shelf area extending from north of Santa Rosalía to about lat 28°40′ N. Elsewhere the southwestern shoreline is bordered only by very narrow benches cut in rocky cliffs. There is a sharp shelf-break, however, along much of this coastline and around most major islands (Figs. 2 and 3). This shelf-break separates a supposedly rocky shelf surface from the steeper, rough upper gulf slopes at about 55 fathoms. The eastern shelf, on the other hand, is wider and more continuous, ranging in width from a few, to as much as 30 miles. The broadest shelf is found southeast of the Río Mayo generally, where abundant sediments may have covered over and smoothed out former areas of irregularity. The shelf surface slopes gradually outward as a depositional terrace spilling down into the Gulf. Even on this side the upper slopes are sharply irregular and steeply ridged wherever little or no alluvial fill occurs. Where not lost under a gradually sloping blanket of sediment, the shelf-break occurs at a depth of about 55 fathoms (Fig. 3) as on the west side. This concordance of depths in the most easily recognized shelf breaks suggests little vertical movement in the Gulf between latitudes 24° N. and 28° N. since Pleistocene lowering of sea level.

Several canyons originate at the shelf-break, or shoreward, and these terminate in small fans at the base of the slopes. One of the largest fans occurs off the Río Fuerte delta, at the base of San Ignacio and Fuerte Canyons. Most of the canyons occur off the tip of the Baja California Peninsula; distinct fans lie at the mouths of several of these canyons. The canyons, fans, and associated sediments are discussed extensively by Shepard (this volume).

Seamounts, pinnacles, and knolls are common in the southern Gulf, rare in the central Gulf, and appear totally absent (except for Consag Rock at lat 31°06′ N., long 114°29′ W.) in the northern Gulf (Pl. 1). The largest submerged bank occurs off Ceralbo Island, to which it is apparently similar. This bank, like Cabrillo Seamount off Cape San Lucas, represents a submerged peninsular unit similar to the extensive island fringe. Cabrillo Seamount has been sampled by coring; these samples consisted of shattered quartz and granite (Shepard, this volume). Numerous knolls and ridges form prominent features on the mainland slope between lat 25° N. and the Tres Marías Islands. Their composition is unknown but other prominences— for example, Tortugas Island in the central Gulf—appear to be totally volcanic. Except for Cabrillo Seamount, the numerous seamounts on the floor of the southern Gulf also appear to be volcanic; basalt fragments have been recovered from several of them by coring or dredging operations. Smaller irregularities abound on the deep sea floor between the southern end of Baja California and the Tres Marías Islands.

In a general way, the bottom morphology of the Gulf thus continues the topography of the adjacent land areas. There are lowlands and moderate slopes, and highlands with steep slopes. Superimposed on these major features are the canyons, fans, and pinnacles. This general correspondence in morphological character is due presumably to similar structural development. The Gulf of California lies between the westward-dipping fault blocks of Baja California and the westward-dipping fault blocks of the Mexican mainland,

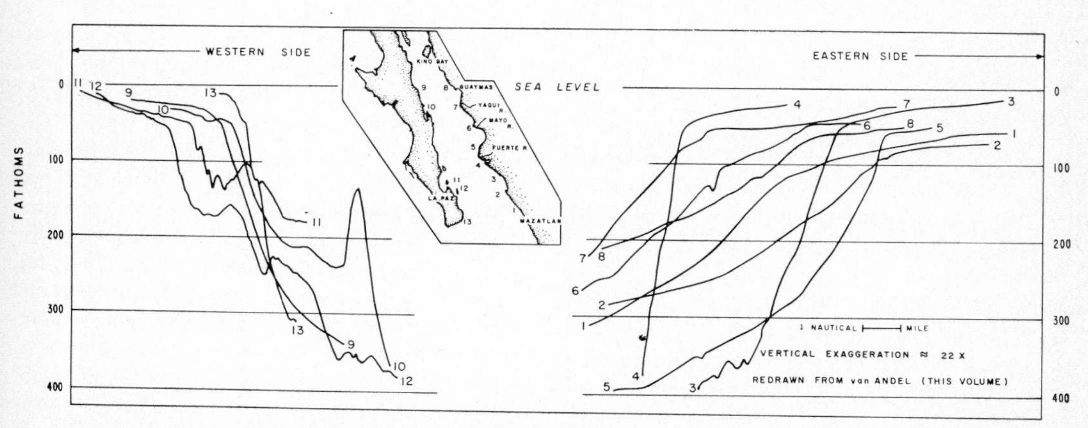

FIG. 3.—Topographic profiles of the shelf edge and upper continental slope in the central and southern Gulf of California. These profiles, traced from fathometer records, have a vertical exaggeration of 22×.

extending from the Colorado River delta to Banderas Bay.

Topography of the Northern Gulf province.—In the northern Gulf, thick sedimentary fill has blanketed any surface irregularities that may have existed in its early history. The shallow Gulf floor dips gently offshore and southward with no obvious shelf-break and with only three small elongated depressions evident on the smooth floor. Two of these depressions are aligned off the Colorado River delta, and probably mark an old river course. Their bottoms lie 10–20 fathoms below sills separating them from each other and from Delfin Basin, the deepest portion of the northern Gulf. More closely spaced contour intervals drawn by van Andel (this volume, Fig. 2) show these depressions to be part of a well-developed valley system. This pattern is probably of pre-Recent fluviatile origin. However, the northern or upstream of these depressions is deeper, lying at the juncture of two supposed channels. This suggests that these depressions may owe their present expression to some movement along a buried structure. The third depression, near lat 30° N., long 113° W., parallels the coastline. This shallow swale, the small mounds lying some miles to the northwest, and the shallow depression trending south from Consag Rock, may be scour and depositional features maintained by strong tidal currents known to exist there.

Two larger basins are found within the northern Gulf as here delineated. Delfin Basin lies at the southern end of one of the submerged river systems traced by van Andel (this volume). In its northern part the floor slopes gently southeast, reflecting a high rate of deposition. The northeast-trending deep portion of Delfin Basin is structurally controlled; steep walled but nearly flat floored, this segment reaches a depth of 500 fathoms near its intersection with the northwest extension of Sal si Puedes Basin. North of Angel de la Guarda Island, Delfin Basin connects, over a 190 fathom sill, with the southeasterly deepening trough lying between Tiburón and Angel de la Guarda Islands. Tiburón Basin, west of Tiburón Island, is a shallow basin of fault or nondepositional origin, with a rather smooth, bowl-shaped profile. There is little recent sediment cover in this basin; corers brought up fine gravel and shells. The constriction to the exchange of tidal waters imposed by Angel de la Guarda-San Lorenzo, and San Esteban-Tiburón, and the resulting scour may account for the absence of fine sediment in the deeper portions of this channel.

Based both on bathymetry and crustal structure (Phillips, this volume), the southwest boundary zone of the northern Gulf includes the very narrow, relatively straight Sal si Puedes Basin and the chain of islands and banks extending southeast from Angel de la Guarda to lat 28° N. Sal si Puedes Basin is a steep-walled cleft (with slopes up to 38°) 75 miles long and less than 8 miles wide (below sill depth). It extends from an abrupt southern termination near lat 28°30′ N. to just west of north-central Angel de la Guarda, where it passes (over a 350-fathom-deep sill) into the southeast-trending portion of Delfin Basin. Its maximum depth, 850 fathoms, lies at the foot of the steepest major escarpment yet found in the Gulf. The east wall characteristically is the steeper. Shepard (1950) presented evidence supporting a fault origin for this scarp. The steep slope and straight trace of the west wall indicate it is a fault-derived surface, as well. Several small depressions lie within the elongated basin which varies between *V*-shaped and trough-shaped in cross section. Off the south end of Angel de la Guarda the northwest trend changes to north for a short distance; here the *V*-bottom locally is flattened. Sounding profiles along the basin axis exhibit a remarkable sawtooth appearance of the floor in the *V*-shaped segments. Even the smoother floors have insignificant sediment cover, and bottom photographs show rock exposed on the floor (Fig. 4). The general absence of fill in Sal si Puedes Basin is remarkable in view of the observations that the nearby northern Gulf contains sediment fill more than 15,000 feet thick (Phillips, this volume) and that the Delfin Basin just to the north, and the Guaymas Basin nearby to the south, both show high sedimentation rates (van Andel, this volume, Table XVII). The lack of fill suggests possible nondeposition because of scour in the constricted channel, as above; it might alternatively be explained by very recent activity of faults between the Angel de la Guarda-San Lorenzo Islands and the Baja California Peninsula.

Topography of the Central Gulf province.—The

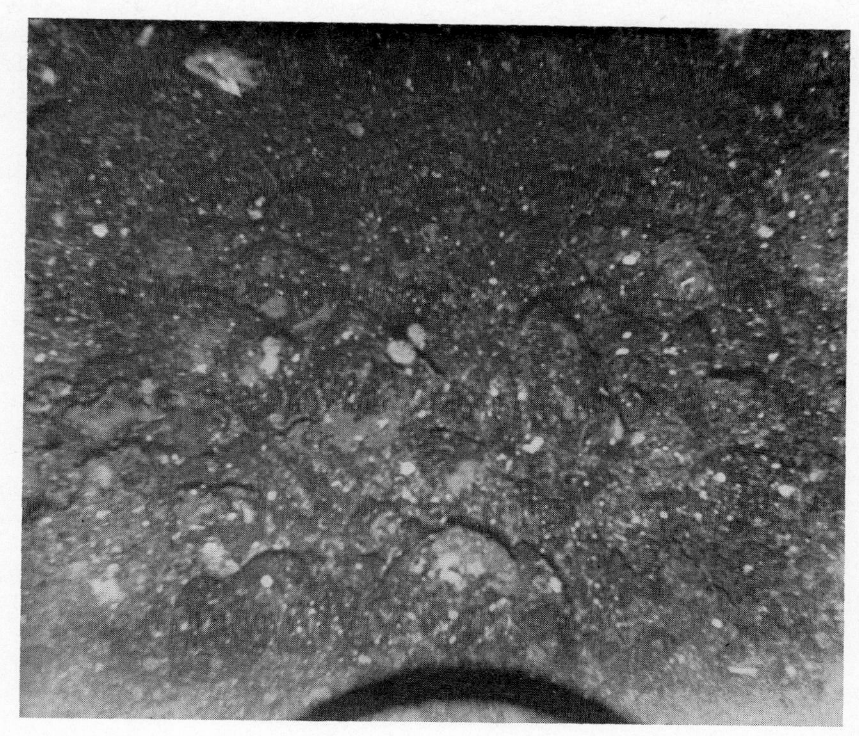

FIG. 4.—Boulders exposed at the base of the west wall of Sal si Puedes Basin, at about 390 fms, west of Angel de la Guarda Island. Photograph by Carl Shipek, U.S. Navy Electronics Laboratory. Field coverage—about 2 square meters.

central Gulf as here delineated lies diagonal to the Gulf axis as a zone of moderate slopes and gentle relief. Extending from the north-trending western shoreline near long. 112°50′ W. to the north-trending shoreline of the Río Fuerte Delta, it includes the largest depression of the Gulf, Guaymas Basin, and a major volcanic island, Tortuga, rising sharply from the east end of a gentle swell.

Shelf characteristics within the area are discussed by Shepard (1950) and van Andel (this volume), who relate shelf development here to the presence of sediment brought to the shore by rivers. Shoal-scale recording on the EDO echo-sounder and gravity surveys (Harrison and Mathur, this volume) reveal strong sub-bottom irregularity of the now-blanketed surfaces.

Guaymas Basin, though the most extensive in the Gulf, has a relief of only 240 fathoms below sill depth. Its northwest trend, extending up to the 600 to 700 fathom contours, is well displayed throughout most of its length. Below these depths the basin floor slopes gently and continuously to the central deep. The dominance here of sedimentation as reflected in morphology is supported by the high accumulation rates of biogenous sediment measured from cores (van Andel, this volume, Table XVII), the common occurrence on PDR records of shallow sub-bottom echoes from slightly more compacted sediments that underlie the soft recent sediments, and the indication from seismic-refraction lines of low-velocity material 1–2 km thick (Phillips, this volume).

The dominant structural pattern of the Gulf first appears clearly in the central province. The most striking characteristic of the deep basins and the eastern slopes south to Islas Tres Marías is the prevalence of long northwest-trending scarps or slopes terminated or offset by shorter north-east-trending structures. The smoothly sloping floor of Guaymas Basin is dissected by two central steep-walled elongated troughs (Fig. 5) that trend almost normal to the basin's axis. Each is flat floored; each has a depth of 80± fathoms below the smooth basin floor. The northern trough is sharply terminated on the northeast by a northwest-trending scarp. The southern trough is similarly terminated on the southwest. The expression of such sharply defined features of local extent in a region of rapid sediment deposition argues for recent structural activity.

Two major fault traces or scarps are suggested by bottom contours in the central Gulf. One of these joins a subsidiary set and with its southerly continuation extends in general in an east-southeasterly direction, as a broadly arcuate scarp with several offsets, from Sal si Puedes Basin along the west face of the San Lorenzo group to a coastal re-entrant on the northwest side of the Río Fuerte delta. As the scarp passes south of Guaymas it is broken by an irregular indentation (lat 27°30′ N. long 111° W.) where several small submarine valleys occur. The sub-parallel subsidiary fault trace, extending through the San Pedro Mártir Basin (Pl. 1, *M-M′*), bounds the east face of San Lorenzo and the small hills to the southeast, apparently cutting these off from the Angel de la Guarda block. The other main scarp of this group extends in a rather uniformly straight line southeast from San Marcos Island, near the southern sill of the Guaymas Basin to the bulge of the Río Fuerte delta, where it reaches Fuerte Canyon.

One of the conclusions advanced by Shepard (1950) was that in the Gulf the larger depressions, specifically Guaymas, Carmen, and Farallón Basins, alternated in trend and shape between broad north-trending deeps—for example, Guaymas Basin—and narrow northwest-trending deeps—for example, Carmen Basin. From this base he evolved a mechanism for rhombic basin origin from strike-slip movement along the Gulf axis. The recent work refining and extending his bathymetric chart suggests that the greater Guaymas Basin is a generally smooth-floored, rectangular basin trending northwest between rather regular scraps. In this basin (as well as in the deeper southern basins to be discussed) the deepest, sharply defined segments have a nearly northeasterly trend. This zig-zag pattern of the steeper slopes, predominating both in the deep basins and on the lower, less-dissected eastern flanks south of the Río Fuerte delta, reflects orthogonal faulting in the whole area, a problem to be discussed in the next section.

Topography of the Southern Gulf province.—In contrast to the sedimented floor of the northern Gulf and the simple, linear basin of the central Gulf, the floor of the deeper southern Gulf is characterized by great irregularity. The dominant northwest and secondary northeast trends—shown by the eastern scarps and the major basins—are especially evident as lineaments here, but knolls, peaks, and swells of more random orientation cover the region south of lat 24° N. where the Gulf of California widens to merge, at less than normal oceanic depths, with the Pacific Basin. Judging from their conical shape, these seamounts are submarine volcanoes like those commonly found west of Baja California; basalt fragments have been recovered from several of them by coring or dredging. Crustal-structure studies (Phillips, this volume) indicate this southernmost portion of the Gulf is of oceanic or near-oceanic character. The knolls and deeper ridges have developed along breaks in the crust, constructing irregularities on a sea floor which lies generally at 1,400–1,600 fathoms in depth.

Several islands and submerged elongated highs, separated from each other and the Baja California Peninsula by shallow troughs or saddles, are present along the western margin. All of these islands consist of "granitic" rocks, deformed volcanics, and local accumulations of Pliocene sediments, as found on the Peninsula nearby (Anderson, 1950) but apparently separated from it by faults. Similarly, the nearshore highs so far sampled—such as Cabrillo Seamount at lat 22°50′ N. long 109°15′ W.—are petrologically part of Baja California. The greatly sheared nature of the quartz-bearing rocks collected from Cabrillo Seamount indicates the faulting that isolated this peak. North of lat 24° N. marginal features are bounded by north-trending scarps that appear to be sliver fault sets. Ceralbo Island, for example, is separated from an elongated bank of comparable size and very similar trend by a steep-walled (15°–20°) trough (previously thought to be a basin) extending south-southeast to the deep floor at lat 24° N. Also on the basis of the few soundings available, La Paz Basin, a shallow depression on

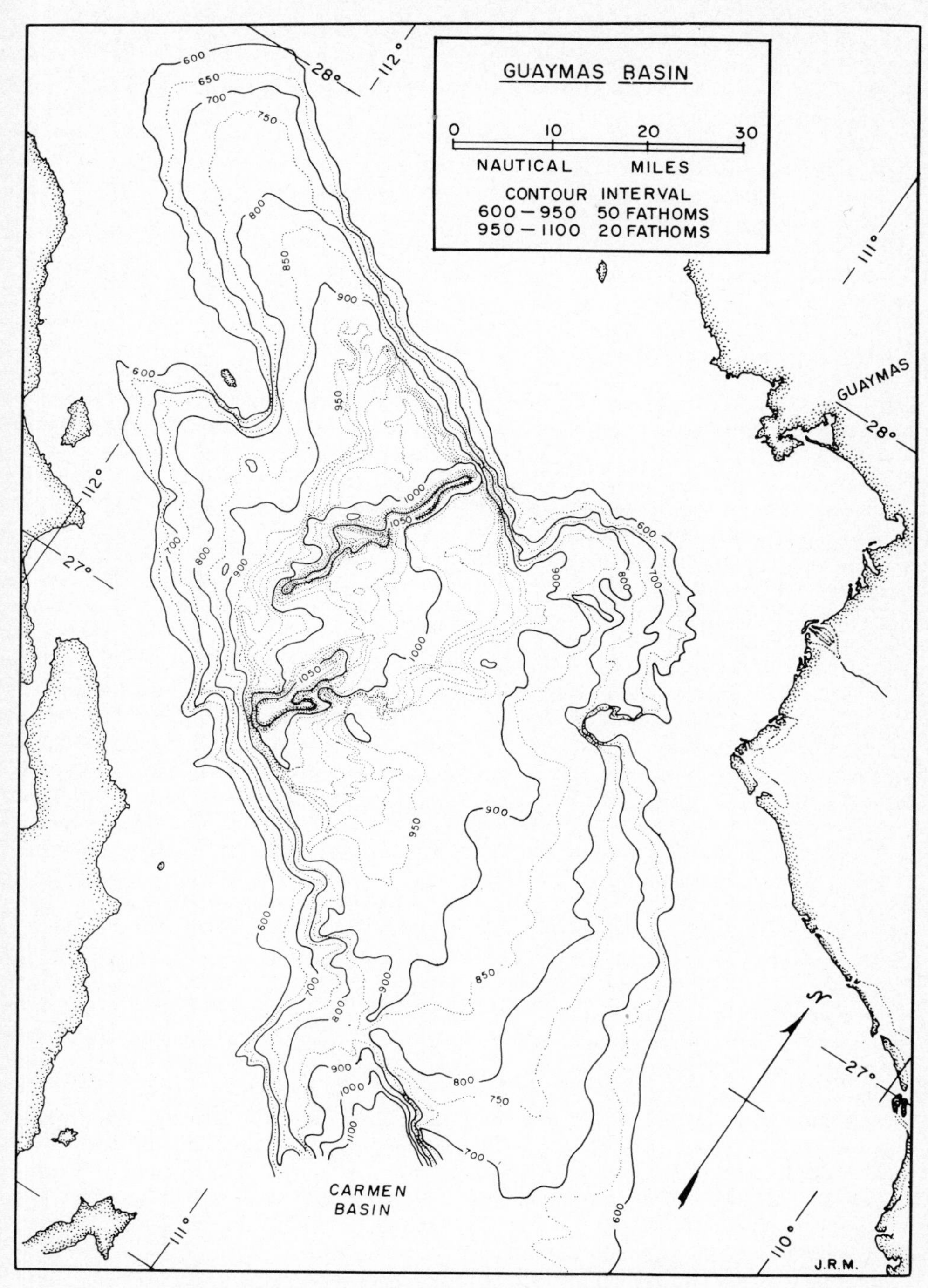

FIG. 5.—Submarine topography of the Guaymas Basin. All contours are in fathoms below sea level; depression contours are not used. See overlay to Chart I for bathymetric control.

the peninsular block, seems separated from the deep Gulf by a spur extending from Ceralbo to the two banks northeast of Espíritu Santo Island. A trans-peninsular fault apparently extends due south of La Paz through Tinaja Trough off the southwest tip of the Peninsula. The separation of two portions of a submarine canyon there bears clear evidence of recent faulting (Shepard, this volume). The offshore depression can be traced clearly northward into the Peninsula. Its northerly trend continues through the embayment west of Espíritu Santo, through the saddles west of San José and Santa Catalina Islands, and into the deep Gulf between Carmen Island and the northern Carmen Basin. A secondary scarp borders the eastern side of the San José-Santa Cruz-Santa Catalina island sequence. East of San José Island, three recent sounding lines across this scarp indicate that the deep elongated basin shown on Shepard's chart (1950) does not exist; from the base of the scarp the floor descends into the western lobe of the Farallón Basin.

Along the eastern margin, southeast of San Ignacio Canyon, the deeper eastern flank of the Gulf and the continental slope to Banderas Bay are characterized by long, steep northwest-trending scarps offset or interrupted by shorter, more gently dipping north-to-northeast-trending slopes or re-entrants. Here, in general, the sedimented upper flank slopes gently, but numerous pinnacles and elongated knolls lie at intermediate depths or at the rim of the steep lower walls (Pl. 1, *A-A′*).

The most striking topographic feature within the southern Gulf is a trio of partially enclosed axial basins separated by sills (Fig. 2 and Chart I). These three—Carmen, Farallón, and Pescadero—increase in maximum depth, in sill depth, in depth below sill level, and in complexity in a southeasterly direction. The over-all trend of each is northwest, as in the simpler Guaymas and Sal si Puedes Basins. They, with Guaymas Basin, appear to form a system of *en echelon* grabens bordered by northwest-trending, high-angle faults oriented slightly west of the median line of the Gulf. Though the basin floors slope gently at moderate depths, the southern two, in particular, have steep-walled (>12°–15°) inner clefts commonly oriented north or northeast of the over-all trend. The inner deeps might be interpreted, as in the case of Guaymas Basin, as tension features caused by right-lateral strike-slip movement along the major boundary faults. Pescadero Basin seems additionally complicated by cross faulting. As noted above for the eastern Gulf flank, knolls or blocks of probably structural origin lie adjacent to the steep inner slopes (Pl. 1, *D-D′*, *G-G′*) of this group. There is no evidence for significant amounts of sediment in the deep portions of Carmen, Farallón, and Pescadero Basins; local deeps are not flat floored. Therefore, the deeps are considered to have been formed rather recently. At intermediate depths all three basins show hummocky or gently irregular topography. Only in the southeast part of Carmen Basin and in the Farallón Basin, both east and west of the central deep, are there continuously sloping floors suggesting blanketing. Sediment in these two basins comes chiefly from the Mayo and Fuerte river systems (van Andel, this volume); in the latter case, sediment would be delivered to the basin through the nearshore San Ignacio-Fuerte canyons.

FAULTS AND FAULTING

Clearly the Gulf of California lies within the boundaries of the structurally complex, much faulted region dominated by the strike-slip faults of the San Andreas system. Although small discontinuous alluvial scarps and recorded earthquake activity indicate a subsurface continuation of the observed faults, attempts at surface mapping of these major California faults into and beneath the thick sedimentary fill of the Imperial Valley-Colorado River delta region have met with little success. Kovach and others (1962; *see* also Biehler and others, this volume) applied various geophysical techniques to trace the subsurface continuity of the San Andreas-Banning-Mission Creek, Imperial, San Jacinto, and the Elsinore-Laguna Salada faults within the Colorado River delta region and have met with moderate success. They conclude that each fault set extends into the delta region as wide zones of branching and interlacing faults rather than as individual breaks. Kovach and others state (1962, p. 2852):

> It is significant that none of these faults of the San Andreas system appears to curve southward so as to

become truly parallel to the Gulf of California, as has been suggested by sketch maps of many previous authors. The Banning-Mission Creek fault, if extended, would continue into the Mexican mainland. Likewise the San Jacinto fault, if extended along the very linear trend evidenced by scarps in the delta region, would pass across the northeast corner of the Gulf and extend into Sonora. From the geological evidence available it thus appears more likely that the San Andreas system enters the Gulf of California as a series of great *en echelon* breaks rather than as a single curving fracture.

Morphologic studies, as well as seismic refraction (Phillips, this volume) and gravity surveys (Harrison and Mathur, this volume) of the crustal structure, indicate similar fault zones within the Gulf proper.

Shepard (1950) has presented the various arguments and criteria applying to the recognition of the many faults by their topographic expression as escarpments in the Gulf. Detailed contouring of the newer and more extensive data now available emphasizes these remarkable *en echelon* structural features as the strong lineaments, discussed individually in the preceding section. Evidence for fault origin, other than that which may be inferred from morphology, is difficult to obtain for many of the submarine structural elements. However, reasonable conclusions can be drawn by assuming that the majority of the lineaments are reflections of faults or fault traces, or have an original fault-controlled structure. Major lineaments are characterized by sharp escarpments; minor structural elements may also include series of volcanic pinnacles, or *en echelon* ridges, knolls, and depressions.

The lineaments illustrated in Plate 2 are marked by heavy lines to emphasize the total pattern observed in the bathymetric chart (Chart I), or in the topography and geology of the land areas as exhibited on aeronautical charts and tectonic maps (USAF Operational Navigation Charts, 1960; Sánchez Mejorada, 1956; Mina U., 1957; de Cserna, 1961; King and others, 1944). They range in size from those of peninsular scale to minor offsets of only a few miles within a basin floor (*see* Bathymetry); and in kind from sharp escarpments with characteristic physiography to distinct boundaries between petrographic provinces. Not all may be assumed to be faults or fault features, however, until such assumptions can be supported by more information than is now available. The degree to which some of the various lineaments may be identified as faults or fault traces follows as (1) observed faults, based on outcrop data, (2) probable faults, based on expression by steep escarpments, and (3) possible faults, suggested by an extension of morphological features or marked by changes in physiography or petrography. Comparison of Plate 3 with Plate 2 distinguishes those lineations considered as faults from those representing other structural elements. In this interpretation, supplementary seismological, gravitational, and geological information has been used wherever available (Beal, 1948; Mina U., 1957; de Cserna, 1961; King, personal communication; King and others, 1944; and this volume).

In the main, the faults figured outline the remarkable zig-zag pattern exhibited by the deep basins, the major morphological offsets, and the slopes, boundaries, and attitudes of islands and escarpments of the Gulf. The most recent studies of right-lateral motion along the San Andreas and related faults in Southern California indicate that the structural block southwest of the fault, including the peninsular range (and thus presumably all of Baja California), has moved toward the northwest some 160 miles (Crowell, 1962). This total distance must have been traversed by most of the Peninsula except where compensated or complicated by local and regional faults. The well-documented history of strike-slip right-lateral movement predicates the interpretation of inferred faults shown here as (1) major *en echelon* right-lateral strike-slip faults, trending about 30° west of the northwest-trending Gulf axis, with (2) complementary orthogonal tension faults, and (3) minor sliver-ridge and splay faulting due largely to the release of tensional stresses imposed on the inner flanks of the central and southern Gulf by basement drag and gravitational adjustment during dilation.

The long strike-slip faults are displayed best in the central Gulf, where they have been shown as the slightly arcuate scarp extending from near lat 27°30′ W., long 111° N. into the Sal si Puedes Basin and the gentler, more linear scarp forming the western boundary of the Guaymas Basin. Although more faults may be present, only two faults subsidiary to the Sal si Puedes Basin seem clearly indicated for the Angel de la Guarda-

FIG. 6.—Bathymetry of the seafloor adjacent to Bahía Sebastián Vizcaíno, showing marked re-entrant offset at its foot, outlined by the 1,000-fathom contour (after Fisher, unpublished).

San Lorenzo string of islands (Chart I and Pl. 1, *K-K′* through *P-P′*), outlining them as two strike-slip, sliver-fault blocks. Judging from the gravity data (Harrison and Mathur, this volume), the bottom contours and the north-trending offset in the Sal si Puedes Basin at lat 29° N., one fault separates Angel de la Guarda from San Lorenzo and extends southeast through the valley between San Esteban and San Lorenzo. Another fault follows the east face of Angel de la Guarda southeast through the small depression near the south end of the island and thence through the Tiburón Basin into the central Gulf region, where it is lost in the complex east scarp near Guaymas. Other sub-parallel northwest-trending faults are indicated in the southern Gulf where they bound the *en echelon* grabens of the southern basins; their linearity has been interrupted by irregular re-entrants, knolls, pinnacles, and ridges. Presence of strike-slip basement faults in the sediment-filled basins of the northern Gulf is only inferred from southeastern extensions of observed California strike-slip faults (as suggested by Kovach and others, 1962). However, possible basement control of the two small shallow depressions at about lat 30° N., long 113° W. and lat 30°45′ N., long 114°10′ W. strongly suggests continuity of such inferred faults, at least here where the axes of the small basins strike parallel to the tectonic grain and appear to be in line with an extension of the newly recognized (trans-peninsular?) Agua Blanca fault (Allen and others, 1960). The Sal si Puedes fault seems to end abruptly at the peninsula shoreline near San Luis Island, but it may continue into the peninsula. Similarly, the fault bordering the southwestern margin of the Guaymas Basin seems to end abruptly near the fault zone of the Santa Rosalía mineral district (Wilson, 1949, 1955), but it may continue as a tectonic element across the Peninsula, as suggested by seismic activity (Richter, 1960), volcanism (Mooser and Lagos, 1961; Ives, 1962), a sharp boundary between petrographic provinces (Sánchez Mejorada, 1956; de Cserna, 1961), and a decidedly offset re-entrant at the south end of Bahía Sebastián Vizcaíno on the Pacific side of the Peninsula (Fig. 6).

Where deposition has not masked their structural character, the transverse tension faults trending north, north-northeast, and northeast are most obvious as the central deeps that are orthogonal to the right-lateral slip traces of the major axial basins. These conjugate depressions have been described as the two north-northeast-trending inner deeps of the Guaymas Basin, a broader north-trending deep in the Carmen Basin, a very deep northeast-trending cleft in the Farallón Basin, and a north-trending cleft, with some indications of cross faulting, in the Pescadero Basin. Similar faulting seems indicated by the irregular northeast-trending outlines of Mazatlán Basin and the generally north- to northeast-striking slopes and re-entrants characterizing the fabric of the eastern Gulf flank. All are presumed to be tensional features, as evidenced by the measured large horizontal displacements along the San Andreas in Southern California (Crowell, 1962) and implicit in the right-lateral slip faces of the basin's major boundary scarps.

It is important to note that contours in the smooth sediment-filled northern Gulf appear to reflect similar tensional fracturing in the underlying basement. Such activity is suggested by the northeast-trending lobes of the 200- and the 400-fathom contours of the Delfin Basin, the northerly offset in the 60-fathom contour of the small depression near lat 30° N., long 113° W., and the northeasterly offset of the 100-fathom contour in the depression near lat 30°45′ N., long 114°10′ W. In the Imperial Valley-Gran Desierto, possible transverse fault control is suggested by the northeast-trending segment of the Colorado River (from lat 32°15′ N., long 115° W. to lat 32°45′ N., long 114°45′ W.) and by a northeasterly aligned set of volcanic outpourings (King and others, 1944; de Cserna, 1961) occurring near lat 31°45′ N., long 113°30′ W., north of Puerto Peñasco (Pl. 2). Notably, most of these suggested fractures of the Gulf appear to be situated in the basin centers, almost equidistant from the shoreline or marginal extremity at each end of the basins. This fact suggests that tensional stress may have been symmetrically imposed and relieved by strike-slip tectonics throughout the history of tensional fracturing in the Gulf.

Less symmetrically disposed are the numerous elongated islands fringing the Baja California Peninsula from Cape San Lucas to San Marcos Island. The inferred normal faults which separate these islands from the Peninsula are recognized in the trend and continuity of adjacent shallow troughs and saddles described in the preceding sections. The faults presumably are the result of tensional stresses caused by a westward component of Gulf dilation and seem to lie nearly parallel to the peninsular shoreline. This tectonic activity seems displayed in the formation of Concepción Bay as well as La Paz Bay and the trans-peninsular fault running through La Paz and into Tinaja Trough off the southwest tip of the Peninsula.

Figure 7 serves to illustrate diagrammatically the major fault-block structures discussed above. Without showing details such as the fringing islands or the modification of slopes, it presents the major tectonic setting.

Escarpments of characteristic slope seem to be related to each class of fault. Cross sections of the Gulf (Pl. 1) vividly portray the nature of these declivities. The characteristic slopes are perhaps best typified by Section *I-I′* (Pl. 1), where the steepest slope is that of the strike-slip escarpment on the east side of the Carmen Basin. A lower slope occurs along the foot of the apparently gravity-adjusted west flank, and a gentle slope is associated with the fault orthogonals to the Guaymas Basin.

Throughout the greater part of the south and central Gulf the strike-slip longitudinal scarps are very steep relative to the transverse basin floors except where very recent tectonic activity has opened deep fractures, as seems indicated by the inner deeps of the Carmen, Farallón, and Pescadero Basins. The more gentle slope relationships are especially clear in the Guaymas Basin where complications by later westward dilation evidently were felt less. It is significant that these distinctly different slopes have not lost their identity even in an area of abundant sediment supply and under a thick blanket of fill, as in the vicinity of the Río Fuerte delta. The difference must be fundamentally a structural one, originating with the formation of the Gulf here as an open crustal break rather than as a foundering of continental crust (Fig. 8), as would appear true for the northern Gulf from the crustal studies of Phillips (this volume). Phillips' seismic refraction results as well as gravimetric studies of the Gulf (Harrison and

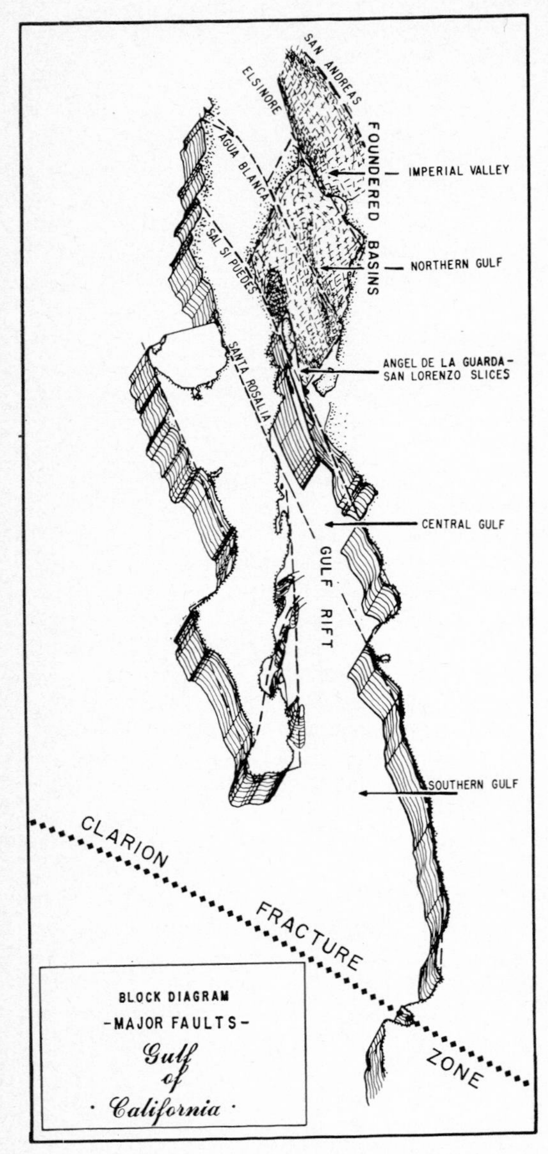

FIG. 7.—Schematic diagram of the Baja California peninsular block, showing faults and structural-rift relations on the south and foundering on the north in the Gulf of California.

Mathur, this volume) are consistent with the conclusion that underlying the sediment cover of the Guaymas Basin and the more southerly basins is dense intrusive or volcanic rock. It might be further suggested that the more gradually sloping floor of the Guaymas Basin, for example, is a constructional feature built by successive intrusions of dike swarms that filled tension fractures created by the strike-slip faults. In contrast, the strike-slip faults were rarely open breaks through which intrusives could reach shallow levels. With such a process, a rectangular basin, having gentle slopes from either end dipping toward the center and bounded throughout its long dimension by steep walls, could be produced. The suggested mechanism is shown schematically for the Guaymas Basin (Fig. 8).

The general rectangular shape and the zig-zag patterns of the basins, then, appear to result from initially offset faults caused by tensional stresses between parallel strike-slip controlling faults. The geometric correspondence between the northern and central Gulf indicates that these two regions are nearly similar in shape and structure, but differ from the southern Gulf in some detail. In the upper two-thirds of the Gulf right-lateral motion seems to have been dominant along the *en echelon* faults of the San Andreas system. In the

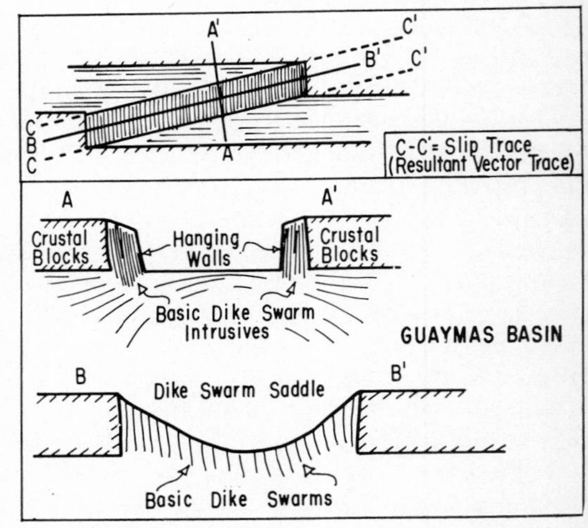

FIG. 8.—Hypothetical diking of the tensional fractures that formed in the Gulf of California rift during dilation. Cross section A-A' shows diking within tight fault-breaks to form steep hanging walls along strike-slip faults. Section B-B' pictures dike swarms filling open tensional fractures conjugate to the strike-slip faults to form a gentle saddle.

lower one-third of the Gulf, however, westward dilation created a wedge-shaped break (*see* also Harrison and Mathur, this volume). The entire southern half of the peninsular block must have swung to the west around a postulated hinge point located just north of Concepción Bay; this is suggested by a matching of zig-zag outlines on each flank of the Gulf as well as by the gravimetric results of Harrison and Mathur (this volume).

Displacement along faults.—Reasonable estimates of the total lateral displacement along strike-slip movements seem to be readily obtainable from the principal physiographic features of the Gulf of California. These estimated distances should, by virtue of geometry, agree with the measured total maximum movement measured on land along the San Andreas fault and its related fractures. Crowell (1962) has reviewed the various field studies of many investigators to reach a figure for the San Andreas displacement; he concludes that the best available evidence indicates a combined movement along the San Andreas and the San Gabriel faults of 160 miles of right-lateral slip (130 miles and 30 miles, respectively). Estimates of up to 350 miles, or even more, have been made by other investigators (Hill and Dibblee, 1953, for example). If we accept the present shoreline configuration as reflecting the outlines of the boundary faults, the evidence from the Gulf and Baja California, although admittedly subject to errors, indicates that Crowell's figure is the more reasonable here. Any derived estimate greater than his value of 160 miles would require "telescopic" extension of the peninsular block, whereas, on the contrary, shortening seems to have prevailed. The evidence from the present study indicates some contraction of the Peninsula, along diagonal trans-peninsular (Agua Blanca-type) faults, to account for the variable distances in estimated displacement along separate longitudinal sections.

On the other hand, by correlation of morphological trends or slopes across the Gulf (Fig. 9),

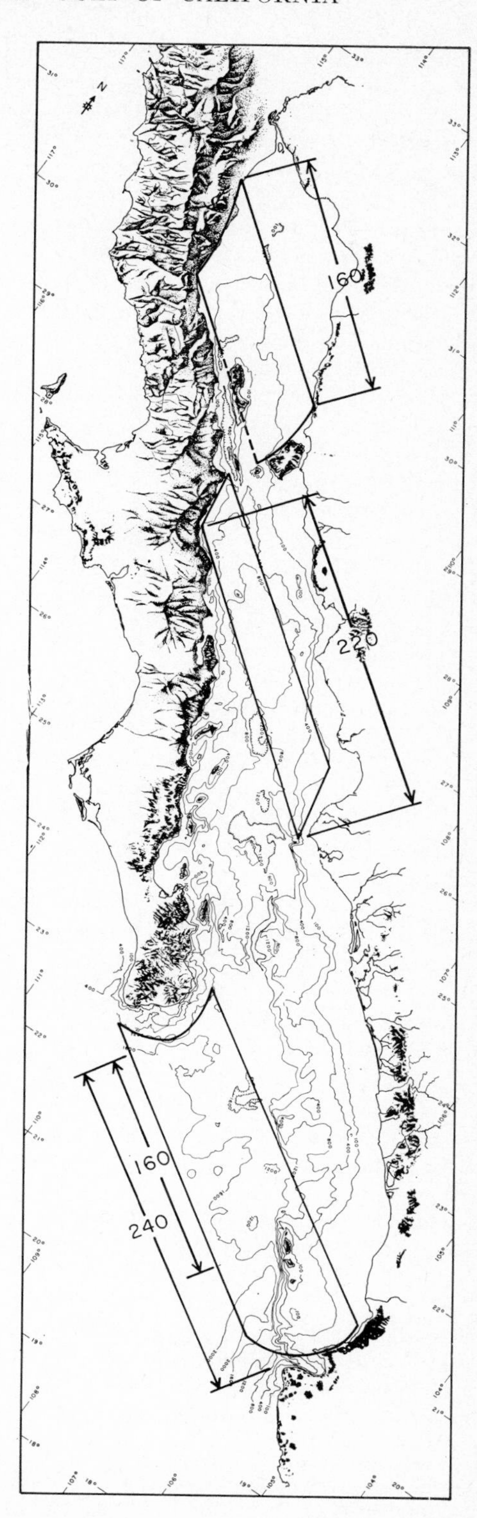

FIG. 9.—Translation of Baja California along *en echelon* strike-slip faults. Displacement shown (in nautical miles) assumes that initial boundary fractures are represented by the shoreline.

the differential movement of the various segments along strike-slip traces appears to be about 240 miles for the segment from Banderas Bay to Cape San Lucas, about 220 miles from Fuerte Canyon to the marked offset south of San Lorenzo, and about 160 miles from the north end of Tiburón Island to the offset at San Felipe. The Angel de la Guarda-San Lorenzo block slices, isolated as they are from the main crustal block, appear to have moved considerably less than has the peninsular block with which they are associated. The fact that apparently there has been marked differential movement between the various peninsular segments indicates that these units may have acted as independent blocks as well, although all moved as a group, and undoubtedly left broken crustal material behind.

Outcrop evidence for right-lateral displacements on the Baja California Peninsula seems limited to the Agua Blanca fault; there Allen, Silver, and Stehli (1960) report that 14 miles of movement has been recognized but more may be present. A similar through-running fault across the Peninsula might be suggested where the Sal si Puedes fault ends abruptly as a recognizable feature; however, evidence for continuity into the land area is not obvious and such a fault, if present, must have negligible displacement. It is likely, therefore, that part of the apparent excessive separation (that is, 220 miles observed versus 160 miles expected from San Andreas movement) measured from shoreline to shoreline across the Guaymas Basin might be due to crustal breakup during dilation, which might also be invoked for the apparently excessive distance between Cape San Lucas and Banderas Bay. On the other hand, if the Peninsula did not break away from the Banderas Bay region but rather from the marked re-entrant, extending well down the east flank, at the north end of the Tres Marías Islands, then the total distance of slip would be 160 miles, and no discrepancy would exist. This easier solution raises some difficulties in geometry, however, as the Peninsula would then be required to move almost due west from its initial position. Inasmuch as none of the observed scarps indicate translation in that direction, the Banderas Bay origin is favored, and, in fact, the trace of the movement seems well recorded in the distinctive northwest-trending scarp occurring near lat 22°45′ N., long 107°45′ W. Such displacements, inferred from morphological evidence, in the Banderas Bay-Cape San Lucas instance receive support from petrographic reconnaissances by Carew McFall, who finds that plutonic rocks (and their inclusions and associated dikes) collected from the south coast of Baja California are essentially identical in plagioclase compositions to such rocks collected from the south coast of Banderas Bay (McFall, personal communication).

Peninsular shortening must then have been caused by crustal breakup in the area of dilation (although fault-block debris is not obviously strewn on the sea floor) and possibly by contraction of the Peninsula along as yet unrecognized trans-peninsular faults, such as might occur from Santa Rosalía through Bahía Sebastián Vizcaíno and/or the observed La Paz fault. Although the hypothetical Sebastián Vizcaíno fault seems marked at its base by a remarkably offset re-entrant on the Pacific floor (Fig. 6) and although the La Paz fault and the positions of islands might be interpreted as resulting from compression of the southern Cape against the Peninsula, direct observations of large-scale compressive evidence are unavailable.

In summary, consideration of the various displacements leads to the conclusion that the present Peninsula was originally offset from the mainland of Mexico by right-lateral movement on several *en echelon* strike-slip faults of the San Andreas system. Concurrently, the entire lower half of the Peninsula swung gradually westward on a curvilinear path hinged somewhere south of Sierra San Pedro Mártir near Concepción Bay. North of the Sal si Puedes-Tiburón constriction the continental crust apparently thinned by low-angle graben-horst *en echelon* normal faulting and foundered, serving as basement beneath fill from the Colorado River system. South of the constriction, the deep Gulf was formed by an open break in the crust. From morphological evidence, as well as crustal studies (Phillips, and Harrison and Mathur, this volume), the Peninsula tip is believed to have broken off the Mexican mainland near Banderas Bay. According to Wilson (1949), the Gulf came into existence and was invaded by marine waters during late Miocene time.

REFERENCES

Allen, C.R., Silver, L.T., and Stehli, F.G., 1960, Agua Blanca fault—a major transverse structure of northern Baja California, Mexico: Geol. Soc. America Bull., v. 71, no. 4, p. 457–482.

Anderson, C.A., 1950, Geology of islands and neighboring land areas, pt. 1 *of* The 1940 E.W. Scripps cruise to the Gulf of California: Geol. Soc. America Mem. 43, 53 p.

——— Durham, J.W., Shepard, F.P., Natland, M.L., and Revelle, R.R., 1950, The 1940 E.W. Scripps cruise to the Gulf of California: Geol. Soc. America Mem. 43, 362 p.

Beal, C.H., 1948, Reconnaissance of the geology and oil possibilities of Baja California, Mexico: Geol. Soc. America Mem. 31, 138 p.

Carey, S.W., 1958, The tectonic approach to continental drift, *in* Continental drift—a symposium: Geol. Dept., Univ. Tasmania, Hobart, Australia, p. 177–355.

Crowell, J.C., 1962, Displacement along the San Andreas fault, California: Geol. Soc. America Spec. Paper 71, 61 p.

de Cserna, Z., 1961, Tectonic map of Mexico; scale 1:2,500,000: Geol. Soc. America.

Drake, C.L., Girdler, R.W., and Landisman, M., 1959, Geophysical measurements in the Gulf of Aden, *in* Internat. Oceanog. Cong. Preprints: Am. Assoc. Adv. Sci., Washington 25, D.C.

Fisher, R.L., 1961, Middle America trench; topography and structure: Geol. Soc. America Bull., v. 72, no. 5, p. 703–720.

Girdler, W.R., 1958, The relationship of the Red Sea to the east African rift system: Geol. Soc. London Quart. Jour., v. 114, pt. 1, no. 453, p. 79–105.

——— 1962, Initiation of continental drift: Nature, v. 194, p. 521–524.

Hill, M.L., and Dibblee, T.W., Jr., 1953, San Andreas, Garlock, and Big Pine faults, California: Geol. Soc. America Bull., v. 64, p. 443–458.

Ives, R.L., 1962, Dating of the 1746 eruption of Tres Virgenes volcano, Baja California: Geol. Soc. America Bull., v. 73, no. 5, p. 647–648.

King, P.B., and others, 1944, Tectonic map of the United States; scale 1:2,500,000: Am. Assoc. Petroleum Geologists, Tulsa, Okla.

Kovach, R.L., Allen, C.R., and Press, F., 1962, Geophysical investigations in the Colorado Delta region: Jour. Geophys. Research, v. 67, p. 2845–2871.

Krause, D.C., 1962, Interpretation of echo sounding profiles: Internat. Hydrog. Review, v. 39, p. 65–123.

Luskin, B., Heezen, B.C., Ewing, M., and Landisman, M., 1953, Precision measurements of ocean depths: Deep-Sea Research, v. 1, p. 131–140.

Mina, U.F., 1957, Bosquejo geológico del territorio sur de la Baja California: Asoc. Mexicana Géol. Petr. Bol., v. 9, nos. 3–4, p. 129–270.

Mooser, F., and Lagos, A.R., 1961, El Grupo volcánico de las Tres Virgenes, MPIO de Santa Rosalía, territorio de Baja California: México Univ. Nac. Inst. Geol. Bol. 61, p. 47–48.

Richter, C.F., 1960, Bulletin of local shocks, January 1947–June 1960: Calif. Inst. Tech. Seismolog. Lab., Pasadena.

Sánchez Mejorada, S.H., compiler, 1956, Carta geológica de la República Mexicana; scale 1:2,000,000: Internat. Geol. Cong., 20th, Mexico, D.F.

Shepard, F.P., 1950, Submarine topography of the Gulf of California, pt. 3 *of* The 1940 E.W. Scripps cruise to the Gulf of California: Geol. Soc. America Mem. 43, 32 p.

Swartz, D.H., and Arden, D.D., Jr., 1960, Geologic history of Red Sea area: Am. Assoc. Petroleum Geologists Bull., v. 44, no. 10, p. 1621–1637.

Wilson, I.F., 1949, Buried topography, initial structures, and sedimentation in Santa Rosalía area, Baja California, Mexico: Am. Assoc. Petroleum Geologists Bull., v. 32, no. 9, p. 1762–1807.

——— 1955, Geology and mineral deposits of the Boleo copper district, Baja California: U.S. Geol. Survey Prof. Paper 273, 134 p.

GRAVITY ANOMALIES IN GULF OF CALIFORNIA[1]

J.C. HARRISON[2] AND S.P. MATHUR[3]
Malibu and Los Angeles, California

ABSTRACT

South of lat 28° N., the axis of the Gulf of California is associated with a gravity high of about 100 mgal Bouguer anomaly which falls off rapidly to about 0 mgal at the sides. This anomaly correlates closely with the deeper water and has been interpreted as a long, narrow strip of dense crust resembling an oceanic section, bordered on either side by a crust of continental type.

North of lat 28° N., this dominant axial high is replaced by a patchwork pattern of anomalies whose magnitude rarely exceeds ±20 mgal. The most pronounced features are a number of relatively restricted areas of low negative anomaly located on both sides of the Gulf and elongated parallel to its general direction. These areas probably mark elongated basins of thicker-than-normal sediment associated with faults, although there is little corroboratory evidence for this interpretation. One of these features, on the mainland side of the Gulf near its head, could mark an extension of the San Jacinto fault.

INTRODUCTION

Gravity measurements were made in the Gulf of California with a LaCoste-Romberg surface-ship gravity meter on board the R/V *Horizon* during the first phase of the *Vermilion Sea Expedition*. During this phase (February 25–April 10, 1959) *Horizon* proceeded from San Diego to Mazatlán by a direct route and then zigzagged her way up the Gulf. A large number of sediment cores were also taken during this phase, and the usual practice was to stop for coring while crossing the Gulf in one direction and to make the return journey without any such stops.

This was the first full-scale survey undertaken with a LaCoste-Romberg surface-ship instrument. During the survey it became apparent that the servo-amplifiers controlling the follow-up mechanism on the long-period pendulums used as vertical references were overloaded, causing the vacuum tubes to deteriorate rapidly. This deterioration led to a worsening of the instrument's performance after leaving Mazatlán. Soon after leaving La Paz, the performance became so poor that a special visit was made to Guaymas to allow an overhaul by manufacturer's representatives. Very little trouble was experienced after this overhaul, and only about 24 hours of data were lost during the remainder of the survey.

ACCURACY OF DATA

Harrison and Spiess (1963) have described tests made on this survey in which results from the shipboard meter were compared with simultaneous measurements by LaCoste-Romberg underwater and geodetic land meters. Figures 1 and 2 show the positions of measurements, the comparison stations, and 20-mgal contours of simple Bouguer anomaly. These comparisons show an apparently consistent difference of 2–3 mgal between the surface and underwater meters, with a scatter of ±1.5 mgal. The profiles are smooth to 1 or 2 mgal. It is concluded that the surface-ship data have an internal consistency of about 2 mgal

[1] Manuscript received, June 25, 1963. Publication 311, Institute of Geophysics and Planetary Physics, University of California, Los Angeles.

We would like to acknowledge with thanks the assistance of F.N. Spiess, M.S. McGehee, J.W. Joy, and E.G. Smith (Marine Physical Laboratory, Scripps Institution of Oceanography), M. Caputo (University of Trieste and Institute of Geophysics), and C.O. Alexis (Office of Naval Research) in making the gravity measurements. G.A. Rusnak, whose leadership as chief scientist on *Horizon* during the period when these measurements were made contributed greatly to the success of the survey, prepared the track charts necessary for reducing the gravity data. Finally, we owe a great debt to L.J.B. LaCoste of the LaCoste and Romberg Company for lending the geodetic and underwater gravity meters used for comparisons. These measurements were made while the senior author was at the Institute of Geophysics, University of California, Los Angeles, and were supported by the Office of Naval Research under contracts with the Institute of Geophysics and the Scripps Institution of Oceanography of the University of California.

[2] Hughes Research Laboratories; formerly at Institute of Geophysics and Planetary Physics.

[3] Institute of Geophysics and Planetary Physics, University of California, Los Angeles.

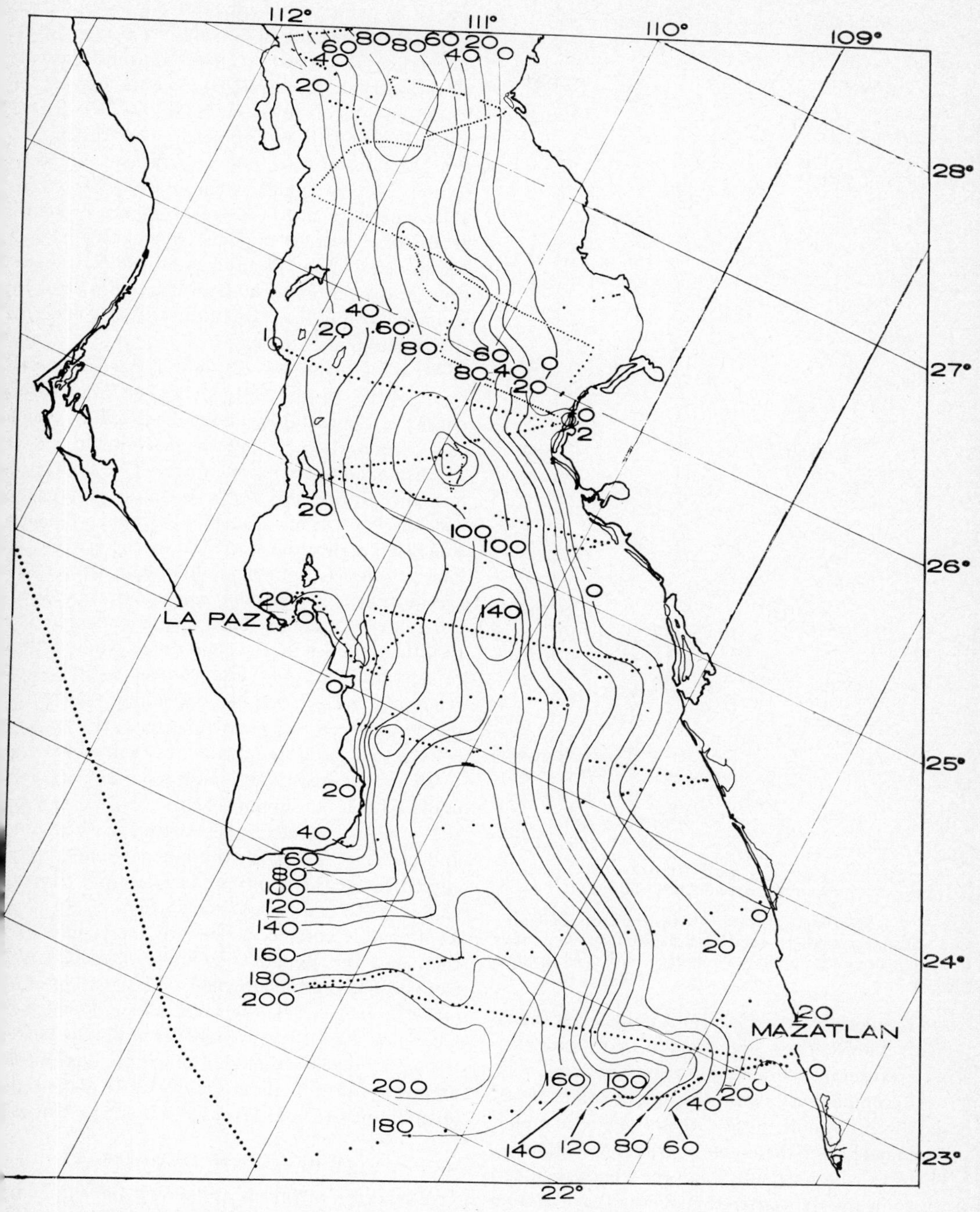

Fig. 1.—Positions of gravity measurements in Gulf of California, southern section, and 20-mgal contours of simple Bouguer anomaly computed with 2.67 g/cm³ density.

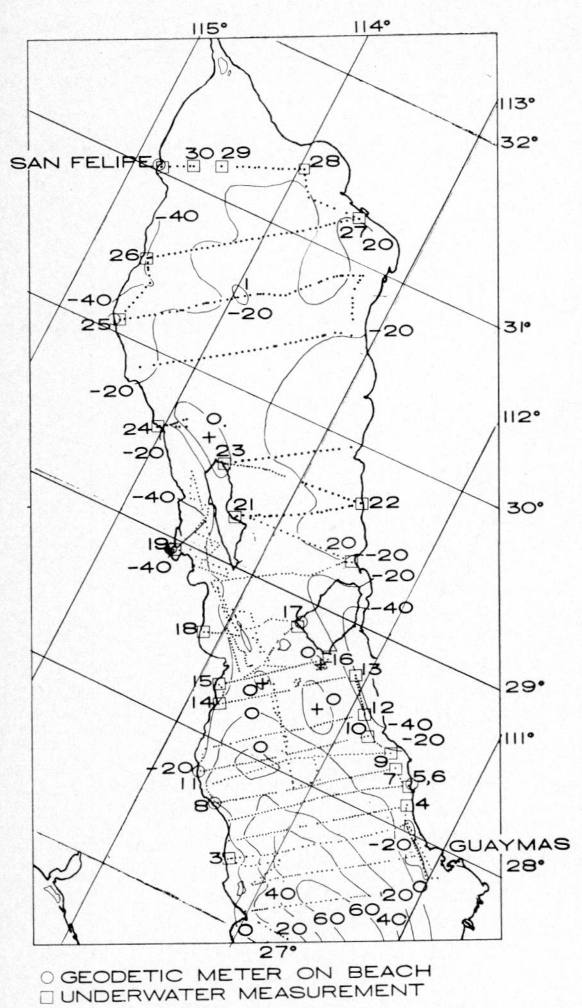

FIG. 2.—Positions of gravity measurements in Gulf of California, northern section, and 20-mgal contours of simple Bouguer anomaly computed with 2.34 g/cm³ density.

and that any systematic error is not greater than 3 mgal. These errors are smaller than errors expected from inaccuracies in the navigation.

All comparisons with the underwater meter, and all but two of those with the geodetic meter, were made after the meter overhaul at Guaymas. There can be no doubt that the greatest uncertainty in the data after this overhaul arises from the navigation. Although frequent landfalls were made for accurate positioning, tidal currents of several knots, which varied rapidly with position and time, made it difficult to estimate ship's true speed, and hence led to uncertainty in the Eötvös correction. The speed estimates are most difficult when frequent stops are made to obtain cores, for it is often difficult to estimate the distance drifted on station and to determine the currents on the short sections of track between stations. The continuous profiles should be considerably more reliable. The data north of Guaymas are probably generally consistent to about ±3 mgal, although occasional sections of track between coring stations in the center of the Gulf may be in error by ±6 mgal, owing to errors in the estimate of ship's speed between stations.

Accuracy before the overhaul is harder to estimate owing to the infrequency of comparison checks and uncertainty about the extent to which the deterioration in meter performance after Mazatlán affected its accuracy. The poor performance during this period certainly resulted in considerable loss of data, especially when the ship was heading into the sea. Clearances between the long-period reference pendulums and their stops are quite small, and poor servo performance allowed a pendulum to touch one of its stops. The resulting impulse set the pendulum swinging, thus causing the servo to lose control entirely and rendering measurements impossible. Although many data were lost from this cause, the authors believe that data taken while the instrument was to all appearances functioning correctly, are generally reliable. In support of this view, one can say that the profiles of free-air anomaly are smooth and correlate well with the bottom topography; agreement at the few track intersections is good, as it is at the two comparison stations in this area. Topographic corrections smooth the profiles further, and the Bouguer anomalies correlate well from profile to profile to yield a consistent over-all pattern. In general, the measurements south of Guaymas are believed to be accurate to better than ±10 mgal, although a few individual measurements south of the southern tip of Baja California appear to be in error by as much as 20 mgal.

REDUCTION OF THE DATA

A small correction is applied to the shipboard measurements to reduce them to sea level, and the value given by the International Gravity Formula is subtracted to yield a "free-air" gravity anomaly. Variations in the free-air anomaly are caused by changes in the sub-bottom structure and by changes in the depth of water beneath the ship. In order to obtain an anomaly map reflecting the sub-bottom changes, it is necessary to correct for the variations in water depth. This is accomplished by applying a topographic correction to each measurement. This correction is the increase in gravity at the station, which would occur if the sea water were replaced by rock of a specified density. If this density is correctly chosen, the effect of varying water depth is completely removed and the anomaly pattern reflects the sub-bottom structure. The topographic correction is laborious to compute exactly when a large number of stations is concerned, and it is often convenient to approximate this correction by the attraction of an infinite slab of thickness equal to the water depth at the station. Anomalies so corrected are referred to as simple, or infinite slab, Bouguer anomalies; this is the anomaly shown in Figures 1 and 2. The infinite slab approximation is good in shallow water and when the depth of water does not change significantly in distances of the order of 5 or 10 times the depth of water at the station. These conditions are not met in many parts of the Gulf, so the full topographic correction has been used in Figures 3, 6 and 8, for all the profiles used in the interpretation.

The choice of a density to use in the correction is important and, unfortunately, a very difficult one to make. Many rock types are found in an area the size of the Gulf, and the use of different densities in different parts of the area under study is confusing because discontinuities will be introduced where the choice of density is changed. In any case, available geologic maps are very generalized and densities can only be guessed at.

In the southern part of the Gulf, water depths range from 1 to 3 km, so it is appropriate to use a mean density typical of the surrounding rocks between sea level and a depth of 2 km below sea level. Extensive outcrops of metamorphic rocks very similar to the Peninsular Range batholith of Southern California occur in the northern half of the Baja California Peninsula and in the southern tip. The eastern portion of the intervening area consists largely of upper Tertiary volcanic rocks. In their study of the Colorado Delta, Kovach, Allen, and Press (1962, Table 2) assign average densities of 2.67–2.68 and 2.61–2.68 g/cm^3 to these two groups of rocks on the basis of sample measurements from various unpublished sources. On the mainland side, the outcrops are mainly of upper Tertiary and Quaternary sediments, although there are also extensive extrusive and intrusive igneous rocks. Densities of well samples given by Kovach, Allen, and Press suggest a sediment density of 2.37 g/cm^3 in the 0–4,000-foot depth range, increasing to 2.47 in the 8,000–12,000-foot range. There are, however, many outcrops of Precambrian, Paleozoic, and Mesozoic formations within 100 km of the shoreline, whose mean densities are probably in the 2.6–2.7 range, if not even denser. A mean density of 2.67 g/cm^3 for the 2-km column below sea level is reasonable except, perhaps, for the coastal belt, where the Quaternary and Tertiary sediments may form an appreciable proportion of the column. A density of 2.67 g/cm^3 has been used for the calculation of the topographic corrections and is fairly well justified, except where there are large thicknesses of sediments, notably in a coastal belt on the mainland side of the Gulf.

INTERPRETATION

The Gulf is conveniently divided into three problem areas for the interpretation. As may be seen from Figures 1 and 2, its axis is characterized by a prominent gravity maximum from its mouth north to about lat 28° N. This is the dominant feature in the southern section and forms the first problem. The transition area in the vicinity of lat 28° N., where this maximum disappears, is characterized by a much higher density of stations than are the areas to the north and to the south, and is conveniently considered as a whole. The section of the Gulf north of Tiburón Island provides the third problem.

SOUTHERN SECTION

Figure 3 shows 20-mgal contours of fully corrected Bouguer anomaly in the portion of the Gulf characterized by the central gravity maximum. This feature generally follows the deepest water; its subsidiary maxima coincide with the deep basins. Figure 4 shows ten profiles whose positions are given in Figure 3. From the map and profiles, it is seen that the 0-mgal anomaly contour generally coincides well with the coast line, although

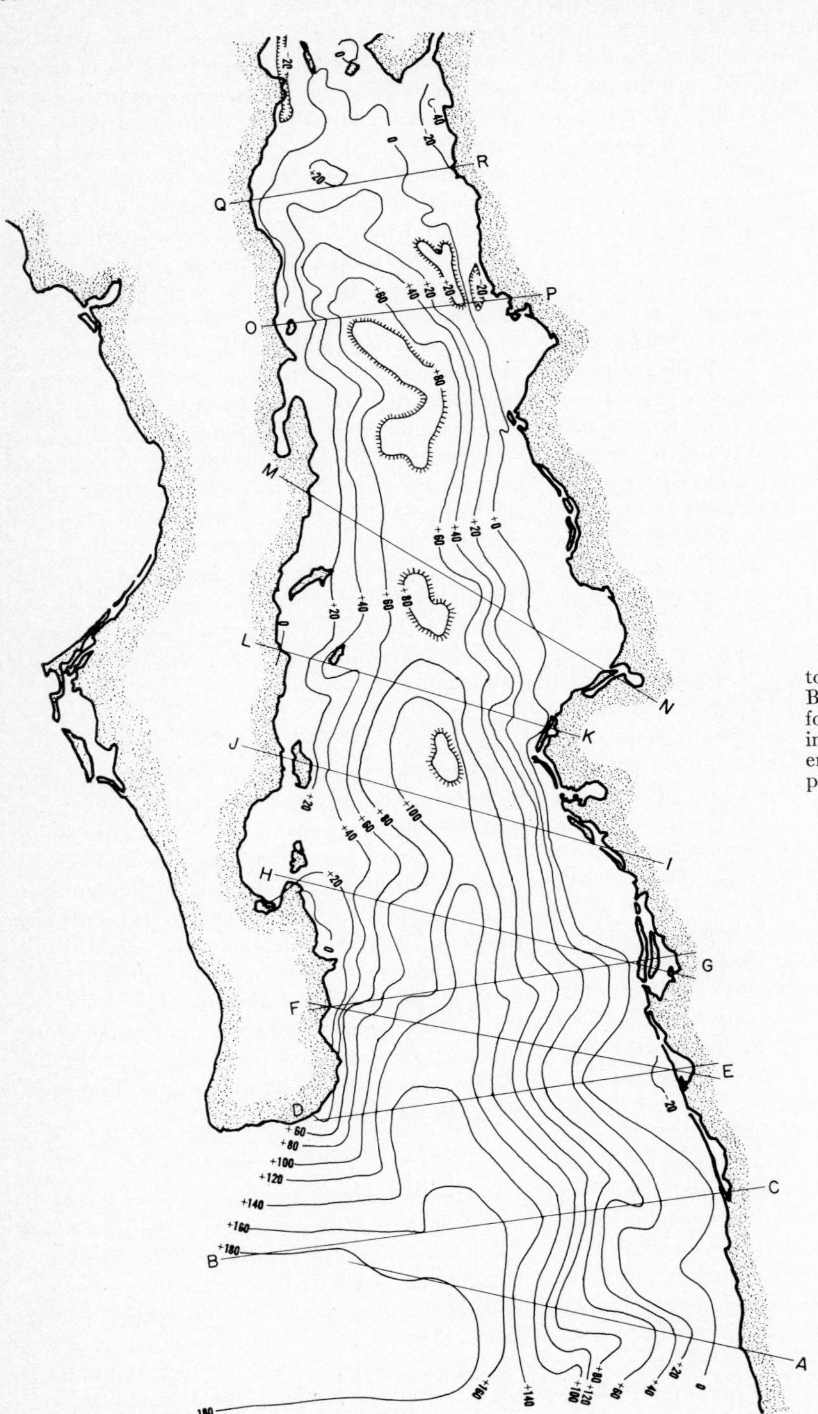

FIG. 3.—20-mgal contours of fully corrected Bouguer anomaly computed for a density of 2.67 g/cm³ in Gulf of California, southern section, together with positions of profiles.

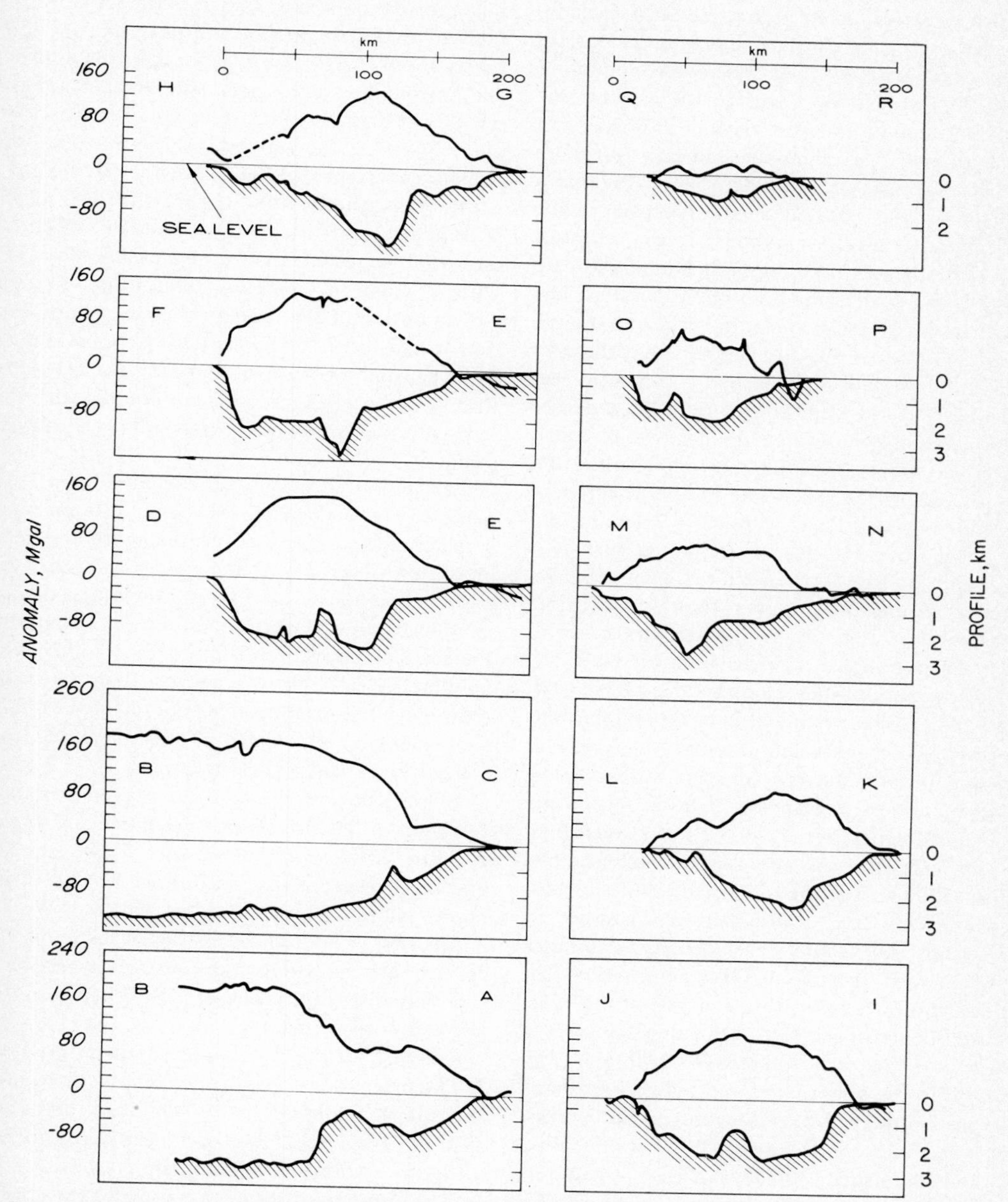

FIG. 4.—Gravity and topographic profiles across Gulf of California. Positions of profiles shown in Fig. 3.

the anomalies on the eastern side tend to be slightly negative, whereas on the western side, they are commonly positive, but still decreasing, as the coast is approached. There is commonly a broad shelf of shallow water on the eastern side which is absent on the western side. This shelf and the negative gravity anomalies indicate that there has been appreciable sedimentation on the mainland side which is absent on the peninsular side.

Clearly this gravity maximum in the center of the Gulf indicates that the Gulf is underlain by denser rocks than is the land on either side. The fact that the Bouguer anomaly is close to 0 mgal along the shores of the Gulf suggests that the land areas are underlain by a normal continental section and that the Gulf is underlain by a denser section, possibly intermediate between a continental and an oceanic crust. Seismic results from lines shot along the axis of the southern section of the Gulf reveal a layer with 6.3–6.7 km/s compressional wave velocity, whose upper surface is at a depth of 4 to 5 km below sea level. This velocity is significantly higher than is typical of continental sections at this depth and confirms the presence of dense rocks beneath the Gulf.

The anomaly profiles along sections *A-B*, *G-H*, *K-L*, and *O-P* were studied in order to determine the distribution of the denser rocks. An anomalous mass of uniform density contrast was assumed, whose upper surface coincides with the seismically determined depth to the 6.3–6.7 km/s layer. This density contrast was supposed to extend to a depth of 30 km, and the computed profiles include a sedimentary layer whose thickness is given by the seismic results and whose density is assumed to be 2.33 gm/cm^3. With these assumptions the profiles can be fitted with a contrast of 0.17 gm/cm^3 and the cross sections outlined in Figure 5, in which the contrast is between 2.90 and 2.73 gm/cm^3 in the upper layer and between 3.20 and 3.03 in the lower. A two-dimensional approximation was made, and the method of Talwani, Worzel, and Landisman (1959) was used to compute the gravity profiles. The mass is a steep-sided body which progressively narrows as one proceeds up the Gulf. It has a width of about 100 km in section *G-H*, 70 km in *K-L*, and has narrowed to less than 50 km in width in *O-P*. The assumption of a uniform density contrast for the mass is undoubtedly an oversimplification. Although seismic information is available from the center of the Gulf so that it is possible to make density estimates for the mass itself, none is available from the surrounding areas, and the section against which the mass is contrasted is unknown. However, by using the seismic information and the density contrast of 0.17 gm/cm^3, one can deduce a continental structure and can discover whether it is compatible with known continental structures and whether its mass per unit area is compatible with a crust in isostatic equilibrium. Vertical redistribution of the mass in the continental section would increase the contrast at some depths while causing a corresponding decrease at others. Provided the changes were not too drastic, this redistribution would not greatly affect the gravity profiles.

The computed gravity profiles in Figure 5 depend only on the density contrast of 0.17 gm/cm^3. The actual densities used in this figure are based on seismic observations along the axis of the Gulf and the assumption that the continental section is in approximate isostatic equilibrium with other Pacific sections. The seismic data (Phillips, this volume, Table II-C) show a discontinuity beneath that which has been taken as the top of the anomalous mass, at which the velocity increases from 6.3–6.7 km/s (6.46 km/s mean) to 7.3–8.2 km/s (7.73 km/s mean). The 6.46 km/s layer averages a thickness of 3.9 km. Seismic velocities of 6.46 and 7.73 km/s correspond to densities of 2.90 and 3.27 gm/cm^3, respectively, according to the Nafe-Drake relationship as given by Talwani, Worzel, and Ewing (1961), and densities of 2.73 and 3.10 gm/cm^3 are implied for the continental section at corresponding depths if a density contrast of 0.17 gm/cm^3 is to be maintained.

Several crustal columns are compared in Table I. The first, for the axis of the Gulf, is the mean of the 3-layer models given by Phillips in his Table II-C (this volume). The second is a continental structure obtained from this on the basis of the 0.17 gm/cm^3 density contrast used for the gravity interpretation. Four well-determined oceanic crustal sections are included for comparison—two from the Atlantic given by Ewing, Worzel, and Ewing (1962, Table 3) and two from the Pacific averages of 14 and 8, respectively, of Raitt's

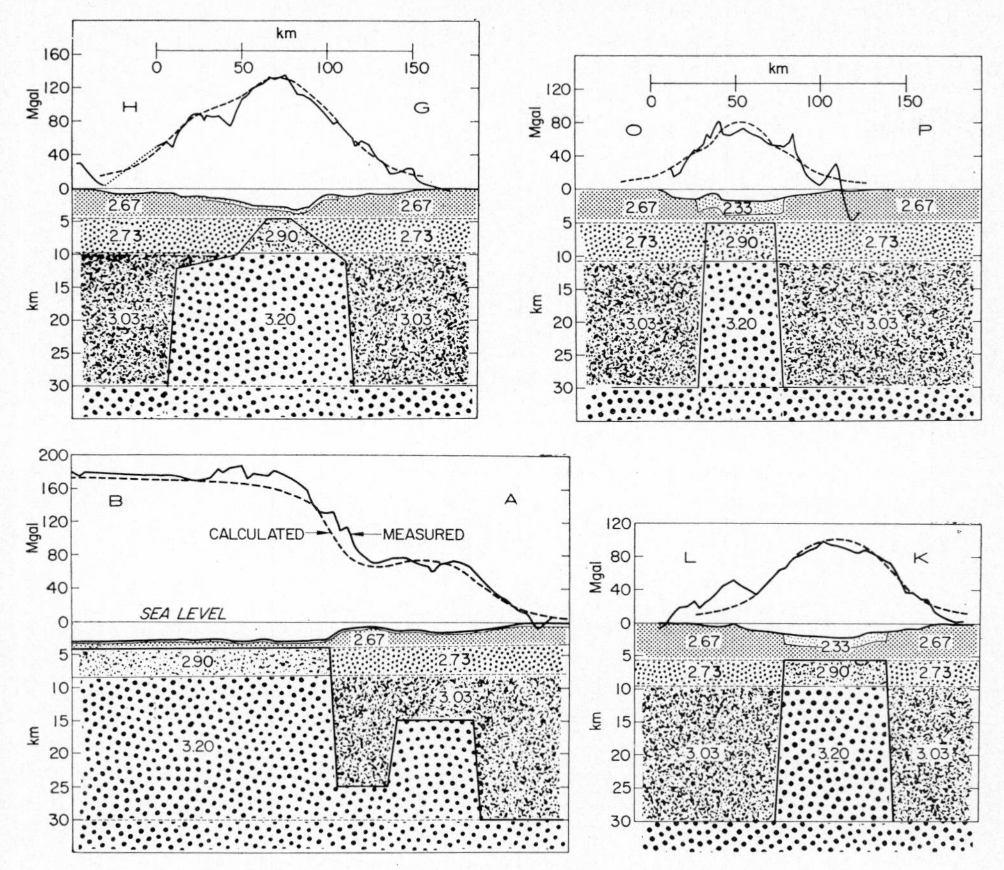

FIG. 5.—Structural sections across the Gulf showing calculated and observed gravity profiles. Positions of sections shown in Fig. 3.

Capricorn and Mid-Pacific seismic stations (Raitt, 1956). Densities have been assigned on the basis of the Nafe-Drake curve and the mass-per-unit area to a depth of 33 km has been calculated for each column from these densities.

The masses of the two Atlantic sections are in reasonable agreement as are the masses of the Pacific columns, although the Pacific columns appear to be somewhat heavier than the Atlantic. The columns on the axis and at the margins of the Gulf are in close agreement and are heavier than both the Atlantic and Pacific columns. However, a departure of only 0.07 gm/cm³ from the Nafe-Drake curve in the lowest layer, or a reduction of only 0.2 km/s in the assigned velocity of 7.73 km/s—an average of measurements ranging from 7.25 to 8.24 km/s—would reduce the density of this layer to 3.20 and bring the continental and Gulf columns into agreement with the two Pacific columns. Neither alternative places an undue strain on the observational data and it can be concluded that the profiles of Figure 5 are consistent with the seismic measurements in the Gulf and with an entirely reasonable continental structure on either side.

Thus the southern portion of the Gulf of California, approximately as far north as lat 28° N., is underlain by rocks about 0.17 gm/cm³ denser than those underlying the land masses on either side. These denser rocks form a wedge-shaped mass some 650 km long in the direction of the Gulf, approximately 100 km wide near its mouth,

TABLE I. COMPARISON OF CRUSTAL COLUMNS

Axis of Gulf			Continental Section			West Atlantic			East Atlantic			Pacific (Capricorn Expedition)			Pacific (Mid-Pacific Expedition)		
Thickness km	Velocity km/s	Density gm/cm^3	Thickness km	Velocity km/s	Density gm/cm^3	Thickness km	Velocity km/s	Density gm/cm^3	Thickness km	Velocity km/s	Density gm/cm^3	Thickness km	Velocity km/s	Density gm/cm^3	Thickness km	Velocity km/s	Density gm/cm^3
2.1	(1.5)	1.03				5.0	1.5	1.03	4.6	1.5	1.03	4.5	1.5	1.03	4.9	1.5	1.03
			5.5		2.67												
1.2	(2.0)	2.33				0.4	1.8	1.8	0.3	1.8	1.8	0.3	2.15	2.0	0.4	2.15	2.0
						0.5	2.1	2.0	0.5	2.1	2.0						
2.2	5.4	2.67				1.5	5.0	2.55	1.5	5.0	2.55	1.1	5.1	2.60	1.6	5.4	2.65
3.9	6.5	2.90	3.9		2.73	5.2	6.7	2.95	4.9	6.5	2.90	4.6	6.76	2.97	4.8	6.77	2.97
			20.6		3.10	-	8.1	3.40	-	7.8	3.30	-	8.25	3.40	-	8.22	3.40
--	7.7	3.27	-		3.27												
Mass per cm^2 to a depth of 33 km ($gm/cm^2 \times 10^6$)																	
9.93			9.90			9.54			9.43			9.83			9.68		
						-mean						mean					
with 3.20 density for 7.7 km/s layer																	
9.77			9.73			9.48						9.75					

and narrowing to a width of approximately 50 km before ceasing rather abruptly. In the vertical dimension they extend from the base of the continental crust, assumed to be at 30 km depth, to within about 5 km of sea level as indicated by the seismic results. Although lack of knowledge of the crustal sections beneath the sides of the Gulf precludes any detailed conclusions, the gravity profiles are consistent with a continental crust in isostatic equilibrium on either side of the Gulf and the structure obtained from the seismic profiles in the center.

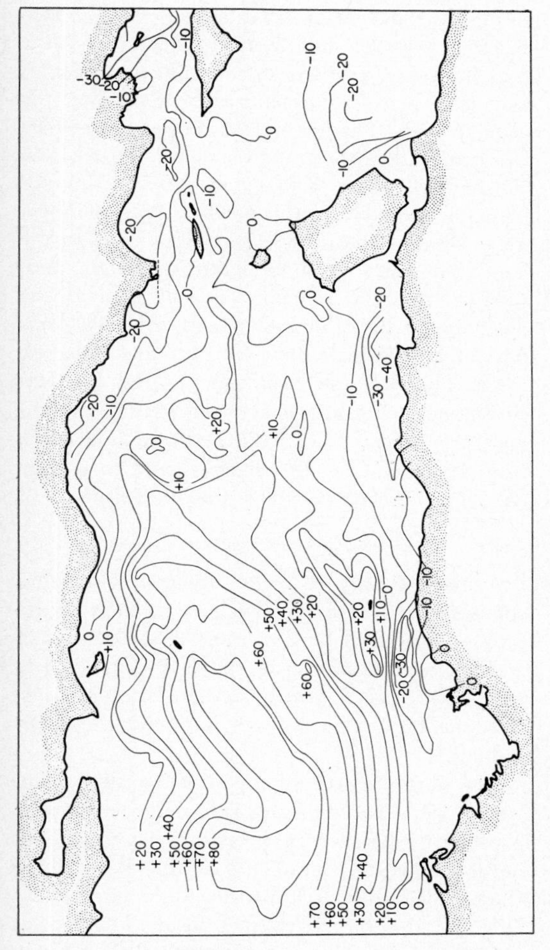

FIG. 6.—10 mgal contours of fully corrected Bouguer anomaly computed for a density of 2.67 g/cm³ in Gulf of California, central section.

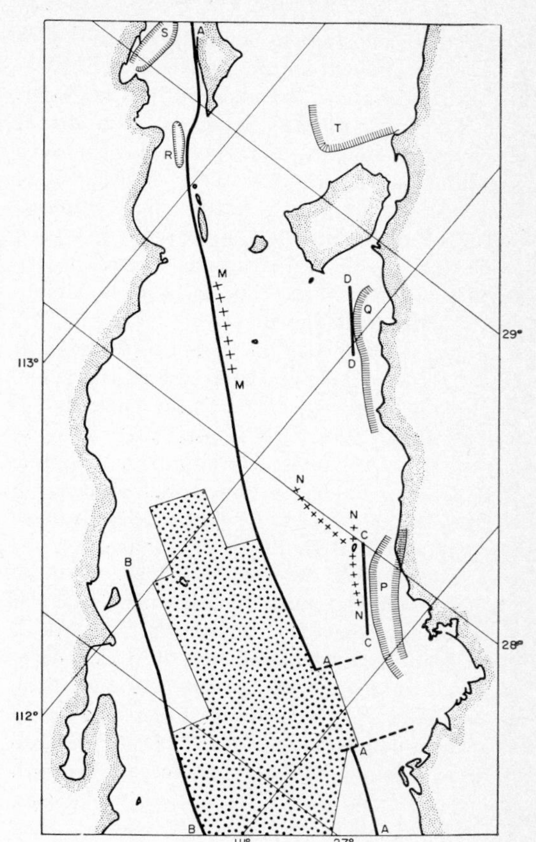

FIG. 7.—Structural map of central section of Gulf of California. Shaded area represents gravity high associated with intrusion of heavy rocks. *A-A*, *B-B*, *C-C*, and *D-D* represent fault scarps and probable faults. *M-M* and *N-N* represent gravity highs. *P*, *Q*, *R*, *S*, and *T* represent gravity lows.

CENTRAL SECTION

A map of fully corrected Bouguer anomalies contoured at 10-mgal intervals is shown in Figure 6, and some of the prominent structural features of the area are shown in Figure 7. The line *A-A* in Figure 7 follows a major scarp in the sea floor. West of San Lorenzo and Angel de la Guarda Islands, it divides these islands from a narrow steep-sided topographic trough, Sal si Puedes Basin, in Ballenas Channel. The same trend can readily be followed in a southeasterly direction across the Gulf where it follows a steep slope between deep water to the southwest and shallower water to the northeast. Similarly, the line *B-B* follows a prominent scarp on the sea floor, marking the southwestern boundary of the deep water. The trough in Ballenas Channel is significant, as its presence suggests that there may be such troughs along both sides of the Gulf north of Guaymas, concealed beneath the sediment. Southwest of the line *A-A*, topography is a good guide to the geological structure, whereas to the northeast of this line, the structure is largely buried under the sediment.

In the southern part of Figure 6, the gravity pattern is dominated by the axial high characteristic of the southern section of the Gulf. As described above, this high is associated with an intrusion of heavy rocks. The approximate outline of the area underlain by these rocks is shaded in Figure 7 and appears to be closely related to the faults *A-A* and *B-B*. North of this feature, the gravitational relief is sharply reduced and the single predominant maximum of nearly +90 mgal amplitude is replaced by a patchwork pattern of minor features in which much of the area is characterized by anomalies between ±10 mgal. The gravity data show no indication that the heavy axial rocks extend north of lat 28° N. and up into Ballenas Channel, and are thus in contrast with the results from seismic lines 8 and 9 (Phillips, Table II-A, this volume) which do indicate such an extension.

The next most prominent feature on the gravity map is a feature just west of Guaymas, consisting of a trough of low anomalies elongated parallel to the shoreline (marked *P* in Fig. 7), bordered on its western side by a ridge of high anomalies (*N-N* in Fig. 7) on which a small island is located. The simplest interpretation is a narrow but deep sedimentary trough *P* associated with a basement uplift *N-N*, the association and strong gravity gradient indicating a fault *C-C* between the two structures. The anomaly in the trough *P* attains −38 mgal. With a density contrast of 0.3 gm/cm^3 for the sediments, this anomaly indicates a thickness of nearly 3 km, about twice the present depth of Sal si Puedes Basin. The structure is, of course, very similar to the relationship between the Sal si Puedes Basin and San Lorenzo Island. There is a second gravity low southeast of Tiburón Island (*Q* in Fig. 7), probably also associated with a sedimentary trough and possibly with a fault *D-D*. There is insufficient evidence to be sure whether *P* and *Q* are connected or whether they are separate troughs. The high *N-N* bifurcates at the small island; one branch follows the direction *C-C*, *D-D* parallel to the coast, whereas the other branch tends to follow the trend *A-A* across the Gulf. A third area of low anomalies, *T* in Figure 7, on the northern side of Tiburón Island belongs with the interpretation of the northern area.

Following *A-A* across the Gulf, one finds a weak, elongated gravity high *M-M* continuing the trend of Angel de la Guarda and San Lorenzo Islands. Between San Lorenzo Island and the coast of Baja California, the Sal si Puedes Basin is associated with no recognizable pattern on the gravity map. Farther north, however, between the two islands, the trough is characterized by a closed gravity low, *R* in Figure 7, indicating appreciable sediment in this portion. West of Angel de la Guarda Island, the gravity low lies to the landward side of the topographic trough, and, judging from the anomaly of −39 mgal on the beach in the Bahia de los Angeles, this bay forms part of a filled-in sedimentary trough. Although the gravity data are insufficient to map this feature completely, there is evidence for a filled sedimentary trough *S*, extending almost due north from the Bahia de los Angeles in an *en echelon* configuration with the Sal si Puedes Basin.

NORTHERN SECTION

A map of fully corrected Bouguer anomalies contoured at 10-mgal intervals is shown in Figure 8. As indicated in Figures 1 and 2, the density of stations in this section of the Gulf is much less than in the central section, so there is considerable freedom in contouring between the measured profiles.

The northern part of the Gulf is a depression with a deep fill of sediment. It would, therefore, be expected to be an area of low gravity anomalies bordered by steep gradients at the edges where the sediments abut against the older rocks. In fact (Fig. 8), the area is characterized by a central maximum and the gravity anomaly generally becomes more negative toward the sides of the Gulf.

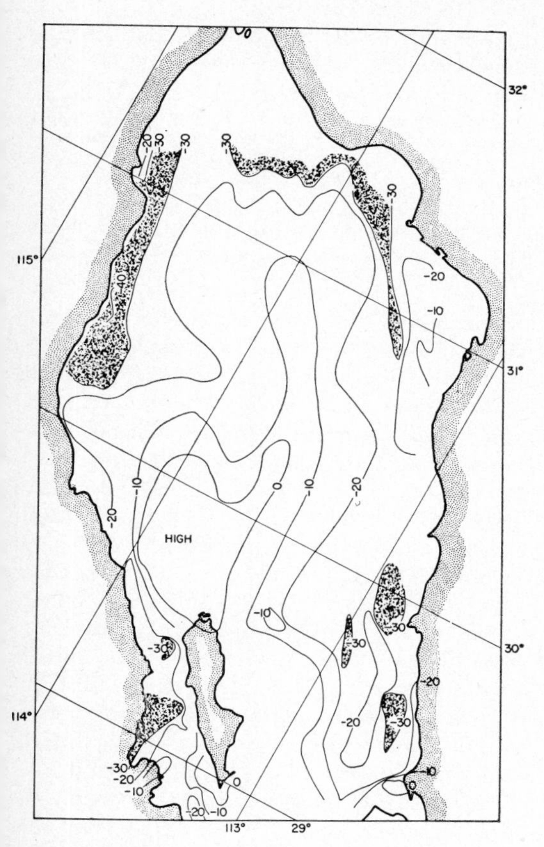

FIG. 8.—10-mgal contours of fully corrected Bouguer anomaly computed for a density of 2.67 g/cm³ in Gulf of California, northern section. Stippled areas indicate areas where the anomaly is more negative than −30 mgal.

Kovach, Allen, and Press (1962) also found no correlation between sediment thickness and gravity anomaly in their study of the Colorado Delta to the north. Their profile from Yuma to San Diego (their Fig. 13) shows more than 15,000 feet (4.5 km) of sediment beneath the Imperial Valley which finds no expression in the gravity profile. They conclude that compaction in such a column of sediments reduces the expected average density contrast, that density differentials in the sediments and in the basement are as important in governing the gravity profile as is the basement-sediment contrast, and that the sedimentary basin may be partially compensated isostatically. Under these circumstances, interpretation of gravity data without detailed seismic, magnetic, and well data becomes impossible.

There is a region of relatively positive (0 to +10 mgal) anomalies north and northwest of Angel de la Guarda Island which decrease very steadily and slowly to the sides and head of the Gulf. There are elongated areas near the edges of the Gulf where the anomaly is more negative than −30 mgal; these areas have been stippled in Figure 8. They could be associated with variations in the thickness or density of the sediments, or with variations in the basement rocks. The seismic lines are on too gross a scale to provide an unambiguous answer to the problem. Stations 4, 5, 6, and 7 (Phillips, this volume, Fig. 1) are located in the central area of high gravity anomalies and, although none of the lines or stations is located in one of the stippled areas of Figure 8, Stations 1, 2, 3, 10, and 11 are placed in areas of relatively low anomaly. The data in Phillips' Tables I-A and I-B (this volume) were examined for systematic differences between results from these two groups of stations. There is some indication that the mean sediment thickness in the second group is about 0.5 km greater than in the first, a result which is largely due to the second sedimentary layer at Stations 2 and 3. Neither the velocity nor the thickness of layer 1*a* differed significantly between the groups and neither did the velocity in layer 2. This layer is slightly thinner in the mean for the stations with the more negative gravity anomalies, bringing the high velocity layer 3 about 0.4 km shallower. Although none of these correlations is really convincing, the data do suggest that variations in sediment thickness are the most probable cause of the anomaly variations. If this is the case, then the sides of the Gulf are marked by elongated troughs of thicker-than-normal sediments, which could be associated with faults generally paralleling the sides.

CONCLUSIONS

The southern section of the Gulf, approximately as far north as Guaymas, is underlain by a crust reminiscent of an oceanic section, in that a velocity of 6.5 km/s is found at a depth of approximately 5 km, and a considerably higher velocity of about 7.7 km/s is found about 9 km below sea level. This higher velocity is, however, significantly lower than that generally associated with the Mohorovičić discontinuity (7.9–8.2 km/s). The gravity data are consistent with a sliver of such a crust some 100 km wide at the mouth, narrowing to 50 km west of Guaymas, which is contrasted with a normal continental crust in isostatic equilibrium.

The only reasonable explanation for such a long, narrow sliver of denser crust in a continental area is that the continental crust was pulled apart and denser material welled up to fill the crack as Baja California moved away from the mainland. Such an explanation has already been given for the Red Sea (Girdler, 1958), which appears to be an analogous area. A component of tension perpendicular to the Gulf is required.

It is to be expected that the material filling the crack was very closely in isostatic equilibrium following the formation of the Gulf. Because this material is dense and the column is similar to that of an oceanic crust, there is no problem in explaining the deep water in the southern part of the Gulf. However, the crack ceases abruptly just south of lat 28° N.; yet the Gulf continues as a very definite topographic depression, albeit of notably shallower depth, for an additional 250 miles, and beyond that as a sediment-filled depression. The evidence for the abrupt ending of the crack is quite definite—the gravity field in the vicinity of San Lorenzo and Tiburón Islands is very uniform, and such variations as do exist are clearly associated with relatively minor surface features. In order to account for the northward continuation of the Gulf, it is necessary to suppose that the continental crust has been thinned by plastic flow without fracture, thus creating an isostatically compensated depression. This crustal thinning helps account for the absence of the negative anomalies expected to accompany the sediments of the Imperial Valley, Colorado Delta, and northern Gulf. On this point of view, the Gulf is an area of tension perpendicular to its axis, decreasing in intensity toward the north. In the south, this tension was sufficient to produce thinning of the continental crust, followed by formation of a tensional fracture, but farther north the critical fracturing stress was not attained, although some crustal thinning did take place.

The Gulf of California lies on a southward continuation of the San Andreas fault zone, although Kovach, Allen, and Press (1962) remark

> It is significant that none of these faults of the San Andreas system appear to curve southward so as to become truly parallel to the Gulf of California.

and

> From the geological evidence available it thus appears more likely that the San Andreas system enters the Gulf of California as a series of great *en echelon* breaks rather than as a single curving fracture.

Unfortunately, the data in the northern section of the Gulf do not give an unambiguous indication as to whether the faults curve to become parallel with the sides of the Gulf, or trend across the Gulf and disappear into the Mexican mainland. In the central section, the evidence favors faulting parallel to the coast line. The Sal si Puedes Basin and the fault *C-C* (Fig. 7) are examples of such faulting. However, neither is followed for any great distance. The fault on the east side of the Sal si Puedes Basin does cross the Gulf in its southern extension and might well cross the coast into Baja California north of Angel de la Guarda Island. In the southern section of the Gulf, the structure is plainly shown in topographic scarps, with a more westerly trend than the Gulf itself, which cross the axis at an angle of about 30°.

Viewed from the central Pacific Ocean, the Gulf lies on the northerly continuation of another major feature, the East Pacific Rise. Quoting from Bullard (1962):

> The mid-Atlantic ridge is not confined to the Atlantic. It is continued round the south of Africa into the Indian Ocean where it branches, one branch running towards the Gulf of Aden and the Red Sea, and the other south of India and Australia into the Pacific where it joins the east Pacific rise and ends near the Gulf of California (the second Red Sea or Mar Vermejo as its discoverers called it).
>
> Clearly, this system of ridges is one of the main features of the earth's surface and any acceptable history of the earth must describe how it came into being. At present theories can only be tentative and are useful more to suggest what should be looked for than as serious accounts of earth history. A linear system of volcanoes suggests a crack up which lava comes and this idea is reinforced by the occurrence of a faulted central valley, itself sometimes obstructed by later volcanoes. Perhaps the ridges mark out a continually widening and self-healing crack in the ocean floor.

Thus the Gulf is associated with *en echelon* faults of the San Andreas system at its northern end and with a world-encircling system of oceanic ridges at its southern end. Although the full significance of the latter feature is speculative at present, it does appear to be associated with crustal tension. Many features of the Gulf-Imperial Valley depression can be explained on the assumption of a belt of southwest-northeast tension perpendicular to this depression which steadily decreases in magnitude from the mouth of the Gulf to Southern California.

In the Gulf, tension is predominant, producing a tensional fracture normal to the tension in the southern half, and plastic thinning of the continental crust in the northern. Still farther north, the tension is of a magnitude comparable with general compression in the crust, producing a stress configuration favoring strike-slip faulting at a small angle (less than 45°) with the axis of the Gulf. Such faults would be produced in the southern half of the Gulf during the initial tensional phases, and, assuming that the plastic flow and tensional fracture did not extend right to the surface, the opening up of the Gulf would tend to steepen the angle between these faults and the axis of the Gulf. Fault *A-A* in Figure 7 appears to show this expected steepening as it crosses the Gulf.

REFERENCES

Bullard, E.C., 1962, The deeper structure of the ocean floor: Royal Soc. Proc., Ser. A, v. 265, p. 386–395.

Ewing, J.I., Worzel, J.L., and Ewing, M., 1962, Sediments and oceanic structural history of the Gulf of Mexico: Jour. Geophys. Research, v. 67, p. 2509–2527.

Girdler, R.W., 1958, The relationship of the Red Sea to the east African rift system: Geol. Soc. London, Quart. Jour., pt. 1, v. 114, p. 79–105.

Harrison, J.C., and Spiess, F.N., 1963, Tests of the LaCoste-Romberg surface-ship gravity meter II: Jour. Geophys. Research, v. 68, p. 1431–1438.

Kovach, R.L., Allen, C.R., and Press, F., 1962, Geophysical investigations in the Colorado Delta region: Jour. Geophys. Research, v. 67, p. 2845–2871.

Raitt, R.W., 1956, Crustal thickness of the Central Equatorial Pacific, pt. 1 *of* Seismic-refraction studies of the Pacific Ocean basin: Geol. Soc. America Bull., v. 67, no. 12, p. 1623–1639.

Talwani, M., Worzel, J.L., and Ewing, M., 1961, Gravity anomalies and crustal section across the Tonga trench: Jour. Geophys. Research, v. 66, p. 1265–1278.

——— and Landisman, M., 1959, Rapid gravity computations for two-dimensional bodies with application to the Mendocino submarine fracture zone: Jour. Geophys. Research, v. 64, p. 49–59.

SEISMIC REFRACTION STUDIES IN GULF OF CALIFORNIA[1]

RICHARD P. PHILLIPS[2]
La Jolla, California

ABSTRACT

During April and May of 1959, 26 seismic refraction stations were completed in the Gulf of California. In the shallow Northern Gulf province the crust of the earth consists of four layers—1.5 km of unconsolidated sediments with a velocity of 2.1 km/sec, 2.0 km of semiconsolidated sediments with a velocity of 4.1 km/sec, 4.3 km of basement material with a velocity of 5.4 km/sec, and a main crustal layer with a velocity of 6.7 km/sec. The total thickness of the crust is not well determined but appears to be about 25 km. In the central and southern sections of the Gulf only two layers can be resolved—a 1.3 km layer of unconsolidated material, and 6.2 km of material with a velocity of 5.8 km/sec. The subcrustal material has an average velocity of 7.8 km/sec and lies at a depth of 9.3 km. South of the Gulf proper the crust can be resolved into three layers—0.4 km of unconsolidated sediments, a 1.3 km layer with an average velocity of 5.5 km/sec, and a 4.3 km third layer with an average velocity of 6.7 km/sec. The upper mantle lies at an average depth of 8.9 km, and has a velocity of 7.7 km/sec. It is concluded that the northern portion of the Gulf of California has a structure similar to the continental borderland off Southern California, and that the southern section has a structure similar to the East Pacific Rise.

INTRODUCTION

During April and May of 1959, as part of the *Vermilion Sea Expedition*, 26 seismic refraction stations were completed in or near the Gulf of California (Fig. 1). The stations had been planned on the basis of existing topographic information (Shepard, 1950) to study the deep crustal structure under the Gulf, the nature of the transition from the continental structure of the mainland of Mexico to the continental borderland and the Middle America Trench, the nature of the shallow north end of the Gulf, and the nature of the long, narrow deeps.

[1] Manuscript received, June 25, 1963. Contribution from Scripps Institution of Oceanography.
The author wishes to acknowledge the services of the members of the *Vermilion Sea Expedition*, both scientific and ships' crews, who obtained the data used in this paper. George G. Shor, Jr., Russell W. Raitt, and Robert L. Fisher acted as chief scientists during the second leg of the expedition. Further, I would like to acknowledge the help of Miss Helen Kirk, Miss Gloria Slack, and Mrs. Wanda Willson who prepared many of the data for analysis. Finally, I would like to thank Clay Perry and the staff, especially Gene Gilbert, of the Computer Center of the University of California, San Diego, for their aid and counsel in developing the computer program that was used for the analysis of the data. Most of the figures for this paper were drafted by David Crouch. This work represents results of research sponsored by the Office of Naval Research under contracts Nonr 2216(05) and 2216(01).

[2] Marine Physical Laboratory of the Scripps Institution of Oceanography, University of California.

The stations were planned and the operations directed by George G. Shor, Jr. and Russell W. Raitt, who were chief scientists on the R/V *Spencer F. Baird*, and Robert L. Fisher, who was chief scientist on the R/V *Horizon*. The author has had responsibility for analyzing the data.

FIELD METHODS

The theory behind refraction profiling has been thoroughly discussed elsewhere (as, Dobrin, 1960). In general, a sound field is created, usually by an explosion, and the minimum time required for this sound pulse to travel from one point to another is determined. When a graph is made of the sound travel time against the distance of travel (termed a travel-time plot; *see* Fig. 2*a–j*) the points will lie in a characteristic pattern which can be related to the structure of the earth's crust through which the waves passed. In the most basic form, the points are seen to lie on segments of straight lines, each of which corresponds to arrivals from separate layers within the crust. The inverse slope of the line is used to determine the velocity of the compressional sound wave through that layer, and the intercept of the line with the time axis is used to determine the depth to the layer.

The field methods used by the Scripps Institution of Oceanography for doing seismic refraction work at sea have been described in detail previously (Shor, 1963). However, a brief description of the method will be given here. During the *Vermilion Sea Expedition* all seismic work was done as a two-ship operation— one, the R/V *Spencer F. Baird*, was the receiving ship, and the other, the R/V *Horizon*, was the shooting ship.

In shallow water the receiving ship is anchored at the receiving station, whereas in deeper water it either steams slowly into the wind to try to hold its position, or is allowed to drift. Pressure detecting devices (the hydrophones) are placed in the water from the receiving ship. They are so arranged as to float at a depth of about 150 feet below the surface, beyond the effects of surface waves. The signals, which are sound waves that have either traveled through the water or through the rocks below the bottom, are received by the hydrophones, amplified, transmitted by wire to the receiving ship, amplified again, filtered, and recorded on an oscillograph.

The sound field to be detected is set up by the detonation of explosives dropped into the water from the shooting ship. The shooting ship proceeds on a course either radially directed with respect to the receiving station (refraction profiling), or directed as an arc of a circle with the receiving station at the center (fan shooting). During the *Vermilion Sea Expedition* all 26 stations were basically profiles; however, short fan lines were shot in connection with four of them (numbers 4, 13, 14, and 23). The lengths of the profiles vary according to conditions of shooting and receiving, but 150 km is about the maximum range at which useful results were obtained. The size of the exposive charge detonated depends on the conditions and range. On the *Vermilion Sea Expedition* shot size ranged from ½ pound near the receiving ship to 200 pounds at the extreme ranges. A total of about 4,400 km of shooting track was run during the 26 stations of the expedition and over 40,000 pounds of explosives were detonated.

Figure 1 shows the locations of the receiving stations and shooting tracks of the 26 stations

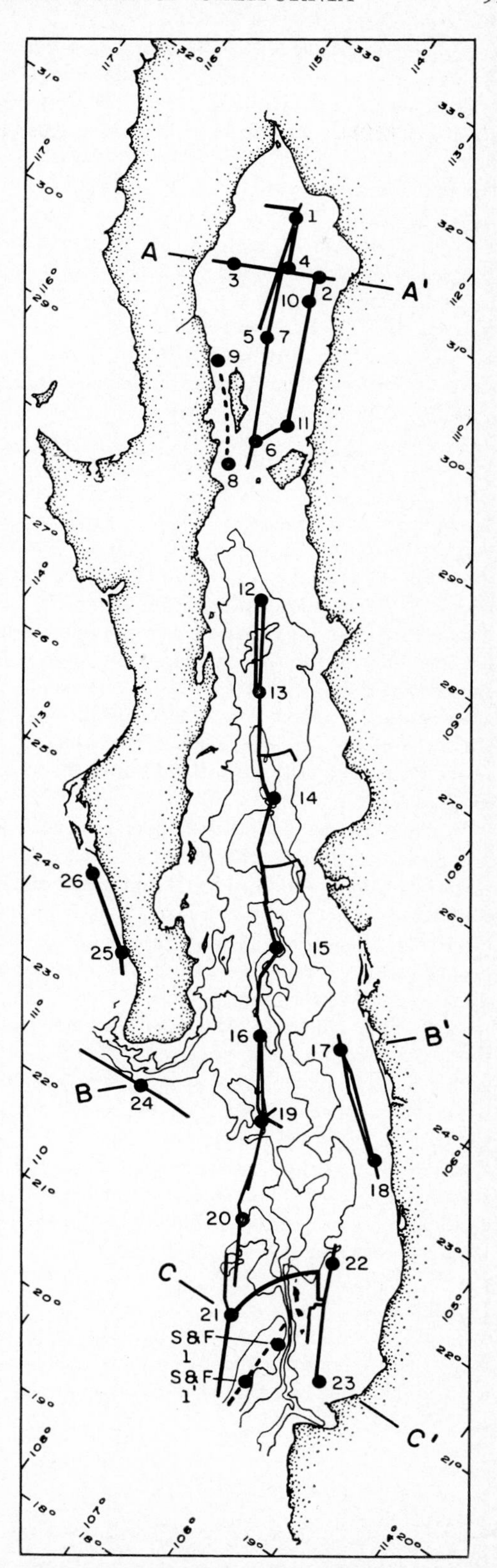

FIG. 1.—Index chart of the Gulf of California, showing locations of shooting tracks of seismic refraction Stations 1–26 of the *Vermilion Sea Expedition* and the Middle America Trench Stations 1 and 1'. Shooting tracks of Stations 8 and 9 are approximate. *A-A'*, *B-B'*, and *C-C'* are traces of cross sections shown in Fig. 10.

completed during the *Vermilion Sea Expedition.* The first 24 of these will be covered in this report.

Stations 25 and 26, both on the continental shelf west of Baja California, will not be discussed in detail here. Preliminary results indicate that the structure here consists of 0.5 km of unconsolidated sediments with a velocity of 1.7 km/sec overlying 1.6 km of material with an average seismic velocity of 2.9 km/sec. Below this is a layer 6.1 km thick with a velocity of 5.0 km/sec, overlying a layer 11.2 km thick with a velocity of 6.1 km/sec. The subcrustal material, lying at a depth of 19.5 km below sea level, has an average velocity of 7.9 km/sec.

COMPUTATIONAL METHODS

In marine seismic work, as done at Scripps Institution of Oceanography, the distance between the shot and the hydrophone is usually determined by the travel time of the direct water wave. For any shot the zero reference time is determined from the explosion as picked up on the echo sounder of the shooting ship and radioed to the receiving ship. This time must be corrected for the distance of the shooting ship from the explosion, which is determined from the time the shot is in the water, before it goes off, and from the speed of the ship.

In some instances the direct water wave does not travel far through the water. In such cases a water-wave time is determined from sound waves that have reflected one or more times from the bottom of the ocean. This is the case in all the deeper water work in the Gulf of California. The direct water wave was not recorded beyond 15 km from the receiving ship. As a result, almost all of the travel-time plots for deep water stations presented in this paper are based on a calculated water-wave travel time, rather than on a measured direct water wave. The method of calculation is similar to that used by Katz and Ewing (1956).

The velocity of sound in the water was calculated using Kuwahara's Tables (1939) from the temperatures and salinities measured by bathythermograph and hydrographic casts made on the *Vermilion Sea Expedition.*

The water velocity and the sound-wave travel times were then entered into punched cards and used as the input to a C.D.C. 1604 computer. The normal sequence of computation followed by the program for any profile was—first, the effect of varying water depth was removed from the travel times, using the computed slopes of the travel-time plot as determined from the input data; these "water delay corrected" data were then used to calculate slopes and intercepts of lines using the method of least squares; these data were screened for points with large residuals which were discarded; the least squares computation was then repeated, using the remaining points; and, finally, a layer solution, assuming plane, horizontal layers, was made for each shooting track. (*See* Tables I-A, II-A, III-A, and IV-A.)

Computations combining the profiles were also made. Several different methods were used, depending on the nature of the profiles and the type of data available. Simple averages and weighted averages were used in some instances, as well as reverse solutions, using both the reverse points as calculated, or recalculating the lines of fit to pass through common reverse points and still give least-squares residuals for the two profiles being combined. (*See* Tables I-B, II-B, III-B, and IV-B.)

RESULTS OF SEISMIC REFRACTION STUDIES

On the basis of the water depth, bottom topography, and nature of the travel-time curves, the seismic stations in the Gulf of California can be divided into four groups.

The first group of stations lies north of Tiburón Island and east of Sal si Puedes Basin. These 9 stations (1–7, 10, and 11) are all in the area designated as the Northern Gulf province by Rusnak, Fisher, and Shepard (this volume).

The second group of 6 stations, (8, 9, and 12–15) follows the line of basins found close to the mid-Gulf line. The mid-Gulf stations are characterized by intermediate water depths and rough bottom topography typical of the physiographic provinces designated as the central Gulf and southern Gulf by Rusnak, Fisher, and Shepard.

South of these mid-Gulf stations is a series of 5 stations (16, 19, 20, 21, and 24) that are not in the confines of the Gulf proper, and in both water depth and bottom topography approach the characteristics of the open ocean. This third group will be referred to as the deep-water stations.

TABLE I-A. VELOCITIES AND LAYER THICKNESSES AT NORTHERN GULF STATIONS

Each profile calculated independently. ( ) indicates assumed value; [ ] indicates anomalous value, not included in averages.

Station	Profile	Water Depth (km)	Layer 1		Layer 1a		Layer 2		3	Total Thickness (km)	Remarks
			Velocity (km/sec)	Thickness (km)	Velocity (km/sec)	Thickness (km)	Velocity (km/sec)	Thickness (km)	Velocity (km/sec)		
1	north south	0.07 0.07	1.78±.03 2.00±.03	1.17 1.25	4.00±.05 3.68±.06	2.31	5.36±.05	4.32	6.72±.02	7.96	
4	north south	0.08 0.08	2.34±.12 1.86±.16	1.98 1.41	4.45±.16 3.97±.08	1.16 2.49	5.13±.02 5.75±.05	5.61 4.16	6.82±.03 6.78±.04	8.83 8.13	{[8.20±.22 km/sec at 18.40 km]
5 5-s & 7	north	0.16 0.15	2.08±.11 1.85±.06	1.14 1.24	3.35±.13 4.09±.07	2.06 2.21	5.93±.02 5.38±.02	7.82 3.64	6.86±.02 6.47±.04	11.18 7.24	{8.31±.02 km/sec at 23.85 km
6	north south	0.39 0.39	2.23±.02 [2.41*]	1.57 1.62	4.58±.08 5.04±.05	2.14	5.49±.08	2.90	6.53±.05	7.00	* 2 points only
10	north south	0.10 0.10	2.11±.05 2.28±.05	1.55 1.95	3.94±.05 4.16±.10	2.09 1.25	5.79±.10 5.14±.03	4.76	6.97±.06	7.96	
11	north south	0.13 0.13	2.19±.07 2.04±.09	1.49 1.18	(4.04) (4.04)	[0.58] [0.63]	5.11±.08 5.19±.02	3.64 3.02	6.24±.14 6.39±.02	5.67 4.94	Layer 1a assumed Layer 1a assumed
Average			2.07±.18	1.46	4.13±.47	1.96	5.43±.31	4.34	6.64±.24	7.66	
2	east	0.07	{1.92±.02 {2.75±.05	0.68} [1.65]}	[6.18±.04]	[2.95]	[13.16±.06]				
	west	0.07	{1.74±.01 {2.70±.09	0.51} 1.58}	4.72±.09	1.96	5.48±.05	4.34	6.46±.11	8.46	[8.35±.03 km/sec at 20.64 km]
3	east	0.07	{1.80±.08 {3.42±.05	1.31} 1.50}	4.45±.08	2.62	5.84±.03	4.76	7.22±.03	10.28	
	west	0.07	{1.80±.02 {3.30±.14	1.19} [1.90]}	[5.33±.04]						

TABLE I-B. VELOCITIES AND LAYER THICKNESSES AT NORTHERN GULF STATIONS
Dipping layer solutions forced to a common reverse or intercept time.

Profiles	*Water Depth (km)*	*Layer 1*		*1a*		*2*		*3*	*Total Thickness (km)*
		Velocity (km/sec)	*Thickness (km)*	*Velocity (km/sec)*	*Thickness (km)*	*Velocity (km/sec)*	*Thickness (km)*	*Velocity (km/sec)*	
1-s 4-n	0.07 0.08	2.01	1.42 1.45	4.00	2.20 1.48	5.22	4.07 6.33	6.83	7.77 9.34
4-n & 4-s	0.08	2.01	1.59	4.17	1.85	5.37	4.94	6.78	8.45
4-s 5-n	0.08 0.16	1.92	1.42 1.21	3.85	2.99 2.04	6.02	3.07 8.77	6.76	7.57 11.18
1-s 5-n	0.07 0.16	2.00	1.21 1.19	3.60	2.98 1.97	5.93	4.35 7.23	6.74	8.60 10.47
5-n & 5-s & 7-s	0.15	1.88	1.23	3.99	2.16	5.63	5.13	6.64	8.68
5-s & 7-s 6-n	0.15 0.39	1.86	1.35 1.11	4.31	2.22 1.92	5.37	4.69 2.69	6.58	8.41 6.10
6-n & 6-s	0.39	2.27	1.57	4.78					
10-s 11-n	0.10 0.13	2.15	1.81 1.52	4.11	1.22 0.56	5.09	5.13 3.04	6.59	8.26 5.24
Average		2.01	1.43	4.10	1.96	5.52	4.95	6.70	8.34
2-w	0.07	1.77 3.01	0.49 2.01	4.50	1.31	5.57	4.32	6.73	8.20
3-e	0.07	1.77 3.01	1.36 0.99		3.29		4.59		10.29

The fourth group is the 4 stations (17, 18, 22, and 23) that were shot in the shallow-water continental terrace areas to the east of the deep-water stations.

In addition to the profiles mentioned above, fan lines were shot in conjunction with four of the stations (4, 13, 14, and 23), and short profile segments were shot in conjunction with Stations 13, 14, 17, 18, and 23.

Each of the four groups of stations will be discussed separately by giving first a general description, then a detailed discussion of the stations involved, and finally a summary interpretation.

NORTHERN STATIONS: INTRODUCTION

North of Tiburón Island and northeast of the Sal si Puedes Basin is a broad area of shallow water which has been termed the Northern Gulf province by Rusnak, Fisher, and Shepard (this volume). In this area the greatest water depth is slightly less than 500 fathoms (900 m) and is for the most part less than 100 fathoms (180 m). The bottom topography is gently undulating, with some small closed basins in the north-central section.

Nine seismic refraction stations were run in this area—Stations 1–7, 10, and 11. Of these, Stations 1, 4, 5, 7, and 6 form a long, multiple reversed profile from near the mouth of the Colorado River to the southern limit of the Northern Gulf province west of Tiburón Island. This northwest-southeast line of stations is crossed at right angles by a reversed pair of Stations—2 and 3—and is paralleled to the east by Stations 10 and 11 (Fig. 1).

In general, four distinct branches of the travel-time curves can be distinguished in the northern Gulf stations (Figs. 2*a*, 2*b*, and 2*c*). Table I-A summarizes the seismic velocities and thicknesses indicated by these travel-time curves, calculated on the assumption that the straight-line segments represent arrivals from flat-lying plane layers. The four layers can be interpreted as follows.

Layer	*Velocity*	*Remarks*
1	2.07 ± .18 km/sec	unconsolidated sediment
1a	4.13 ± .47 km/sec	semiconsolidated sediment
2	5.43 ± .31 km/sec	metamorphic basement
3	6.64 ± .24 km/sec	main crustal layer

In addition to the above four layers, it was possible to resolve the unconsolidated sedimentary arrivals into two branches for profiles 2 and 3.

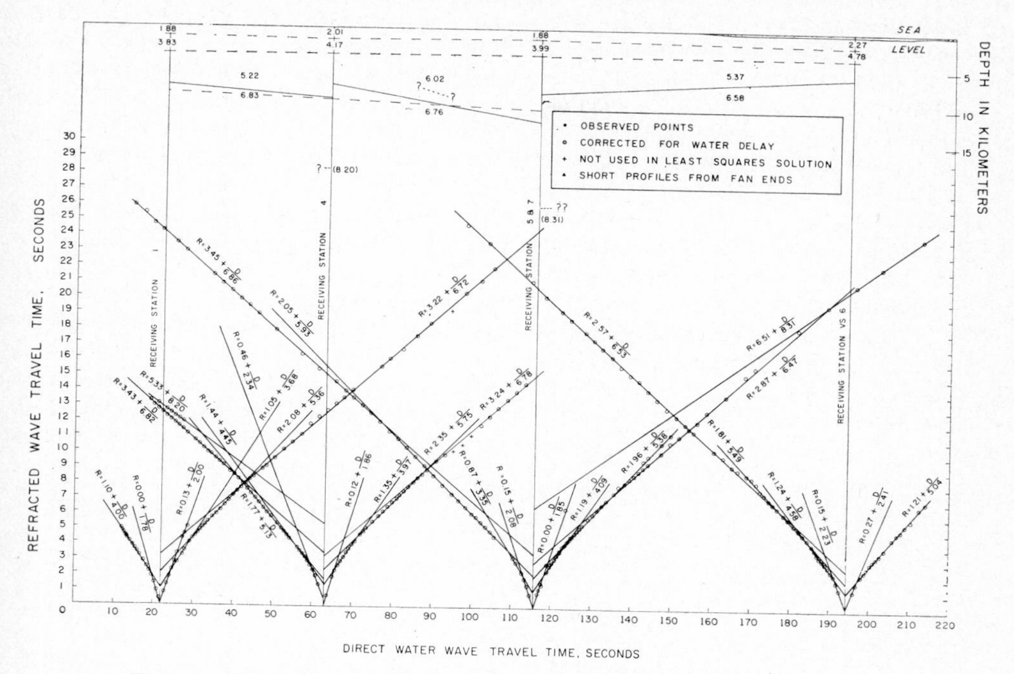

FIG. 2*a*.—Travel-time plot of Stas. 1, 4, 5, 7, and 6 in Northern Gulf province.

Further, velocities above 7.5 km/sec were indicated on 4 individual travel-time plots.

No direct correlation has been made between the seismic velocities observed in the Northern Gulf province and the rock types. In the Salton Sea trough, to the north, similar velocities and layering have been found (Kovach and others, 1962; Biehler and others, this volume). All layers with velocities less than 5 km/sec were found to be correlated with sedimentary deposits of Tertiary age. Correlation of individual seismic horizons with stratigraphic units within these sediments was attempted by Kovach and others (1962). Wells drilled subsequently within the area of profiling show, however, that no such correlation exists. It seems probable that the vertical changes in velocity have a closer relationship with depth of burial and degree of lithification than with age.

The average velocity of 5.4 km/sec and the variability of the material that makes up layer 2 suggest a similarity to the metamorphic basement of the Imperial Valley to the north.

NORTHERN STATIONS: DISCUSSION OF THE DATA

Stations 1, 4, 5, 7, and 6 form a long, multiple reversed profile running in a generally southeasterly direction from near the mouth of the Colorado River to the southern edge of the Northern Gulf physiographic province. These 5 stations shall be considered first. Figure 2*a*, which presents the travel-time curves of these five stations showing reverse and intercept relationships among them, reveals the basic similarities found in them all.

The receiving Stations 5 and 7, though near each other, were not identical. However, Station 7 had no north run, and the profile south from Station 5 was short. In Figure 2*a* and in the solutions presented it is assumed that 7-south is the split run of 5-north, and the shots of run 5-south have been included in the data of 7-south. Therefore, only 8 separate profiles were used in the solution of this long line of profiles.

Arrivals that can be interpreted as having been transmitted by layer 1, the unconsolidated sediments, are present in all the profiles. These arrivals give velocities ranging from as low as 1.78 km/sec to as high as 2.41 km/sec. This high value, however, is determined by only two points, those from Station 6-south, so it is not included in the over-all average value calculated for this layer.

The average value of the velocity for this layer, 2.07 km/sec, is higher than that found in the laboratory for unconsolidated sediments (Hamilton, 1959). The arrivals recorded may be from partially consolidated sediments slightly below the sea floor, because in every case except Station 1-north the line determined by these arrivals has a slight positive intercept after the removal of the effect of the water depth.

Layer 1*a*, with an average velocity of 4.13 km/sec and a range of values from 3.35 km/sec to 5.04 km/sec, appears to have the most variable velocity of the layers. If this layer is composed of consolidated sediments and/or volcanic rocks, then such a variation in velocity might be expected. It is known, for example, that the sediments in the Imperial Valley trough, to the north, have great lateral variations in short distances (Dibblee, 1954).

The high value for the velocity of layer 1*a* associated with Station 6-south may be due to lateral variations in the sediment thickness or to the introduction of large amounts of volcanic ro k into the section, both of which appear likely as the sill south of Tiburón Basin is approached.

A thick fill of sediments, becoming more com-

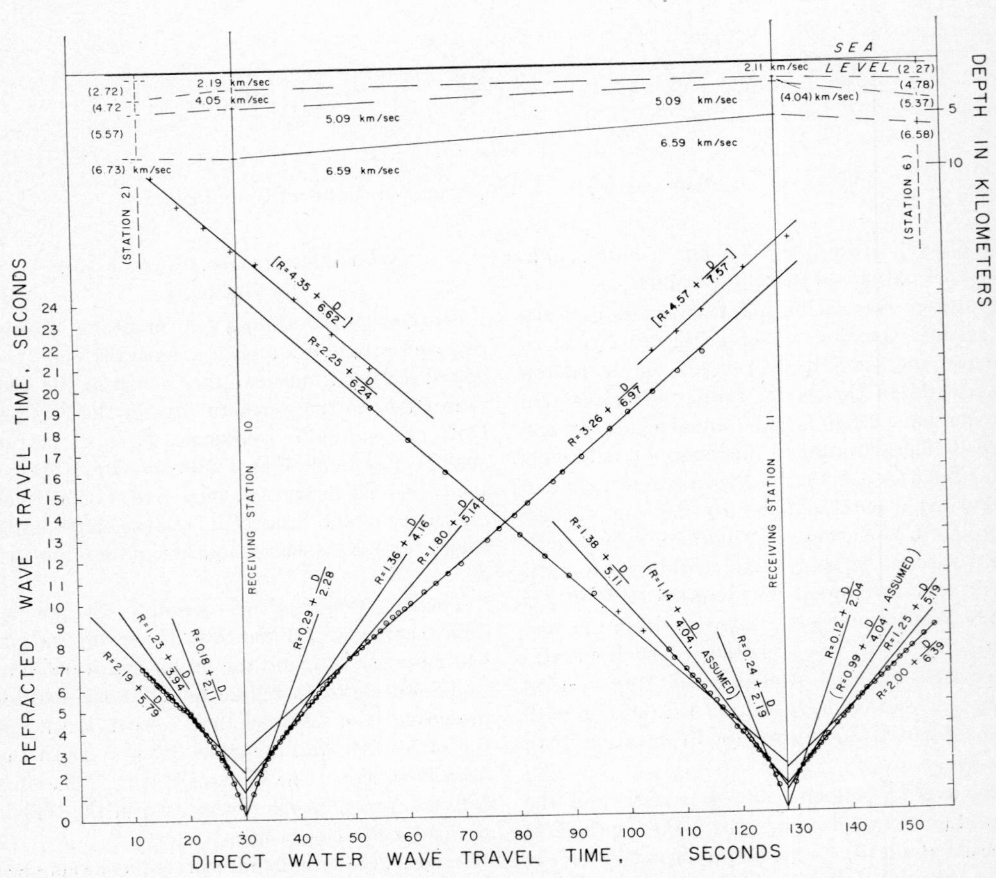

FIG. 2*b*.—Travel-time plot of Stas. 10 and 11 in the Northern Gulf province. For an explanation of the symbols see Fig. 2*a*.

pacted with depth, would be expected to give rise to a continuous velocity increase with depth rather than layers with constant velocities. The profiles from the northern Gulf were analyzed to find the closest linear velocity-depth function consistent with the data. The function derived is

$$V = (1.74 + 0.91Z)\text{km/sec}$$

where 1.74 km/sec is the velocity at the sediment-water interface, 0.91 sec^{-1} is the velocity gradient, and Z is the depth in kilometers.

Layer 2, the igneous and metamorphic basement complex, has an indicated average velocity of 5.43 km/sec and a range of values from 5.13 to 5.93 km/sec. Its presence is indicated on the travel-time plots of each profile (Fig. 2*a*) except the two short ones, 1-north and 6-south. The surface of this layer appears to lie about 3.6 km below sea level in the region of the long central line of profiles, and from the fair agreement of intercept times it is presumed that the surface is nearly flat. The large mismatch of intercepts seen in the lines representing this layer from 4-north and 4-south may be due to a change of dip south of Station 4.

In contrast to the overlying sediments this basement layer appears to have a highly variable thickness, ranging from less than 3 km in the southern part of the line of profiles to almost 8 km in the central section. The bottom surface of this layer may have marked irregularities on a smaller scale. The travel-time curve of Stations 4-south and 1-south both contain points that are up to 0.4 second earlier than expected from the least squares fit of the line to layer 3 arrivals. Station 5-north, however, shows no such irregularity at the appropriate distance, and at that distance arrivals from the second layer still appear. This may indicate that there is an irregularity of as much as 1.5 km in the interface between layers 2 and 3, which is not reflected in the interface between 1*a* and 2.

Layer 3, which has an average seismic compressional wave velocity of 6.64 km/sec, is the dominant line segment in most profiles. The wide range of velocity values as measured for layer 3 at first suggests that the layer is rather variable. Most of this variation can be accounted for by the irregularities of the upper surface of this layer, and the variations in the overlying material. This

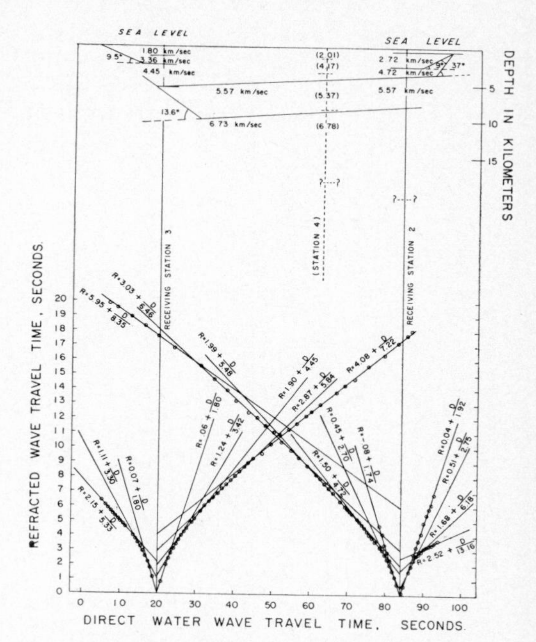

FIG. 2*c*.—Travel-time plot of Stas. 2 and 3 in the Northern Gulf province. For an explanation of the symbols see Fig. 2*a*.

can be seen when computations are made taking the profiles two at a time and combining them. If the arrivals attributed to a single layer are all from the same layer, and if the surface of that layer is plane, then two profiles on opposite sides of a receiving point should give the same intercept time. Further, two profiles that reverse each other should give the same reverse time. The method of least squares can be used to determine a pair of lines that pass through a common point (either the intercept in the case of a split profile, or the reverse time in case of a reverse pair). This procedure tends to average out the effects of lateral variations in the structure of the overlying material.

The resulting pairs of slopes and intercepts can be solved under the assumption that the remaining differences of slope are due to sloping interfaces between the layers. Table I–B shows the results of such a solution for the stations in the northern part of the Gulf. The average values for the velocities of sound in the individual layers are not significantly changed from the value obtained

(*Text continued on page 101.*)

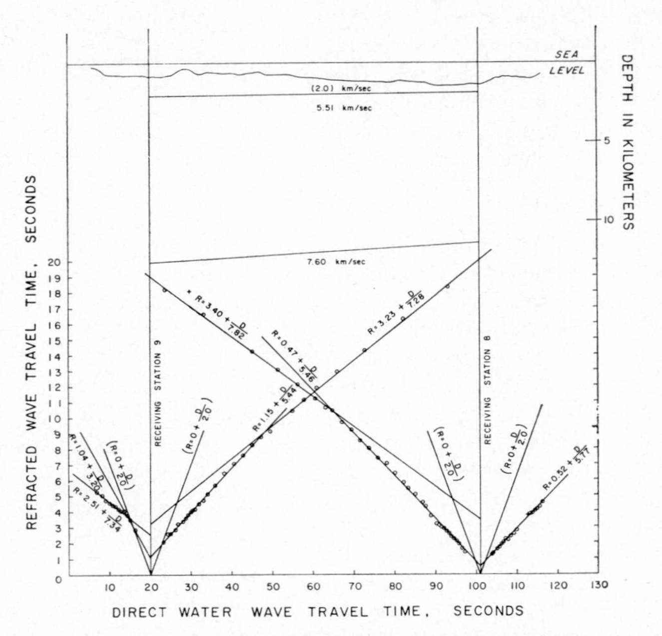

FIG. 2*d*.—Travel-time plot of Stas. 8 and 9, in the mid-Gulf region. For an explanation of the symbols see Fig. 2*a*.

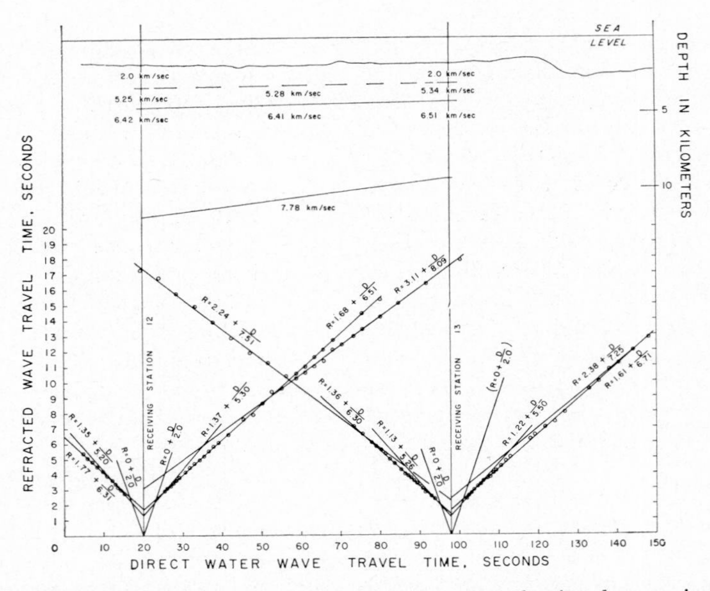

FIG. 2*e*.—Travel-time plot of Stas. 12 and 13 in the mid-Gulf region, showing the grouping of points used in the 3-layer model. For an explanation of the symbols see Fig. 2*a*.

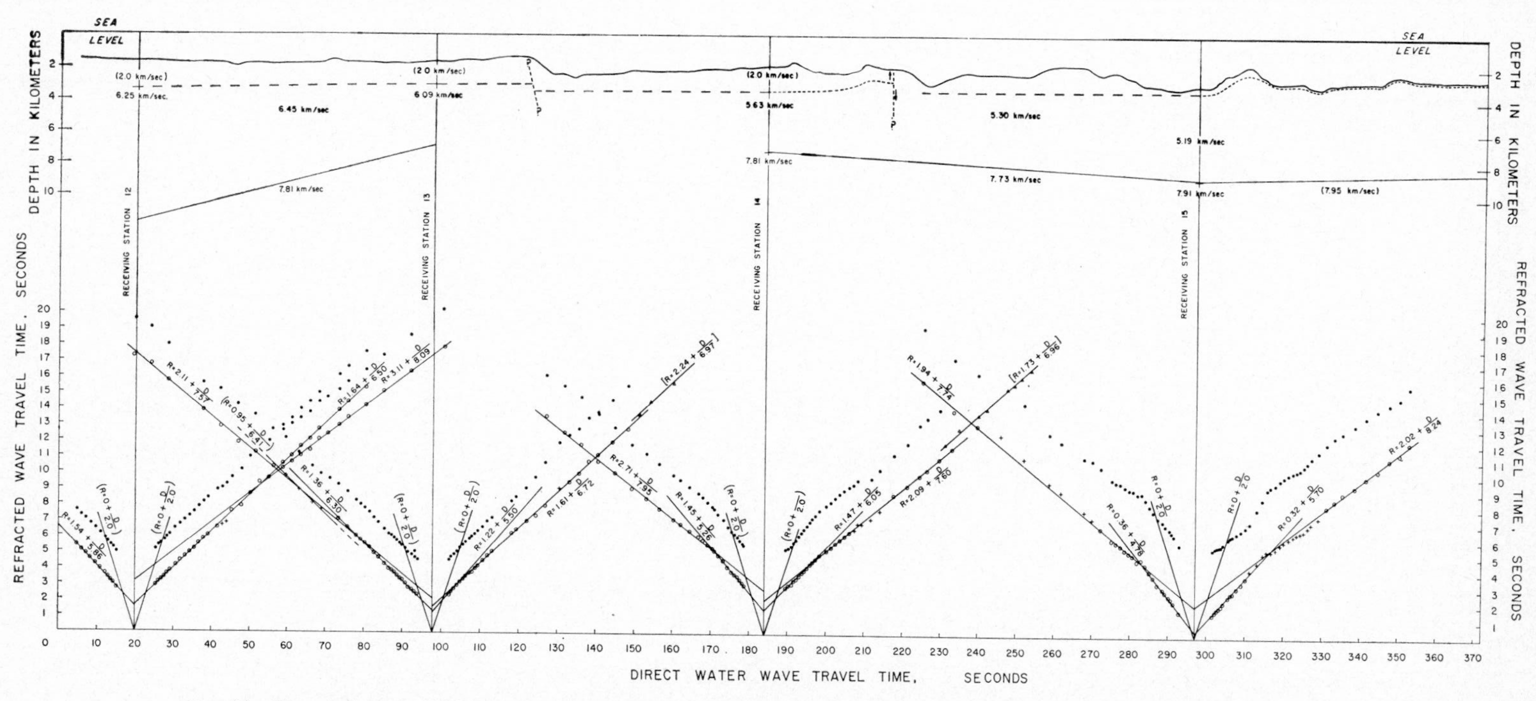

FIG. 2*f*.—Travel-time plot of Stas. 12, 13, 14, and 15 in the mid-Gulf region, showing the lines used in the 2-layer interpretation. For an explanation of the symbols see Fig. 2*a*.

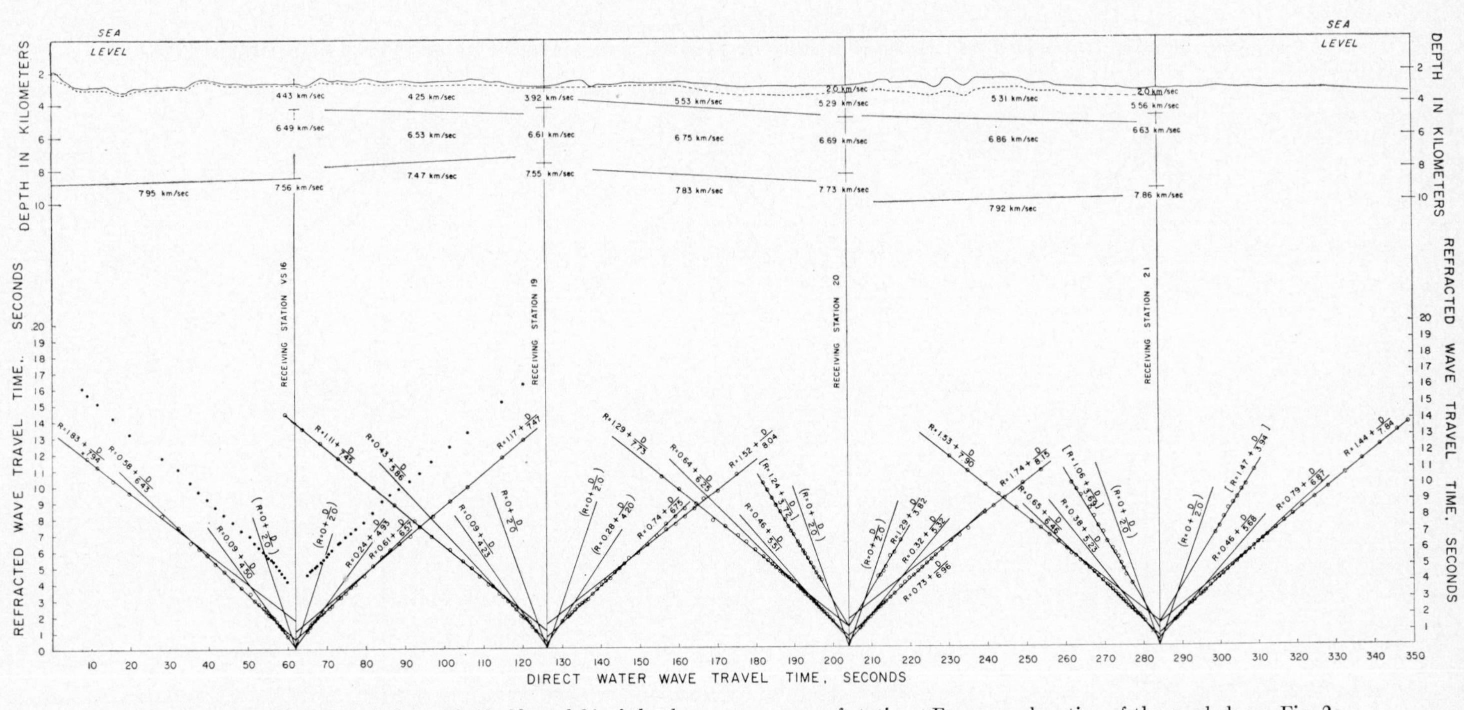

FIG. 2*g*.—Travel-time plot of Stas. 16, 19, 20, and 21 of the deep-water group of stations. For an explanation of the symbols see Fig. 2*a*.

by a simple averaging method. For layers 1, 1*a*, and 2 the spread of values so obtained is little changed. This fact indicates that the variations in velocity previously noted for these layers are real.

On the other hand, the range in the calculated velocity for layer 3 is reduced from almost 1 km/sec to 0.25 km/sec. It appears that layer 3 in the Northern Gulf province has a nearly uniform velocity of a value near 6.70 km/sec. This is called the main crustal layer and is analogous to the third layer of Raitt (1956) and Shor and Fisher (1961).

Stations 10 and 11 form a long (approx. 144 km) reversed pair parallel to and east of the long compound set of stations discussed above. Station 10 is due west of the mouth of Río Concepción and Station 11 is approximately 25 km north of Tiburón Island. The travel-time plot obtained from this compound reverse pair is shown as Figure 2*b*. Station 10 shows the typical four-segmented curve that is characteristic of the northern stations previously discussed; these segments have been correlated with layers 1, 1*a*, 2, and 3 as defined above. The travel-time curves of Station 11, however, do not seem to show the arrivals from layer 1*a*, the semiconsolidated sediments. A layer as thick as 0.6 km could fail to show up as first arrivals. Thinning of the sedimentary layer toward Tiburón Island is to be expected, for volcanic and metamorphic rocks crop out on the island (Anderson, 1950). The gravity low north of Tiburón Island (Harrison and Mathur, this volume) may represent a filled basin to the east of Station 11.

Near the ends of profile 10-south and 11-north the transmission of the refracted wave became very poor. It appears that what were thought originally to be first arrivals are later events, and the true first arrivals of energy have faded so as to be unreadable on the record. The five arrivals at the southern end of profile 10 may be interpreted as arrivals from a higher velocity layer below the main crustal layer. If so, this would give a crustal thickness of 19 km below Station 10. On the other hand, the corresponding arrivals from profile 11-north give a lower velocity that is probably correlative with a multiple refracted arrival from layer 3. It is felt that this is the most probable explanation of the southern end of profile 10, also.

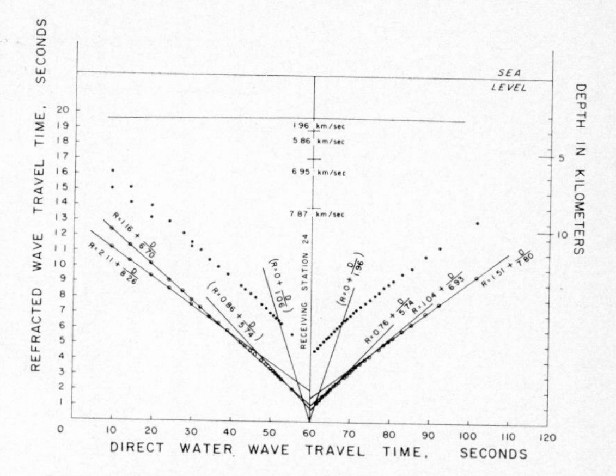

FIG. 2*h*.—Travel-time plot of Station 24 of the deep-water group of stations. For an explanation of the symbols see Fig. 2*a*.

A compound reverse pair, Stations 2 and 3, was shot at right angles to the other profiles in the Northern Gulf province, and presumably across the structure of the Gulf proper. In several ways these profiles are anomalous. The travel-time plots are presented as Figure 2*c*.

Two layers with velocities less than 4 km/sec can be distinguished from both Stations 2 and 3. The upper one has a thickness of about 0.6 km on the east and 1.2 km on the west side of the Gulf, and a velocity averaging 1.8 km/sec. The lower of these layers is about 1.6 km thick both on the east and the west, with a seismic velocity of 3.0 km/sec. Both these layers are presumed to represent unconsolidated sediments, and thus correspond to layer 1 as defined above.

Another anomaly found in the travel-time plots of Stations 2 and 3 is the high velocities indicated at shallow depths by the short profiles 2-east and 3-west. In view of the velocities found by the long reverse profiles 2-west and 3-east, it must be concluded that the high velocities indicated by the third and fourth branches of the travel-time plot of Station 2-east and the third branch of 3-west are not real velocities, but are rather the result of shooting "up dip" across layers with rather steep dips.

If it is assumed that the velocities of the various

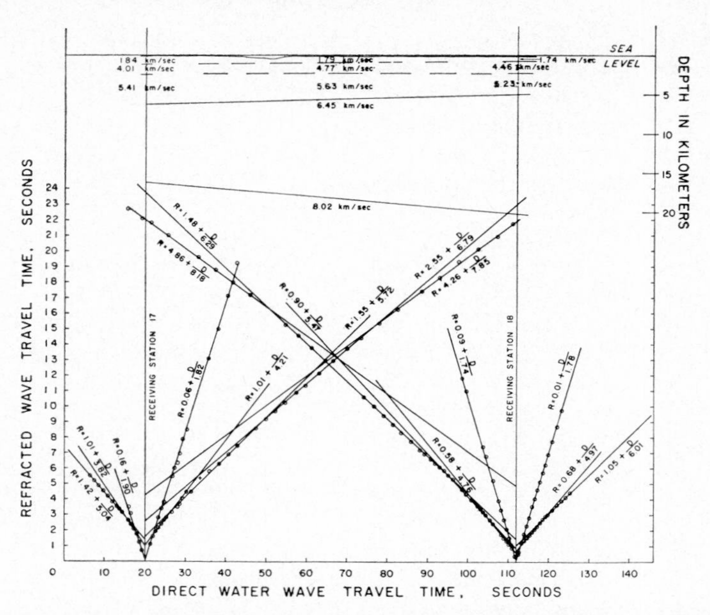

FIG. 2*i*.—Travel-time plot of Stas. 17 and 18 on the continental shelf west of Mazatlán. For an explanation of the symbols see Fig. 2*a*.

layers are known from the averages that can be calculated from the stations in the northern Gulf where such steep dips do not exist, then the angle of dip can be calculated from the relationship

$$\text{dip angle} = \sin^{-1}(V_1/V_2) - \sin^{-1}(V_1 S)$$

where S is the observed slope of the travel-time plot, V_1 is the velocity above the dipping interface, and V_2 is the velocity below it. Figure 2 shows the result of such calculations.

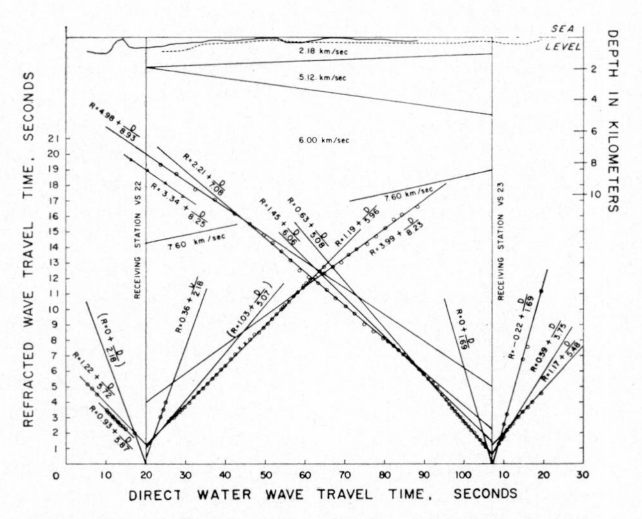

FIG. 2*j*.—Travel-time plot of Stas. 22 and 23 in the Tres Marías Basin west of Nayarit. For an explanation of the symbols see Fig. 2*a*.

The reversed profiles 2-west and 3-east can be interpreted in two different ways. If the agreement of the reverse times for the last segments of 2 and 3 is interpreted as indicating that the two segments, one with an observed velocity of 8.35 km/sec for Station 2, and the other with an observed velocity of 7.22 km/sec from Station 3, are representative of the same layer, then the reverse time solution requires that a layer with a seismic velocity of 7.64 km/sec lies at a depth of 10.5 km below Station 3, but at 19.4 km below Station 2. The velocity of 7.64 km/sec is in agreement with the average velocity of the subcrustal material found to the south of Tiburón Island, but the calculated dip to the east would be much too great to be consistent with the observed gravity profile across the Gulf (Harrison and Mathur, this volume). On the other hand, on the basis of seismic evidence, such an interpretation cannot be rejected because the reverse times at Stations 2 and 3 do agree; the indicated velocity is similar to that found farther south; and the depth is similar to the depth found for the subcrustal layer under Station 10 if the problematical segment of the travel-time plot of station 10-south is accepted as being from subcrustal arrivals.

A second interpretation, and the one preferred here, is that the high velocity indicated by the last segment of the travel-time plot of Station 2-west is not due to arrival from a high-velocity layer, but rather due to a sharp change in the dip of the interface between layers 2 and 3. If this is so, and if the measured velocities of 6.46 km/sec for Station 2 and 7.22 km/sec for Station 3 are assumed to represent layer 3, then a cross section of the Gulf can be drawn that is consistent with the travel-time plots of Stations 2 and 3, with the gravity data from the northern Gulf, and with the long section defined by Stations 1, 4, and 5. According to this interpretation, the structure across the northern Gulf is that of a basin, with the deepest portion to the west (Fig. 2*c*).

Some evidence in favor of the interpretation that the 8.35 km/sec branch of the travel-time plot of Station 2 truly represents a high-velocity layer at a depth of about 20 km, is found in the second arrivals plotted on the nothern end of the travel-time plot of Station 4. These second arrivals are strong and persistent, and can be correlated from shot to shot for 7 shots. They indicate the presence of a layer with a seismic velocity of 8.20 km/sec at a depth of 18.4 km.

The easily recognizable second events corresponding to this 8.20 km/sec velocity are also observed on the records of the three shots that make the fan sections of this run. The arrival times of these events are slightly later than might be expected for corresponding water-wave travel times, but not significantly so (Fig. 3). This would indicate that the arrivals are from a plane that is essentially horizontal, or dipping slightly to the west.

On the other hand, the long profiles that cover the same area fail to show such a layer. No high-velocity layer is indicated in the travel-time curves of 1-south, 5-north, or 6-north. The only other good evidence that such a layer exists is found in the travel-time plot of Station 7-south. The last four points of this travel-time plot fall on a line indicating a velocity of 8.31 km/sec at a depth of 23.8 km. A similar high velocity, however, is not indicated by Station 6-north (the reverse of 7-south), even though the reverse times agree well. The highest velocity and shallowest depth consistent with the last two points of 6-north is 7.80 km/sec at 26.8 km. The high velocity indicated by the travel-time curve of 7-south might be due to the presence of volcanic material near the surface of the section toward the sill south of Tiburón Basin. This is indicated by the high velocities found for layer 1 and 1*a* at Station 6.

On the other hand, the base of the crust may lie at about 24 km below sea level at Station 7 and be dipping to the north. The last two points of profile 5-north (the split partner of 7-south) can be interpreted as indicating material with a seismic velocity of 7.80 km/sec at a depth of 24 km.

To summarize the evidence for the thickness of the crust in the northern section of the Gulf of California—velocities greater than 7.5 km/sec are indicated on only 4 of the 16 profiles in the northern section. None of these velocities is reversed, and none is indicated on the split partners of the stations. All but one, 4-north, can be explained by an alternate interpretation, and that one is in an area that may be expected to have structural complexities inasmuch as it is an area of active faulting. On the other hand, the long reversed profiles in the center of the Gulf indicate that the base of the crust must lie at least 25 km below sea level. Evidence from profile 7-south indicates that this minimum depth is near the true depth.

NORTHERN STATIONS: SUMMARY

The seismic evidence (Fig. *2a*, *2b* and *2c*) indicates that the northern Gulf is essentially a large basin averaging 3.5 km deep, with the deeper section to the west. This basin is filled with approximately 2 km of semiconsolidated sediments that may include some volcanic rocks, underlying approximately 1.5 km of unconsolidated sediments.

The basin is floored by material of highly variable nature, probably similar to the igneous and metamorphic material that forms the mountains bordering the Northern Gulf province on the east and west. This basement material is from about 3 km to almost 8 km thick, and is perhaps offset by faulting.

Under the basement material is a main crustal layer with a nearly constant seismic velocity of 6.70 km/sec. The thickness of this layer is not clearly defined by the present data, but is at least 10 km thick and probably closer to 17 km.

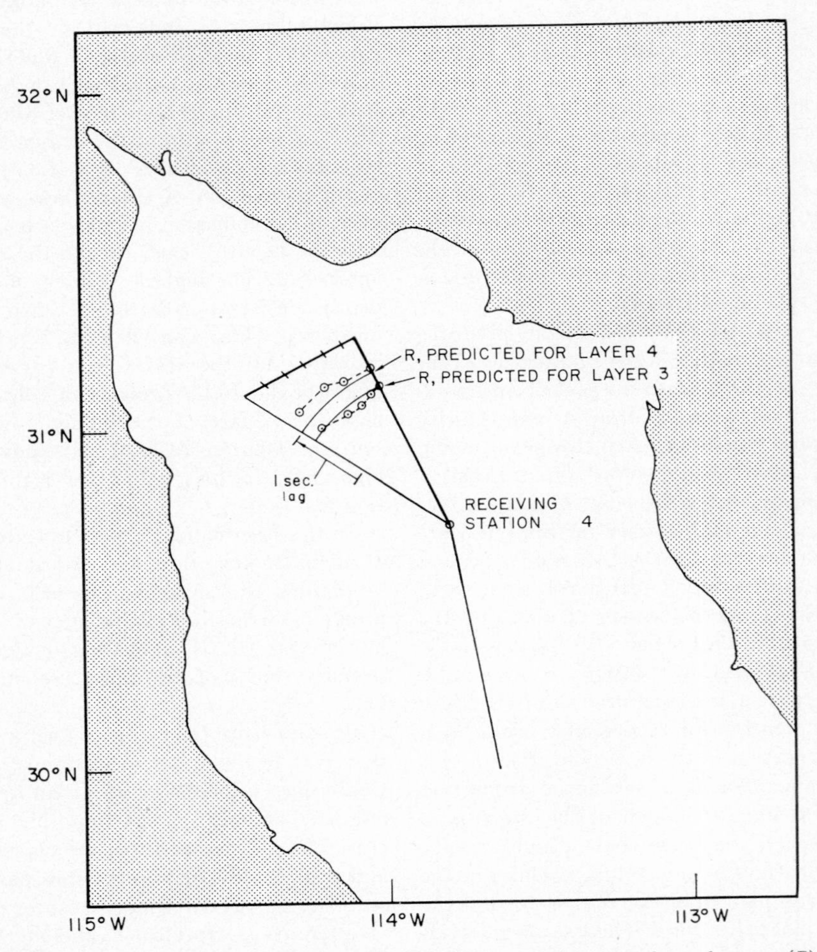

FIG. 3.—Fan line from Sta. 4-north showing relative travel time for refracted waves (*R*).

Below this, probably at a depth no less than 24 km below sea level, is the subcrustal material with a seismic velocity between 7.80 and 8.3 km/sec. In view of the values determined to the south, the lower value is the more probable.

This structure is similar to that reported by Shor and Raitt (1958) for the continental borderland off the Pacific coast of Southern California, particularly that in the shallow-water region east of San Clemente Island.

MID-GULF STATIONS: INTRODUCTION

A series of stations was completed to investigate the nature of the crust under the deep basins along the approximate midline of the Gulf. These six stations (8, 9, and 12–15) were planned using the best information available at the time (Shepard, 1950), but without the knowledge of the strong *en echelon* pattern of the basins within the Gulf indicated by more detailed soundings (Chart I, Rusnak, Fisher, and Shepard, this volume).

The shooting tracks of these stations deviate somewhat from the deepest parts of the basins (*see* Fig. 1). This deviation has introduced a large water-delay correction into the travel-time plots (Fig. 2*d*, 2*e*, and 2*f*) of these stations, increasing the scatter and reducing the precision of the results.

The region covered by the mid-Gulf stations is structurally complex, another factor that makes the interpretation of refraction seismic results difficult. Unlike the travel-time plots of the northern Gulf stations, the travel-time plots of the mid-Gulf stations fail to agree for either reverse times or intercepts.

Of the models that can be used to interpret the travel-time plots, the simplest, and in some ways the most satisfactory, consists of a two-layer crust overlying subcrustal material which has a seismic velocity of about 7.8 km/sec. The two layers of the crust would be about 1.1 km of unconsolidated sediments with an assumed velocity of 2.0 km/sec underlain by 6.2 km of material with a velocity of about 5.7 km/sec (Table II-A).

On the other hand, the northern Gulf stations, and the deep-water stations to the south, indicate that the crust has three distinct layers. The upper layer, consisting of the sediments, is underlain by a "second layer" of material with a velocity of about 5.4 km/sec, and under this is the main crustal layer consisting of material with a velocity close to 6.7 km/sec.

Both a two-layer and a three-layer crustal model will be considered.

MID-GULF STATIONS: DESCRIPTION OF THE DATA

For the layer solutions of all of the mid-Gulf stations, the velocity of sound in the unconsolidated sediments was assumed to be 2.0 km/sec. There is little direct evidence on which to base this choice of velocity.

Five rather uncertain arrivals in the records of Station 13-north could be interpreted as refracted arrivals from a sedimentary layer. A least-squares line fitted to these indicates a velocity of 1.67 ± 0.15 km/sec. No other arrivals that could be interpreted as refracted arrivals from layer 1 were found for the mid-Gulf stations.

Events interpreted as reflections from below the surface of the sediments were found in the records of Station 14-north. Four such sub-bottom reflections were picked, and a depth to the reflecting horizon and an average velocity were calculated according to the $T^2 - x^2$ method (Dix, 1955). The indicated velocity is 1.81 km/sec for a layer 0.7 km thick. This thickness is about half that calculated from the refraction results; therefore it is assumed that the reflections did not come from the base of the sediments but from some horizon within the sedimentary layer. If the velocity increases with depth, as is normally found to be true, then the average velocity for the entire sedimentary section would be expected to be higher than that found from the reflections from the upper half of the layer.

Station 24, one of the deep-water stations to the south, has 9 sub-bottom reflections that can be used to calculate the velocity and the thickness of the unconsolidated sediments. The thickness so calculated agrees well with the thickness calculated from the refraction results. The velocity is 1.97 km/sec.

The velocity of sound in the unconsolidated sediments in the Northern Gulf province averaged 2.0 km/sec for the solutions that required the intercepts or reverse times to agree (Table I-B).

A velocity of 2.0 km/sec, then, is in agreement

TABLE II-A. VELOCITIES AND LAYER THICKNESSES AT MID-GULF STATIONS

Each profile calculated independently; two layer crustal model. ( ) indicates assumed value; [ ] indicates anomalous value not included in averages.

Station	Profile	Water Depth (km)	Layer 1		2 & 3		4	Total Thickness (km)
			Velocity (km/sec)	Thickness (km)	Velocity (km/sec)	Thickness (km)	Velocity (km/sec)	
9	north	0.81	(2.0)	[1.39]	[3.20 ± .23]	[2.09]	[7.34 ± .04]	[4.29]
	south	0.81	(2.0)	1.25	5.44 ± .03	8.31	7.28 ± .12	10.37
8	north	1.35	(2.0)	0.51	5.46 ± .04	11.08	7.82 ± .12	12.95
	south	1.35	(2.0)	0.56	5.77 ± .08			
12	north	1.72	(2.0)	1.64	5.86 ± .10			
	south	1.72	(2.0)	1.72	6.50 ± .01	7.86	8.09 ± .06	11.30
13	north	1.69	(2.0)	1.44	6.30 ± .04	4.13	7.57 ± .18	7.26
	south	1.69	(2.0)	1.31	5.50 ± .18	[1.69]	[6.72 ± .02]	[4.69]
14	north	1.91	(2.0)	1.57	5.29 ± .08	4.19	7.95 ± .08	7.67
	south	1.91	(2.0)	1.56	6.05 ± .07	2.95	7.60 ± .05	6.42
15	north	3.10	(2.0)	0.39	4.78 ± .12	4.73	7.74 ± .01	8.22
	south	3.10	(2.0)	0.34	5.70 ± .05	6.65	8.24 ± .15	10.09
Average 9–15			(2.0)	1.12	5.70 ± .48	6.24	7.79 ± .31	9.29
Average 9–14				1.28	5.80 ± .42			

with the reflection data to the south and the refraction data from the northern Gulf stations.

Although the thickness of the layer of unconsolidated sediments may vary considerably between stations, the thickness at the receiving stations is about 1.5 km for Stations 12 to 14 (Table II-A). The deepening of the water by a little more than 1 km between Stations 14 and 15 can be accounted for by a corresponding thinning of the sediments. The depth to the top of the second layer is nearly the same at Stations 14 and 15.

The reversed pair of Stations 8 and 9 present a typical set of travel-time curves for the mid-Gulf stations (Fig. 2*d*). Although several choices of shorter groups of points can be made in both 8-north and 9-south other than those shown, it is difficult to do so and retain any sort of agreement of reverse times and intercept times. Also, some choices lead to velocities that appear incompatible with the other stations.

The high velocity and shallow depth indicated by the second branch of the travel-time plot of Station 9-north are probably due to a sharp up-

TABLE II-B. VELOCITIES AND LAYER THICKNESSES OF MID-GULF STATIONS

Dipping layer solutions forced to a common reverse or intercept time; two layer crustal model.

Profiles	Water Depth (km)	Layer 1		2 & 3		4	Total Thickness (km)
		Velocity (km/sec)	Thickness (km)	Velocity (km/sec)	Thickness (km)	Velocity (km/sec)	
9-s	0.81	(2.0)	1.36	5.51	10.41	7.60	12.58
8-n	1.35		0.47		9.50		11.31
12-n & 12-s	1.72	(2.0)	1.71	6.25			
12-s	1.72	(2.0)	1.71	6.45	8.35	7.81	11.78
13-n	1.69		1.48		3.78		6.95
13-n & 13-s	1.69	(2.0)	1.42	6.09			
13-s	1.69	(2.0)	1.23	5.28			
14-n	1.91		1.60				
14-n & 14-s	1.91	(2.0)	1.56	5.63	3.80	7.81	7.28
14-s	1.91	(2.0)	1.26	5.30	3.72	7.73	6.88
15-n	3.10		0.65		4.58		8.33
15-n & 15-s	3.10	(2.0)	0.36	5.19	5.47	7.91	8.93
Average		(2.0)	1.23	5.71	6.20	7.77	9.26

TABLE II-C. VELOCITIES AND LAYER THICKNESSES AT MID-GULF STATIONS
Each profile calculated independently. Three layer crustal model. ( ) indicates assumed values; [ ] indicates anomalous value not included in averages.

Station	*Profile*	*Water Depth (km)*	*Layer 1*		*2*		*3*		*4*	*Total Thickness (km)*	*Remarks*
			Velocity (km/sec)	*Thickness (km)*	*Velocity (km/sec)*	*Thickness (km)*	*Velocity (km/sec)*	*Thickness (km)*	*Velocity (km/sec)*		
12	north	1.72	(2.0)	1.49	5.20± .20	1.71	6.31± .13				
	south	1.72	(2.0)	1.51	[5.30*]	1.00	6.51± .01	7.51	8.09± .06	11.74	* 2 points only
13	north	1.69	(2.0)	1.30	(5.26)	0.68	6.30± .04	4.15	7.51± .18	7.82	Layer 2 assumed
	south	1.69	(2.0)	1.32	5.50± .18	1.69	6.72± .02	6.67	7.25± .26	11.57	
14	north	1.91	(2.0)	1.61	5.29± .18	2.95	(6.56)	2.10	7.95± .08	8.57	Layer 3 assumed
	south	1.91	(2.0)	1.57	6.05± .07	1.03	(6.56)	2.43	7.60± .05	6.94	Layer 3 assumed
15	north	3.10	(2.0)	0.42	4.78± .12	3.20	(6.16)	2.52	7.74± .01	9.24	Layer 3 assumed
	south	3.10	(2.0)	0.26	5.70± .05	5.10	(6.96)	1.83	8.24± .15	10.29	Layer 3 assumed
Average		2.18		1.18	5.42± .41	2.17	6.46± .19	3.89	7.73± .11	9.42	

dip to the north toward the north edge of the Sal si Puedes Basin. However, a high apparent velocity at shallow depth is associated with the west end of Station 2-west and the north end of 4-north; that is, in general with the north-west corner of the Gulf.

The long overlapping series of the 8 profiles of Stations 12–15 can be interpreted in the light of a two-layer crust. Except for the pair 13-south and 14-north, this assumption allows the calculation of lines that have consistent reverse and intercept times. (*See* Fig. 2*f* and Table II-A.) If such a solution is made, the crustal layer below the sediments has a velocity from 4.78 km/sec to 6.50 km/sec. The low value, 4.78 km/sec, is associated with other low values farther to the south in the deep-water stations, and will be included in the averages and discussion of those stations.

The high velocities associated with Stations 12-south and 13-north suggest that these are arrivals from the material designated layer 3 in the Northern Gulf province.

The presence of material with a velocity of 6.7 km/sec is further suggested by the arrivals from Station 13-south. There the second branch of the travel-time plot is obviously later than is to be expected from its reverse partner 14-north, and the intercept is earlier than is to be expected from 13-north. The velocity indicated by these arrivals is only 6.72 km/sec, rather than 7.5 km/sec, as might be expected at the ranges covered by these points. In other words, it would seem as if arrivals from the material below the crust were not received for Station 13-south. Perhaps because of this, arrivals from the 6.7 km/sec layer could be recognized in the record.

If it is assumed that material with seismic velocities of 6.2 km/sec and above is associated with layer 3, and that material with velocities from 4.5 to 6.1 km/sec is associated with layer 2, then a three-layer model can be calculated. The results of such a calculation are shown in Table II-C and Figure 2*e*.

Comparing the solutions of Tables II-A and II-C, it can be seen that the different models make a difference of about 0.8 km in the average depth to the mantle. For the two-layer model the average depth below Stations 12–15 is 8.49 km, whereas for the three-layer model the comparable average is 9.26 km.

The material below the crust is represented in the mid-Gulf travel-time plots except 13-south and the three short profiles—9-north, 8-south, and 12-north. From the 8 profiles that indicate the subcrustal material, it can be calculated that this material has an average seismic velocity of 7.78 km/sec. When the reversed solutions are considered, the range of velocities indicated is only 0.3 km/sec.

After the normal water-delay correction has been applied to the data for the mid-Gulf stations, many points still have an excessive scatter from any line that might be fitted to the data. These points are generally associated with large changes in the water depth, and the large residual might result from changes in thicknesses of the sediments, or from changes in thicknesses of the underlying high-velocity material.

If areas of shallower water are associated with

early arrivals, then it can be assumed that these are regions of thinner sediments, and that the high areas represent areas of near-surface high-velocity material. If the arrivals are late, then the shallow areas can be taken as representing areas of thickened sedimentary cover. Figure 2*f* illustrates both situations.

MID-GULF STATIONS: SUMMARY

In the mid-Gulf region, where the bathymetry is characterized by deep, irregular, closed basins, the typical three-layer crust is not well expressed; instead, a two-layer crust consisting of 1.3 km of unconsolidated sediments overlying 6.2 km of material with a seismic velocity of 5.80 km/sec seems to be the most probable interpretation of the data available. However, the data are not accurate enough to eliminate the possibility of a three-layer crust existing. If there are three layers they probably consist of a layer of unconsolidated sediments of a thickness of 1.2 km, overlying a layer 2.2 km thick and with a velocity of 5.4 km/sec; overlying a layer with a velocity of 6.5 km/sec and a thickness of 3.9 km. If this layer 3 is correlative with the "main crustal layer" in the deep ocean, it is thinner here than in all but 2 of the 28 stations reported by Raitt (1956).

Although the precision of the data is not sufficient for detailed numerical calculations, the rough bottom topography along the shooting tracks can be loosely associated with two causes—(1) Changes in thickness of the sedimentary layer are found. The deepening of the bottom into Pescadero Basin appears to be associated with a thinning of the sedimentary layer of about 1 km. (2) Changes in the depth of the higher velocity material are found, with the sediments more or less uniformly mantling the underlying material. The sill between Pescadero and Mazatlán Basins appears to be associated with such an effect.

DEEP-WATER STATIONS: INTRODUCTION

Generally south of lat 24° N., and west of the continental terrace off the mainland of Mexico, the sea floor takes on a more typically "open ocean" aspect. The depths are greater than farther north in the Gulf, though not as great as the average of the Pacific Basin, and the bottom topography is less rugged. Five stations were completed in this region during the *Vermilion Se Expedition*. Four of these—numbers 16, 19, 20 and 21—continue the line of profiles started wit Stations 12–15. The fifth station, number 24, is split profile to the west of the line of stations an about 50 km south of the tip of Baja California

Stations 1 and 1′ of the *Acapulco Trench Expedition*, completed in November 1954, lie just t the east of Station 21-south, and are include here, even though they have been previously re ported (Shor and Fisher, 1961).

As might be expected from the more oceani appearance of the area, the travel-time plot (Figs. 2*g* and 2*h*) are more nearly typical of thos found in the deep sea basins (as Raitt, 1956). Th travel-time plots can be interpreted as represent ing the arrivals from three distinct layers, wit velocities and depths similar to those found in th deep Pacific Basin to the west.

DEEP-WATER STATIONS: DESCRIPTION OF THE DAT

As with the mid-Gulf stations, the velocity c layer 1 was estimated for all the profiles of th deep-water stations, with the exception of Sta tion 24. Sub-bottom reflections were recorded a Station 24, which allowed the computation of th average sediment velocity. This velocity is 1.9 km/sec, and the thickness of the sedimentar section was calculated from the reflections to b 0.75 km.

Strong persistent sub-bottom reflections wer recorded also at Station 21. Here, on the basis c 25 reflected arrivals, a sediment velocity of 1.6 km/sec for the top 0.27 km of sediment was ir dicated.

The 7 sub-bottom reflections recorded at Sta tion 20 also indicate a value of 1.63 km/sec fc the velocity of sound in the unconsolidated sedi ments. The reflection time here indicates that th reflections were from 0.18 km below the surfac of the sediments.

For all profiles with the exception of 19-sout and 24-west, the travel-time plots indicate arriva from a layer having an average velocity of 5.1 ±0.54 km/sec. For computational purposes th layer was assumed to be present for the two pro files where it was not recorded. The velocity wa assumed to be similar to that of the split profi associated with the deficient profile, and th

TABLE III-A. VELOCITIES AND LAYER THICKNESSES AT DEEP-WATER STATIONS
Each profile calculated independently. ( ) indicates assumed value.

Station	Profile	Water Depth (km)	Layer 1		2		3		4	Total Thickness (km)	Remarks
			Velocity (km/sec)	Thickness (km)	Velocity (km/sec)	Thickness (km)	Veloctiy (km/sec)	Thickness (km)	Velocity (km/sec)		
16	north	2.60	(2.0)	0.10	4.50±.13	1.51	6.43±.03	6.43	7.94±.29	10.64	
	south	2.60	(2.0)	0.29	4.93±.10	1.33	6.57±.07	3.45	7.47±.05	7.66	
19	north	2.80	(2.0)	0.10	4.23±.18	1.02	5.86±.11	2.90	7.45±.02	6.83	
	south	2.80	(2.0)	0.32	(4.20)	1.18	6.75±.03	4.57	8.04±.18	8.87	Layer 2 assumed
20	north	2.94	(2.0)	0.49	5.51±.28	1.02	6.25±.04	2.93	7.73±.05	7.38	
	south	2.94	(2.0)	0.35	5.32±.30	1.65	6.96±.06	6.28	8.15±.14	11.21	
21	north	3.19	(2.0)	0.42	5.23±.33	1.11	6.46±.05	4.50	7.90±.08	9.23	
	south	3.19	(2.0)	0.50	5.68±.12	1.59	6.87±.03	4.12	7.84±.01	9.40	
24	east	2.74	1.96*	0.80	5.74±.19	1.33	6.93±.08	3.11	7.80±.05	7.97	*From reflections
	west	2.74	1.96*	0.89	(5.74)	1.60	6.70±.02	4.74	8.26±.04	9.97	Layer 2 assumed
verage 16–24		2.85	(2.0)	0.43	5.14±.54	1.33	6.57±.35	4.30	7.86±.26	8.92	
verage 20–24					5.50±.22						
verage [illegible], 16, 19					4.83±.56						

earest refracted arrival to the receiving point as assumed to lie on the line. This computation ives a maximum value for the thickness of the nrecorded layer.

The values calculated for the velocity of sound this layer (Table III-A) appear to be grouped to two separate populations. One has a mean elocity well below 5.0 km/sec and the other a ean velocity of 5.5 km/sec. In considering the roups of stations reported on here, we see that very group has a population of velocities with eans near 5.6 km/sec. The ten profiles in the orthern Gulf province with an average velocity r layer 2 of 5.43±0.31 km/sec, the eight pro- les (not including 15-north and 15-south) of the id-Gulf stations indicating a velocity of 5.80 ±0.42 km/sec, the eight profiles of the shelf group dicating a velocity of 5.66±0.33 km/sec, nd the five profiles in the deep-water group—20- orth and south, 21-north and south, and 24-east -have an average value for the velocity in layer 2 f 5.50±0.22 km/sec. No one of these groups in- icates a velocity for layer 2 significantly differ- nt from 5.6 km/sec. The over-all average of the tal of 35 profiles is 5.61±0.20 km/sec. The alues of the mean and of the standard deviation re lowered somewhat if the high velocities indi- ited in the mid-Gulf stations are associated with yer 3, rather than layer 2, as is proposed in the three-layer solution for those stations.

In contrast, of the six profiles 15-north, 15-south, 16-north, 16-south, 19-north, and 19-south, four have indicated velocities more than three standard deviations away from the average for layer 2; one (19-south) has no arrivals that can be associated clearly with layer 2; and the one (15-south) that indicates a normal velocity has a rapidly shoaling bottom, which may be the cause of an apparently high velocity for this area. Averaging the measured values of the velocities in layer 2 for these profiles gives a velocity of 4.83±0.56 km/sec, which is significantly lower than the average velocity for the second layer.

This material with a lower-than-normal velocity appearing in the transition zone between the Gulf of California proper and the open ocean to the south may well represent volcanic material accumulating on the sea floor, inasmuch as the velocity is close to that measured for volcanic islands (as Shor, 1960) and the topographic highs in this area are closely associated with magnetic highs (Hilde, this volume).

The main crustal layer, layer 3, is represented in the travel-time plots of all of the deep-water stations. The average velocity indicated by the 10 profiles included here is 6.57±0.35 km/sec when each side is calculated separately. As with the

TABLE III-B. VELOCITIES AND LAYER THICKNESSES AT DEEP-WATER STATIONS
Dipping layer solutions forced to a common reverse or intercept time.

Profiles	Water Depth (km)	Layer 1		2		3		4	Total Thickness (km)
		Velocity (km/sec)	Thickness (km)	Velocity (km/sec)	Thickness (km)	Velocity (km/sec)	Thickness (km)	Velocity (km/sec)	
16-n & 16-s	2.60	(2.0)	0.11	4.43	1.49	6.49	4.29	7.56	8.49
16-s 19-n	2.60 2.80	(2.0)	0.08 0.11	4.25	1.40 1.59	6.53	3.75 2.59	7.47	7.85 7.09
19-n & 19-s	2.80	(2.0)	0.09	3.92	1.50	6.61	2.93	7.55	7.33
19-s 20-n	2.80 2.94	(2.0)	0.66 0.49	5.53	0.50 1.69	6.75	3.93 2.79	7.83	7.89 7.92
20-n & 20-s	2.94	(2.0)	0.39	5.29	1.53	6.69	3.44	7.73	8.30
20-s 21-n	2.94 3.19	(2.0)	0.34 0.45	5.31	1.41 1.71	6.86	5.41 4.43	7.92	10.11 9.78
21-n & 21-s	3.19	(2.0)	0.48	5.56	1.21	6.63	4.33	7.86	9.22
24-e & 24-w	2.74	1.96	0.83	5.86	1.80	6.95	3.19	7.87	8.57
Average			0.37	5.02	1.44	6.69	3.73	7.72	8.41
1 & 1′ of Shor & Fisher (61)	4.40 3.76	2.15	1.64 1.38	5.71	1.77 1.79	6.49	3.84 6.05	8.29	11.68 12.98

northern Gulf stations, this average is increased slightly, and the spread of values calculated is reduced greatly when the average is based on the values of the velocity calculated from common intercept or reverse times. The latter average is 6.69 km/sec, and the spread of values is reduced from 1.1 km/sec to 0.46 km/sec. (*See* Table III-B.)

The main crustal layer has an average thickness of 4.3 km for the 10 profiles included in the deep-water group of stations. Combining layer 3 (4.30 km), layer 2 (1.33 km), and layer 1 (0.43 km) gives an average thickness for the crust o 6.06 km. This is not significantly different fron the average of the Pacific Ocean basin reporte by Raitt (1956), of 6.31±1.01 km. However, be cause the water depth at the present stations i closer to 3 km than to the 5 km of the typica deep ocean basins, the base of the main crusta layer is at a depth that averages only 8.92 kn below sea level.

TABLE III-C. SHEAR WAVE VELOCITIES FOR LAYER 3 AT THE DEEP-WATER STATIONS

Station	Profile	Comp. Velocity Layer 3 (km/sec)	Shear Wave Velocity (km/sec)	Ratio V_c/V_s
20	north south	6.25 6.96	3.72 3.82	1.68 1.82
21	north south	6.46 6.87	3.69 3.94	1.75 1.75
1′ of Shor and Fisher	north	6.66	3.84	1.73
Average		6.64	3.80	1.75

(Poisson's ratio = 0.26)

In addition to the compressional wave arrival recorded at Stations 20 and 21, events were re corded that could be interpreted as energy trans mitted as shear waves along the interface at th top of layer 3. The velocities indicated by suc arrivals are listed in Table III-C. Also included i Table III-C are shear wave arrivals that wer recorded by Shor during the shooting of th Middle America Trench Station 1′, but not pre viously reported.

Each of the travel-time plots for the 1 profiles included in the deep-water stations ind cates material with a velocity of 7.4 km/sec c higher underlying the main crustal layer. Thes 10 sets of data show a mean velocity for the sul crustal material of 7.86±0.26 km/sec. As wit the mid-Gulf stations, this velocity seems sig nificantly lower than the 8.2±0.2 km/sec velocit for the subcrustal material in the average dee Pacific Ocean basin.

TABLE IV-A. VELOCITIES AND LAYER THICKNESSES AT THE CONTINENTAL TERRACE STATIONS
Each profile calculated independently. ( ) indicates assumed value; [ ] indicates anomalous value, not included in averages.

Station	*Profile*	*Water Depth (km)*	*1*		*1a*		*2*		*3*		*4*	*Total Thick-ness (km)*
			Velocity (km/sec)	*Thick-ness (km)*	*Velocity (km/sec)*	*Thick-ness (km)*	*Velocity (km/sec)*	*Thick-ness (km)*	*Velocity (km/sec)*	*Thick-ness (km)*	*Velocity (km/sec)*	
17	north	0.08	1.90± .08	1.10	3.82± .10	1.01	5.04± .05					
	south	0.08	1.82± .01	1.02	4.21± .05	1.52	5.72± .16	4.78	6.79± .04	9.54	7.85± .10	16.95
18	north	0.08	1.74± .01	0.54	4.76± .07	1.51	5.47± .05	2.51	6.29± .02	14.93	8.18± .03	19.64
	south	0.08	1.78± .01	0.93	4.97± .05	1.48	6.01± .02					
22	north	0.81	(2.18)	1.43			5.72± .03					
	south	0.81	2.18± .11	1.49	(5.07)	(0)	5.96± .03	11.67			8.23± .16	13.97
23	north	0.32	(1.69)	0.58	5.08± .05	3.79	6.06± .05	3.03	7.08± .02	[13.71]	[8.93± .21]	[21.45]
	south	0.32	1.69± .05	0.56	3.75± .21	1.40	5.48± .14					
Average			1.85± .18		4.40± .49		5.66± .33		6.65± .31		8.09± .21	

TABLE IV-B. VELOCITIES AND LAYER THICKNESSES AT CONTINENTAL TERRACE STATIONS
Dipping layer solutions forced to a common reverse or intercept time.

Profiles	*Water Depth (km)*	*Layer 1*		*1a*		*2*		*3*		*4*	*Total Thick-ness (km)*
		Velocity (km/sec)	*Thickness (km)*	*Velocity (km/sec)*	*Thickness (km)*	*Velocity (km/sec)*	*Thickness (km)*	*Velocity (km/sec)*	*Thickness (km)*	*Velocity (km/sec)*	
17-n & 17-s	0.08	1.84	1.04	4.01	1.30	5.41					
17-s 18-n	0.08 0.08	1.79	1.13 0.55	4.77	1.54 1.69	5.63	3.53 2.73	6.45	9.89 15.40	8.02	16.18 20.45
18-n & 18-s	0.08	1.74	0.54	4.46	0.77	5.23					
22-s 5 layer 23-n solution	0.84 0.32	2.18	1.79 0.76	5.12	0.00 3.92	6.01	12.20 2.02	7.25	0.50 15.76	8.54	15.19 22.78
22-s 4 layer 23-n solution	0.84 0.32	2.18	1.79 0.76	5.12	0.00 3.89			6.00	10.73 3.57	7.60	13.17 8.53

TABLE V. VELOCITIES AND INTERCEPT TIMES OF SHORT LINE SEGMENTS RUN IN CONJUNCTION WITH FAN SHOOTING OR THE CONTINENTAL TERRACE STATIONS

Station	*Profile*	*Length (km)*	*Layer 3*		*Layer 4*		*Remarks*
			Velocity (km/sec)	*Intercept (sec)*	*Velocity (km/sec)*	*Intercept (sec)*	
13	east	13.4	6.97± .03	2.24			From end of 13 south fan
14	east	35.4	6.96± .03	1.73			From end of 14 south fan
17	west	26.0			8.33± .09	4.15	Shot from 19 toward 17
18	west	15.9	6.77± .02	1.00			Shot from 19 toward 18
23	west	19.5			8.25± .02	3.34	From end of 23 north fan

Three short profiles were shot in the area of the deep-water stations and were recorded at receiving stations on the continental terrace. These three profiles are—Station 17-west, shot from the site of receiving station 19 toward the receiving Station 17; 18-west, shot from the receiving Station 19 toward 18; and a short segment 23-west shot in conjunction with the fan line from 23-north, and from the site of receiving Station 21. Station 18-west is the shortest, only 15.9 km long. The arrivals from these shots indicate a layer with velocity of 6.77 km/sec, and so are presumed to be from layer 3. The small intercept (1.00 sec) of the least-squares line agrees with this interpretation. On the other hand, Station 17-west, 26 km long, and Station 23-west, 19.5 km long, indicate arrivals from material with a seismic velocity of 8.33 and 8.25 km/sec, respectively. From their higher velocities and their larger intercepts it is presumed that these arrivals represent energy from the subcrustal material. (*See* Table V.)

DEEP-WATER STATIONS: SUMMARY

In the deep-water area south of the Gulf of California proper, the seismic refraction results indicate an area with a crust composed of a thin layer of unconsolidated sediments (about 0.5 km) overlying a 1.3-km-thick "second layer" with an average velocity of 5.5 km/sec, and a third layer 4.3 km thick with a velocity of 6.7 km/sec.

Within the second layer an area with a low velocity (average of 4.83 km/sec) is found in the transition region between the Southern Gulf province and the open ocean to the south. It may represent an extensive area of volcanic material that has accumulated on the sea floor.

The velocity of the second layer as measured in the deep-water stations (5.50 km/sec) is not significantly different from that measured in the Northern Gulf province (5.43 km/sec), where it was correlated with the igneous and metamorphic basement. Though slightly higher than the Pacific Basin averages reported by Raitt (1956), the scatter in both sets of data is so high that the difference is not significant.

The third or main crustal layer seems to have a velocity very close to 6.7 km/sec, here, as well as in the Northern Gulf province. This average is similar to that found for the Pacific Basin as a whole.

The average thickness of the crust in the area of the deep-water stations, 6.06 km, is a little less than the Pacific Basin average, and the seismic velocity of the material below the crust (average 7.86 km/sec) is lower than the average found by Raitt in the Pacific (8.2 km/sec).

Though once considered rare, these lower-than-normal velocities associated with the subcrustal material have been reported widely from areas in both the Atlantic and Pacific Oceans. In every instance they seem to be associated with regions of unusual tectonic activity. Such low velocities are found under the Mid-Atlantic Ridge (Ewing and Ewing, 1959), the Puerto Rico Trench (Bunce and Fahlquist, 1962), and the East Pacific Rise (Menard, 1960), to name a few.

A further point of interest is the association of

TABLE VI. HEAT-FLOW MEASUREMENTS IN THE GULF OF CALIFORNIA
(From Von Herzen, 1963)

Sta.	*Lat*	*Long*	*Depth (m)*	*Therm. Cond.*[1]	*Heat Flow*[2]
V-1	27°08′N	111°38′W	1,840	1.77	2.80
V-2	27°17′N	111°22′W	1,870	1.65	2.94
V-3	27°38′N	111°44′W	1,775	1.64	4.19
V-4	26°46′N	111°04′W	1,750	1.75	2.95
V-5	24°09′N	108°55′W	3,020	1.99	4.24
V-6	22°58′N	108°04′W	2,900	1.81	0.62
V-7	21°59′N	107°41′W	3,055	1.86	5.51
V-8	21°00′N	107°04′W	3,300	1.89	3.98
V-9	20°55′N	106°25′W	4,450	2.00	2.14
V-10	20°10′N	107°43′W	3,290	1.76	1.25
V-11	19°45′N	108°28′W	2,600	1.82	1.43
V-12	20°48′N	109°34′W	2,910	1.81	2.40
V-13	22°33′N	109°29′W	2,860	2.08	6.15

[1] (10^{-3} cal °C^{-1} cm^{-1} sec^{-1}).
[2] (10^{-6} cal cm^{-2} sec^{-1}).

these low seismic velocities and high geothermal heat flows through the crust. Von Herzen (1963) reports, on the basis of 13 measurements in or near the Gulf of California (Fig. 4), that the average heat flow is 3.12×10^{-6} cal/cm^2/sec (Table VI), compared to 1.2 to 1.4×10^{-6} cal/cm^2/sec as the mean oceanic value. Similar high heat flow values have been reported from other areas where the seismic velocity of the material below the crust is low.

On the basis of topography, seismicity, and heat flow, Menard (1960) postulated that the East Pacific Rise continued northward from Easter Island and that the Gulf of California was coincident with the crest of this feature. The similarity between the crustal structure under the Gulf of California, as reported here, and that of the East Pacific Rise as determined by Raitt (Menard, 1960), lends support to this hypothesis.

It would appear that the low velocity of subcrustal material as found near the mouth of the Gulf, and that found by Raitt in the equatorial East Pacific, are parts of a continuous low-velocity area associated with the East Pacific Rise. Studies of the dispersion of surface waves traveling a path across the eastern Pacific Ocean (Kovach and Press, 1961) indicate that the upper mantle may have a lower than normal velocity over a broad area roughly coincident with the East Pacific Rise. Over the oceanic path from Easter Island to Pasadena the data show that the

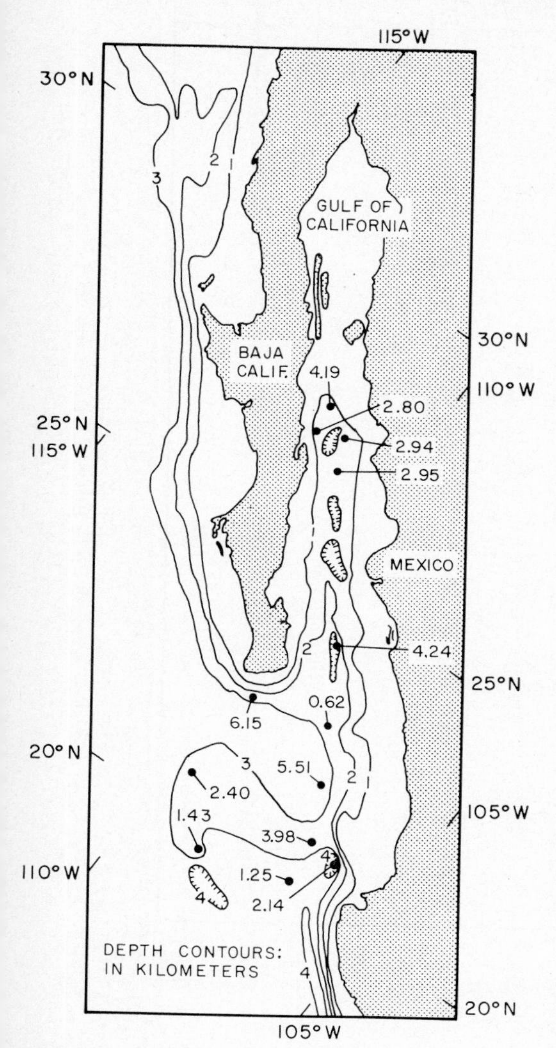

FIG. 4.—Location diagram (after Von Herzen, 1963) showing heat-flow measurements in the Gulf of California. Value of heat flux in microcal/cm²/sec.

material with a normal velocity of 8.2 km/sec is either very thin or absent. The major portion of the upper mantle should have a compressional wave velocity near 7.8 km/sec to agree with the observed surface wave dispersion.

CONTINENTAL TERRACE STATIONS: INTRODUCTION

Four stations—17, 18, 22, and 23—were located in the shallow-water continental-terrace region west of the mainland of Mexico. All four stations were split profiles giving eight independent solutions; Stations 17 and 18 were reversed, which allowed dipping-layer solutions.

Stations 22 and 23, though not reversed, and beset with water-wave propagation troubles, can be used to give limits, at least, on the depth of the base of the crust in the region east of the Tres Marías Islands.

In addition to these split profiles, two short profile segments were shot in shallow water and received in deep water, in conjunction with the fan lines from Station 13-south and from 14-south.

Because of the similarity of the travel-time plots of Station 17 and Station 18 to the travel-time plots of the stations in the northern Gulf, a similar interpretation is made for the layers. This is not possible for the pair of Stations 22 and 23 (Figs. *2i* and *2j*).

SHELF STATIONS: DESCRIPTION OF THE DATA

Arrivals from the unconsolidated sediments are particularly well represented in the data from Stations 17 and 18. They can be distinctly recognized as second arrivals from shots as far out as 20 km from the receiving ship. The average velocity calculated from these four lines is 1.8 km/sec, lower than that measured in the northern Gulf, but in keeping with values determined in the laboratory for unconsolidated sediments (Hamilton, 1959).

Arrivals that can be attributed to layers having seismic velocities similar to layers 1*a*, 2, and 3 are apparent from the travel-time plots of 17-south and 18-north. However, unlike the arrivals from the stations in the Northern Gulf province, the reverse pair 17-south and 18-north contain arrivals that can be associated with subcrustal material. The close agreement of the reverse times and of the intercepts for the layers of these profiles tends to give added confidence in the solutions of this compound pair of stations (Fig. *2i*).

Interpretations of Stations 22 and 23, on the other hand, are less certain. The travel-time plot (Fig. *2j*) for them shows that the four-layer model of the crust adopted for Stations 17 and 18 is not suitable here.

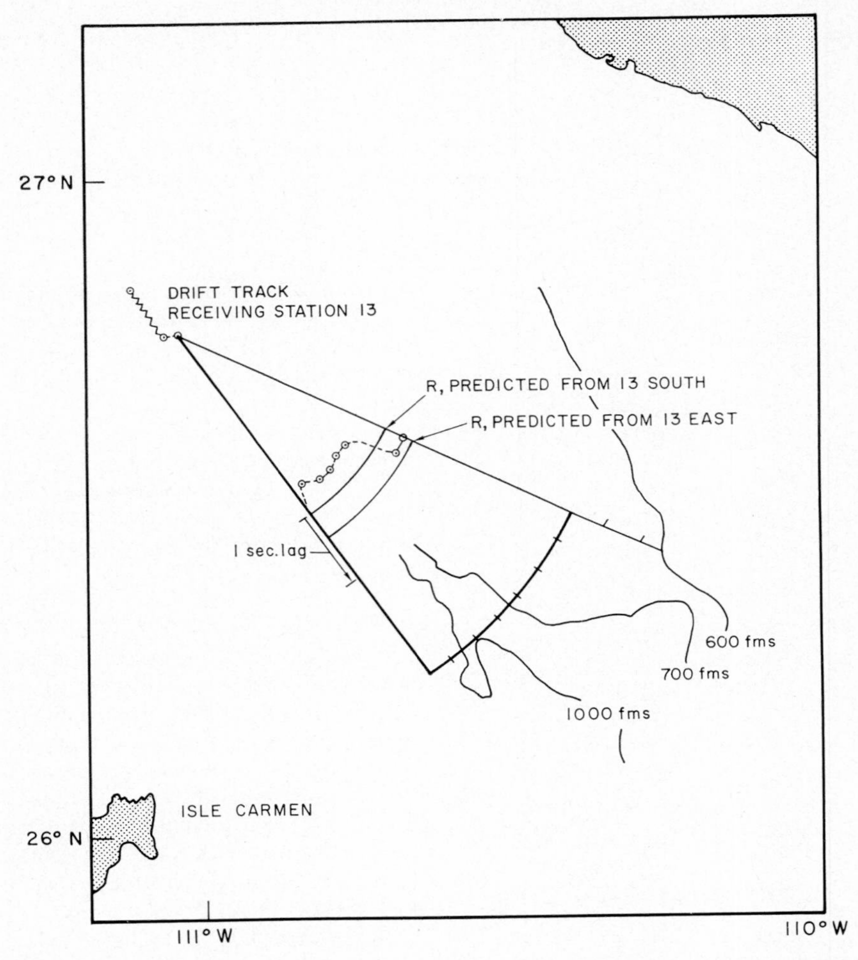

FIG. 5.—Fan line from profile 13-south to 13-east, showing relative travel time for the refracted waves (*R*).

The offset of 0.4 sec in the travel-time plot of Station 22-north, which is associated with a small topographic high, indicates the presence of high-velocity material near the surface. This small hill may be volcanic in origin.

Station 22-south can be interpreted as a simple two-layer crust overlying a higher velocity material at a depth of about 14 km. In order to allow a reversal of this profile with 23-north, a layer of small thickness and a velocity of 5.07 km/sec is presumed to exist under Station 22.

Although no arrivals that can be associated with the unconsolidated sediments were recorded at Station 23-north, the travel-time curve indicates four distinct branches. Only one seems directly correlative with the branches of the travel-time plot of 22-south. This is the second branch, corresponding to a velocity of 5.96 km/sec, which appears to be the same as the main section of the plot of 22-south, with a velocity of 6.06 km/sec.

The interpretation of the last two branches of the travel-time plot of Station 23-north is open to doubt. The indicated velocities of 7.08 and 8.93 km/sec are either too high or too low to correlate with the last branch of the travel-time plot of 22-

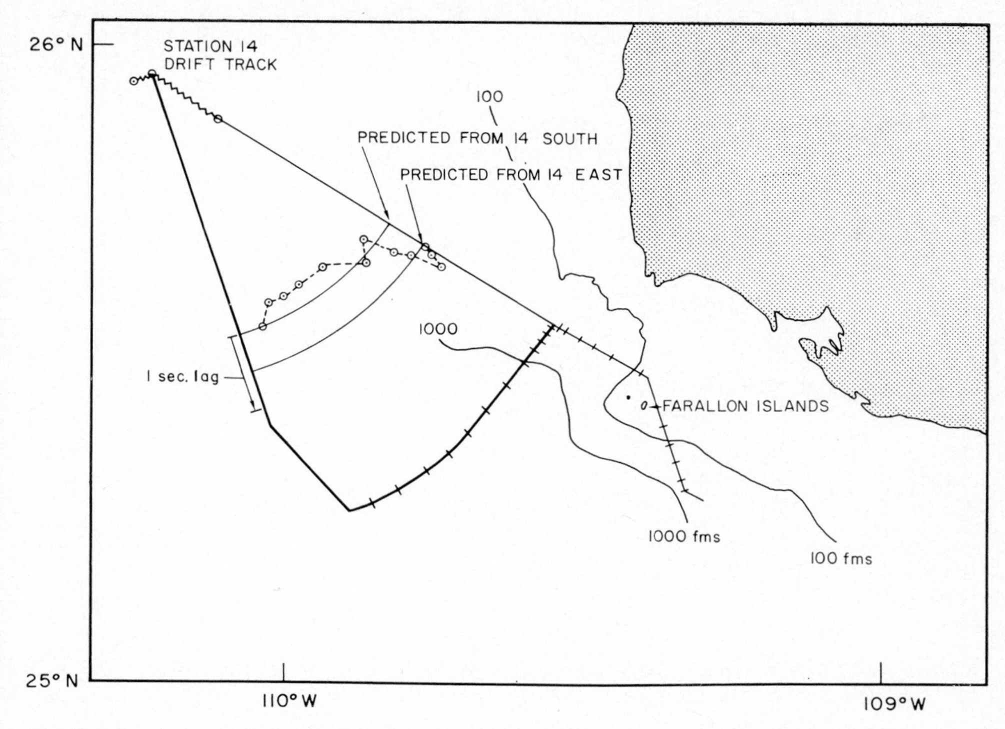

FIG. 6.—Fan line from profile 14-south to 14-east, showing the relative travel time for the refracted wave (*R*).

south. The higher velocity may be due to a marked thinning of the sedimentary cover associated with the increase of water depth at the end of the profile, and the 7.08 km/sec segment may correspond to the 8.23 km/sec material from Station 22-south. If this is so, it would indicate a very strong dip down to the north, and a velocity of about 7.6 km/sec for the material below the main crustal layer. It would also indicate that the crust is extremely thin under Station 23. On the other hand, if the 8.93 km/sec velocity is correlated with the 8.23 km/sec velocity for Station 22-south, then the interface at the base of the crustal material dips strongly down to the south, and the subcrustal material has an indicated seismic velocity of 8.59 km/sec. Both of these interpretations appear unlikely.

Fan lines were shot from the deep-water ends of Stations 13-south and 14-south eastward toward the continental mainland. Though the fan from 13-south never reached true shelf depths, that from 14-south reached rather shallow water, and the profile run from the end of the fan (14-east) reached water of less than 100 fathoms.

A fan line was shot from profile 23-north westward across the shelf edge, behind the Tres Marías Islands and into deep water to the site of receiving Station 21 (*see* Figs. 5, 6, and 7). These three fans all show a similar pattern of arrivals. At the crossing of the 1,000-fathom contour by the shooting ship, the travel times of the arrivals seem to shift abruptly, and the first arrivals appear to be associated with a distinctly lower velocity zone in the shallow-water region than in the deep-water region. The short profiles from the end of the 13-south fan, called 13-east, and the 14-south fan, called 14-east, indicate that these arrivals are associated with the main crustal layer rather than with the subcrustal material. This is interpreted to mean that the base of the crust deepens considerably and the main crustal layer thickens correspondingly, at the edge of the continent. This pattern is shown on the cross sections in *B-B′* and *C-C′* of Figure 10.

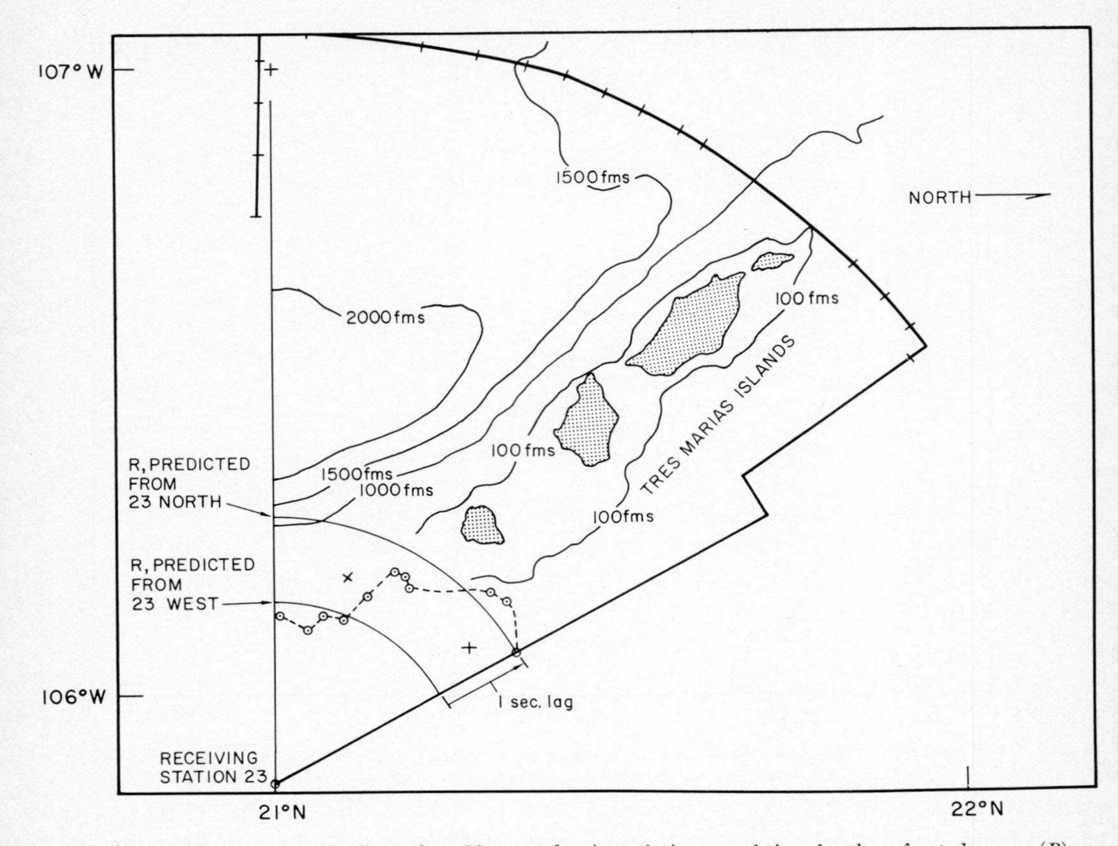

FIG. 7.—Fan line from profile 23-north to 23-west, showing relative travel time for the refracted waves (*R*).

CONTINENTAL TERRACE STATIONS: SUMMARY

The continental shelf off the west coast of Mazatlán appears to be a depositional feature with layering and seismic velocities similar to the area of the Northern Gulf province. The crust appears to be from 16 to 20 km thick in this region with the deeper portions to the south.

On the other hand, east of the Tres Marías Islands higher velocity material seems to be nearer the surface. Though the seismic results are not clear, the crust seems to be about 16 km thick, with the underlying material having a velocity of about 8 km/sec.

This high-velocity material at a shallow depth may be a southern continuation of the shallow dense material indicated farther north in the gravity profile *A-B* of Harrison and Mathur (this volume).

SUMMARY AND CONCLUSIONS

Figures 9 and 10 present a summary of the data detailed above. Figure 9 is a longitudinal section extending from the United States–Mexico Border southeast to the latitude of the Tres Marías Islands. This long section is roughly coincident with the line of stations that follow the center of the Gulf of California from the Colorado Delta southeast into deep water. The bathymetry shown is generalized from the bathymetric chart (Chart I, Rusnak, Fisher, and Shepard, this volume) rather than the water depths along the shooting tracks. The section has been continued to the north to the International Border to include Stations 5 and 6 of Kovach, Allen, and Press (1962).

Figure 10 presents three cross sections, each roughly at right angles to the trend of the Gulf.

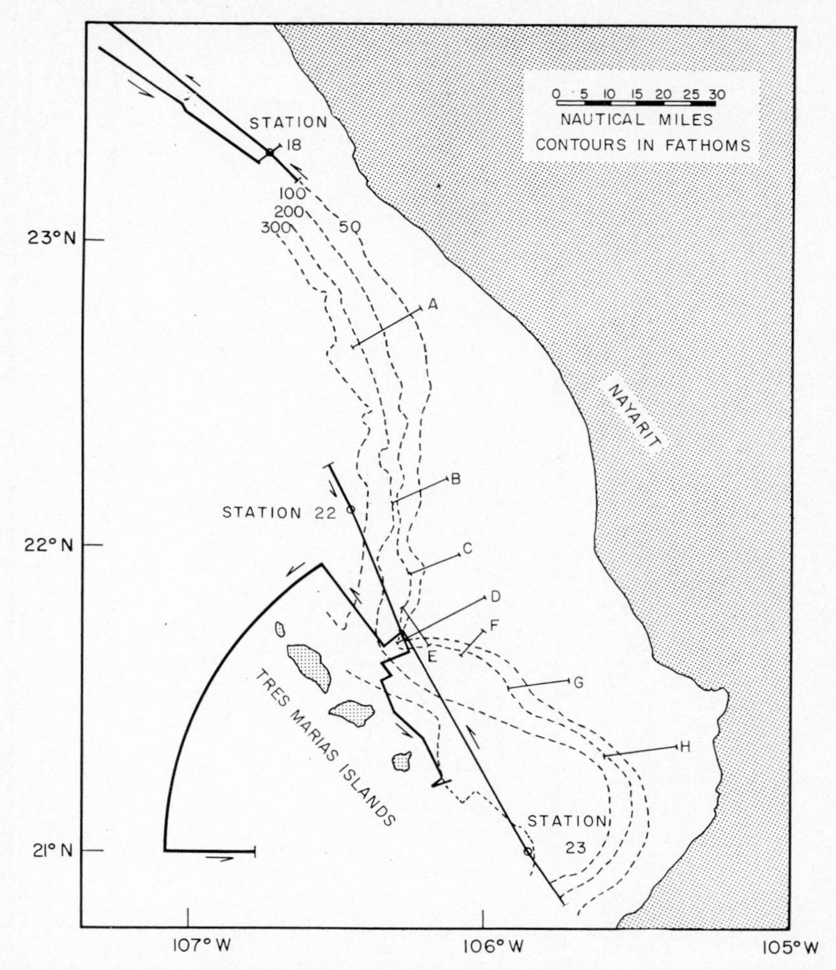

FIG. 8.—Location diagram showing the relationship between the continental terrace Stas. 17, 18, 22, and 23 and the arcer sections of Curray and Moore (this volume).

The northernmost one, *A-A′*, in the shallow-water Northern Gulf province, follows the shooting tracks of Stations 2 and 3 and passes slightly to the south of Station 4.

The cross section from the southern Gulf, *B-B′*, includes the receiving positions of Station 17 on the continental shelf north of Mazatlán, and Station 24 in the deep water south of the tip of Baja California. This section passes just to the south of the receiving position of Station 16.

The third cross section, *C-C′* off the coast of Nayarit, is drawn west from the town of San Blas, across the continental shelf, where the basement-sediment contact shown on section *H* of Curray and Moore (this volume) has been included. The section passes north of receiving Station 23, south of the Tres Marías Islands, through Station 1, Shor and Fisher (1961), and west to the receiving position of Station 21.

A fundamental difference appears to exist between the Northern Gulf province and the deep-water region south of the Gulf of California proper. This difference, as indicated on the longitudinal section, is similar to that found between the deep sea and the continental borderland west of California, as presented by Shor and

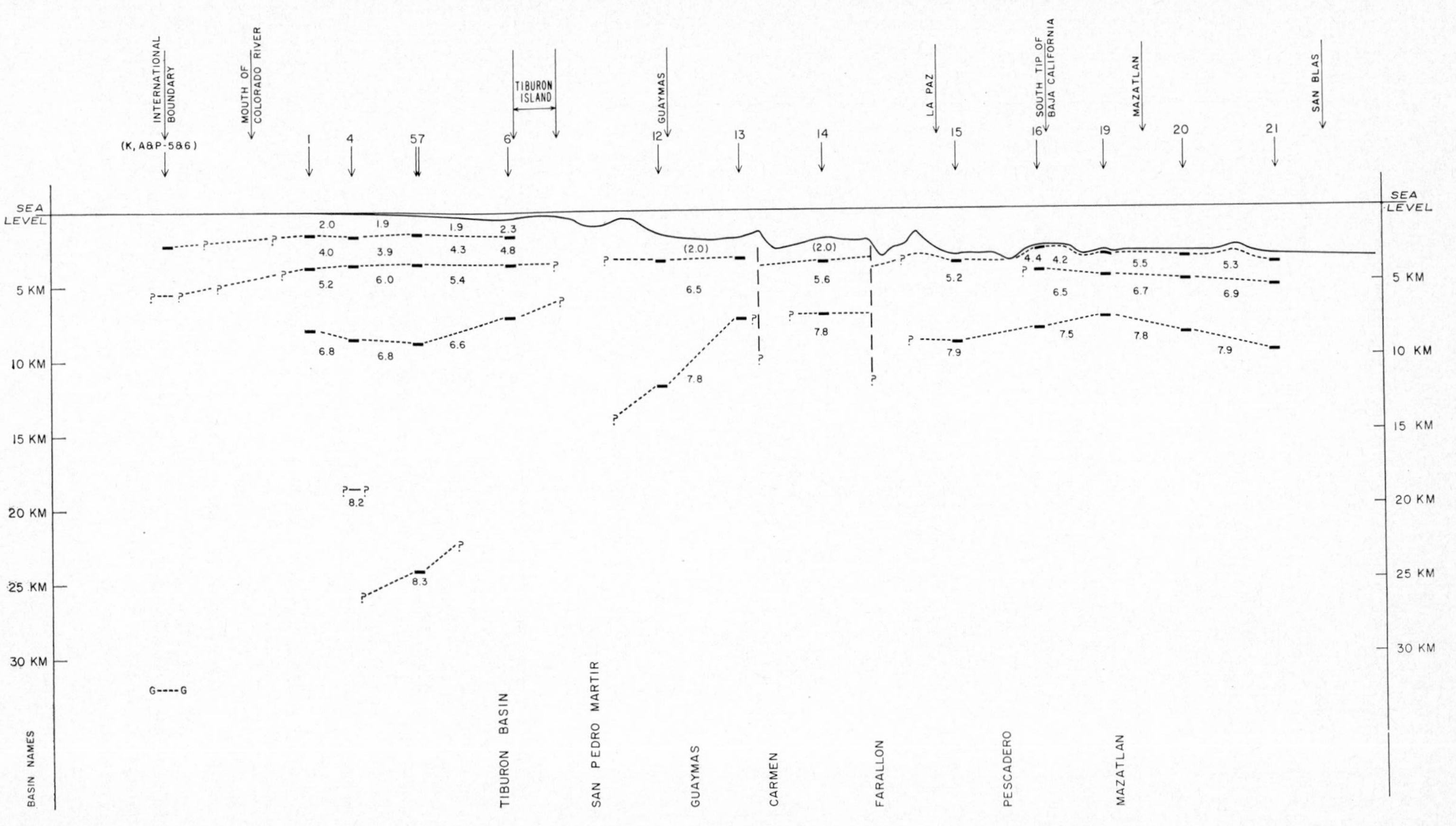

FIG. 9.—Longitudinal section from the International Boundary (on the left) southeast to the latitude of the Tres Marías Islands. Vertical exaggeration approximately 20 to 1. Velocities directly below the stations are based on calculations using the station as a split profile; those between stations are based on calculations using stations as reverse pairs. Profile at International Boundary from Kovach and others (1962).

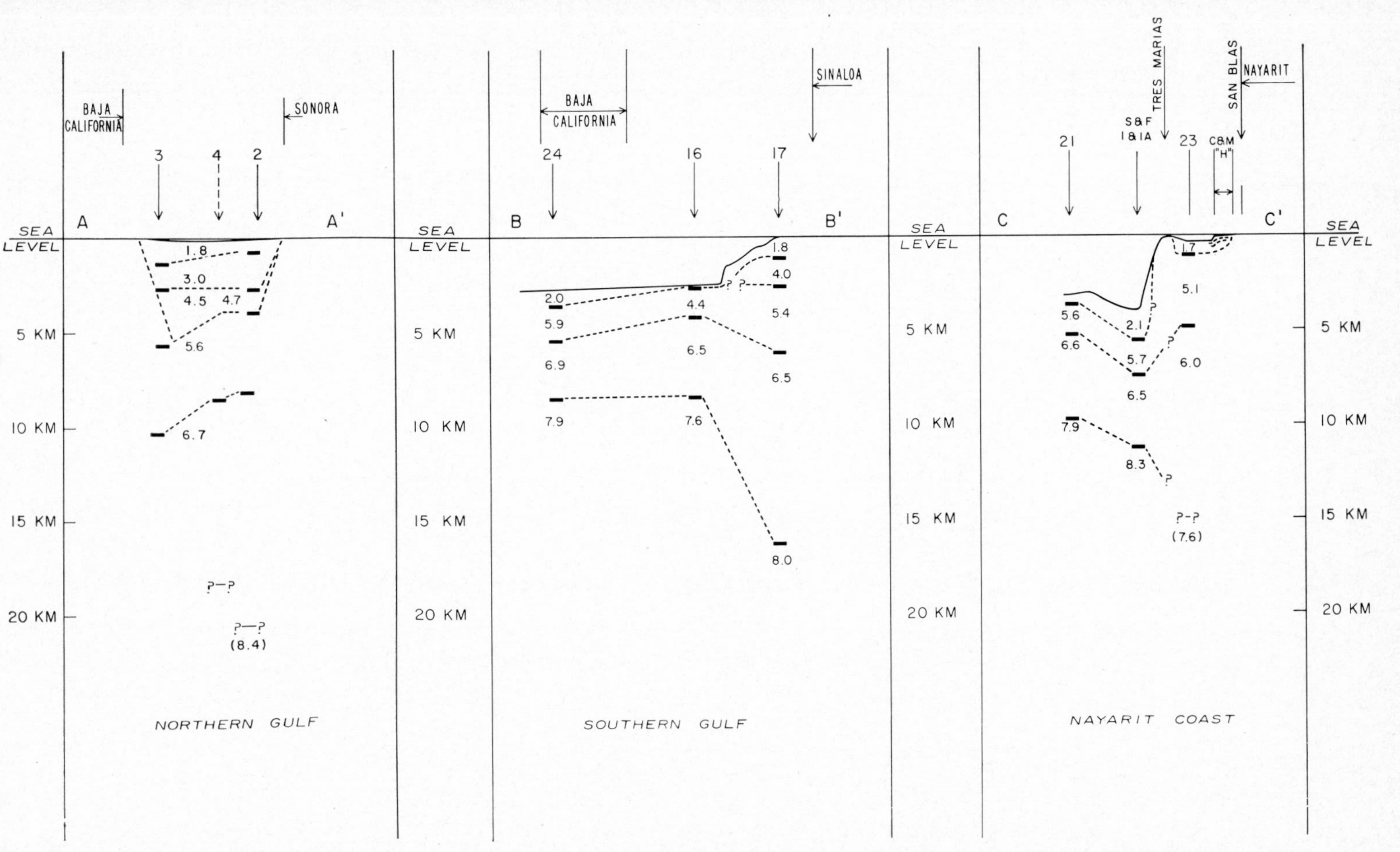

FIG. 10.—Cross section across the structure of the Gulf. For location of the sections see Fig. 1. Section *C-C'* includes section *H* from Curray and Moore (this volume).

Raitt (1958). It would appear that a simple filling of a trench similar to the present central Gulf region is not enough to account for the structure of the northern Gulf. The layer of material with a seismic velocity of 6.7 km/sec that has a maximum thickness of 7.5 km south of Tiburón Island thickens rapidly to the north; it has a minimum thickness of 15 km to the east of Angel de la Guarda Island.

A similar thickening of the main crustal layer and the "second layer" seems to take place generally at the continental slope on the east side of the Gulf of California, as indicated by the fan lines that were shot in connection with the seismic profiles 13-south, 14-south, and 23-north and the profiles from Stations 17, 18, and 22.

The structure of the crust in those areas of the Gulf where the water depth is less than 0.5 km can be summarized as follows:

Layer	*Seismic Velocity*	*Thickness*	*Remarks*
1	2.00 km/sec	1.5 km	unconsolidated sediments
1a	4.23	2.0	semiconsolidated sediments
2	5.53	4.3	igneous and metamorphic basement
3	6.70		main crustal layer

The total thickness of the crust in the shallow-water regions is not clearly defined on the basis of this work. The base of the crust appears to be no deeper than 20 km, and probably closer to 15 km under much of the shelf west of Sinaloa and Nayarit. In the northern Gulf it appears to lie no shallower than 20 km and probably closer to 25 km below the surface.

South of the Gulf of California proper and west of the continental slope appears a region where the crust can be characterized by a three-layer structure similar to that found for the average of the deep Pacific. This structure can be summarized as follows:

Layer	*Seismic Velocity*	*Thickness*	*Remarks*
water	1.47 km/sec	2.9 km	deep ocean average = 5 km
1	(2.0)	0.4	unconsolidated sediments
2	5.50	1.3	the "second layer"
3	6.69	4.3	main crustal layer
4	7.86		mantle

The average value of the crustal thickness here is 6.0 km, not significantly different from that of 6.3 km for the deep Pacific Basin as a whole.

The seismic velocity of the upper mantle, as determined in this study, seems lower than the value of 8.2 km/sec that has become accepted as normal. It is similar to values obtained for the East Pacific Rise. On the basis of the bathymetry, heat flow, and seismic velocity, the East Pacific Rise can be projected from Easter Island to the Gulf of California.

Due to the topographic and structural complexity of the major portion of the Gulf of California, the seismic refraction results could not be resolved with the detail desired. However, from the Sal si Puedes Basin to the mouth of the Gulf, the structure can be interpreted as consisting of:

Layer	*Seismic Velocity*	*Thickness*	*Remarks*
1	(2.0 km/sec)	1.28 km	unconsolidated sediments
2	5.80	6.24	the "second layer" and main crustal layer
4	7.79		mantle.

The thickness of the crust below the unconsolidated sediments appears to be similar to that found in the deep-water region to the south. The general shallowing of the water to the north is due to a thickening of the sedimentary blanket. Therefore, though it is interrupted by faulting, the general level of the base of the sediments, and the depth to the Mohorovičić discontinuity do not change greatly as one goes up the Gulf until the shallow water region to the north is reached.

The transition zone between the open ocean and the Gulf of California proper is marked by a topographic rise (the sill between the Pescadero and Mazatlán Basins), that seems to have a thin sedimentary cover, and an anomalously low seismic velocity in the second layer of 4.8 km/sec. Perhaps this transition zone is marked by an accumulation of volcanic material on the sea floor.

The transition zone between the mid-Gulf region and the shallow water region to the north is marked by a more or less abrupt thickening of the main crustal layer, and the appearance of a layer of semiconsolidated sediments and volcanic rocks.

REFERENCES

Anderson, C.A., 1950, Geology of the islands and neighboring land areas, pt. 1 *of* The 1940 E.W. Scripps cruise to the Gulf of California: Geol. Soc. America Mem. 43.

Bunce, E.T., and Fahlquist, D.A., 1962, Geophysical investigations of the Puerto Rico Trench and outer ridge: Jour. Geophys. Research, v. 67, no. 10, p. 3955–3972.

Dibblee, T.W., Jr., 1954, Geology of the Imperial Valley region, California, *in* Geology of Southern California: Calif. Div. Mines Bull. 170, pt. 2, ch. 2, p. 21–28.

Dix, C.H., 1955, Seismic velocities from surface measurements: Geophysics, v. 20, no. 1, p. 68–86.

Dobrin, M.B., 1960, The refraction method, *in* Introduction to geophysical prospecting: McGraw-Hill, New York, ch. 5, p. 69–104.

Ewing, J., and Ewing, M., 1959, Seismic-refraction measurements in the Atlantic Ocean basins, in the Mediterranean Sea, on the mid-Atlantic ridge, and in the Norwegian Sea: Geol. Soc. America Bull., v. 70, no. 3, p. 291–318.

Hamilton, E.L., 1959, Thickness and consolidation of deep-sea sediments: Geol. Soc. America Bull., v. 70, no. 11, p. 1399–1424.

Katz, S., and Ewing, M., 1956, Atlantic Ocean basin west of Bermuda, pt. 7 *of* Seismic-refraction measurements in the Atlantic Ocean: Geol. Soc. America Bull., v. 67, no. 4, p. 475–510.

Kovach, R.L., Allen, C.R., and Press, F., 1962, Geophysical investigations in the Colorado Delta region: Jour. Geophys. Research, v. 67, no. 7, p. 2845–2871.

——— and Press, F., 1961, Raleigh wave dispersion and crustal structure in the eastern Pacific and Indian Oceans: Roy. Astron. Soc. Geophysics Jour., v. 4, p. 202–216.

Kuwahara, S., 1939, Velocity of sound in sea water and calculation of the velocity for use in sonic soundings: Hydrographic Rev., v. 16, p. 127–140.

Menard, H.W., 1960, The East Pacific Rise: Science, v. 132, no. 3441, p. 1737–1746.

Raitt, R.W., 1956, Crustal thickness of the Central Equatorial Pacific, pt. 1 *of* Seismic-refraction studies of the Pacific Ocean basin: Geol. Soc. America Bull., v. 67, no. 12, p. 1623–1639.

Shepard, F.P., 1950, Submarine topography of the Gulf of California, pt. 3 *of* The 1940 E.W. Scripps cruise to the Gulf of California: Geol. Soc. America Mem. 43.

Shor, G.G., Jr., 1960, Crustal structure of the Hawaiian ridge near Gardner pinnacles: Seismol. Soc. America Bull., v. 50, no. 4, p. 563–573.

——— 1963, Refraction and reflection techniques and procedures, *in* The sea—ideas and observations: Interscience Publishers, New York, v. 3, p. 20–38.

——— and Fisher, R.L., 1961, Middle America Trench: seismic-refraction studies: Geol. Soc. America Bull., v. 72, no. 5, p. 721–730.

——— and Raitt, R.W., 1958, Seismic studies in the Southern California continental borderland: Internat. Geol. Cong., 20th, Mexico, D.F., Rept., sec. 9, p. 253–259.

Von Herzen, R.P., 1963, Geothermal heat flow in the Gulfs of California and Aden: Science, v. 140, no. 3572, p. 1207–1208.

MAGNETIC PROFILES ACROSS GULF OF CALIFORNIA[1]

THOMAS W.C. HILDE[2]
La Jolla, California

ABSTRACT

A total magnetic intensity survey in the southern Gulf of California revealed a close association between topography and the magnetic anomalies. Negative anomalies were found over steep scarps. Positive anomalies were found over the basins, hilly topography, and island ridges. The anomaly pattern is northwest-southeast, the same as the pattern of topographic features. Size and shape of anomalies indicate the magnetic rock is in the second crustal layer and has considerable relief on its surface.

INTRODUCTION

During November 1959 the Scripps Institution of Oceanography research vessel *Orca* carried out a geomagnetic survey of the Gulf of California. Lines normal and diagonal to the geographical axis of the Gulf were traversed in the southern Gulf. The portion of the cruise for which magnetic records were obtained is shown in Figure 1.

Positioning of the ship was by celestial navigation and land sights. Although the navigation was not of high accuracy, a check was obtained from echo-sounder data and adjustments required to make fathometer depths match at crossing points were less than one mile.

A total intensity proton precession magnetometer was towed 500 ft behind the ship; it is unlikely that the ship's field contributes significantly to the records in comparison with the size of anomalies observed. The regional gradient was removed from the profiles by inspection, as the gradient is uniform throughout this area (*see* U.S. Navy Hydrographic Office chart 1703) and could be seen plainly as a nearly constant slope in the plotted profiles. No attempt was made to remove the diurnal variation. During the time of this survey there were no magnetic storms (N.A.S. IGY, 1959). The lines running across the Gulf were checked by a longitudinal control line running through them, and at crossings differences were all in the range of 30 gammas except for one difference of 60 gammas. It is therefore unlikely that any effect in excess of 30 gammas was contributed by diurnal variation.

Five profiles of total magnetic intensity, corrected for regional gradient, are plotted in Figure 2. A definite relationship can be seen between the magnetic anomalies and the topography of the southern Gulf, confirming the interpretation by Rusnak and others (this volume) that the topography reflects the underlying structure. In general, three relationships between the magnetic anomalies and topography can be seen—(1) broad positive anomalies are associated with the basins; (2) sharp negative anomalies are associated with scarps; and (3) sharp positive anomalies are associated with seamounts and volcanic islands.

DISCUSSION OF PROFILES

Profile A-A′.—Profile *A-A′* extends northeast from the east side of San José Canyon across the Gulf of California trough to a point approximately 250 fathoms below the shelf break on the northeast side of the Gulf (Figs. 1 and 2). For a detailed representation of topography and for geographical names see Chart I of Rusnak and others, in pocket.

A broad positive anomaly, with three sharp positive anomalies superimposed on it, exists over the main Gulf trough. The three high posi-

[1] Manuscript received, June 25, 1963. Contribution from Scripps Institution of Oceanography.

The cooperation of the magnetic section of the Marine Physical Laboratory of the Scripps Institution of Oceanography, University of California, is most gratefully appreciated. The author is especially indebted to Robert Warren of the Marine Physical Laboratory, who conducted the survey in 1959. Thanks are also extended to the many individuals at Scripps for the helpful discussion of the magnetic data. This work was supported by the Office of Naval Research under contracts Nonr 2216(01) and Nonr 2216(05).

[2] Scripps Institution of Oceanography, University of California.

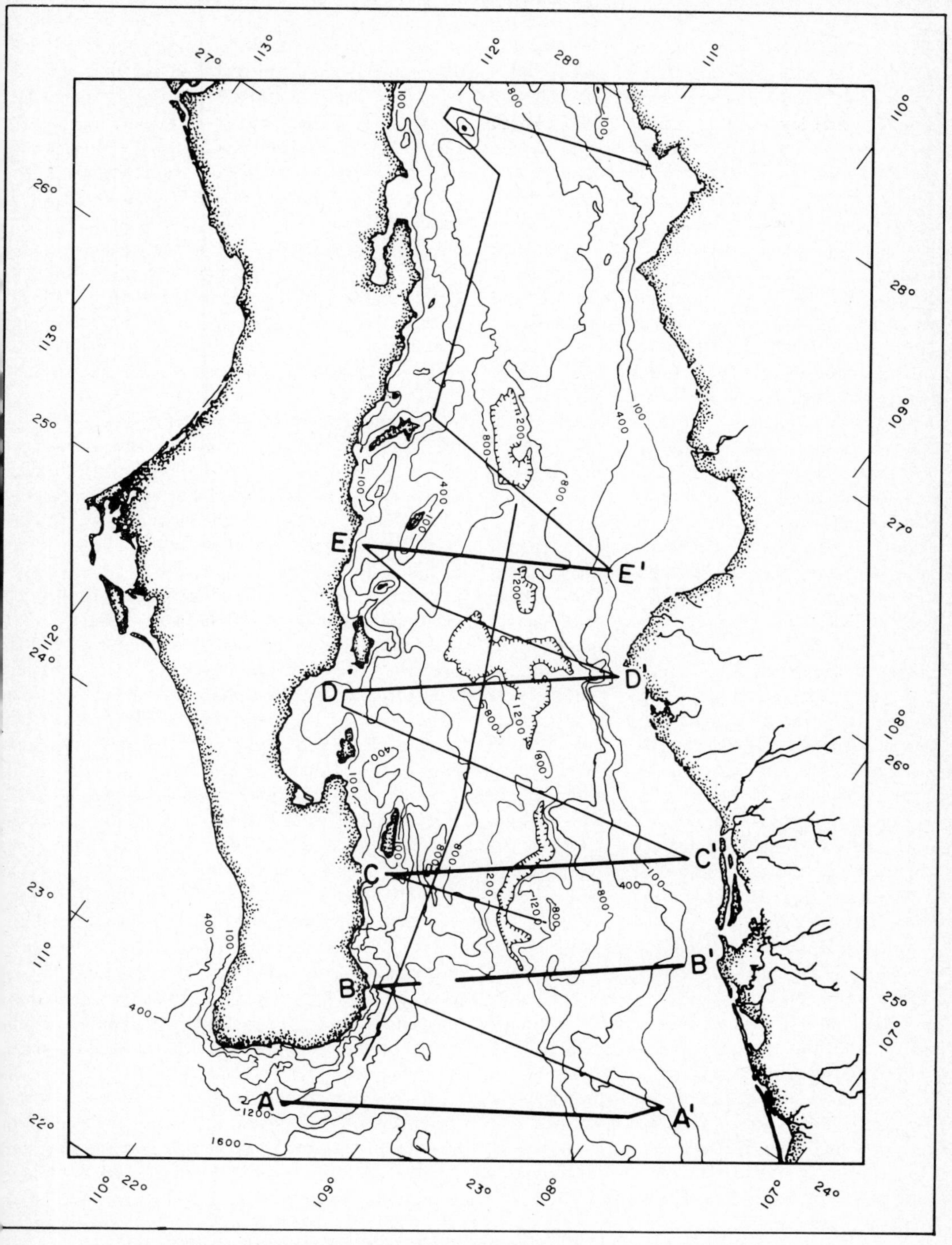

FIG. 1.—Ship track of the R/V *Orca* showing lines of the magnetic survey. Heavy lines locate profiles shown in Fig. 2.

tive anomalies (180 gammas, 210 gammas, and 455 gammas) are over an area of rough, hilly topography. Phillips' seismic data (this volume) indicate a first layer of 0.43 km average thickness in this area and a lower-than-normal velocity of 4.83 ± 0.56 km/sec for the second layer. With the thin cover of unconsolidated sediments the topography may well be an expression of relief in either the second or main crustal layer. The narrowness of the magnetic anomalies indicates the magnetic rock unit is not deeply buried, and the magnitude of the anomalies indicates a highly magnetic rock such as basalt (Dobrin, 1960; Vacquier and others, 1951; Reford, 1960). Fragments of basalt have been dredged from seamounts in the southern Gulf (Rusnak and others, this volume).

A sharp negative anomaly (310 gammas) exists over the steep scarp bordering the northeast side of Pescadero Basin. This scarp has been shown as a fault by Rusnak and others (this volume). Another negative anomaly (220 gammas) is over the submerged slope of Baja California near Cabrillo Seamount. Samples of fractured quartz and granite have been recovered from Cabrillo Seamount (Shepard, this volume).

Profile B-B′.—Profile *B-B′* crosses the deepest part of the Pescadero Basin running from near Punta Arena on the coast of Baja California to the shelf on the northeast side of the Gulf. Here, as in Profile *A-A′*, broad positive anomalies are seen over the greater extent of the Gulf trough. Less anomalous negative values exist over the shoal area to the east, and a negative anomaly appears very near the Baja California Peninsula to the west.

When comparing the magnetic profile with the topographic profile for the central deep of Pescadero Basin and the adjacent ridges, a similarity in shapes can be seen. It seems likely, therefore, that the relief in the surface of the magnetic rock body is reflected in the topography.

The dashed lines in the magnetic profile to the west represent an area of no magnetic record. The diagonal line connecting lines *A-A′* and *B-B′* (Fig. 1) has a similar distribution of anomalies to that in profiles *A-A′* and *B-B′*, and a negative anomaly exists on this line adjacent to the area of no magnetic record on line *B-B′*. A sharp negative anomaly (220 gammas) exists on the diagonal line over the scarp on the east side of Pescadero Basin, thus relating a negative anomaly to the length of this scarp.

Profile C-C′.—Profile *C-C′* shows a broad positive anomaly over the main trough of the Gulf and over the shelf on the northeast side of the Gulf. A feature not seen in the two sets of profiles previously discussed is the sharp anomaly associated with little topographic relief. Phillips' seismic data (this volume) indicate a thicker unit of unconsolidated sediment in this area than in the areas of *A-A′* and *B-B′*. This additional sediment may mask some of the subsurface structural relief.

Two sharp negative anomalies exist in this profile—one (115 gammas) over the scarp bordering the west side of Ceralbo Trough and the other (135 gammas) over the slight change in slope just below shelf break on the northeast side of the Gulf. The latter of these two anomalies lies directly in line with the strike of the linear scarp to the northwest. Both of these scarps are shown as faults by Rusnak and others (this volume).

A sharp positive anomaly (305 gammas) exists over the 400-fathom knoll east of the deep basin. The northeast side of the deep basin crossed here is not part of the same linear scarp crossed by profiles *A-A′* and *B-B′*, and no sharp negative anomaly is observed here.

As on the two previous profiles, there is a negative anomaly near the east coast of Baja California. This anomaly also covers the southward extension of the Isla Ceralbo ridge.

Profile D-D′.—Profile *D-D′* extends from the entrance to Bahia de la Paz on the southwest to the shelf break on the northeast side of the Gulf near the Río Fuerte Delta. The magnetic profile is characterized by generally high positive anomalies broken by three sharp negative anomalies. Each of the three negative anomalies is associated with moderate topographic relief.

The extremely large negative anomaly (575 gammas) to the southwest is over the southern portion of the scarp that fronts Isla San José on the east. A large negative anomaly (420 gammas) exists on the diagonal line connecting *C-C′* and *D-D′* (Fig. 1) near the north end of Isla Esperítu Santo in direct line with a southward projection of the scarp fronting Isla San José. These two anomalies fall very nearly on the long fault that cuts across Baja California as mapped by Rusnak and others (this volume).

The other two large negative anomalies are found over northeast-facing scarps within the main Gulf trough. The fault as shown by Rusnak and others (this volume) along the southwest side of Farallón Basin is marked by a 200-gamma negative anomaly. A smaller scarp to the west is marked by the other sharp anomaly (175 gammas).

Profile E-E′.—Profile *E-E′* extends across the north end of Farallón Basin, normal to the Gulf axis. This magnetic profile exhibits a different character from those discussed to the south. There is no large positive anomaly across the main Gulf trough, rather a single sharp positive anomaly (310 gammas) over the Isla Santa Catalina ridge and a single sharp negative anomaly (190 gammas) over the north end of a scarp which borders the northeast side of Farallón Basin. One small negative anomaly lies over the small narrow depression in the Farallón Basin.

The topographic profile shows much less relief than is seen in those to the south. The only two topographic irregularities of any size correspond to the two sharp magnetic anomalies.

Phillips' seismic data (this volume) indicates a thicker layer of unconsolidated sediment here (1.2 to 1.3 km) than there is to the south, and a higher velocity for the second layer. The higher seismic velocity and the lack of large positive anomalies suggest change in composition of the material of the second layer; the magnetic rock unit may be a deeper structure.

CONCLUSIONS

Where the lower-than-normal-velocity second layer exists in the southern Gulf of California there is a thin sediment cover and a large amount of topographic relief. The magnetic data indicate shallow structures of high magnetic susceptibility for this same area. The anomaly patterns correspond very closely to topographic relief; and as it is unlikely that the sediment is highly magnetic, one may assume that the magnetic data shows relief in the second layer which is directly reflected in the topography. This assumption necessitates a fairly uniform composition or polarization contrast for the second layer underlying a large portion of the southern Gulf of California.

Girdler (1962) discusses structural similarities of the Gulf of California and the Red Sea and their association with rift zones. Comparison of the patterns of magnetic anomalies for these two troughs shows that in both cases the patterns strike the axial direction of the trough. However, the Red Sea has anomalies of larger amplitude at much closer spacing. Part of this effect is due to the lesser water depth in the Red Sea. Girdler's hypothesis that the central deeps are underlain by closely spaced dikes is, therefore, not as strongly supported by the Gulf of California data. In the Gulf of California many of the magnetic anomalies are associated with topographic features interpreted as faults.

REFERENCES

Dobrin, M.B., 1960, Introduction to geophysical prospecting: McGraw-Hill Book Co., New York, 2nd ed., 446 p.

Girdler, R.W., 1962, Initiation of continental drift: Nature, v. 194, no. 4828, p. 521–524.

National Academy of Sciences, IGY Bulletin, 1959, World days report for IGC-1959: Transactions of the American Geophysical Union, v. 41, no. 3, p. 537–539.

Reford, M.S., 1960, Airborne magnetometer surveys for petroleum exploration: Aero Service Corporation, Philadelphia, Pa., 56 p.

Vacquier, V., Steenland, N.C., Henderson, R.G., and Zietz, I., 1951, Interpretation of aeromagnetic maps: Geol. Soc. America Mem. 47, 151 p.

GEOPHYSICAL FRAMEWORK OF NORTHERN END OF GULF OF CALIFORNIA STRUCTURAL PROVINCE[1]

SHAWN BIEHLER,[2] ROBERT L. KOVACH,[2] AND CLARENCE R. ALLEN[2]
Pasadena, California

ABSTRACT

More than 3,000 gravity observations in the Northern Gulf province, including an underwater gravity survey of the Salton Sea, show the over-all trend of isogal contours to be northwest, parallel to the tectonic pattern dominated by the San Andreas fault system. Contours northeast of the trough trend east, probably reflecting Transverse Range structures in this area. A prominent and linear gradient of 5 mgal/km marks the Banning-Mission Creek fault in the Coachella Valley but dies out southeastward at about the same point the surface trace disappears. The San Jacinto fault zone is characterized by a series of maxima and minima that tend to confirm continuity of this fault zone to the Gulf of California. A 15–20 mgal maximum over the Obsidian Buttes suggests a large anomalous mass at depth, or may be related to contemporaneous metamorphism of the Tertiary sedimentary section that has recently been observed in nearby steam wells. The regional gravity gradient indicates a crustal thickening northwest from the Gulf of California; inferred crustal thicknesses are 32 km at the International Border and 40 km at San Gorgonio Pass. Ten seismic refraction profiles in the Imperial and Coachella Valleys indicate several throughgoing velocity zones, but we are unable to correlate these with known stratigraphic units. The maximum thickness of sediments in the trough appears to be about 6.4 km (21,000 ft) just south of the International Border, with basement becoming shallower both to the north and south. The Salton trough has many geophysical and structural similarities to the Dead Sea rift, but the markedly *en echelon* pattern of major faults in the Salton trough and Gulf of California appears unique. A particular problem is presented by their orientation, which would suggest left-lateral displacement across the zone rather than the right-lateral displacement that is known to characterize at least the northern end of the province.

INTRODUCTION

Although the head of the Gulf of California terminates 100 km south of the International Border, the structural trough characterized by the Gulf continues another 300 km northwest to San Gorgonio Pass (Fig. 1). In this northern segment the trough is filled by Cenozoic deposits derived from the surrounding mountain ranges and from the Colorado River, but the general structural framework appears similar to that of the Gulf of California proper. It is this primarily dry-land segment of the Gulf of California structural province that is the subject of the present study and is herein called the Salton trough. Although considerable geologic work has been done in the various mountain ranges bordering the Salton trough, geophysical studies are necessary within the basin itself because of widespread alluvial cover.

One of the principal objectives of the geophysical study of this region was to gain a better understanding of the nature of the structural control of the Gulf of California. The great linear depression of the Gulf itself is certainly the distinguishing feature of the province, but it is clear from the known geology of mountain ranges bordering the depression that it is not a simple graben, at least at its northern end. The Gulf of California is characterized throughout its length by northwest-trending faults of the San Andreas fault system, but major breaks of this system such as the Banning-Mission Creek, San Jacinto, and Elsinore faults (Fig. 1) which trend at a definite angle to the length of the Gulf, are not simple parallel breaks outlining the borders of a dropped block. It

[1] Manuscript received, June 25, 1963. Contribution No. 1139, Division of Geological Sciences, California Institute of Technology.

The gravity measurements in Mexico were made in collaboration with the Instituto de Geofísica, Universidad Nacional Autónoma de México, through the participation of Ing. Julio Monges C. We are indebted to Dr. Lucien LaCoste of LaCoste and Romberg for supplying the underwater gravimeter, and to Aerial Control, Inc., and Pacific Air Industries for the use of their Tellurometers. Dr. Frank Press helped supervise most of the work reported herein, and Dr. Charles Helsley was particularly helpful in the field program. Others who assisted us in the field include S. Alexander, D. Harkrider, J. Healy, A. Ibrahim, R. Phinney, and L. Teng. Most of this work was supported by National Science Foundation Grant G-19778 and by the American Petroleum Institute.

[2] Seismological Laboratory and Division of Geological Sciences, California Institute of Technology.

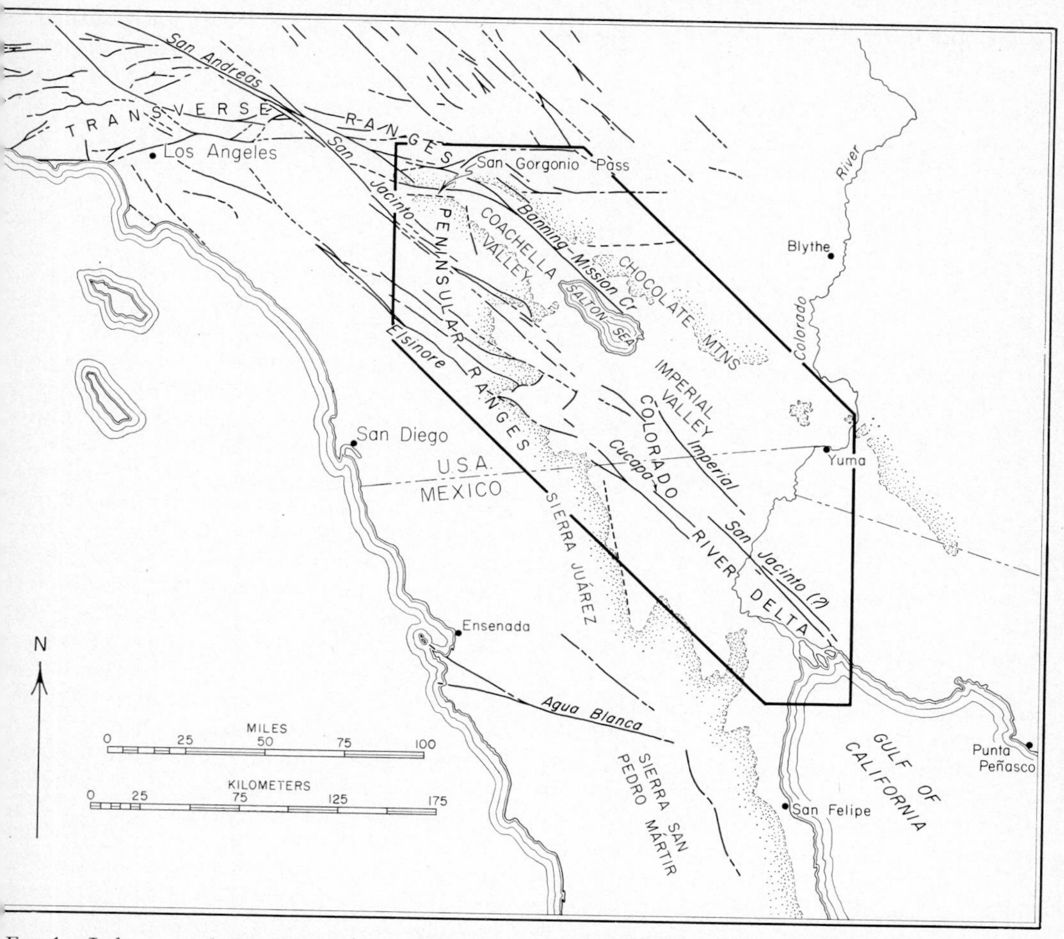

FIG. 1.—Index map, showing names of principal faults and area covered by gravity map, Chart I, in pocket. Stippling indicates generalized outline of pre-Tertiary crystalline rocks bordering the Salton trough.

as hoped that geophysical studies might help to lineate these breaks under the alluvium of the lton trough and thus lead to a better under-anding of their trends, displacements, and rela-e importance in creating major features of the ılf province. In addition, the Cenozoic sedi-ents that fill the Salton trough at the northern d have been of considerable interest in them-ves, because they include thick marine deposits potential petroleum importance. Recently, ere has been renewed interest in the commercial oduction of steam from deep wells in the Salton ough both north and south of the International rder. The location of these wells is apparently closely related to trends of active faults.

Most of the results of gravity and seismic refraction work south of the Salton Sea have been published previously (Kovach and others, 1962; Kovach and Monges, 1961) and are merely summarized here. Gravity studies north of this region (by Biehler), including the survey of the Salton Sea, are presented herein for the first time.

TECTONIC FRAMEWORK

Faults.—Even though individual faults of the San Andreas system cannot be delineated everywhere within the Gulf province, the continuity of earthquake epicenters along the axis of the Gulf leaves little doubt that it indeed represents the southeastward prolongation of the San Andreas fault zone. The narrowing and termination of the Gulf province at its northern end, on the other hand, are caused by truncation and conflict between northwest-trending faults of the San Andreas system and east-trending faults of the Transverse Range province. At San Gorgonio Pass these two systems come into conflict with one another, amid great structural complications (Allen, 1957), but southeast of this point, faults of the San Andreas system have remarkable linearity, parallelism, and apparent mechanical coherence. Considerable geologic data, as well as evidence from historic earthquakes and geodetic observations, indicate that the predominant displacements on northwest-trending faults of this region have been right-lateral strike slip. Individual faults of the San Andreas system will be discussed later in this report, where geophysical as well as geological evidence can be considered.

Rocks.—The northern end of the Gulf province is ringed by mountain ranges including the highest peaks of Southern California. West of the Salton trough, these mountains are largely underlain by massive plutonic rocks of the mid-Cretaceous batholith of Southern and Baja California; whereas those to the east comprise more diverse igneous, metamorphic, and volcanic types. As was emphasized by Hamilton (1961), there is no geologic or geochronologic evidence that the Gulf of California necessarily represents the eastern border of the batholith, which may simply be transected and possibly pulled apart by the San Andreas fault system in this region. Nevertheless, all the pre-Tertiary rocks that bound the Salton depression are crystalline types whose geophysical characteristics are in contrast to the Cenozoic sedimentary rocks that constitute the bulk of the material filling the trough. Cenozoic volcanic rocks occur sparsely around the edges of the trough as well as within the sedimentary section of the basin itself. Continued volcanic activity into Quaternary time is indicated by the well-preserved crater of Cerro Prieto, 30 km southeast of Mexicali, and by the very young Pinacate volcanic field north of Punta Peñasco, Sonora (Ives, 1956; Jahns, 1959). In addition, cores from steam wells drilled recently near the south end of the Salton Sea suggest that contemporaneou metamorphism of the Tertiary sedimentary rock is taking place here, presumably related to magmatic activity at depth (White and others, 1963) Abnormally high heat flow also characterizes th floor of the Gulf of California farther south (vo Herzen, 1963).

Detailed stratigraphy of the sedimentary section within the Salton trough is incompletel known, inasmuch as these rocks are only sparsel exposed, and records of the few deep wells withi the valley are not easily interpreted. Dibble (1954) has summarized the known stratigraphy. major marine incursion of lower Pliocene age fro the Gulf is represented by deposits of the Imperia Formation exceeding 3,000 ft in thickness. Th subsequent history of deposition has been charac terized by intermittent and interfingering deposit derived from local alluvial fans, lakes ancestral t the present Salton Sea, the delta of the Colorad River, and occasional marine incursions from th Gulf of California. Intermittent strike-slip faul ing within the basin may have strongly affecte original depositional environments, and has sub sequently displaced many formerly continuou units, perhaps by several tens of miles.

Seismicity.—In terms of minor and moderat sized earthquakes, the Salton trough has been th most seismically active part of California an adjacent Mexico within historic time, although n truly great earthquakes have been reported fro here (Fig. 2). Several of these shocks have cause considerable damage and loss of life, and th 1940 earthquake on the Imperial fault was ass ciated with well-documented ground displac ment for more than 60 km; the Internation Border was displaced a few meters by right-later strike slip at this time (Fig. 3). The 1934 eart quake in the delta region of Mexico was also prob ably associated with ground displacement (Fig. *see* also Kovach and others, 1962, p. 2848).

The seismicity map of the region portrays broad band of activity trending southeast into th Gulf of California, but if attention is restricted earthquakes of magnitude 6 and greater, one fin a remarkable alignment and spacing of eart quakes along the general zone of the San Jacin fault (Fig. 2). From northwest to southeast, the shocks include the 1918 San Jacinto earthquak

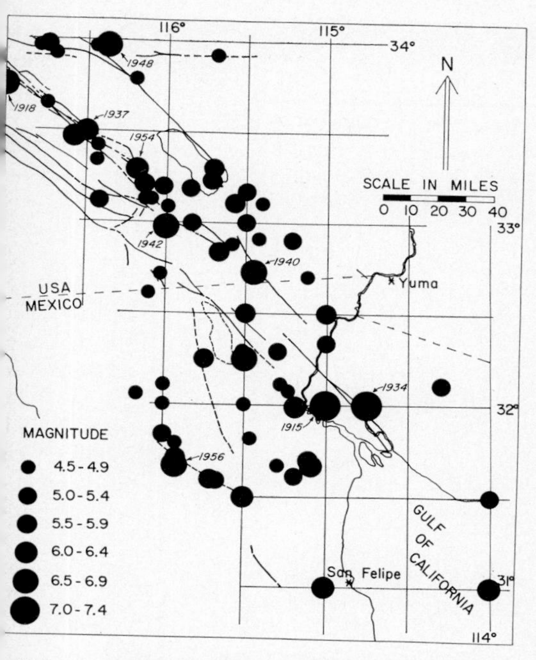

FIG. 2.—Seismicity map of Salton trough and adjacent areas, showing shocks of magnitude 4.5 and greater that occurred between 1904 and 1960. Listing prior to 1934 is very incomplete. Largest shocks, with dates shown, are mentioned in the text. Data from Gutenberg and Richter (1954) and local bulletins of the Pasadena Seismological Laboratory.

(M = 6.8), the 1937 Terwilliger Valley earthquake (M = 6.0), the 1954 Santa Rosa Mountains earthquake (M = 6.2), the 1942 Lower Borrego Valley earthquake (M = $6\frac{1}{2}$), the 1940 Imperial Valley earthquake (M = 7.1), and the 1915 and 1934 earthquakes in the delta region south of the border (M = 7.1; 7.1). Indeed the only large earthquakes of the region that did not occur along the San Jacinto fault zone are the 1948 Desert Hot Springs earthquake (M = 6.5) on the Mission Creek fault and a few very poorly located shocks in Baja California. Some of the earthquakes of the Laguna Salada area just south of the International Border may have occurred on the Elsinore fault. Farther south in Baja California, the 1956 San Miguel earthquake (M = 6.8) was clearly associated with faulting at some distance from the main San Andreas zone, and at a distinct angle to it. References to detailed studies of these various earthquakes are given by Richter (1958).

Geodetic surveys across the Imperial Valley segment of the Salton trough (Whitten, 1956, 1960) indicate that shear strain is continuing to build up in this region. If one compares the rate of strain accumulation with the known strain release through earthquakes, using assumptions similar to those of Benioff (1955), it appears that over a 30-year period roughly as much strain is released

FIG. 3.—Aerial view of orange grove displaced horizontally along Imperial fault during earthquake of May 1940. Photograph taken looking north from about over International Border between United States and Mexico.

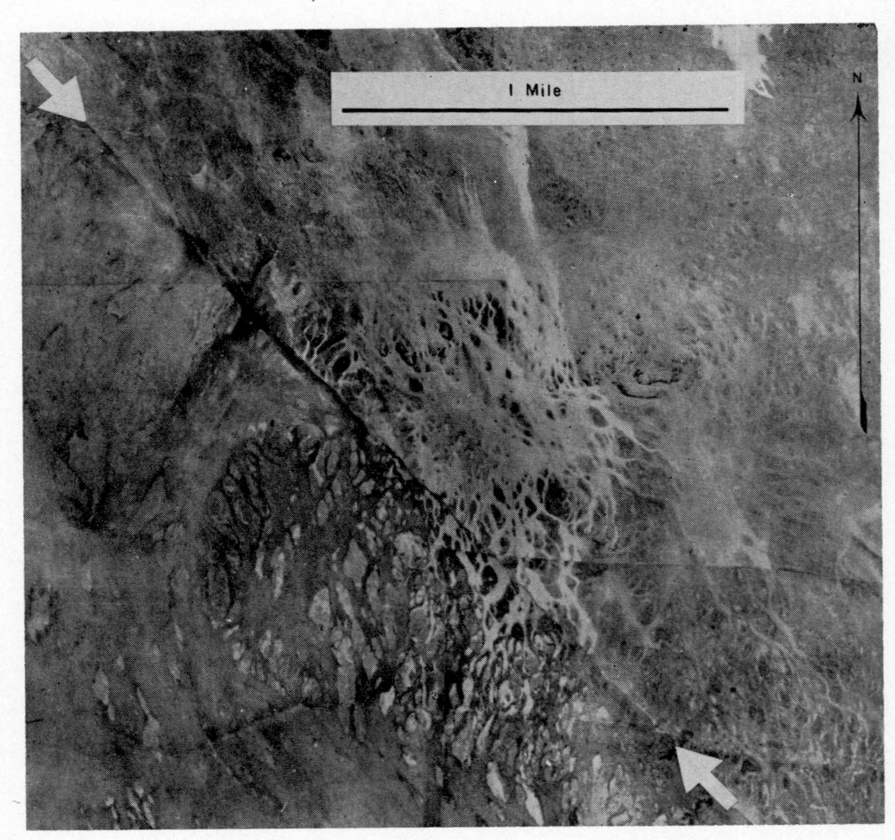

FIG. 4.—Vertical aerial view of San Jacinto? fault where it cuts across tidal flats near the head of the Gulf of California, near lat 31° 50′ N., long 114° 40′ W. This segment of the fault probably broke in the earthquake of Dec. 31, 1934; photograph taken in 1935.

as is accumulated. This is in sharp contrast to the segment of the San Andreas fault zone northwest of this region, where there has been remarkably little seismic activity in the same 30-year period despite the probable accumulation of shear strain across the fault at about the same rate. It appears, therefore, that the typical seismic "habit" of the Northern Gulf province at present is that of relatively frequent moderate-sized earthquakes, as opposed to infrequent great earthquakes along other segments of the San Andreas fault zone.

SEISMIC REFRACTION PROFILES

Ten refraction profiles have been shot within the Salton trough for the purpose of determining the nature of the Tertiary sedimentary section and the depth to the underlying crystalline basement rocks. Six of these profiles, between the International Border and the Salton Sea, were described by Kovach and others (1962); Biehler has subsequently added four more, three of which are around the borders of the Salton Sea, and one of which is north of Indio in the Coachella Valley (Fig. 5). Detailed results of these surveys will be published elsewhere, but the most significant of the new profiles is along an east-west line 2 km north of Westmorland, which was shot to a distance of almost 32 km and for the first time clearly establishes the depth to basement in the very axis of the Salton trough. All other profiles have been shot in desert areas outside the agricultural lands that occupy the floor of the Imperial Valley. Basement arrivals were not reversed along the Westmorland profile, but if basement depth i

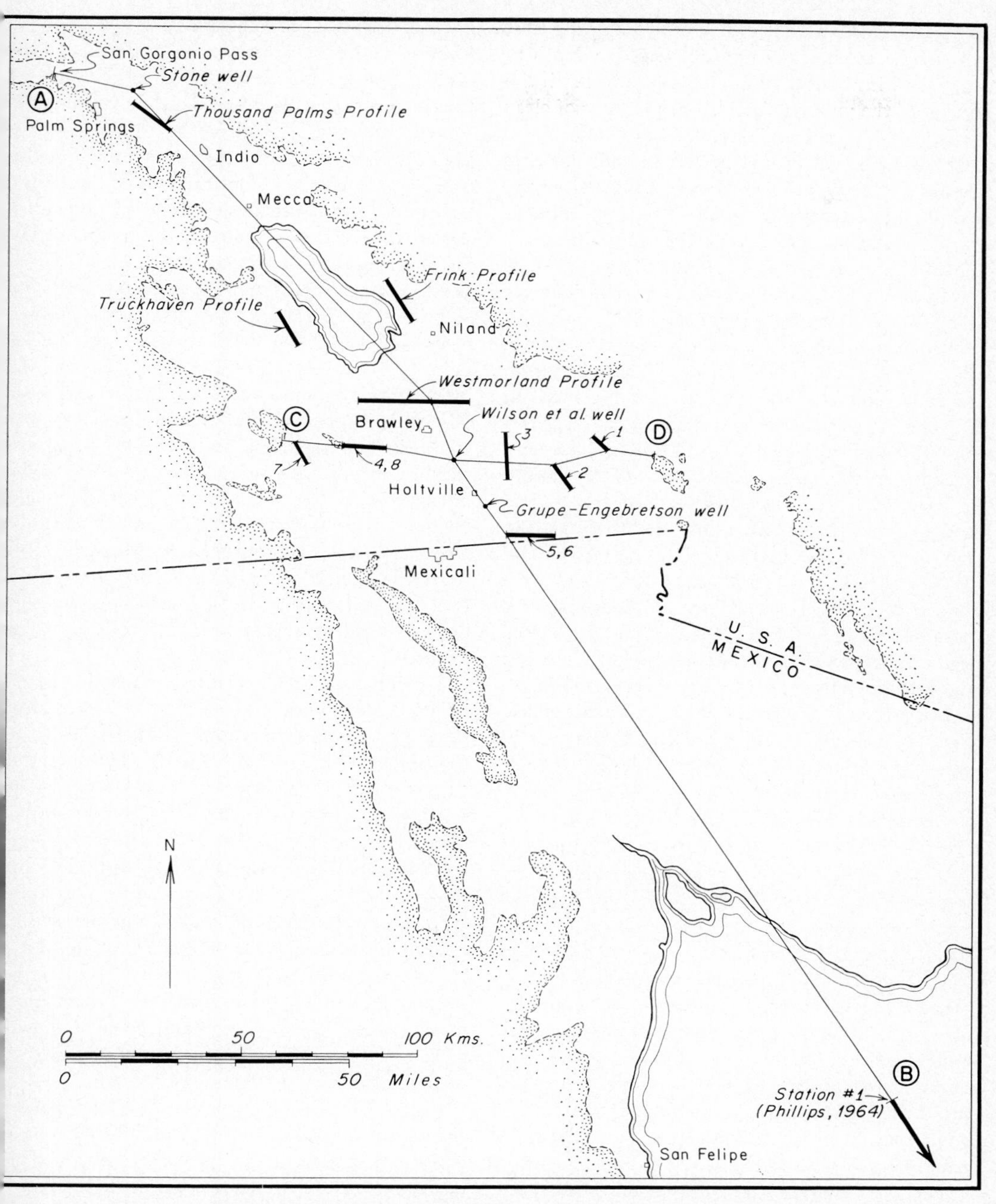

FIG. 5.—Index map of Salton trough showing locations of seismic refraction profiles and cross section lines –*B* (Fig. 6) and *C–D* (Fig. 7). Numbers refer to seismic profiles described by Kovach and others (1962). Reference Phillips, 1964, is to this volume. Stippling indicates generalized outline of pre-Tertiary crystalline rocks bordering he Salton trough.

projected eastward with the same shallow dip that characterizes all of the upper layers, the depth to basement is about 5.9 km (19,400 ft) beneath the center of the valley (Fig. 6). The presence of clear basement arrivals and the striking similarity of the shallower velocity structure to that of other Imperial Valley profiles suggest that contemporaneous metamorphism of the Tertiary sedimentary section, such as is reported from the steam wells near Niland (White and others, 1963), is localized in "hot spots" and is not pervasive over the floor of the entire valley.

Basement arrivals from the various profiles in this region show seismic velocities varying from 5.2 km/sec (17,100 ft/sec) at the head of the Gulf to 6.4 km/sec (21,000 ft/sec) beneath the Westmorland profile. Such wide variations in basement velocity are not unexpected in view of the variety of basement rock types exposed in the region, which range from low-rank metasedimentary schists to plutonic bodies including granites and gabbros. That the 4.7 km/sec (15,500 ft/sec) layer beneath the Imperial Valley cannot be considered basement is indicated by the fact that two deep wells have penetrated sedimentary rocks below the calculated upper contact of this layer (Fig. 6).

In contrast to the variations in basement velocities, the velocity structure of the Tertiary sedimentary section is so similar from profile to profile that one is tempted to assign stratigraphic names to the individual seismic layers. This has not been possible with the limited subsurface geological data available to date. For example, the Grupe-Engebretson well south of Holtville penetrated four seismic zones (Fig. 6) to a total depth of 3.76 km (12,300 ft) yet all of the rocks from this well were assigned by geologists to a single stratigraphic unit—the Plio-Pleistocene Borrego Formation. If the other formations that are known to underlie the Borrego Formation along the west side of the Imperial Valley are present at depth in the center of the valley, they have not to our knowledge been identified either in wells or in geophysical profiles.

The Westmorland seismic profile has been combined in Figure 6 with others located near the axis of the Salton trough to give a longitudinal cross section from the northern end of the trough at San Gorgonio Pass southeast 400 km to the head of the Gulf of California, where we tie to Phillips' (this volume) northernmost seismic profile. The most noteworthy feature of this section is the greater basement depth in the Imperial Valley than at the head of the Gulf, suggesting that the Salton trough represents a sedimentary basin that is distinct from the rest of the Gulf of California. From our limited data it is difficult to say where the deepest part of the basin may lie but if basement is projected southward from the Westmorland profile with the same dip that characterizes the shallower layers (Fig. 6), basement would lie at 6.23 km depth beneath profiles 5– (Fig. 5) and at 6.37 km (20,900 ft) beneath the broad gravity minimum 20 km farther southeast (Chart I, in pocket). For reasons discussed elsewhere in this report, it is hazardous to assume that gravity directly reflects basement depth, but in the absence of other information in this region we tentatively suggest that this gravity minimum located 35 km east-southeast of Mexicali represents the deepest part of the Salton trough and that the sedimentary section then becomes thinner as traced southeast toward the Gulf of California.

The Thousand Palms seismic refraction profile (Figs. 5, 6) shows basement at a considerably shallower depth than would be suggested by the regional gravity data or by the nearby Stone well. Inasmuch as this profile is located only 4 km southwest of and parallel to the Banning fault—a major branch of the San Andreas—we can only conclude that basement under this profile represents a local faulted block in a zone of complex structure; numerous anomalies on the seismic records from this profile substantiate the idea of structural complications in the basement. Further supporting evidence is given by the magnetic measurements of Soske (1935), which show a distinct magnetic maximum along the axis of the seismic profile.

Figure 7 is a seismic cross section transverse to the axis of the Salton trough near Brawley, based mainly on the refraction profiles of Kovach and others (1962). The basement configuration is undoubtedly more complicated than indicated inasmuch as the section crosses a number of important active faults; but the section illustrates well the effect observed in many parts of the va

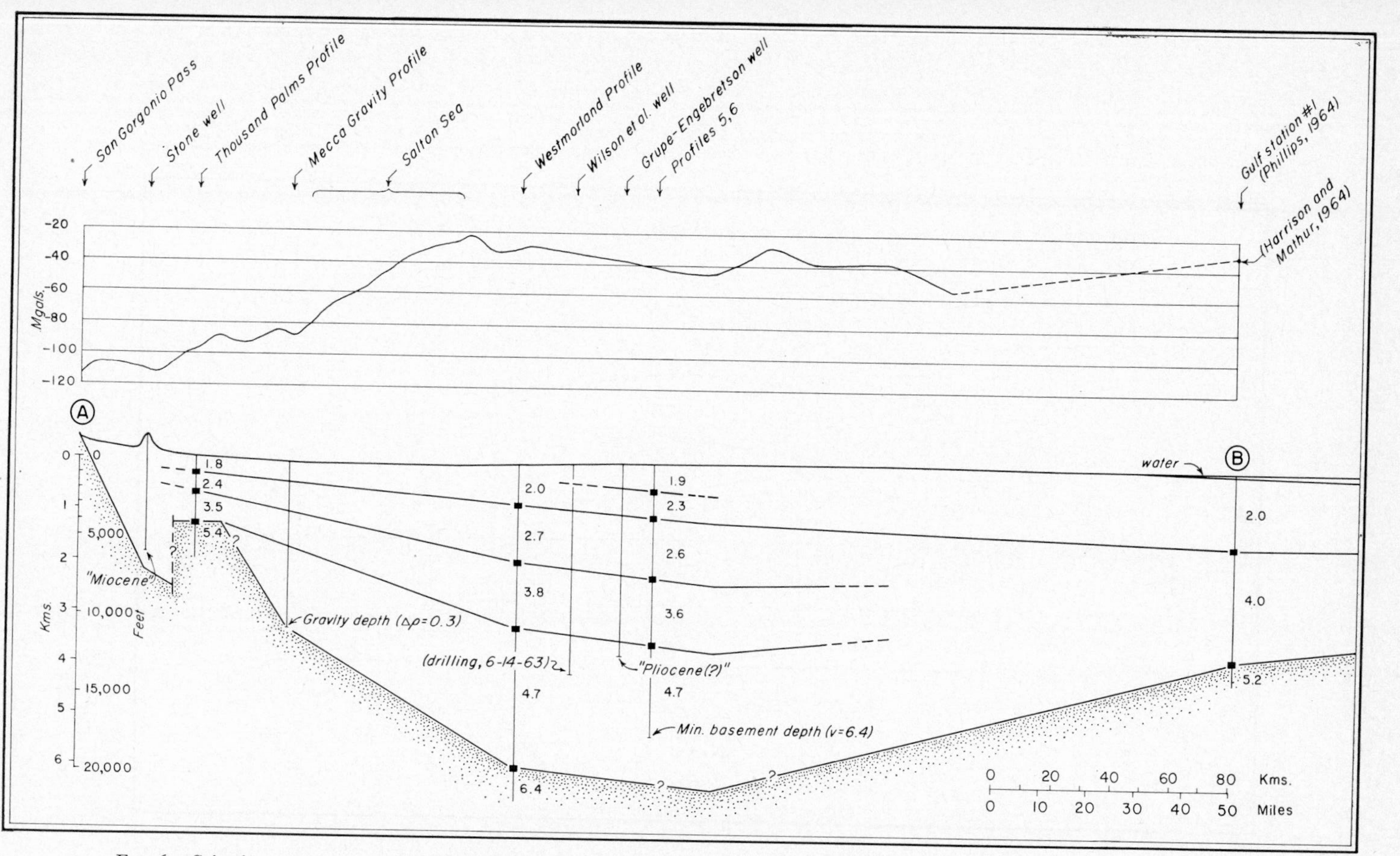

FIG. 6.—Seismic cross section and simple Bouguer gravity profile along line *A–B* of Figure 5. Numbers indicate velocities in km/sec. References to Phillips, 1964, and Harrison and Mathur, 1964, are to this volume.

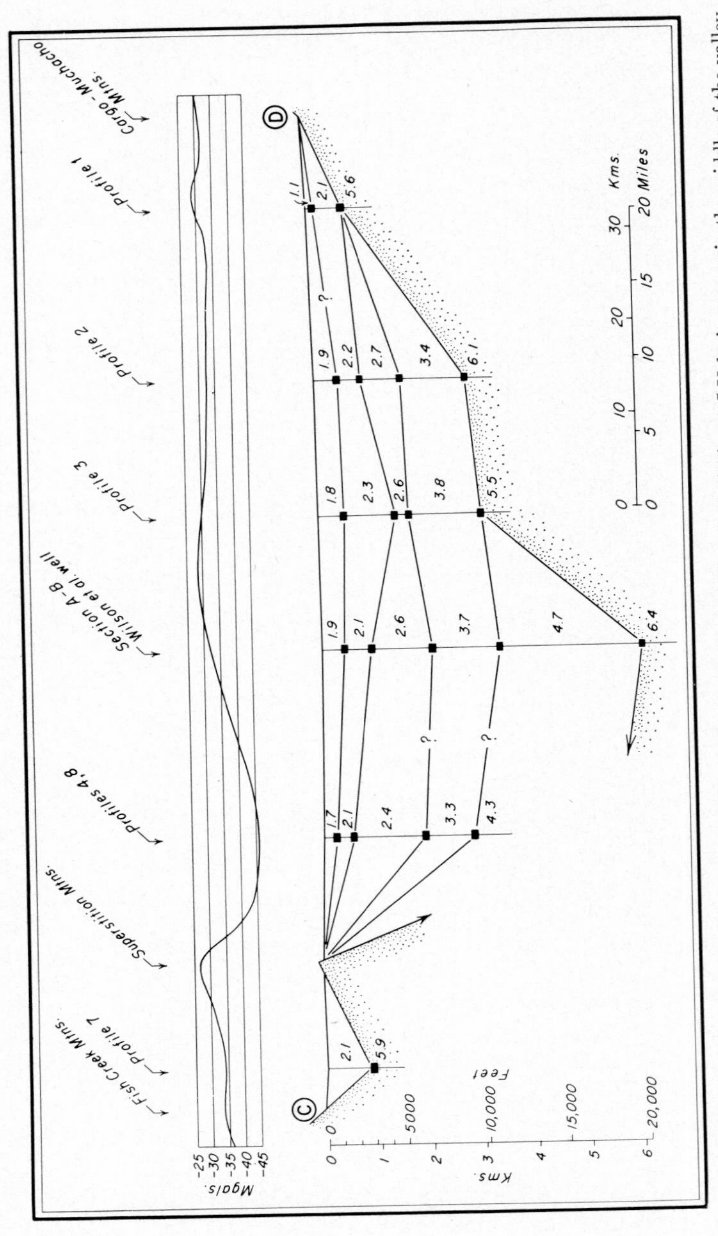

FIG. 7.—Seismic cross section and simple Bouguer gravity profile along line *C–D* of Figure 5. Velocity zones in the middle of the valley are extrapolated from section *A–B*, Figure 6. Note that ratio of horizontal to vertical scales is different on Figures 6 and 7.

ley that some of the seismic layers in the deepest part of the trough are not represented in the shallower areas toward the flanks. If these layers truly indicate stratigraphic units, this pinch-out effect has an important bearing on the sedimentary history of the basin.

GRAVITY OBSERVATIONS

About 3,000 gravity observations were made in the United States and Mexico using a Worden gravimeter (Chart I, in pocket). The observations are tied to a network of base stations in the Salton trough which has been ultimately tied to the University of Wisconsin geodetic base station No. WU4 in Pasadena, California (Behrendt and Woollard, 1961). Adjustment of the 1,250 gravity stations reported in an earlier paper (Kovach and others, 1962) to the University of Wisconsin base station in Pasadena required that about 1.5 mgal be added to the observed gravity values based on this network of gravimeter base stations. However, it should be emphasized that this base station adjustment does not change any of the conclusions reached in the earlier paper, which are all based on a discussion of *relative* Bouguer anomalies. The present map differs from the earlier maps of Kovach and others (1962) in that an elevation factor of 0.060 mgal/ft corresponding to a rock density of 2.67 g/cm^3, has been used in order to facilitate comparison with maps of other workers. The earlier map was reduced using a factor of $0.069 \times 1{,}000 + 0.060(h - 1{,}000)$, where h is the station elevation in feet. 0.069 mgal/ft corresponds to a rock density of 2.00 g/cm^3. This change has little effect except for the few stations on the flanks of the Peninsular Ranges west of the Imperial Valley.

The gravity observations in the Salton Sea were made with a LaCoste-Romberg underwater gravimeter, and the gravity stations were located using Tellurometers and transits. The underwater observations are considered accurate to 0.3 mgal.

Station elevations for the land stations in the United States were obtained from survey bench marks, level survey lines, and altimeter readings. In Mexico most of the station elevations were determined by altimeter differences from a network of bench marks of the International Boundary and Water Commission. Considering all the elevation and location factors, the precision of the Bouguer gravity anomalies in the United States is estimated to be 0.3 mgal; in Mexico the precision is estimated to be 1 mgal, although some stations could be in error by more than 1 mgal. The precision of the Mexican stations is hindered by the inadequate maps available.

Terrain corrections have not been made for the gravity stations. Failure to make terrain corrections does not have a significant effect on the majority of the stations, except in the San Gorgonio Pass area and along the extreme edges of the Salton trough. The Bouguer gravity values for these stations would be raised relative to stations in the broad alluviated areas. The average terrain effect in the San Gorgonio Pass area is about 4–6 mgal. Gravity values were reduced to the complete Bouguer anomaly with respect to the International ellipsoid.

GRAVITY INTERPRETATION

Regional anomaly and crustal thickness.—The northwest trend of structural elements of the Salton trough is reflected by the over-all northwest trend of the isogal contours (Chart I, in pocket). Contours in the mountainous area northeast of the Coachella Valley have a general east trend that is in agreement with the major structural features of this area. Thus, in a gross way, the gravity anomalies outline the general tectonic framework that is apparent from the major surface features of the region.

The Bouguer anomalies range from a low of −121 mgal just west of Desert Hot Springs, California, to a high of −10 mgal southeast of Yuma, Arizona. This gravity difference of 110 mgal over a distance of 240 km is an indication of the regional gradient of the area which is approximately parallel to the axis of the Salton trough. The northwest regional gradient is, however, not uniform throughout the length of the trough. From San Gorgonio Pass southeast to about the middle of the Salton Sea, the regional gradient is approximately 0.6 mgal/km; from this area southeast to the International Border the regional gradient is relatively flat—about 0.2 mgal/km. This gradient suggests a very gradual thickening of the crust from the International Border to the Salton Sea and then a more rapid thickening northwest toward San Gorgonio Pass and the northern end of the Salton trough. However, this is based on regional gravity values on pre-Tertiary crystalline rocks and may reflect the crustal thickness under the mountains along the flanks of the trough and not under the Salton trough itself.

Assuming a crust-mantle density contrast of 0.3 g/cm^3, a crustal thickening of about 8 km is needed to explain a regional anomaly of 100 mgal. If a density contrast of 0.4 g/cm^3 is assumed, then a thickening of only 6 km is necessary. From Woollard's (1959) empirical curve relating Bouguer anomaly to crustal thickness, a -110 mgal anomaly indicates a crustal thickness of about 40 km, and a -10 mgal anomaly a thickness of 32 km; this is consistent with the above simple computation.

Unfortunately, the sparsity of gravity data and the large distances involved do not justify a detailed extrapolation of our data to the area studied by Harrison and Mathur (this volume) at the head of the Gulf of California. However, the average Bouguer gravity at the head of the Gulf is about 10 mgal higher than at the International Border, which is in agreement with the concept of a continental crust thinning toward the southeast. Seismic refraction measurements (Phillips, this volume) verify that a thin crust is present beneath the Gulf south of lat 27° 30′ N., and that the crust becomes progressively thicker and more continental toward the northern end of the Gulf.

Thickness of sediments.—The problem of estimating thickness of sedimentary fill in the Salton trough from gravity data alone is a hazardous one, as has been emphasized by Kovach and others (1962). Peculiar problems of this region include (1) known density complications, such as reversals with depth, in the sedimentary section; (2) abrupt facies changes that occur throughout the basin; (3) a wide variety of crystalline rock types constituting the regional basement, ranging from granite to gabbro to low-rank metasedimentary schists, many of which are in complex fault relationship to one another; (4) volcanic rocks that are known to occur locally within the section; (5) recently documented contemporaneous metamorphism of parts of the Tertiary section, with markedly increased densities relative to unmetamorphosed parts of the section; and (6) the possibility of local isostatic compensation beneath the trough.

In some areas the gravity contours appear directly to reflect the basement configuration, but marked failure to do so in other areas causes hesitancy in drawing general conclusions from the gravity map. For example, gravity values across the eastern half of the Imperial Valley near Holtville (Fig. 7) are nearly constant and have little apparent relation to basement depths that are here well documented from seismic data. Undoubtedly one contributing factor is the presence of deep high-velocity zones in the sedimentary section that are restricted to the central parts of the basin; sedimentary rocks with seismic velocities of 4.7 km/sec (15,400 ft/sec) may well have densities above 2.6 g/cm^3 (Woollard, 1962), which is as high a density as that of some of the basement rocks of the region. Thus in computing a depth to basement on the basis of a single density contrast, we are in some areas undoubtedly "seeing" horizons that are within the sedimentary section rather than the true crystalline basement.

The problem of increased density associated with contemporaneous metamorphism of the Tertiary section near Obsidian Buttes is discussed elsewhere in this report, but it is obvious that the possibility of similar effects elsewhere in the Salton trough adds to both the interest and the hazards in gravity interpretation. In the absence of heat-flow measurements, we cannot say whether or not some of the other gravity maxima might be related to similar magmatic effects, but it is clear that generalized conclusions as to depth to basement cannot be drawn until more is known of this problem.

Banning-Mission Creek fault and Coachella Valley area.—The Banning-Mission Creek fault is the most northeasterly representative of the San Andreas system in the Gulf province and indeed has often been called *the* San Andreas fault in this region. The fault is particularly well exposed near Indio (Fig. 8), but as traced southeast the surficial evidence for faulting dies out abruptly near Pope (Chart I, in pocket). This is disturbing because the fault near Indio possesses many features characteristic of the fault in its "type area" in central

FIG. 8.—Aerial view of Banning-Mission Creek fault 5 km northeast of Indio, in the area of the greatest magnetic and gravity anomalies across the fault. Photograph taken prior to excavation of the Coachella Canal in this area.

California—the trace is exceptionally linear; scarps are continuous and well developed; and right-lateral stream offsets are particularly evident in the Indio Hills (Popenoe, 1959). Furthermore, very large lateral displacement along this fault zone has been suggested by Crowell (1962) on the basis of similar geologic terranes north of the fault in the Salton Sea area and south of the fault in the central Transverse Ranges; this appears to be incompatible with the fault terminating abruptly at the Salton Sea. If the fault is projected southeast in line with its very linear trace where well exposed, it would miss the northern end of the Gulf of California entirely and extend into Sonora. However, there is no presently known geologic or seismic evidence for continuing this fault into Sonora. Much of this region, however, is covered by wind-blown sand, and portions south of the International Border have not been mapped geologically even in reconnaissance. Toward the northwest, the two branches of the Banning-Mission Creek fault diverge and veer westward into the complex region of San Gorgonio Pass, becoming north-dipping thrusts (Allen, 1957).

A steep gravity gradient of about 5 mgal/km characterizes the Banning-Mission Creek fault from the point where the two faults coalesce southeast to the Salton Sea. This steep gradient indicates a near-surface anomalous mass probably caused by higher density basement rocks northeast of the fault being juxtaposed against thick sedimentary rocks of the Coachella Valley across the fault to the southwest. Preliminary calculations based on simple Bouguer anomalies and assuming a density contrast of 0.3 g/cm^3 indicate a depth of fill of 3.2 km (10,500 ft) at Mecca; a density contrast of 0.2 g/cm^3 would nearly double this depth. At the southern end of the exposed trace of the fault near Pope the gravity gradient dies out, and the contours swing sharply southwestward. This may be due in part to the influence of the large gravity maximum over the Obsidian Buttes at the south end of the Salton Sea. Even southeast of the Obsidian Buttes, however, there is no indication of a steep gravity gradient along the projected trace of the fault similar to the gradient farther north.

It is significant that in the 14 magnetic profiles across the fault in this region that were described by Soske (1935), the greatest magnetic anomalies occur across the fault near Mecca—in the same area as the most pronounced gravity anomalies. Furthermore, the magnetic anomalies gradually dissipate southeastward, and Soske's long profile across the Imperial Valley south of the Obsidian Buttes shows no marked magnetic anomaly across the projected trace of the Banning-Mission Creek fault in this area.

A gravity gradient similar to that along the Banning-Mission Creek fault exists on the opposite side of the Coachella Valley but is neither as steep nor as continuous. This probably indicates a fault system along the front of the Santa Rosa Mountains that is buried beneath the alluvium at shallow depth. Discontinuities in the trend of the gradient are possibly caused by cross faults that strike northeast, similar to the fault exposed northwest of Truckhaven.

The large gravity maximum north of Truckhaven is of the same magnitude as the maximum on the opposite side of the Salton Sea, and a similar maximum is present just northeast of Borrego Springs. These closures are all located over localized exposures of metamorphic rock and may reflect a higher density as compared to the surrounding granite intrusive rocks.

Obsidian Buttes area.—A large gravity maximum of 15–20 mgal is present over the Obsidian Buttes (Salton volcanic domes) at the southern end of the Salton Sea. Although the surface expression of volcanic activity appears to be along a line trending northeast, the gravity anomaly indicates an approximately circular mass distribution. The center of the anomaly is located about 2 km east of Red Island, which is near the middle of the linear distribution of the four buttes. Undoubtedly, part of this gravity maximum is due to volcanic rocks which have a higher density than that of the surrounding sediments. However, a larger contributing factor to the mass anomaly may be the increased density of sediments that are undergoing contemporaneous metamorphism in this area (White and others, 1963). The density of these metamorphosed sediments is approximately 0.3 to 0.4 g/cm^3 greater than that of the equivalent unaltered rock. Assuming a density contrast of this magnitude, a considerably larger anomalous mass is necessary to explain the gravity maximum than is indicated by the surface exposure of the domes; such an explanation is in agreement with the magnetic observations of Kelley and Soske (1936). The broadness of the anomaly indicates that the center of the mass may be located at considerable depth, possibly as deep as 5 or 6 km with an equal lateral subsurface extent. Alternatively, this broadness may be the result of a horizontal decrease in the density of the altered sediments outward from the center of metamorphism. More detailed geophysical studies of this area are currently underway and will be published elsewhere.

San Jacinto fault.—The San Jacinto fault zone is probably the straightest and most throughgoing member of the San Andreas system in southern California, although even it cannot be followed continuously into the Gulf of California. Conspicuous features of recent displacement mark the trace of the fault southeast from where it diverges from the main San Andreas, across the high Peninsular Ranges, and into the Borrego-Clark Valley area. Here the fault seems to fray out into several branches, all of which lose surface expression as traced toward the International Border. Southeast from Cerro Prieto, 30 km south of the Border, a distinct surface break can be followed continuously for the remaining 100 km to the Gulf of California (Fig. 4; Kovach and others, 1962). This segment has tentatively been called the San Jacinto fault on the basis of its close alignment to the trend of the fault where well exposed in the Peninsular Ranges to the northwest and because of the continuity of earthquake epicenters along the zone. If continuous, however, the fault must be characterized by a wide zone of fractures, and the faults of the Superstition Mountains and possibly even the Imperial fault must be considered members of the San Jacinto zone. It is interesting to note that if the San Jacinto fault is projected into the Gulf of California along the line of very linear scarps in the delta region, it does not parallel the axis of the Gulf, but instead cuts across the northeast corner of the Gulf and into Sonora.

In the high Peninsular Ranges the San Jacinto fault is characterized by a series of small gravity lows along the length of the zone. There is no pronounced gradient such as is seen across the Banning-Mission Creek fault. In this area the entire fault zone is located in pre-Tertiary crystalline rocks, and as a result the absence of large density contrasts is not surprising. The presence of gravity lows may indicate a slightly lowered density of the crushed rocks within the fault zone.

Southward in the Borrego Valley area a steep gravity gradient is present between the minimum of Borrego Valley and the maximum over the metasedimentary rocks of Coyote Mountain, 10 km northeast of Borrego Springs. From here south to the International Border the fault zone is characterized by numerous gravity maxima and minima, including the minimum in Lower Borrego Valley, the maximum over the Superstition Mountains, the minimum west of El Centro, and the maximum near Mexicali. These highs and lows are evidently indicative of small uplifted and downdropped blocks, such as are typical of the San Andreas fault zone where better exposed elsewhere in California. A relatively steep gravity gradient is seen along the projection of the San Jacinto fault in Mexico between Cerro Prieto and Mexicali, and a buried 2 km scarp along the fault is indicated by gravity data near Victoria (Kovach and others, 1962, Fig. 15).

Elsinore-Laguna Salada fault.—Unlike the Banning-Mission Creek and San Jacinto faults, the Elsinore fault does not coalesce with the San Andreas fault as traced toward the northwest. Its assignment to the San Andreas system is instead based primarily on its being one of the *en echelon* fractures of the system farther south in the Gulf of California province. The Elsinore fault is marked by evidence of recent displacements throughout most of its trace through the batholithic rocks of the Peninsular Ranges (Jahns, 1954; Dibblee, 1954), and it lines up very closely with the Laguna Salada fault of Baja California—a correlation that is supported by the gravity data. The Laguna Salada fault is best exposed in the Sierra de los Cucapas, but this range is typical of other structural features of the Gulf province in being oriented more northerly than the obvious throughgoing faults of the area—that is, northwest-trending fractures such as the Laguna Salada and Cucapa faults (Fig. 9) appear to cut across the trend of the range rather than completely delineating its borders; other less obvious fractures of different orientation must be present beneath the bordering alluvium.

The steep gravity gradient along the southwest flank of the Sierra de los Cucapas is one of the most noteworthy features of the gravity map. Although the detailed configuration of contours is obviously not well defined by the available stations, it is clear that a very steep gradient must exist and that its average trend is more northerly than that of individual breaks such as the Laguna Salada fault. The gradient suggests a depth to basement of about 5.8 km (19,000 ft) in Laguna Salada (Kovach and others, 1962, p. 2870), although any estimate is difficult without a better knowledge of gravity values west of Laguna Salada toward the Sierra Juárez.

East-trending faults of the Little San Bernardino Mountains.—Three east-trending lineaments dominate the structure of the mountainous country northeast of the Banning-Mission Creek fault. The northern two, through Twentynine Palms and through the Pinto Basin, are distinct fault zones marked by Recent scarps and crushed zones; the southern lineament, between Indio and Desert Center, is inferred to be fault controlled because of the gross physiography. These three zones are particularly interesting because they appear to indicate continuity of east-trending structures of the Transverse Range province into this region, possibly offset somewhat to the south by the San Andreas fault. The Transverse Ranges, in turn, probably represent the continental prolongation of the offshore Murray fracture zone, so that very major and deep-seated tectonic features may be represented by these lineaments. They certainly extend east beyond the area of Chart I, but their total extent is unknown.

The fault zone through the Pinto Basin, called the Eagle Mountain lineament by Hill (1928) and

FIG. 9.—Aerial view southeast along Cucapa fault, 25 km south of Mexicali, Baja California. Trench is cause primarily by erosion of crushed rock within the fault zone, rather than by Recent fault displacements.

apparently including the Blue Cut fault of Pruss and others (1959), has a particularly marked gravity effect. The three traverses that cross the fault all show a distinct minimum at the fault, although additional work will be necessary to delineate the anomaly completely, particularly as traced west toward Desert Hot Springs. A less pronounced gravity low occurs along the lineament between Indio and Desert Center, but data are insufficient to make any comment on possible anomalies along the northernmost lineament. Certainly the over-all east trend of contours in the northeast segment of the gravity map is in contrast to the northwest trend that characterizes the Salton trough, and it tends to confirm the geological observation that a grossly different tectoni pattern—perhaps related to the Transvers Ranges—typifies this northeastern region.

REGIONAL COMPARISONS AND PROBLEMS

It is tempting to compare the Salton troug with other regions in the world of possible simila tectonic setting. However, the Gulf of Californi province, including the Salton trough, appears t be unique in that it combines some of the attr butes of rift valleys with those of major strike-sli fault systems, and in this respect is not directl comparable to features such as either the Eas African rift valleys or the northern part of the Sa Andreas fault zone. Perhaps the most intriguin comparison is with the Dead Sea rift of the Near East, which has many striking analogies to the Salton trough.

(1) Both are sediment-filled troughs, in part below sea level, characterized by great length and linearity and by steep fault-controlled valley walls.

(2) Although current seismicity is considerably lower in the Dead Sea rift than in the Salton trough, the presence of numerous Recent scarps and closed depressions in both these regions testifies to vigorous continuing tectonic activity.

(3) Both troughs have been ascribed to rifting and extension, but evidence of a significant strike-slip component has been recognized in recent years in both areas, with possible total displacements of at least 260 km (right-lateral) for the Salton trough (Crowell, 1962) and 107 km (left-lateral) for the Dead Sea rift (Quennell, 1959).

(4) As traced southward toward the open ocean, both rift zones become progressively wider, suggesting rotation of adjacent continental blocks (Hamilton, 1961; Quennell, 1959). Furthermore, crustal structure becomes progressively more oceanic in character toward the south (Drake and others, 1959; Nafe and others, 1959; Phillips, this volume).

(5) Relative Bouguer gravity minima characterize both rift zones, with negative anomalies of 50–100 mgal reported from the Gulf of 'Aqaba and Lebanese segments of the Dead Sea rift (de Bruyn, 1955; Girdler, 1958), and similar values from parts of the Salton trough. On the other hand, southward from each of these areas, in the wider and more oceanic parts of the rift structures —the Red Sea and the Gulf of California—the Bouguer anomalies change from negative to positive, with definite relative gravity maxima along the axes of the rifts (Girdler, 1958; Harrison and Mathur, this volume).

(6) Although striking magnetic anomalies are present over the median rift valley of the Red Sea, these anomalies die out northward and do not characterize either the Gulf of Suez or the Gulf of Aqaba (Drake and others, 1959; Girdler, 1962). Likewise, Soske's (1935) 50-mile profile across the Imperial Valley of the Salton trough shows no linear magnetic anomalies that are at all comparable to those of the Red Sea or some of the mid-ocean ridges. Preliminary analysis by Hilde (this volume) of magnetic measurements by R. Warren in the Gulf of California south of Guaymas indicates sharp magnetic anomalies associated with submarine scarps and basins in this area.

Despite the many similarities, there remain some significant contrasts between the Salton trough and the Dead Sea rift that imply fundamental tectonic differences. The Salton trough is collinear with the Gulf of California and appears to share its structural pattern in every way, whereas the Dead Sea rift is at a marked angle to the Red Sea. Left-lateral displacement along the Dead Sea rift is thus mechanically compatible with almost pure extension across the Red Sea, as has been pointed out by a number of workers. Such is not the case in the Gulf of California, where right-lateral displacement across the Salton trough suggests that the same sense of displacement characterizes the entire Gulf province.

One of the most intriguing aspects of the structure of the Gulf of California is the *en echelon* fault pattern, in that major faults of the trough trend more westerly than the axis and borders of the trough itself. In the Salton trough, these breaks are typified by the Banning-Mission Creek, San Jacinto, and Elsinore faults, and the submarine topography of the floor of the Gulf (Rusnak and others, this volume) leaves little doubt that the same pattern characterizes most of the rest of the Gulf province as well. At least at the northern end of the province, these *en echelon* faults clearly cut across the adjacent mountain ranges and are by no means limited to the floor of the trough itself.

Subsidiary *en echelon* breaks associated with great strike-slip faults are not in themselves unusual, and indeed are reported from the region of the Dead Sea rift (Vroman, 1961, p. 329). Those of the Gulf of California, however, can hardly be considered "subsidiary," inasmuch as there is no one throughgoing master fracture, at least at the surface. Nor has such a pronounced *en echelon* pattern been recognized in any of the other major circum-Pacific strike-slip fault zones that are otherwise very similar to the San Andreas (Allen, 1962). But the most puzzling aspect of the faults of the Gulf of California is that the *en echelon* pattern is in the wrong orientation for right-lateral displacements across the zone and would instead suggest left-lateral movements. That is, a regional stress pattern oriented so as to produce right-lateral displacement across the Gulf of California would seemingly lead to *en echelon* fractures trending more northerly than the Gulf axis (*see* Hills, 1953, p. 132–133) if these *en echelon* fractures are at all similar in origin to those that have consistently been observed in glaciers, ore deposits, dike swarms, earthquake fractures, and numerous model studies. Even though one might argue that the sense of displacement across most of the Gulf of California has not been documented and could indeed be left-lateral, this cannot be claimed for the *en echelon* faults of the Salton trough, which are not only clearly right-lateral, but have apparently had a long history of such displacement. Furthermore, the relative motion between opposite walls of the Salton trough is likewise right-lateral, as demonstrated by geodetic observations (Whitten, 1956, 1960), which is important because one might otherwise argue that right-lateral displacement on *en echelon* faults within the trough is the result of rotation of these faults in response to left-lateral displacement across the zone as a whole.

Perhaps the answer to the anomalous *en echelon* pattern is that present displacements are associated with faults that were initially formed under a very different stress system, or that possibly different members of the system have originated sequentially at different times. On the other hand, there is no known geologic evidence for either of these hypotheses, and it is significant that all of the faults are apparently active at the present time.

An important difference between the San Andreas fault zone in the Gulf of California and in its "type area" in central California is the abundant evidence for extension perpendicular to the fault zone in the Gulf, possibly associated with the prolongation of the East Pacific Rise into this region (Menard, 1960). Supporting evidence of extension is given by Quaternary volcanism, which is absent along the San Andreas zone north of the Salton trough but is relatively abundant within the trough and farther south. Other geologic contrasts have been cited by Hamilton (1961), who pointed out that the Transverse Ranges mark the dividing line between these two structural realms of the San Andreas fault. It seems reasonable that the extensional history of the Gulf has had a direct bearing on the development of the unique *en echelon* pattern, but no known mechanical model combining extension with right-lateral displacement satisfactorily explains the existing pattern. Shepard (1950, p. 17–19) pointed out that the deep rhomb-shaped basins of the Gulf may have resulted from tensional forces set up between adjacent parallel strike-slip faults, and this explanation may well apply to the dropped blocks of the Salton trough as well. The origin of the major *en echelon* faults themselves, however, remains an enigma.

REFERENCES

Allen, C.R., 1957, San Andreas fault zone in San Gorgonio Pass, Southern California: Geol. Soc. America Bull., v. 68, no. 3, p. 315–350.

——— 1962, Circum-Pacific faulting in the Philippines-Taiwan region: Jour. Geophys. Research, v. 67, p. 4795–4812.

Behrendt, J.C., and Woollard, G.P., 1961, An evaluation of the gravity control network in North America: Geophysics, v. 26, p. 57–76.

Benioff, H., 1955, Mechanism and strain characteristics of the White Wolf fault as indicated by the aftershock sequence: Calif. Dept. Nat. Res., Div. Mines Bull. 171, p. 199–202.

Crowell, J.C., 1962, Displacement along the San Andreas fault, California: Geol. Soc. America Spec. Paper 71.

de Bruyn, J.W., 1955, Isogam maps of Europe and North Africa: Geophys. Prospecting, v. 3, p. 1–1[illegible]

Dibblee, T.W., 1954, Geology of the Imperial Valley region, California, *in* Geology of Southern California: Calif. Dept. Nat. Res., Div. Mines Bull. 170, p. 21–28.

Drake, C.L., Girdler, R.W., and Landisman, M., 195[illegible] Geophysical measurements in the Red Sea [abs.] Internat. Oceanogr. Cong. Preprints, p. 21.

Girdler, R.W., 1958, The relationship of the Red Sea to the east African rift system: Geol. Soc. London Quart. Jour., v. 114, p. 79–105.

——— 1962, Initiation of continental drift: Nature, v. 194, no. 4828, p. 521–524.

Gutenberg, B., and Richter, C.F., 1954, Seismicity of the earth: Princeton Univ. Press, Princeton, N.J., 2d ed.

Hamilton, W., 1961, Origin of the Gulf of California: Geol. Soc. America Bull., v. 72, p. 1307–1318.

Hill, R.T., 1928, Southern California geology and Los Angeles earthquakes: Southern Calif. Acad. Sc[illegible] L.A.

Hills, E.S., 1953, Outlines of structural geology: John Wiley & Sons, New York, 3d ed.

Ives, R.L., 1956, Age of Cerro Colorado crater, Pinacate, Sonora, Mexico: Am. Geophys. Union Trans., v. 37, p. 221–223.

Jahns, R.H., 1954, Geology of the Peninsular province, Southern and Baja California, *in* Geology of Sout[illegible] ern California: Calif. Dept. Nat. Res., Div. Mines Bull. 170, p. 29–52.

——— 1959, Collapse depressions of the Pinacate volcanic field, Sonora, Mexico, *in* Ariz. Geol. Soc. Guidebook 2: Ariz. Geol. Soc. Digest, 2d Ann., p. 165–183.

Kelley, V.C., and Soske, J.L., 1936, Origin of the Salton volcanic domes, Salton Sea, California: Jour. Geology, v. 44, p. 496–509.

Kovach, R.L., Allen, C.R., and Press, F., 1962, Geophysical investigations in the Colorado Delta region: Jour. Geophys. Research, v. 67, p. 2845–2871.

——— and Monges Caldera, J., 1961, Medidas de gravedad en la parte norte de Baja California, Mexico: An. Inst. Geofísica, Univ. Nac. Mexico, v. 7, p. 9–14.

Menard, H.W., 1960, The East Pacific Rise: Science, v. 132, p. 1737–1746.

Nafe, J.E., Hennion, J.F., and Peter, G., 1959, Geophysical measurements in the Gulf of Aden [abs.]: Internat. Oceanogr. Cong. Preprints, p. 42–43.

Popenoe, F.W., 1959, Geology of the southeastern portion of the Indio Hills, Riverside County, California: unpub. M.S. thesis, Univ. Calif., L.A.

Pruss, D.E., Olcott, G.W., and Oesterling, W.A., 1959, Areal geology of a portion of the Little San Bernardino Mountains, Riverside and San Bernardino Counties, California [abs.]: Geol. Soc. America Bull., v. 70, no. 12, p. 1741.

Quennell, A.M., 1959, Tectonics of the Dead Sea rift: Internat. Geol. Cong., 20th, Mexico, D.F., Asoc. de Serv. Africanos, Actas y Tr., p. 385–403.

Richter, C.F., 1958, Elementary seismology: Freeman, San Francisco, Calif.

Shepard, F.P., 1950, Submarine topography of the Gulf of California, pt. 3 *of* The 1940 E.W. Scripps cruise to the Gulf of California: Geol. Soc. America Mem. 43.

Soske, J.L., 1935, Theory of magnetic methods of applied geophysics with an application to the San Andreas fault: unpub. Ph.D. thesis, Calif. Inst. Technology.

von Herzen, R.P., 1963, Geothermal heat flow in the Gulfs of California and Aden, Science, v. 140, p. 1207–1208.

Vroman, A.J., 1961, On the Red Sea rift problem: Israel Resch. Council Bull., sec. G, v. 10G, p. 321–338.

White, D.E., Anderson, E.T., and Grubbs, D.K., 1963, Geothermal brine well—mile-deep drill hole may tap ore-bearing magmatic water and rocks undergoing metamorphism: Science, v. 139, p. 919–922.

Whitten, C.A., 1956, Crustal movement in California and Nevada: Am. Geophys. Union Trans., v. 37, p. 393–398.

——— 1960, Horizontal movement in the earth's crust: Jour. Geophys. Research, v. 65, p. 2839–2844.

Woollard, G.P., 1959, Crustal structure from gravity and seismic measurements: Jour. Geophys. Research, v. 64, p. 1521–1544.

——— 1962, The relation of gravity anomalies to surface elevation, crustal structure, and geology: Geophys. and Polar Resch. Center, Univ. Wisconsin, Resch. Rept. 62–9.

STRUCTURAL HISTORY AND EVOLUTION OF GULF OF CALIFORNIA[1]

GENE A. RUSNAK[2] AND ROBERT L. FISHER[3]
Miami, Florida and La Jolla, California

ABSTRACT

The geology of the Gulf of California region is discussed as it pertains to developing a hypothetical structural model presented to describe Gulf evolution. The Gulf of California supposedly evolved as fractured plates of crustal material moved northwestward and Pacific-ward by gravitational sliding, on extremely gentle slopes, from the regions of western Mexico uplifted by batholithic intrusions. The source of the uplift and westward tilting, and perhaps the formation of the intrusions, is ascribed to the development of the East Pacific Rise. This rise is the present expression of a subcrustal welt that reaches the North American continent near the south end of the Gulf of California, as demonstrated by the work of Menard and others.

INTRODUCTION

Considerable geological reconnaissance work has been done in the area surrounding the Gulf of California, but detailed studies have yet to be made. Mapping on a quadrangle scale is certainly desirable but this has been done only in a very few areas; even there, except for special studies it has been mostly of a more detailed reconnaissance nature. Allison (this volume) presents a summary and synthesis of most of what has been learned about the geology of the Peninsula of Baja California. Together with the studies of Beal (1948), Anderson (1950), and R.E. King (1939), this provides a comprehensive general picture of the Peninsula and the mainland (see also Mina U., 1957). The present paper is largely a theoretical morphological-structural analysis of the available additional topographic, geological, and geophysical information gained during the past several years. The main objective of this study is an attempt to extract the red thread of the region's structural grain from the complex deformational history of this orogenic belt. The interpretation presented must be considered as a working hypothesis based on the best information currently available.

Manuscript received, June 25, 1963.

[1] Contribution No. 498 from the Marine Laboratory, University of Miami. Contribution from Scripps Institution of Oceanography, University of California.
Illustrations were prepared by Richard Marra, James Moriarty, and David Crouch.

[2] Marine Laboratory, University of Miami.

[3] Scripps Institution of Oceanography, University of California.

REGIONAL GEOLOGIC SETTING

The Gulf of California plays a key role in the late history of the orogenic cycles which have been active intermittently since the Mesozoic along the Pacific Coast of North America. Centered in the Pacific Coast Cordillera, itself intermittently active from the Jurassic (Hill and Dibblee, 1953) through the present day (Benioff, 1962; Crowell, 1960, 1962; Figueroa A., 1959), the Gulf apparently is an extension of the structurally complex East Pacific Rise. It is flanked on the west by the mountainous peninsular block of mid-Cretaceous granitic rocks which are covered in part by late-Cretaceous volcanics and by mid-Tertiary-to-Recent sediments and volcanics. On the east it is flanked by gently westward-dipping mid-Tertiary and later sediments and volcanics that are blanketed on the coastal plain by broad Recent alluvial fans and deltas.

The Gulf is bordered by seven of the physiographic provinces of Mexico,—four on the west, one on the north, and two on the east (Fig. 1, after Byrne and Emery, 1960). Each physiographic province is characterized by a distinctive geology resulting from and shaped by the tectonic activities of the region. Composites of geologic and tectonic maps of Mexico compiled by P.B. King (1947), Sanchez Mejorada (1956), Mina U. (1957), and de Czerna (1961) show numerous large-scale faults cutting the land masses into a series of irregular fault blocks roughly outlining the physiographic provinces.

The Peninsular Southern Cape province (Fig. 1) consists of an elevated granite block intruding highly metamorphosed sediments that are overlain locally by north-northwest-dipping Miocene and Pliocene sediments. This block is separated from the mountainous South-Central Peninsula province by the narrow, depressed, and sediment-covered Isthmus of La Paz (Fig. 2, Section VII). A westward-tilted volcanic tableland of Miocene, Pliocene, and Recent volcanic flows and pyroclastics forms the mountainous backbone of the south-central Peninsula (Fig. 2, Sections IV, V, and VI). The northern Peninsula is a continuation of this elevated Peninsular backbone but differs from the southern Peninsula in having greater elevation (Fig. 2, Sections I, II, and III) and an exposed core of Middle Cretaceous crystalline rocks of the Southern California batholith (Larson, 1948; Beal, 1948; Anderson, 1950; Dibblee, 1954; Silver and others, 1956; Allen and others, 1960; and Woodford, 1960).

The head of the Gulf is bordered by the Colorado River delta, resting on the floor of the Colorado Desert province and blocking Gulf waters from entering the Salton Sea in the depressed Imperial Valley trough. The Imperial Valley, a structural continuation of the Gulf, is filled by as much as 19,400 feet of Pliocene-to-Recent deltaic deposits, and some Miocene marine sediments (Tarbet, 1951; Dibblee, 1954; Biehler and others, this volume). In the northern Gulf, the thickness of sediments is more than 15,000 feet (Phillips, this volume). To the south, the eastern margin of the Gulf is bounded by two low broad provinces, the Sonoran Desert and the Pacific Coastal Plain. The Sonoran Desert is largely an alluvium-covered surface through which protrude Paleozoic and Mesozoic mountain ranges composed of intrusive, metamorphic, sedimentary, and volcanic rocks. Toward the Gulf these mountains gradually decrease in elevation (Fig. 2). The Pacific Coastal Plain is a gently sloping alluvial surface, unbroken except for a few volcanic flows in the vicinity of Guaymas which rest on a granodiorite basement.

The geologic and structural framework of the desert and plain east of the Gulf does not appear to be as complex as the strongly faulted western coast. The surface of Sonora has a gently westward-dipping slope, with numerous exposures of normal faults parallel to and flanking the mountains of the Sierra Madre Occidental (P.B. King, 1947). In contrast, the Peninsula consists of folded blocks bounded by normal and thrust faults of complex origin; these are related to the formation of the Gulf by deep-seated tectonic activity. In the southern half of the Peninsula the folded and faulted crystalline and sedimentary rocks are cut by an angular unconformity that is overlain by a thick accumulation of lava flows which dip gently toward the west.

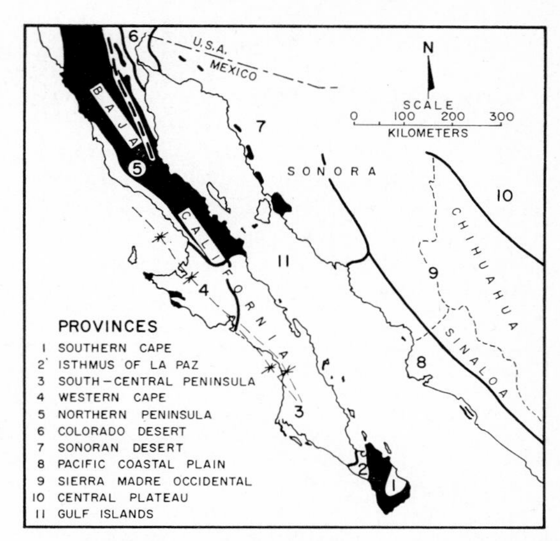

FIG. 1.—Physiographic provinces and crystalline rocks (in black) of the region surrounding the Gulf of California (after Byrne and Emery, 1960, Fig. 1, modified after Ordoñez, 1936; and, Beal, 1948). The trend of the Baja California syncline, after Mina U. (1957), has been added.

The entire post-Mesozoic history seems one of only mild deformation but extensive volcanism with vast outpourings of andesites and basalts. The main orogenic movements associated with the Gulf seem to be gentle westward tilting, mild to strong uplift, and extensive horizontal translations along longitudinal, transcurrent, and subsidiary faults.

Topography and relief.—Along the Mexican mainland elevations of the Gulf margins are low; broad alluvial plains dip gently to the coast and extend seaward as a wide submerged shelf (Fig. 2). In contrast, the Baja California side of the Gulf is elevated several thousand feet; significantly, it, too, has a westward tilt identical with that of the mainland. The maximum uplift of the

Peninsula occurs on its east side, but, in addition, the greatest elevations occur where batholithic rocks are exposed; this suggests isostatic adjustment to deeper roots. The fact that the batholithic bodies do not seem to have markedly influenced the tilt, and that the tilted tableland extends so uniformly over such broad areas of tectonic activity, leads to the conclusion that a very large, deep-seated orogenic process is here operative.

Menard (1960) has shown that the trend of the East Pacific Rise intersects the North American continent at the Gulf of California. Crustal studies (Phillips, this volume) support this conclusion. Clearly, this subcrustal welt must be related in some way to the observed orogenesis on the continent, as was suggested by Menard (1961). Not only has there been relative uplift of local individual blocks but also regional uplift in the absolute sense. This has apparently resulted in broad zones of tensional fractures of which the Gulf is a part.

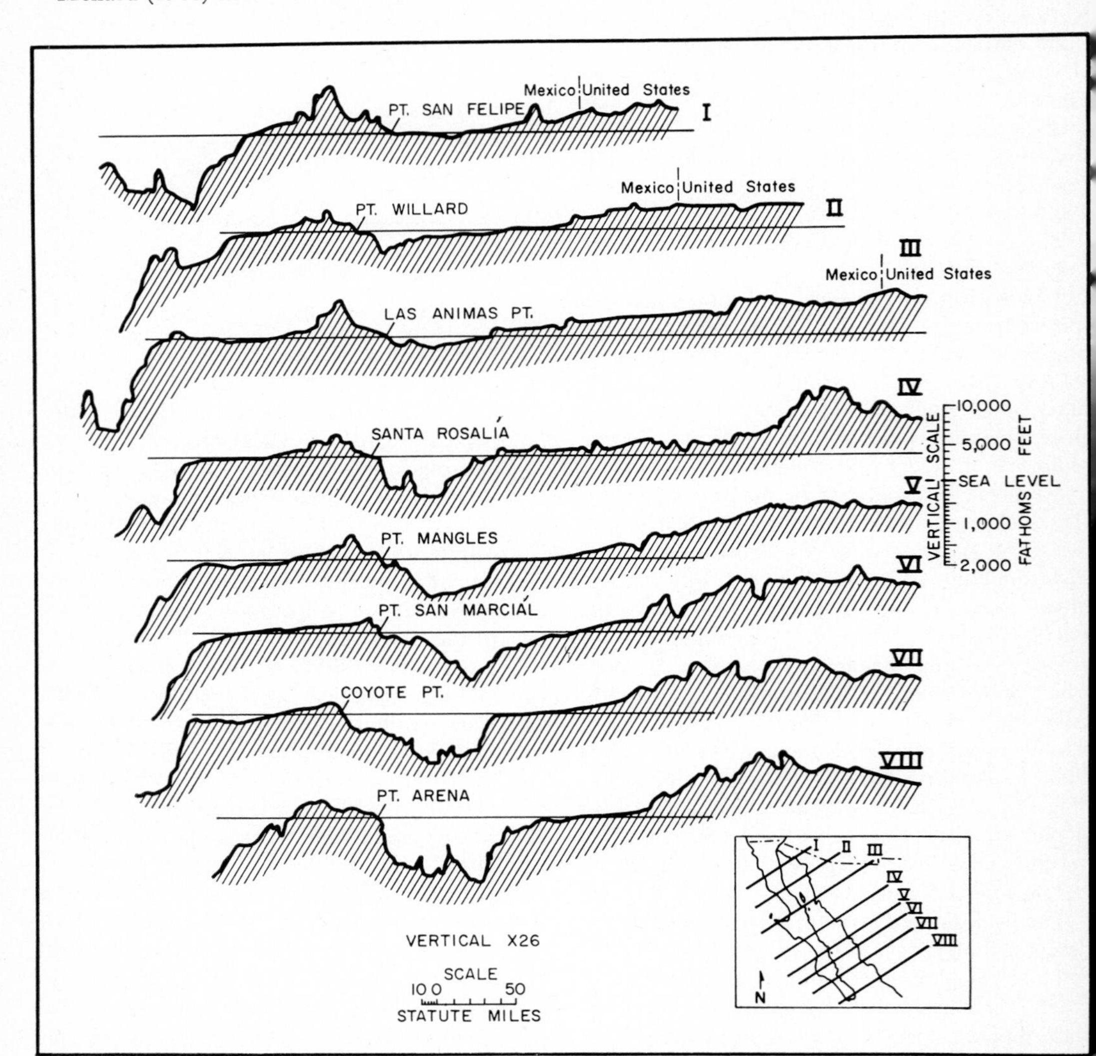

FIG. 2.—Physiographic cross sections showing regional tilt of surfaces and variable land elevations in the provinces surrounding the Gulf of California (modified from Byrne, 1957).

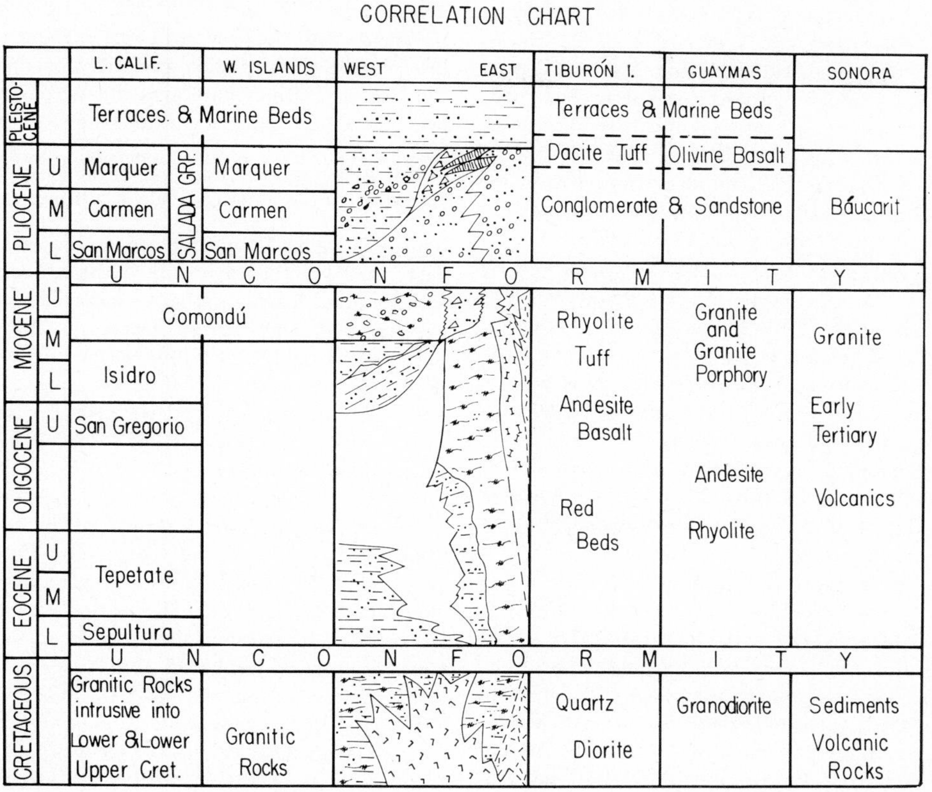

CORRELATION CHART

		L. CALIF.	W. ISLANDS	WEST / EAST	TIBURÓN I.	GUAYMAS	SONORA
PLEISTOCENE		Terraces & Marine Beds			Terraces & Marine Beds		
PLIOCENE	U	Marquer (SALADA GRP.)	Marquer		Dacite Tuff	Olivine Basalt	Báucarit
	M	Carmen (SALADA GRP.)	Carmen		Conglomerate & Sandstone		
	L	San Marcos (SALADA GRP.)	San Marcos				
U N C O N F O R M I T Y							
MIOCENE	U	Comondú			Rhyolite Tuff Andesite Basalt Red Beds	Granite and Granite Porphory Andesite Rhyolite	Granite Early Tertiary Volcanics
	M						
	L	Isidro					
OLIGOCENE	U	San Gregorio					
EOCENE	U	Tepetate					
	M						
	L	Sepultura					
U N C O N F O R M I T Y							
CRETACEOUS		Granitic Rocks intrusive into Lower & Lower Upper Cret.	Granitic Rocks		Quartz Diorite	Granodiorite	Sediments Volcanic Rocks

FIG. 3.—Correlation chart of outcrop stratigraphy in and around the Gulf of California, compiled from Anderson (1950), Beal (1948), and R.E. King (1939).

The rock record.—Two igneous rock types dominate along the Pacific margin of North America. These are the granites (in the sense of Buddington, 1959) and the andesites. They occur as linear bodies lying approximately parallel to each other and to major tectonic elements such as metamorphic foliation, fold axes, volcanic flows, and major fault strikes (Eardley, 1951; P.B. King, 1959; Moore, 1959; Moore, Grantz, and Blake, 1961). The granitic rocks within this tectonic belt have a distinctive character. Moore (1959) and Moore and others (1961) recognize "the quartz diorite line" as extending from Baja California to Alaska. This line, based on the compositional zonation of the plutonic masses, delineates quartz diorites on the west and granodiorites on the east.

Moore and others (1961) conclude that the Mesozoic and Cenozoic granitic rocks of the Pacific margin are largely first cycle, that is, emplaced in a basement containing no older granitic rocks. To the west of the "quartz diorite line" the crust was thinner than to the east, and was composed of a larger percentage of eugeosynclinal sediments and volcanic rocks. In the northern part of Baja California, these were intruded by the Baja California batholith (Cretaceous) for which Larsen and others (1958) give a mean value of 103 million years, based on four lead-alpha ages. For convenience a summary of the rock record as reported by R.E. King (1939), Beal (1948), Anderson (1950), Woodford (1960), and others, may be started from this point in time (Fig. 3).

By early Cretaceous time, when plutonic rocks invaded the area, some marine sediments had already been deposited in northern Sonora and on the western margin of Baja California. These were then eroded, covered by extensive sheets of volcanics, and then tilted during the mid-Upper Cretaceous. Upper and Lower Cretaceous rocks are separated by an erosional unconformity. Some Upper Cretaceous marine deposits were formed in northern Sonora, but by late Cretaceous time marine transgressive deposits were forming only on the plutonic rocks of Baja California.

Paleocene and Eocene times were marked by important subsidence as the sea covered the western flanks of the Peninsula and possibly extended across the isthmus to the present southern Gulf. In Sonora, activity was confined largely to volcanism and continental red-bed formation. The close of Eocene time was marked by the beginning of local folding and erosion. Sandstones were deposited and overlain by volcanics, and the granites of the Southern Cape were invaded and covered by volcanics.

Volcanic rocks continued to accumulate in the Sonora area throughout mid-Tertiary time. In Baja California, the gently depressed area of the Baja California syncline was forming in lower and middle Miocene time; it was bordered by uplifted crystalline islands at Bahía de Magdalena. Marine invasion submerged the east coast of the present Peninsula from Punta San Marciál to La Paz. This marked the first Tertiary sea invasion of the Gulf coasts, with thick Miocene accumulations of coarse breccias and marine conglomerates. In the Miocene the synclinal area as far as Cedros Island was submerged, and the Southern Cape region near La Paz was an elevated block. After deposition of marine shales between the higher standing blocks, the northern half of the Peninsula was uplifted and eroded considerably; there was little erosion in the synclinal area.

During late Miocene time, extensive volcanism formed thick deposits (Comondú) of several kinds of volcanic rocks. The volcanic centers appear to have coincided with the western margin of the present Gulf. Anderson (1950, p. 47–48) notes that

> The location of the volcanic centers is indicated by the following points; to the west only sandstones appear, and they grade eastward into volcanic conglomerates which in turn pass into volcanic breccias, tuff, and lava flows.

There is no indication of interfingering of marine sediments with the Comondú (the volcanic rocks), implying that the region presently occupied by the Gulf was still a land area during part of the late Miocene. Anderson continues

> After accumulation of the Comondú volcanics and associated sediments, deformation along the eastern border of Lower California resulted in tilting. . . .

This was followed by invasion of the sea to the east, isolating the Peninsula of Baja California. Faulting and folding probably occurred along the eastern side, and further movement may have occurred along the Ceralbo, Sal si Puedes (Ballenas), San Lorenzo, and other fault zones. Dips of the Comondú indicate that elevation (or sinking) of the islands in the southern Gulf continued as independent structural events, not being dependent upon the movements of one another, or of the Peninsula (Beal, 1948), although all must derive from the basic structural movement. This independence is indicated by the steeper dips in the mantling Comondú volcanics on the islands than in those on the Peninsula. The separate island units apparently broke off the Peninsula as the Gulf depression opened in late Miocene time (Wilson, 1949). By Pliocene time, a very narrow gulf already existed along the eastern side of the Peninsula; its extension northward into the Imperial Valley of southeastern California is indicated there by late Miocene-early Pliocene marine assemblages. During this time shallow-water marine deposits filled embayments carved out of the deformed Comondú. Uplift continued into the Pleistocene, and some, or much, of the deformation recorded may have occurred then, with major structural driving forces being more effective on the east side of the Peninsula. The structural processes responsible for the Peninsula's westward tilting must be controlled by the configuration of the peninsular basement.

In Sonora, some of the rocks of the Sierra Madre Occidental and the high ranges to the west apparently were pushed westward, along small overthrust faults, over valleys filled with sediments of Pliocene (Báucarit) age. R.E. King (1939, p. 1716) records that

> The normal faults extensively developed south of the 28th parallel and farther west in central Sonora were somehow related to the thrust faults.

The regional forces appear to have been dominantly tensional, although locally compressional structures have developed. Such seemingly contradictory coexistence of tension and compression within the area fits into a coherent picture in the light of gravity tectonics and a consideration of the East Pacific Rise, the broad welt to which local as well as regional structural features owe, either directly or indirectly, their existence.

The geophysical record.—Some of the seismic refraction information from the *Vermilion Sea Expedition* of 1959 reported by Shor (1959) was used by Hamilton (1961) in interpreting the basin structure but the compilation of detailed topographic charts, gravity observations, heat-flow measurements, and magnetic anomaly maps has only now been completed (Phillips; Harrison and Mathur; Biehler, Kovach, and Allen; all, this volume). Von Herzen (1963) has reported heat-flow measurements made in the Gulf of California. These studies show that (1) the crustal structure in the central and southern Gulf of California is more nearly oceanic than continental in character, (2) for all practical purposes, the Gulf is in isostatic equilibrium, and (3) the Gulf is characterized by a zone of surprisingly high heat flow. The first and second of these observations eliminate the hypothesis that the Gulf is a graben; the Gulf could not have formed by downfaulting of continental blocks alone, although such foundered structure perhaps seems possible as a partial explanation for the area north of Tiburón and Angel de la Guarda. In its southern two-thirds the Gulf appears to be a rift between two continental blocks separated by a crust of oceanic character (*see* Phillips; and Harrison and Mathur, this volume); in its northern reaches, the Gulf contains an abnormally thin crust (Phillips, this volume). In east-west cross sections the basic crustal structure appears to be remarkably similar to corresponding portions of the Red Sea (Girdler, 1958, 1962; Swartz and Arden, 1960; Drake, personal communication); in each, an oceanic crustal character is evident in the south, whereas crustal thinning is observed in the north. The third observation—that the Gulf is a zone of high heat flow—suggests that convection currents in the mantle are rising beneath this region, providing the basic mechanism to maintain the East Pacific Rise here (Menard, 1960, 1961; Hamilton, 1961).

Various crustal relations of the continental plates, blocks, and margins to the ocean floor are pictured in Figure 4. These sections are only slightly modified from the seismic-refraction studies discussed by Raitt and Shor (1958), Shor and Raitt (1956), Shor and Fisher (1961), Phillips (this volume), Fisher and Hess (1963), and Kovach, Allen, and Press (1962).

The structure section off western Guatemala (Fig. 4-*A*, after Fisher, 1961) is accepted as a standard section, uncomplicated by extreme deformation or faulting, but including a portion of the Middle America Trench at the base of the continental slope. The section off Banderas Bay and Islas Tres Marías (Fig. 4-*B*) shows a markedly thinner crust, underlain at the edge of the continental margin by material with lower-than-normal mantle seismic velocities; it is thus more nearly like the section across the central Gulf but shows clearly the volcanic construction of the Islas Tres Marías. To the north and west, the structure of the Peninsula near Bahía Sebastián Vizcaíno (Fig. 4-*C*) again shows a thicker crustal section, more nearly like that off Guatemala, but separated from the continental mainland by the open, shallow-mantled oceanic? crust of the opened Gulf rift. North and west of San Diego (Fig. 4-*D*) the transition from oceanic crust to continental block is complicated by the structurally disturbed anomalous plate of the continental borderland (Shor and Raitt, 1958; Harrison, personal communication); this may be comparable to the section in the northern Gulf basin (Fig. 4-*E*).

These data provide evidence unquestionably favoring a rifted gulf. They also provide a basic model from which the evolutionary history of the Gulf can be developed. The model chosen for this purpose is relatively simple—it consists of continental crust, oceanic crust, and superjacent sediments, which have slid down the flank of the East Pacific Rise.

Structural model of the Gulf of California.—Local deformation, faulting, or uplift in the Gulf of California certainly appears to be related to the regional orogenesis exhibited along the Pacific Coast; all may derive from a basic orogenic mech-

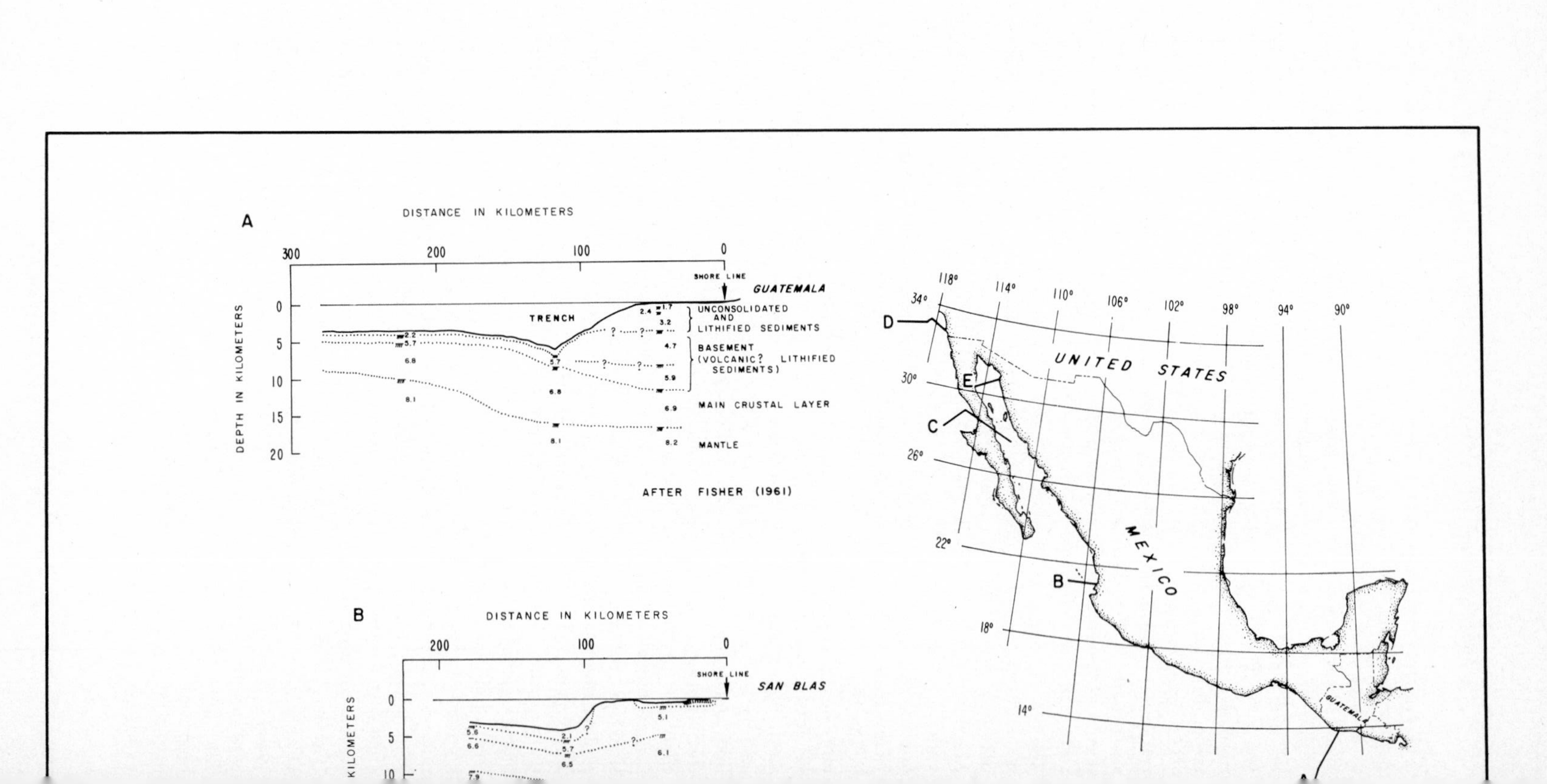
A
DISTANCE IN KILOMETERS
300
200
100
0
SHORE LINE
GUATEMALA
DEPTH IN KILOMETERS
TRENCH
UNCONSOLIDATED AND LITHIFIED SEDIMENTS
BASEMENT (VOLCANIC? LITHIFIED SEDIMENTS)
MAIN CRUSTAL LAYER
MANTLE
AFTER FISHER (1961)
B
DISTANCE IN KILOMETERS
SAN BLAS
KILOMETERS
UNITED STATES
MEXICO
GUATEMALA
D
E
C
B
118°
114°
110°
106°
102°
98°
94°
90°
34°
30°
26°
22°
18°
14°

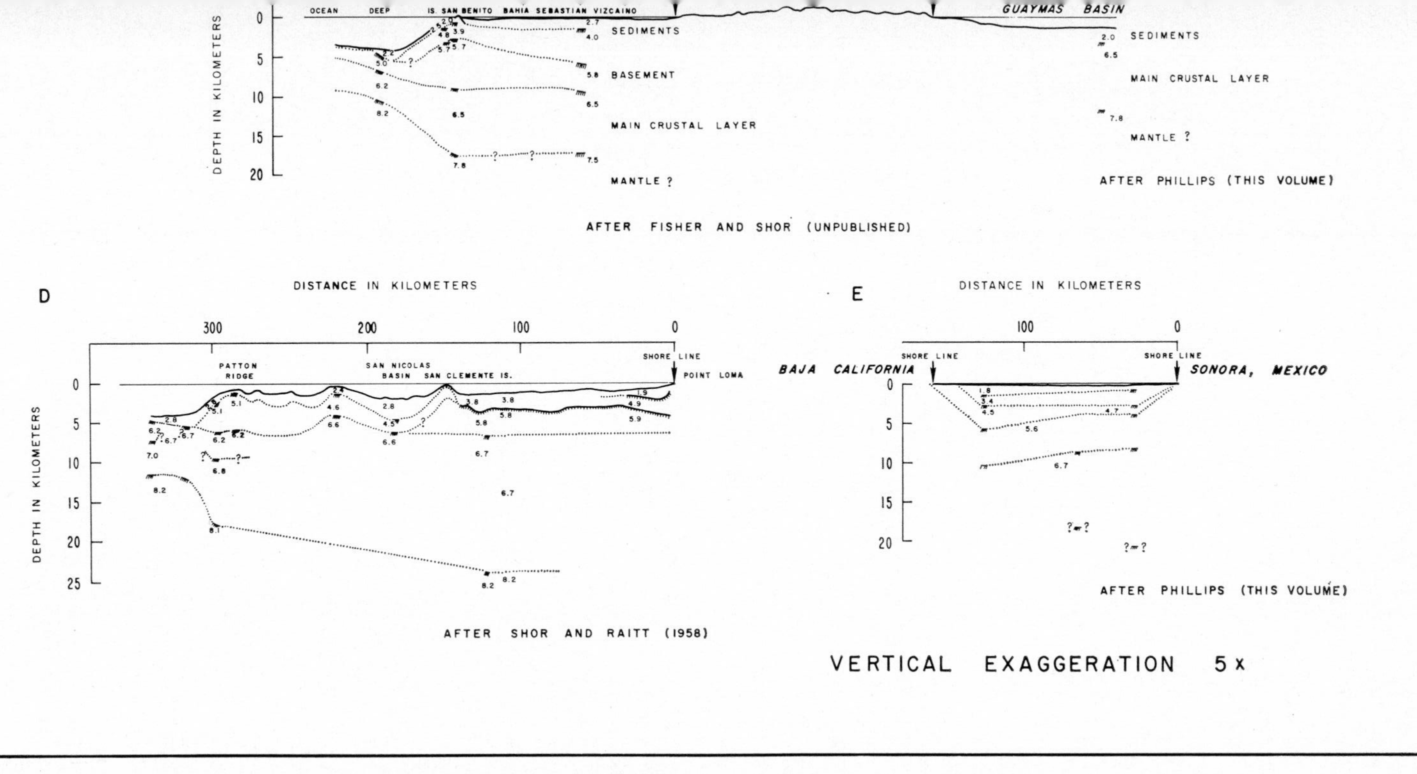

FIG. 4.—Crustal structure transverse to the Gulf of California and within the adjacent Pacific, from seismic-refraction data.

anism (Menard, 1955, 1960, 1961). It appears that the main crustal movement has been regional uplift. A hypothesis of Gulf evolution may be constructed around this fact.

The present shape and structure of the Gulf of California reflect lines of structural weakness in the pre-existing rocks in and adjacent to the continental margin. That these lines were shaped by the vertical and horizontal movements of the crystalline basement is clearly recorded, in a relative sense, by the rocks; however, these relative movements are superimposed upon the absolute uplift of the East Pacific Rise. Menard (1955, 1960, 1961) argues convincingly, on the basis of heat-flow data, in favor of convective-current mantle forces for uplift.

Oceanic crustal motion on a regional scale has been established from an analysis of the major east-west fracture zones—Mendocino, Pioneer, Murray, Clarion, Clipperton—of the Northeastern Pacific sea floor (Menard, 1955, 1960, 1961) and from fault-plane solutions for earthquakes in the Eastern Pacific (Benioff, 1962; and others). The topographically demonstrated fractures outline major oceanic plates which have rotated counterclockwise with respect to the North American continent and have been translated up to hundreds of miles east-west relative to each other, as shown by magnetic anomaly studies (Vacquier and others, 1961; Vacquier, 1962; Mason, 1958; Mason and Raff, 1961; and Raff and Mason, 1961). The Baja California Peninsula lies along the east face of the oceanic plate bounded by the Murray fracture zone on the north and the Clarion fracture zone on the south.

It is important to emphasize these features and to reiterate that the crest of the East Pacific Rise intersects the North American continent near the mouth of the Gulf of California (Menard, 1961). In the model proposed here, the oceanic plates drape the flanks of the rise and apparently move east-west, in response to differential uplift, by gravitational adjustment along subcrustal planes of plastic flow. The San Andreas fault zone and its subsidiary fractures, lying adjacent to the oceanic plates and on the flank of the rise, are controlled in part by this motion, possibly after having formed along lines of weakness inherited from pre-existing basement rock. Uplift along the East Pacific Rise thus is thought to provide the potential energy through which motion could take place by the action of gravity-induced body forces. The structural model proposes a continental marginal block resting in an area of regional uplift and tension.

Figure 5 shows a simplified structural model, based on crustal-structure studies, of the Baja California Peninsula within the zone of regional tectonic activity. It represents the hypothetical general configuration of the continental basement with its overlying Tertiary and pre-Tertiary cover, adjacent to the Pacific margin. The batholithic core of the Peninsula may have developed from an older eugeosynclinal belt (*see* Moore and others, 1962) which had formed as an arcuate undulating marginal deep that filled with sediments and volcanics along the ancestral "California" coast. In shape and general bathymetry, the original marginal deep may have resembled the present Middle America Trench (*see* Fisher, 1961). Thus, this supposed trench may have had a depth that varied along the trench axis, later resulting in, and developing as, an uneven batholithic root. Where a thick root existed, the uplifting (convective) subcrustal welt might abut against and around it, forcing it high by uplift and far by lateral translation. A shallow root might thus be uplifted less, causing a saddle in the backbone. Adjacent oceanic plates uplifted by this process might be either depressed or elevated relative to each other depending upon differential elevation along the continental block. In areas of large batholithic thickness, where such uplift would be greater, marginal oceanic plates might remain less elevated, thereby explaining some often uncompensated? depressions bordering structurally active areas. The following evolutionary history may be suggested as a working hypothesis fitting the geological and geophysical observations and proceeding directly from the theoretical model proposed.

Evolution of the Gulf of California.—Initial stages of the Gulf of California evolution undoubtedly began with gentle upwarping of the pre-batholithic continental margin as the East Pacific Rise became an effective force under the continent. Contemporaneous increases in the heat flow apparently acted on the roots of the existing

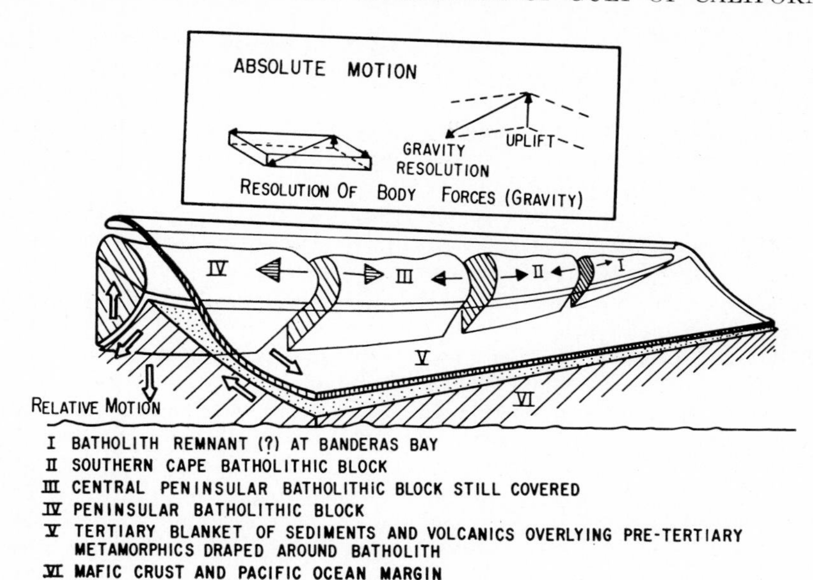

FIG. 5.—Schematic diagram of hypothetical crustal structure and forces on the Baja California Peninsula in the broader zone of regional tectonic activity. Upper—absolute uplift of the western flank of the East Pacific Rise, together with the resultant induced gravitational sliding of crustal plates. Lower—arrows indicate relative movement of adjacent units as suggested by presently known faulting.

geosyncline sufficiently (Moore and others, 1962; Fisher and Hess, 1963) to have resulted in a synorgenic phase that emplaced the granitic plutons, dating the uplift as Middle Cretaceous (Larsen, 1954; Larsen and others, 1958; Hsu and others, 1963). The San Andreas fault system became operative at about this time (Hill and Dibblee, 1953) and may have been accompanied (then or a little later) by a continuous series of *en echelon* faults of the Agua Blanca type to create the initial complementary *en echelon* offsets which persist across the entire length of the present Gulf. These cut off the Angel de la Guarda-San Lorenzo island slice and extend into the Imperial Valley (Kovach and others, 1962; Biehler and others, this volume). The initial fault offsets continue to be a part of the Peninsula structure to the present day. As regional uplift continued, the sedimentary cover appears to have been removed in part by erosion—evidenced by a major unconformity (*see* Fig. 3)—and perhaps in part by tectonic denudation. The Peninsula moved to the northwest down the flank of the East Pacific Rise by gravitational adjustment along parallel strike-slip faults, causing complementary orthogonal offset faults where tensional stress was greatest. These tensional features seem to have created fissures through which upper Miocene volcanic eruptions rose to cover the exposed land surface. They apparently follow the Miocene orogenic phase which is recorded in the San Gabriel Mountains of Southern California (Hsu, Edwards, and McLaughlin, 1963) by the emplacement of quartz monzonite plutons. The dominantly tensional faults lying transverse to the Gulf axis carried the bulk of the abundant volcanic flows which apparently were continually fractured and welded as uplift and northwestward drift of the Peninsula block proceeded (*see* Rusnak and others, this volume). Abundant upwelling volcanics appear to have formed in the Tres Marías island group very early (mid-Miocene?) during the initial southern rifting, as evidenced by geologic and seismic-refraction cross sections (Phillips, this volume). Initial eruptive products consisted of andesitic flows (Beal, 1948), but as the separation of the continental blocks increased, the volcanics became more basaltic in type.

By the end of Miocene time a narrow gulf had formed (Wilson, 1949). The northern and central

Peninsula continued to slide northwest; the southern Peninsula followed, but rotated slightly more to the west on the tilted flank of the subcrustal welt. The Angel de la Guarda-San Esteban slice and the San Lorenzo Island string were formed and were shifted toward their present position along parallel faults—influenced in part by the westward rotation—subsidiary to the major strike-slip break. If any other large scale slices of like nature are present, they are now covered by sedimentary fill, as are those subsurface ridges observed in gravity profiles (Harrison and Mathur, this volume) and sub-bottom acoustic profiles from the east flank of the southern Gulf (Curray and Moore, this volume). Kovach and others (1962, p. 2848, 2870) suggest such a possible fault-slice origin for the Sierra de los Cucapas and Superstition Mountains of the Imperial Valley, which are bounded by faults of the Elsinore-Laguna Salada-San Jacinto system. Such an origin seems suggested as well for Consag Rock, an andesitic (van Andel, personal communication) islet in the northern Gulf and for a shoaling basement separating the Imperial Valley from the northern Gulf.[4] Geophysical investigations (Biehler and others, this volume; Kovach and others, 1962; Shor, 1959; Phillips, this volume; and Harrison and Mathur, this volume) supply evidence that the continental crust of both the Imperial Valley and the northern Gulf was being thinned during dilation by possible complementary sets of low-angle normal faults, forming foundered troughs on a basement of graben-and-horst lineaments.

In Sonora, westward tilting and drift seem to have occurred as continental crustal blocks underwent increasing tension over the crest and flanks of the subcrustal welt. Sediments covering the differentially uplifted crystalline basement appear to have been in part stripped by tectonic denudation (of the type described by Rubey and Hubbert, 1959) to create some observed local thrust sheets of previously deposited sediments (R.E. King, 1939).

As a result of deep batholithic roots in the northern Peninsula, uplift seems to have outraced erosional denudation; the tilted superjacent strat[a] appear to have slid off the batholith backbone, b[y] gravity, to form a large thrust sheet of the conti[-] nental borderland on the floor of the Pacific (*se[e]* for example, the structural relations shown in th[e] seismic-refraction cross sections, Fig. 4)[5]. Th[e] thrust plate apparently broke into several larg[e] fragments forming the northern and the souther[n] continental borderland (*see* also Krause, 1961 1964). Small gravitational adjustments may hav[e] occurred in the "saddle" of the central Peninsula western Cape, and at the Isthmus of La Paz Dilation in the zone between the crystallin[e] blocks of the northern Peninsula and the souther[n] Cape seems to have caused a gentle syncline t[o] have formed in the sedimentary mantle as well a[s] to have created an apparent underlying "pull apart" of rock plates, as suggested by gravity data of Mina U. (1957) and by the offset structur[e] observed in the contours (especially outlined by 1,000-fathom contour) at the foot of the Bahí[a] Sebastián Vizcaíno depression entering the Pacifi[c] (*see* Rusnak and others, this volume). The Pen insula's gradually submerging tilted erosion sur face allowed deposition of sediments on the cen tral Peninsula (Beal, 1948; Mina U., 1957). As th[e]

[4] The notable depression of the Laguna Salada may be analogous to the Delfin Basin northwest of the Angel de la Guarda-San Lorenzo slices in the northern Gulf.

[5] Similar large-scale thrusting of continental crusta[l] plates in the Appalachians and adjacent Atlantic wa[s] recently reported by Drake (1963, and personal com munication), Woodward (1963, 1964, and personal com munication), and Dennison and Woodward (1963). T[o] explain such seemingly difficult crustal translations, [a] corollary is made here with the fluid-pressure concep[t] for lubricating the sole of large-scale thrust plates t[o] allow gravitational sliding on low slopes, as describe[d] by Hubbert and Rubey (1959) and Rubey and Hub bert (1959). Platt (1962) has recently suggested [a] similar corollary in drawing on the fluid-pressure con cept to explain the Taconic allochthon, calling upo[n] water derived from remobilized granitic rocks, instea[d] of the sedimentary pore fluid pressures subscribed to by Hubbert and Rubey (1959), to provide the abnormally high fluid pressures required to reduce glide-plane fric tion. It is theoretically possible that the hypothetica[l] continental-borderland thrust plate was lubricated by such deep-seated injection of metasomatic fluids a[s] may be evidenced in the puzzling field relations ex hibited by the glaucophane schists of the Californi[a] Coast Ranges and Baja California (Taliaferro, 1943 Turner and Verhoogen, 1951; Brothers, 1954; and Va[n] West, 1958). High pore-fluid pressures in the Lo[s] Angeles Basin have been noted, however, by Hubber[t] and Rubey (1959), and highly mineralized pneumato litic? waters are reported by White, Anderson, and Grubbs (1963) from the tectonically active Salton Sea hydrothermal area in the Imperial Valley.

Peninsula moved toward the northwest, the Pacific sea floor adjacent to the Vizcaíno Peninsula-block was depressed by the overburden of the Baja California allochthon, forming a moat—Cedros Deep. The strongly disturbed sea floor between the Peninsula and Guadalupe Island, termed the "Arrugado" by Krause (1961), may be viewed as a dominantly tensional area, disrupted by local faults, small folds, and dotted with volcanic outpourings, lying between an oceanic plate and the Peninsula.

This interpretation, or a very similarly constructed mechanical model, may account for the observed basic elements of the tectonic belt, as indicated by the structural pattern, fault displacements, geophysical observations, and diastrophic activity. The earthquake model, suggested by Benioff (1962) to account for the peculiar behavior of earthquake shocks arising from the San Andreas and associated earthquakes, fits well into this hypothesis—it proposes a mechanical analog consisting of two crustal plates, sliding against one another on a lubricated (plastic) horizontal plane, radiating earthquake shocks almost entirely from the nearly vertical strike-slip fault between the two plates. P.B. King's (1959) general reconstruction of the structural history of the Southern California Coast Range appears to the authors to be a natural consequence of the model suggested here. Numerous details of local deformation in future studies of the unknown remote areas may well fit this framework of reference.

REFERENCES

Allen, C.R., Silver, L.T., and Stehli, F.G., 1960, Agua Blanca fault—a major transverse structure of northern Baja California: Geol. Soc. America Bull., v. 71, p. 457–482.

Anderson, C.A., Geology of islands and neighboring land areas, pt. 1 *of* The 1940 E.W. Scripps cruise to the Gulf of California: Geol. Soc. America Mem. 43, 53 p.

Beal, C.H., 1948, Reconnaissance of the geology and oil possibilities of Baja California, Mexico: Geol. Soc. America Mem. 31, 138 p.

Benioff, H., 1962, Movements on major transcurrent faults, *in* Continental drift: Internat. Geophys. Series, v. 3, Academic Press, New York, p. 103–134.

Brothers, R.M., 1954, Glaucophane schists from the north Berkeley Hills, California: Am. Jour. Sci., v. 252, p. 614–626.

Buddington, A.F., 1959, Granite emplacement with special reference to North America: Geol. Soc. America Bull., v. 70, p. 671–748.

Byrne, J.V., 1957, The marine geology of the Gulf of California: Unpub. Ph.D. thesis, Univ. Southern Calif., L.A.

——— and Emery, K.O., 1960, Sediments of the Gulf of California: Geol. Soc. America Bull., v. 71, p. 983–1010.

Crowell, J.C., 1960, The San Andreas fault in Southern California: Internat. Geol. Cong., 21st, Copenhagen, Denmark, Proc. sec. 18, p. 45–52.

——— 1962, Displacement along the San Andreas fault, California: Geol. Soc. America Spec. Paper 71, 61 p.

de Cserna, Z., 1961, Tectonic map of Mexico; scale 1:2,500,000: Geol. Soc. America.

Dennison, J.M., and Woodward, H.P., 1963, Palinspastic maps of the central Appalachians: Am. Assoc. Petroleum Geologists Bull., v. 47, p. 666–680.

Dibblee, T.W., Jr., 1954, Geology of the Imperial Valley region, California: Calif. Dept. Nat. Res., Div. Mines Bull. 170, chap. 2, p. 21–28.

Drake, C.L., 1963, Atlantic margin of North America [abs.]: Program booklet, AAPG 48th ann. mtg., Houston, Texas, March 25–28, 1963, p. 38–39.

Eardley, A.J., 1951, Structural geology of North America: Harper & Bros., New York, 624 p.

Figueroa, A.J., 1959, Carta sismica de la Republica Mexicana: Anales Nac. Univ. Mexico Inst. de Geofisica, v. 5, p. 45–162.

Fisher, R.L., 1961, Middle America trench—topography and structure: Geol. Soc. America Bull., v. 72, p. 703–720.

——— and Hess, H.H., 1963, Trenches, *in* The sea—ideas and observations: v. 3, Interscience Pub., New York, p. 411–436.

Girdler, R.W., 1958, The relation of the Red Sea to the east African rift system: Geol. Soc. London Quart. Jour., v. 114, p. 79–105.

——— 1962, Initiation of continental drift: Nature, v. 194, p. 521–524.

Hamilton, W., 1961, Origin of the Gulf of California: Geol. Soc. America Bull., v. 72, p. 1307–1318.

Hill, M.L., and Dibblee, T.W., Jr., 1953, San Andreas, Garlock, and Big Pine faults, California: Geol. Soc. America Bull., v. 64, p. 443–458.

Hsu, K.J., Edwards, G., and McLaughlin, W.A., 1963, Age of the intrusive rocks of the southeastern San Gabriel Mountains, California: Geol. Soc. America Bull., v. 74, p. 507–512.

Hubbert, K., and Rubey, W.W., 1959, Mechanics of fluid-filled porous solids and its application to overthrust faulting, pt. 1 *of* Role of fluid pressure in mechanics of overthrust faulting: Geol. Soc. Am. Bull., v. 70, p. 115–166.

King, P.B., 1947, Carta geologica de la parte septentrional de la Republica Mexicana: Nac. Univ. Mexico, Cartas Geol. y Min. de la Republica Mexicana, no. 3, 24 p.

——— 1959, The evolution of North America: Princeton Univ. Press, Princeton, New Jersey, 189 p.

King, R.E., 1939, Geological reconnaissance in the northern Sierra Madre Occidental of Mexico: Geol. Soc. America Bull., v. 50, p. 1625–1722.

Kovach, R.L., Allen, C.R., and Press, F., 1962, Geophysical investigations in the Colorado Delta region: Jour. Geophys. Research, v. 67, p. 2845–2871.

Krause, D.C., 1961, Geology of the southern continental borderland west of Baja California, Mexico: Unpub. Ph.D. thesis, Univ. of Calif. at San Diego, 205 p.

——— 1964, Structural geology and geomagnetism of the southern continental borderland west of Baja California, Mexico: Geol. Soc. America.

Larsen, E.S., Jr., 1948, Batholith and associated rocks of Corona, Elsinore, and San Luis Rey quadrangles, Southern California: Geol. Soc. America Mem. 29, 182 p.

——— 1954, The batholith of Southern California: Calif. Dept. Nat. Res., Div. Mines Bull. 170, chap. 7, p. 25–30.

——— Gottfried, D., Jaffe, H.W., and Waring, C.L., 1958, Lead-alpha ages of the Mesozoic batholiths of western North America: U.S. Geol. Survey Bull. 1070, p. 35–62.

Mason, R.G., 1958, A magnetic survey off the west coast of the United States between latitudes 32° and 36° N and longitudes 121° and 128° W: Roy. Astron. Soc. Geophys. Jour., v. 1, p. 320–329.

——— and Raff, A.D., 1961, Magnetic survey off the west coast of North America, 32° N latitude to 42° N latitude: Geol. Soc. America Bull., v. 72, p. 1259–1266.

Menard, H.W., 1955, Deformation of the northeastern Pacific basin and the west coast of North America: Geol. Soc. America Bull., v. 66, p. 1149–1198.

——— 1960, The east Pacific rise: Science, v. 132, p. 1737–1746.

——— 1961, The east Pacific rise: Scientific American, v. 205, no. 6, p. 52–61.

Mina U., F., 1957, Bosquejo geológico del territorio sur de la Baja California: Asoc. Mexicana Geól. Petroleros Bol., v. 9, p. 139–270.

Moore, J.G., 1959, The quartz diorite line in the United States: Jour. Geology, v. 67, p. 198–210.

——— Grantz, A., and Blake, M.C., Jr., 1961, The quartz diorite line in northwestern North America: U.S. Geol. Survey Prof. Paper 424-C, p. 87–90.

Ordoñez, E., 1936, Principal physiographic provinces of Mexico: Am. Assoc. Petroleum Geologists Bull., v. 20, p. 1277–1307.

Platt, L., 1962, Fluid pressure in thrust faulting, a corollary: Am. Jour. Sci., v. 260, p. 107–114.

Raff, A.D., and Mason, R.G., 1961, Magnetic survey off the west coast of North America 40° N latitude to 52° N latitude: Geol. Soc. America Bull., v. 72, p. 1267–1270.

Raitt, R.W., and Shor, G.G., Jr., 1958, Seismic studies in the Southern California continental borderland: Internat. Geol. Cong., 21st, Mexico, D.F., Proc. sec. 9, v. 2, p. 243–259.

Rubey, W.W., and Hubbert, K., 1959, Overthrust belt in geosynclinal area of western Wyoming in light of fluid-pressure hypothesis, pt. 2 *of* Role of fluid pressure in mechanics of overthrust faulting: Geol. Soc. America Bull., v. 70, p. 167–205.

Sanchez Mejorda, S.H., 1956, Carta geologica de la Republica Mexicana; scale 1:2,000,000: Internat. Geol. Cong., 20th, Mexico, D.F.

Shor, G.G., Jr., 1959, Preliminary report on seismic-refraction survey, Gulf of California: Am. Petroleum Inst. Proj. 51 Quart. Rept. 1, 12 p.

——— and Fisher, R.L., 1961, Middle America trench—seismic refraction studies: Geol. Soc. America Bull., v. 72, p. 721–730.

——— and Raitt, R.W., 1956, Seismic studies of the Southern California continental borderland: Marine Phys. Lab., Scripps Inst. Oceanography, SIO Ref. 58–78, 17 p.

Silver, L.T., Stehli, F.G., and Allen, C.R., 1956, Lower Cretaceous pre-batholithic rocks of northern Baja California, Mexico [abs.]: Internat. Geol. Cong., 20th, Mexico, D.F., Resumenes de los Trabajos Presentados, p. 30.

Swartz, D.H., and Arden, D.D., Jr., 1960, Geological history of Red Sea area: Am. Assoc. Petroleum Geologists Bull., v. 44, p. 1621–1637.

Taliaferro, N.L., 1943, Franciscan-Knoxville problem: Am. Assoc. Petroleum Geologists, v. 27, p. 109–219.

Tarbet, L.A., 1951, Imperial Valley: Am. Assoc. Petroleum Geologists Bull., v. 35, p. 260–263.

Turner, F.J., and Verhoogen, J., 1951, Igneous and metamorphic geology: McGraw-Hill Book Co., New York, 602 p.

Vacquier, V., 1962, Magnetic evidence for horizontal displacement in the floor of the Pacific Ocean, *in* Continental drift: Internat. Geophys. Series, v. 3, Academic Press, New York, p. 135–144.

——— Raff, A.D., and Warren, R.E., 1961, Horizontal displacements in the floor of the northeastern Pacific Ocean: Geol. Soc. America Bull., v. 72, p. 1251–1258.

Van West, O., 1958, Geology of the San Benito Islands and the southwest part of Cedros Island, Baja California, Mexico: Unpub. M.S. thesis, Claremont College, California, 78 p.

Von Herzen, R.P., 1963, Geothermal heat flow in the Gulfs of California and Aden: Science, v. 140, p. 1207–1208.

White, D.E., Anderson, E.T., and Grubbs, D.K., 1963, Geothermal brine well; mile-deep drill hole may tap ore-bearing magmatic water and rock undergoing metamorphism: Science, v. 139, p. 919–922.

Wilson, I.F., 1949, Buried topography, initial structures, and sedimentation in the Santa Rosalía area, Baja California, Mexico: Am. Assoc. Petroleum Geologists, v. 32, p. 1762–1807.

Woodford, A.O., 1960, Bedrock patterns and strike-slip faulting in Southern California: Am. Jour. Sci., Bradley Volume, v. 258-A, p. 400–417.

Woodward, H.P., 1963, Appalachian tectonic deformation and the deep basin [abs.]: Program booklet, AAPG 48th ann. mtg., Houston, Texas, March 25–28, 1963, p. 59–60.

——— 1964, Central Appalachian tectonics and the deep basin: Am. Assoc. Petroleum Geologists Bull., v. 48, no. 3, p. 338–356.

SEA-FLOOR VALLEYS OF GULF OF CALIFORNIA[1]

FRANCIS P. SHEPARD[2]
La Jolla, California

ABSTRACT

Valleys of various types have been found in the Gulf of California. Of these the most impressive is the series of deeply incised canyons that extend down the slopes around the lower end of Baja California. Crystalline rocks together with sedimentary formations of Miocene and Pliocene age have been dredged from the steep walls of these canyons. The canyons head near the shore and wind outward with many dendritic tributaries terminating at depths from about 900 to 1,300 fathoms. Narrow vertical to overhanging walled gorges at the head of some of these canyons, very different from local land canyons, are probably being excavated at the present time by the sand flows and other gravity-induced movements which have been observed along their steep courses. Sand with underlying gravel and rock fragments found in cores and box samples have been taken from the canyon axes over a wide range of depths. These indicate that a scouring action is working on the canyon floor. Despite these evidences of present-day marine erosion it seems likely that the pattern of the valleys was established by old, deeply submerged stream valleys that have been considerably modified by marine processes, especially as they sank below sea level.

Some valleys of the Gulf floor are the result of tectonism and it is possible that such movements may have helped form the canyons. In one place a canyon appears to have been cut off by faulting, and in another place a narrow gorge cuts through what appears to be a fault scarp. Other valleys owe their origin entirely to slumping and other types of mass movements on the steep slopes. This last group, like the tectonic valleys, is very distinct in character from the eroded canyons.

A problem of considerable interest is the explanation of the deeply weathered granitic rocks found on the walls of several of the canyons.

INTRODUCTION

During a Scripps Institution expedition in 1940 a preliminary study was made of two of the submarine canyons at the southern end of the Gulf of California (Shepard, 1950). Since 1959 the writer has spent the major part of five short expeditions obtaining further information on the canyons and on other types of marine valleys in this area. Most of the work has been concentrated around the lower end of Baja California. Preliminary results based on the first two of these recent expeditions have been published (Shepard, 1961). Since submission of this earlier paper the three following expeditions yielded many new data on the nature of the canyons, and have led to some modifications of the earlier interpretations.

The work has included a network of closely spaced sounding lines (*see* Figs. 1, 8, 11, 13, 16, 17). The surveys of all of the canyons around the lower end of the Peninsula have been extended out to the point where they terminate. Most of the canyon heads have been charted in detail even where they extend in virtually to the shore.[3] For this last purpose an Edo fathometer was used on a 30-foot launch because of the danger of bringing the larger ships in close to the shore. All soundings are given without correction for sound velocities or for slopes, because of the difficulty of conversion and because the uncorrected soundings allow

[1] Manuscript received, June 25, 1963. Contribution from Scripps Institution of Oceanography.

This work was supported in part by the Office of Naval Research under Contract Nonr-2216(01), and in part by the National Science Foundation Grant G-15547.

Many people helped in the work reported here. Of considerable importance has been the information from divers, for which I am grateful to R.F. Dill, Conrad Limbaugh, W.J. North, and J.R. Stewart. The cooperation of A.H. Bouma during the last expedition, and the use of the box corer which he helped develop were of great significance. Sample analyses were made by Ruth Y. Manar and N.F. Marshall. Plotting of soundings was made largely by F.J. Emmel. The cooperation of the Navy Electronics Laboratory in allowing Dill, C.J. Shipek, and various other members to accompany us, is also acknowledged. Organisms have been interpreted by Frances L. Parker, Jean P. Hosmer, E.C. Allison, W.K. Emerson, G. Dallas Hanna, F.L.G. Hertlein, and E.L. Martini. Appreciation is also due to my wife for her valuable volunteer help during all of the expeditions.

[2] Scripps Institution of Oceanography, University of California.

[3] Shown only in part on charts because of surveys made in 1963 just prior to submitting this report.

a better comparison with depths observed in subsequent sounding lines. At some future date, when directional echo sounders are available allowing the measuring of steep slopes, a new charting should be made of the walls of these canyons, since there are many indications that precipitous slopes exist and the large cone (30° on each side) echo-sounder heads do not show the exact character of these slopes.

Another important phase of the study has been the dredging of the walls of the canyons. For this purpose it has been found that a cast iron pipe dredge with a diameter of about 1 foot and a length of 6 feet is the most satisfactory (*see* Shepard, 1963, Fig. 16*A*). It is better for canyon-wall dredging than a rectangular dredge with a chain bag, used extensively elsewhere, because the pipe dredges rarely catch on large outcrops in such a manner that they cannot be broken loose. The rectangular dredges are frequently snagged and often lost on steep slopes with crystalline or other hard rock.

Samples referred to in the text are described in Table I. Coring along the axis of the canyons in this area proved to be rather unsuccessful because of the numerous instances where the bottom was so hard as to bend the core barrel and prevent any appreciable core from being obtained. Gravity cores have sometimes been more successful than piston cores because the former often obtain a thin mud covering that overlies hard sand, whereas the latter frequently push aside the mud at the top and fail to penetrate far into the underlying sand and gravel. However, a few good cores have been recovered and the nature of the bottom in areas with coarse sand and fine gravel has been determined in many other places by dredging. The dredge often brings up masses of sand and gravel that are distinct and easily separated from the mud or rock of the canyon walls.

During the 1963 expedition a box sampler adapted by Arnold H. Bouma, from an instrument of Reineck (1958, 1963), has been used to obtain rectangular cores with a cross section of 8 by 12 inches and depth up to 18 inches, when full. This proved very successful in sampling the canyon axes. The samples are now being studied. The locations of all the 1963 sampling stations referred to in this report are given in the overprints.

A particularly important phase of the work has been accomplished by the SCUBA divers who have accompanied three of the expeditions and have concentrated their efforts around the heads of two of the canyons. Most of the work of these divers during the 1962 *Bacanyon Expedition* and the 1964 *San Juan Expedition* is reported separately by Dill (1963) so that only a brief résumé of their results will be included here.

Other information has come from use of a strobe flash camera lowered to the bottom, the work of Carl J. Shipek of Navy Electronics Laboratory who accompanied us on the 1959 *Vermilion Sea Expedition*.

CAPE SAN LUCAS AREA (LOWER PENINSULA)

The area with the most interesting and diversified submarine topography of the entire Gulf borders the lower end of Baja California, extending from a point 20 nautical miles up the west side of the Peninsula to about 40 nautical miles up the east coast. This is the area that has been most carefully investigated and where the submarine canyons are most impressive.

Nature of adjacent land and coast.—Very little geological work has been undertaken in the mountainous terrain of the lower end of the Peninsula, although the maps of Beal (1948), Anderson (1950), and the Tectonic Map of Mexico (de Czerna, 1961) indicate that the area is largely a granitic batholith. According to Beal, a small coastal zone of Tertiary sandstone exists east of San José del Cabo, but the Tectonic Map of Mexico shows this belt as "subsequent volcanics." The same alternative interpretation is given for a coastal area in the vicinity of Palmas Bay (30 miles up the east side of the Peninsula). The form lines in the U.S. Hydrographic Office Chart (H.O. 1664, reproduced in part in Chart I) show the main features of land relief. Inasmuch as the mountains have been used extensively for fixes in our own charting operations, it can be stated that most of them show good locations at least relative to each other, despite the fact that the surveys here, as in most of the Gulf, were made by the U.S. Navy in the 19th century. The north-south backbone range, with heights of 3,000 to 6,500 feet, rises abruptly from a plateau of low relief on

(*Text continued on page 168.*)

TABLE I. DESCRIPTION OF SAMPLES FROM FOUR EXPEDITIONS[1]

New No.	Old No.	Lat.	Long.	Depth (fathoms)	General Location	Type of Sampler	Length of core	Description of Sample
1	VSS 2	22°48.1'	110°11.2'	870	Tinaja Trough	Petterson Grab		Muddy sample, contains <u>Neopilina</u>
2	VSS 3	22°49.3'	109°49.4'	780	San Lucas Canyon	Gravity Core		Only a few grains sand
3	VSS 4	22°49.3'	109°49.4'	780	San Lucas Canyon, west wall	Shipek Camera		Sediment with abundant brittle stars
4	VSS 5	22°48.0'	109°47.3'	875-750	Northwest wall, Santa Maria Canyon	Dredge		Cobbles, conglomerate with sea lion bone
5	VSS 6	22°48.2'	109°47.4'	780-260	Inner fan near San Lucas Canyon	Parker Biol. Dredge		<u>Neopilina</u> dredged
7	VSS 9	22°57.7'	109°33.3'	462	San Jose Canyon	Gravity Core		Few grains of sand only
8	VSS 10	22°58.6'	109°33.6'	460	San Jose Canyon	Shipek Camera & 2 small cores		Ripple marks in one photograph
9	VSS 11	22°52.7'	109°36.7'	642	San Jose Canyon	Gravity Core	43cm	Sand above, mud in hose
10	VSS 13	22°35.5'	109°36.7'	1450	On fan outside San Jose Canyon	Gravity Core		A few grains of sand
11	VSS 14	22°35.2'	109°34.8'	1480	On side of levee outside San Jose Canyon	Petterson Grab		A little muddy sand with Foraminifera
12	VSS 15	22°46.3'	109°48.6'	950-900	West wall, San Lucas Canyon	Dredge		One mudstone fragment
13	VSS 18	22°47.9'	109°44.2'	220-117	Pinnacle between San Jose and Santa Maria Canyon	Dredge		Numerous rocks including granite

[1] Samples from 1963 expedition, as yet only briefly examined, are not included here.
Cores are in axis of canyon unless otherwise marked.
Dredge is pipe dredge unless marked otherwise.
Note that dredge depths are approximate.

(Continued on the following page.)

TABLE I (*Continued*)

New No.	Old No.	Lat.	Long.	Depth (fathoms)	General Location	Type of Sampler	Length of core (cm)	Description of Sample
14	VSS 19	22°45.7'	109°48.3'	1030-920	West wall, San Lucas Canyon	Dredge		Granite broken from wall
15	VSS 20	22°45.4'	109°49.4'	800-1020	Floor and W. wall San Lucas Canyon	Shipek Camera		Poor ripple marks, pieces of wood, rocks (?)
16	VSS 21	22°52.0'	109°50.7'	400-200	Northeast wall San Lucas Canyon	Dredge		Dredge empty
17	VSS 22	22°51.8'	109°52.3'	52-38	Southwest wall San Lucas Canyon	Shipek Camera		Shows rocks and profuse organisms, fans, large sponges
18	VSS 23	22°51.4'	109°51.0'	400-250	Southwest wall San Lucas Canyon	Dredge		Brecciated granite
19	VSS 24	23°49.0'	109°35.7'	400-180	Pinnacle north wall Pescadero Canyon	Dredge		Granitic outcrops
21	VSS 26	23°47.5'	109°35.4'	700	Palmas Canyon near juncture Pescadero Canyon	Gravity Core		Sand with small granite fragments
22	VSS 33	25°26.0'	109°24.0'	55	San Ignacio Canyon	Petterson Grab		Dark brown mud
23	VSS 37	25°31.4'	109°23.8'	500-400	South wall San Ignacio Canyon	Dredge		Mud, shells, hard clay
25	VSS 39	25°31.7'	109°22.5'	325-283	Near axis San Ignacio Canyon	Chain bag dredge		Soft shale and mud
26	VSS 40	25°31.7'	109°22.5'	301	San Ignacio Canyon	Gravity Core	113	Mud with sand increasing at top
26a	VSS 41	25°33.4'	109°24.9	263	San Ignacio Canyon axis	Shipek Camera		Slump scars and overhang Probably compacted clay walls
27	VSS 42	25°26.4'	109°52.0'	1725	Outermost Fuerte Canyon	Piston Core	100	Soupy sandy mud, obsidian in nose

TABLE I (*Continued*)

New No.	Old No.	Lat.	Long.	Depth (fathoms)	General Location	Type of Sampler	Length of core (cm)	Description of Sample
28	CAB 1	22°44.6'	109°49.6'	1000-870	West wall, San Lucas Canyon	Dredge		Granitic rock broken from outcrops (see fig. 7)
29	CAB 5	22°35.5'	109°51.0'	1669	Fan off San Lucas Canyon	Gravity Core		Green mud high in mica
30	CAB 7	22°31.8'	109°41.8'	1545	Fan between San Lucas & San Jose canyons	Gravity Core	22	Green mud (12% sand, half mica)
31	CAB 8	22°31.3'	109°46.3'	1535	Fan off San Lucas Canyon	Gravity Core		
32	CAB 10	23°39.8'	109°40.0'	150	Palmas Canyon axis	Orange Peel		Sandy mud with grains up to 1ϕ
33	CAB 11	23°49.4'	109°33.7'	885	Pescadero Canyon	Gravity Core		Small amount sandy mud
34	CAB 15	23°26.0'	109°22.0'	500-400	South wall Frailes Canyon	Dredge		Mudstone and mud lumps
35	CAB 16	23°21.7'	109°23.7'	258	South wall Frailes Canyon	Dredge		No sample
36	CAB 17	23°22.6'	109°23.3'	280	North wall Frailes Canyon	Dredge		Angular blocks of weathered granite and other igneous types. Manganese and limonite crusts have partly recemented the rock fragments Numerous shells partly shallow water origin and includes Pectens of probable Pliocene age.
37	CAB 18	22°52.3'	109°35.2'	680-550	West wall San Jose Canyon	Dredge		No sample but dredge was rock scarred
38	CAB 19	22°45.5'	109°34.1'	1000-950	West wall San Jose Canyon	Dredge		Gneissic crystal rock, claystone with quartz grains up to granule, graywacke

TABLE I (*Continued*)

New No.	Old No.	Lat.	Long.	Depth (fathoms)	General Location	Type of Sampler	Length of core (cm)	Description of Sample
39	CAB 20	22°37.3'	109°31.5'	1400-1380	Levee outside San Jose Canyon	Chain dredge		Manganese nodules, green mud
40	SL 1	22°43.6'	109°36.0'	1100-1000	West wall San Jose Canyon	Chain dredge		Mud, coarse sand, hard clay with liminite
41	SL 2	22°45.0'	109°32.8'	1039-800	West wall San Jose Canyon	Chain dredge		Basaltic andesite, basalt and granite cobble
42	SL 3	22°50.5'	109°49.7'	640	San Lucas Canyon	Piston core		A few sand grains
43	SL 4	22°47.0'	109°48.1'	940	San Lucas Canyon	Piston core	318	Thick graded sand layer near top, other sand layers below
44	SL 5	22°45.3'	109°34.2'	1175	San Jose Canyon	Piston core	548	Thick sand layers especially in upper portion
45	SL 6	22°59.3'	109°35.1'	406	San Jose Canyon	Piston core	256	All sand, few organisms, but disturbed by coring
46	SL 7	23°00.1'	109°31.8'	270-230	Head of Gorda Canyon	Dredge		No sample
47	SL 8	23°00.5'	109°32.4'	280-250	Head of Gorda Canyon	Dredge		Mudstone
48	SL 9	23°22.5'	109°22.7'	380-230	North wall Frailes Canyon	Dredge		Ang. biotite granite rounded volc.
49	SL 10	23°22.0'	109°23.3'	370	Frailes Canyon	Piston core	382	Disturbed sand, low in organisms, 87-98 cm sand
50	SL 11	23°22.1'	109°25.0'	100-50	North wall Frailes Canyon	Dredge		Granitic rocks and cobbles, sheared
51	SL 12	23°22.3'	109°25.4'	120	Frailes Canyon	Gravity core		Small chips granite, nose bent
52	SL 13	23°22.2'	109°25.4'	125	Frailes Canyon	Gravity core	3	Fine sand. High mica and plant frags. Some rock frags.

TABLE I (*Continued*)

New No.	Old No.	Lat.	Long.	Depth (fathoms)	General Location	Type of Sampler	Length of core (cm)	Description of Sample
53	SL 14	23°21.8'	109°25.3'	150-50	Frailes Canyon Southwest wall	Dredge		Anchored ship. No sample
54	SL 15	23°26.0'	109°21.7'	500-340	NE wall Pulmo Canyon	Dredge		Large outcrops, highly fractured igneous rocks
55	SL 16	23°01.3'	109°27.6'	50-35	Gorda Bank	Dredge		Granite block broken off
56	SL 17	22°34.9'	109°46.1'	1480	Fan off San Lucas Canyon	Piston core	50	Pilot core had sand and gravel in nose. Angular gravel in piston core.
57	SL 18	22°34.8'	109°49.2'	1440	Fan off San Lucas Canyon	Piston core	374	Many sand layers. Very fine sand with silt. Considerable mica. Pl.Forams
58	SL 19	22°50.9'	110°13.3'	900	Tinaja Trough	Piston core	20	Hard clay,free of organisms
59	SL 20	22°51.0'	110°14.3'	700-600	West wall Tinaja Trough	Dredge		Claystone granodiorite weathered granite
60	SL 21	22°52.0'	110°13.0'	880	Tinaja Trough	Gravity core	8	Hard clay
63	BAC 4	23°00.6'	110°12.4'	626	Upper Tinaja Trough	Piston core	156	Shallow Forams (see fig.6) Graded sand with ungraded sand and gravel below
64	BAC 5	22°36.6'	109°33.4'	1425-1390	Levee off San Jose Canyon	Dredge		Woody material. Considerable sand and fine gravel
65	BAC 7	22°36.8'	109°32.2'	1385	East levee off San Jose Canyon	Piston core	175	Coarse sand. Mud and sand layers. Rock frags. Granite
66	BAC 9	22°40.6'	109°48.7'	1235	Outer San Lucas Canyon	Piston core	140	Fine sand grading to coarse sand with gravel. Lower ungraded. Very clean sand except at top. Low organisms

TABLE I (*Continued*)

New No.	Old No.	Lat.	Long.	Depth (fathoms)	General Location	Type of Sampler	Length of core (cm)	Description of Sample
67	BAC 10	22°45.0'	109°47.1'	980-830	West wall San Lucas Canyon	Dredge		Mud only
68	BAC 11	22°51.4'	109°44.0'	642-500	East wall Santa Maria Canyon	Dredge		Claystone, cobbles of granite, dacite, & basalt
69	BAC 12	22°55.5'	109°36.7'	480-300	West wall San Jose Canyon	Dredge		Claystone fragments only, but anchored ship
70	BAC 14	23°01.8'	109°37.2'	250-180	West wall San Jose Canyon	Dredge		Mud only
71	BAC 15	23°02.1'	109°37.0'	281	San Jose Canyon	Piston core		A little mud
72	BAC 16	22°52.5'	109°34.7'	740	San Jose Canyon	Piston core		No core
73	BAC 17	22°50.0'	109°16.7'	680-550	West side Cabrillo Seamount	Dredge		Greatly sheared, high in quartz, manganese crusts
74	BAC 18	23°14.3'	109°18.8'	940-870	North wall Salado Canyon	Dredge		Anchored, but only shells and one granite
75	BAC 19	23°17.9'	109°22.7'	540-400	North wall Salado Canyon	Dredge		Granite outcrops. Beach rock with arkosic sand, shells
76	BAC 21	23°22.5'	109°18.7'	750	Frailes Canyon	Piston core		No core
77	BAC 22	23°24.6'	109°23.2'	340-260	Salatito Canyon	Dredge		Shale fragments, stratified sands, pectens
78	BAC 23		109°26.2'	470-400	NW wall Arena Canyon	Dredge		Hard mud lumps
79	BAC 24	23°30.8'	109°24.5'	240-100	SE Arena Canyon	Dredge		Large cobbles and rather angular igenous rocks, shells and sand
80	BAC 25	23°41.0'	109°32.5'	360-240	Trinidad Canyon	Dredge		Green mud, a little wood

New No.	Old No.	Lat.	Long.	Depth (fathoms)	General Location	Type of Sampler	Length of core (cm)	Description of Sample
81	BAC 26	23°41.4'	109°33.1'	400-316	Trinidad Canyon	Dredge		Mud, shells and wood
82	BAC 28	25°30.8'	109°27.1'	800	San Ignacio Canyon	Piston core	185	Gray clay, sandy at top, small pieces of rock in bottom
83	BAC 29	25°24.5'	109°27.2'	680-480	Escarpment off San Ignacio Farallon Is.	Dredge		Basalt,Pelecypods, mud
84	BAC 30	25°12.8'	109°06.0'	430-270	Southeast wall Sinaloa Canyon	Dredge		Siltstone, probably harder rock also as dredge was badly bent
85	BAC 31	25°11.7'	109°07.7'	600-480	Sinaloa Canyon	Dredge		Clay with shells
86	BAC 32	25°12.0'	109°08.5'	670	Sinaloa Canyon	Piston core	350	Gray clay
87	BAC 33	25°34.75'	109°31.3'	580	Fuerte Canyon North branch	Piston core	370	All mud
88	BAC 34	25°28.1'	109°27.2'	650-300	SE wall San Ignacio Canyon	Dredge		Greatly sheared metamorphic or plutonic rock
89	BAC 35	25°35.8'	109°25.3'	20	San Ignacio Canyon	Snapper		Mud
90	BAC 37	23°46.7'	109°38.3'	314	Pescadero Canyon	Petterson Grab		Green mud
91	BAC 38	23°47.0'	109°38.1'	610	Pescadero Canyon	Piston core Small Gravity core		Hit rock, bent nose. Mud in pilot core.
92	BAC 39	23°45.7'	109°40.6'	360	Pescadero Canyon	Piston core		No sample but polished by sand
93	BAC 41	23°48.2'	109°36.0'	795	Pescadero Canyon	Piston core		No core, bent barrel
94	BAC 42	23°46.9'	109°34.7'	640-550	Palmas Canyon East wall	Dredge		Anchored but no sample except sponge
95	BAC 43	23°47.0'	109°35.2'	773-700	Palmas Canyon East wall	Dredge		No sample, but caught very hard

TABLE I (*Continued*)

New No.	Old No.	Lat.	Long.	Depth (fathoms)	General Location	Type of Sampler	Length of core (cm)	Description of Sample
96	BAC 44	23°21.7'	109°18.5'	780-550	Floor and wall, Frailes Canyon	Dredge		Granite outcrop,manganese coating, coarse sand, cross-bedding abraded mollusks
97	BAC 45	23°16.4'	109°20.3'	700-450	North wall Salado Canyon	Dredge		Granite, partly weathered. Apparently pulled up vertical cliff
98	BAC 46	23°24.2'	109°18.1'	820	On fan near Salatito Canyon	Piston core	168	Planktonic Foram, mud, sand, grass
99	BAC 47	23°14.8'	109°18.9'	954	Salado Canyon	Piston core		Mud on top
100	BAC 48	23°22.2'	109°20.0'	675	Frailes Canyon	Piston core		Nose damaged, sand in pilot snapper
101	BAC 49	23°47.0'	109°39.9'	300-175	Head axis Pescadero Canyon	Dredge		Sand, gravel, shells, a few rock fragments
102	BAC 50	23°48.0'	109°38.3'	500-400	Pescadero Canyon Northwest side	Dredge		Coarse sand, mud, clay, shells and cobbles. Shells indicate fauna less than 50 meters.
103	BAC 52	23°40.6'	109°35.7'	360-250	East wall Santiago Canyon	Dredge		Basalt with flow structure
104	BAC 53	23°42.1'	109°36.7'	505-400	East wall Palmas Canyon	Dredge		Large slabs of shale,partly laminated, partly nodular Miocene age
105	BAC 54	23°42.1'	109°37.0'	535	Palmas Canyon	Piston core small snapper		Badly bent core tube. Muddy sand in snapper.
106	BAC 55	22°55.5'	109°36.5'	520-300	West wall San Jose Canyon	Dredge		Weathered igneous rock
107	BAC 56	22°49.0'	109°34.0'	864-700	West wall San Jose Canyon	Dredge		Igneous rock, shale with angular fragments

TABLE I (*Continued*)

New No.	Old No.	Lat.	Long.	Depth (fathoms)	General Location	Type of Sampler	Length of core (cm)	Description of Sample
108	BAC 57	22°50.3'	109°45.0'	730	Santa Maria Canyon	Piston core		Nose badly bent, no core, sand grains
109	BAC 58	22°50.3'	109°45.2'	750-700	East wall and floor Santa Maria Canyon	Dredge		Pockets coarse sand, large igneous rocks. Shells from shelf fauna less than 50 m. deep
110	BAC 59	22°49.0'	109°14.5'	525-400	Top of Cabrillo Seamount	Dredge		Granitic highly fractured fault zone, Mn crust
111	BAC 60	22°46.9'	109°52.9'	670-600	West wall Vigia Canyon	Dredge		Laminated, shale granite boulders. Porphyritic andesite
112	BAC 61	22°49.8'	109°54.2'	640-530	NW wall Vigia Canyon	Dredge		Rotten granite with manganese. Also some fresh granite.
113	BAC 62	22°45.4'	109°55.0'	1012	Vigia Canyon	Piston core Small snapper		Core nose bent, small amount mud
114	BAC 63	22°52.5'	109°53.2'	100-40	NW wall San Lucas Canyon	Dredge		Granite from outcrop, gneiss, quartz, diorite, abundant organisms
115	BAC 64	22°49.8'	110°03.9'	780-650	NW Cardonal Canyon	Dredge		Diatomite, Miocene or Pliocene laminated shale
116	BAC 65	23°01.9'	110°09.3'	475-380	North side Calabasa Canyon	Dredge		Angular pebbles, shells, coarse sand, wood, mud.

either side. Near the south end of this range there is a transverse outlier, Sierra San Lazaro, that extends for 5 miles or more in an east-west direction. All along the coast there are mountains of lower elevation, with summits mostly less than 2,000 feet in elevation. The greater heights in the backbone range allow these mountains to be seen from the offshore area in most places, helping navigation considerably. Cutting the coastal range there are a number of arroyos, mostly with wide fans along their course. A number of these valleys head inland beyond the coastal mountains, draining the interior plateau and the high central range. The most pronounced valleys are at San Lucas and San José del Cabo on the south coast, and on the east coast inside Frailes Bay and at the south end of Palmas Bay.

Climatically, this area should be considered as semidesert. The rainfall is about 5–10 inches. Occasional cloudbursts transport coarse sediment down along the fans to the sea.

The coast is mostly rocky, although there are broad beaches and dunes along the shore at the mouths of the large valleys. Small barriers and saline lagoons exist along the shore at San Lucas, San José del Cabo, Frailes Bay, Riviera, and Buena Vista. The lagoons are intermittently filled and dried.

General description of the submarine topography.—Around the lower end of Baja California the continental shelf is very narrow or missing (Chart I, in pocket). It shows bulges of a few miles off Cabo Falso, Palmilla Point, and the widest bulge of about 7 miles off the southeast corner extends for 10 miles to the east of Gorda Bank. Beginning near Cabo Falso, the southwest corner of the Peninsula, there is a virtually continuous series of submarine canyons that extend out 10–20 nautical miles from the coast to points where they terminate at depths from 900 to 1,300 fathoms. Because the high mountains and the generally clear weather allowed visual fixes during most of the daytime operations, all of these canyons were surveyed with considerable accuracy. The canyons thus delineated proved to be steep-sided and *V*-shaped with winding courses and numerous tributaries. Along the west coast, north of Cabo Falso, on the other hand, there is a straight-sided valley extending virtually parallel to the coast in contrast to the canyons farther south and east that extend out roughly at right angles to the coast. A more detailed description of each of these valleys along with the information from diving, dredging, and coring operations will follow.

San Lucas Canyon (*Fig. 1*). San Lucas Canyon, in many ways the most interesting of the canyons, extends out of San Lucas Bay at the south cape and comes up to the end of the pier at the fish cannery (Fig. 2). Several short, steep tributaries enter the inner canyon on the south side, coming down from the north side of the granite promontory. This point protects the bay entrance from the full effect of all but easterly wave approaches although large refracted waves come around the point under some conditions. One of the tributaries is unique because it has a small projecting rock rising out of an axial depth of about 40 fathoms. When the water is clear, a swimmer using a face plate can look down from the surface at a vertical wall of granite that forms one side of a steep gorge. This is a tributary to the main channel of the canyon. Shoreward of this rock one can swim into the head of the gorge at a point a few feet from the beach.

The seaward tip of Cape San Lucas consists of a series of granite stacks, the shorewardmost being connected to the mainland by a tombolo. This beach is overtopped by waves during storms and sand is carried into a tributary down which it moves as a sand flow. This phenomenon has now been seen in both southern tributaries in three out of six periods of diving. It was first photographed by a group of biologists under the leadership of Conrad Limbaugh (Fig. 3; North, 1960) and later studied with great care by geologists (Dill, 1964). Both groups obtained excellent moving pictures that show the slow sand flow (about 0.1–0.2 knot) down a 37° slope and the rapid falling of the sand over low cliffs along the descent

→

FIG. 1.—Showing the granite-walled San Lucas Canyon which heads off the large arroyo entering the coast at San Lucas. The principal head of Santa Maria Canyon is shown extending into the rocky gorge just west of Palmilla Point. The fans outside of San Lucas and Vigia Canyons are indicated. Contour interval 50 fathoms, with 25-fathom intervals added beyond 1,350. Sounding lines and samples shown in overprint.

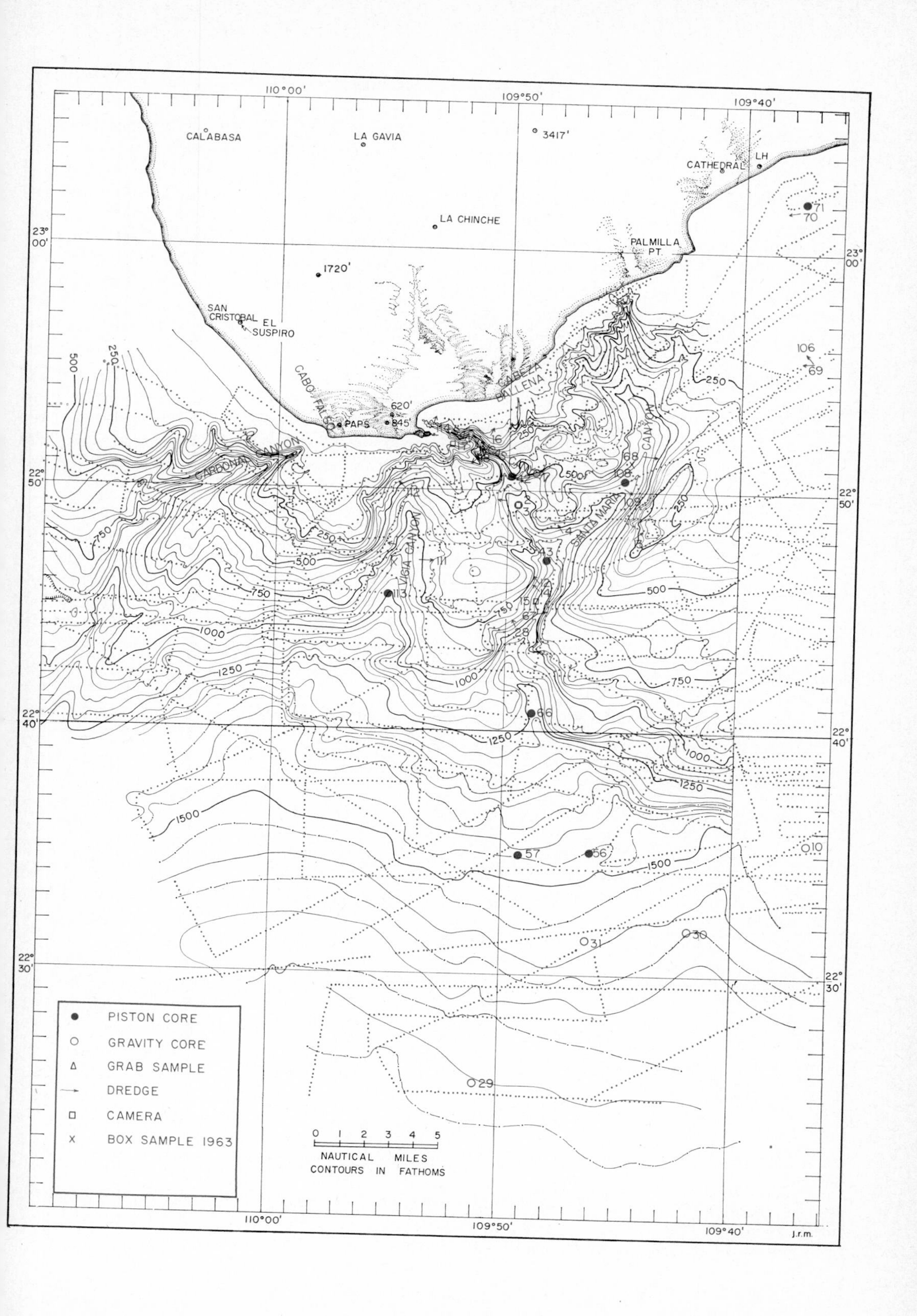
110°00'
109°50'
109°40'
23° 00'
22° 50'
22° 40'
22° 30'
CALABASA
LA GAVIA
3417'
CATHEDRAL
LH
LA CHINCHE
PALMILLA PT.
1720'
SAN CRISTOBAL
EL SUSPIRO
CABO FALSO
PAPS
620'
845'
CABEZA BALLENA
CARDONAL CANYON
VIGIA CANYON
SANTA MARIA CANYON
250
500
750
1000
1250
1500
PISTON CORE
GRAVITY CORE
GRAB SAMPLE
DREDGE
CAMERA
BOX SAMPLE 1963
0 1 2 3 4 5
NAUTICAL MILES
CONTOURS IN FATHOMS
J.r.m.

into the deep gorge below. From the vast extent of the flows and from the fact that they have been seen three times, it seems highly probable that these sand flows carry large quantities of sediment into the main axis of the canyon. The sand is evidently supplied from the beach on the outside of the point, although it presumably comes originally from the arroyo that lies north of the town, direct transportation over the low pass west of the 500-foot peak (called Vigia) being provided by the wind. Thence, waves move it along the beach and rocky coast as the result of the diagonal approach of the westerly swell.

According to Dill (1964), the granite walls along the path of the sand flows are greatly smoothed and even undercut in some places, suggesting erosive effects of the sand-flow action combined with gravity creep. The sand that comes over the tombolo is coarse, with a median diameter of about 1 mm. According to Dill, the sand is graded in cross section like a turbidity-current deposit, although the flow is decidedly different from any turbidity current observed either in tanks or in theory, as it shows no surface turbulence. Locally there are concentrations of coarse debris in the low ridges on the sand flow that look like miniature medial or lateral moraines on a glacier (Fig. 4). Blocks of rock of large size are carried along on the surface of the flow. No mud is present in the flow so far as has been determined, and the sand must flow down the steep gorge to the floor of the main canyon without much opportunity to pick

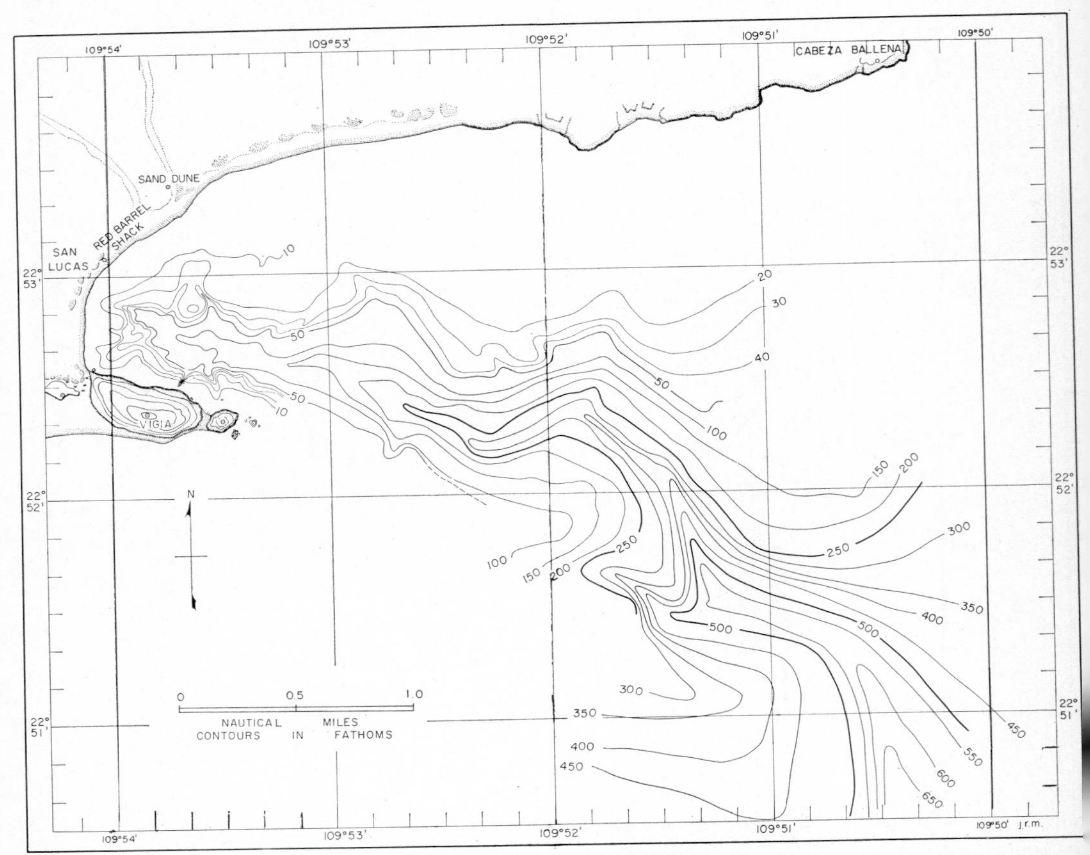

FIG. 2.—The head of San Lucas Canyon. Shows also the sand source from the west which is carried over the tombolo during high waves and moves into the small tributary to the north. Contour interval 10 fathoms to 50, and 50 fathoms beyond.

FIG. 3.—Flowing sand and sandfall at 27 fathoms depth in the tributary north of the tombolo on San Lucas Point. The total fall is of the order of 15 feet. This movement was observed after large waves had swept across the tombolo. Photograph by Conrad Limbaugh in March 1959.

up mud for the development of a possible turbidity flow at a lower level.

The head of the canyon outside the pier at San Lucas and the head of a tributary to the north, both have coarse sand bottom with well-developed ripple marks down to a depth of 30 feet. Below this depth the bottom is relatively flat with a slight hummocky topography indicating near-surface slumping down to depths of 70 feet. Below this, outcrops of cemented beach rock were found by Dill. The north wall of the canyon near the entrance to the bay was dredged at about 100 fathoms, yielding angular granite blocks, some clearly broken from outcrops, along with other types of igneous rocks, the latter partly rounded. Large numbers of organisms were also recovered

FIG. 4.—Flowing sand in the small tributary west of the point where Fig. 3 was taken. Note the rock debris that is moving down the sand flow like a medial moraine on a glacier. Photograph by R.F. Dill, in April 1962. See beer can for scale.

in the dredge, including mollusks, Gorgonian corals, sponges, and an assortment of wood fragments.

Photographs by Carl J. Shipek of the southwest wall outside of the bay show an irregular rocky bottom and a profuse growth of organisms (*see* Shepard, 1961, Fig. 5). At an axial depth of 930 fathoms the walls rise to a high peak of 158 fathoms on the east and to 571 fathoms on the west, giving the canyon an average depth of 570 fathoms (3,420 feet). This is as deep as all but a few of the deepest of North American land canyons and is surpassed by only a few submarine canyons such as that off Monterey, California. The gradient of San Lucas Canyon out to 1,000 fathoms maintains a slope of about 10 per cent (5°40′) and thence to the fan at 1,300 fathoms the slope is about 4 per cent (2°20′). Beyond, the fan

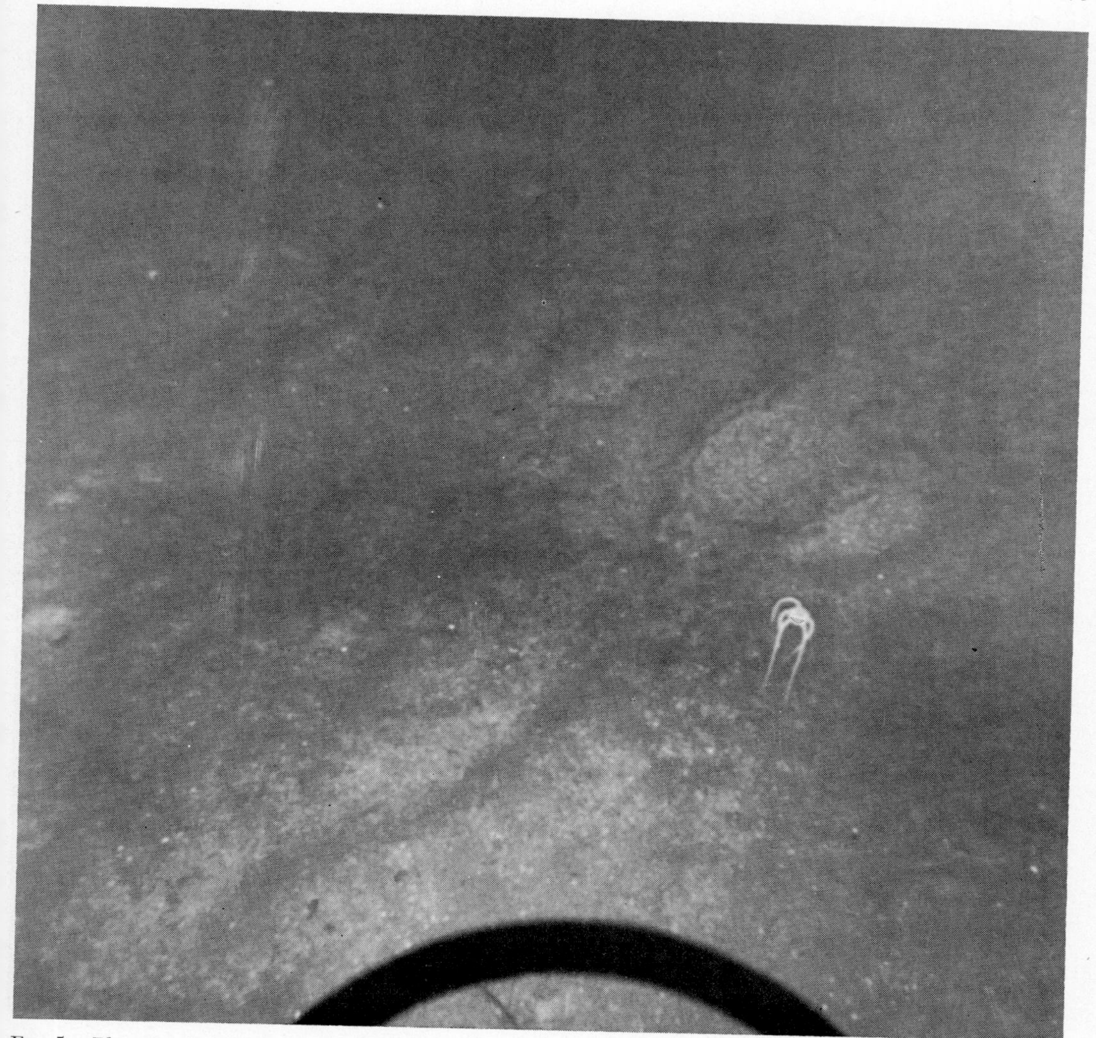

FIG. 5.—Photograph in approximately 1,000 fathoms depth showing what appear to be ripple marks on the bottom of San Lucas Canyon. The brittle star is about 4 inches across. Photograph by Carl J. Shipek.

drops at a slope of about 2 per cent (1°10′) to 1,650 fathoms.

A considerable number of tributaries come in to the main canyon—perhaps more than are shown by the contours, for lines along the walls are not so well developed as would be desirable. A large tributary, called Santa Maria Canyon, comes in from the east joining the San Lucas branch at about 930 fathoms. This eastern branch has about the same length as San Lucas Canyon. It also extends in close to the shore, particularly in its eastern branch. Like the head in San Lucas Bay, the eastern arm of Santa Maria Canyon is located off an arroyo. Santa Maria Canyon is wider and has much less precipitous walls than San Lucas Canyon. The difference between the two canyons may be due to the softer rock into which Santa Maria Canyon is cut. Dredging here has yielded mostly mudstone and cobbles, the latter including crystalline rock. The shallow bank that has a high point of 111 fathoms on the east side of the canyon has outcrops of granite, however, so that the wall rock of this canyon is not all soft. On the west side of the main canyon there is a small tributary that heads in about 600 fathoms and comes nowhere near either the coast or any source of present day sediment.

One dredge sample coming from a depth of about 350 fathoms (Sample 18)[4] included brecciated granite blocks that are recemented with a matrix containing benthic Foraminifera. Examination of these Foraminifera by Robert R. Lankford showed that they were characteristic of the present depths and thus suggest that the cementation has taken place after the canyon reached at least approximately its present level. A dredge sample from the floor and east wall of Santa Maria Canyon at 750 to 700 fathoms (Sample 109) yielded shells that represent a shelf fauna interpreted by E.C. Allison as coming from a depth of less than 27 fathoms.

A photograph taken at about 1,000 fathoms by the Shipek camera in or near the axis of the San Lucas Canyon showed the presence of what appear to be ripple marks (Fig. 5). These are not nearly as pronounced as ripple marks obtained along the axis of a small canyon outside Tokyo Bay (Shepard and others, in preparation).

Attempts to core both the floors of San Lucas and Santa Maria canyons have been disappointing except at depths of 950 and 1,235 fathoms. The latter core came from the very outer portion of the combined canyon (Sample 66). This core, 140 cm long, consists largely of sand and has complete gradation down into coarser material with a considerable amount of gravel (Fig. 6). The lower portion of the core is variable in texture and rather poorly sorted but has no fines. It appears to resemble some turbidites in the southern French Alps described by Bouma (1962, Fig. 10 T_a, and Pl. A-4, H-1). The largest gravel fragment was about 4 cm in diameter. The gravel is rather angular, consisting of granite and other intrusives. The material, aside from the gravel, is similar to the sand that comes down in the sandfall in San Lucas Bay. Analyses of sections of the core are given in part in Figure 6. The percentage of silt is generally less than 0.5, and very little material is less than 0.25 mm in diameter. Hence, it does not fit the usual definition of a graywacke. The medians run from +3 *phi* to −1 *phi*, the coarsest at the base of the graded layer. The mica content shows a sharp decrease from the top to 10 cm, whereas the calcareous organisms are most abundant at about 40 cm where there are many shell fragments. Foraminifera in the core, according to Frances L. Parker, include *Elphidium* that live only in shallow water.

Several box cores have been obtained from the axis of Santa Maria Canyon. Preliminary study shows the following—at 183 fathoms thin, slightly folded sand layers were found between muddy sediments. At 368 fathoms a gravel and coarse sand layer at the base of the sample is cut off abruptly and covered unconformably by silty sediments. The latter appear to grade upward into finer material and contain a few drag folds. At 655 fathoms there are gravelly sand beds with some indication of graded bedding. These are interbedded with thin clayey layers and 3 inches of silty clay is found on top.

The walls of the lower canyon are variable in character, much of them covered by sediment. There are some places where dredges were pulled for about a mile up the wall but failed to yield rock or signs of rock. A series of photographs in 800- to 1,000-fathom depths also showed no rock on the west wall at a place where the canyon axis is 1,000 fathoms deep. Angular blocks of rock, clearly broken off and including granite, however, were dredged in slightly less than 1,000 fathoms (Fig. 7). Also a dredging showed coarse sediment, presumably from the axis, at 1,000 fathoms. Claystone was obtained from wall depths of 800

[4] For locations of samples, see Table I.

→

Fig. 6.—Photographs of cores. Bac. No. 4 was taken at 626 fathoms in Tinaja Trough at the lower end of Inner Candalaria Canyon. Bac. No. 9 was taken at 1,235 fathoms in the outer portion of San Lucas Canyon. Rather angular pieces of gravel in the lower portions of the cores are shown. The upper portions have graded bedding, as is shown by the median diameters. The sorting is good but in both cores there is a decrease in sorting below the top. In both cores mica decreases from top to bottom.

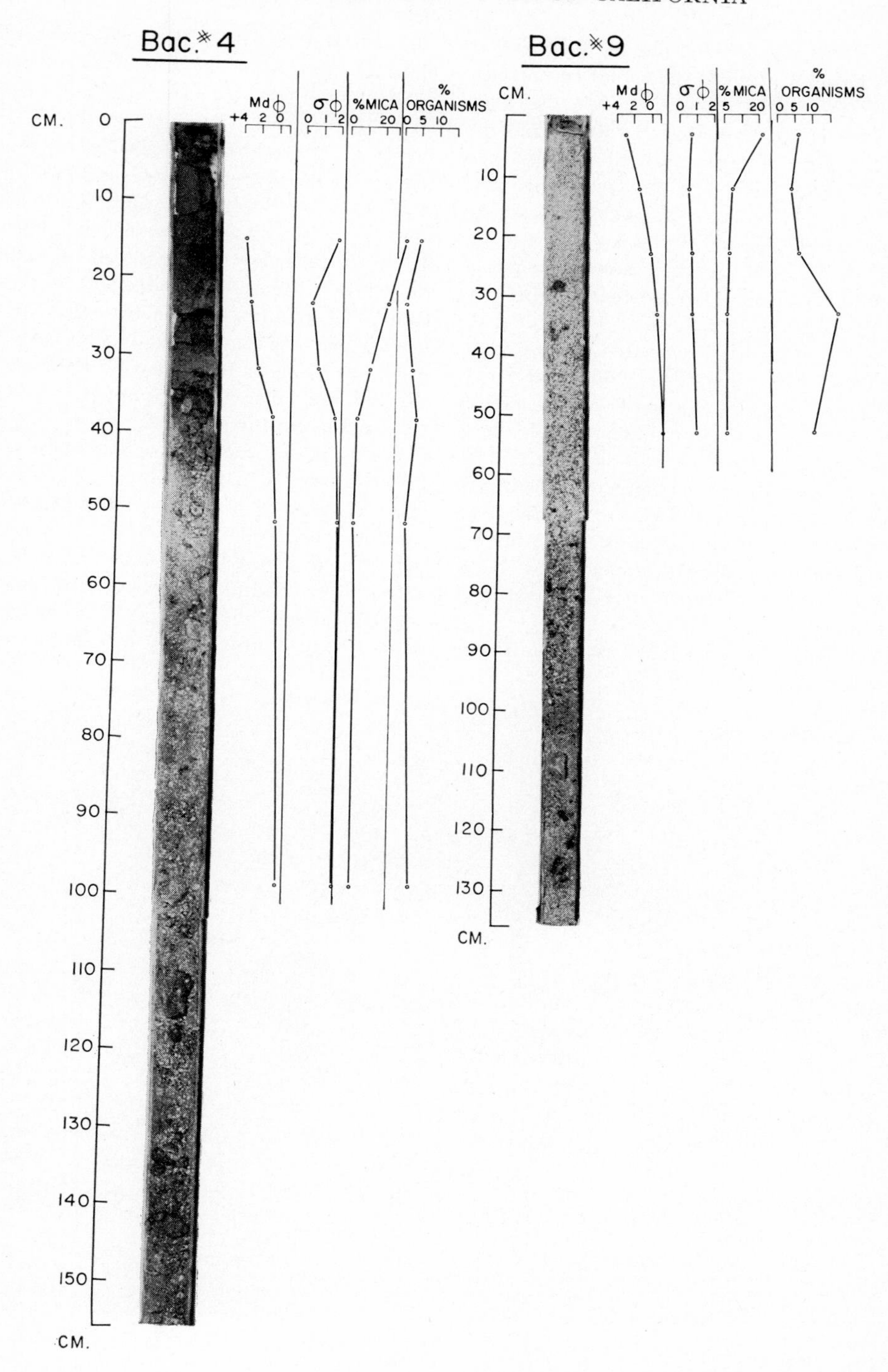
Bac.* 4
CM.
0
10
20
30
40
50
60
70
80
90
100
110
120
130
140
150
CM.
Md ϕ
+4 2 0
σ ϕ
0 1 2
% MICA
0 20
% ORGANISMS
0 5 10
Bac.* 9
CM.
10
20
30
40
50
60
70
80
90
100
110
120
130
CM.
Md ϕ
+4 2 0
σ ϕ
0 1 2
% MICA
5 20
% ORGANISMS
0 5 10

fathoms. Dredging at a depth of 980 to 830 fathoms, however, yielded only mud on the east wall.

Beyond axial depths of about 1,150 fathoms the canyon appears to enter a fan with a small channel and a natural levee on the west side. The channel swings left as do the deep channels off the west coast of the United States as described by Menard (1955). However, the channel becomes of negligible dimensions or nonexistent a short distance out on the fan.

The terminal fan has been cored and found to contain thin layers of fine or very fine sand. Some benthonic Foraminifera of a shallow-water facies, identified by Jean P. Hosmer in one sample, indicate the importance of recent transportation of sand out onto the fan. The thinness of the layers and their fine grain seem to indicate that the relatively powerful transporting agent suggested by the thick coarse sediments emplaced at 1,200 fathoms in the outer canyon, does not continue out onto the fan.

Vigia Canyon (*Fig. 1*).—Just west of San Lucas Canyon there is another deep valley extending ir close to the coast off the beach south of the towr of San Lucas. Detailed soundings of its head shov that it comes within $\frac{1}{4}$ mile of the beach where a depth of 10 fathoms was sounded between fathoms. Vigia Canyon has several tributaries a its head but no sign of any important branche lower down. In some sections it has a floor abou 400 fathoms below the crests of the bordering ridges, but the walls are less precipitous thar those of San Lucas Canyon. At 1,200 fathoms i has become a channel with a natural levee on th west side. This outer valley or channel, unlik that off San Lucas Canyon, apparently bends t the right in entering the fan.

Coring in the canyon was attempted at 1,00 fathoms but failed to produce results, owing t hitting hard sand or rock bottom, as shown by th bend in the core barrel. In 1963 a box sample a 926 fathoms showed a few rock fragments unde a thin layer of sand and gravel with rough grad ing. Dredging on the west wall of the inner canyo at depths of approximately 600 fathoms yielde

Fig. 7.—A group of angular granitic rocks, some with fresh fractures, obtained from approximately 1,000 fathoms on the west wall of San Lucas Canyon. Scale is in centimeters.

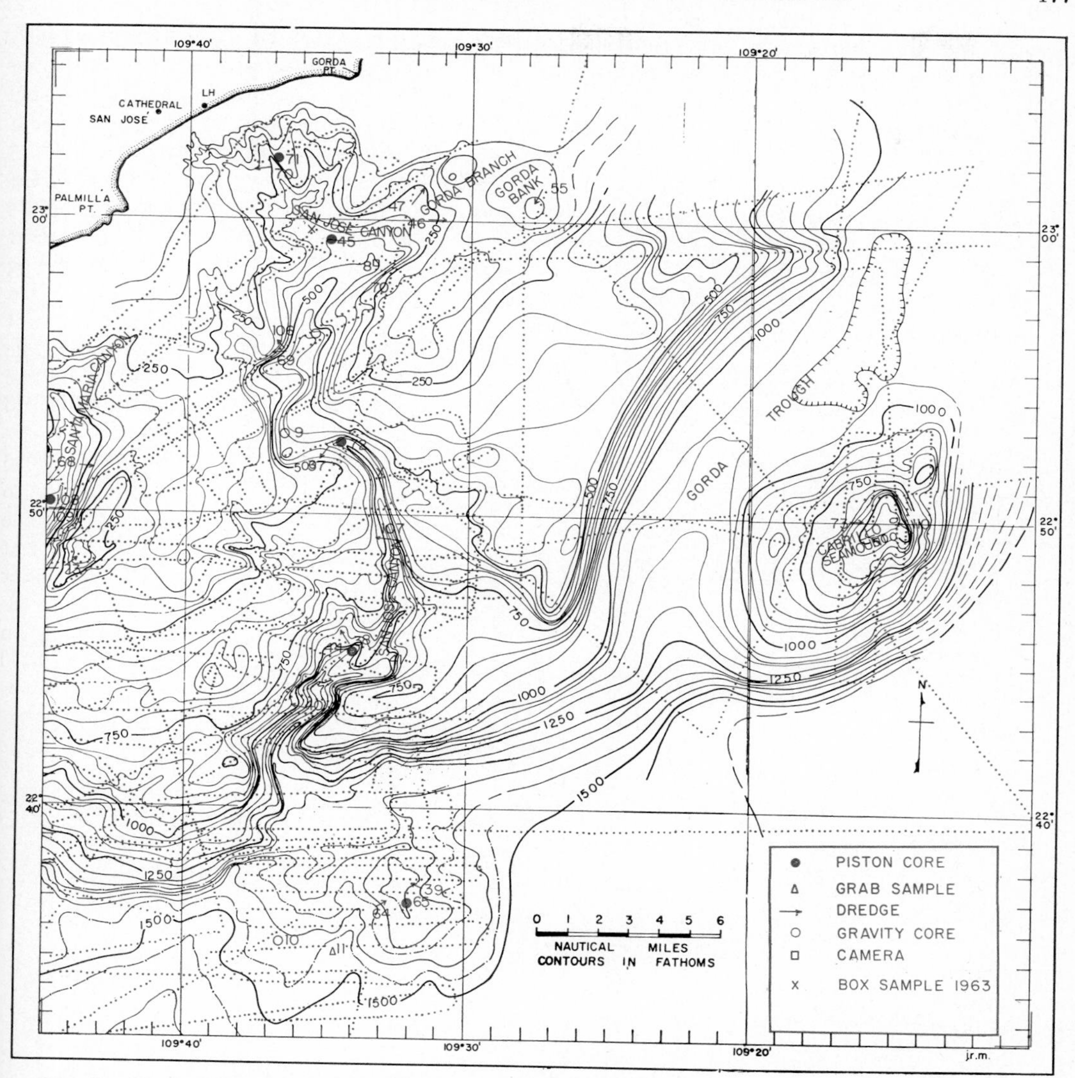

FIG. 8.—Showing San José Canyon off the southeast corner of Baja California. The canyon apparently terminates at the base of the escarpment but farther out there is a winding valley with ridges rising above it, shown in more detail in Fig. 10. Also indicated are Gorda Trough and Cabrillo Seamount. Contour interval 50 fathoms, with 25-fathom intervals included locally in the southwest corner. Sounding lines and samples shown in overprint.

granite blocks, some deeply weathered. Dredging at 750 fathoms on the east wall brought up large boulders of granite and blocks of laminated shale (Sample 111). The fresh fractures indicate that the shale must crop out. The shale contains Foraminifera which according to Frances L. Parker appear to be Pliocene or possibly Pleistocene.

San José Canyon (*Fig. 8*).—The second largest canyon of the Gulf area is located off the town of San José del Cabo. On land, here, the largest of the intermontane valleys, probably a fault valley, crosses the coastal range and there is a relatively wide coastal plain bordered by a barrier and a narrow saline lagoon. The submarine canyon head lies somewhat east of the axis of the intermontane valley and east of the lagoon outlet so that one cannot say that the present land drainage is definitely connected to the canyon. The head of the canyon (Fig. 9), unlike neighboring San Lucas Canyon, is apparently cut into unconsolidated sediment. Out to depths of 500 fathoms no dredging obtained rock. Like the valleys in other alluvial fills at submarine canyon heads, the inner valley has many branches, one extending in to at least ¼ mile from the shoreline. A dive by Dill showed that cobbles and sand occur in this inner channel. As in San Lucas Canyon, San José Canyon has one main tributary. This tributary, called Gorda Canyon, has two heads extending into portions of the shallow Gorda Bank. This bank has solid granite outcrops on its summit at 25 fathoms, but along Gorda Canyon dredging yielded only hard clayey material. As this canyon is in line with the outer portion of Santa Maria Canyon, a structural connection is suggested. Possibly these valleys were cut along the same fault line. A core in the branch yielded a fine-sand layer between muddy material. Near the juncture with the main canyon a photograph by Shipek showed possible ripple marks in 458 fathoms.

Beyond the juncture of the two heads, the canyon becomes more deeply incised, having some sections with walls 300 fathoms high. The walls have yielded freshly broken granite and gneiss

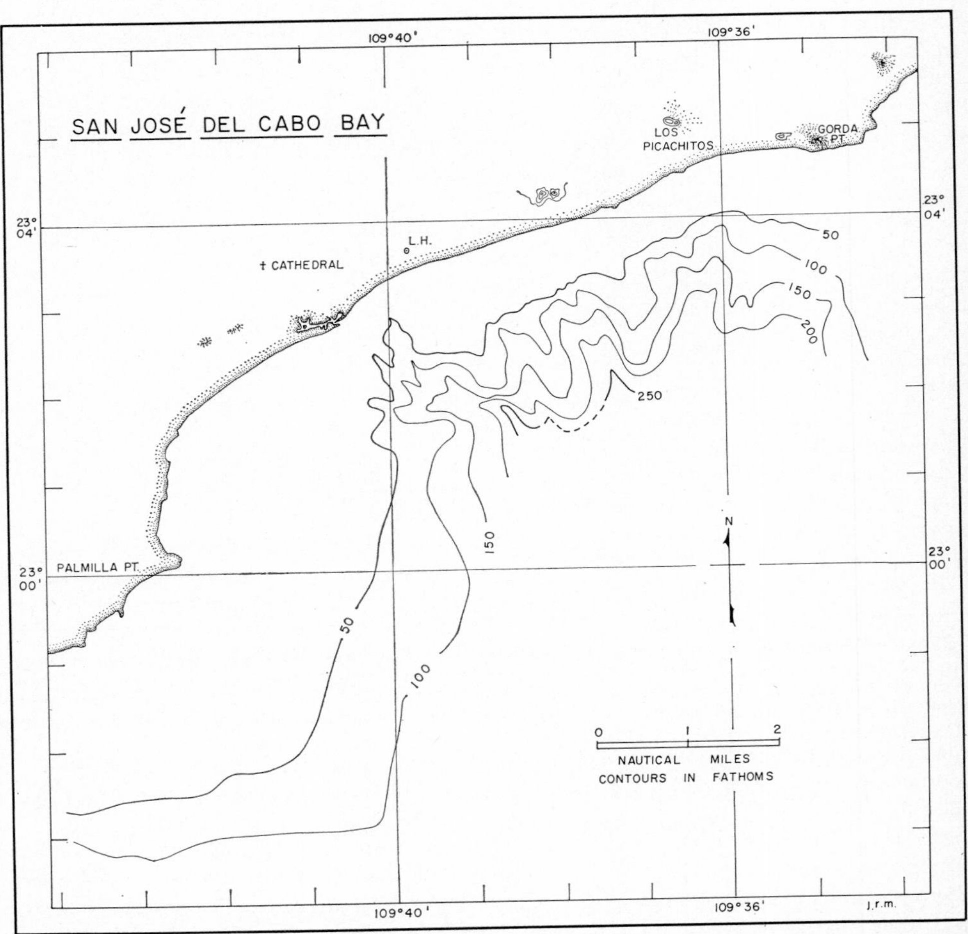

FIG. 9.—Showing the head of San José Canyon with its numerous branches. Contour interval 50 fathoms.

even at a depth of about 1,000 fathoms. Several of the dredgings from San José Canyon and its tributaries were found to contain granite and other igneous rocks, some of the rocks being deeply weathered. At greater depths, however, as in outer San Lucas Canyon, the walls appear to be entirely covered with sediment. Claystone was found at several places on the walls of the middle section of the canyon.

Cores were difficult to obtain here, also. A short core at 406 fathoms consisted entirely of fine sand. One core at 600 fathoms and another at 1,050 fathoms had sand layers of fine to very fine grain interbedded with silty clay. When dredges were pulled across the axis of the canyons, however, considerable coarse sand and gravel were recovered. Box cores showed the following—at 130 fathoms a small sample of sand and fine gravel, at 390 fathoms coarse sand and fine gravel 18 cm thick with some layering but no grading, and at 760 fathoms angular gravel up to 2 cm in diameter intermixed with coarse sand.

The outer canyon has a few rather small tributaries that head in water 400–800 fathoms deep and show no connection to coastal drainage. The deep part of the canyon continues to about 1,300 fathoms. The outer canyon is deeply incised into a steep, straight escarpment which suggests a fault scarp. Beyond where the gorge terminates, a shallow depression extends northeast along the base of the escarpment. This same escarpment apparently continues well to the northeast where there is a possible fault valley with a depth below surroundings of 500 fathoms and an outlying fault block—Cabrillo Seamount—from which highly sheared granitic rock with large quartz crystals and manganese coating was dredged.

Still farther out along the line of San José Canyon, but apparently connected with it, there is an elongate depression between ridges rising about 00 fathoms above the floor (Fig. 10). These ridges have been dredged without yielding rock. Cores show that the ridges have fan material with layers of sand. These sand layers were found by ean P. Hosmer to have a few shallow-water Foraminifera.

Tinaja Trough (*Fig. 11*).—North and west of the San Lucas area the sea floor is dominated by a north-south valley that runs in a comparatively straight line almost parallel to the coastal trend. This valley will be referred to as Tinaja Trough, although it has a narrow floor like a trench except in its northern portion. This valley has slopes approximately as steep as the submarine canyons to the southeast. So far as soundings are now available, the trough lacks appreciable entering tributaries on the west side although there are some small valleys or canyons coming into it on the northeast side. Near the southern end of the trough there appears to be another similar valley on the east, but the two are not connected although they both trend parallel to the coast.

A small canyon, called Candalaria, enters near the north end of Tinaja Trough. This canyon apparently is a continuation of Arroyo Candalaria on land, the most prominent valley along this part of the coast. The submarine canyon dies out in the trough, but virtually in line of continuation with it there is another canyon located on the outside of the outer bank, extending down the outer slope to at least 500 fathoms—the end of the soundings. It has a rocky bottom at 450 fathoms. The head of this outer canyon crosses a divide in the bank that borders the west side of Tinaja Trough, and along the inside of the bank a horizontal-floored depression extends for 1.4 miles to the northeast where it merges into the slope. The explanation of these two canyons that are in line appears to be that they have been cut in two by faulting. The existence of turbidity currents is attested to by a core from 626 fathoms in the center of the trough (Fig. 6) that contains a thick sand layer with gravel and coarse sand in its lower portion. The sediment of this core is like that found in the outermost portion of San Lucas Canyon, increasing in size downward consistently for the first 60 cm, below which it contains gravel mixed with rather coarse sand all the way to the bottom. The material in these core samples, as in the San Lucas Canyon core, is progressively better sorted downward for 22 cm; below that, sorting is of a lower order, but still relatively good, throughout. The mica content decreases with depth in the core, but the remains of organisms show no consistent change.

Cores taken farther down the axis of Tinaja Trough yielded only short lengths of a rather hard clay lacking Foraminifera and sand layers. This

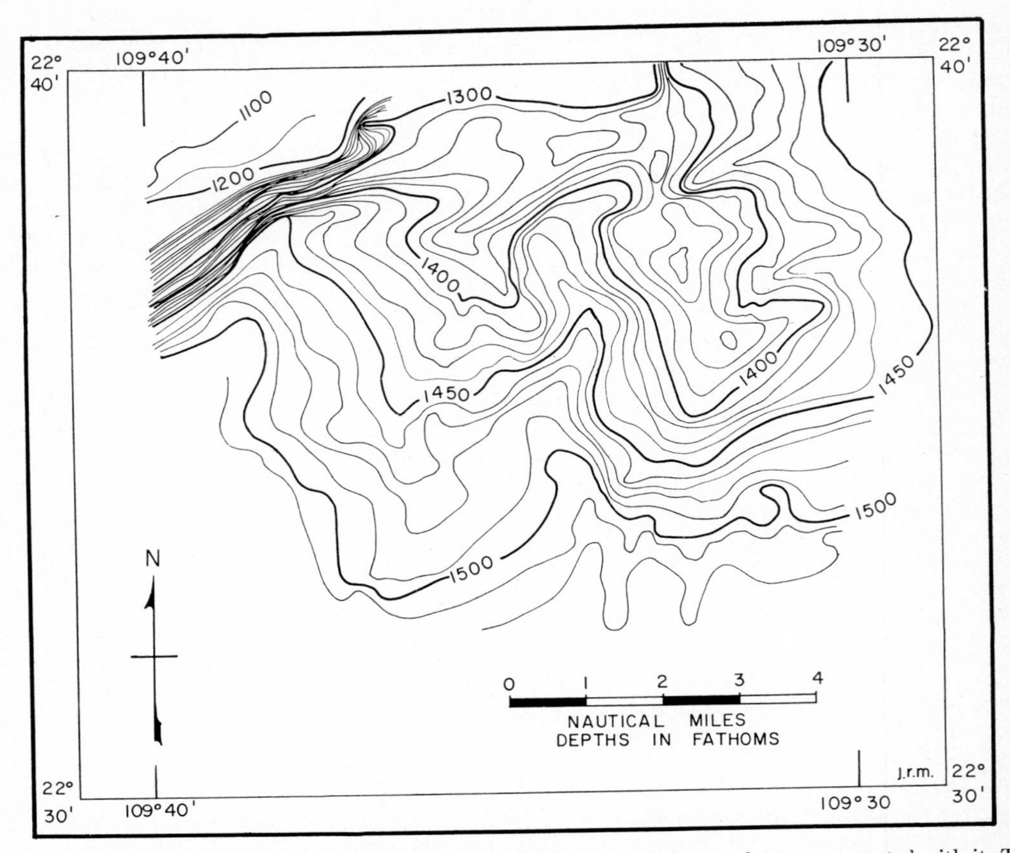

FIG. 10.—An enlargement of the fan valley found outside San José Canyon but not connected with it. Th ridges are thought to be natural levees because of sand layers found in the cores from the top of one of ther Contour interval 10 fathoms.

clay was found in two cores, both taken at about 850-fathom depths. Dredging of the western trough wall produced an abundance of angular granodiorite fragments along with other types of intrusive rock and some claystone that failed to yield any diagnostic fossils.

A grab sample taken on the floor of the eastern trench at about 900 fathoms contained the living fossil *Neopilina* (first recognized by R.H. Parker and confirmed by H. Lemche). This Paleozoic type of mollusk was first described by Lemche (1958) from the *Galathea Expedition* samples off Costa Rica. Parker found another specimen o the deep fan outside of San Lucas Canyon.

A significant submarine canyon, called Ca donal (named from the ranch at its head), is foun in the vicinity of the trough, although it does nc connect with it but turns and runs parallel to th outer portion of the trough. It extends out to depth of about 1,300 fathoms. Cardonal Canyo has a series of tributaries entering from both side Shoreward it heads near Cabo Falso, the sout west point of land, coming in to about ¼ mile fro shore. A dredging on the northwest wall of th

FIG. 11.—Tinaja Trough and associated submarine canyons. The relatively straight walls, the extension the trough parallel to the coast, and the apparent break between Inner and Outer Candalaria canyons are thoug to indicate a fault origin of the trough. Contour interval 50 fathoms, with local addition of 25 fathoms in the sout east corner. Sounding lines and samples shown in overprint.

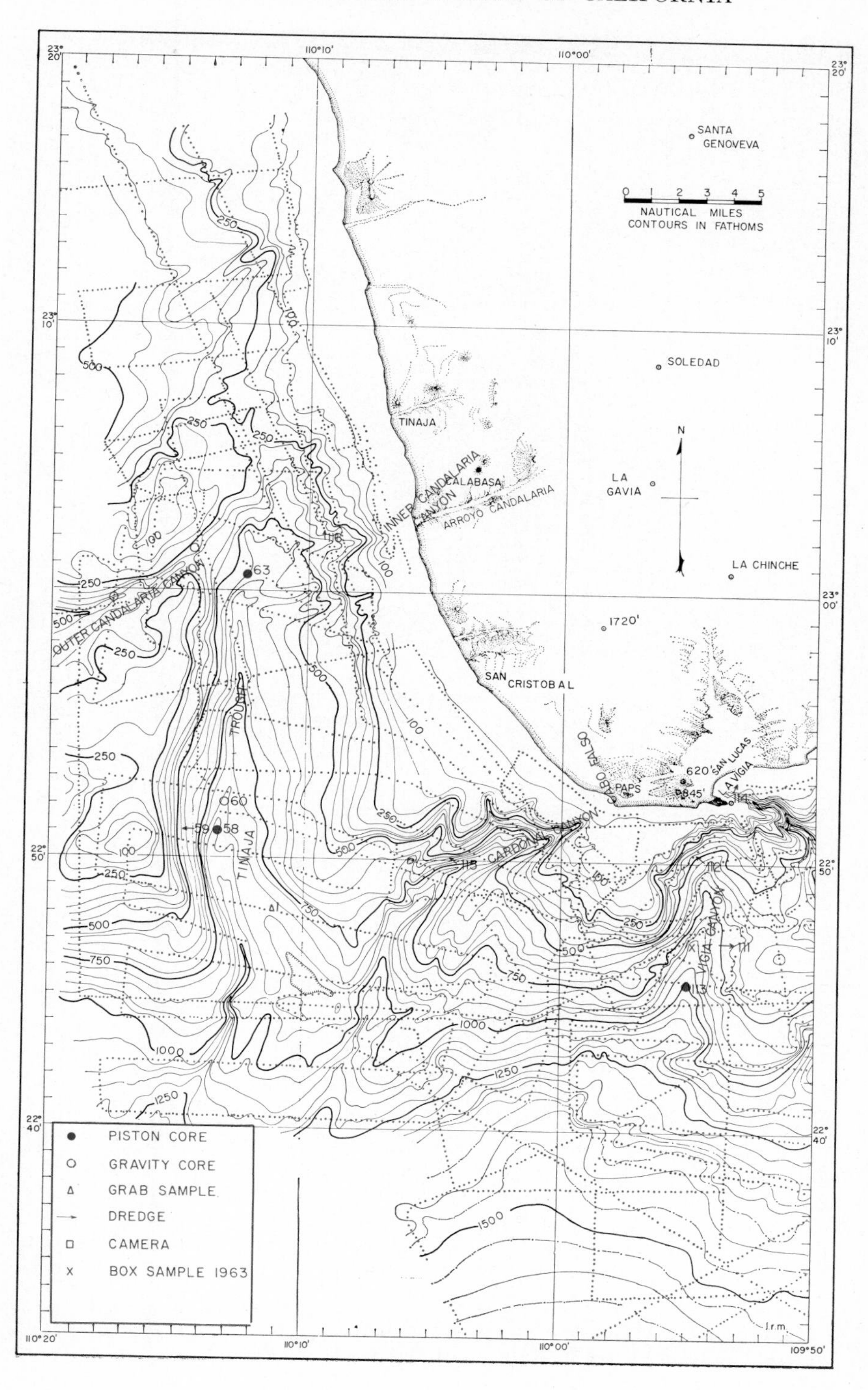

SANTA GENOVEVA
0 1 2 3 4 5
NAUTICAL MILES
CONTOURS IN FATHOMS
SOLEDAD
TINAJA
INNER CANDALARIA CANYON
CALABASA
ARROYO CANDALARIA
LA GAVIA
N
LA CHINCHE
OUTER CANDALARIA CANYON
1720'
SAN CRISTOBAL
TROUGH
TINAJA
CABO FALSO
SAN LUCAS
LA VIGIA
PAPS
620'
845'
CARDONAL CANYON
VIGIA CANYON
PISTON CORE
GRAVITY CORE
GRAB SAMPLE
DREDGE
CAMERA
BOX SAMPLE 1963
110°20'
110°10'
110°00'
109°50'
23° 20'
23° 10'
23° 00'
22° 50'
22° 40'

FIG. 12.—Photograph of a slice through a laminated formation obtained on the wall of Cardonal Canyon. Note the small normal faults. Slice prepared by Arnold Bouma.

canyon (Sample 115) yielded outcrop material of diatomite and laminated shale, the latter cut by small faults (Fig. 12). The study of the silicoflagellates from this sample, according to Erlend L. Martini of Scripps Institution (personal communication), indicated that, despite the resemblance to the Monterey diatomite of California, it was more likely of Pliocene age, making it comparable to the shale dredged from Vigia Canyon. However, G. Dallas Hanna considered the diatoms as more likely Miocene in age. A dredge sample from the southeast wall of the inner canyon between 350 and 200 fathoms (obtained in 1963 and not yet studied) contained sedimentary and igneous rocks. Some of the latter are cemented to the sediments by material resembling phosphorite.

Canyons of Los Frailes Bay and vicinity (*Fig. 13*).—Ten miles north of Gorda Bank is a series of canyons centering around Los Frailes Bay. Of these, Los Frailes Canyon is the best known. Flying over the canyon head, one can see its outline by the contrast between the green color of the shoal water and the dark blue water of the canyon. The head has been intensively explored by Dill (1964), who found that it has several closely spaced branches in Los Frailes Bay (Fig. 14).[5] These extend in almost to the shore where they have sand chutes in very shallow water continuing down into granite-walled gorges. The latter are very narrow above and broaden at the base so that walls overhang in some places. According to Dill, the granite along the bottom of these gorges is considerably smoothed, suggesting that the seaward-moving sand has produced erosion, widening the base into a bottle-shaped cross section.

[5] Dill reported in 1964 that there was one newly opened canyon head and three additional branches not discovered previously.

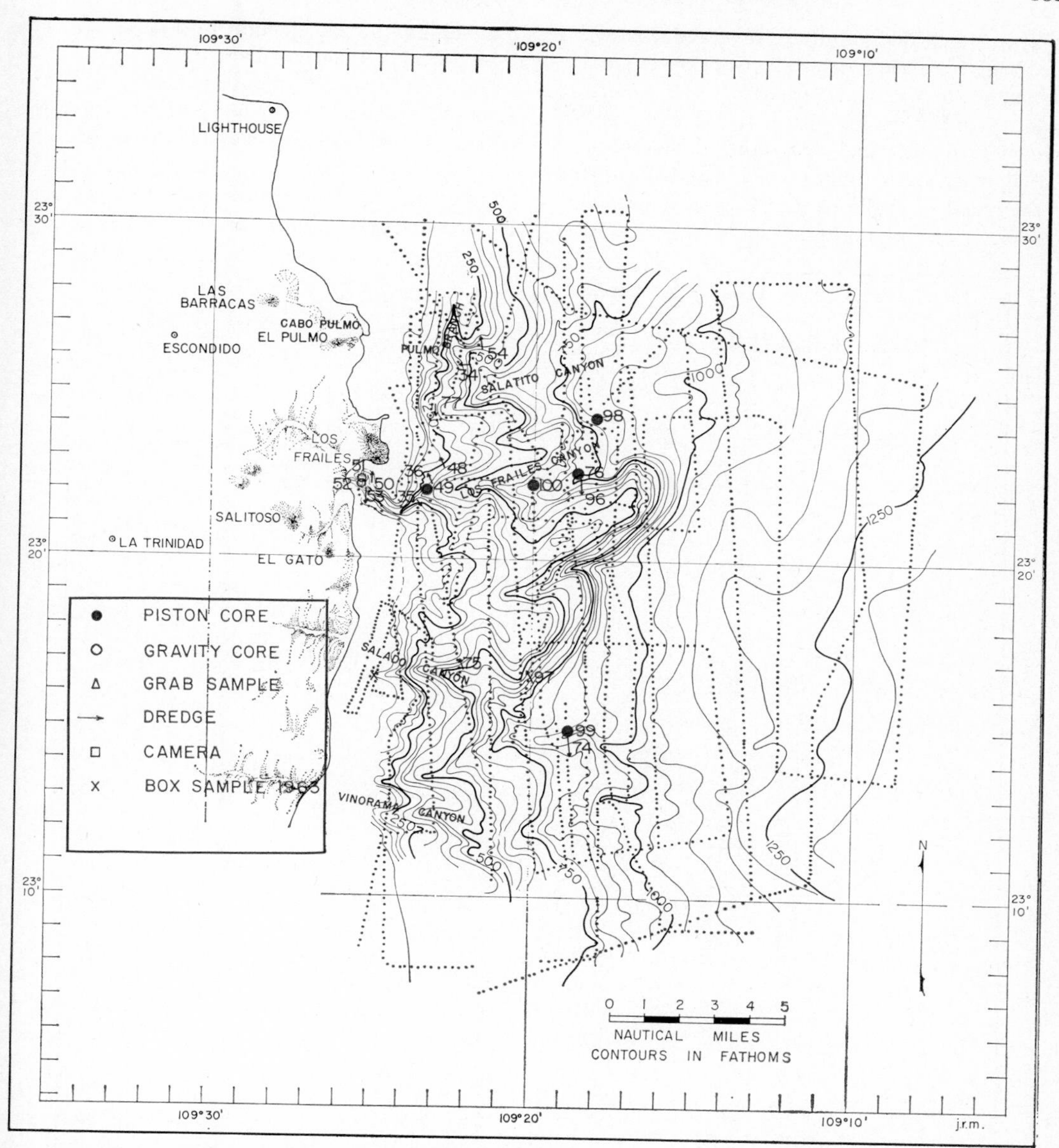

FIG. 13.—The group of canyons in the vicinity of Los Frailes Bay on the southeast coast of Lower California. It was found that Salado Canyon is directly off the arroyo shown farther north on the Hydrographic Office chart. Contour interval is 50 fathoms. Sounding lines and samples shown in overprint.

The group of canyon heads is located off the largest arroyo along this part of the coast, showing again a relationship to a land valley.

Los Frailes Canyon winds seaward with wall heights of 200 fathoms or more, terminating at about 900 fathoms. Beyond this depth is a fan-like protuberance but no definite channel or natural levee.

Dredgings on the canyon walls showed that the granite continues out to at least 250 fathoms and then reappears on the south side at about 750 fathoms. The ridge on the south of the canyon at that point yielded granite in two dredge hauls. A dredging from the north wall of this outer portion (Sample 36) contained weathered fragments of granite and other igneous intrusive rocks partly recemented with manganese and limonite crusts. In addition, these dredge hauls included assorted fossil shells of shallow-water origin as diagnosed by W.K. Emerson. Some specimens of *Pecten* from this group were thought by F.L.G. Hertlein to be probably Pliocene in age.

Coring in Los Frailes Canyon also was not very successful. Apparently the floor is covered largely with sand. One long core of sand is thought to be unreliable as it was badly distorted by piston withdrawal. The sand in this core is fine to very fine and has 4–24 per cent mica in it. One dredge

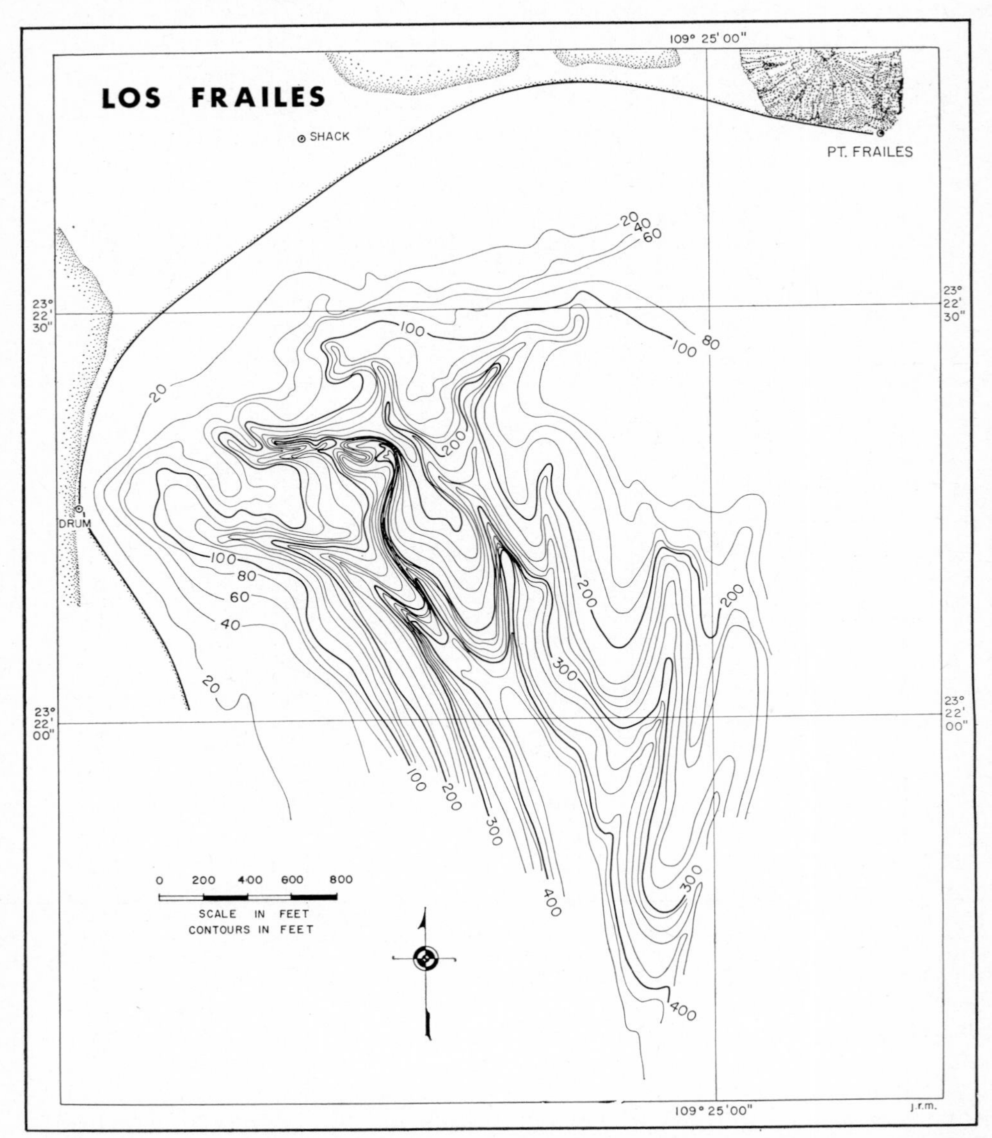

Fig. 14.—Detail of the head of Los Frailes Canyon prepared by R.F. Dill and partly based on his numerous dives into the canyon heads. A new branch discovered by Dill in 1963 has been added. Contour interval 20 feet.

that crossed the canyon axis at about 780 fathoms brought up a large lump of cross-bedded sand that had remained relatively undisturbed. This sand had a median diameter of about 0.5 mm. One core along the axis near the canyon head hit rock and brought up a few chips of granite.

To the south of Los Frailes Canyon, Salado Canyon comes in to less than a mile from the beach. Traced outward it bends to the south and joins Vinoramo Canyon at about 900 fathoms. The united canyons can be traced seaward to about 1,090 fathoms. Beyond, there is a definite bulge indicating a fan but there is no clear evidence of channels or levees crossing the fan. Both of these canyons appear to be related to land valleys although the evidence is not so clear as is the case at Los Frailes Canyon. A box sample in the head of Salado Canyon in 80 fathoms showed graded sediment with fine sand on top and small gravel at the bottom.

Dredging in Salado Canyon showed that it is also cut into granite or a similar type of crystalline rock. The dredge was hung up on bottom at 950 fathoms indicating the presence of hard rocks, although only a small fragment of granite was recovered when the dredge finally broke loose. Granite came from several other places in shoaler water. A dredging operation on the escarpment on the north side near the juncture of the two canyons produced evidence that there might be a vertical or overhanging cliff in deep water. After contacting the bottom at the base of the cliff, as shown by a significant jerk on the wire, the dredge showed no signs of making contact again until the ship had progressed about ½ mile to the north, during which time the dredge must have been pulled nearly to the top of the escarpment. At the time of this operation there was a strong south wind so that the dredge was being pulled constantly into the escarpment. Normally there are plenty of indications of catching bottom when a dredge is moving up a steep rocky slope and even a sediment slope produces moderate strains of varying intensity. Therefore, it is likely that the dredge was hanging over a vertical cliff and that the wire was being dragged up over the edge of the cliff without interference from the suspended dredge. Additional evidence, such as could be obtained from a bathyscaph or other deep-diving submarine, seems desirable before suggesting this overhang is an established fact. The soundings do not indicate a particularly steep slope, but this could be an example of the failure of echo sounding apparatus to discover very steep slopes without the narrow-beam transducers that are now in the experimental stage.

To the north of Los Frailes Canyon there are some canyon-like valleys of short length, but with rocky walls. Of these, the south wall of Saltito Canyon yielded shale rock and some *Pecten* shells, the latter indicative of shallow water conditions of deposition, much shoaler than the depth from which they were dredged. Saltito Canyon does not extend landward of the 300-fathom contour. Pulmo Branch enters the north side of Saltito Canyon. Its head runs essentially north and south parallel to the coast but it turns eastward lower down and enters Saltito Canyon at a small angle. Pulmo Canyon has not been traced in beyond approximately 400-fathom depths. A dredge on the outer wall of this canyon brought up angular fragments of highly fractured felsite and other types of igneous flow breccia with some indications of slickensides.

Valleys off Point Arena (*Fig. 15*).—In running between Los Frailes and Palmas Bays it was observed that traverses off Point Arena, a low sandy point without rock outcrops, showed a series of highly irregular valleys and ridges. A closely spaced grid of lines was run across these valleys so that they could be contoured in some detail. It was found that these valleys are quite different from those farther south along the Peninsula. One or possibly two of them are fairly continuous seaward to more than 1,000 fathoms, but the others die out along the slope and show little if any tendency to join adjacent valleys. Tributary systems are clearly lacking. There may be one basin depression and one or more possible hills. The outbend of the 500-fathom contour on either side of the principal valley is somewhat suggestive of the natural levees occurring in deep sea fans along the side of channels. The topography is also similar to that found off the Mississippi Delta (Shepard, 1955) although the slopes are much steeper (10% *versus* 1%) and the valleys considerably deeper below the general slope. The deepest valley has a floor about 100 fathoms below the adjacent ridges.

A box core in the axis of the principal valley at

565 fathoms yielded a layer of unsorted sand, gravel, and shell fragments overlain by several inches of muddy sediment that may be graded. Dredgings of the walls on either side of these valleys failed to give any indication of ledge rock, but to the south Sample 79 contained small cobbles of crystalline rock along with sand and shells.

Palmas Bay canyons (*Fig. 16*).—Palmas Bay to the north has another group of branching submarine canyons. This group represents the northernmost extent of the rock-walled canyons of the western Gulf. Reconnaissance lines farther north showed only minor depressions in the slope. The Palmas Bay canyons are similar to those off Cape San Lucas and the Los Frailes area. By flying along the coast south of Pescadero Point when the water is clear, the head of at least one of these canyons can be detected. Dives into Pescadero Canyon head did not show any close correspondence with what was seen in the canyons farther south. No outcrops were found, but gravel and cobble deposits were observed (Conrad Limbaugh, personal communication). Robert F. Dill dived in the canyon head off Buena Vista and found sandy slopes up to 30° in declivity.

The most significant Palmas Bay canyon is the combined Pescadero-Palmas group with their series of tributaries that come in close to shore all along the coast from Arroyo de Santiago, on the south, to Pescadero Point, on the north. The Palmas Bay canyons appear to have the typical winding dendritic drainage pattern of land canyons, unlike the valleys off Point Arena that trend directly down slope. There are some indications that the tributaries in Palmas Bay are not continuous outwardly but this impression may be the result of a lack of a complete coordination between all of the sounding lines or of the too wide spacing of some lines, resulting in failure to show connections between different segments of a valley. Tracing the combined Palmas and Pescadero canyons seaward, a sizeable fan is found. This fan is crossed by a channel with natural levees on the side, and in this respect differs from most of the

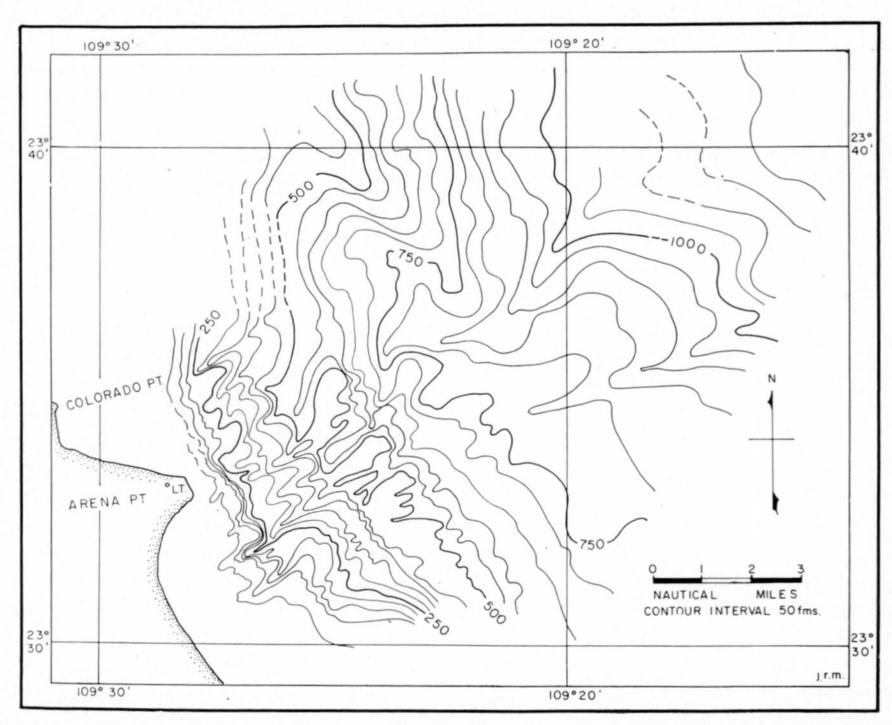

FIG. 15.—The group of highly irregular valleys found in the vicinity of Pt. Arena. So far as known, these valleys do not have rock walls. Contour interval 100 fathoms, with 50 fathoms added near shore. Sounding lines and samples shown in Fig. 16 overprint.

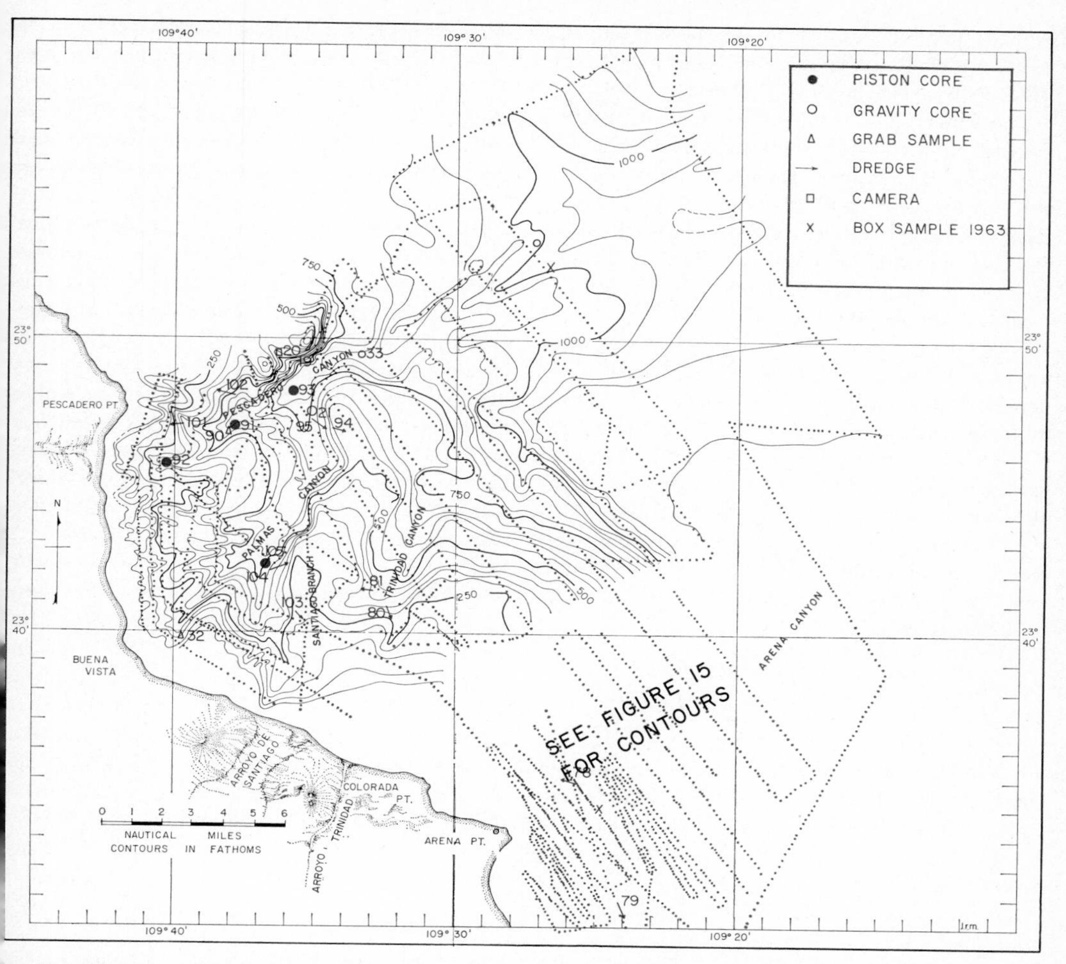

ɪɢ. 16.—The group of canyons in Palmas Bay. The existence of natural levees along the outer portion of Pescadero Canyon was definitely confirmed in 1963. Contour interval 50 fathoms.

ther fans outside the canyons of the Baja Cali-ɔrnia canyon province.

The walls of the Palmas Bay canyons have onsiderable declivity in some places. Thus, the orthwest wall of Pescadero Canyon at Long. 09°35′ is as steep as can be depicted on a fatho-ram, and may be vertical. As may be judged om the dredgings, these steep walls, as well as ɔme of those of gentler slopes, have rock out-rops. Elsewhere, however, a number of dredgings n the canyon walls failed to produce any rock xcept rounded cobbles. On the west wall of Santi-go Canyon the dredge brought up a basalt lava Sample 103) that has the appearance of having flowed like tar, although it is a finely crystalline basalt with flow surfaces shown in finger-like protuberances. Lower down, near where Santiago Canyon joins Palmas Canyon, shale was dredged which is partly laminated and partly nodular, and has a manganese coating (Sample 104). Foraminifera from this shale were identified by Frances L. Parker as being probably Miocene in age. Dredging farther down Palmas Canyon indicated the presence of rock out to 750 fathoms because the dredge was hung up at this depth although only a small fragment of rock was recovered when it was finally broken loose. A dredging on the north wall of Pescadero Canyon (Sample 102) brought up a shell fauna from depths of 500 to 400 fathoms including a group which lives in less than 30 fathoms, according to E.C. Allison.

The inner slopes of Pescadero Canyon were dredged in a number of places but the dredge came up empty in most of these hauls or yielded only cobbles and shells, some of the latter being clearly of a type living in shoaler water than the depths from which they were obtained. The bank directly north of the outer part of this canyon yielded large, angular, granitic rocks.

The coring in this group of canyons was also unsuccessful, although short cores of sand were obtained, some of the sediment being up to 2 mm in diameter. Hard sand bottom appears to be the rule on these canyon floors. Sand and gravel were dredged from the floor of Pescadero Canyon in about 500 and 300 fathoms, respectively. This shows some dirty sand layers, but a core nearby had clean sand and gravel. Also, a core on the north levee showed a clean sand layer about 20 cm below the top.

CANYONS SOUTH OF FUERTE DELTA (FIGURE 17)

On the east side of the Gulf, almost directly north of Los Frailes Bay, there are some valleys or canyons adjacent to the volcanic island, San Ignacio Farallón. These canyons have walls up to 2,000 feet or more in height. This group was at first thought to join outwardly into one large trough (Shepard, 1961), but with additional soundings it was found that San Ignacio Canyon, the southernmost of the valleys, does not join the more northerly Fuerte Canyon. Each of these canyons has three known branches at its head. San Ignacio Canyon is bordered on the south by a broad shelf. The steep slope on the canyon wall next to this shelf does not appear to have any appreciable valleys cut into it so that all of the tributaries come down from the narrow shelf off the Fuerte Delta. Slopes of about 25 per cent (14°) exist at the heads of these clustering tributaries and this inclination continues down to the 500-fathom contour, beyond which it is reduced to an average of about 5 per cent (2°50′) out to 1,100 fathoms. Equally steep heads occur in the northern canyon. These slopes may be compared with the 40–50 per cent (22°–26°) slopes along the south rim of San Ignacio Canyon, and to the almost equally steep slopes along a portion of the north wall of Fuerte Canyon. A probable continuation of the northern escarpment was discovered north of the deep trough-like valley that is found where the 1,250-fathom contour crosses Fuerte Canyon.

Dredging near the canyon heads did not result in the discovery of anything but a soft mudstone however along the escarpment on the southeast side of San Ignacio Canyon a large block of a greatly sheared igneous or metamorphic rock was brought up, so much altered as to make its identification difficult. Large cores from the canyon floor were found to consist of silty clay with no appreciable stratification or sand layers, with one core in what may be the outer part of Fuerte Canyon in 1,725 fathoms yielding an 8-cm fragment of obsidian under a cover of one meter of sandy mud.

Sinaloa Canyon, discovered in 1962 by soundings on the *Argo*, lies 20 miles southeast of San Ignacio Farallón Island. This canyon, which has at least one tributary on the southeast wall, extends slightly into the shelf terminating headward at 50 fathoms and can be traced down the slope to at least 800 fathoms. A dredging on the same wall came up with only a relatively hard clay, whereas a core from the canyon center produced an unstratified silty clay, similar to the cores in San Ignacio Canyon.

OTHER GULF VALLEYS

It is quite likely that there are submarine canyons in the Gulf of California that have not yet been discovered because insufficient sounding lines have been run along many of the slopes. It is unlikely, however, that there are any comparable in size to those around the lower Peninsula. From available sounding lines it is clear that most of the escarpments, all presumably of fault origin, have small valleys cut into them. The fathograms show that such valleys commonly have depths of 50–7[illegible] fathoms below surroundings. An attempt was made to investigate some of these valleys along the submerged escarpment on the northeast side of Ceralbo Island and along the west side of Angel de la Guarda Island. Lines approximately 0.1 mile apart were run along Ceralbo taking bearings

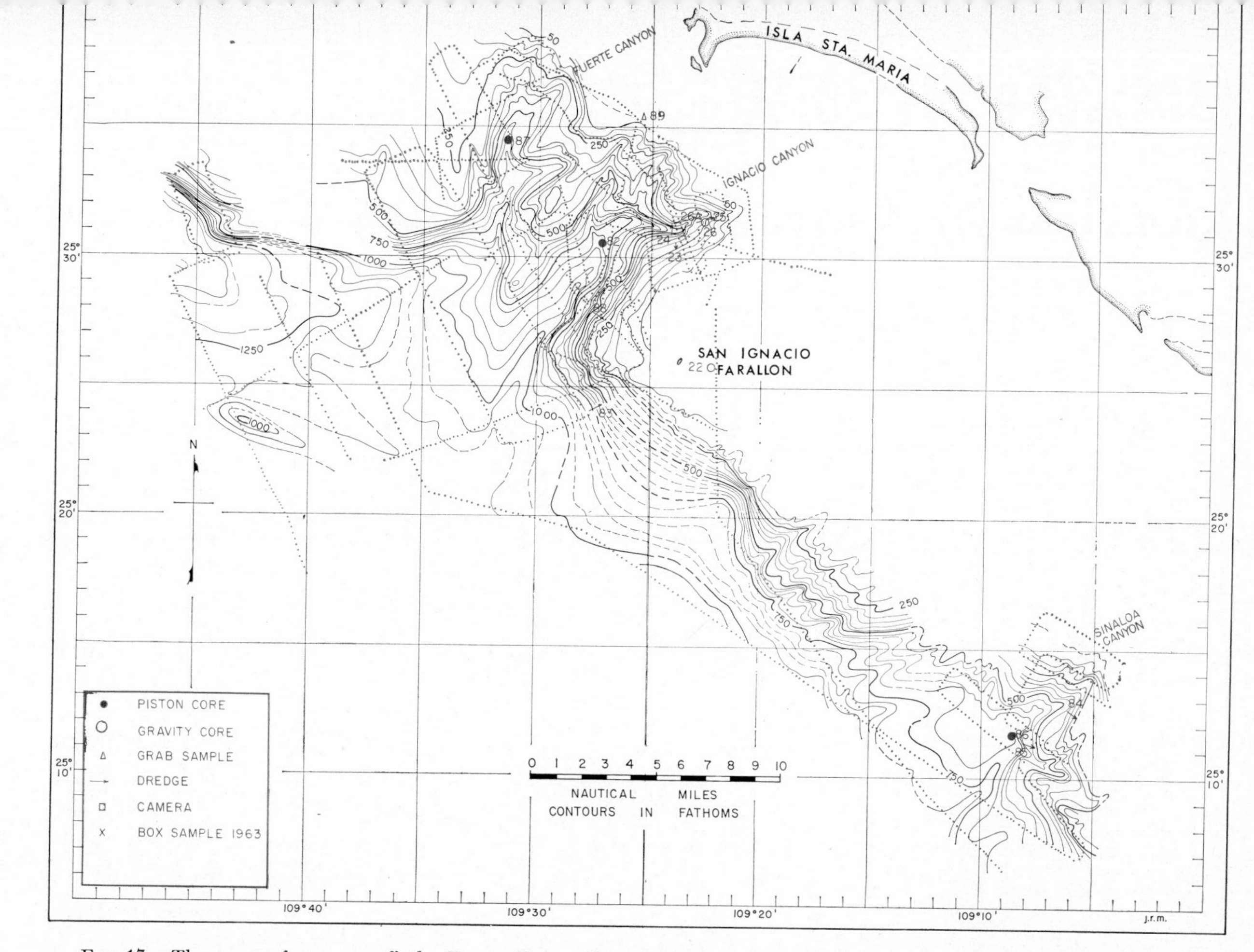

FIG. 17.—The group of canyons off the Fuerte Delta. Note the steep escarpments northwest of Fuerte Canyon and southeast of San Ignacio Canyon. The small island of San Ignacio Farallón is an eroded volcano. Contour interval 50 fathoms. Sounding lines and samples shown on overprint.

on a prominent white boulder on shore and distances off the straight cliffs by radar. The results of this survey (Fig. 18) show that the valleys are very different from any other types explored elsewhere in the area—they extend only part way down the slope and are more common on the upper than on the lower slope; they are straight and so far as can be determined, no tributaries enter them. Outside each valley there is an indication of a slight bulge or fan.

Valleys observed in the steep escarpment adjacent to Angel de la Guarda appear to be of the same type, although they were not as well sur veyed. Similar valleys have been found cut int the fault scarp northeast of San Clemente Islan and west of Palos Verdes Hills (Emery and Terry 1956) off Southern California. There is no evi dence that any of these valleys have rocky walls

Off the Rio Mayo Delta, south of Guaymas there are several shallow valleys which extend a least part way down the slope and appear to b similar to the valleys outside the Mississipp Delta (Shepard, 1955) and off the Fraser Delt (Mathews and Shepard, 1962).

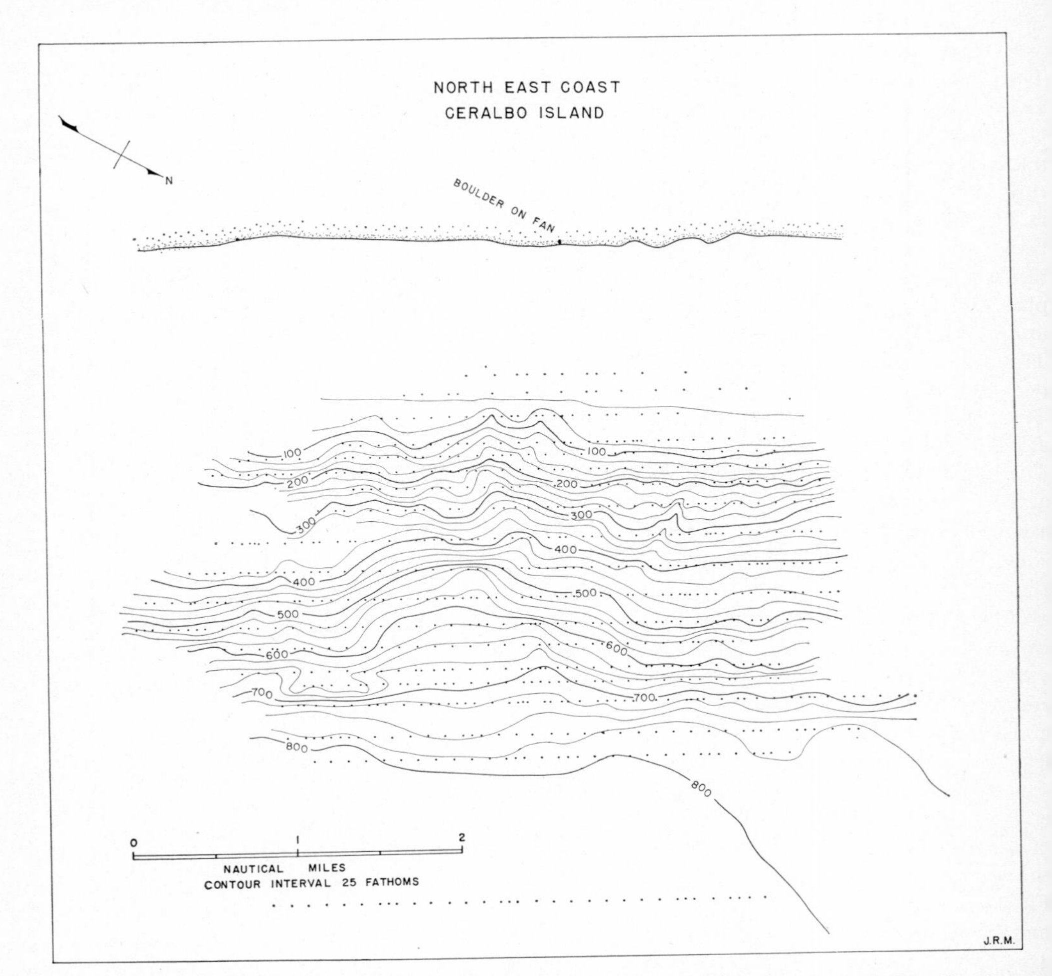

Fig. 18.—A large-scale detail of the steep slope on the northeast side of Ceralbo Island. Sounding lines a shown by dots. The base of the map shows the juncture of the slope with Ceralbo Trough. Note the contra between these slope valleys and the submarine canyons.

ORIGIN OF THE TYPES OF VALLEYS

The preceding descriptions of the Gulf of California submarine valleys have shown that they are definitely of several genetic types and as pointed out elsewhere (Shepard, 1961; 1963, p. 317) each type appears to have a different explanation. Thus, there are the winding rock-walled canyons with dendritic tributaries, the relatively straight-walled valleys that extend down slopes with few if any tributaries, and the straight-walled valleys that extend along the coast rather than down the slopes. Each of these will be considered separately.

Explanation of canyons of the lower Peninsula.—The canyons that cut the slopes of the lower Peninsula from Cabo Falso to Pescadero Point on the Gulf side (shown collectively on Chart I, in pocket) are definitely similar to river-cut land canyons. Most of them occur directly off the larger of the land valleys. The walls of most of these valleys have crystalline rock types, although locally the rock is deeply weathered and in some places soft sedimentary rocks occur. The canyons are narrow, steep walled, and roughly *V*-shaped. Tributaries are fairly common and enter with a dendritic pattern much like that of land canyons. The canyons terminate at rather similar depths—a fact that is hard to explain by marine erosion. There is, therefore, some reason for favoring subaerial erosion to explain the submarine canyons around the lower Peninsula.

On the other hand, there is no indication that the land canyons landward of submarine canyons are of the same type as the heads of the submarine canyons. The landward continuations of the sea valleys are broad arroyos with rather flat floors resulting from extensive but intermittent wash and fill. The heads of several of the sea-floor valleys have narrow, precipitous gorges of a type not seen on the adjacent land. Furthermore, the gradients of the sea valleys are much steeper than those of the land. Therefore, the sea canyons cannot be the submerged lower end of the land valleys. Finally, we know that the sea valleys have active movement of sand and gravel down along their axes. This movement is probably cutting the gorges at the head of the canyons as claimed by Dill (1964). How far down this action goes is not certain. The evidence that turbidity currents or other transporting agents carry sand and gravel into the lower limits of the outer canyons shows that erosion may be occurring all along the canyon lengths.

There are reasons, however, to doubt that the canyons were cut entirely or even perhaps largely by submarine processes. If they were due to marine erosion alone, the canyons should extend as single valleys down the slopes rather than having dendritic tributaries. There would be little sediment entering the sides to produce tributaries, some of which have heads at depths as great as 500 to 600 fathoms. It is hardly conceivable that under present conditions the sediments necessary for active erosion could be provided at such points. Finally, the shallow-water shells dredged from the deep walls are indications of submergence. It is possible that the deep weathering of the igneous rocks found in several places is further evidence of submergence, although the alternative that such weathering can take place on the sea floor must be kept in mind at least until more study has been made of the weathered products to see whether they suggest subaerial processes.

To the writer the most reasonable explanation of the facts now available is that the granite canyons were initiated when the Cape stood higher above sea level than now and that the dendritic erosion pattern was formed at that time. Subsequently, both during and after submergence, marine processes have been reshaping old land valleys to produce the present type of submarine canyon with the rock gorge heads, the product of recent erosion. The fans built outside the canyon mouths may be a combination of old delta deposits later covered over by turbidity-current flows that moved down the submerging canyons and built fans widely out over the slopes.

Fault valleys.—Tinaja Trough (Fig. 11), although it resembles a canyon in its general *V*-shape, differs from the canyons in its straight course and the virtual absence of tributaries. Furthermore, this trough apparently cuts a submarine canyon in two. It closely resembles San Clemente Rift valley, found at the southern end of San Clemente Island off Southern California and clearly related to regional faulting (Shepard and Emery, 1941, Fig. 11). The origin of Tinaja

Trough seems, therefore, to be faulting, probably similar to the faults that formed Sal si Puedes Basin in the northern Gulf. Whether or not this faulting is strike slip, as has been suggested for San Clemente Rift valley, can be judged only from the fact that the two ends of Candalaria Canyon, cut by the trough, appear to line up fairly well. This may indicate that the faulting has not had any large horizontal slip component. In any case, marine erosion and deposition have considerably modified the head of the trough.[6]

Farallón and Fuerte canyons on the east side of the Gulf may also have been formed at least in part by faulting, as suggested by the fault-scarp type walls occurring at the northwest and southeast sides of this valley group.

Landslide valleys.—The valleys found extending discontinuously down the submarine escarpments can be explained most easily by landsliding. The valleys on the escarpment of Ceralbo (Fig. 18) are clearly of such an origin. The possibility should be considered that valleys like this may represent an early stage in the growth of the more normal type of submarine canyon with its branching and curving course, but there seems to be no particular reason why submarine erosion should produce such changes.

Another example of probable landslide valleys is found off Point Arena (Fig. 16). Here the slopes are considerably less than off Ceralbo, only about 12 per cent (6°50′), compared to 50 per cent (28°), but the forward building of Point Arena as a cuspate foreland may have produced the instability of the slope due to failure of the rapidly depositing sediment that was in a metastable condition (Terzaghi, 1956).

The steep-headed valleys of San Ignacio and Fuerte Canyons can be explained as slope failures on a steep fan or foreset slope built out into a fault trough. The multi-heads of San Jose Canyon, where no rock has been dredged, are very likely another example of landslide activity.

[6] Information obtained in 1964 suggests that erosion has played an important part in forming this valley.

REFERENCES

Anderson, C.A., Durham, J.W., Shepard, F.P., Natland, M.N., and Revelle, R.R., 1950, The 1940 E.W. Scripps cruise to the Gulf of California: Geol. Soc. America Mem. 43, 362 p.

Beal, C.H., 1948, Reconnaissance of the geology and oil possibilities of Baja California, Mexico: Geol. Soc. America Mem. 31, 138 p.

Bouma, A.H., 1962, Sedimentology of some flysch deposits—a graphic approach to facies interpretation: Elsevier, Amsterdam, 168 p.

de Czerna, Z., 1961, Tectonic map of Mexico; scale 1:2,500,000: Geol. Soc. America.

Dill, R.F., 1964, Submarine erosion: Unpub. Ph.D. dissertation, Univ. Calif., San Diego, Scripps Inst. of Oceanography.

Emery, K.O., and Terry, R.D., 1956, A submarine slope off Southern California: Jour. Geology, v. 64, p. 271–280.

Lemche, H., 1958, Neuer Tiefsee-Fund eines rezenten Vertreters der Kambro-silurischen molluskengruppe Tryblidiacae: Geol. Rundschau, v. 47, no. 1, p. 249–251.

Mathews, W.H., and Shepard, F.P., 1962, Sedimentation of Fraser River delta, British Columbia: Am. Assoc. Petroleum Geologists Bull., v. 46, no. 8, p. 1416–1438.

Menard, H.W., 1955, Deep-sea channels, topography, and sedimentation: Am. Assoc. Petroleum Geologists Bull., v. 39, no. 2, p. 236–255.

North, W.J., 1960, Fabulous Cape San Lucas: Skin Diver Magazine, May, 1960, p. 24–26, 52.

Reineck, H.E., 1958, Kastengreifer und Lotröhre "Schnepfe": Sencke. Lethaea, v. 39, nos. 1, 2, p. 45–48.

——— 1963, Der Kastengreifer: Natur und Museum, v. 93, no. 2, p. 65–68.

Shepard, F.P., 1950, Submarine topography of the Gulf of California, pt. 3 *of* The 1940 E.W. Scripps cruise to the Gulf of California: Geol. Soc. America Mem. 43, 32 p.

——— 1955, Delta-front valleys bordering the Mississippi distributaries: Geol. Soc. America Bull., v. 66, no. 12, p. 1489–1498.

——— 1961, Submarine canyons of the Gulf of California: Internat. Geol. Cong., 21st, Copenhagen, Denmark, Repts., pt. 26, p. 11–23.

——— 1963, Submarine geology: Harper & Row, New York, 2d ed., 560 p.

——— and Emery, K.O., 1941, Submarine topography off the California coast—canyons and tectonic interpretation: Geol. Soc. America Spec. Paper 31, 171 p.

Shepard, F.P., Niino, Hiroshi, and Chamberlain, T.K. (in preparation), Submarine canyons and Sagami Trough, east-central Honshu, Japan: Geol. Soc. America Bull.

Terzaghi, Karl, 1956, Varieties of submarine slope failures: 8th Texas Conf. on Soil Mech. and Found. Eng., Proc. Spec. Pub. 29, Bureau Eng. Research, Univ. Texas, Austin, 41 p.

PLEISTOCENE DELTAIC PROGRADATION OF CONTINENTAL TERRACE, COSTA DE NAYARIT, MEXICO[1]

JOSEPH R. CURRAY[2] AND DAVID G. MOORE[3]
La Jolla and San Diego, California

ABSTRACT

The sedimentary structure of the continental terrace of the Costa de Nayarit, on the west coast of mainland Mexico, has been investigated geophysically by means of continuous acoustic reflection profiling. Facies interpretations are made from these records and profiles on the basis of shape, attitude, nature of internal reflecting horizons, and relationship to adjacent facies.

The framework of this continental terrace is composed of a sequence of wedges of deltaic sediments, interspersed with strata of other paralic and open-shelf facies, which grade seaward into continental-slope facies. The deltaic platforms are correlated and matched with flanking erosional shorelines to obtain a chronology of deltaic progradation to the edge of the terrace. Low positions of sea level below −65 fathoms are postulated for early Wisconsin time. Younger sequences, believed to be of late Wisconsin age, were formed during fluctuations of sea level between −35 and −68 fathoms. The youngest low stand of sea level at −68 fathoms is dated 17,600 years B.P.

The northern part of this terrace is nondeltaic and consists of a thick section of open-shelf sediments grading seaward over a deep, rounded shelf-break into a thick section of slope sediments. Faulting in the reflection records shows that this thick section was deposited on a subsiding platform. It is concluded that shelf and slope deposits are volumetrically very important in regions like the Costa de Nayarit.

The break in slope at the edge of the southern and central Costa de Nayarit shelf is very complex in origin, but is primarily controlled by Pleistocene deltas. The edge of the northern subsiding portion of the shelf is also depositional in origin, but is only indirectly controlled by lowered sea level. Long-term balance between deposition and removal of sediment, controlled by wave action well below surf-base (about 5 fathoms), and by surf erosion during past transgressions and regressions, must form terrace structures of this northern type. These may have been processes of geological importance in pre-Quaternary time. Thus the explanation for the world-wide origin of the shelf-break as caused primarily by surf erosion during lowered sea level appears oversimplified.

INTRODUCTION

The continental terrace is defined as the zone around the continents, extending from low water line to the base of the continental slope (A.G.I., 1957). The inadequacy of this definition of one of the earth's major geomorphic provinces exemplifies the meager state of our knowledge of the regions of juncture between continents and ocean basins. Although many studies of the continental terrace, or its component parts, have been completed, most have dealt with the surface characteristics, such as Holocene sediments and bathymetry, or with deep structure as revealed by seismic refraction methods. Details of internal structural framework have remained largely unknown because geological and geophysical techniques were not available for obtaining this information. As a result, the geological literature is fraught with rank speculation on this internal structure. With the recent development of acoustic reflection profiling techniques, it is no longer necessary to speculate on the internal framework of the continental terrace; it can be observed in detail. With proper interpretation of such observations, great advances should be forthcoming toward understanding the sedimentary and tectonic history of the continental margins.

The most direct evidence for determining the

[1] Manuscript received, June 25, 1963. Contribution from Scripps Institution of Oceanography.

The authors are indebted to E.C. Buffington, W.B. Huckabay, C.L. Barker, and S.H. Abernethy for assistance in preparation for, and execution of, work at sea. Radiocarbon dating was done by G.S. Bien, on shells selected by R.H. Parker. Administrative assistance was provided by the University of Mexico and particularly by G.P. Salas and A. Ayala-Castañares, of that institution.

Cartography, editing, typing, and laboratory assistance were rendered by J.R. Moriarty, G.L. Prible, Miss J.M. Witte, Mrs. M.F. Franklin, and P.J. Crampton. The studies were supported by the U.S. Navy Electronics Laboratory and by grants of the American Petroleum Institute and the Office of Naval Research at Scripps Institution of Oceanography. The Socony-Mobil Oil Company provided a Sonoprobe for use in the Gulf of California project.

The manuscript benefited significantly as a result of critical reading by Tj.H. van Andel, E.L. Hamilton, G.H. Curl, E.C. Buffington, and H.R. Gould.

[2] Scripps Institution of Oceanography, University of California.

[3] U.S. Navy Electronics Laboratory.

method of emplacement of sedimentary bodies is depositional structure. For the recognition of facies and environments of deposition, the shape,

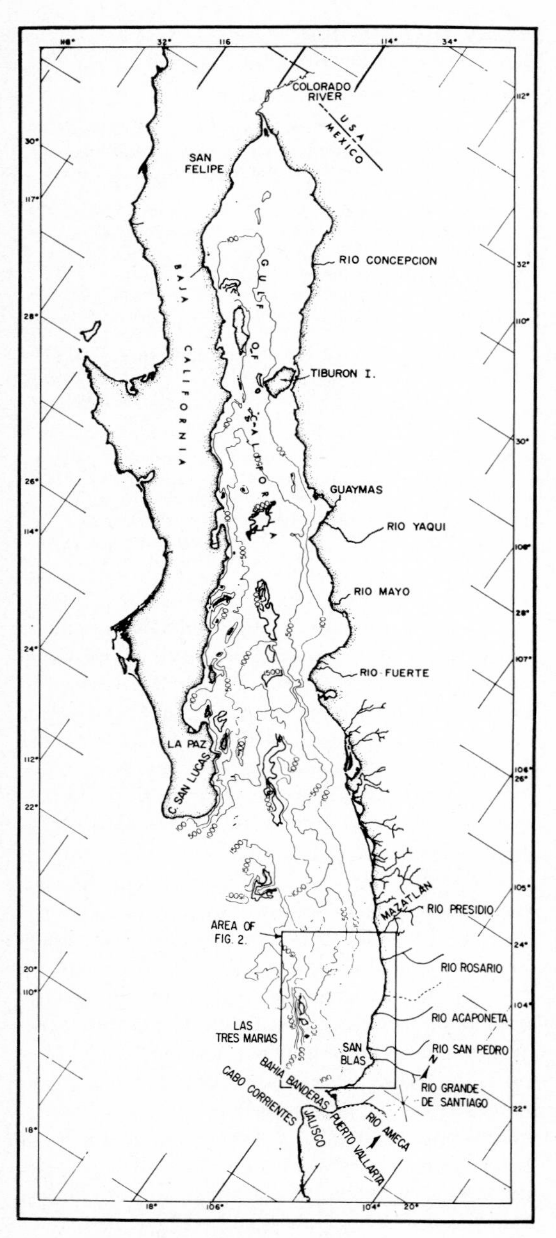

FIG. 1.—Index chart showing regional location of the Costa de Nayarit, Mexico.

size, and attitude of internal boundaries of sedimentary bodies are generally easier criteria to apply than examination of isolated samples. Thus, the significant advances in acoustic profiling have made the study of depositional structures a significant part of sedimentology. An important follow-up task is direct sampling of the sedimentary environments now being identified by structure and morphology in acoustic reflection records.

As a part of the speculation of the last few years concerning origin of the continental terrace, considerable doubt has been cast on the importance and even on the existence of permanent deposits on the continental shelf and slope. Both shelf and slope facies will be shown in this paper to be of great significance in continental margins of the Costa de Nayarit type. Continental terraces, like mountain ranges, are, we believe, genetically and regionally different. Generalizations on structure and origin will, therefore, require detailed examination of many different terraces.

In the spring of 1959, the Scripps Institution of Oceanography organized a study of the geology, biology, geophysics, and oceanography of the Gulf of California. As a part of that investigation, study of the coastal plain and continental shelf of the mainland coast of the Gulf was undertaken as a joint effort of the U.S. Navy Electronics Laboratory, the University of Mexico, and the Scripps Institution. This investigation was initiated in 1959 with a reconnaissance of the entire coastal plain from the head of the Gulf to Puerto Vallarta, Jalisco (Fig. 1). From this reconnaissance, several areas of greatest geological interest were selected for detailed investigation. The area referred to in this paper as the Costa de Nayarit was one of these selected areas.

The over-all investigation of this area has included study of morphology and sediments of the coastal plain, the continental shelf, and upper continental slope, and geophysical studies of shelf and slope structure. This paper deals with the structure of the continental shelf and upper continental slope, as interpreted from geophysical studies. A later paper will report on investigations of the surface sediments of the continental shelf and on studies of the sediments and depositional history of the coastal plain.

REGIONAL GEOLOGY AND PHYSIOGRAPHY

The physiography of the mainland coast of the Gulf of California (Fig. 1) is divided into three provinces—(1) a coastline of alternating rocky headlands and alluvial fans north of Guaymas, (2) a wide central coastal plain of coalescing alluvial plains and deltas between Guaymas and San Blas, and (3) the rocky coastline south of San Blas. The Costa de Nayarit straddles the boundary between the latter two provinces, and lies at the structural southern end of the Gulf of California.

The coastline is steep and rocky south of San Blas where it projects seaward as a double point. The continental shelf adjacent to this rocky coastline is narrow and is cut by a deep trough, probably structural, which enters Bahía de Banderas and Valle de Banderas near Puerto Vallarta. North of San Blas, the coast opens into a wide (9–30 nautical miles) coastal plain covered by littoral and alluvial late Quaternary sediments. This coastal plain slopes gently upward to the foothills of the Sierra Madre Occidental. The geology of the foothills, the western flanks of the Sierra Madre, and the drainage basins of the rivers of the Costa de Nayarit is unknown in detail, but it is generally summarized as middle Tertiary volcanics, probably Oligocene to lower Pliocene, which range from andesite to rhyolite in composition.

The coastal plain of the Costa de Nayarit (Curray, 1959, 1961a; Curray and Moore, 1964) is of great geological interest because of its marshy strand plain of about 250 abandoned, regressive beach-dune ridges (Figs. 2 and 3). This strand plain, which averages about 6 miles wide, overlaps the seaward-dipping flood plain of the Rio Grande de Santiago and smaller adjacent rivers to the north and south (Figs. 1 and 2). The maximum width from the present beach to the oldest ridge is about 9 miles.

The pre-transgressive (Pleistocene) alluvial and deltaic surface of the coalescing river systems underlies the Holocene strand plain sand. This same surface has also been traced under the Holocene sediments on the continental shelf by subbottom reflections on the Sonoprobe records discussed in the following sections. Because this surface predates the Holocene transgression, it is older where traced on the continental shelf.

The continental shelf and upper continental slope, the main subjects of this paper, are contoured in detail in Figure 2. Most of this bathymetric control was obtained during two cruises of this survey (Fig. 4), supplemented by tracks of previous Scripps expeditions through this area and by soundings from the U.S. Hydrographic Office's published chart of the area.

The continental shelf immediately north of Mazatlán is both deeper and narrower than that of the Costa de Nayarit. Off Mazatlán it is 14 nautical miles wide to the shelf-break at about 120 fathoms. In the Costa de Nayarit region, the continental shelf widens to a maximum of 40 miles at lat 21°40′ N. The shelf-break ranges in depth from 50 to 125 fathoms, but lies at an average of 55 fathoms in most of the area. South of San Blas, near the southern edge of the Costa de Nayarit, the shelf again narrows to 7 nautical miles adjacent to the rocky coastline at lat 21° N.

The central portion of the shelf from lat 21°30′ N. to 22°30′ N. is very nearly flat between 25 and 35 fathoms (Fig. 2). Low elongate ridges a few fathoms high lie parallel to the contour, separated by irregular depressions. Some of these ridges and depressions may be related to the lowered sea-level Pleistocene deltas which form the outer terrace, whereas others are probably related to the Holocene transgression as relict shoreline deposits.

The Tres Marías Islands (Fig. 1) lie off the edge of the continental shelf west of the Costa de Nayarit. These islands are poorly known geologically, but are tentatively plotted on the geological map of Mexico as including lower Cenozoic intrusives, Mesozoic metamorphics, and Miocene and Pliocene marine sediments. Two small islands (Fig. 2) lie on the continental shelf of the Costa de Nayarit—Isla Isabel (21°52′ N., 105°54′ W.) and Piedra Blanca del Mar (21°35′ N., 105°31′ W.). Isla Isabel is a cluster of breached volcanic cones forming a main island about $1\frac{1}{2}$ miles long, slightly over $\frac{1}{2}$ mile wide, and approximately 280 feet high. Piedra Blanca del Mar is a circular volcanic neck about 300 feet in diameter and 145 feet high, rising vertically out of the ocean. Both islands are composed of volcanics of probable andesitic composition.

South of the protuberance in the shelf edge at

(Curray and Moore, in preparation) on the surface sediments of the continental terrace. Examples are shown here only to summarize briefly the structure of the Holocene sedimentary veneer of the terrace.

Surface sediment distribution of this continental shelf is similar to most other wide shelves of the world which have been studied in detail. Littoral sands form the shoreface and longshore bars and continue seaward as neritic sands, in equilibrium with present conditions, into water depths of about 4 fathoms, 1 mile from shore, where they give way to shelf-facies muds (predominantly silty clays). These shelf muds exist only to distances of no more than 15–20 miles from shore off rivers which presently supply sediment to the open ocean. Beyond these modern silty clays and in the zones not adjacent to the presently active rivers, the shelf is covered with relict littoral sand from the Holocene transgression. This is particularly true of the outer shelf of most of the area, where the surface sediments are clean, well-sorted, medium-grain sands.

These relationships are clearly shown in the Sonoprobe records, and have been in part confirmed by the coring program. Other confirmation of interpretation of Sonoprobe records has been presented by Moore (1960) and Curray and Moore (1963b). Sonoprobe line 1 (Figs. 6 and 7) shows the thick nearshore section of shelf-facies muds, interbedded with and overlying neritic and littoral sands, and a probable pre-transgressive, subaerial erosional surface. The shelf-facies muds thin to seaward, as shown in line 2 (Figs. 6 and 8), and finally pinch out completely where the basal sands crop out a few miles farther seaward. Line 3 (Figs. 6 and 9), collected nearshore south of San Blas, shows a smooth cover of Holocene sediment overlying an irregular rock surface. Channels in the rock have been filled with layers of sediment until they are now completely and smoothly buried.

Arcer records.—Most of the discussion in the following sections of this paper is based on interpretation of Arcer records in terms of structural framework and sedimentary facies. Experience

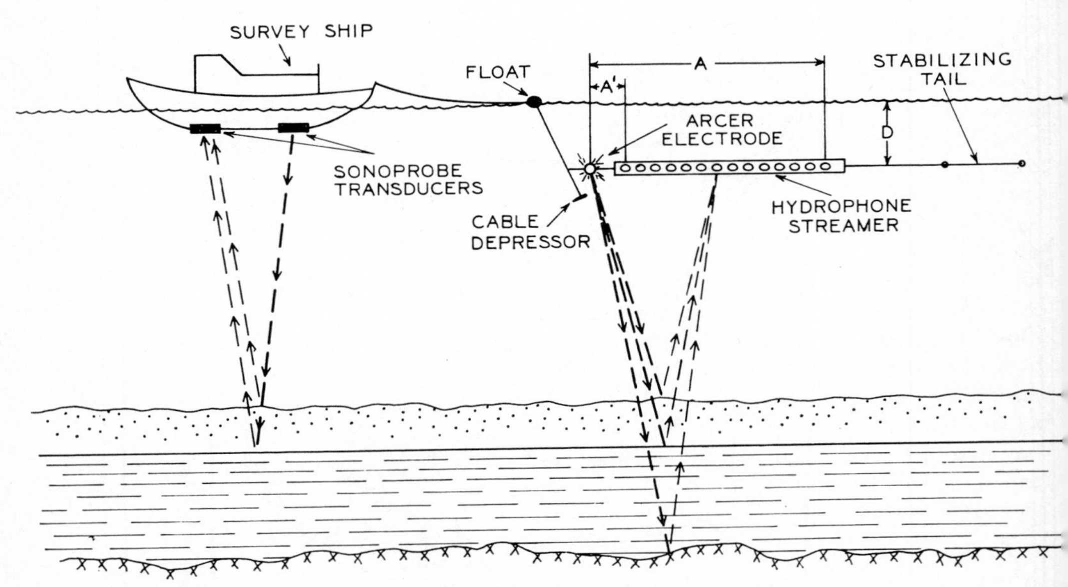

FIG. 5.—Diagram of field use of Sonoprobe and Arcer components. Directional Sonoprobe transducers are mounted under ship's hull. Transmitting and receiving components of Arcer are towed behind ship on depressor at predetermined depth. Distances A and A' are regulated to determine geometric optimum depth below streamer for detection of reflectors. Depth D at which streamer is towed generally is set to equal one-quarter wave length (about 6 feet for the present study). As hydrophones are connected in parallel, streamer has directivity and null fore and aft with phone spacing adjusted to one-half wave length.

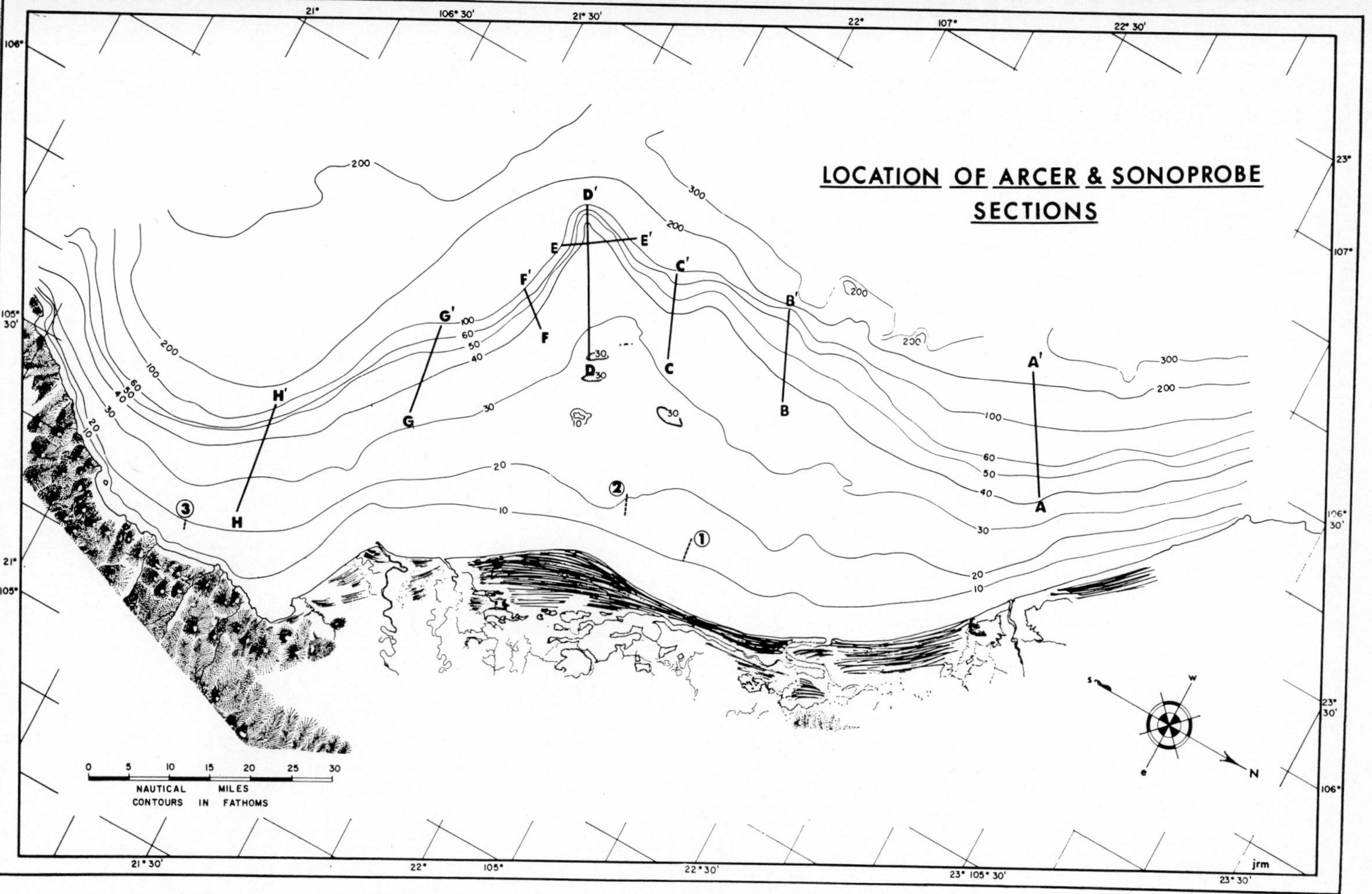

FIG. 6.—Location of Arcer and Sonoprobe sections shown in Figs. 7 through 17.

from examination of the suite of records collected from two cruises to the Costa de Nayarit and from previous work with similar records (Moore and Curray, 1963; Curray and Moore, 1963; Moore, 1964) has resulted in definition of several basic sedimentary structural types within the Costa de Nayarit region. Unfortunately, no deep borings are available from the continental shelf or slope off the Costa de Nayarit, and only limited confirmation of interpretive efforts can be gained through conventional piston and gravity coring. It is important, therefore, to realize the interpretive nature of our data and to understand the basis of these interpretations.

Interpretation of Arcer records is complicated by the multiplicity of signals recorded from a single reflecting surface as a result of bubble pulses generated by the electric arc explosion. Thus a single surface may appear on the record as a series of parallel lines. Separation of a series of actual reflecting horizons from the multiplicity of lines recorded from a single reflector generally can be accomplished by careful observation of line spacing and parallelism, or lack of parallelism. Interpretation is made much easier where angular discontinuities exist between key horizons (Fig. 10, notation 1).

A problem common to all continuous recording profiling systems is recognition of multiples. Multiples are the result of the reflection of sound energy from the sea floor or from other strong reflectors, travel back to the air-water interface, and reflection downward again. If sufficient energy is involved, a second, or even third, round trip between the air-water interface and the sea floor, or other strong reflector, may be completed and recorded on the chart. Interpretation generally is no problem in conventional sea-floor ech sounding, but where multiples are mixed in wit sub-bottom reflecting horizons, the interpretatio can be complex. In records such as those pre sented here, it is well to recognize that the firs multiple of the sea floor plots at twice the dept and twice the slope of the sea floor. Many geo metric possibilities exist for complicated sub bottom multiples. Most commonly, however, th first multiple of sub-bottom reflections plots i identical position relative to the bottom multipl as does the original sub-bottom reflection to th original bottom reflection; that is, both the bo tom and the sub-bottom multiple reflections ar displaced downward a distance equal to the dept of water.

It is somewhat difficult to define rigidly th criteria utilized in record interpretation, and certain amount of intuitive geological reasonin must contribute to the final picture evolved. Bas cally, however, four kinds of evidence must b considered in making a decision concerning th nature of the geology recorded on this type record—(1) lateral continuity of bedding (reflec ing horizons believed to be bedding), (2) attitud of bedding with respect to underlying, overlyin and flanking strata, (3) nature of upper contac of sequences of beds, and (4) thickness of unit both individual and in sequence. In short, we a looking for familiar geological forms, such deltaic structure, angular unconformities, ero sional surfaces, lenticularity and cross-beddin original dip structure, faults, folds, and the man other structural forms used for interpretive geo ogy. In some records, these forms are better di played than by any other method. In other re ords, the case for these forms is very tenuous an

→

FIG. 7.—Sonoprobe record from line 1 shown in Fig. 6. Water depth ranges from 95 to 120 feet (16 to fathoms). Water depths and thicknesses of sediment units are shown at a sound velocity of 4,800 fps. (1) Holoce shelf-facies silty clays. (2) Probable interbedded silty clays and littoral sands, the basal sands of the Holocene tran gression. (3) Probable pre-transgressive (Pleistocene) subaerial erosional surface on alluvium.

FIG. 8.—Sonoprobe record from line 2 shown in Fig. 6. (1) Surface layer of Holocene shelf-facies sil clays. (2) Holocene basal transgressive sands, locally interbedded with shelf muds. (3) Subaerial pre-transgressi alluvial surface. This surface is covered with basal sands under the shelf muds and where it crops out seawa from this record.

FIG. 9.—Sonoprobe record from line 3 shown in Fig. 6. (1) Holocene shelf-facies silty clays. (2) Subaerial eroded rock surface, probably covered with thin veneer of sand and rubble. (3) Channel in rock surface is fill with several layers of sediments draped in to subdue contours of channel.

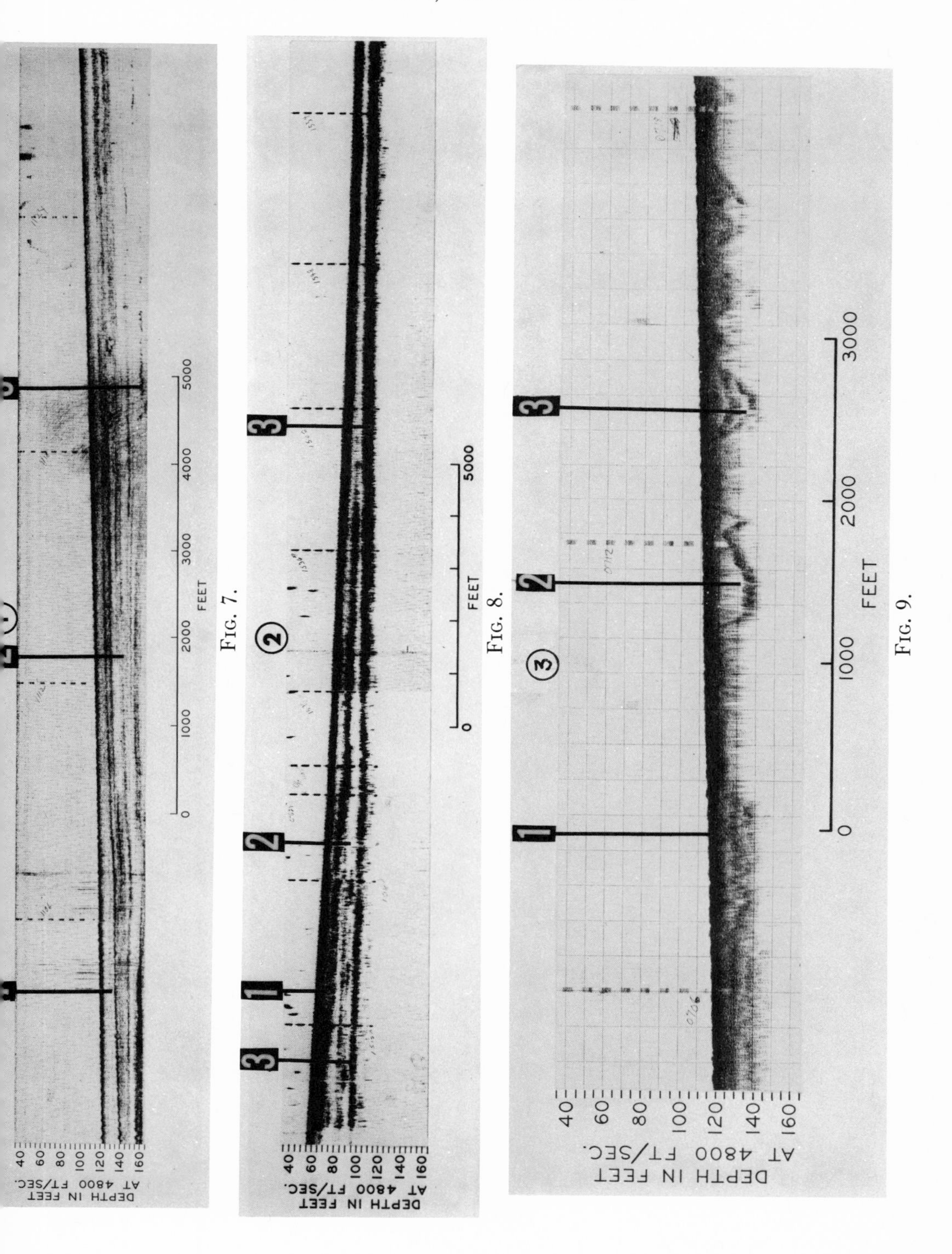

FIG. 7.

FIG. 8.

FIG. 9.

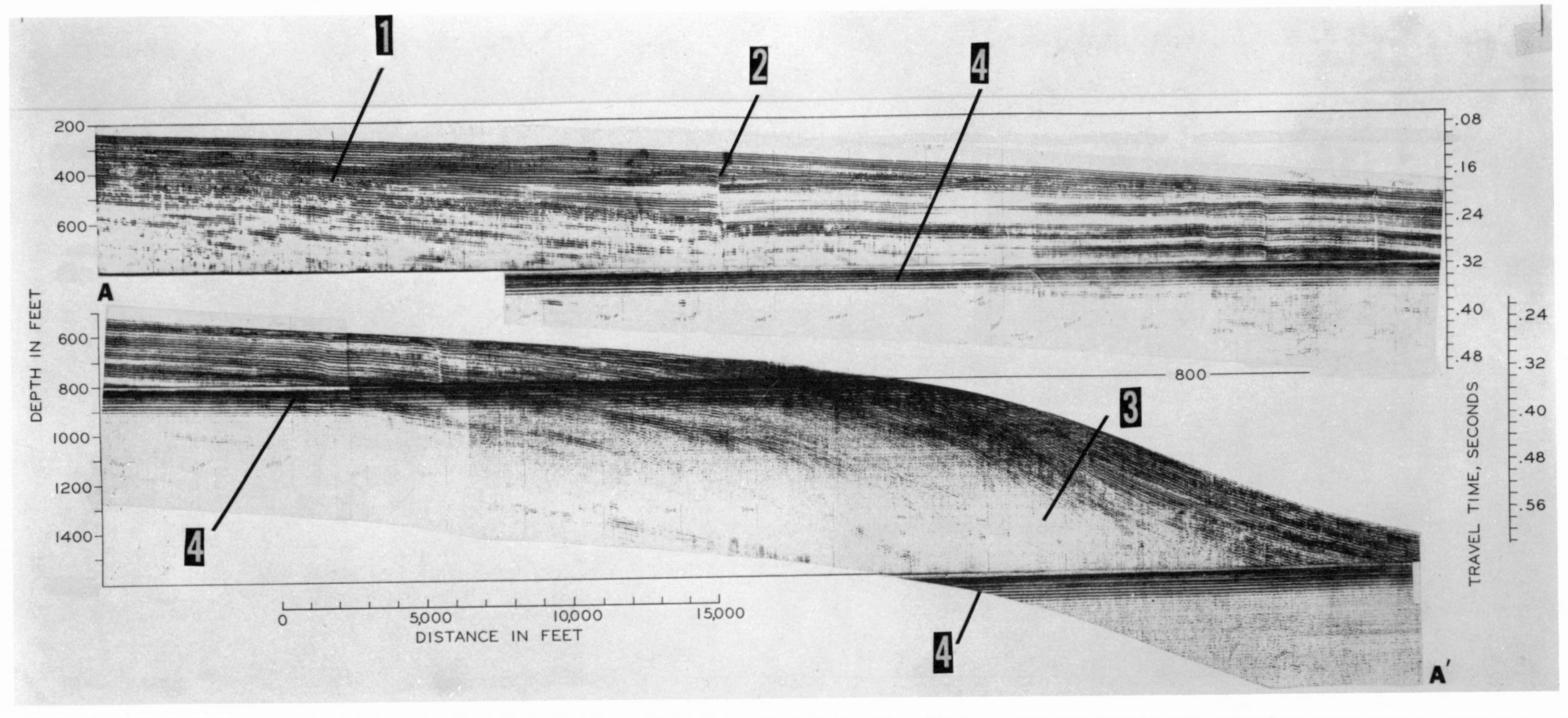

FIG. 10.—Arcer record *A-A′* from position shown in Fig. 6. In this and following series of Arcer records, primed letter of section (*A′*) is on the seaward end of the traverse. Each section was recorded continuously, but is broken for convenience of presentation. Section covers water depth range of about 200 to 1,350 feet (33 to 225 fathoms). (1) Thick accumulation of evenly bedded shelf sediments interfingering with littoral and alluvial facies, detectable by angular discontinuity of reflecting layers to those of enclosing beds. (2) Down-to-basin normal faults are shown with throw increasing with depth. (3) Very thick accumulation of slope deposits has built terrace outward and upward with continued subsidence. Steepest of these slope deposits is about 4°; present slope surface is about 2°. (4) Records were cut for easier presentation, causing outgoing signal to appear within sections.

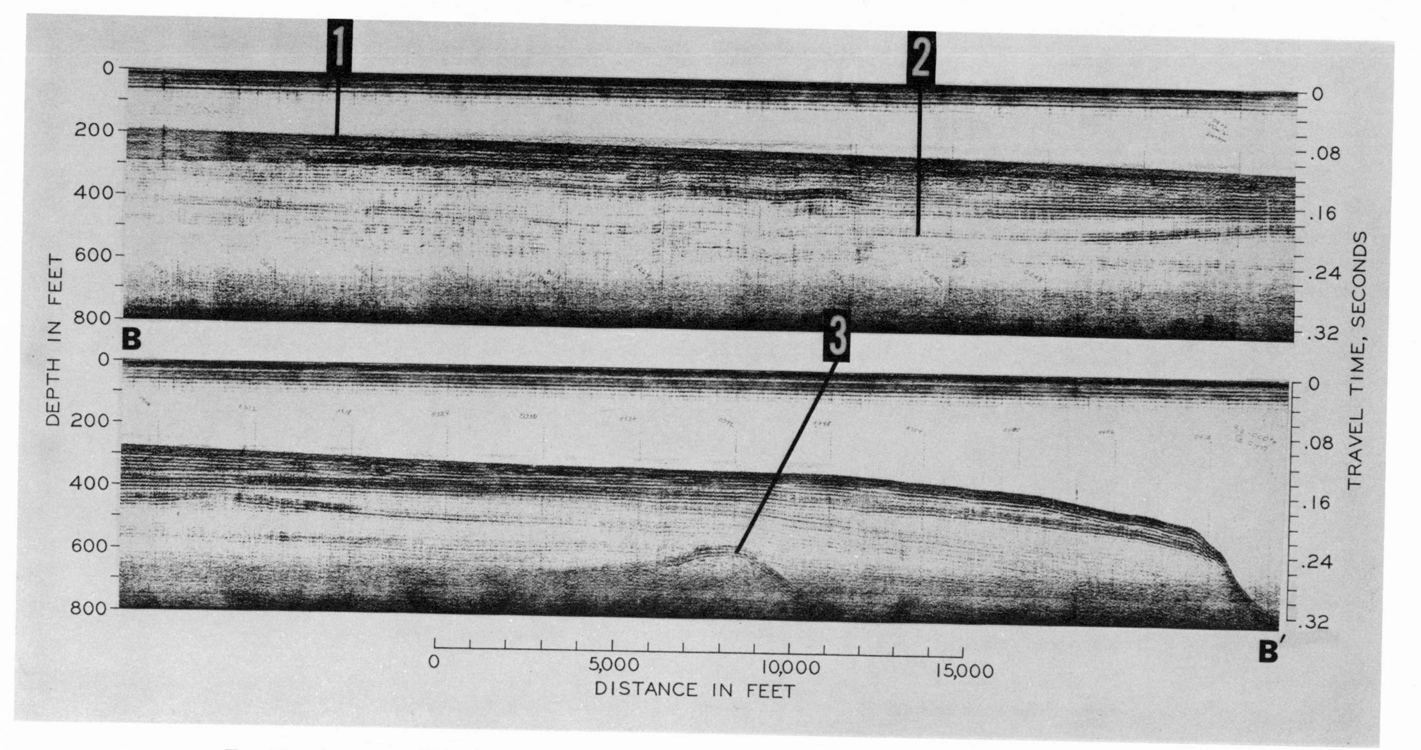

FIG. 11.—Arcer record *B-B′* from position shown in Fig. 6. (1) Sea floor slopes gently from a depth of 200 feet to nearly 400 feet (33 to 67 fathoms) near the shelf-break. (2) Continuity of subsurface bedding and conformity to present shelf profile suggests long period of shelf deposition. Reflecting beds in upper 200 feet of subsurface near outer shelf appear to crop out on upper slope, suggesting slump. This is the only surveyed section to show outcropping beds on slope. It is immediately adjacent to an area on the continental slope (Fig. 2), where the depth contours show an indentation suggestive of a slump scar or area of concentration of slope erosion. (3) A buried hill of unknown rock type appears underlying outer shelf.

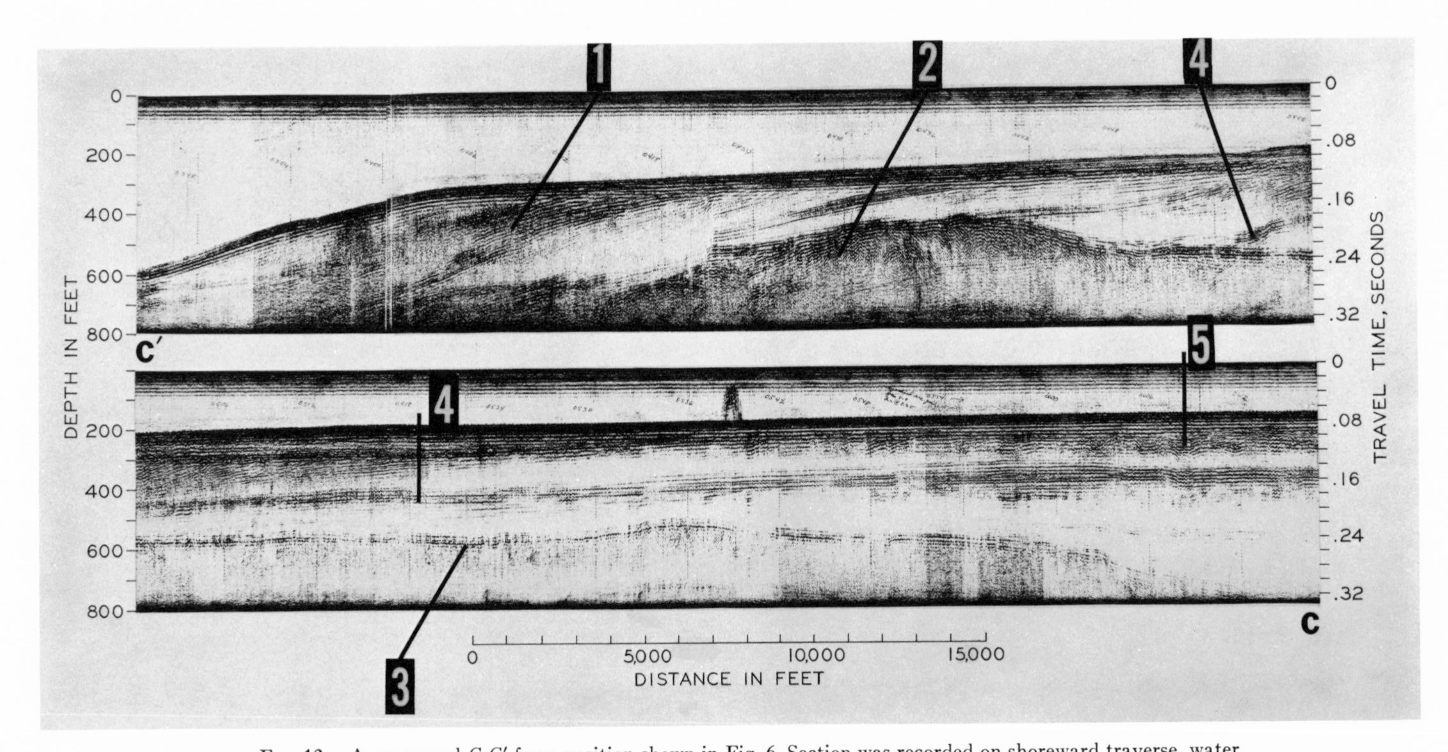

Fig. 12.—Arcer record C-C' from position shown in Fig. 6. Section was recorded on shoreward traverse, water depths from 600 to 200 feet (100 to 33 fathoms). Seaward part of section underlain by (1) probable thick delta foreset beds covering (2) buried hill of unknown rock type, which formed shelf-break of pre-delta time. (3) Reflections from same probable rock surface extend beneath 600 to 800 feet of sediment to near end of section. (4) Multiple of bottom reflection runs through record. Discontinuous, irregular reflections (5) near shoreward end suggest marsh and alluvial facies related to delta.

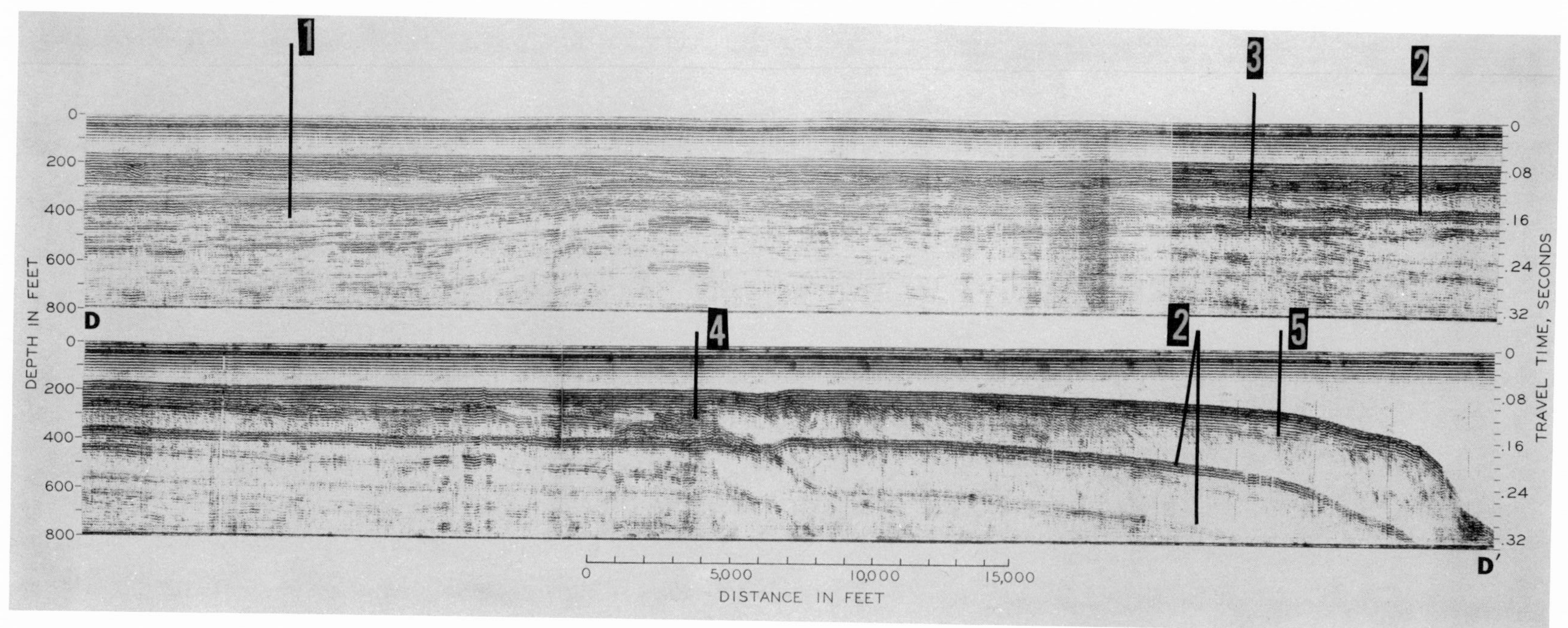

FIG. 13.—Arcer record *D-D′* from position shown in Fig. 6. Section from 150 to 750 feet (25 to 125 fathoms) of water depth across principal topographic bulge in Costa de Nayarit terrace. Inner part of section has shelf-facies muds underlain by (1) irregularly bedded probable paralic facies. (2) Multiples of bottom reflection run through record. (3) Probable fossil shelf-break. Seaward, a deltaic sequence is recorded ending at a well-defined old shelf-break having (4) an apparent shelf-edge reef buried beneath shoreward part of (5) another deltaic sequence which ends at, and forms, the present shelf-break. Steepest of the foreset beds is about 9° and average is about 7°.

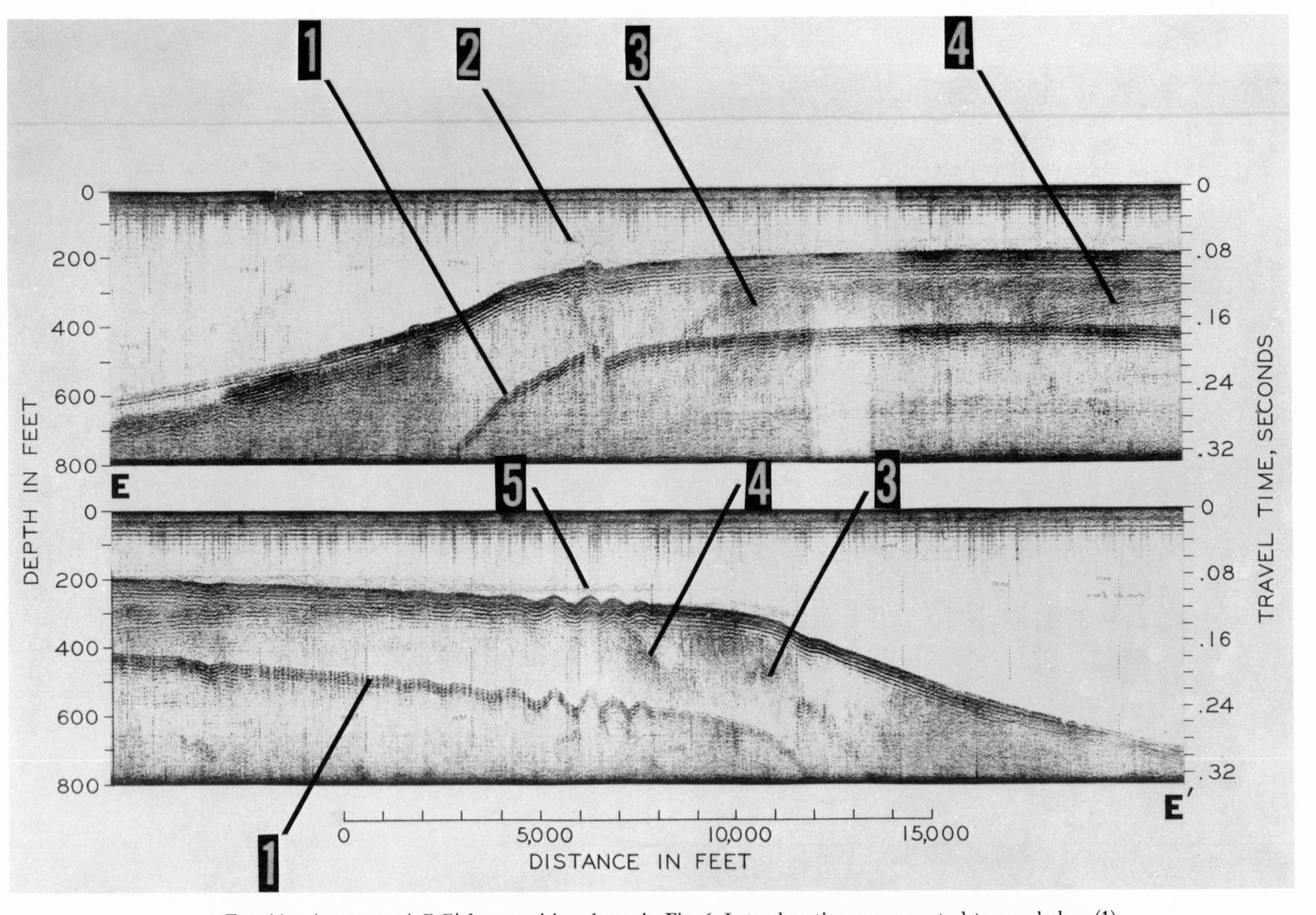

Fig. 14.—Arcer record *E-E'* from position shown in Fig. 6. Lateral section across central terrace bulge. (1) Strong bottom echo multiple. (2) Probable rock or reef protuberance near southern shelf-break. (3) Youngest delta foreset beds flank both sides of topographic bulge and prograde slope into deeper water from (4) older slope face.

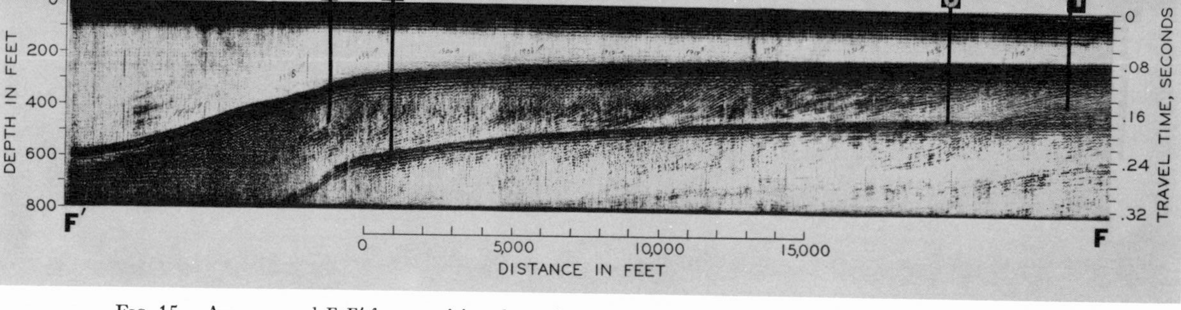

FIG. 15.—Arcer record *F-F'* from position shown in Fig. 6. Section from shoreward traverse. (1) Steep dipping, arcuate, concave-upward bedding typical of records of foreset deltaic deposition in this area. Termination of this deltaic phase forms present shelf-break. (2) Strong bottom multiple runs through section. (3) Probable fossil shelf-break predating deltaic deposition is shown dipping down through multiple. Delta foresets grade landward into more gently dipping strata of probable marsh or alluvial origin.

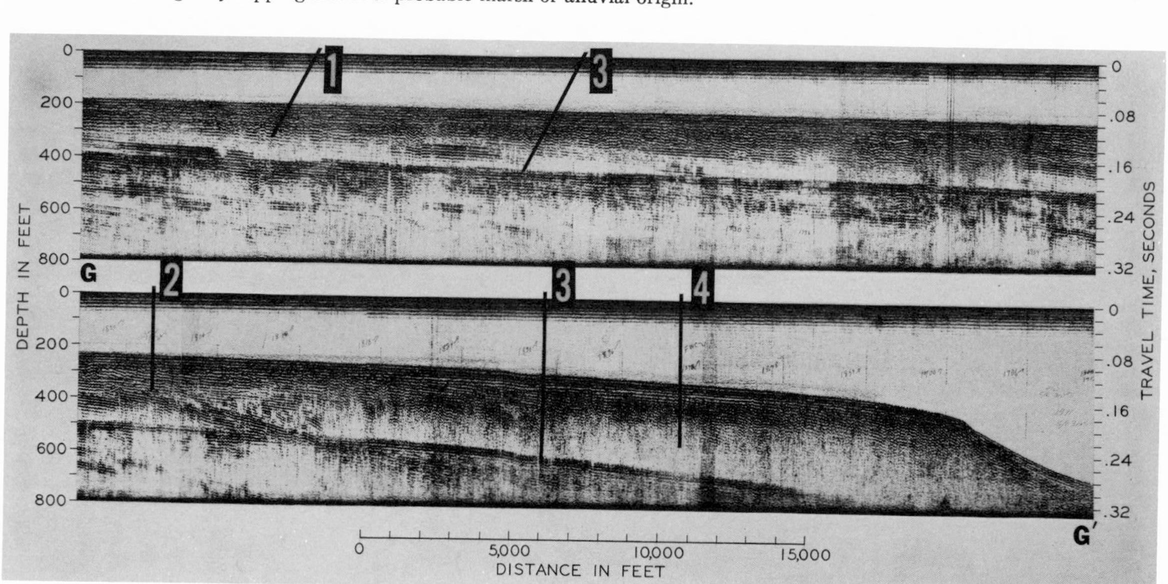

FIG. 16.—Arcer record *G-G'* from position shown in Fig. 6. Traverse from 200 to 650 feet (33 to 116 fathoms) water depth. (1) Irregularly bedded probable alluvial or marsh deposits over more uniform shelf facies which terminate at (2) a buried fossil shelf-break. (3) Strong bottom multiple runs through entire section. Seaward of this break a thick section of delta foreset beds, related to the inshore marsh and alluvial deposits, extends to, and forms, the present shelf-break.

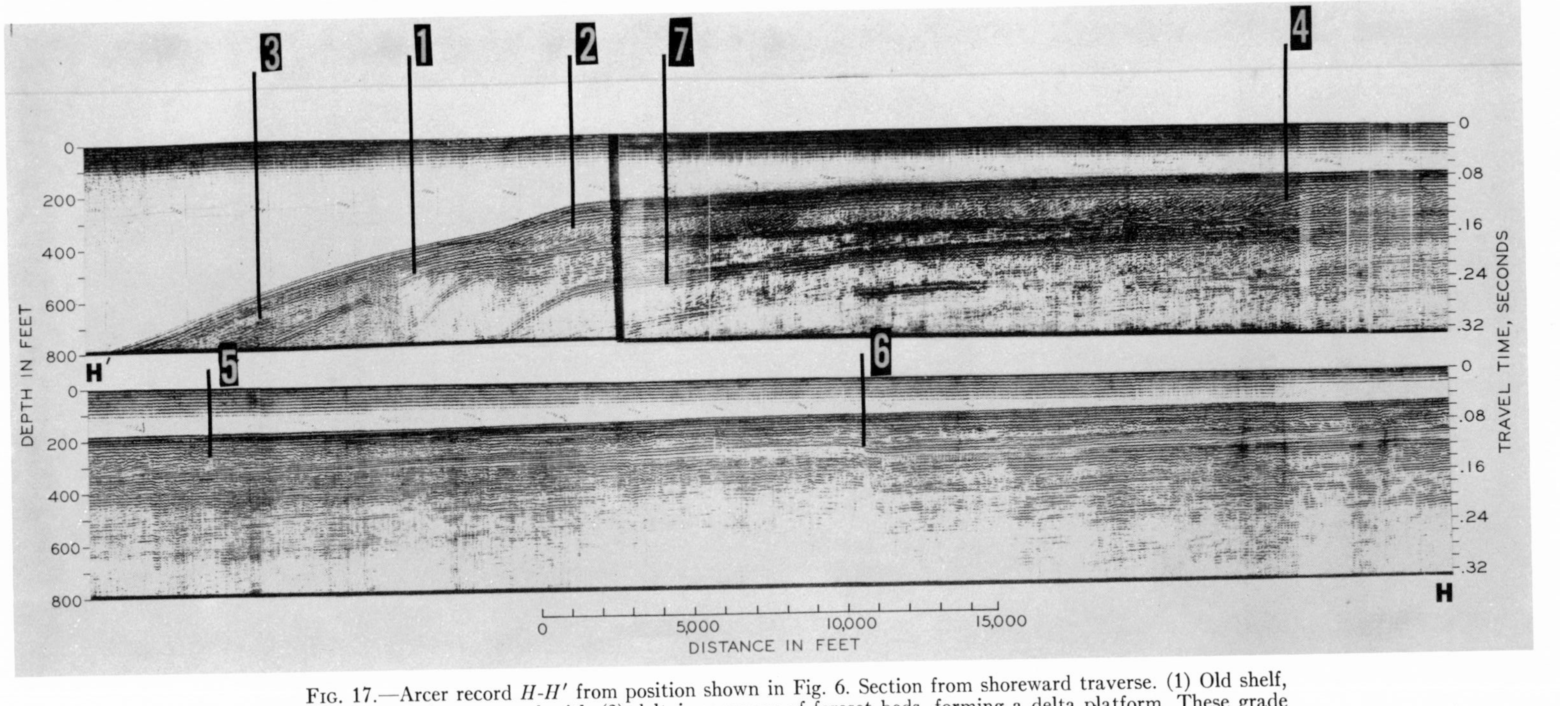

FIG. 17.—Arcer record H-H' from position shown in Fig. 6. Section from shoreward traverse. (1) Old shelf, shelf-break, and slope covered with (2) deltaic sequence of foreset beds, forming a delta platform. These grade seaward into (3) slope deposits, actually the bottomset beds of the deltaic sequence; landward into (4) less steeply dipping beds of probable interdistributary origin, and finally to (5) irregular beds of probable alluvial origin. (6) Up-to-basin normal fault of considerable displacement. (7) Strong bottom multiple is shown in the outer half of the section.

can be justified only by association with related structures.

In using the evidence described, the recorded subsurface of the Costa de Nayarit has been divided into alluvial facies; littoral, neritic, and basal transgressive sand facies; open-shelf facies; deltaic foreset and topset facies; and slope facies. Topset delta facies are, in fact, commonly indistinguishable from basal transgressive sands; similarly, slope facies in the areas of delta sequences must be considered the bottomset beds of the delta system.

The Arcer records presented and described in captions (Figs. 10–17) were selected to point out pertinent structural features and facies units within the area.

CORRELATION OF EVENTS

Formation of the various facies units revealed by interpretation of the Arcer records involves a rather complicated sequence of events. These include progradation of the shelf edge by deltaic deposition, and erosional truncation of pre-existing sediments at former sea levels. These events occurred during Quaternary eustatic fluctuations of sea level. They are preserved as former surfaces of the continental shelf and slope and former positions of the shelf-break, and are detectable in the records (Figs. 10–17). Correlations of these surfaces between adjacent survey lines are postulated to establish a sequence which, supplemented by radiocarbon dates, can be extrapolated into a chronology of the depositional history and fluctuations of sea level for a portion of the late Quaternary.

The correlated fossil surfaces represent only those positions of the former sea floor which existed as interfaces for a sufficiently long time to develop into acoustic reflecting horizons by changes in lithology, by desiccation under subaerial conditions, or by more complete consolidation. To develop such characteristics, the fossil surfaces must have formed during changes in the depositional, oceanographic, or sea-level conditions.

Correlation of contemporaneous geological events is most straightforward if we consider only those surfaces and morphological features with known relationships to sea level.

The break in slope between the topset beds and the foreset beds of a delta occurs approximately at sea level. This position is easily determined on the records and is used as an indication of the position of sea level at the time of deposition of the sediments. All the delta sequences of the area shown in the records apparently were formed during periods of falling sea level, because the depth of this break in slope becomes deeper in a seaward direction. The most seaward positions of these breaks in each deltaic sequence are correlated in Figure 18.

The deltaic break in slope in some cases correlates laterally with what might be termed normal shelf breaks. These are the breaks in slope between shelf sediments and slope sediments. As will be discussed more fully later, such a break in slope might be expected to occur somewhat below sea level in a nondeltaic, depositional area. For the sake of simplicity, these breaks will still be called "old shorelines," although they were probably formed slightly below sea level.

The most recent of the old shorelines also include surface erosional terraces. These terraces were shown most clearly by the echo-sounding profiles of the bathymetric survey as approximately horizontal notches cut into the lower continental shelf and upper continental slope. Such terraces have been shown by Dietz and Menard (1951) to be related to "surf-base," at a maximum of about 30 feet below sea level at the time of formation. Because most of this coastline is exposed to the open swell of the Pacific Ocean, the 30-foot depth of surf abrasion suggested by Dietz and Menard is reasonable.

Four distinct former shorelines have been traced by correlations between the Arcer lines over parts of the area (Fig. 18). These correlations are based on relative geographic position, depth below present sea level, and in some cases on genesis—such as deltaic or erosional. The assumption has been made that depth may change systematically from line to line, reflecting regional tectonic activity. Local unsystematic depth changes may reflect not only changes in shoreline type, but also local variations in the balance between rate of deposition and rate of removal. Erosional notches might be expected to be deeper in areas of more open exposure and lower rate of sediment supply.

Despite these sources of variation, the four old shorelines show some consistency in depth

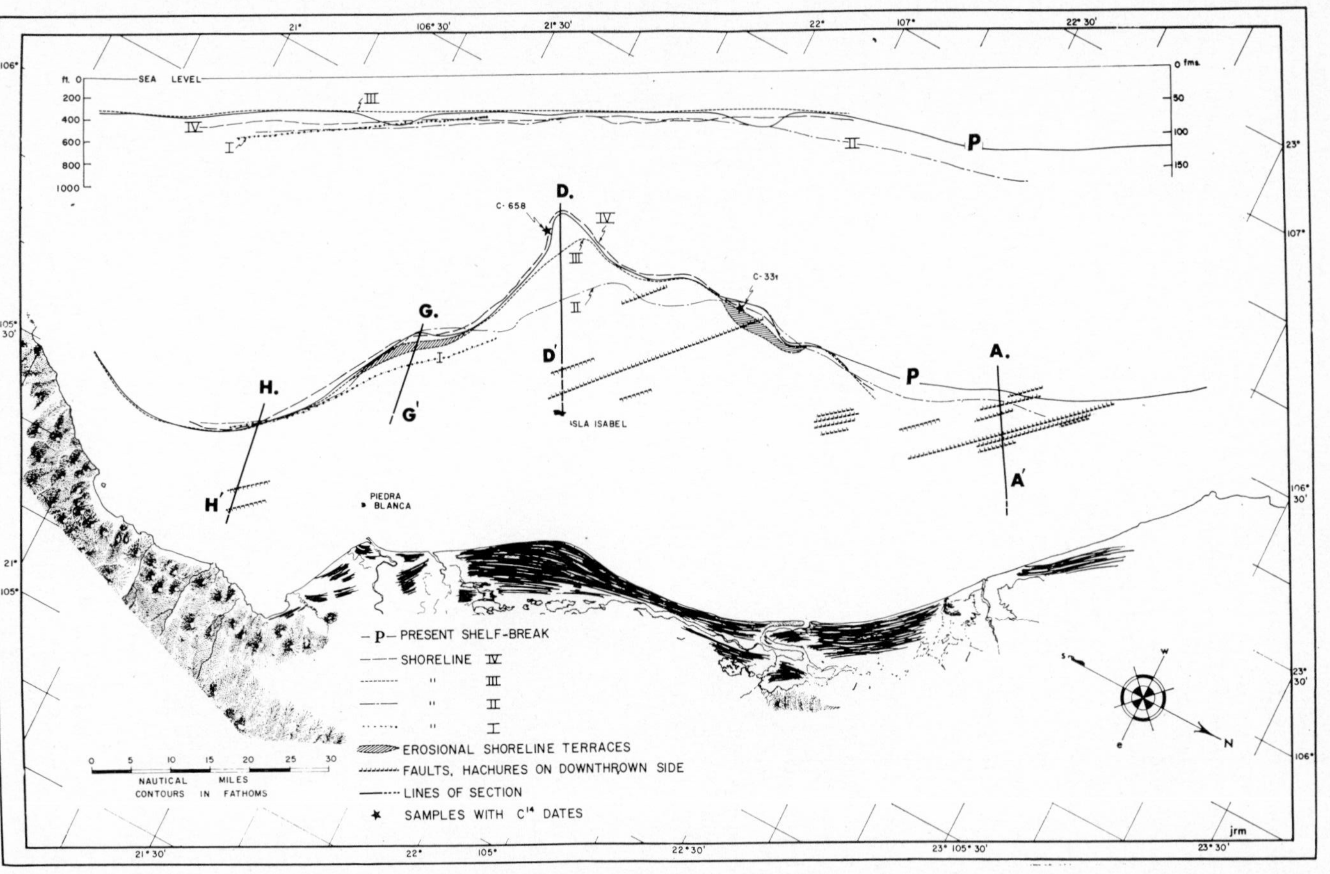

FIG. 18.—Chart of the Costa de Nayarit showing former positions of shoreline during late Pleistocene lowered sea level. Positions were obtained by correlation of old shelf-breaks shown in the Arcer records of the area, and in some cases also by correlation with erosional terraces in the present surface of the shelf and upper slope. Radiocarbon dates from the two starred positions average about 17,600 years B.P., showing that shoreline IV must be late Wisconsin. Assignment of ages to the other shorelines is explained in the text. The section plotted above the chart is a projected longitudinal section of depths of old shorelines and present shelf-break. The oldest shorelines show some downwarping by faulting to the north and south. The present shelf-break is shown to be related to several different controlling parts of the terrace structure and to vary widely in depth.

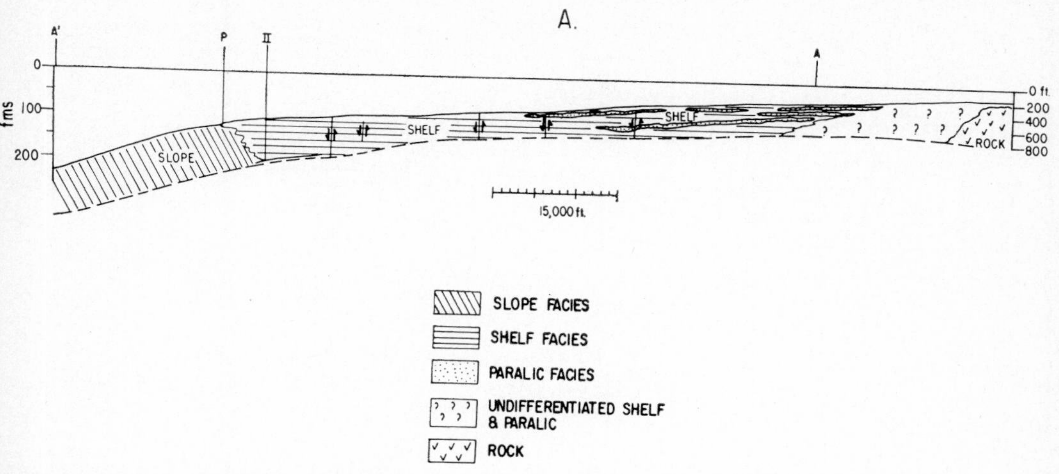

FIG. 19.—Line drawing of Arcer record including section *A-A'* (Fig. 10), with facies interpretations and notations on the positions of old shorelines plotted in Fig. 18.

throughout the area. A vertical profile in the upper part of Figure 18, plotted longitudinally along the edge of the shelf by projection normal to the profile line, shows the depths of the shoreline below present sea level. The older shorelines (I and II) clearly show downwarping to the south, and shoreline II also shows downwarping to the north. The younger features show mainly local variation.

The old shorelines, deltaic sequences, and faults also are shown in section in Figures 19, 20, 21, and 22. They are plotted directly from the records, which include sections *A-A'*, *D-D'*, *G-G'*, and *H-H'* (Figs. 10, 13, 16, and 17).

Section *A-A'* (Fig. 19) lies near the northern part of the Costa de Nayarit, just south of Mazatlán. The edge of the continental shelf in this vicinity is deep, averaging about −750 feet (125 fathoms), and is indistinct because of rounding. The cause of this deeply downwarped shelf edge obviously is related to faulting, as shown in the Arcer records and plotted in Figure 18. All faults crossed on this traverse are normal, with down-to-basin displacement. Further, all these faults are growth

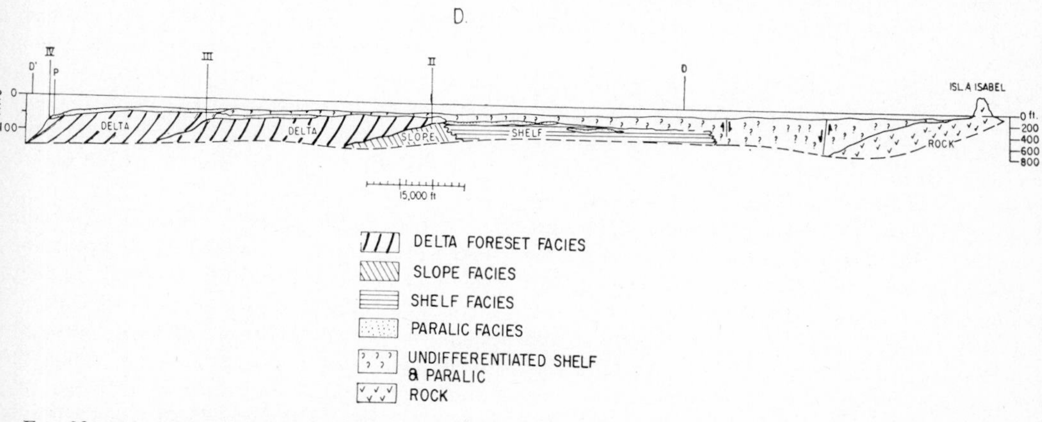

FIG. 20.—Line drawing of Arcer record including section *D-D'* (Fig. 13), with facies interpretations and notations on the positions of old shorelines plotted in Fig. 18.

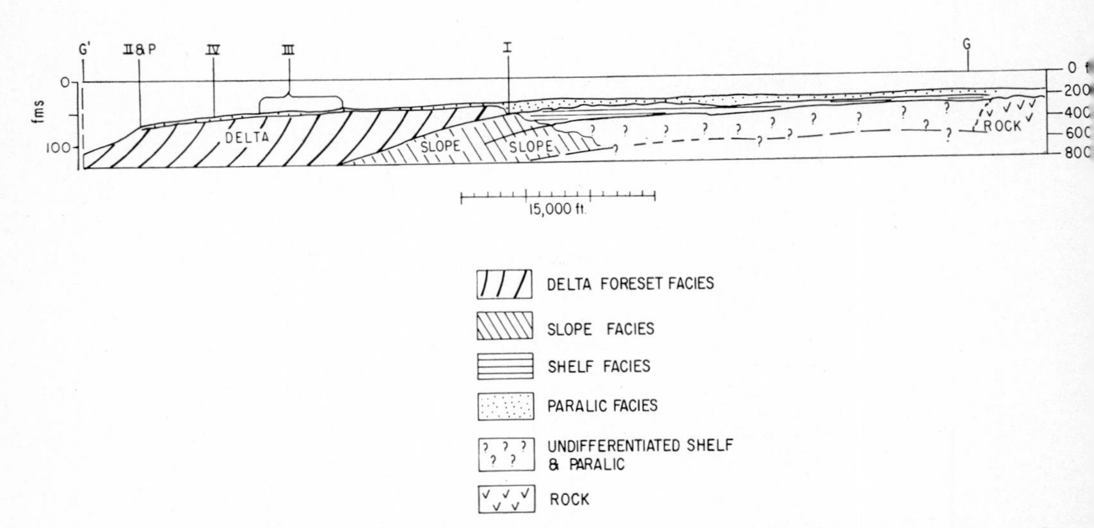

FIG. 21.—Line drawing of Arcer record including section *G-G'* (Fig. 16), with facies interpretations and notations on the positions of old shorelines plotted in Fig. 18.

faults active through a long period of deposition of sediments, and they show increased displacement downward. A consequence of the gradual subsidence is the thick section of sediment draping across the shelf and down the slope. The contact shown between the shelf facies and the slope facies is based on depositional dip.

Landward from the break in slope, the shelf facies are interbedded with probable paralic facies (neritic, littoral, lagoonal, and deltaic topset sediments).

The section through the main protuberance in the edge of the shelf, line *D-D'* (Fig. 20), shows the sequence of deltas which prograded the edge of the shelf in this vicinity. This section extends from Isla Isabel across the old continental shelf which existed at the time of shoreline II, presumably in early Wisconsin time. The edge of the shelf, and hence the position of sea level at that time, was at about 400 feet (67 fathoms) below present sea level. Overlying and seaward of this shelf-break are the foreset beds of the delta that formed prior to stabilization of sea level of shoreline III. This delta must have formed during a period of slowly falling sea level, because the break in slope between the topset and foreset bed slopes seaward from about 260 feet (43 fathoms to about 350 feet (58 fathoms) below present se level. Thus 58 fathoms represents the final lov stand of sea level of shoreline III.

The final deltaic sequence in this section lie over and seaward of shoreline III. This delta als must have formed with falling sea level, as it oldest foreset beds extend to about 210 feet (3 fathoms) below present sea level, whereas it youngest foresets come to −406 feet (68 fathoms) Part of, but probably not all, this change in slop could have been caused by erosion. Thus th change also represents a regressive delta phas formed during a drop in sea level from about 3 fathoms to 68 fathoms.

Proceeding toward the south, the next sectior *G-G'* (Fig. 21), also shows deltaic progradation t the edge of the continental terrace. This sectio extends from a point where rock appears to b shallowly buried under the sediment on the inne shelf, and across an old surface of the shelf, shel break, and continental slope. This ancient shel break (I) at −450 feet (75 fathoms) has bee correlated with other records and has been dete

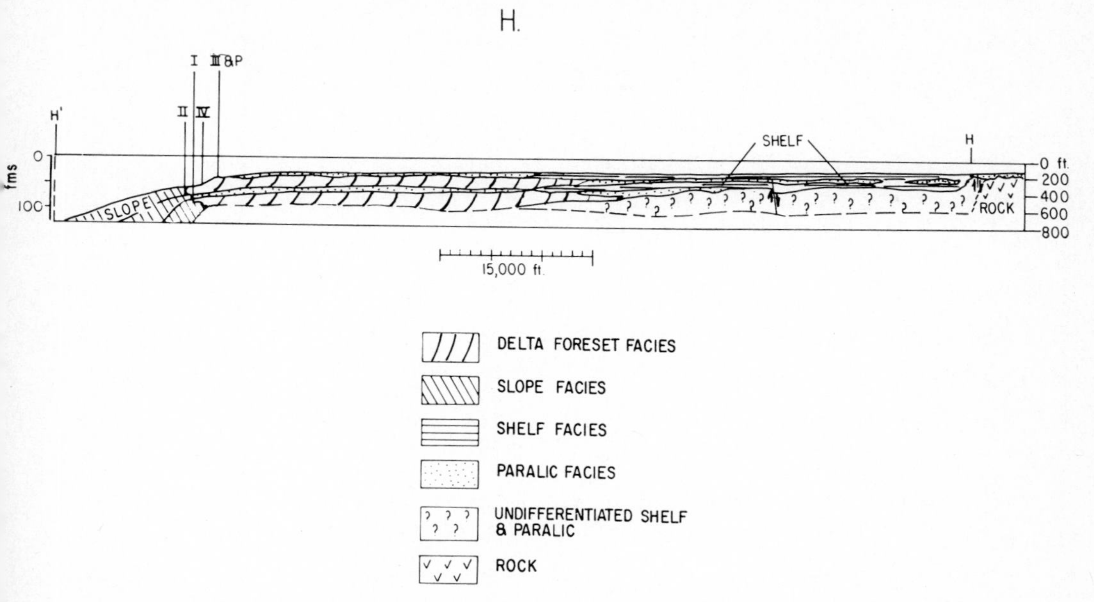

FIG. 22.—Line drawing of Arcer record including section *H-H′* (Fig. 17), with facies interpretations and notations on the positions of old shorelines plotted in Fig. 18.

mined to be the oldest identifiable fossil shelf-break in the area. Overlying and seaward of this is the younger deltaic sequence (II) at −472 feet (79 fathoms). Shorelines III and IV are both erosional terraces in this part of the area. The terrace corresponding to III is a wide, flat surface at about 345 to 350 feet of depth (58 fathoms), whereas the terrace corresponding to IV is a slight erosional notch in the slope at about −410 feet (68 fathoms).

Section *H-H′* (Fig. 22) shows a vertical succession of deltas of different ages, but no deltaic progradation to the edge of the continental terrace. Stage I and II shorelines and surfaces (−550 and −520 feet, or 92 and 87 fathoms, respectively) are distinctly shown, but the correlations are somewhat tenuous. The stage III delta clearly overlies the previous shelf surface and apparently represents a regressive deltaic sequence formed during a drop in sea level from about 35 fathoms to about 53 fathoms. The regression did not carry the shoreline seaward of the previous shelf edge, but the former shelf edge was buried under the bottomset beds of the delta, which are, in effect, the continental-slope deposits in this region. The stage IV shoreline, which marks the termination of delta foreset beds on the central shelf protuberance, shows very distinctly as an erosional notch at −410 feet (68 fathoms).

A basic morphological difference can be observed between delta foreset beds and slope deposits, in that normal delta foreset beds in this area are predominantly concave upward, whereas upper continental slope deposits are convex upward. In addition, delta foreset beds are 7°–9° on their steepest slopes, whereas slope deposits are about 4°, measured on steepest beds, and more nearly 2.5° on the present slope surface. The delta of the Rio Grande de Santiago is predominantly composed of sand. Deltas of rivers such as the Mississippi, which carry predominantly silt and clay, may show a more subdued concavity to the foresets as well as gentler slopes, or in some instances may even show convex-upward foresets.

CHRONOLOGY

On the basis of the correlations and the inferred depth variations shown by the deltaic sequences and the erosional levels, a tentative chronology of sea-level fluctuations and events is suggested.

TABLE I. RADIOCARBON DATES

Sample	*Water Depth (fathoms)*	*Age (years B.P.)*	*Correlation in Fig. 18*	*Material and Comments*
C-331 a	67	19,300±300	IV	Dated *Strombus grannulatus*, with living depth rang 1–10 fathoms (Parker, personal communication) Previously published depth $62\frac{1}{2}$ fathoms (Curray 1961b). Re-examination of echo-sounding record shows depth to be about 67 fathoms.
C-331 b	67	16,490±600	IV	Dated *Megapitaria squalida*, and *Chione gnidia*, livin depth ranges 1–10 fathoms (Parker, personal com munication).
C-658 b	57	17,850±700	IV	Dated *Anomia adamas* (Gray), living depth range inter tidal to 5 fathoms (Parker, personal communication)
C-658 c	57	16,800±700	IV	Dated *Arca pacifica* (Sow. 1833) and *Arca mutabili* (Sow. 1833), living depth ranges 1–3 fathoms (Parker personal communication).

These events have been related to an absolute time scale by four radiocarbon dates run on molluscs of known intertidal or shallow water living-depth range. Robert H. Parker selected these shells for dating from dredge hauls made by the writers from Stations C-331 and C-658 (Fig. 18). Both samples from which dates were obtained were dredged from shelly sands near or at the edge of the continental shelf and correlated with the stage IV shoreline, or the latest low stand of the sea in this area. The dates (Table I) average about 17,600 years B.P., indicating that the stage IV delta must represent a late Wisconsin age. We may further reason that if our correlations are correct between the stage III delta and the erosional terraces in the nondeltaic part of the area, then stage III must also be very recent, probably late Wisconsin. If it were older (for example, early Wisconsin), the erosional terraces in all probability would have been buried and concealed. Stages I and II are older and thus may represent early Wisconsin, or possibly even earlier Pleistocene. These age assignments and the sequence of events are tentative and must remain so until more samples and radiocarbon dates can add substantiation.

The proposed sequence of events inferred from the bathymetry and sub-bottom structure and published literature is as follows.

1. During early Wisconsin time, stage I and stage II shorelines were formed. Both are deltaic shorelines in part and nondeltaic in part, with sea level at −65 fathoms or lower. It is postulated that both stages were formed during the same general period of time, because they are no widely separated either in distance or in dept below present sea level.

2. An interstadial higher stand of sea level i middle Wisconsin time (Curray, 1961b; Frye an Willman, 1961) drowned these old shorelines, an deposition of sediment probably occurred on th broad continental shelf that was created.

3. Following this interstadial, sea level fell t −53 to −58 fathoms at the beginning of the lat Wisconsin glacial phase. During this drop in se level, the stage III delta was formed as a regres sive deposit. At the termination of the sea leve drop, there was a stillstand of sufficient duratio to form the extensive erosional terraces at −5 fathoms.

4. Sea level rose again to −35 fathoms, an stood long enough to form the broad, flat surfac of the central shelf at depths of −25 to −35 fath oms (Fig. 2). This must have been an alluvia plain and perhaps a marshy surface, possibly wit a strand plain like the modern strand plain. distinct break in slope occurs at −35 fathoms o this shelf, as on many other broad shelves of th world (Shepard, 1948; Curray, 1960).

5. Sea level dropped for the second time in th late Wisconsin, this time to about −68 fathom During this fall of sea level, the regressive stag IV delta was formed, probably very quickly, b concentration of deposition of the major rivers o the area into this one deltaic bulge. Elsewher along the upper continental slope, this shoreline i locally shown as a slight erosional notch cut int the unconsolidated sediments. Rate of fall of se

level may have varied from relatively slow between the depths of −35 to −63 fathoms to relatively more rapid from −63 to −68 fathoms. This final stand of the sea correlates with the radiocarbon dates of Table I, as late Wisconsin.

6. Subsequent events belong to the Holocene transgression and will be discussed in a later paper (Curray and Moore, in preparation) on the surface sediments, morphology, and Sonoprobe studies of the continental shelf.

CONTINENTAL TERRACE STRUCTURE

Little more than a decade ago the geologic literature indicated a flowering of interest in the origin and structure of the continental margins. This interest probably was sparked by the postwar availability of records from numerous widespread echo sounding traverses which gave, for the first time, relatively detailed topographic information on many shelves and slopes. Additional motivation for speculation on the origin of continental terraces was provided by the data of seismic refraction studies, principally on the eastern coast of the United States.

Although several papers dealing with the origin of continental terraces appeared within a very few years (Umbgrove, 1947; Shepard, 1948; Bourcart, 1949; Stetson, 1949, 1953; Kuenen, 1950a, 1950b; Dietz, 1952; for example), there was remarkably little basic agreement among the contributors. Essentially all possible mechanisms of terrace origin have been proposed and published either in the above examples or in earlier papers. The writers have previously suggested that several of these mechanisms will be found valid with further exploration, and they have proposed a simple descriptive classification (Moore and Curray, 1963), based only on the internal structure of the rock and sediment mass comprising the terrace (Fig. 23). This classification summarizes the models previously theorized in the literature. It is not intended as a detailed nor an original classification; further varieties can be conceived by different combinations of these basic types and by combining them with adjacent features such as bordering trenches, thick sediment sections underlying rises at the base of the continental slope, and substitution of regional downwarping of continental margins for folding and faulting as the mechanism of structural emplacement. These further variations will not be considered here, but a brief outline of the simple classification will assist in the presentation of structural data of the Costa de Nayarit profiles.

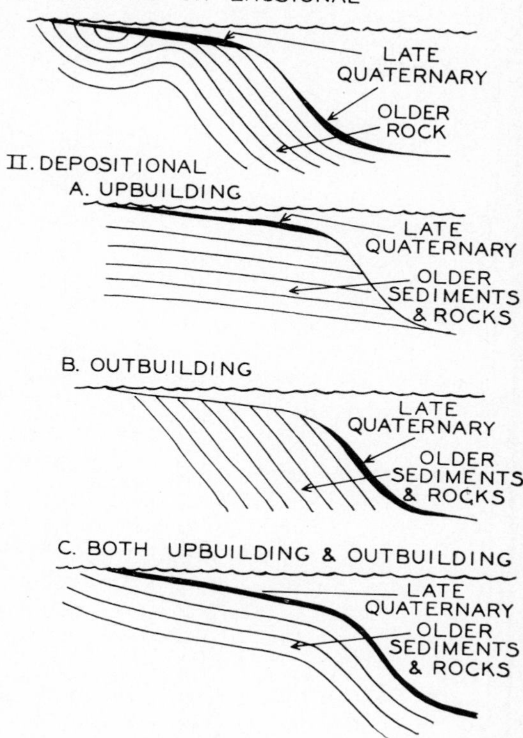

FIG. 23.—Basic descriptive classification of continental terrace structural types (from Moore and Curray, 1963).

I. *Tectonic or erosional terraces* (Fig. 23, *I*).—Deposition is not continuous, but is interrupted by extensive modification by folding, faulting, and erosion. Internal structure may be complex, and the present shelf surface normally is formed by erosion during the Pleistocene, whereas the present slope is little modified from the original tectonic form.

II. *Depositional terraces.*—Deposition, generally accompanied by subsidence, dominates internal structure, with interruptions of insufficient duration or intensity to cause major distortion. Three subtypes are recognized.

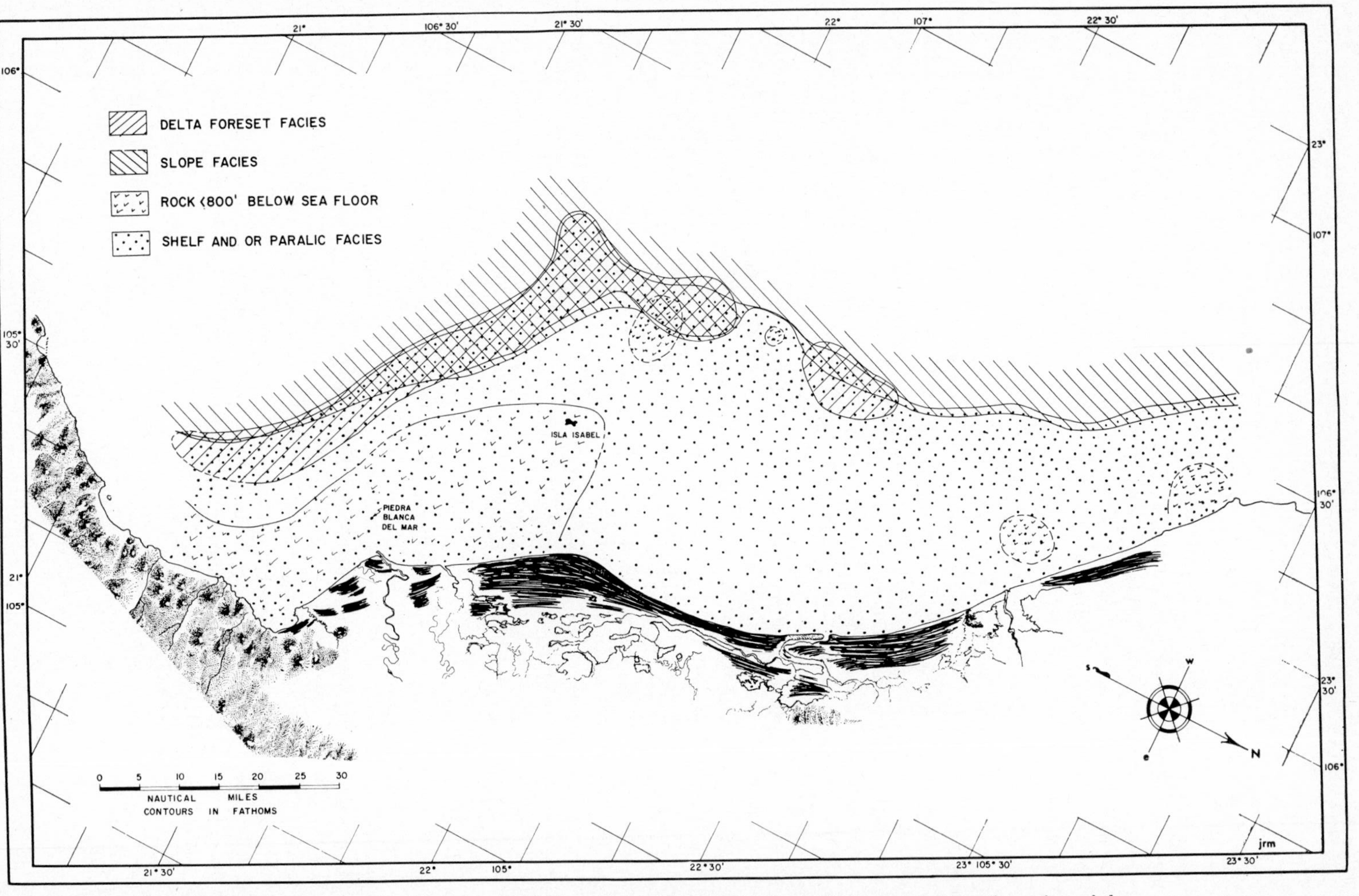

FIG. 24.—Chart of the Costa de Nayarit, showing distribution of the facies types underlying the surface of the shelf and upper slope within about the upper 800 feet.

A. *Dominantly upbuilding* (Fig. 23, *IIA*). This model assumes permanent deposition on the shelf, but not on the slope (Heezen and others, 1959). Thus internal structure consists of shelf, continental, or paralic (alluvial, lagoonal, littoral, and neritic) facies only, and any slope deposits ultimately are removed by mass movements and turbidity currents which may erode the slope landward.

B. *Dominantly outbuilding* (Fig. 23, *IIB*). This model reverses the assumptions of the previous model and allows permanent deposition on the slope, but not on the shelf. This can be considered the classic wave-built terrace, with shelf-break at "wave base" and all sediment bypassing the shelf to come to rest on the slope.

C. *Both upbuilding and outbuilding* (Fig. 23, *IIC*). In this model, the possibility of both shelf and slope deposits is admitted, and the internal structure is composed of sedimentary layers roughly paralleling the surface configuration of the terrace. Shelf facies are both paralic and open shelf, and may interfinger with alluvial facies. Slope deposits may interfinger with those of the continental rise or with basin sediments at their distal end. Most possible continental terrace structures may be simplified sufficiently to fit into one type or a composite of these types.

The structural framework of the continental terrace of the Costa de Nayarit is fundamentally similar to type *IIC* of this classification. It is, however, more complex in detail as a result of the inclusion of deltaic sequences in parts of the terrace body, whereas in other parts, open shelf and prograding slope deposits are the dominant components. The relatively abrupt changes in facies laterally parallel to the shoreline of this region are probably typical of areas of medium-sized rivers carrying an abundant load of predominantly sand-sized sediment. Under such conditions, in contrast to large rivers carrying predominantly a mud load, small deltas with sharply defined limits are formed. Basal transgressive sands, regressive sands of the present stand of sea level, and alluvium, marsh, and littoral deposits of former lowered sea levels are also recognized in the complex body of the inner central terrace.

The approximate distribution of these various facies units is shown in plan in Figure 24. Large areas are underlain by probable volcanic rock, like that of the nearby coastal hills. This rock is buried under the sedimentary facies, broadly grouped as paralic, shelf, slope, and deltaic. The deltaic

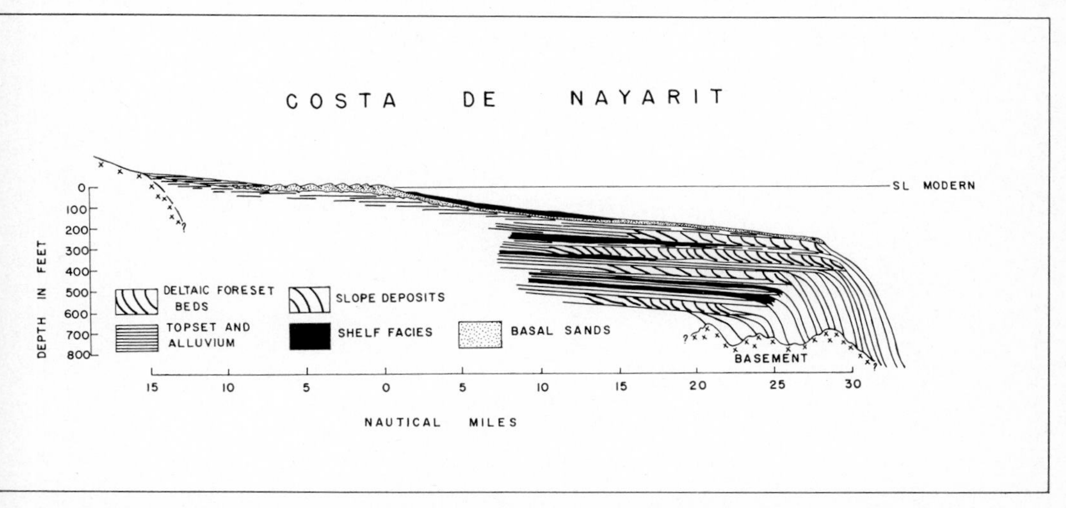

FIG. 25.—Composite structural cross section of the continental terrace of the Costa de Nayarit, showing distribution of the facies types.

facies, as plotted, includes only the foresets; the topsets are included in the paralic grouping, and the bottomsets are generally indistinguishable from shelf and slope facies.

The seaward parts of the southern and central terrace are predominantly deltaic in structure, whereas the deep, down-faulted northern area is not related to delta deposition (Figs. 7–17, 19–22). A third type, possibly related to slope failure, is illustrated by only one section (Fig. 11, *B-B′*). This lies within the deltaic province, but shows apparent outcropping of shelf deposits on the upper slope. Bathymetry in this locality (Fig. 2) shows an indentation in the slope, best seen in the 200-fathom contour, resembling a possible slump scar.

A composite model of these sections has been constructed to convey the over-all impression of the structural framework to be expected within a region having the environmental factors of the Costa de Nayarit (Fig. 25). Deltaic sediments are shown to be an important part of the body of the terrace, and, as on the present shelf, local thick sections of shelf sediments composed of neritic sand facies and open-shelf silty clays were accumulated in the past as important components within the sedimentary framework of the terrace body. The landward, or inner half, of the terrace wedge has important deposits of alluvium interfingering with the paralic and open-shelf facies. A boring through the outer shelf or upper slope of a region such as this should pass through several hundreds, or perhaps even thousands, of feet of slope deposits, probably of more or less uniform lithology such as those presently exposed on the slope. In contrast, a boring through the mid-shelf area would pass through a succession of open-shelf, neritic, alluvial, and deltaic foreset sedimentary facies.

The development of this complex structure requires concurrent deposition during lowered sea level of paralic and deltaic topset facies, marine delta-front facies, open-shelf silty clays, and slope deposits. The open-shelf silty clays and some continental-slope deposits are essentially the bottomset beds of the delta complex. As these various deposits accumulate, the sea recedes, with delta building keeping pace. On the flanks of the delta, open-shelf bottomset beds may accumulate, indistinguishable from the shelf silty clays beyond the deltaic influence. With a rise of sea level, basal transgressive sands form over the old marsh and alluvial deposits of the coastal plain. With another stillstand or drop in sea level, the stage is set for a new cycle of delta building and marine deposition, with the old delta mass forming the platform on which to build. Concurrent with the accumulation of these facies, but outside the delta influence, there also may be formation of regressive littoral sands and nondeltaic open-shelf and slope facies.

These slope deposits must accumulate very slowly in comparison to the delta platform, regressive sands of the paralic zone, and open-shelf muds. Thick sections are built because fluctuations in sea level do not expose them to the vigor of wave attack.

The upper part of the continental terrace of the Costa de Nayarit is the product of deposition of sediment under conditions of Quaternary eustatic fluctuations of sea level. Those portions of the terrace with relatively lower rates of supply of sediment and relatively rapid subsidence consist of thick sections of slope and shelf deposits, the latter interspersed with a minor proportion of paralic sediments. The portions of the shelf with greater tectonic stability and higher rates of sediment supply are characterized by delta masses distributed both laterally and vertically throughout a section in which the shelf facies are relatively less important. The complexity of structure apparently is a function primarily of the balance between rate of subsidence and the rate of deposition within this area. The Quaternary, however, is not typical for geological time, because of its rapid and wide eustatic fluctuations of sea level.

Throughout most of pre-Quaternary geological time, such eustatic fluctuations of sea level probably were rare. Transgressions and regressions, instead, were controlled by the balance between rate of regional or local subsidence and rate of deposition (Curray, 1964). Continental terraces with relatively rapid subsidence were probably then, as now, dominantly built of shelf and slope sediments. Those continental terraces with relatively less subsidence and higher rate of sediment supply probably were more complex because of a shifting balance between transgression caused by the subsidence, and regression caused by deposition. They would have consisted of complex facies changes with delta masses, other paralic and continental facies, and shelf and slope sediments, much like the facies changes of the Costa de Nayarit. Progradation of the continental terrace by deltaic deposition might also have resembled that shown in this study.

ORIGIN AND SIGNIFICANCE OF THE SHELF-BREAK

The change in slope at the continental shelf margin, or shelf-break, in the region of the Costa de Nayarit ranges in depth from about 50 to 150 fathoms. The change is shown (Fig. 18) to be variously related to deltaic platform edges, to the seaward edge of erosional terraces, to the transition between outbuilding and upbuilding facies in deeper sedimentary terrace platforms, and possibly to the upper edge of a slump scar on the upper continental slope (line *B-B'*, Figs. 6 and 11). This relationship of the shelf-break to several different events within a relatively small area like the Costa de Nayarit is not believed to be the result of unusual regional complexities, but rather the result of a greater than usual concentration of data.

In the past, the only data bearing on the origin of the shelf-break have been topographic profiles, with little or no information on internal structure beneath these profiles. Bottom-penetrating, continuous profilers now give us ample subsurface information that requires explanation not entirely in accord with previous theory. Dietz and Menard (1951) reviewed the literature on origin of shelf and slope and analyzed the origin of the shelf-break. They concluded that it was related primarily to erosion at "surf-base" (defined as about 5 fathoms) during glacially lowered sea level. They downgraded the importance of deltaic deposition as a mechanism of forming abrupt slope changes. They also emphasized the fallacy of the wave-base concept of a terrace built by wave motion carrying sedimentary particles across the shelf and dropping them over the edge of the slope at a sharply defined depth, beyond which no wave-induced transportation can occur. Discarding this old wave-base concept, in view of present knowledge of wave motion, deep currents, and transportation of sediment by turbidity currents, is certainly justified. Present subsurface data, however, show equally strong evidence that wave action on a shelf surface must play an important role in sediment transportation and in the ultimate shape of the terrace profile.

Two important lines of evidence from these and other subsurface studies (Moore and Curray, 1963) suggest that re-evaluation of important factors in shelf-break origin is necessary. The first of these factors is the prevalence of shelf-breaks related to delta platform edges in this area. These breaks are indeed relict from times of lowered sea level, but they are depositional, not erosional, in origin (Figs. 12–17). Of the 19 shelf crossings made with the Arcer off the Costa de Nayarit, 12 crossings had shelf-breaks formed by the tops of delta foreset beds. Although it is not suggested that deltaic shelf-breaks are universally more important than the erosional forms, it is suggested that constructional forms, particularly off the larger streams of a region, should be reinstated as an important component of the outer continental terrace and should be locally recognized as the cause of the abrupt change in slope at the edge of the continental shelf.

Of greater significance is the second line of evidence concerning the origin of the shelf-break. The deeply downfaulted northern part of the Costa de Nayarit terrace is not a part of the deltaic system that is so well developed off the wide central part of the area. It is certainly not an erosional form, as its deeper portions are well below the accepted range of eustatically lowered Quaternary sea level. Sedimentation on the shelf has erased surficial evidence of the former shorelines, which must have been developed on this deep, gently sloping shelf contemporaneously with those of the deltas to the south. The terrace profile along the northern part of the area is depositional in origin, and, as is well illustrated in Figure 10, this deposition has been very active on the continental slope as well as on the shelf. The result has been the formation of a shelf, shelf-break, and slope through outbuilding and upbuilding on a subsiding platform. Thus the origin of this shelf-break is inseparable from the origin of the terrace body, and it has been constructed by depositional processes, with its upper boundary describing a flat shelf, a relatively abrupt change in slope, and a relatively steep slope to oceanic depths.

To explain the break in slope at the continental-shelf edge as a nondeltaic depositional feature, one must re-examine the concept of wave base. Early proponents of the wave-built terrace form of continental terrace were not aware of the turbidity current nor of the existence of deep currents capable of transporting sand-sized particles. They envisioned the depths below which wave action could act as an eternally quiet graveyard of sediment where accumulation could proceed uninterrupted by complicating physical processes. We now know that these complicating processes do exist—slumps, turbidity currents, deep currents, submarine mud flows, and other processes act to erode the slopes beneath depths which possibly could be affected by wave action. We also now know, from acoustic reflection profiles such as those in Figure 10, that in spite of the agents of degradation, thick sections of continental-slope deposits are accumulating, which in places make up a very important percentage of the bulk of the terrace. This is evidence *per se* of the prevalence of deposition over erosion in these localities. It also supports the contention (Moore, 1960 and 1961; Moore and Curray, 1963; Curray, 1964) that submarine slumps and turbidity currents act not in a general degradation of the slope face, as suggested by Heezen and others (1959, p. 50) and Dietz (1952), but in repeated flushing out of localities of steep slope and/or rapid accumulation, such as canyon walls and areas off mouths of large rivers. The old idea of wave base must be compromised accordingly, but not abandoned.

Wave action on the shelf can erode consolidated materials to surf-base, and with the transgressions and regressions which must inevitably occur across the shelf during formation of a sedimentary continental terrace wedge, wave action can remove large amounts of shelf sediments to the slope. Below the depth of surf-base, waves can prevent deposition by maintaining suspended loads. Further, waves can resuspend surficial, highly fluid sediments of low cohesion to depths of at least 55 fathoms (Moore, 1963). A local balance must exist between deposition from local or regional sediment supply and the removal of cohesionless sediments by the effect of waves and currents. The net effect of deposition or nondeposition must be averaged over the natural cyclical periods of the region (perhaps in the range of 1 to 100 years). This concept demands a relatively wide depth range of several tens of fathoms as a zone of transition from shelf to slope and, consequently, a relatively shallow, rounded shelf-break.

The rounded break off the northern Costa de Nayarit was probably formed in this way, but at a somewhat greater depth regulated by Pleistocene eustatic sea-level fluctuations. In this case, Pleistocene transgressions and regressions have contributed to terrace formation by moving the zone of maximum deposition back and forth across the shelf. The shelf-break exhibited must be primarily related to balance between wave-induced deposition and removal during low sea-level stands, and further modified by downfaulting.

CONCLUSIONS

1. Deltas are an important, integral part of the continental-terrace body off the Costa de Nayarit and probably off similar regions throughout the world.

2. Deposition of nonparalic, open-shelf deposits forms an important part of the volume of the Costa de Nayarit terrace. These deposits are intimately in contact with, and gradational to, paralic facies.

3. Deposition of permanent, thick continental-slope sediments is shown to be a reality off the Costa de Nayarit. These sediments are not related to deltaic deposition along the northern part of the area. There is no reason to believe that these extensive slope deposits are unique to this area, and we conclude, therefore, that the process of terrace progradation by slope deposition is established.

4. A possible chronology of the depositional history of the deltaic part of the region is suggested with correlation of two early Wisconsin shorelines, an interstadial, and two periods of late Wisconsin maximum lowering of sea level. During the late Wisconsin, sea level fell to between −53 and −58 fathoms, rose to −35 fathoms, and fell again to −68 fathoms. This last lowering occurred about 17,600 years B.P.

5. Outer terminations of drowned delta plat-

forms form the shelf-break off much of the Costa de Nayarit area. These breaks are depositional in origin, and, although they are related to glacially lowered sea levels, they show that in this deltaic region, erosion at surf-base is not the dominant cause of the break in slope at the edge of the continental shelf.

6. Nondeltaic, depositional, rounded shelf-breaks are believed to form by balance between deposition and wave removal in a broad depth zone below surf-base. The northern part of this area has a shelf-break formed in this way, modified by Pleistocene eustatic fluctuations in sea level and local subsidence.

REFERENCES

American Geological Institute, 1957 (Howell, J.V., chm.), Glossary of geology and related sciences: Natl. Research Council Pub. 501, x, 325 p.

Bourcart, J., 1949, Géographie du fond des mers; étude du relief des océans: Payot, Paris, 307 p.

Curray, J.R., 1959, Coastal plain-continental shelf studies, *in* Study of Recent sediments and their environments in the Gulf of California: Univ. of Calif., Inst. of Marine Resources, IMR Ref. 59-7, Quart. Rept. A.P.I. Project 51.

——— 1960, Sediments and history of the Holocene transgression, continental shelf, *in* Shepard and others, Recent sediments, northwest Gulf of Mexico: Am. Assoc. Petroleum Geologists, p. 221–226.

——— 1961a, Continental shelf-coastal plain of northwest mainland Mexico: 1st Natl. Shallow Water Conf. Proc., publ. by N.S.F. and O.N.R., p. 533–536.

——— 1961b, Late Quaternary sea level—a discussion: Geol. Soc. America Bull., v. 72, no. 11, p. 1707–1712.

——— 1964, Transgressions and regressions, *in* Papers in marine geology: Shepard Commemorative Volume, Macmillan, New York, p. 175–203.

——— and Moore, D. G., 1963, Facies delineation by acoustic-reflection, northern Gulf of Mexico: Sedimentology v. 2, p. 130–148.

——— 1964, Holocene regressive littoral sand in deltaic and shallow marine deposits, Costa de Nayarit, Mexico: 6th Internatl. Sedimentological Cong., Amsterdam and Antwerp.

Dietz, R.S., 1952, Geomorphic evolution of continental terrace (continental shelf and slope): Am. Assoc. Petroleum Geologists Bull., v. 36, p. 1802–1819.

——— and Menard, H.W., 1951, Origin of abrupt change in slope at continental shelf margin: Am. Assoc. Petroleum Geologists, v. 35, no. 9, p. 1994–2016.

Frye, J.C., and Willman, H.B., 1961, Continental glaciation in relation to McFarlan's sea-level curves for Louisiana: Geol. Soc. America Bull., v. 72, p. 991–992.

Heezen, B.C., Tharp, M., and Ewing, M., 1959, The North Atlantic, Pt. 1 *of* The floors of the oceans: Geol. Soc. America Spec. Paper 65, 122 p.

Kuenen, Ph.H., 1950a, The formation of the continental terrace: Adv. Sci., v. 7, no. 25, p. 76–80.

——— 1950b, Marine geology: Wiley & Sons, Inc., New York, 568 p.

McClure, C.D., Nelson, H.F., and Huckabay, W.B., 1958, The marine sonoprobe system, new tool for geologic mapping: Am. Assoc. Petroleum Geologists Bull., v. 42, p. 701–716.

Moore, D.G., 1960, Acoustic-reflection studies of the continental shelf and slope off Southern California: Geol. Soc. America Bull., v. 71, p. 1121–1136.

——— 1961, Submarine slumps: Jour. Sed. Petrology, v. 31, p. 343–357.

——— 1963, Geological observations from the bathyscaph Trieste near the edge of the continental shelf off San Diego, California: Geol. Soc. America Bull., v. 74, p. 1057–1062.

——— 1964, Acoustic reflection reconnaissance of continental shelves, eastern Bering and Chukchi Seas, *in* Papers in marine geology: Shepard Commemorative Volume, Macmillan, New York, p. 319–362.

——— and Curray, J.R., 1963, Structural framework of continental terrace, northwest Gulf of Mexico: Jour. Geophys. Research, v. 68, p. 1725–1747.

Shepard, F.P., 1948, Submarine geology: Harper and Bros., New York, 348 p.

Stetson, H.C., 1949, The sediments and stratigraphy of the east coast continental margin; Georges Bank to Norfolk Canyon: Papers in Phys. Oceanog. & Meteor., Mass. Inst. Tech. & Woods Hole Oceanog. Inst., v. 9, no. 2, p. 1–60.

——— 1953, The continental surface of the western Gulf of Mexico; its surface sediments, origin, and development, Pt. 1 *of* The sediments of the western Gulf of Mexico: Papers in Phys. Oceanog. & Meteor., Mass. Inst. Tech. & Woods Hole Oceanog. Inst., v. 12, no. 4, p. 1–45.

Umbgrove, J., 1947, The pulse of the earth: Martinus Nijhoff. The Hague, The Netherlands, 358 p.

RECENT MARINE SEDIMENTS OF GULF OF CALIFORNIA[1]

TJEERD H. VAN ANDEL[2]
La Jolla, California

ABSTRACT

The Gulf of California is a long, narrow basin which is almost completely separated from the Pacific Ocean by the mountainous Peninsula of Baja California and bordered on the east by a coastal plain and the Sierra Madre Occidental of Mexico. The northern Gulf, with the exception of the deep Sal si Puedes Basin, is at shelf depth and receives sediment mainly from the Colorado River. Modern deposition is restricted to the vicinity of the Colorado River delta, to areas of sandy littoral sediments fringing the margins, and to somewhat diatomaceous clays in the deepest basin. Over most of the area, glauconitic sands, thought to belong to the post-Pleistocene transgression, occur at the surface.

The central and southern portions of the Gulf consist of a series of basins which increase in depth southward from 500 to nearly 2,000 fathoms. A fairly wide and depositional shelf occurs on the eastern side; the western shelf is narrow, rocky, and mainly erosional. Sediment supply is lateral, and dispersal is essentially perpendicular to the basin axis. The eastern supply is dominant. The distribution and characteristics of the shelf facies are controlled by the rate of sediment supply and the rate of marine redispersal, which are functions of climate and basin shape, respectively. In areas of very low sediment supply, calcarenites occur; elsewhere, the shelf sediments are similar to those of the Gulf of Mexico.

In the deeper portion, several fans occur with thin sand layers, which are presumed to be turbidites. Such fans are found in areas of major sediment supply off the Fuerte and Yaqui Rivers and around Cape San Lucas, where numerous submarine canyons channel turbidity-current flow. Well-defined slope facies can be recognized. The slope facies of the western margin, which is starved with respect to terrigenous material, is fairly calcareous. The deposits of the central basins are diatomites, as a result of the very high organic productivity in surface waters caused by a circulation pattern of wind-driven surface currents which remove surface water to the open Pacific. This surface water is replaced by upwelling of deeper Pacific water rich in nutrients and dissolved silica. All deposited biogenous silica can be accounted for by this mechanism. The southern basins are predominantly terrigenous and very fine grained, notwithstanding the nearness of the sources of sediments.

INTRODUCTION

OBJECTIVES AND ORGANIZATION

Throughout the publications and teaching of P.D. Krynine, frequent expression is given to the

[1] Manuscript received, April 1, 1963. Contribution from Scripps Institution of Oceanography, University of California.

The investigation has been supported by a contract of the Office of Naval Research with the University of California for all cruise expenses (contract Nonr 2216[01]), and by the American Petroleum Institute Project 51 for field work on land and all other activities. Some additional support was received from the Institute of Marine Resources of the University of California, whose former Director, C.C. Wheelock, has been a source of continuous encouragement.

The author is deeply indebted to numerous people for support and encouragement of many kinds. Only a few can be mentioned here; to the others he wishes to acknowledge his debt collectively.

The basis of the investigation is formed by samples collected by the staff and crew of the R.V. *Horizon*, under leadership of Captain L.E. Davis and Chief Scientist G.A. Rusnak. The staff of A.P.I. Project 51, at various times consisting of Mrs. Sandra Southworth, Miss Leanne Hinton, Miss Janet Witte, S.P. Huffman, F.B. Denman, T. W. Hilde, G.A. Davis, P.J. Crampton, and W.L. Cozad, has made important contributions to the work. Above all, Mrs. Mary Franklin deserves much credit for the organization and execution of the voluminous laboratory work. The thin-section work was done by R.A. Wadge, and J.R. Moriarty is responsible for the construction of all topographic base maps and for many illustrations. In the difficult subject of electronic data processing, J.R. Curray and the writer were generously assisted by L.C. Bonham of the California Research Corporation, M. Sprague, M.A. Rosenfeld, and G. Brunton of the Pure Oil Company, and C.L. Perry of the University of California at San Diego.

The entire undertaking would not have been possible without the cooperation of Mexican scientists, and their valued assistance is acknowledged here in the person of Ing. G. Salas.

The ideas expressed in this paper have been shaped in discussions with colleagues at Scripps and elsewhere, in particular with S.E. Calvert, J.R. Curray, R.L. Fisher, F.B Phleger, R.R. Revelle, G.G. Shor, and especially with F.P. Shepard, all of Scripps Institution, and with O. Weser of the Standard Oil Company of California. C.M. Gilbert and R.L. Hay of the University of California in Berkeley reviewed the manuscript and made many helpful suggestions.

[2] Scripps Institution of Oceanography, University of California.

notion of the "determining background" or geological setting of a basin as one of the primary controls of its depositional facies. It is Krynine's contention that, notwithstanding the large variety of environments possibly included within any one depositional basin, deposits from similar settings will be comparable, and those from different settings dissimilar.

In the final report on the Gulf of Mexico studies of American Petroleum Institute Project 51, van Andel and Curray (1960, p. 364) pointed out that most regional studies of modern sediments deal with basins of similar geological settings. In essence, all of the studies discuss sedimentary facies in basins of subdued relief which is controlled by depositional factors. The degree of diastrophism is low, the supply of terrigenous material is abundant, and contact with the world's oceans is essentially unrestricted. The sedimentary facies in such basins and the factors that control them are similar and allow direct comparison.

The present paper deals with the sediments of a basin with very different background characteristics. The Gulf of California possesses a high relief, which is largely of structural origin and only partially obscured by the effects of sedimentation. It is, to a large extent, isolated from the Pacific Ocean, and as a result is characterized by special physical and chemical conditions. In proportion to its size, the Gulf does possess substantial sources of terrigenous sediments, but they are irregularly distributed along the Gulf margins. The general purpose of this paper is to describe and interpret the depositional facies formed in this geological setting and to compare them with those of other settings, particularly the Gulf of Mexico type. The following problems are corollaries to this main objective. It has been postulated, most explicitly by Ph.H. Kuenen (1957), that sediment dispersion in deep, oblong basins is parallel to the basin axis. This contrasts with the Gulf of Mexico, where center-directed dispersion alternates with transportation along the margins, in dependence of variations of the rate of supply (van Andel, 1960). A study of the dispersal patterns of the Gulf of California is one of the objectives of this paper.

The submarine morphology of the Gulf of California is marked by extreme changes in relief, both in the form of steep boundary slopes and of isolated ridges and banks. Moreover, the Gulf is subdivided into several partially isolated basins. The influence of this topography on sedimentary facies will be examined.

It has been known for many years that the Gulf of California is a region of high organic productivity. It must be expected that this productivity, which is localized in certain areas of the basin, is reflected in the sediments.

In recent years, following many important papers on the effect of turbidity currents, it has been customary to attribute a major importance to this mechanism in the filling of deep basins of the Gulf of California type, which possess a relatively high supply of sediment, narrow shelves, and steep slopes. This hypothesis can be examined to a certain extent in the area of this study.

Several earlier papers have appeared on the marine geology of the Gulf of California. F.P. Shepard (1950) published a discussion of the submarine morphology of the Gulf based on data of two expeditions in 1939 and 1940. The samples collected on these expeditions formed the subject of a brief discussion by R.R. Revelle (1950) and, with additional material, of the most comprehensive papers on Gulf sediments to date, by J.V. Byrne and K.O. Emery (1960), and O.L. Bandy (1961).

The investigation in the Gulf under A.P.I. Project 51 was designed in two phases—a regional reconnaissance study of the marine geology, sediments, and structure of the entire Gulf, followed by more detailed studies of specific areas or problems. This report covers the regional investigation of the sediments. Three more detailed studies fall in the area of this report and are included elsewhere in this volume—an investigation by Shepard of the submarine canyons and associated sediments; a study by J.R. Curray and D.G. Moore of the Costa de Nayarit; and a study by S.E. Calvert of the layered diatomites. Consequently, these subjects will be only briefly discussed here.

FIELD AND LABORATORY WORK

The majority of the samples and observations on which this paper is based (Fig. 1) were collected under the direction of G.A. Rusnak, during a portion of Scripps' *Vermilion Sea Expedition* in 1959. Additional material was obtained in 1959–1961 by J.R. Curray, S.E. Calvert, R.R. Lankford, and the writer. Most samples were taken by gravity corer; some by various grab samplers or on land. The laboratory work was carried out under the supervision of Mrs. Mary Franklin; the writer is responsible for all microscopic studies. Nearly all techniques are conventional and will be referred to briefly at the proper places in the text. Punch-card data recording and processing were used extensively, following initial suggestions by L.C. Bonham of the California Research Corporation. In all, more than 3,000 analyses have been made on approximately 250 samples. Only part of the data is included in this paper; complete tabulations can be made available upon application to the author.

As can be seen from the detailed bathymetric chart presented by Rusnak and others (this volume, Chart I, in pocket), the Gulf is characterized by extreme topographic irregularity. Consequently, there is considerable local variability in sediment properties, which is not adequately reflected by the sampling grid. Mapping of sediment parameters thus is often a subjective matter. The paper emphasizes, and perhaps overemphasizes, regional trends. Further work doubtlessly will show that conditions are far more complex than indicated here.

MORPHOLOGY

The Gulf of California is a narrow, approximately rectangular basin, 600 nautical miles long and of variable width. It consists of two wide portions, the northern Gulf which is approximately 100 nautical miles wide, and the central and southern Gulf, 110 nautical miles wide at the entrance. The two portions are separated by a constriction studded with large islands.

The Gulf is bordered on the western side by the Peninsula of Baja California, an elevated, westward-tilted tableland. The precipitous Gulf coast is interrupted only by the low Isthmus of La Paz and by large, isolated alluvial fans. On the eastern side, south of Guaymas, an extensive coastal plain of Quaternary deltaic and littoral sediments borders the high range of the Sierra Madre Occidental. North of Guaymas, the Sonoran coastal area consists of several mountain ranges rising through extensive alluvial plains. The coast is fringed by alluvial fans, deltas, and low cliffs, except just north of Guaymas and north of Tiburón Island, where the Gulf is bordered by mountains.

Northward, the Gulf depression continues for another 125 nautical miles as the Imperial Valley, separated from the Gulf proper by the delta of the Colorado River.

A detailed discussion of the morphology and structure of the Gulf is provided by Rusnak and others (this volume). Only a few comments on aspects of particular interest from a sedimentation viewpoint will be made here.

The northern Gulf is relatively shallow with depths not exceeding 200 fathoms, except in the Sal si Puedes and Tiburón Basins (Fig. 2). In various places, large, shallow, fan-shaped areas occur along the margins. Well-developed bulges are found off the Concepción River and south of Puerto Peñasco. The latter is not connected with a modern river system. The Colorado River does not possess a submarine bulge, but is fronted by a shallow, funnel-shaped area. Much of the northern Gulf is at shelf depth, but a shelf-break is generally absent.

Between approximately 30 and 200 fathoms, the topography is complex (Fig. 2). A well-developed valley system, which consists of several branches and is somewhat similar to the Pleistocene Mississippi Valley (Fisk and McFarlan, 1955), extends southward from the Colorado River delta, entering the northern Sal si Puedes Basin with a sharp westerly turn and terminating at 200 fathoms. Two isolated depressions in the middle portion suggest a partially structural origin. Farther east, several parallel, smaller systems occur, which originate under the Puerto Peñasco bulge at 50 fathoms. Some of them are interrupted by the Concepción bulge, but reappear at 80 fathoms; all terminate in the Tiburón Basin at 200 fathoms. The coastal area north of these systems consists of a complex, little-known terrain of Quaternary sediments.

During the last Pleistocene low stand of sea level, a large portion of the northern Gulf must have been exposed, and the middle and upper parts of the valley systems may be fluviatile in origin. Because they seem to disappear landward

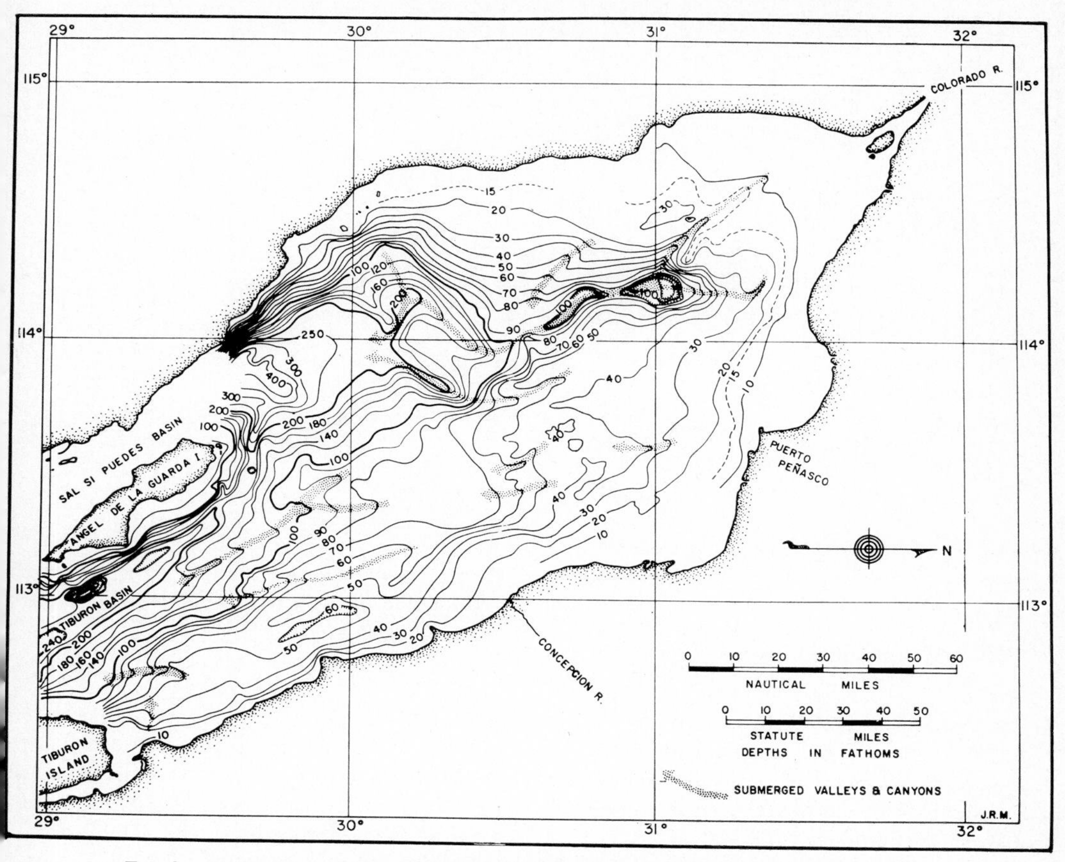

FIG. 2.—Bathymetry of the northern Gulf of California. Contours by R.L. Fisher and Tj.H. van Andel, based on all available data.

elow modern sediments most of them must be of re-Recent origin.

The southern and central portions of the Gulf ossess well-developed continental shelves. On the vestern side, the shelf is generally rocky and arrow, with a sharp shelf-break between 55 and 5 fathoms and a steep upper slope studded with ills and pinnacles (Fig. 3, II, V, VI). About 30 niles north of Santa Rosalía (Fig. 3, XII), the helf widens and the upper slope becomes smooth nd more gentle. The topography appears deposi-ional in nature, but no large drainage system ccurs on the adjacent land.

The eastern shelf is wider, ranging from a few niles opposite prograding deltas to approximately 0 miles (Fig. 4). The surface shows little relief nd a very low slope. South of the Fuerte River delta, a very indefinite shelf-break occurs at 100–120 fathoms (Fig. 3, I, III), and the upper slope is generally smooth and gentle. This and the internal structure (Curray and Moore, this volume) indicate a slowly subsiding depositional terrace.

Off the Fuerte River delta, the shelf is narrow, with a sharp edge and a somewhat rough upper slope (Fig. 3, VII, VIII). Rocky islands and many volcanic outcrops within the delta indicate a thin sediment cover on an irregular substrate. The absence of a well-developed depositional terrace may be explained by the draining of sediment through submarine canyons into the deep Gulf. Similar shelf development occurs off the Yaqui River delta (Fig. 3, XI), but the Mayo River delta is fronted by an apparently depositional shelf (Fig. 3, IX). A large, rounded, depositional

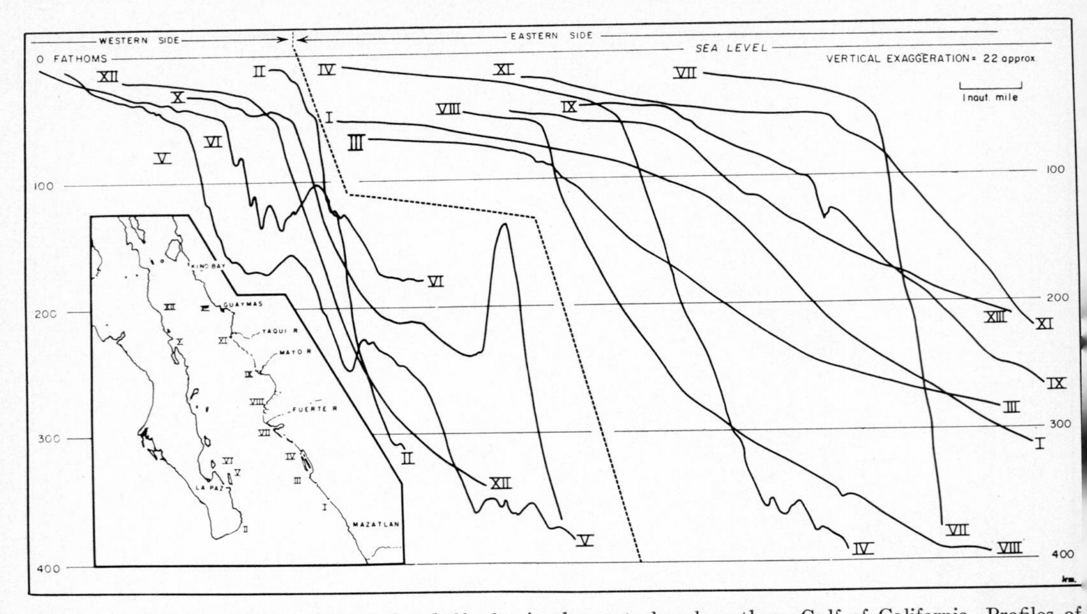

FIG. 3.—Topographic profiles of the shelf edge in the central and southern Gulf of California. Profiles of the western margin on the left, of the eastern margin on the right. Traced directly from fathometer records. Vertical exaggeration approximately 22×.

terrace without a clear shelf-break occurs off the Kino Bay region (Fig. 3, XIII). Thus it appears that, in contrast to the largely wave-cut western shelf, the eastern continental terrace is predominantly depositional in nature.

The Gulf is characterized by a series of partially enclosed basins, separated by sills and increasing in depth from 500 fathoms near Tiburón Island to 2,000 fathoms at the entrance (Fig. 4, Table I). The basins range in shape from broad troughs

TABLE I. BASINS OF THE GULF OF CALIFORNIA

Basin	*Max. Depth (fathoms)*	*Sill Depth (fathoms)*	*Area Below Sill Depth (sq nautical mi)*
Sal si Puedes[1]	830	240	594
Tiburón	400	230	118
San Pedro Martir	540	450	127
Guaymas	1,090	850	1,868
Carmen	1,480	930	585
Farallón	1,740	1,740	1,547
Pescadero	2,030	1,340	1,094
Mazatlán	1,700	1,580	204
La Paz	440	350	119

[1] Includes Delfin Basin of Rusnak, Fisher, and Shepard (this volume).

with gentle slopes (Guaymas and Carmen) to narrow, steep-walled depressions (Pescadero, Farallón, San Pedro Martir). The area below sill depth is generally hummocky; flat floors are rare except in the Guaymas Basin (Fig. 5).

Among the most striking topographic features of the Gulf are the steep slopes shown on many fathometer records (Shepard, 1950; Byrne and Emery, 1960). When discussing large grabens and half-grabens or geosynclines, geologists are inclined to think in terms of prominent and extensive areas of steep slopes and their influence on sedimentary facies. Therefore, it appears desirable to examine the occurrence of high-angle slopes in the Gulf in some detail.

The approximate regional distribution of slope areas in the Gulf is shown in Figure 5, based on the examination of fathometer records for approximately 8,000 nautical miles of ship's track. Three classes of slopes have been recognized; their percentages are based on total record mileage (Table II). Slopes greater than 15° cannot be accurately reduced from sounding records which have a highly exaggerated vertical scale; those greater than 30° are commonly not recorded. A 5° lower

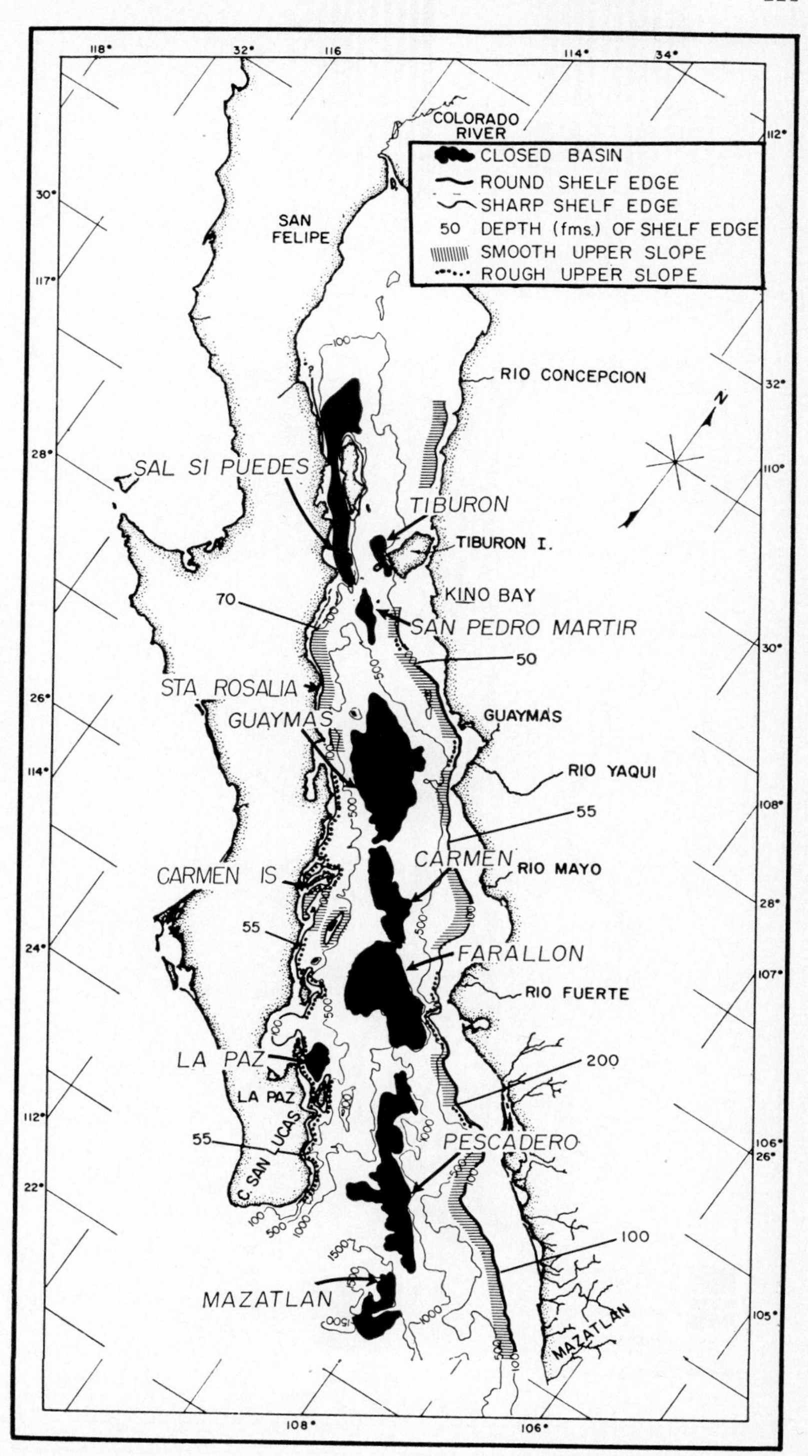

FIG. 4.—Shelves and basins in the central and southern Gulf of California. Basins defined by depth contour at sill depth (Table I). Nature of shelf edge and upper continental slope determined from fathometer records.

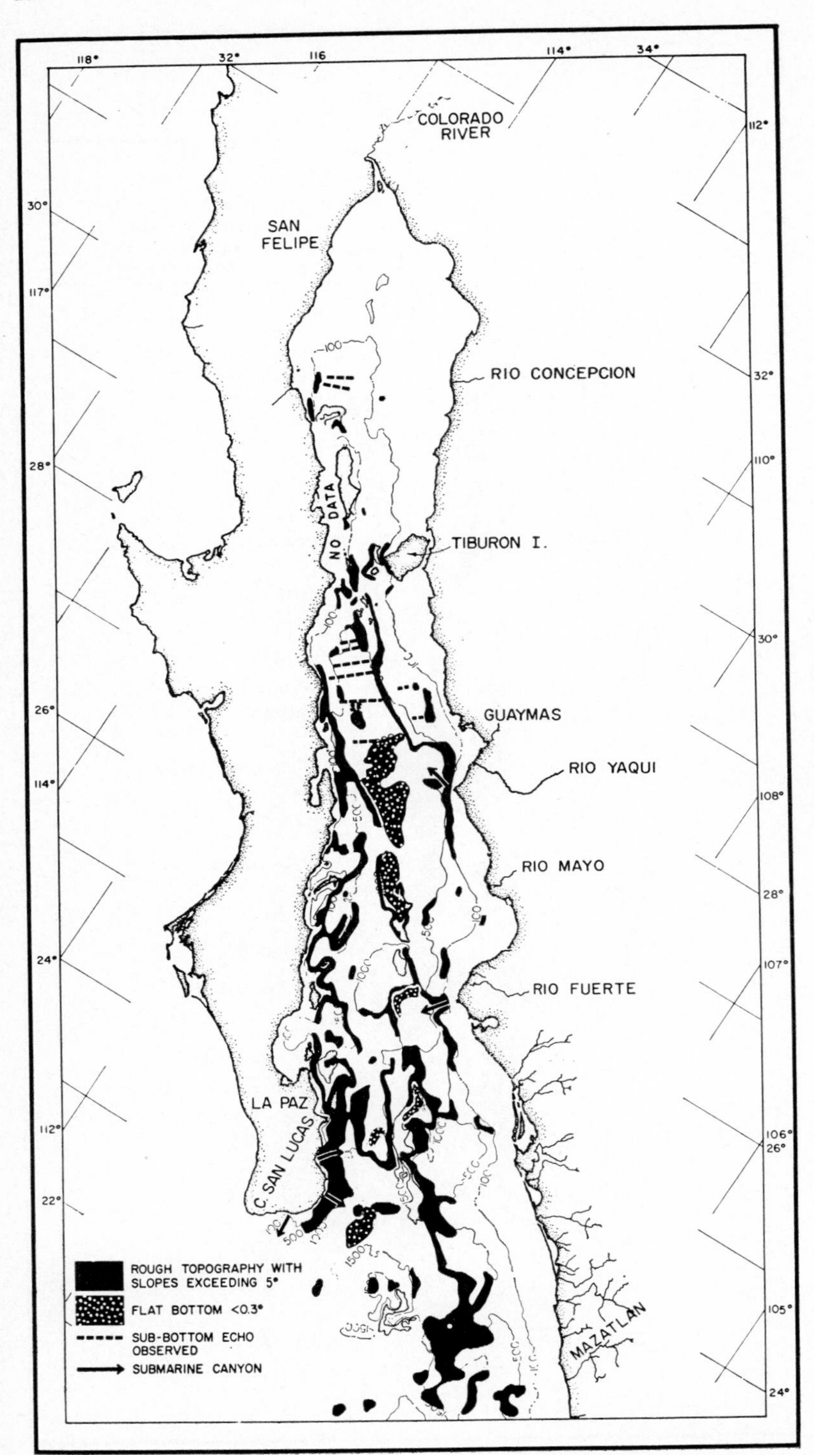

FIG. 5.—Degree of relie in the central and southern Gulf of California. Slope angles measured from al fathometer records of the *Vermilion Sea Expedition* Flat bottom not indicate on continental shelf and in the northern Gulf. Contour in fathoms.

limit was selected to exclude minor relief on the shelf and on basin floors. Table II and Figure 5 show that only a relatively small portion of the southern and central Gulf is occupied by intermediate (5°–30°) slopes. Most of these slopes are in the 5°–8° range. Very steep slopes occupy such a small area that they cannot be mapped with the available information. Most of the Gulf is occupied by low slopes (0.3°–5°) or by almost flat bottom. These observations illustrate a situation very different from the rugged relief that is generally accepted for this type of basin.

The western continental slope is almost everywhere of intermediate steepness, and most of the steep slopes also occur on this side. The eastern slope is generally of low declivity, except off the Yaqui and Fuerte River deltas and locally at the very bottom of the continental slope. Steep slopes also border the deeper portions of many basins, especially the southernmost, below sill depth. Only the Guaymas Basin is characterized by gentle slopes. This, and the universal presence of sub-bottom echoes at 12–25 feet below the sediment surface in the deeper parts of the central Gulf, indicate either very rapid sedimentation or very soft deposits.

A submarine fan with low slope occurs off the Fuerte River and probably is the main area of deposition of its sediment. Other fans are associated with the canyons of Cape San Lucas (Shepard, this volume. Although submarine canyons are not common in the Gulf, several major ones occur around the southeastern extremity of the Peninsula, and two large ones are found off the Fuerte River delta. These canyons and their associated sediments are discussed extensively by Shepard (this volume).

The Gulf of California contains an abundance of small and intermediate islands, particularly along the western side. Moreover, there are numerous submerged banks and seamounts, many of which are covered with special sediment types.

SOURCE AND DISPERSAL OF SEDIMENTS

The problem of the source and dispersal of sediments in deep, oblong basins has acquired special importance as a result of recent interest in sediment transportation in ancient geosynclines. The concepts derived from studies have been

TABLE II. AREAL DISTRIBUTION OF SLOPES IN THE GULF OF CALIFORNIA

Slope Type	*Per cent of Track (Exclusive of Shelf)*	
	Northern Gulf (per cent)	*Southern Gulf (per cent)*
<5°	99	75
5°–30°	1	24.5
>30°	—	0.5

stated by Kuenen (1957, p. 189) as follows:

> It is generally tacitly assumed that the detrital sediment of oblong basins is derived from one or both of the two sides and carried in transversely. The graded graywackes of Flysch, Kulm and Macigno type have been deposited from turbidity currents, and in the majority of the cases studied to date the transport was longitudinal, at least at the point of deposition. Most oblong landlocked basins of the present day receive sediment mainly at one end. It is suggested that longitudinal filling by delta building and/or turbidity currents must have been common in the past.

A somewhat modified concept, including lateral supply in the marginal zones, has been suggested by Knill (1959). It is this problem in particular which will be examined in this chapter.

METHODS OF INVESTIGATION

Samples from the sediment surface or from the 1–10 cm section of cores were treated with hydrogen peroxide (10 per cent), dispersed in a 0.005 molal sodium oxalate and 0.001 molal sodium carbonate peptizer, and material finer than 0.062 mm was removed by wet sieving. After separation in tetrabromoethane and mounting, the composition of the heavy fraction was obtained by line count of 100 transparent grains. A subsample of the light fraction, after removal of carbonate in 2N HCl, was impregnated with *Glas-Skin* plastic resin, and a thin section was prepared and stained for feldspar identification (Hayes and Klugman, 1959). The composition was determined by point counting (Chayes, 1949) of 200–300 points, omitting biogenous components. Another subsample was split into five size fractions by sieving, or settling and washing, and the composition was determined under a polarizing stereomicroscope by line count of 100 grains in each fraction. The terrigenous components of this "coarse fraction" analysis are useful for source studies. By using weight percentages of the various size classes, the percentages by number were converted into percentages by weight.

The data used in this chapter are all based on the sand fraction, and the conclusions should be evaluated in this light.

SOURCE AREAS AND HEAVY-MINERAL ASSEMBLAGES

The geology of the land areas bordering the Gulf of California is only imperfectly known (*see* Beal, 1948; Anderson, 1950; Durham and Allison, 1960; Allison, this volume). Conclusions concerning the sources of detrital sediments have to be drawn from general geologic maps (Fig. 6).

Three source-rock groups occur in the Peninsula. In the northern and southern parts, are acid to intermediate plutonic rocks and associated metamorphics, which are probably of Upper Cretaceous age. The two batholithic zones are separated by an extensive area of thick Miocene lavas, volcanic breccias, and tuffs with associated continental sediments, belonging to the Comondú Formation. Heavy-mineral analyses of sands from pocket beaches along the Gulf shore (Table III) show two distinct suites, an amphibole assemblage with minor amounts of apatite and epidote obviously derived from the batholiths, and a pyroxene assemblage with varying proportions of augite, hypersthene, and basaltic hornblende, which appears related to the Comondú volcanics (Fig. 7). The rainfall on the Peninsula east of the watershed is no more than 4–10 inches per year, and

TABLE III. HEAVY-MINERAL COMPOSITION OF BEACH AND NEARSHORE SANDS ALONG THE EAST SIDE OF THE PENINSULA OF LOWER CALIFORNIA
(In per cent by number. For sample locations *see* Fig. 7.)

Number	*Probable Source*	*Tourmaline*	*Zircon*	*Apatite*	*Garnet*	*Epidote*	*Amphiboles*	*Basaltic Hornblende*	*Augite*	*Hypersthene*	*Titanite*	*Olivine*	*Others*
R- 41	batholithic	—	3	5	—	6	74	—	6	2	3	1	—
R- 55	batholithic	—	1	6	—	9	66	—	9	1	5	3	—
R- 67	mixed	1	1	2	1	8	47	1	22	15	2	—	—
R- 78	mixed	—	1	—	1	3	32	6	47	5	4	—	1
R- 89	volcanic	—	—	1	—	2	11	8	68	8	1	—	1
R- 94	volcanic	—	1	—	—	1	15	20	55	8	—	—	—
R-102	volcanic	—	—	—	—	—	19	19	43	18	1	—	—
R-127	volcanic	—	—	—	—	—	5	16	58	20	1	—	—
R-139	volcanic	—	—	—	—	1	7	4	57	32	—	—	—
R-140	volcanic	—	—	—	—	3	4	3	63	25	—	2	—
R-143	volcanic	—	1	1	—	1	16	6	30	44	1	—	—
R-147	volcanic	—	—	—	—	1	4	10	58	26	—	1	—
R-156	mixed	—	1	—	—	—	54	5	28	9	2	—	1
R-175	mixed	—	1	1	—	5	32	5	32	17	6	—	1
R-157	batholithic	—	—	—	—	1	90	1	2	2	4	—	—
R-180	batholithic	1	4	—	1	3	84	1	4	2	—	—	—
R-182	volcanic	—	—	—	—	—	—	3	32	65	—	—	—
R-188	mixed	—	—	—	—	3	45	19	24	5	1	—	1
R-199	batholithic	—	1	1	—	4	59	5	19	6	3	1	1
R-211	batholithic	—	—	—	—	—	55	11	14	18	2	—	—
R-218	batholithic	4	3	2	—	10	58	3	7	3	8	2	—
A- 9	batholithic	1	—	—	—	1	78	1	6	2	10	—	1
A- 10	batholithic	—	—	—	7	1	75	1	7	—	9	—	—

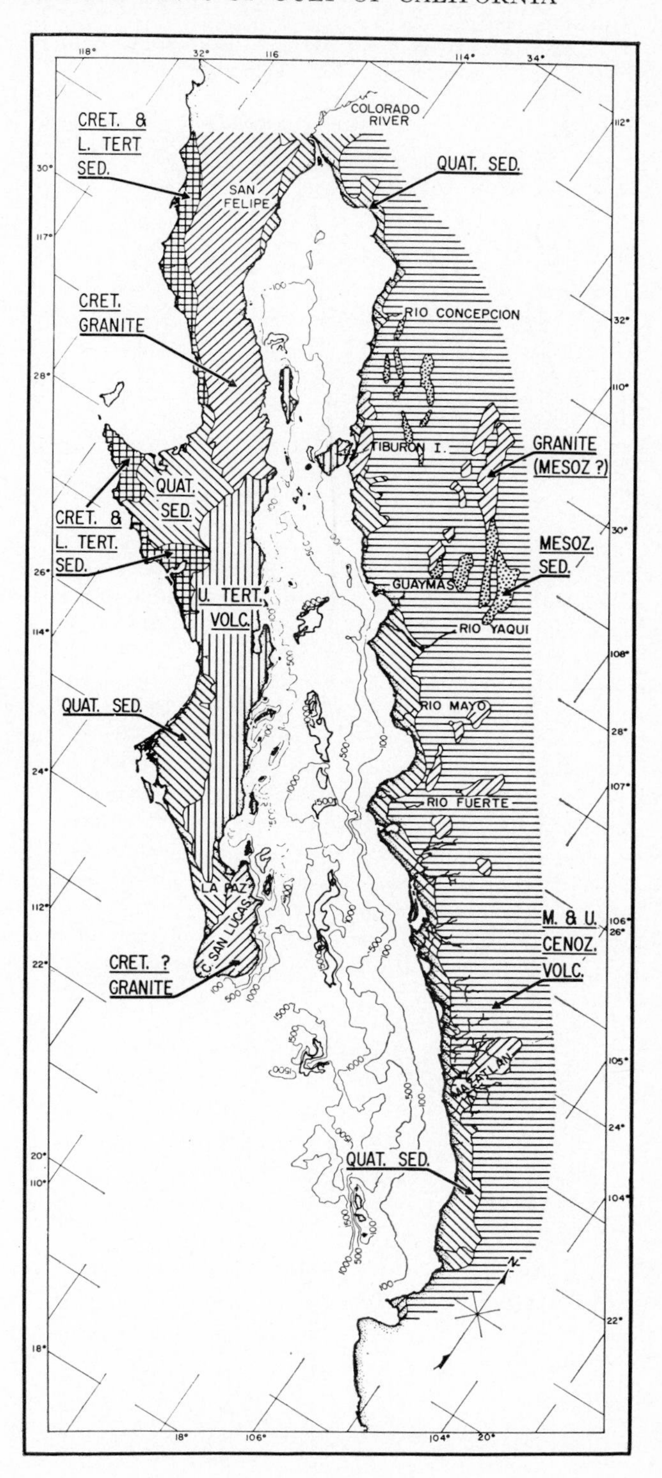

FIG. 6.—Simplified geological map of the Gulf of California region. Compiled from Beal (1948), Mejorado (1956), and de Czerna (1961). Depth contours in fathoms.

TABLE IV. AVERAGE RUNOFF FOR DRAINAGE AREAS OF THE GULF OF CALIFORNIA
(After Byrne, 1957, Table 12. Estimates from various sources.)

Drainage Area	*Per Cent of Total Drainage Area*	*Average Annual Flow (millions m^3)*	*Estimated Annual Sediment Load (tons)*[1]
Colorado River[2]			
1911–1935	68	17,985	161,000,000
1935–1951	—	8,077[3]	15,000,000[3]
Concepción River	7	742	7,422,894
Sonora River	4	770	7,703,003
Yaqui River	6	2,666	26,670,397
Mayo River	2	829	8,293,233
Fuerte River	3	4,707	47,088,357
Sinaloa River	2	1,659	16,596,470
Culiacán River	2	3,833	33,843,194
San Lorenzo River	3	4,728	47,298,439
Baja California	3	—	—
Total 1911–1935 period	100	37,469	374,836,987

[1] Sediment load for all rivers except Colorado estimated by using runoff estimate and amount of sediment per cubic meter of water in the Colorado. Actual amounts are probably slightly higher.
[2] At Yuma. [3] Not included in totals.

permanent streams are absent. Sediment is supplied to the Gulf by ephemeral streams, large alluvial fans, and coastal erosion.

The Colorado River was, until completion of Hoover Dam, the largest single contributor of sediment to the Gulf (Table IV). In its drainage basin, Paleozoic and Mesozoic sediments and Tertiary volcanics are predominant. However, in large source areas of mixed igneous, metamorphic, and sedimentary rocks, the deposits of major rivers are generally characterized mainly by igneous and metamorphic components (van Andel, 1960). Similarly, the Colorado suite (Table V) is characterized by more than 75 per cent igneous minerals, whereas the vast area of sedimentary rocks is only weakly reflected by 15 per cent stable minerals. These minerals distinguish the Colorado suite from most others in the Gulf.

Along the eastern side, from northwest to southeast, the precipitation increases from less than 4 inches of summer rains in the Sonoran Desert to more than 50 inches in the extreme southeast. North of Guaymas the streams are seasonal; south of Guaymas they are permanent with large seasonal changes and considerable discharges (Table IV).

North of Guaymas, the hinterland of the Gulf consists of a vast plain of Quaternary and Tertiary sediments and volcanics, penetrated by low mountains of Paleozoic and Mesozoic intrusive

TABLE V. HEAVY-MINERAL COMPOSITION OF COLORADO RIVER SEDIMENTS
(In per cent by number. For sample locations *see* Fig. 1.)

Number	*Location*	*Tourmaline*	*Zircon*	*Apatite*	*Garnet*	*Epidote*	*Amphiboles*	*Basaltic Hornblende*	*Augite*	*Hypersthene*	*Titanite*	*Others*
A- 6	River mouth	3	3	2	1	21	45	2	17	3	2	1
A- 1	Upper estuary	6	1	5	—	24	35	3	20	4	—	2
A- 4	Delta	3	—	5	2	14	45	1	28	—	1	1
A- 5	Delta	4	—	5	2	18	31	2	35	3	—	—
A-13	River near Yuma Ariz.	3	5	2	11	8	31	1	26	6	5	2
C- 4	Rio Sonoita	2	2	5	4	28	28	—	18	8	2	3

and sedimentary rocks. South of Guaymas, a wide coastal plain borders the Sierra Madre Occidental, which consists of a thick cap of Tertiary volcanics overlying Paleozoic and Mesozoic batholithic rocks and geosynclinal sediments and metamorphics.

The predominant minerals in the stream sediments (Table VI) are volcanic (pyroxenes) and plutonic-metamorphic (amphiboles and epidote). Three major suites can be distinguished.

The Concepción suite is characterized by a high epidote content and, notwithstanding the abundance of volcanics in the drainage basin, less than 10 per cent of volcanic minerals. Except for the low volcanic content, the suite is rather similar to that of the Colorado, but a large difference in the epidote/amphibole ratio (Concepción 1.0: Colorado 0.5) shows that it cannot have been derived from the Colorado suite by selective weathering of the pyroxenes.

A second well-defined suite is represented by the amphibole assemblages of the San Lorenzo, Piaxtla, and Presidio Rivers, which apparently is of batholithic origin and similar to the amphibole suite of the Peninsula. A third group is formed by the volcanic suites, similar to the assemblages derived from the Comondú Formation, of either hypersthene or augite of the Cañas, Grande de Santiago, Santa Cruz, and Chico Rivers.

Many streams are characterized by mixed volcanic and plutonic-metamorphic suites. The three largest rivers in the area—the Yaqui, Mayo, and Fuerte Rivers—belong in this group. A rapid lateral variation of source areas is reflected by a series of beach and stream sediments between Mazatlán and the Chico River (Fig. 8), which also demonstrates that there is little lateral displacement along the shore.

Notwithstanding the small number of basic assemblages, the provenance of sediments in the Gulf of California can be traced in some detail, because of fortunate alternation of source areas and the existence of characteristic mixed assemblages.

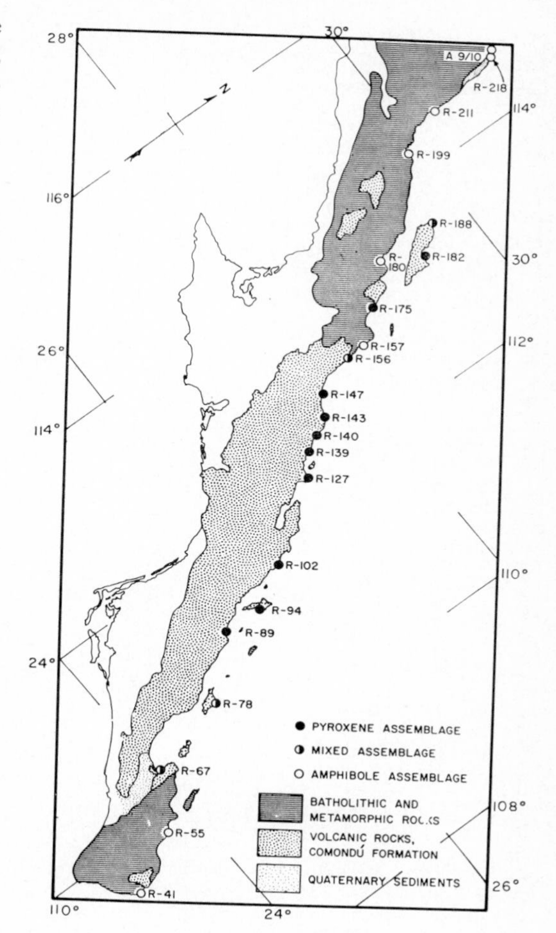

FIG. 7.—Source areas, heavy-mineral assemblages and sample locations of Baja California beaches. Heavy-mineral analyses in Table III.

HEAVY-MINERAL ASSOCIATIONS

Visual inspection of the approximately 250 heavy-mineral analyses available and comparison with the composition of source materials reveal the presence of several associations (Table VII; *see also* Appendix A) characteristic of different areas. One group of sediments, the Sinaloa-Nayarit complex, possesses multiple sources of widely divergent composition. The number of samples available does not allow the definition and use of individual associations, but mappable groups, as for example the Mazatlán group, can be recognized.

The relatively large values of the standard deviation around the mean and the results of a *chi* square test for homogeneity within groups (Eisenhart, 1935; Poole, 1958; Crow, Davis, and Max-

Table VI. Heavy-Mineral Composition of Eastern Gulf of California Rivers
(In per cent by number. For sample locations *see* Fig. 1.)

Number	*River*	*Tourmaline*	*Zircon*	*Apatite*	*Garnet*	*Epidote*	*Amphiboles*	*Basaltic Hornblende*	*Augite*	*Hypersthene*	*Titanite*	*Others*
C- 5	Rio Concepción	—	5	3	1	28	37	5	8	4	5	4*
C- 6	do	—	5	2	—	27	40	1	8	6	6	5
C- 7	do	1	3	1	5	48	26	1	11	1	1	2*
C- 13	do	1	2	3	3	40	33	4	7	2	4	1*
C-140	Rio Yaqui	—	—	—	1	14	20	11	45	5	4	—
C-141	do	—	—	5	1	29	23	4	28	7	3	—
C-142	do	—	1	1	3	14	26	5	36	11	3	—
C-139	Rio Mayo	—	1	—	2	13	24	7	35	13	3	2*
C-138	Rio Fuerte	—	—	2	6	17	33	1	29	7	5	—
C-136	do	—	—	—	1	12	47	2	29	9	—	—
C-135	Rio Sinaloa	1	—	1	—	6	50	5	26	8	2	1
C-134	Rio Mocorito	—	2	—	1	13	32	6	42	4	—	—
C-133	Rio Culiacán	—	1	—	4	27	32	1	27	6	2	—
C-132	Rio San Lorenzo	—	3	—	1	13	66	1	11	5	—	—
C-131	Rio Elota	—	—	—	14	13	29	1	29	12	2	—
C-130	Rio Piaxtla	—	1	—	2	19	72	—	4	1	1	—
C-129	Rio Quelita	—	—	2	—	13	43	2	32	8	—	—
C- 40	Rio Presidio	—	4	2	—	13	64	—	10	1	3	3*
C- 39	Rio Rosario	1	—	—	2	29	13	2	42	8	1	2
C- 38	Rio de las Cañas	1	1	—	—	20	14	—	57	4	2	1*
C- 37	Rio Acaponeta	—	8	2	—	40	3	—	40	7	—	—
C- 49	Rio Grande de Santiago	—	—	—	—	17	7	—	61	15	—	—
C- 35	do	—	2	—	—	11	9	—	62	15	1	—
C- 48	Rio Santa Cruz	—	1	—	—	1	7	1	20	70	—	—
C- 45	Rio Chico	—	—	—	—	2	16	4	23	54	1	—
C- 41	Rio Ameca	—	1	2	1	27	23	4	31	5	4	2*

* C-5—Andalusite 1, Staurolite 1; C-139—Andalusite 1, Sillimanite 1; C-40—Andalusite 1, Sillimanite 2; C-38—Andalusite 1; C-41—Olivine 2.

field, 1960, p. 97) indicate that the variability within individual associations is considerable (Table VII). This inhomogeneity is due to a variety of causes.

Grouping by simple visual inspection in the absence of rigorous criteria may lead to an inadequate distinction between pure and mixed assemblages. With a small number of samples, such grouping may greatly increase the variability. In addition, the cumulative effect of sampling and laboratory errors (Dryden, 1931; Poole, 1958) probably represents a large portion of the total variability.

The influence of size and sorting on mineral composition, although generally insignifican (van Andel, 1959), may occasionally be of majo importance. In Table VIII and Figure 9, the relation between median size and mineral compositio has been tested on the assumption that the regressions are linear. For most minerals, the correlatio is not significant, but in some cases variation i size may obscure the difference between associations. Thus, a fine-grained Baja Hypersthen sample may be very similar to a Baja Augit sample, and size variation may render mediun and coarse-grained Yaqui samples similar to thos of the Sinaloa-Nayarit complex. On the othe hand, size control cannot account for the differ

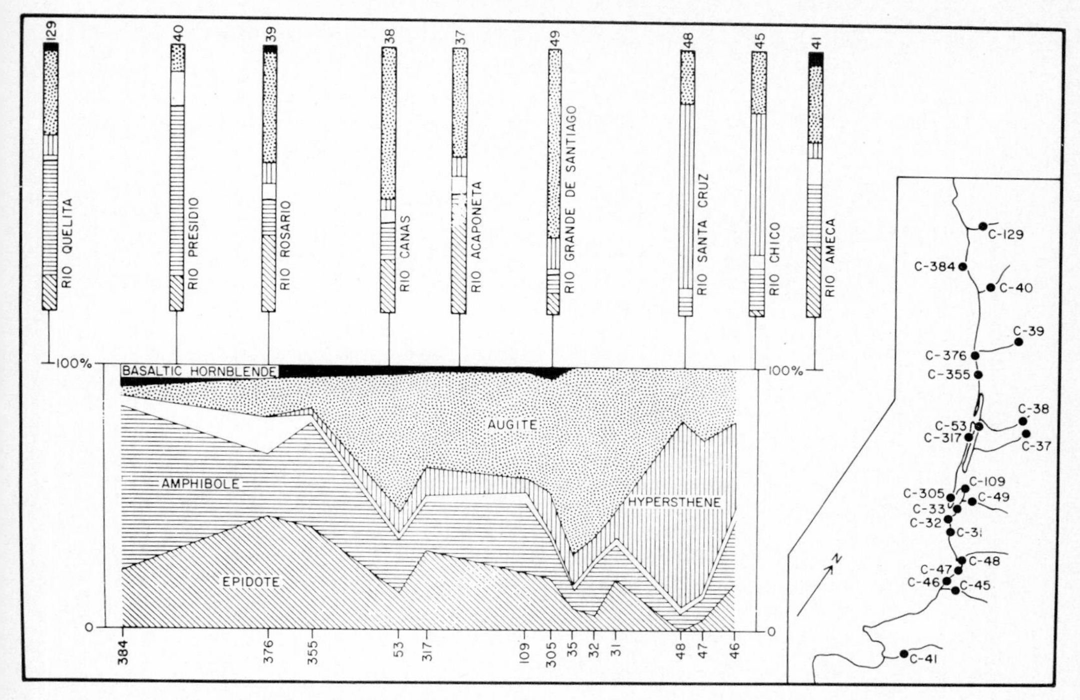

Fig. 8.—Heavy-mineral assemblages of streams and beach sands between Mazatlán and San Blas, southeastern margin of the Gulf of California. Ordinate of graph indicates cumulative mineral per cent; abscissa indicates sample location. Batholithic minerals plotted from bottom, volcanic minerals from top.

ence between the Yaqui and Kino Bay assemblages or the Colorado and Concepción assemblages. The wide range of augite percentages in the Colorado association may, in part, be a size effect.

A major cause for inhomogeneity within associations is the variability of the sediments supplied to the Gulf. This is clearly shown by the beach sands of the Peninsula (Table III) and the sands of the Colorado (Table V), Concepción, and Yaqui (Table VI) Rivers.

Finally, selective removal of unstable minerals by weathering can greatly change mineral suites (van Andel and Poole, 1960; Weyl, 1952). On the shelves of the Gulf, such a process may have been effective.

REGIONAL DISTRIBUTION OF HEAVY-MINERAL PROVINCES

In the northern Gulf of California, the sediments are characterized by four heavy-mineral associations, the Baja Amphibole, Baja Augite, and Concepción and Colorado suites (Table VII, Fig. 10). The small number of samples available, their wide spacing, and the very inadequate knowledge of the Quaternary geology of the surrounding coastal area do not allow more than a very general discussion of sediment sources and distribution.

On the western side, the Gulf is bordered by a narrow zone of Baja Amphibole material, mixed locally with volcanic elements near outcrops of volcanic rock. East of Angel de la Guarda Island, the influence of Comondú volcanics is visible in the high augite and hypersthene percentages of nearshore samples. Another amphibole zone borders the northeastern margin between Tiburón Island and Cape Lobos, where Cretaceous intrusives form a coastal range. Farther northwest, the marginal zone is characterized by the epidote assemblage of the Concepción River, which forms a fan in the Gulf basin.

TABLE VII. AVERAGE COMPOSITION (MEAN, $\overline{X}$) AND VARIABILITY (STANDARD DEVIATION, σ) OF HEAVY-MINERAL ASSOCIATIONS OF GULF OF CALIFORNIA, WITH DEGREE OF HOMOGENEITY (CHI SQUARE, χ^2, AND LEVEL OF SIGNIFICANCE, P)

Association		*Tour-maline*	*Garnet*	*Epidote*	*Amphi-boles*	*Basaltic Horn-blende*	*Augite*	*Hyper-sthene*	*Titan-ite*	*Olivine*	*Others*	χ^2	*P*	*N**
SAN LUCAS amphibole	$\overline{X}$	0.2	0.4	11.0	69.5	1.3	9.4	3.3	1.7	0.2	2.9	73.87	<0.005	18
	σ	0.4	0.6	4.8	8.4	1.3	5.6	3.3	1.2	0.2	2.3	—	—	—
BAJA CALIFORNIA amphibole	$\overline{X}$	0.6	0.5	4.5	71.0	2.7	8.4	4.8	4.1	0.3	1.9	153.07	<0.005	9
	σ	1.2	0.7	3.5	11.0	3.1	5.4	5.1	3.5	2.0	1.4	—	—	—
BAJA CALIFORNIA augite	$\overline{X}$	0.1	0.1	3.3	14.7	11.5	54.6	12.0	1.1	0.1	1.1	236.19	<0.005	10
	σ	0.3	0.3	3.5	3.6	5.5	4.5	4.2	0.5	0.3	1.5	—	—	—
SANTIAGO augite	$\overline{X}$	0.1	0.1	14.8	10.3	1.5	58.3	12.6	0.4	0.1	1.8	131.34	<0.005	15
	σ	0.3	0.2	4.5	5.2	1.9	9.3	3.7	0.6	0.2	—	—	—	—
BAJA CALIFORNIA hypersthene	$\overline{X}$	—	—	1.5	7.8	5.7	52.0	31.7	0.2	0.7	0.5	—	—	4
	σ	—	—	0.7	4.8	2.8	10.0	7.7	0.4	0.8	0.8	—	—	—
SANTA CRUZ hypersthene	$\overline{X}$	—	—	6.2	14.5	1.8	22.5	54.3	0.5	—	0.2	65.73	<0.005	4
	σ	—	—	6.9	8.0	1.3	2.9	13.7	0.5	—	—	—	—	—
CONCEPCIÓN epidote	$\overline{X}$	3.0	5.2	44.2	27.2	2.3	6.5	2.0	3.0	—	6.7	41.43	0.033	6
	σ	1.4	1.7	5.6	6.0	1.1	1.5	1.4	1.3	—	2.7	—	—	—
ACAPONETA epidote	$\overline{X}$	0.2	1.2	41.0	22.3	3.7	21.8	3.7	1.0	—	5.1	111.98	<0.005	12
	σ	0.4	1.5	5.1	9.4	3.8	9.1	2.8	0.9	—	—	—	—	—
COLORADO	$\overline{X}$	2.3	3.3	18.3	43.3	4.5	14.5	5.5	2.0	0.1	6.1	146.46	<0.005	19
	σ	1.5	2.4	4.8	5.5	3.0	5.5	3.7	2.0	0.7	2.4	—	—	—
KINO BAY	$\overline{X}$	0.8	4.5	22.8	39.9	5.1	13.8	4.3	4.1	—	5.6	131.78	<0.005	14
	σ	0.4	2.5	7.1	6.0	3.2	5.2	5.0	2.8	—	2.1	—	—	—
YAQUI RIVER	$\overline{X}$	1.2	2.3	20.0	28.1	4.9	31.3	4.6	3.4	0.1	4.1	51.32	<0.005	10
	σ	0.9	2.1	6.2	4.3	2.4	6.2	2.1	1.4	0.9	3.2	—	—	—
SINALOA-NAYARIT complex	$\overline{X}$	0.5	2.5	24.6	42.2	2.0	18.0	3.6	2.1	—	4.4	162.29	<0.005	26
	σ	0.7	2.3	6.7	6.7	1.9	5.5	2.4	0.9	—	2.4	—	—	—
MAZATLÁN amphibole	$\overline{X}$	—	0.5	20.0	61.5	2.2	9.0	2.0	1.8	—	3.2	13.82	0.1	6
	σ	—	0.7	5.9	7.3	3.0	3.7	3.7	1.1	—	—	—	—	—

* Number of samples

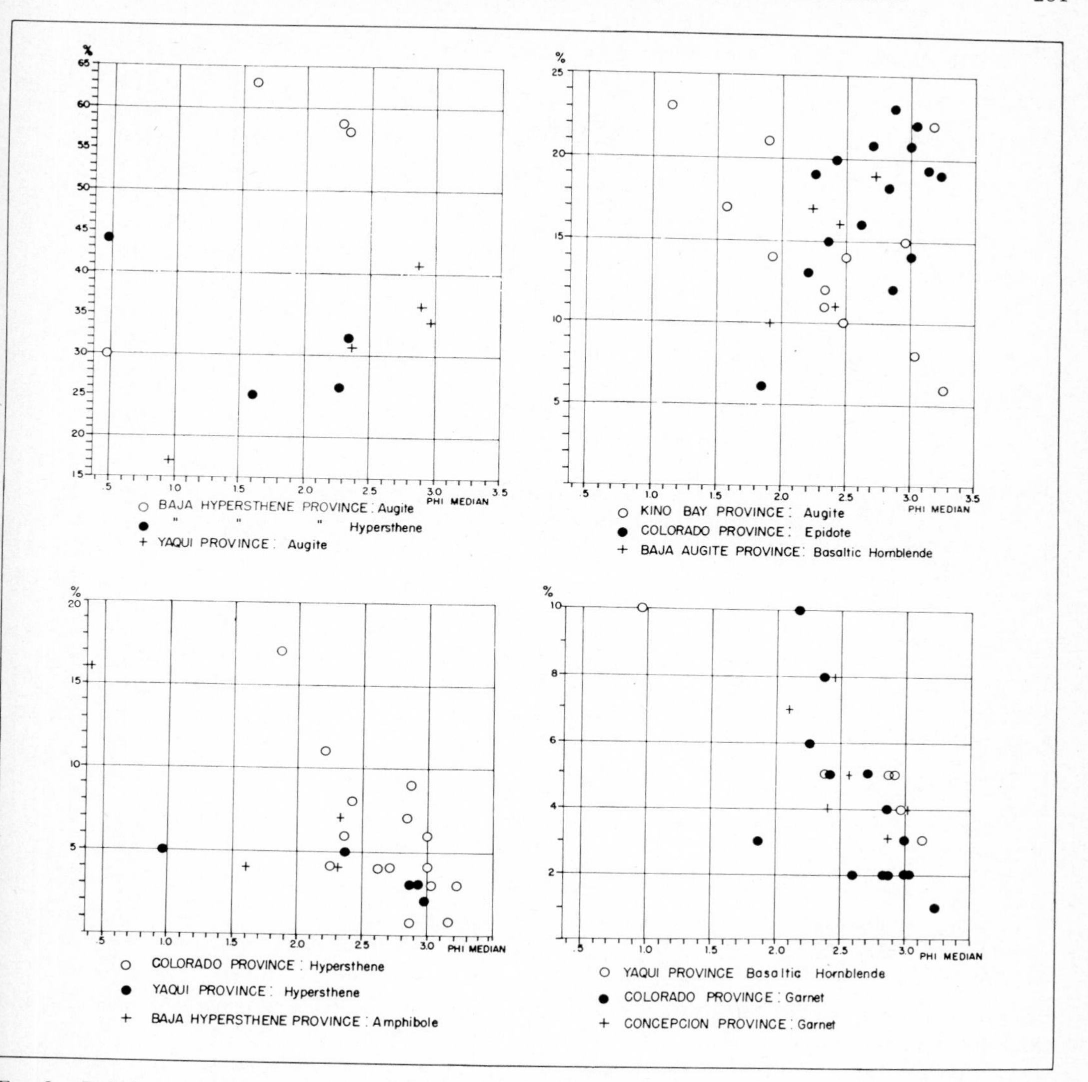

FIG. 9.—Relation between median grain size of sand fraction (2.00–0.06 mm) and heavy-mineral percentage for principal assemblages of the Gulf of California. Correlation coefficients and regression functions in Table VIII.

These narrow marginal provinces fringe an extensive central area occupied by sediments with a mineral composition similar to that of the Colorado. This area extends from the front of the present delta to the deepest portions of the basins west of Angel de la Guarda Island, and into the Tiburón Basin. At the southern edge of this basin, sediments are found that are possibly of Colorado origin, but they may in large part also have been derived from volcanic and batholithic rocks cropping out on nearby islands. The Colorado province does not extend beyond the southern sill of the Tiburón Basin or into the southern part of the Sal si Puedes Basin. Within the Colorado province there is a systematic decrease of the augite percentage from the shore into deeper water (Fig. 10), which may in part be caused by a decrease in grain size (Table VIII). However, it may also be

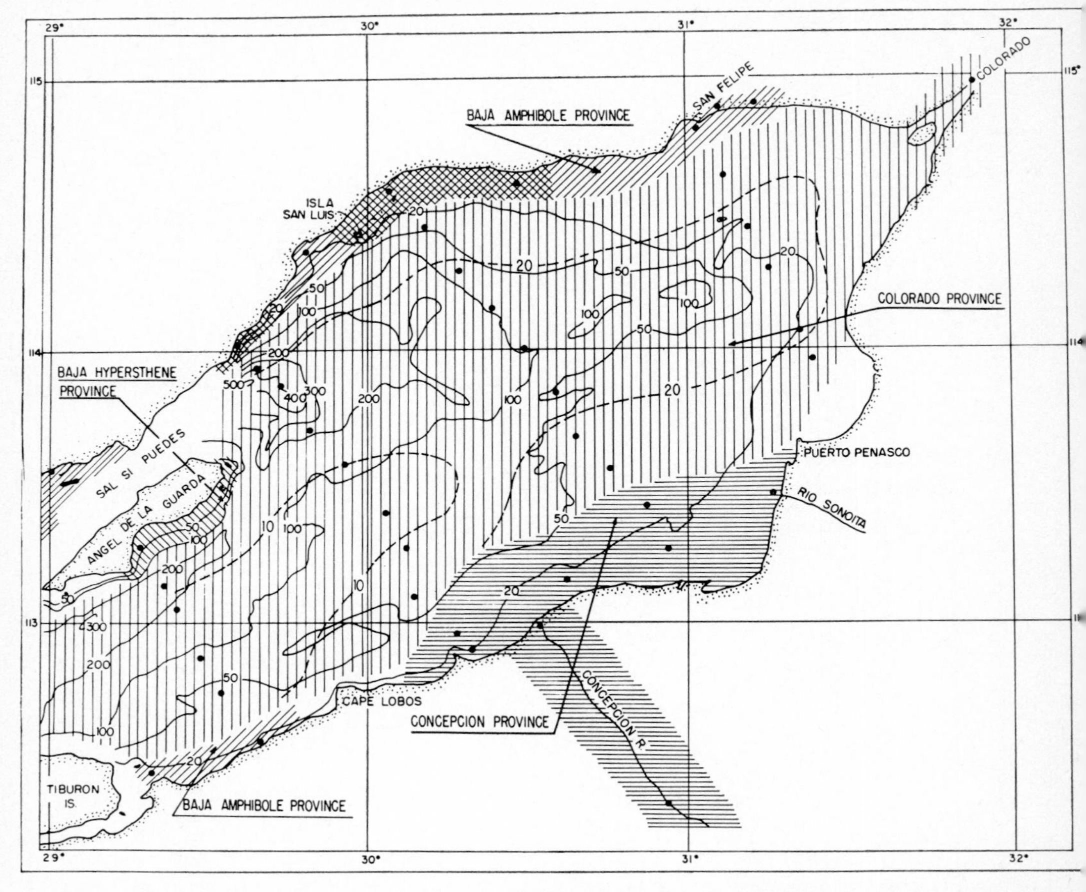

FIG. 10.—Heavy-mineral provinces of the northern Gulf of California. Black dots are sample locations. For composition of heavy-mineral suites see Table VII. Depth contours in fathoms. Broken lines indicate augite-per cent contours.

related to selective weathering during Pleistocene exposure, because during the last sea-level low stand, much of the area was subaerially exposed.

As will be discussed later, most of the Colorado River sediments in the northern Gulf probably are not Recent, but are related to the post-Pleistocene sea-level rise, and the dispersion of minerals must be attributed largely to nearshore processes associated with the transgression.

In the central and southern Gulf, the mineral distribution is very different from that of the northern region, where a large central province with longitudinal dispersal trend occurs, fringed by narrow marginal zones of laterally supplied sediment. In contrast, the sediments of the southern Gulf appear to be supplied from the sides, and dispersion is almost completely transverse.

The province map (Fig. 11) clearly shows the existence of distributive regions originating from the southern Peninsula, the central Peninsular volcanics, the Kino Bay area south of Tiburón Island, and from many of the rivers along the eastern margin. With few exceptions, the contacts are approximately transverse with respect to the Gulf axis. The same pattern of numerous local sources and transverse spreading into the basin of fans separated by mixed zones also is evident from the composite province map. The complex structure of the Sinaloa-Nayarit group cannot be shown with the available data, but a few of the

TABLE VIII. RELATION BETWEEN HEAVY-MINERAL PERCENTAGE AND MEDIAN SIZE OF THE SAND FRACTION OF GULF OF CALIFORNIA HEAVY-MINERAL ASSOCIATIONS

Association Minerals	*Mean Mineral %*	*Correlation Coefficient*	*Significant at 95% Lev.*	*Regression Function*	*% at Md=* 0.5 mm.*	*% at Md= 0.06 mm.*	*Number of Samples*
SAN LUCAS/BAJA AMPHIBOLE							13
Epidote	6.7	0.41	no	$\%=-0.96+2.94xMd\phi$	0	11	
Amphiboles	72.2	−0.35	no	$\%=88.61-6.32xMd\phi$			
Augite	5.6	0.39	no	$\%=-0.94+3.91xMd\phi$			
Hypersthene	4.5	−0.12	no	$\%=7.27-1.05xMd\phi$			
BAJA CALIF. AUGITE							5
Amphiboles	14.2	−0.02	no	$\%=15.18-0.41xMd\phi$			
Basaltic Hornblende	14.6	0.78	no	$\%=-9.97+10.4xMd\phi$	0	32	
Augite	53.8	−0.44	no	$\%=96.73-18.17xMd\phi$	97	24	
BAJA CALIF. HYPERSTHENE							4
Amphiboles	7.8	−0.84	x	$\%=17.06-5.56xMd\phi$	17	0	
Basaltic Hornblende	5.8	0.17	no	$\%=4.74+0.61xMd\phi$			
Augite	52.0	0.84	x	$\%=27.58+14.58xMd\phi$	28	86	
Hypersthene	31.8	−0.77	no	$\%=44.91-7.86xMd\phi$	45	13	
CONCEPCIÓN EPIDOTE							6
Garnet	5.2	−0.66	no	$\%=14.85-3.75xMd\phi$	15	0	
Epidote	44.2	0.35	no	$\%=31.77+4.80xMd\phi$	32	51	
Amphiboles	27.2	0.25	no	$\%=16.52+4.13xMd\phi$			
Augite	6.5	−0.20	no	$\%=8.94-0.95xMd\phi$			
COLORADO							15
Garnet	3.9	−0.61	x	$\%=14.41-3.92xMd\phi$	14	0	
Epidote	17.2	0.58	x	$\%=-0.67+6.64xMd\phi$	0	26	
Amphiboles	43.1	0.42	no	$\%=27.71+5.73xMd\phi$	28	41	
Basaltic Hornblende	4.5	−0.01	no	$\%=4.72-0.10xMd\phi$			
Augite	14.9	−0.48	no	$\%=33.26-6.84xMd\phi$	33	6	
Hypersthene	5.9	−0.73	x	$\%=26.65-7.72xMd\phi$	27	0	
KINO BAY							12
Garnet	4.8	−0.21	no	$\%=6.91-0.87xMd\phi$			
Epidote	21.9	0.03	no	$\%=21.15+0.32xMd\phi$			
Amphiboles	39.7	0.34	no	$\%=32.74+2.91xMd\phi$			
Basaltic Hornblende	5.1	0.30	no	$\%=2.86+0.93xMd\phi$			
Augite	14.4	−0.53	no	$\%=24.81-4.37xMd\phi$	25	7	
YAQUI							5
Epidote	16.6	0.14	no	$\%=14.50+0.87xMd\phi$			
Amphiboles	29.4	−0.38	no	$\%=34.47-2.10xMd\phi$			
Basaltic Hornblende	6.2	−0.99	x	$\%=13.97-3.22xMd\phi$	14	1	
Augite	31.0	0.93	x	$\%=7.12+9.91xMd\phi$	7	33	
Hypersthene	4.0	−0.55	no	$\%=7.08-1.28xMd\phi$	7	2	
SINALOA-NAYARIT COMPLEX							18
Epidote	25.0	0.12	no	$\%=21.78+1.29xMd\phi$			
Amphiboles	40.9	0.17	no	$\%=36.79+1.65xMd\phi$			
Augite	17.7	−0.18	no	$\%=21.52-1.53xMd\phi$			
Hypersthene	4.1	−0.0	no				

* Calculated from regression function.

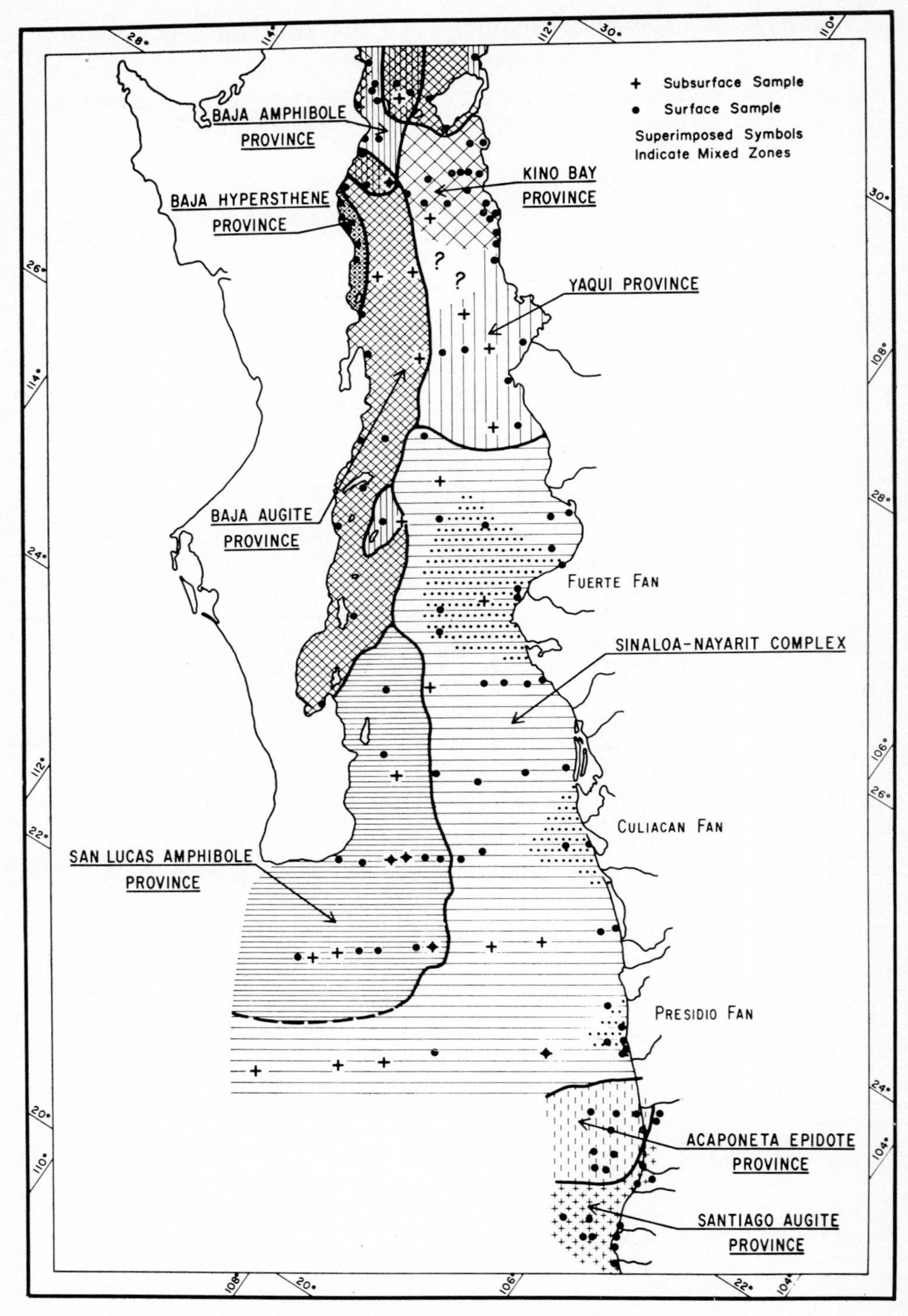

Fig. 11.—Heavy-mineral provinces of the central and southern Gulf of California. See Table VII for composition of heavy-mineral associations.

ıore conspicuous distributive fans have been ıdicated. The pattern of numerous local sources nd transverse spreading into the basin offers ttle evidence for longitudinal transport in excess f 100 miles.

LIGHT-MINERAL COMPOSITION

Heavy-mineral assemblages frequently do not eliably reflect the petrography of source areas ecause of overrepresentation of igneous and ıetamorphic components (Koldewijn, 1955; van ndel, 1960), and light-mineral studies are necesıry for a balanced interpretation. Moreover, the omposition of the light fraction is the basis of arious classifications of sandy sediments (Klein, 963) and of concepts related to tectonic control f sedimentation. Studies of modern sediments ave not yet contributed fully to these concepts Folk, 1956; Curray, 1960; van Andel, 1960). The ollowing discussion will be based on the sand actions of sediments that themselves may be redominantly fine grained.

Nearly all proposed classifications of sandy ediments are based on a three-end-member sysem, including (Krynine, 1948; Dapples, Krumein, and Sloss, 1953; Pettijohn, 1957) or rejecting Folk, 1954; Williams, Turner, and Gilbert, 1954) lt and clay as an end member. Folk (1956) and an Andel (1960) have argued that texture is a roperty almost entirely controlled by deposional environment and virtually independent of ediment source and basin tectonics. The Gulf of alifornia sand fractions are either graywackes or rkoses. In both groups, bimodal and polymodal ze distributions predominate (Fig. 12) with ariable matrix percentages that are independent f the composition of the sand fraction (Table X). Unimodal distributions are restricted to ttoral sands. If matrix content is accepted as a asis for petrographic classification, all Gulf of alifornia sand fractions, with the exception of ome arkose beach sands, would be graywackes.

Some authors (for example, Packham, 1954) ave restricted the term graywacke to sandstones igh in matrix and possessing structural properes and lithological associations normally consided to be produced by turbidity currents in a eosynclinal facies. In the Gulf of California, rkose and graywacke deep-water sands of bimodal texture, locally with graded bedding and associated with deep-water clays, are related by a series of textural transitions to unimodal beach sands of the same composition. It appears unjustified to restrict the term graywacke to the turbidite member of such a homogeneous series, if the principal emphasis of the study is on provenance.

For the present study, a classification system based on quartz+chert, feldspar, and rock fragments has been adopted (Fig. 13). This system allows distinction between a feldspar-rich and a feldspar-poor type. The rock fragments are dominantly volcanic, and even some arkoses near volcanic outcrops contain appreciable amounts of volcanic material.

The distribution of the sand types in the Gulf is simple (Fig. 14). The San Lucas batholith is surrounded by an aureole of arkose which is distinguished by a high mica content and a high plagioclase/orthoclase ratio from the arkose south of Tiburón Island (Table IX, R-138, R-153). Arkoses also occur in most of the northern Gulf, but more stable feldspathic sands border the Colorado River delta and occur in the Colorado River (A-13). The marginal deposits on the western side of the northern Gulf are well defined by admixture of volcanic material, but the influence of the Concepción supply cannot be recognized.

The graywackes of the Gulf are more varied than the arkoses (Table IX), but, on the basis of light-mineral analyses alone, no sharp distinction can be made between eastern and western supply, except in the southeastern and north-central areas.

The light-mineral suites of the Gulf indicate differences in source-area composition, but not as sensitively as do the heavy-mineral associations. The most stable sands are supplied by the Colorado River; they are remarkably similar to those of the Mississippi River (Russell, 1937), which also are derived from a large source area composed mainly of sedimentary rocks.

The regional distribution of three diagnostic light-mineral components—mica, red detritals, and volcanic ash—is more conveniently studied by means of loose-grain counts than in thin section.

The regional distribution of mica in the 0.062–0.250 mm fraction is presented in Figure 15. Pat-

TABLE IX. COMPOSITION OF THE LIGHT FRACTION OF TYPICAL GULF OF CALIFORNIA SEDIMENTS
(Fraction 0.062–0.250 mm. Composition by point count, sand content in weight per cent. For locations *see* Fig. 1.)

Station No.	*Sand Content*	*Quartz*	*Chert*	*Plagioclase*	*Orthoclase*	*Microclase*	*Mica*	*Metamorphic Fr.*	*Volcanic Fr.*	*Plutonic Fr.*	*Sedimentary Fr.*	*Other*	*End Member Per cent*		
													Quartz	*Feldspar*	*Rock Fragments*
							ARKOSES								
R- 24	5.1	41	—	9	14	—	16	1	4	—	—	15	73.3	18.8	7.
R- 43	44.0	58	—	9	24	—	3	—	3	1	—	2	59.2	33.7	7.
R- 78	17.3	48	—	17	12	1	1	—	8	10	2	1	48.5	30.3	21.
R- 91	26.7	40	2	11	21	—	3	—	6	1	—	16	50.0	38.1	11.
R-138	63.4	50	2	3	27	1	1	1	6	2	—	7	53.1	31.6	15.
R-142	68.8	49	3	4	27	6	1	—	6	3	—	1	52.5	37.4	10.
R-145	41.0	47	1	8	28	4	—	—	4	5	1	2	49.0	40.8	10.
R-152	26.5	42	1	5	40	—	1	—	3	4	—	4	44.8	46.9	8.
R-153	78.7	45	6	9	26	3	2	1	1	6	—	1	51.5	38.4	10.
R-161	73.6	64	3	3	21	2	2	—	1	3	—	1	67.0	26.0	7.
R-162	40.6	27	1	11	28	—	1	—	23	2	—	7	29.8	41.5	28.
R-194	65.7	62	2	2	24	—	—	2	3	3	1	1	64.6	26.3	9.
R-200	81.5	49	3	6	27	1	1	4	3	4	1	1	52.5	34.3	13.
R-204	87.9	61	2	5	23	—	—	—	3	5	1	—	63.0	28.0	9.
R-212	59.6	67	1	3	21	2	1	—	3	1	—	1	68.7	26.3	5.
							FELDSPATHIC SANDS								
R-203	61.7	69	4	1	18	—	—	1	3	1	—	3	75.3	19.6	5.
R-213	74.6	76	2	2	16	—	—	—	3	—	—	1	78.8	18.2	3.
R-215	80.4	64	2	4	19	—	3	2	4	1	—	1	66.7	23.2	10.
R-216	4.3	75	1	2	12	—	—	5	2	—	—	2	76.0	15.0	9.
A- 13	—	72	2	4	14	1	—	3	2	1	2	—	73.3	18.8	7.
							GRAYWACKES								
R- 21	2.7	21	—	12	16	—	1	—	44	1	3	2	21.4	28.6	50.
R- 52	59.7	40	4	6	11	—	6	11	18	2	—	2	44.0	17.0	39.
R- 59	3.3	32	2	1	20	—	3	—	33	8	—	1	34.3	21.2	44.
R- 67	83.9	12	—	29	5	—	2	—	49	—	3	—	12.0	34.0	54.
R- 87	10.9	27	4	4	15	—	5	3	33	3	—	6	33.0	20.2	46.
R- 94	21.9	24	1	17	2	—	2	—	44	1	—	9	27.5	20.9	51.
R-102	75.9	29	—	17	15	1	—	—	32	—	—	6	30.9	35.1	34.
R-109	52.9	33	4	7	16	—	4	1	23	2	—	10	40.2	25.0	34.
R-119	33.4	17	—	9	14	1	3	2	47	4	—	3	17.5	24.7	57.
R-139	68.4	12	1	6	6	—	1	—	62	—	2	10	14.4	13.3	72.
R-143	28.8	14	—	6	1	—	4	—	71	1	—	2	14.3	7.1	78.
R-166	28.9	32	1	2	8	1	—	13	29	11	2	1	33.3	11.1	55.
R-188	47.6	14	—	35	2	—	1	—	42	4	—	2	14.3	37.8	48.
R-189	83.6	48	—	6	12	1	1	—	32	—	—	—	48.0	19.0	33.

terns for other size classes are similar. The micas are mainly muscovite, with minor amounts of chlorite and biotite. Large amounts of mica occur in three well-defined areas—around the lower Peninsula, in a coastal zone bordering the northern Peninsular batholith, and between the Fuerte River and Mazatlán. These areas are virtua identical to the distribution of the batholit heavy-mineral suites (Fig. 11) and confirm th the light fraction is of the same origin.

Within the micaceous zone around Cape S Lucas, there is an outward decrease from 25–

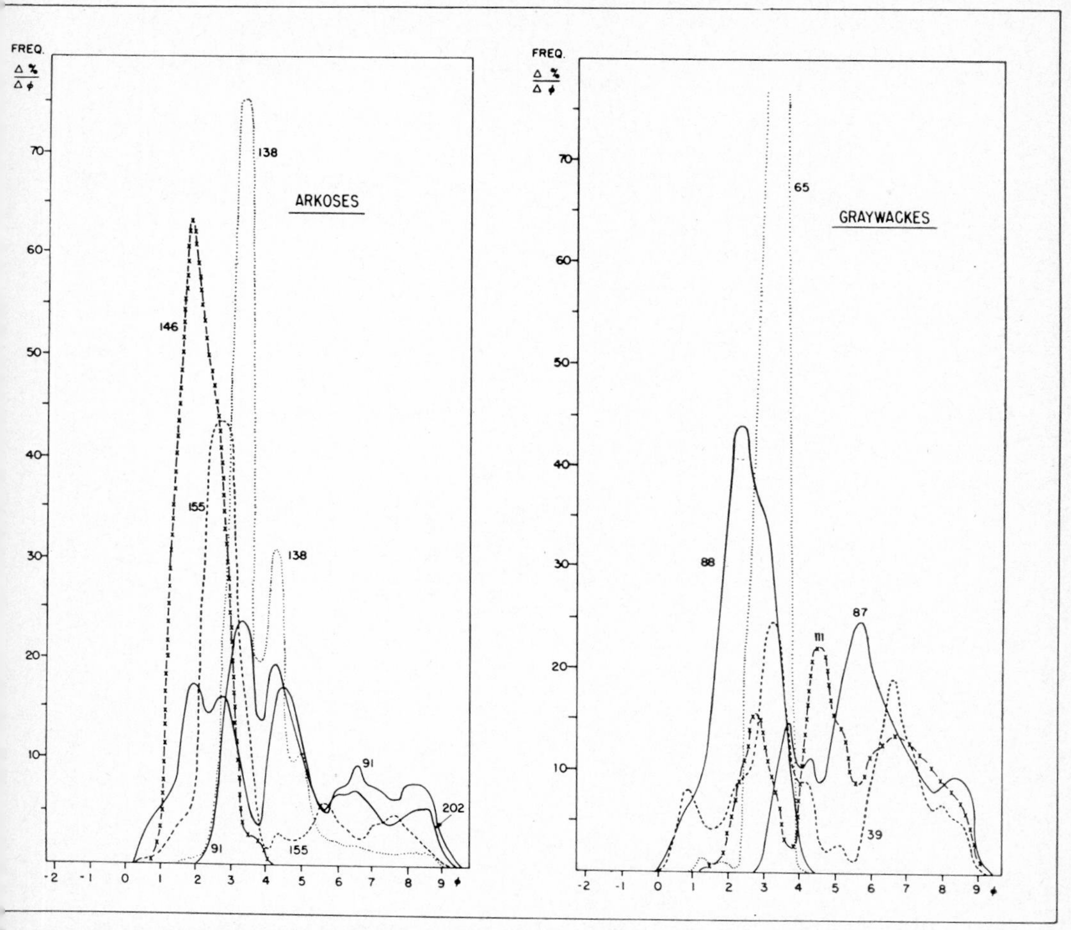

ɪɢ. 12.—Characteristic size-frequency distributions of arkose and graywacke samples. Sample numbers correspond with Table 9. Grain size in *phi*, frequency in per cent per unit *phi*.

er cent, by number, to less than 5 per cent, 50 to 5 miles away (Fig. 16), which is not due to dilu- ion with biogenous or authigenic elements. Mica more abundant in coarse than in fine sizes, and pparently during long-distance transportation is rogressively eliminated with respect to quartz, ldspar, and rock fragments.

The regional distribution of red detritals (Fig. 7) is approximately opposite to the mica distri- ution. The group combines red-orange, brown- ained, and coated quartz; fragments of red rock, ostly volcanic; and well-indurated aggregates. general, the Peninsula appears to produce little red material, but a wide zone fringes the eastern lowlands from Mazatlán to Tiburón Island, and occurs off the Colorado River delta. Red detrital grains are restricted to shallow water and coarse deposits; of 60 samples containing more than 3 per cent red detritals in the sand fraction, only 15 samples are fine grained. Because other components of the same source are carried into deep water, it seems probable that the red pigment is removed by reducing conditions prevalent in the fine-grained, deep-water sediments.

A clear, fresh-looking, brown to colorless volcanic glass, with a refractive index of 1.520–1.598,

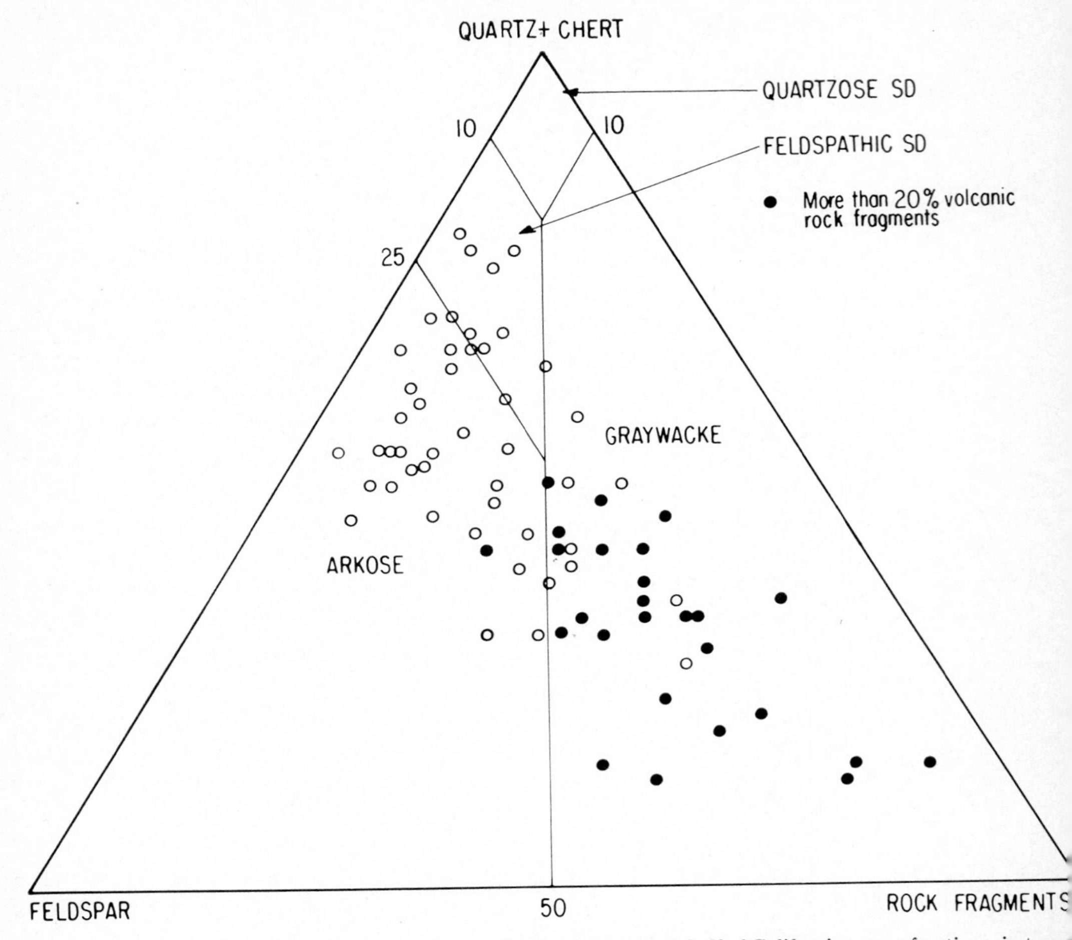

FIG. 13.—Triangular diagram of the composition of the light fraction of Gulf of California coarse fractions, in terms of terrigenous constituents, and classification of petrographic sand types.

occurs in many samples. The regional distribution of this glass (Fig. 18) is strikingly different from that of the other volcanic components (Fig. 14). Very large amounts—up to 15 per cent by weight—occur in a few localities along the central and northern Peninsula, particularly near two areas of young volcanoes, one of which—the Tres Virgenes—has been active in historic time (Ives, 1962). Smaller amounts are widely distributed in deep-water sediments in and near the Gulf entrance, where other volcanic components are very rare. These glass fragments, with an index of 1.596–1.598, are very coarse, indicating a mode of transportation, possibly aeolian, which is independent of that of the rest of the sediment. A source for this glass may be sought in the Holocene volcanoes of Jalisco and Colima, Mexico.

CONCLUSIONS

Three principal types of source areas supply sediment to the Gulf of California, all of which are mountainous with relatively arid climates, little chemical weathering, and rapid erosion. The light- and heavy-mineral associations supplied are highly to moderately unstable, reflecting source area composition and tectonic instability. The acid-intermediate batholiths provide an amphibole-rich arkose; the Tertiary and Quaternary supply basic volcanics with graywackes rich in pyroxenes, basaltic hornblende, and volcanic roc

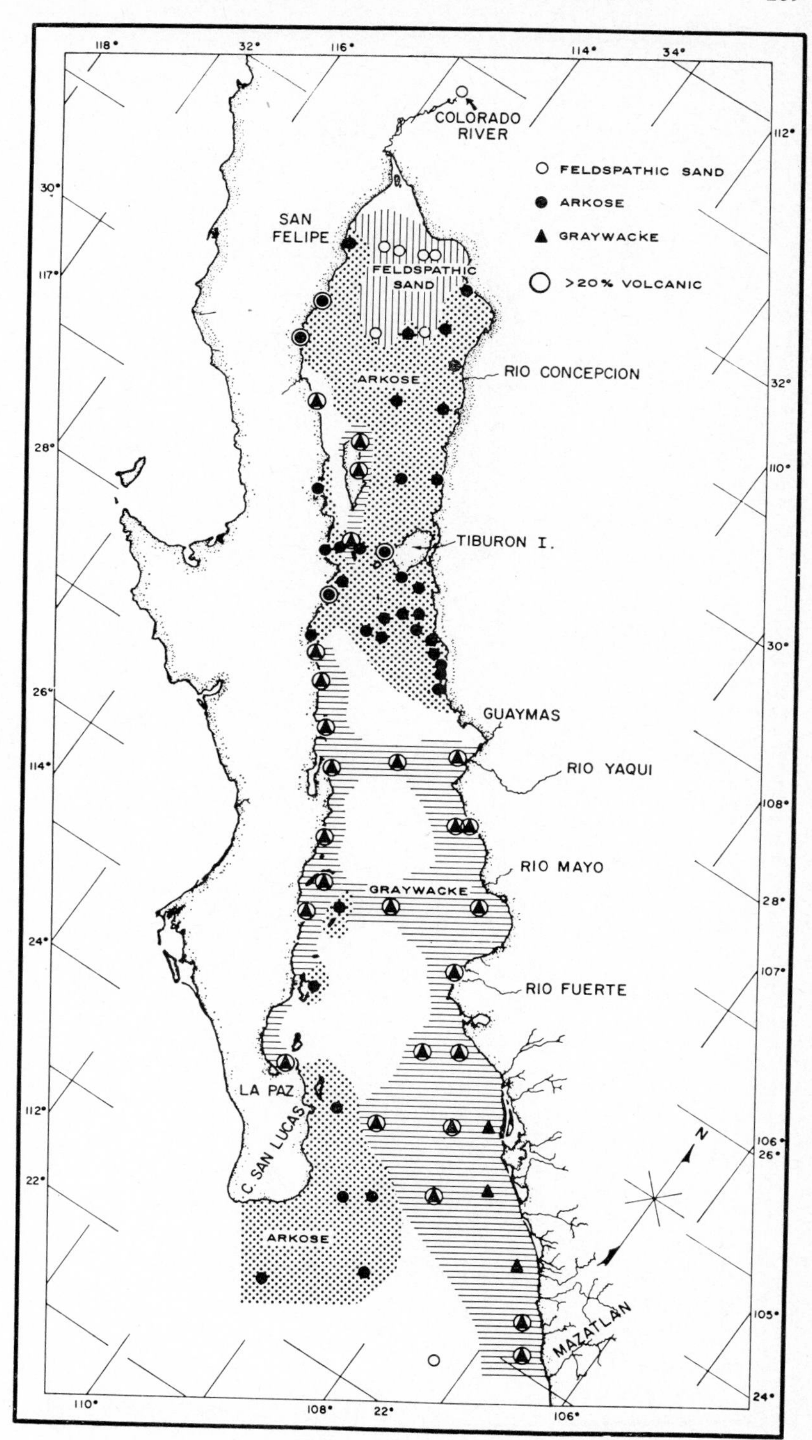

FIG. 14.—Regional distribution of petrographic sand types in the Gulf of California, based on classification of Fig. 13. Blank areas—insufficient sand fraction for analysis.

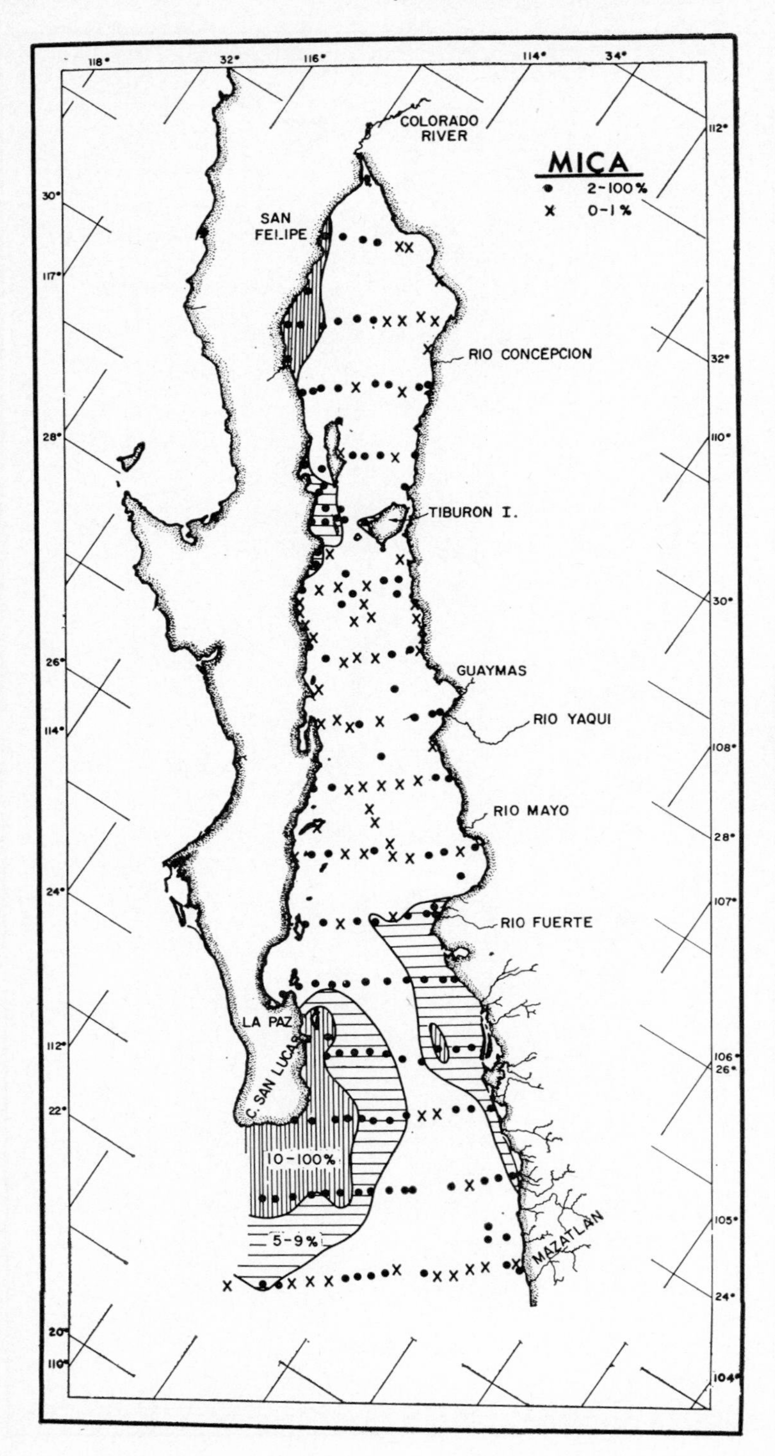

FIG. 15.—Regional distribution of mica in the Gulf of California, in per cent by number of the 0.06–0.25 mm fraction. Dark shading, 10–100 per cent; light shading, 5–9 per cent.

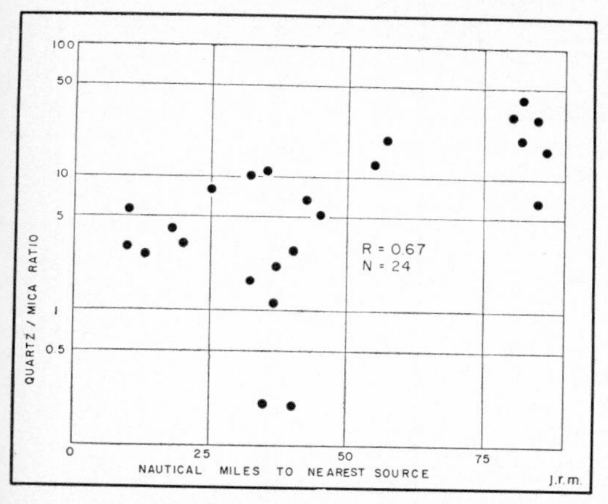

FIG. 16.—Relation between ratio of terrigenous grains (exclusive of mica) and mica, and the distance to nearest source. Correlation significant at one per cent level.

fragments. The mixed drainage basins of the Colorado, the Concepción, and the Costa de Hermosillo (Kino Bay province) are the source of arkosic or feldspathic sands with a heavy-mineral suite containing characteristic amounts of stable minerals.

In the northern Gulf (Fig. 19), the largest area is covered with Colorado sediments, probably largely deposited during the post-Pleistocene sea level rise and now in a nondepositional zone. Many unsolved problems are connected with the sources and dispersal of these sediments. The basin is fringed by marginal deposits derived from the local hinterland, but on the whole, transportation appears to be mainly longitudinal.

The central and the southern Gulf, on the other hand, are filled entirely from the sides, and the configuration of province boundaries indicates little if any longitudinal transportation (Fig. 19). The sediment sources are batholithic and volcanic, and well-defined distributive regions can be recognized in the Gulf sediments. On the western side, the boundaries of these provinces coincide rather precisely with outcrop boundaries on land. On the eastern side, the situation is more complex because of the presence of many mixed-supply areas. A well-defined distribution fan occurs south of Tiburón Island. The origin of the material is not entirely clear, but the transverse dispersal pattern is evident. Farther south, the complex pattern of provinces can be only partially resolved, but the predominantly transverse transportation, extending from the foot of the mountains through the wide coastal plain and into the deep basins of the Gulf, is unmistakable. Longitudinal trends do not exceed a few tens of miles. The eastern margin of the Gulf, as a result of its higher precipitation and the presence of many permanent streams, is a much more prolific supplier of sediment than the Peninsula with its steep, arid mountains devoid of rivers. Consequently, the zone of marine sediments derived from the Peninsula is relatively narrow and terminates approximately at the foot of the western slope. The eastern sources, on the other hand, supply not only all the sediment forming the wide coastal plain and covering the continental shelf and slope, but also extend into most of the Gulf basins. Studies by Harrison and Mathur, Phillips, and Curray and Moore (all, this volume) indicate that sediments are not only extensive but also thick.

The maximum width of the western zone is approximately 30 miles, except in the area of the southern Peninsula, where the zone extends 75–85 miles from the source area. This probably is a result of the activity of turbidity currents issuing from the many submarine canyons surrounding the cape.

The Gulf of California derives its highly immature sediments primarily from local and rather unstable sediment sources, in contrast with the Gulf of Mexico or the Orinoco region, which receive their sediments from distant and predominantly stable sources. The heavy fractions of the Gulf of California reflect the composition of the source areas much more faithfully than do the assemblages of the other two areas. The light fraction of the Gulf of California is very immature and fits existing concepts of tectonic control. The composition of the Colorado River sediment, similarly to that of other large rivers of the world, is not truly representative of the nature of its drainage basin.

Studies of sediment transportation in the Gulf of Mexico (van Andel and Curray, 1960; van Andel and Poole, 1960) have shown that there is a clear relation between the sediment dispersal pattern and the balance between rate of sediment supply and rate of reworking by waves. In areas of major sediment supply, such as off major deltas,

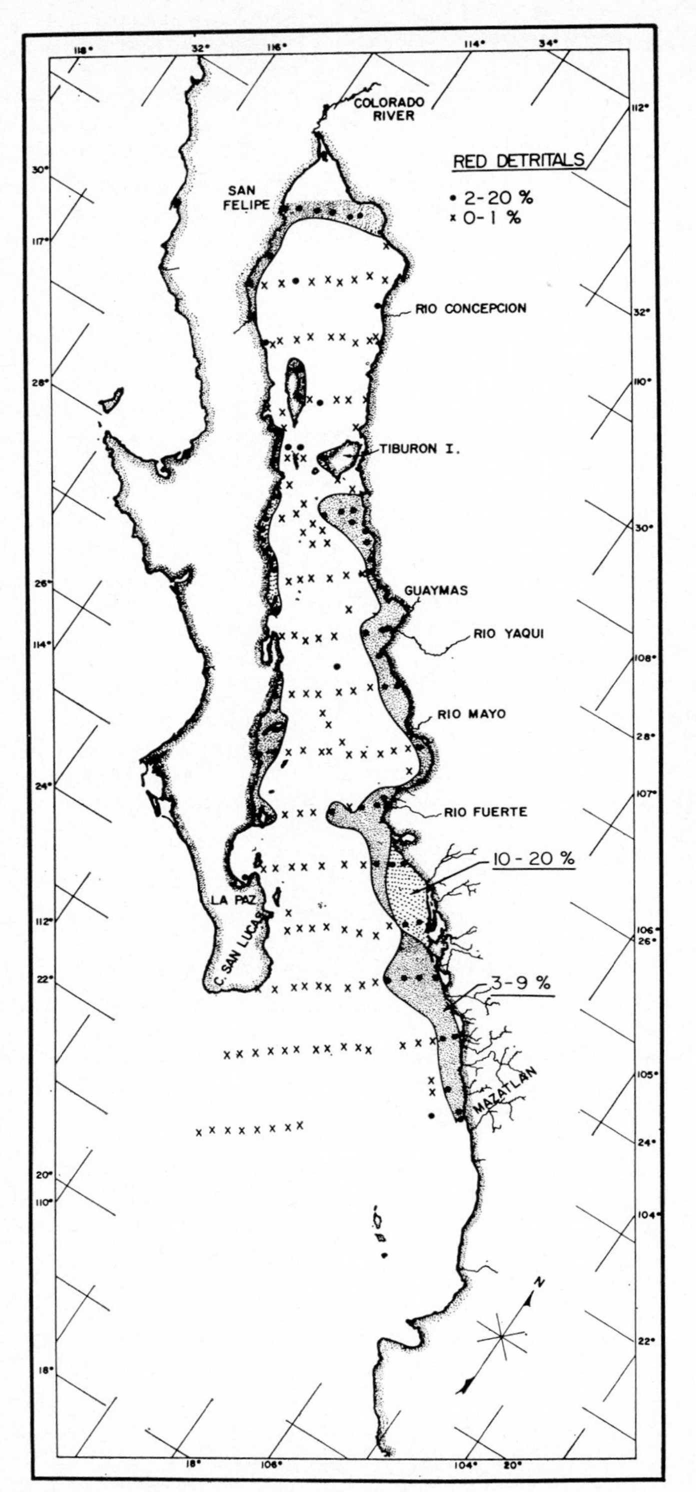

FIG. 17.—Regional distribution of red-stained detritals in the Gulf of California, in per cent by number of the 0.06–0.25 mm fraction. Light shading, 3–9 per cent; dark shading, 10–20 per cent.

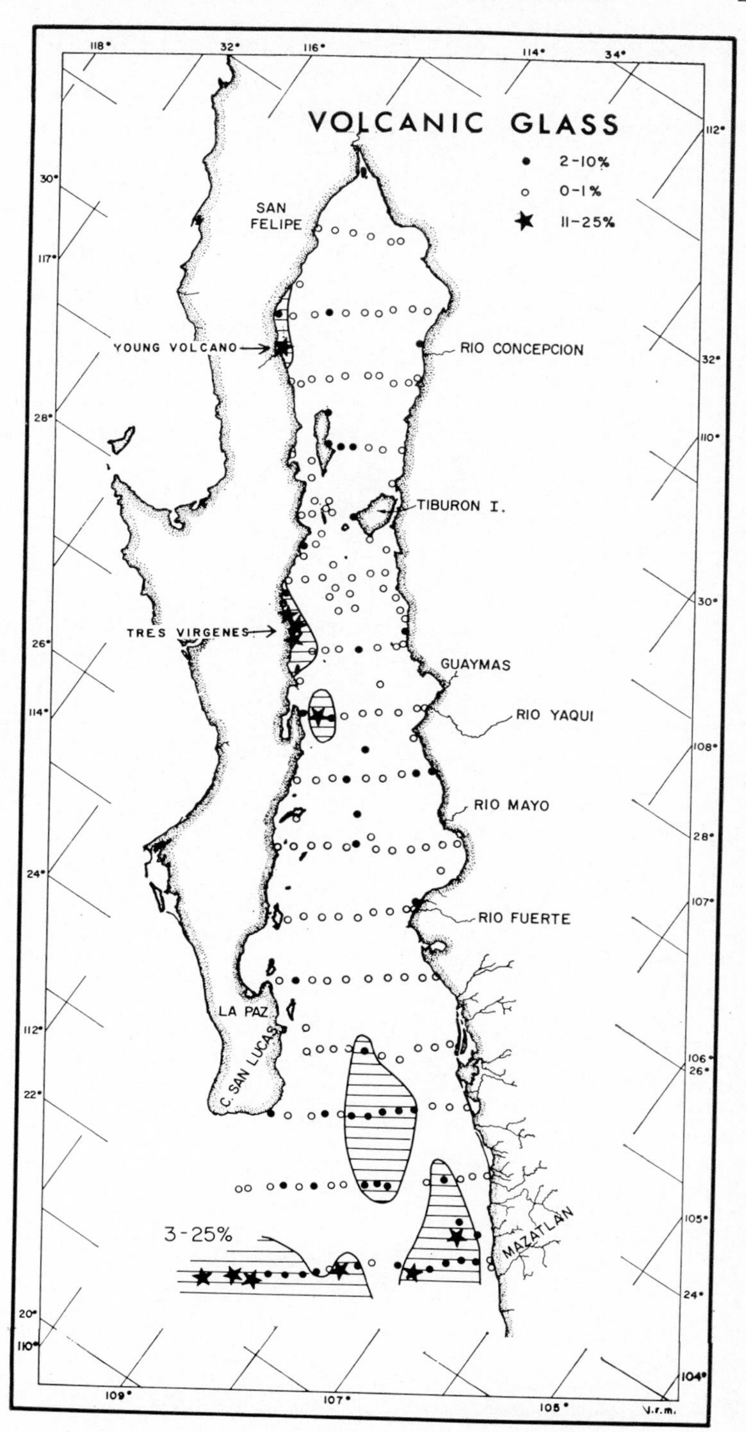

FIG. 18.—Regional distribution of clear volcanic glass in the Gulf of California, in per cent by number of the 0.06–0.25 mm fraction. Note occurrence in the southeastern Gulf and adjacent Pacific, possibly derived from Jalisco and Colima volcanoes.

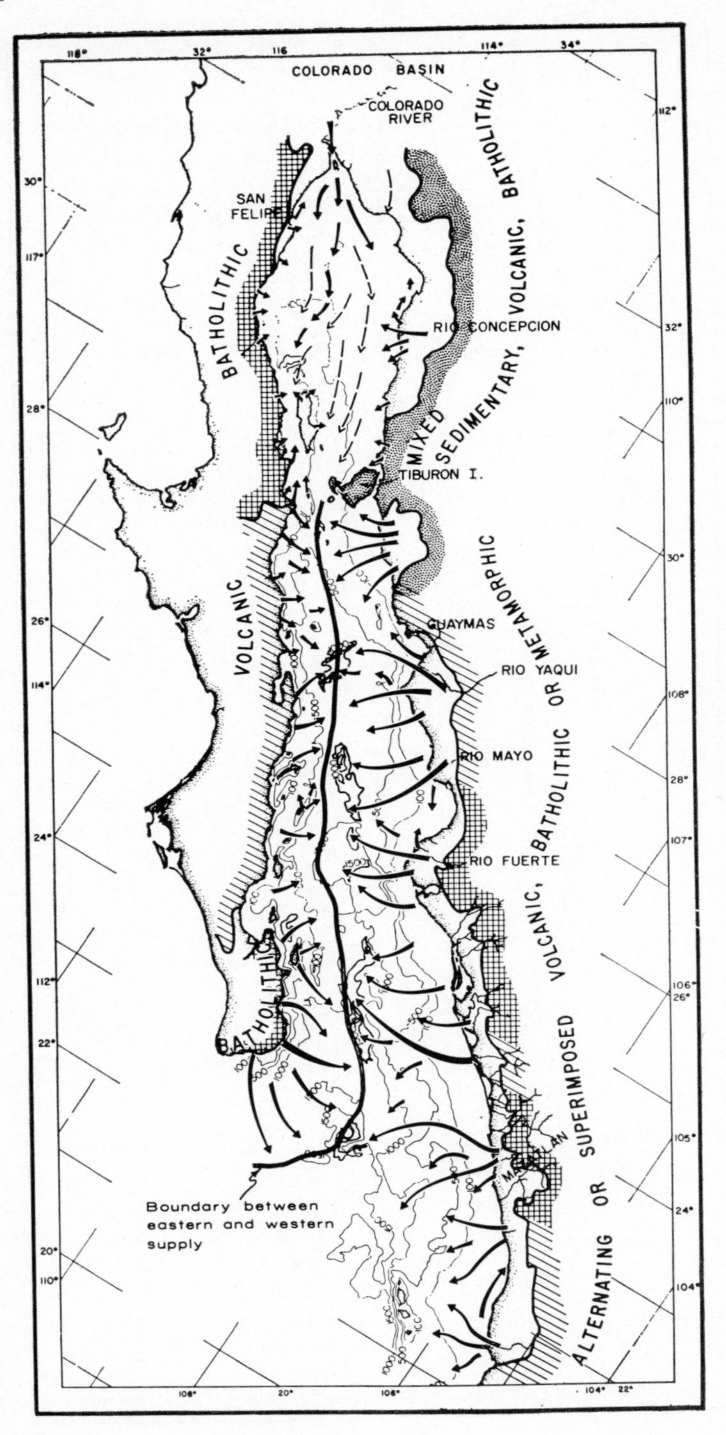

FIG. 19.—Sources and dispersion of sediments in the Gulf of California. Based on heavy- and light-mineral analyses of the sand fraction. Generalized composition of source areas shown along Gulf margins.

transportation is predominantly directed toward the center of the basin. Elsewhere, for example along the Texas coast, sediment dispersal is mainly parallel to the margin of the basin. The transportation patterns observed in the studies mentioned are all in shallow water.

In the Gulf of California many shelves are narrow, and coastal plain formation has been so rapid, particularly along the eastern side, that much sediment is carried directly into deep water. As a result, the effects of shallow-water redistribution by waves, and of the post-Pleistocene transgression, so conspicuous in the Gulf of Mexico, do not play the same important role, and transportation is generally directed away from the shore. Examples of this transverse pattern occur everywhere in the southern Gulf and are especially striking south of Tiburón Island, off the Yaqui River and Fuerte River deltas, and around Cape San Lucas. Dispersal patterns more parallel to the basin margin occur along the Costa de Nayarit south of Mazatlán (Curray and Moore, this volume). In this area, exposure to the Pacific swell creates substantial longshore drift, and the balance between sediment supply and marine reworking is in favor of the latter. Similar patterns can be observed in the northern Gulf, and longshore drift may have been very important during the post-Pleistocene transgression.

From the foregoing, it appears that the present-day Gulf of California does not present a case of longitudinal filling of oblong basins. Whether or not in the course of a long history a major portion of the basin ultimately will be filled from the north is a problem that will be discussed at the end of this paper.

LITHOFACIES OF RECENT GULF OF CALIFORNIA SEDIMENTS

The purpose of this chapter is to discuss the broad lithologic properties of the Gulf deposits and the regional lithofacies distribution. Data are presented in Appendix B. Subsequent chapters will deal in more detail with the distribution of biogenous components, with size distributions and sorting, and with the characteristics and genesis of deep-water sands.

LITHOLOGICAL CHARACTERISTICS

Texture.—The textural classification used here has been proposed by Shepard (1954) and was applied in the regional description of the Gulf of Mexico sediments (Shepard and others, 1960). It is based upon a triangle diagram with sand (2.000–0.062 mm), silt (0.062–0.004 mm), and clay (finer than 0.004 mm) as end members. All Gulf of California surface samples analyzed for grain-size distribution are shown on such a diagram in Figure 20.

Two textural groups—sands with or without minor amounts of silt and clay, and silty clays to very clayey silts—make up the bulk of the Gulf sediments. Clays, silts and clayey silts, and sand-silt-clay are conspicuously rare. This is particularly striking when the Gulf of California diagram is compared with diagrams for the Gulf of Mexico and the Gulf of Paria, where these classes are well represented. Both the Gulf of Mexico and the Gulf of Paria, in contrast to the Gulf of California, are of low relief and possess vast and distant source areas. Possibly the nearness of the sources, the low degree of chemical weathering, and the high relief explain in part the scarcity of very-fine-grained material in the Gulf of California.

The deep basins of the northern Gulf and almost the entire central and southern Gulf beyond the upper continental slope are covered with silty clay (Fig. 21). Well-defined belts of clayey silt occur along the upper slope and outer shelf of the eastern side from the Yaqui Delta southward, and off the Colorado and Concepción Deltas.

The most extensive zone of sandy sediments occurs in the northern Gulf, between the coast and approximately 100 fathoms, extending as far south as the southern sill of the Tiburón Basin. Sand is found at considerable depth in the southern part of the Sal si Puedes Basin and on the sill of the Tiburón Basin. In the central and southern Gulf, sands occur only along the margins. The sandy belt is narrow and calcareous along the western side and wider and predominantly terrigenous along the eastern margin. Sands are restricted to continental shelves, except for the fan south of Tiburón Island, where they are found to a maximum depth of 300 fathoms. A zone of clayey sand, in which the sand fraction is calcarenite, occurs in intermediate depth along the central Peninsula.

In deep water, occasional thin sand layers are interbedded with the silty clays; sand-silt-clay

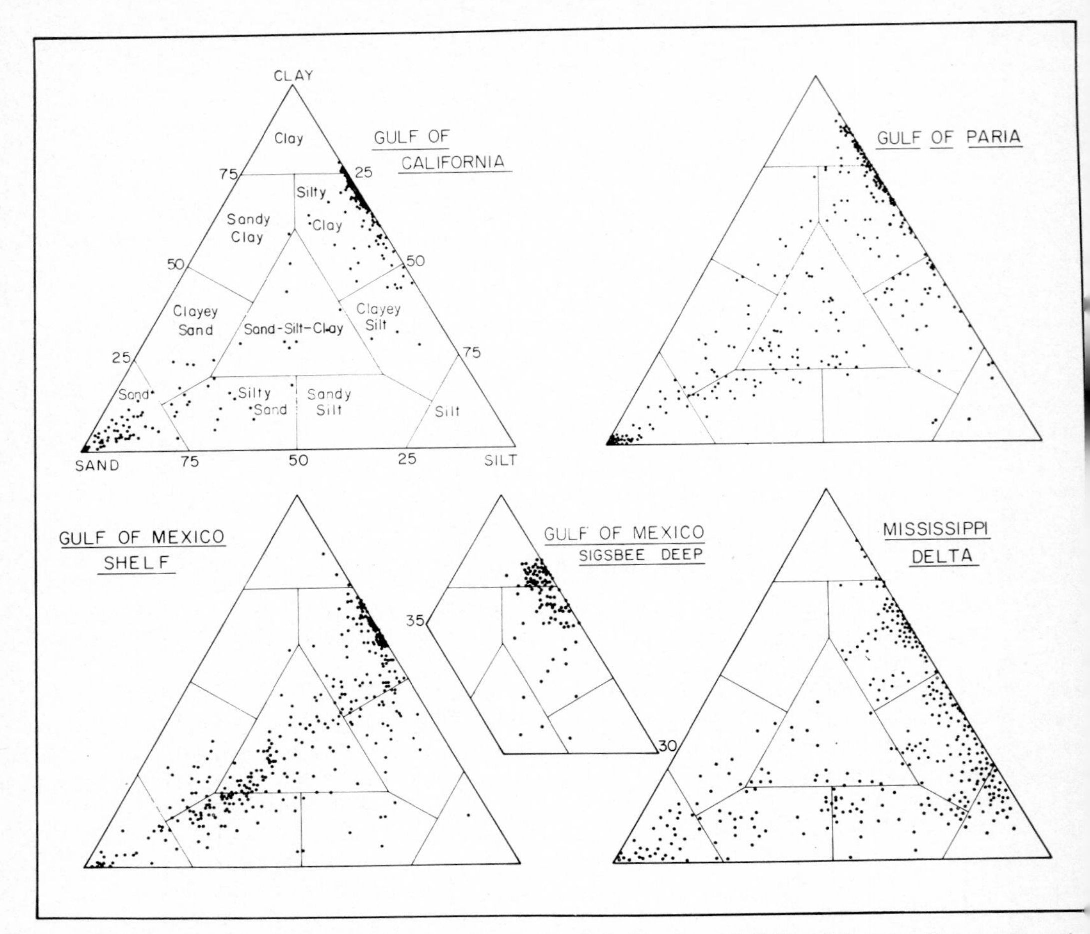

FIG. 20.—Textural diagrams of Gulf of California, Gulf of Paria, and Gulf of Mexico sediments. Data for Gulf of Paria from van Andel (unpublished), for the Gulf of Mexico shelf from J.R. Curray (1960, and original data), for the Sigsbee Deep from Stetson (1953, and original data), and for the Mississippi Delta from Shepard (1956).

and silty sand cover some of the banks and seamounts. These sediments are not shown in Figure 21, and will be discussed later.

Color.—Field determinations of color were made on wet samples with the aid of the Rock Color Chart (Geol. Soc. America, 1951). Nearly all cores have a thin (up to 2 cm), very fluid, yellowish-brown oxidized surface layer. Beneath that, medium to light olive gray and grayish olive predominate. Sandy or calcarenitic sediments generally are a paler olive gray or grayish olive green, but there are many exceptions. On the southeastern continental shelf, sediments are locally yellowish brown. In general, the color range is similar to that of other modern marine sediments, but very dark colors and black are absent.

Water content.—The water content of all fresh fine-grained surface samples has been determined by drying a portion of the 9–10 cm level of each core at 105°. Water content is expressed in per cent by weight of the wet sample. Grain size expressed as the percentage of clay (finer than 0.004 mm), is the dominant controlling factor for variations in water content (Fig. 22). Excessively high water contents are found in highly diatomaceous sediments.

Carbonate content.—Two separate sets of meas

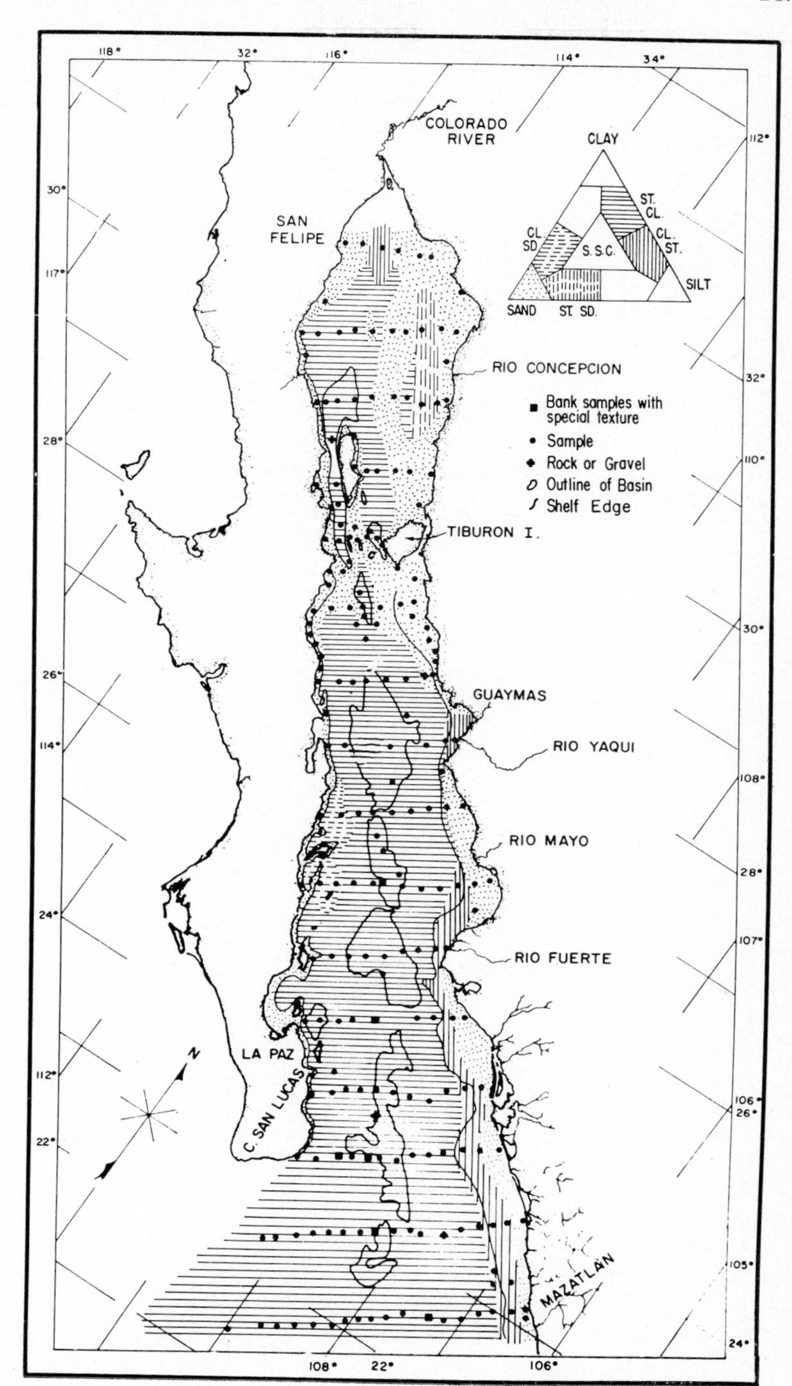

FIG. 21.—Regional distribution of textural types in the Gulf of California. Textural classification after Shepard (1954); See also Fig. 20.

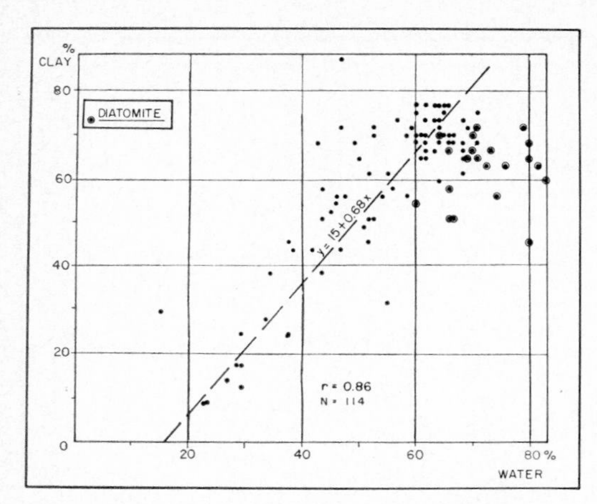

FIG. 22.—Relation between clay content (finer than 0.004 mm) and water content (per cent wet weight) of Gulf of California sediments. Diatomaceous samples circled. Correlation significant at one per cent level.

ures of the calcium carbonate content are available. (1) a weight percentage of coarse carbonate (0.80–0.06 mm) calculated from the coarse fraction analyses, and (2) a weight per cent of total carbonate, obtained by difference from two carbon analyses with a LECO[3] Carbon Determinator —one of the untreated sample, and one of an aliquot after treatment with 9.5% HCl. The computed coarse-carbonate weight percentages may show a large error if based on small-number percentages in a large coarse fraction.

The coarse-carbonate fraction contains Foraminifera ("foraminiferal carbonate") and a variety of other skeletal components, mainly Mollusca, algae, corals, and bryozoans ("skeletal carbonate").

Foraminiferal carbonate is an important constituent in the deposits of some submarine banks and hills, in some deep-water sands, and in slope deposits of the central Peninsular coast. It also occurs in modest amounts from 2 to 10 per cent in many shallow-water calcarenites.

Skeletal carbonate is an important constituent of all beach and shelf sands along the western side of the central and southern Gulf (Fig. 23), where the total amount of coarse carbonate commonly exceeds 25 per cent. Similar highly calcarenitic sands and calcarenites also occur elsewhere along steep and rocky coasts. Skeletal carbonate is most abundant in the coarsest fractions; above 0.25 mm, it may be the only constituent.

On the eastern shelf and in the northern Gulf, coarse carbonate is much less abundant. Moderately calcarenitic sand (5–10 per cent; mostly shell) occurs predominantly in areas remote from active deposition. In deep-water sediments, except in a few thin sand layers, coarse carbonate occurs in less than 1 per cent.

The total carbonate content ranges from 1 to 23 per cent, but from 96 samples only 6 contain less than 3 per cent, and 3 samples more than 17 per cent. The amount of total carbonate is independent of the size distribution of the samples (correlation with per cent clay: $r=0.15$, $N=96$; not significant at 5% level). In all fine-grained samples, the total amount of carbonate is far in excess of the coarse foraminiferal and skeletal material, and there is no correlation between the two variables (Fig. 24). Because few Foraminifera are smaller than 0.03 mm, the bulk of the fine carbonate probably consists of finely comminuted calcareous debris and of smaller calcareous organisms, such as coccoliths.

Highly calcareous silty clays (9–20 per cent) occur along the western slope of the Gulf from the Sal si Puedes Basin to Cape San Lucas (Fig. 23). In general, the floors of the adjacent basins, with the exception of the Sal si Puedes Basin, have a much lower carbonate content (3–8 per cent). Along the eastern slope, highly calcareous muds are much more localized and are restricted to areas where modern deposition probably is relatively slow.

The general distribution pattern thus suggests that relative rates of deposition control, at least in part, the amounts of both coarse and total carbonate. The principal areas of calcareous sediments seem to be the result of a restricted supply of terrigenous material.

Biogenous silica.—Many Gulf of California sediments, particularly those of the central and southern areas, contain appreciable quantities of biogenous opal in the form of radiolarian skeletons and diatom frustules and fragments. Weight percentages of coarse (larger than 0.03 mm) biogenous opal can be calculated from coarse-fraction

[3] Laboratory Equipment Corporation, St. Joseph, Michigan.

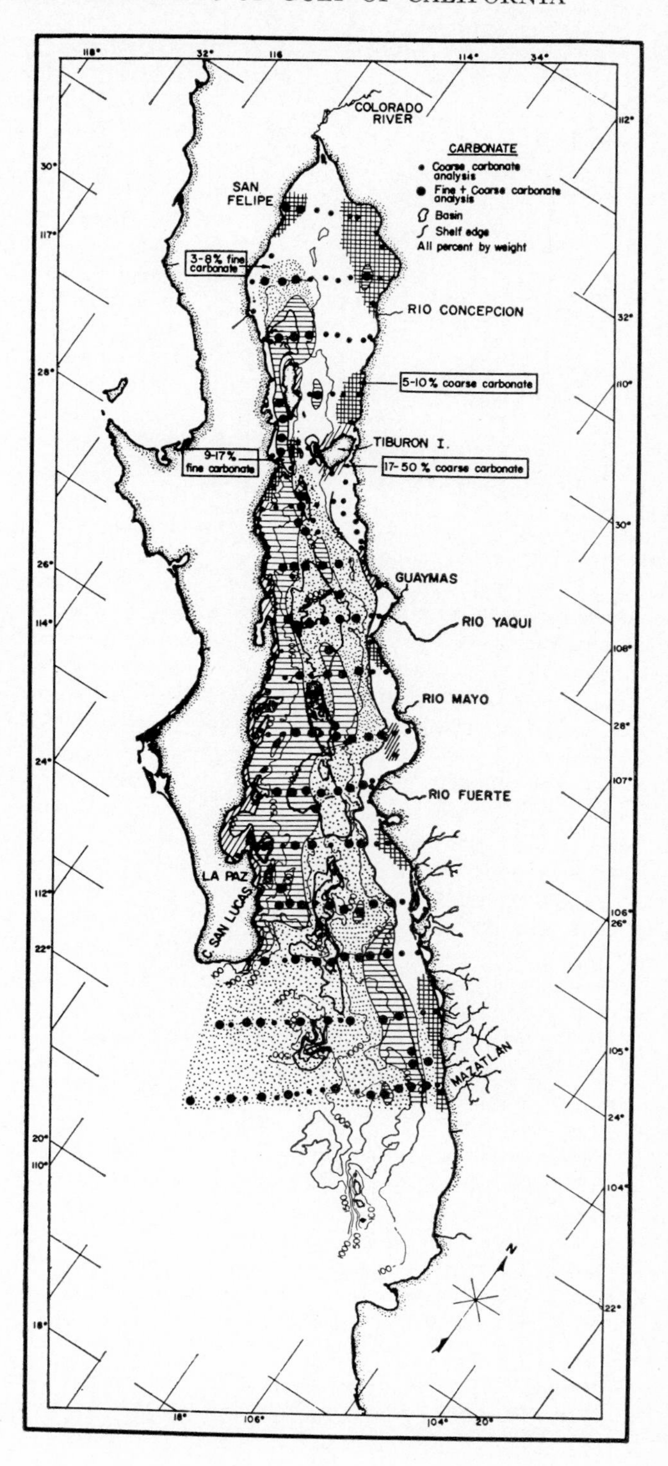

FIG. 23.—Regional distribution of coarse carbonate (0.06–2.00 mm) and total carbonate in the Gulf of California, in per cent by weight of the total sample. Coarse carbonate is most prominent on the shelf, particularly along the western side; fine carbonate is concentrated on the western slope, but low in the basins. Depth contours in fathoms.

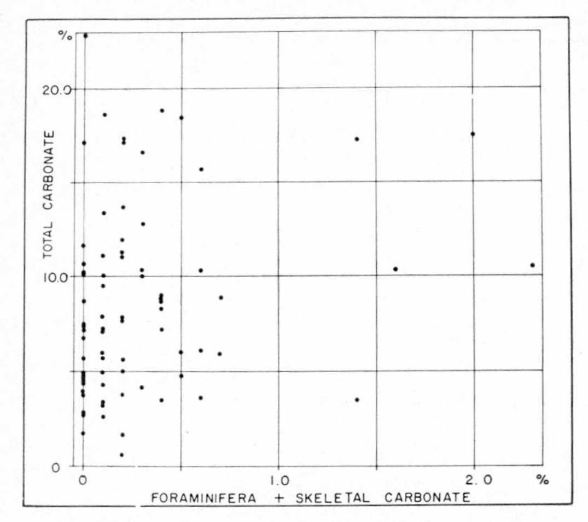

FIG. 24.—Relation between percentage by weight of coarse (0.06–2.00 mm) and total carbonate in Gulf of California samples. No significant correlation.

counts. The accuracy of these computed values is low, especially for low-number percentages. Calvert (in preparation) has carried out quantitative analyses of opal in Gulf of California samples, using a method based on conversion of opal into cristobalite (Goldberg, 1958). The results of this investigation, not complete at this time, show that the total amount of opal may be as much as 10 to 30 times larger than the amount of coarse opal. Apparently, a very large portion of the opal consists of very finely comminuted or very small diatoms. The proportion between total and coarse opal may vary in dependence of the predominant organisms. Consequently, the distribution map of coarse silica (Fig. 25) represents the distribution of only a small fraction of the total opal in the sediments, but may be used as a first approximation.

Coarse biogenous silica is concentrated primarily on the slopes of the southern and central Gulf and is scarce or absent on the basin floors. The narrow San Pedro Martir and Sal si Puedes Basins, which are close to steep slopes, are exceptions. The largest amounts of opal are found on the western slopes; on the eastern slope the distribution is more irregular and the maximum values are lower, certainly because of a higher dilution with terrigenous material. South of lat 26° N., the silica is almost exclusively radiolarian; north of this parallel, it is predominantly diatomaceous, although in most samples appreciable numbers of Radiolaria occur. Significant quantities of diatoms are found in a few nearshore areas, particularly along the western side of the Gulf.

Glauconite.—Glauconite is a fairly common constituent of Gulf of California sediments; more than 50 per cent of all samples contain trace amounts, and 30 per cent of the samples have more than 0.1 per cent by weight as calculated from coarse-fraction analyses. In incident light, the grains vary from pale yellowish green to an almost blackish green, with a bright emerald green as the prevailing color. In thin section, the grains are mostly bright green, some with enclosed terrigenous particles. A variety of shapes can be found, such as ovoid, botryoidal, coprolithic, irregular, or angular fragmental. A substantial portion—1–30 per cent—consists of casts of Foraminifera, many partially or entirely surrounded by the tests. Probably some of the irregular and fragmental grains also are foraminiferal. Large amounts of foraminiferal glauconite have been reported from many neritic sediments of slow deposition (for example, Curray, 1960, p. 244; van Andel and Postma, 1954, p. 186; Pratt, 1962).

Glauconite is concentrated in the 0.06–0.25 mm fraction. In some deep-water sediments, 30–50 per cent of the grains coarser than 0.25 mm also may be glauconitic; in shallow-water sediments, large glauconite grains are rare.

The occurrence of glauconite is positively correlated with sediment texture, as is shown by the first tabulation on page 251.

The depth range of glauconite in the Gulf of California is great—much greater than the 10–400-fathom range given by Cloud (1955), as the second tabulation on page 251 indicates.

The largest area of glauconitic sediments, containing from 1.0–2.8 per cent of glauconite by weight, occurs in the northern Gulf in intermediate depths (Fig. 26) in a zone which is largely nondepositional. Only where deposition is fairly rapid is the mineral entirely absent, or present only in low values. Shelf glauconite also is found in the southern Gulf, again predominantly outside areas of active deposition. However, on the western shelf, where deposition rates also are slow, neritic glauconite occurs only sporadically. In

Tabulation 1:

sand, silty sand, clayey sand	43 samples	average 2.3% glauconite
sand-silt-clay	7 samples	average 0.8% glauconite
clayey silt, silty clay, clay	12 samples	average 0.4% glauconite

Tabulation 2:

0–10 fathoms	13 samples with more than 0.1% glauconite
11–50 fathoms	19 samples with more than 0.1% glauconite
51–400 fathoms	15 samples with more than 0.1% glauconite
401–1,000 fathoms	8 samples with more than 0.1% glauconite
>1,000 fathoms	7 samples with more than 0.1% glauconite

deep water, glauconite occurrences are very localized and are restricted mostly to banks, where the percentages may be very large.

Minor sedimentary structures.—The basic primary structures of water-laid sediments are horizontal bedding, cross-bedding, and homogeneous structure. No cross-bedding has been observed in the Gulf of California cores, but horizontal layering occurs in three ways (Fig. 27)—bedded sand; interbedded sand and mud; and finely laminated, commonly biogenous muds. After deposition, these primary structures may be partially or entirely destroyed by the activity of burrowing organisms, resulting in the formation of secondary structures—irregular bedding, mottling, and secondary homogenization (Fig. 27, R-173, R-204, R-214). Preservation of primary structures is furthered by a high rate of deposition or by an absence of benthonic life.

Thin sand layers interbedded with homogeneous deep-water silty clay occur in the deep Gulf (Fig. 27, R-11). More disturbed deposits with irregular layering and mottling (Fig. 27, R-173) are locally found on submarine hills and banks. In some instances the entire core consists of well-bedded, coarse sand layers, some of which are graded (Fig. 27, R-150). All these deposits will be discussed in detail later.

An interesting type of primary structure is represented by finely laminated, generally highly diatomaceous sediments in the central Gulf (Fig. 27, R-151). These cores consist of sequences of alternating light diatomaceous and dark, more clayey layers, averaging 2.5 mm in thickness. The lamination has been explained by Revelle (1950) and by Byrne and Emery (1960) as the result of seasonal fluctuations in diatom productivity (*see also* Hülsemann and Emery, 1961). The laminated diatomites are similar to many Tertiary diatomites in California and form the subject of a detailed study by S.E. Calvert (this volume), to which the reader is referred for further discussion.

Although some diatomite cores show undisturbed lamination throughout, occasional intervals provide evidence of temporary periods of increased burrowing, as also is observed in the Santa Barbara Basin, Southern California (Hülsemann and Emery, 1961). The horizontal extent of individual layers or groups of layers is not known, but it is probably small, inasmuch as correlation between a group of closely spaced cores (approximately 1-mile spacings) proves impossible.

The few laminated cores available for this paper came from depths between 250 and 800 fathoms in the central Gulf. Laminated, nondiatomaceous clays and silts occur locally (Fig. 27, R-17) on the slopes of the southern Gulf. The majority of all deep-water cores are homogeneous. Slightly mottled intervals can sometimes be observed, and some of the homogeneous sediments may be secondary.

Secondary structures, consisting of disturbed layering and mottling, are very common in the sandy neritic sediments of the eastern continental shelf and of the northern Gulf. All stages of transformation, from barely disrupted bedding to complete homogenization, can be observed (Fig. 27, R-204, R-214). Curray (1960) states that the sandy littoral sediments deposited in the 10–65 fathom zone of the Gulf of Mexico by the post-Pleistocene transgression are commonly characterized by such structures. Their distribution in the Gulf of California agrees with this observation and suggests that, in large parts of the northern Gulf, nondepositional conditions prevail.

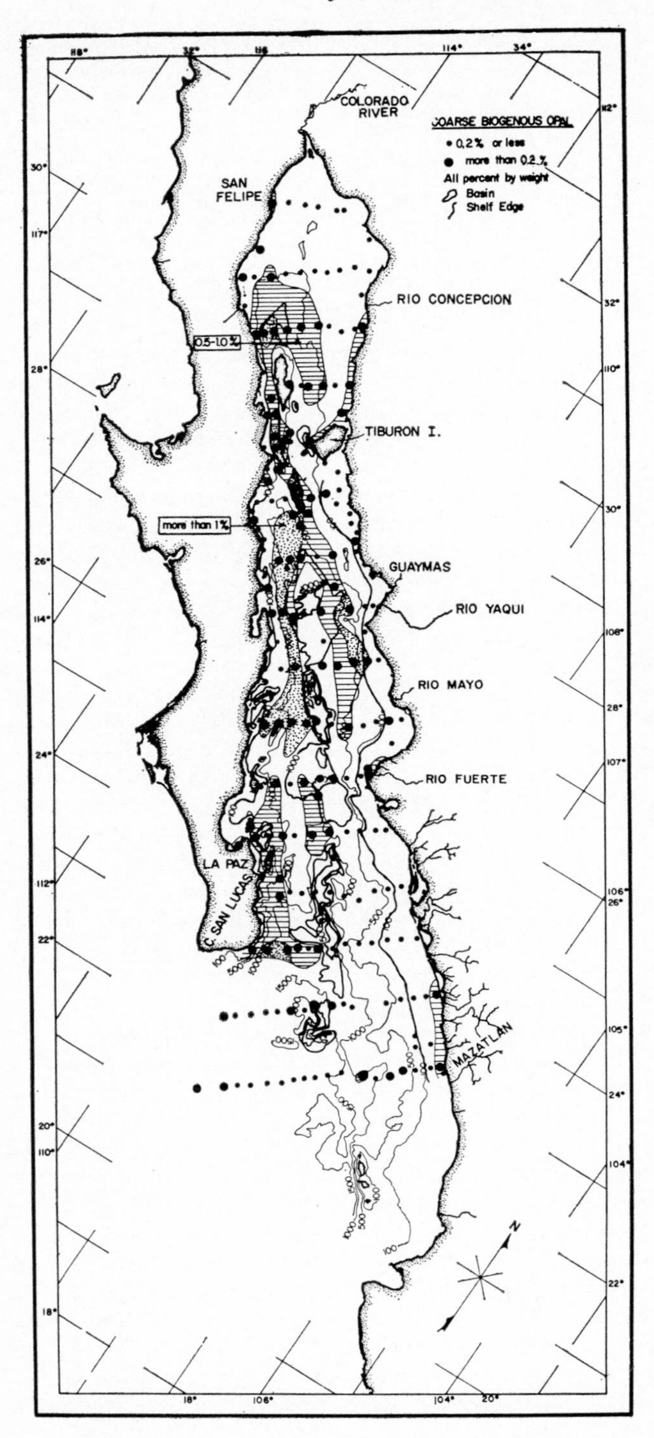

FIG. 25.—Regional distribution of coarse biogenous opal in the Gulf of California, in per cent by weight of the total sample. Dotted pattern: more than 1 per cent; horizontal shading: 0.5–1.0 per cent. Coarse opal is concentrated on continental slopes. Depth contours in fathoms.

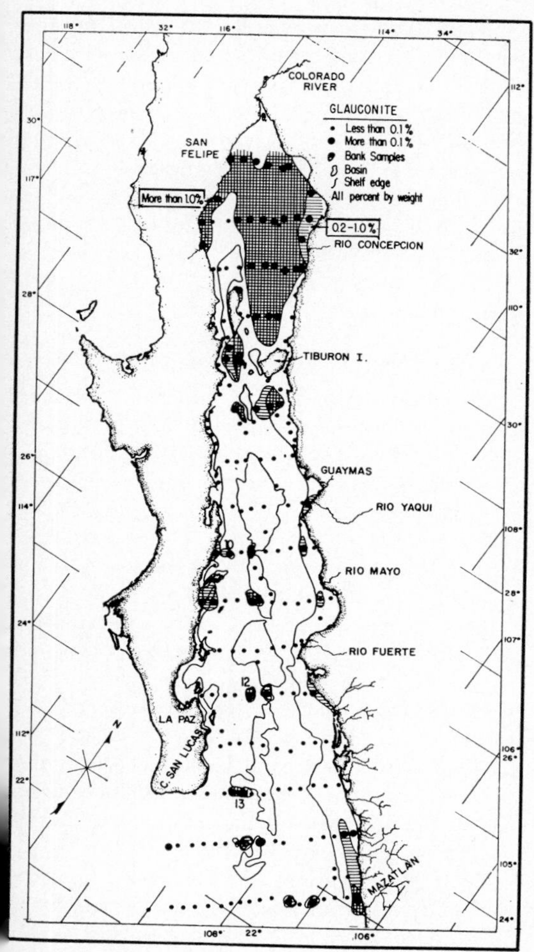

FIG. 26.—Regional distribution of glauconite in the Gulf of California, in per cent by weight of the total sample. High amounts occur locally on banks in the southern Gulf; smaller but more widely spread percentages are found on the continental shelf and in the northern Gulf.

LITHOFACIES DISTRIBUTION

On the basis of the sediment properties discussed above, the system below has been devised for the classification of all Gulf of California samples. The principal sediment name is derived from the texture of the sample by Shepard's (1954) sand-silt-clay classification, except that the term *calcarenite* replaces *sand* where the coarse fraction contains more than 25 per cent by weight of foraminiferal and skeletal carbonate combined. The sediment name is preceded, in order of increasing quantitative importance, by qualifiers derived from several important components. A color description and a description of minor structures are added. With only very minor generalization, these sediment types can be grouped into a small number of mappable categories, listed in the caption of Figure 28.

Fine-grained sediments predominate, particularly in the southern and central Gulf. More than half of these deposits are diatomaceous. The diatomites begin north of the Fuerte River as slope deposits, but they soon widen to include nearly the entire central Gulf below the edge of the continental shelf. They continue well into the northern Gulf.

In the southern Gulf, biogenous silica production evidently is much lower with respect to terrigenous sediment supply, and silty clays predominate both on the slopes and in the basins. Silty clays also fringe the deep-water portion of the Sal si Puedes Basin in the northern Gulf and occur in some of the deepest parts east of Angel de la Guarda Island. A fan-shaped area of silty clay off the Yaqui River probably represents the distal portion of the deltaic bottomset beds.

Sandy foraminiferal and radiolarian sediments are found on and around isolated hills and banks. More of these deposits probably exist, but only a few banks have been sampled. On the rugged and complex western slope north of La Paz, coarse, locally highly glauconitic, foraminiferal calcarenites are found which are similar to bank sediments, but contain less clay and silt. Their depth range extends from the shelf edge to approxi-

Qualifier	*Weight Per Cent*
glauconite	0.2– 2.0% glauconite
very glauconitic	>2.0% glauconite
diatomaceous or radiolarian	0.2– 2.0% biogenous silica
very diatomaceous or radiolarian (depending on predominance)	>2.0% biogenous silica
foraminiferal or calcarenitic	2.0–10.5% coarse carbonate
very foraminiferal or calcarenitic (depending on predominance)	10.6–25.0% coarse carbonate

mately 300 fathoms; they are commonly layered and show ample evidence of down-slope displacement.

A rather extensive area of coarse sands and gravels that are highly volcanic in composition is found north and south of the sills separating the Sal si Puedes Basin from the central Gulf. The complex lithology of this area is inadequately represented by the available samples. Much finer and more uniform sands occur southeast of Tiburón Island to a depth of 300 fathoms.

The sediments of the eastern and western shelves of the central and southern Gulf are markedly different. The narrow western shelf is covered with coarse, very calcareous sands and calcarenites; the deposits abruptly changed into calcareous silty clays at the edge of the shelf. Such sediments are absent from the eastern shelf except in a few places where the coast is mountainous and the shelf rocky and narrow. The other deposits of the eastern shelf are also sandy, but the sands are not so coarse and generally are not very calcareous. Almost everywhere, a transitional zone of clayey silt is well developed on the outer shelf and upper slope. Similar clayey silts occur off the Colorado and Concepción River deltas.

These clayey silts are separated almost everywhere from the coast and the rivers that supplied the material by a wide belt of glauconitic and foraminiferal sand, commonly mottled in structure. Two main types of this sand, which are different in glauconite content and in the absence or presence of mottled structures, can be distinguished. Similar sands occupy a very large, shallow area in the northern Gulf and are considered equivalent to Curray's (1960) basal transgressive deposits, which are exposed in nondepositional areas of the Gulf of Mexico. The sands southeast of Tiburón Island are different from all other shelf sands in the general absence of glauconite and calcareous components.

On the basis of gross lithology alone, it appears possible to distinguish between a fairly large number of depositional environments. In following chapters, with additional data, this picture of sedimentary facies will be further developed.

BIOGENOUS DEPOSITS OF THE GULF OF CALIFORNIA

The observations of the previous chapter indicate the abundance of biogenous sediments in the Gulf, and tentatively suggest that some biogenous components are concentrated on the slopes rather than in the basins, and that the amounts of biogenous material increase from the entrance toward the central Gulf. It is the purpose of this chapter to examine in more detail the properties and distribution of the biogenous components, and to discuss their origin. The genesis of the laminated diatomites will be mentioned only briefly as they form the subject of a separate study by S.E. Calvert (this volume).

COARSE-FRACTION BIOGENOUS COMPONENTS

The weight per cent data for opal and carbonat used in the previous chapter do not distinguis between different types of organisms, and, be cause the coarse fraction forms only a very smal part of most deep-water sediments, they do no sensitively reflect variations. The original per centage counts by number of several size fraction are not subject to these limitations.

The regional distribution map of Radiolari (Fig. 29) shows (1) that percentages are hig outside the Gulf and decrease from the Pacifi toward the upper Gulf, (2) Radiolaria are concen trated on the slopes rather than on basin floors particularly in the central Gulf, and (3) the per centages are reduced in areas of rapid depositio as, for example, around Cape San Lucas and o the Fuerte and Yaqui River deltas.

With few exceptions, the Radiolaria form les than one per cent by weight of the Gulf sediment In deep-water deposits outside the Gulf and i slope sediments of the southern Gulf, however, u to 50 per cent of the coarse fraction may consist c Radiolaria, except where dilution with terrigenou material is high. In the central Gulf, they ar important only in slope deposits, and their pe centage is much reduced because of the high fr quency of diatoms. In the north-central an northern basins, Radiolaria are restricted to th fine-grained sediments of the deepest parts; no mally they are absent in the coarser sediment the zone above 200–300 fathoms, because of dil tion with terrigenous sand. The diatoms a quantitatively much more important than th Radiolaria, and, according to Calvert (person communication), they may constitute up to 50 p cent of the sediments of the central Gulf. Coar diatoms form but a small portion of the whol The regional distribution pattern (Fig. 30) sho

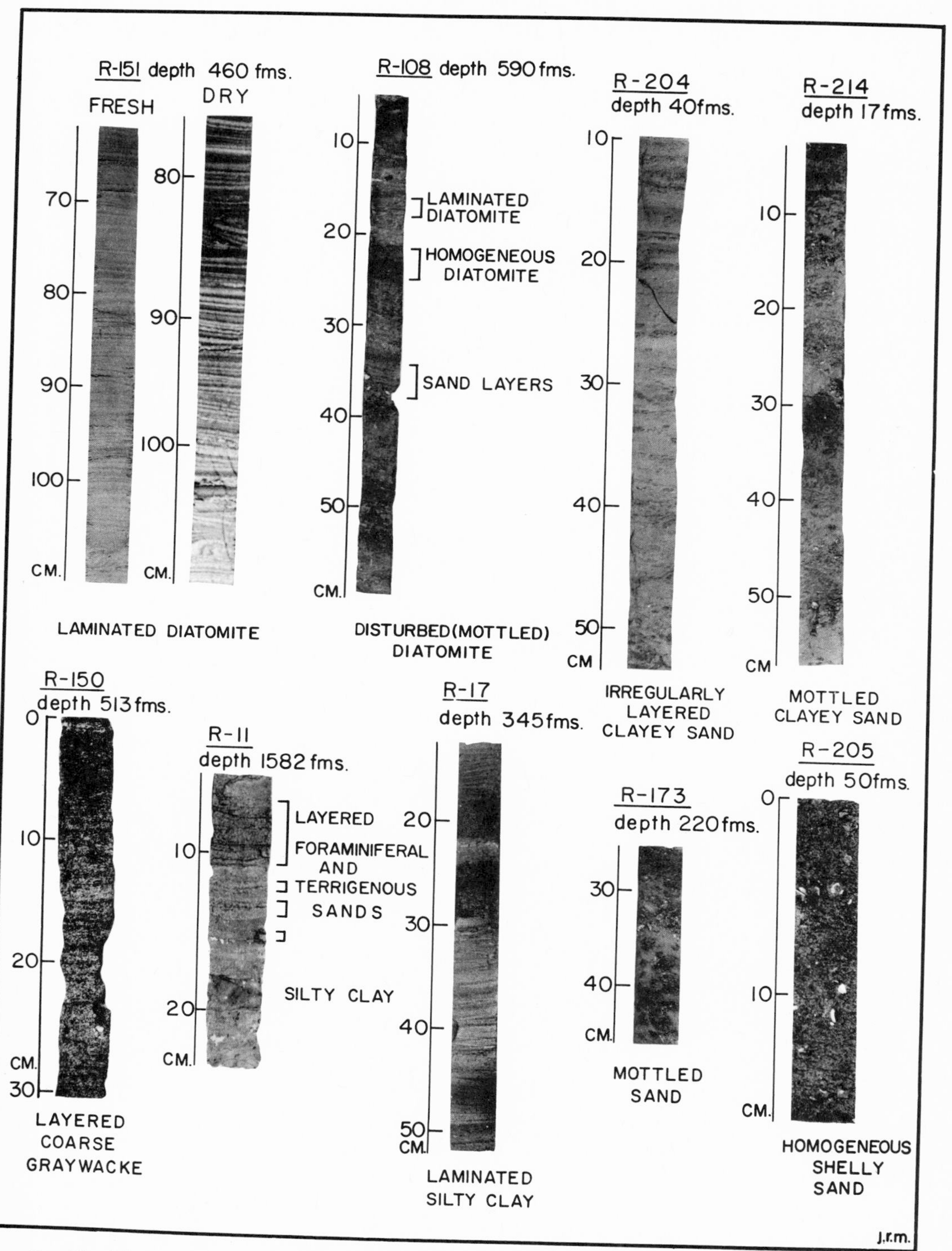

FIG. 27.—Minor structures of the Gulf of California sediments. Terminology after Moore and Scruton (1957). R-11, R-108, R-150, and R-205 from glue peels, the others from split, slightly dried cores. Sample locations in Fig. 1.

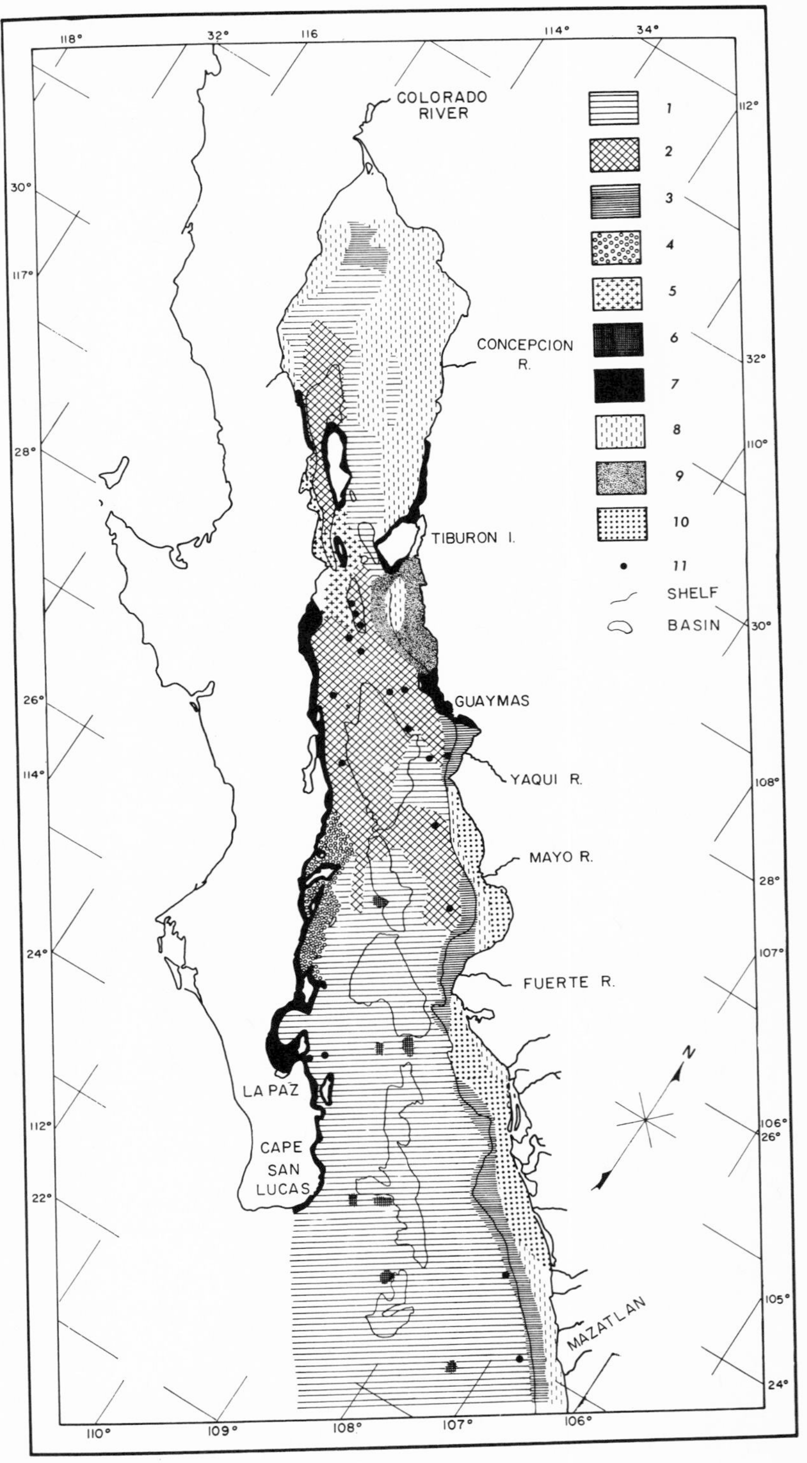

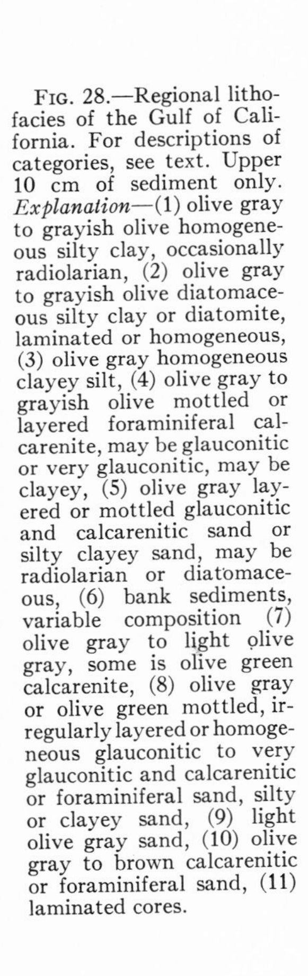
FIG. 28.—Regional lithofacies of the Gulf of California. For descriptions of categories, see text. Upper 10 cm of sediment only. *Explanation*—(1) olive gray to grayish olive homogeneous silty clay, occasionally radiolarian, (2) olive gray to grayish olive diatomaceous silty clay or diatomite, laminated or homogeneous, (3) olive gray homogeneous clayey silt, (4) olive gray to grayish olive mottled or layered foraminiferal calcarenite, may be glauconitic or very glauconitic, may be clayey, (5) olive gray layered or mottled glauconitic and calcarenitic sand or silty clayey sand, may be radiolarian or diatomaceous, (6) bank sediments, variable composition (7) olive gray to light olive gray, some is olive green calcarenite, (8) olive gray or olive green mottled, irregularly layered or homogeneous glauconitic to very glauconitic and calcarenitic or foraminiferal sand, silty or clayey sand, (9) light olive gray sand, (10) olive gray to brown calcarenitic or foraminiferal sand, (11) laminated cores.

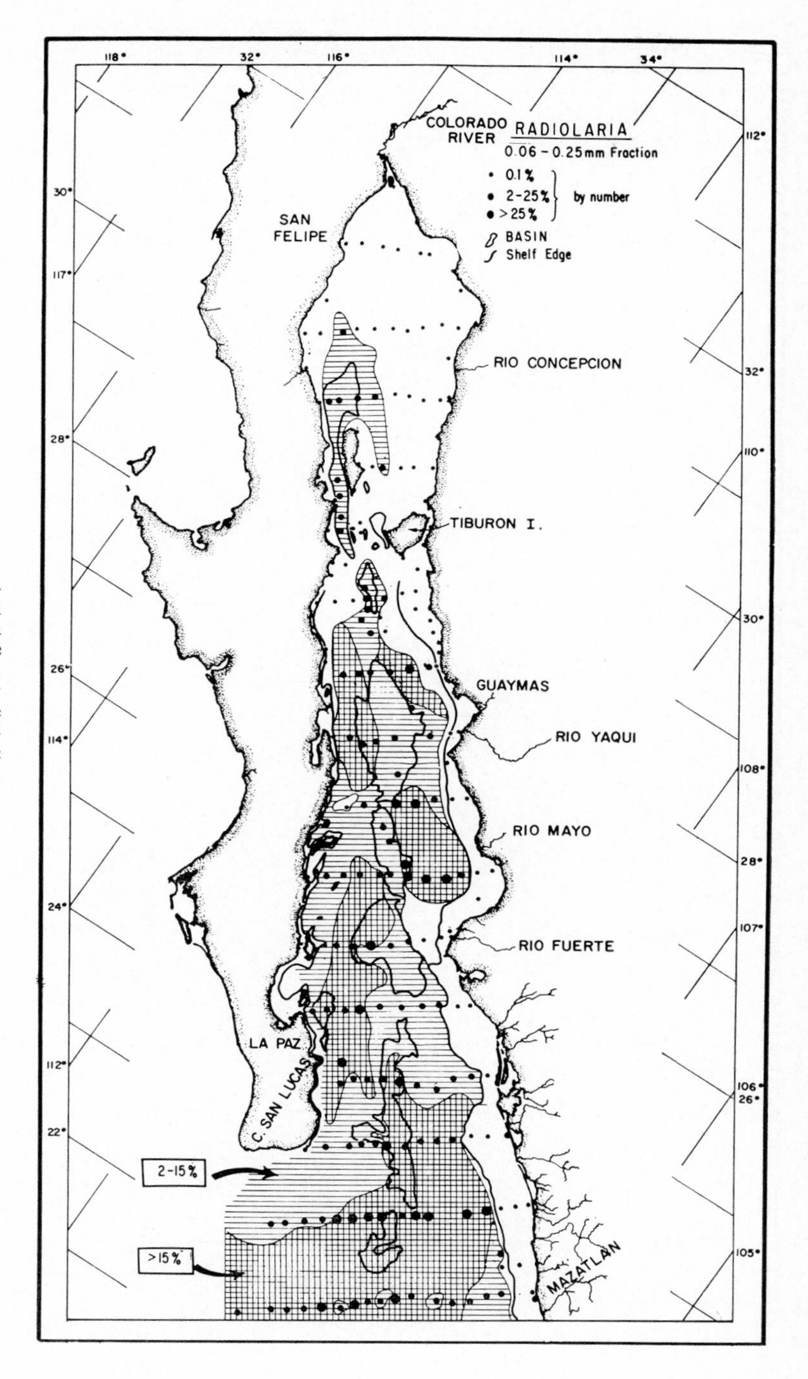

FIG. 29—Regional distribution of Radiolaria in the Gulf of California, in per cent by number of the 0.06–0.25 mm fraction. Horizontal lines—2–15 per cent; cross-hatching—more than 15 per cent. Note concentration in open Pacific and on continental slopes.

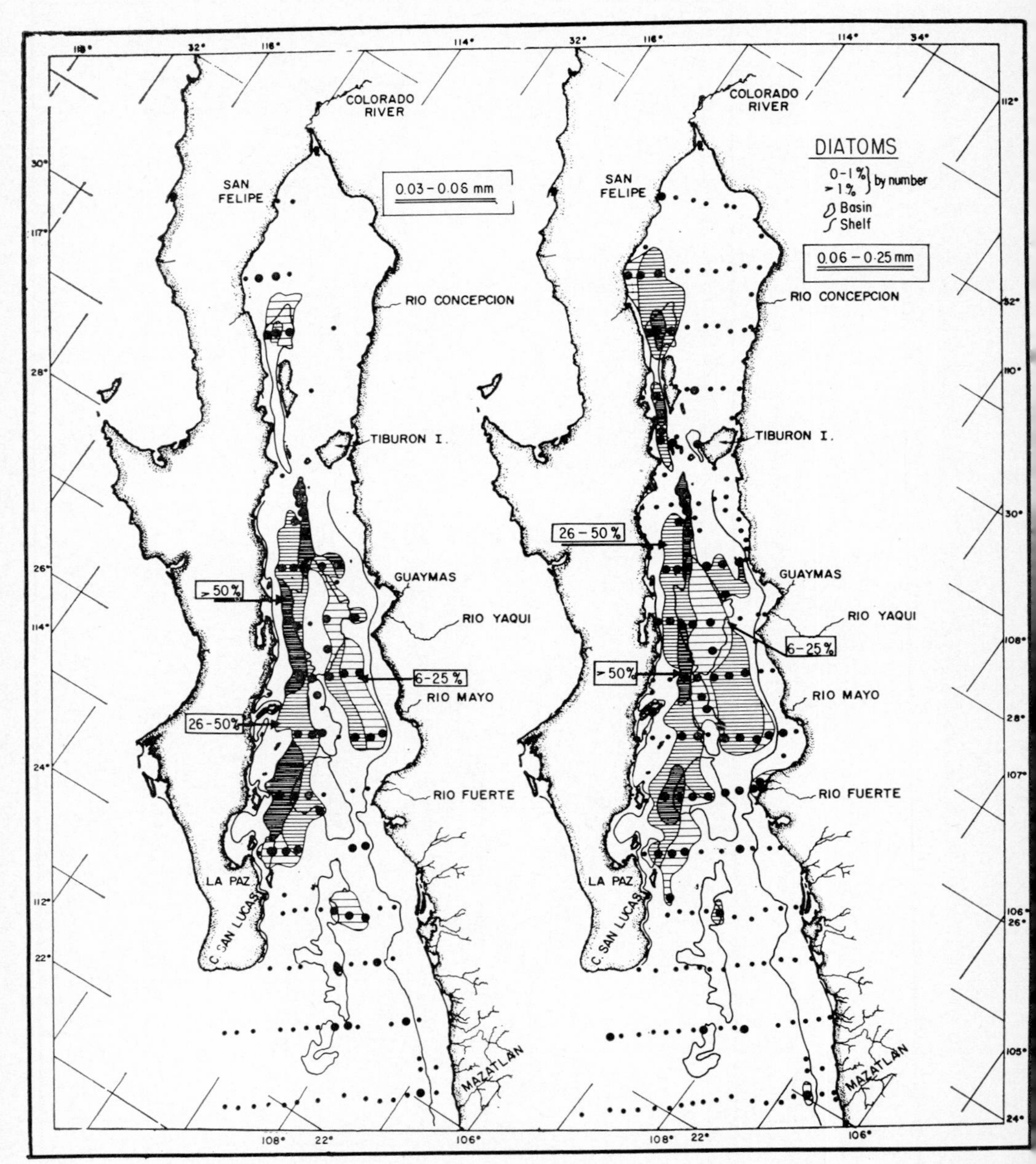

FIG. 30.—Regional distribution of diatoms in the Gulf of California, in per cent by number of the 0.03–0.06 and 0.06–0.25 mm fractions. Lightest shading—6–25 per cent; intermediate shading—26–50 per cent; darkest shading—more than 50 per cent. Diatoms are highly concentrated on slopes.

that the entire southern and central Gulf region can be subdivided in a southern radiolarian and a northern diatomaceous province. In the southern and central Gulf, the concentration of the diatom percentages on the slopes is marked. On the western side, diatomaceous deposits, with percentages ranging between 25 and 50 and locally up to 65, are continuous between La Paz and the northern Gulf. On the eastern side, a diatomaceous slope zone begins north of the Fuerte River delta but is interrupted off the Yaqui River delta, and terminates north of Guaymas. The percentages are lower than on the western side, because of dilution with terrigenous sand. In the north-central and northern Gulf, the situation is reversed; the fine-grained deposits of the basins contain large numbers of diatoms, whereas the sandy slope deposits are barren. The coarse fractions of shelf and near-shore areas only locally contain significant percentages of diatoms, and their distribution is irregular.

In contrast to the diatoms, the Foraminifera occur principally in the coarse fraction. In several places, they contribute important amounts of material to the Gulf sediments. Planktonic Foraminifera are widespread in the Gulf (Fig. 31), except near Cape San Lucas, on the sandy slopes of the north-central Gulf, and in shelf areas. Their distribution is very uniform, and large numbers occur only in a few isolated places. In contrast, benthonic Foraminifera are most abundant on slope areas. The highest and most uniform values occur along the western slope; the distribution along the eastern slope is more patchy. In the basins of the central and southern Gulf, benthonic forms are almost absent. On the continental shelves, benthonic Foraminifera are not very abundant, except in the northern Gulf where they are widespread both in deep and shallow water. Normally, benthonic Foraminifera decrease in abundance with increasing water depth. The relative maximum on the slopes of the Gulf of California is the result of an even more rapid decrease of coarse terrigenous components. Bandy (1961) has shown the presence of several depth zones in the Foraminifera distribution and has drawn attention to the existence of numerous displaced faunas in the slope region.

ORGANIC MATTER

Determinations of organic carbon and nitrogen have been made on approximately 100 Gulf of California core samples (Appendix B) at the 9–10 cm level. Organic carbon determinations were made using a LECO Carbon Determinator. The samples were treated with 9.5 per cent hydrochloric acid to remove carbonates, dried at 100°C and oxidized in an induction furnace at 1,480°C, using tin and iron accelerators. The carbon dioxide was filtered to remove sulfur gases, and measured gasometrically. This method allows rapid and precise (reproducibility approximately 0.02 per cent carbon) determination of carbon in very small samples. Nitrogen was determined by a micro-Kjeldahl technique.

The carbon content of the Gulf samples is positively correlated with the amount of clay in the samples (Fig. 32). Inspection of samples with comparable clay content suggests, however, that factors other than grain size control the variability. This is illustrated by Figure 33, which shows that the largest amounts of carbon are found in intermediate depths on the slopes of the southern and central Gulf. Low values occur in sediments outside the Gulf entrance and in the deep basins of the Gulf itself. Very high values—up to 7 per cent by dry weight—occur on the slope south of Mazatlán and along the southwestern Gulf margin; intermediate values occur on the other slopes of the southern and central Gulf. The data suggest that the shelves represent another area low in carbon, but the values are influenced by the very low clay content of many samples. In order to solve this problem, a trend surface analysis of carbon in dependence of clay content and water depth (Miller, 1956; Krumbein, 1959) has been carried out through the courtesy of H. Slack and M.A. Rosenfeld of the Pure Oil Company Research Center, Crystal Lake, Illinois. Samples from the southern Gulf only were utilized (R-1 to R-99). The results of this analysis are shown in Figure 34. The linear surface, represented by $C=-1.958-0.00137D+0.102S$ (C=per cent organic carbon, D=depth in fathoms, S=per cent clay), has a large standard deviation of ± 1.26, with respect to the average carbon content of 3.33 per cent and range of from 0.64 to 7.44 per cent.

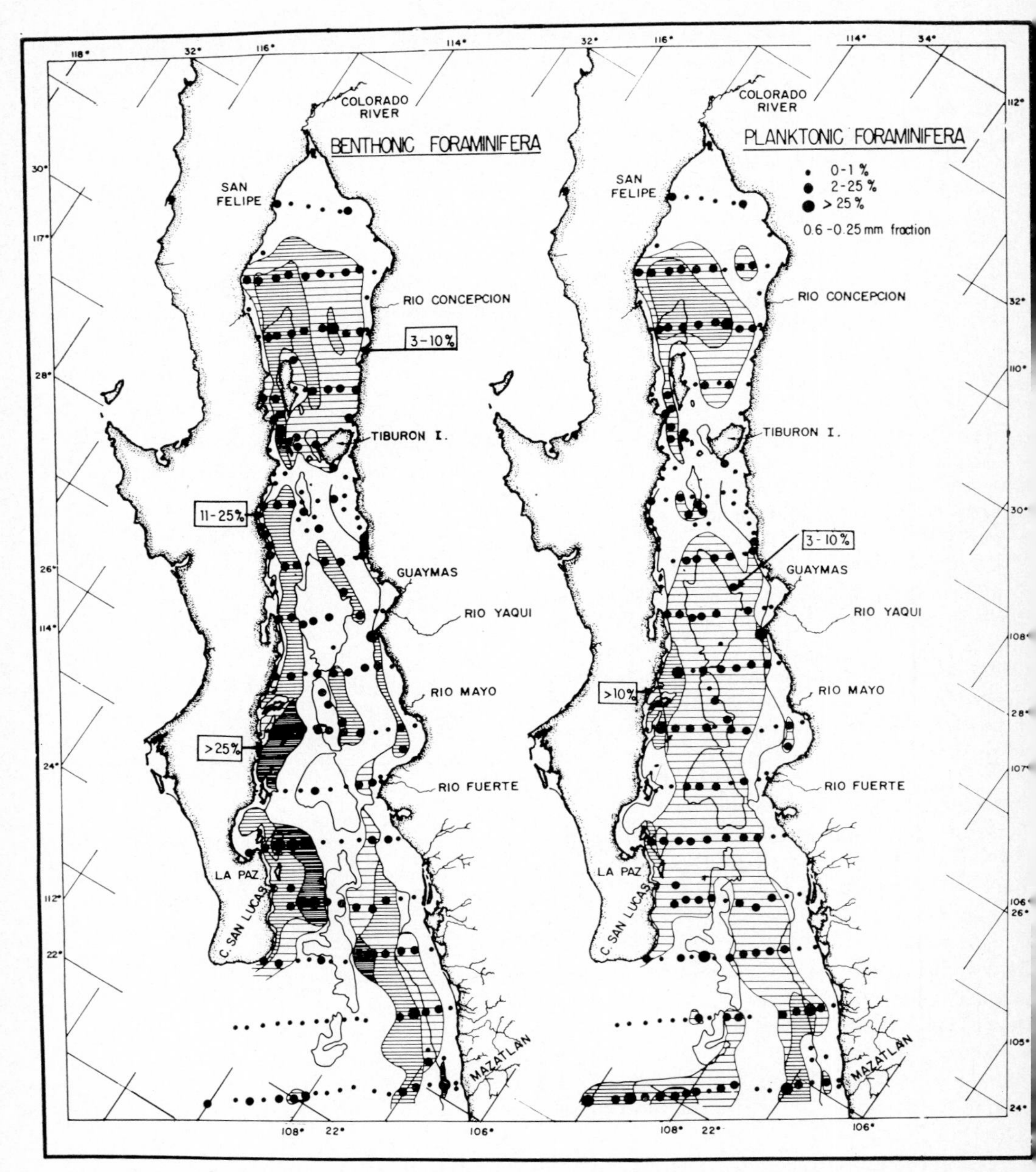

FIG. 31.—Regional distribution of benthonic and planktonic Foraminifera in the Gulf of California, in per cent by number of the 0.06–0.25 mm fraction. Light shading—3–10 per cent; intermediate shading—11–25 per cent (benthonic Foraminifera) or more than 10 per cent (planktonic Foraminifera); darkest shading—more than 25 per cent. Planktonic forms are uniformly distributed; benthonic Foraminifera are concentrated on slopes.

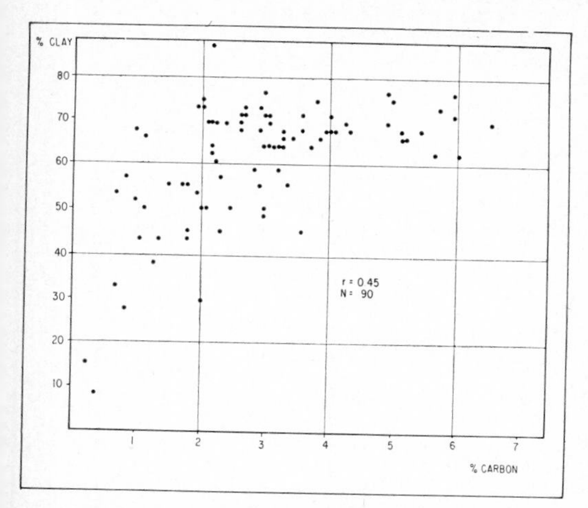

FIG. 32.—Relation between per cent organic carbon and per cent clay (finer than 0.004 mm) in Gulf of California sediments. Correlation significant at one per cent level.

The anomalies associated with the linear surface are in part distributed in a geologically meaningful manner. A somewhat better fit is obtained with the quadratic surface—$C=-1.55+0.0075D + 0.028S - 0.00078DS - 0.000022D^2 + 0.0008S^2$ with a standard deviation of ± 1.07 and randomly distributed anomalies. Figure 34 shows that there is a high carbon maximum, independent of grain size, in water depths of approximately 300–800 fathoms. A clear minimum is found below 1,000 fathoms. Another minimum may exist in shallow water above the shelf edge. Thus, the organic carbon distribution appears to possess the same concentration on slopes that is found for other previously discussed biogenous constituents. The concentration is less well defined in the central Gulf. Undoubtedly water depth is a secondary variable, and the primary factors probably are the rates of organic productivity, deposition, and decomposition, which cannot be assessed quantitatively.

The average carbon content of Gulf samples of slopes and basins is compared (Table X) with the carbon contents of other recent marine sediments. The Gulf of California values are strikingly high, even in comparison with as high a productivity region as the Peru-Chile Trench, and are comparable only to those of the offshore basins of Southern California and the highly productive Baltic Sea. Higher values are found only under very special conditions.

As is generally the case in recent sediments, carbon content is well correlated with nitrogen (Fig. 35). The regression function, $C=1.46N^{1.6}$ (C=carbon; N=nitrogen), is similar to the one obtained by Arrhenius (1950) for a large group of samples from a variety of marine environments ($C=46.8N^{1.3}$). With the exception of a few extreme values, the C/N ratios range from 6.1 to 18.3, with a median value of 8.8. In a study of

TABLE X. ORGANIC CARBON CONTENT OF RECENT MARINE SEDIMENTS

Area	*Per Cent Organic Carbon*		*Reference*
	Average	*Range*	
Gulf of California			
slope	3.60	0.8–7.4	
basins	2.55	0.4–4.0	
Gulf of Paria	0.71	0.1–1.4	van Andel and Postma, 1954
Mississippi Delta	0.61	0.1–1.3	unpublished data, API 51
Aransas Bay, Texas	1.26	0.6–1.7	unpublished data, API 51
San Antonio Bay, Texas	0.82	0.3–2.7	unpublished data, API 51
California offshore basins	4.32	—	Emery and Rittenberg, 1952
Gulf of Mexico shelf	0.36 (median)	—	Trask, 1953
Gulf of Mexico slope	0.82 (median)	—	Trask, 1953
Sigsbee Deep	0.47 (median)	—	Trask, 1953
Abidjan Lagoon, W. Africa	6.43	4.5–12.8	Debyser, 1961
Arcachon Basin, France	2.07	0.3–5.2	Debyser, 1961
Baltic Sea	2.55	2.3–4.8	Debyser, 1961
Bengal shelf	0.77	0.2–1.6	Rao, 1960
Peru-Chile Trench, basin	0.67	0.1–0.9	Trask, 1961
slope	1.92	0.3–9.6	Trask, 1961

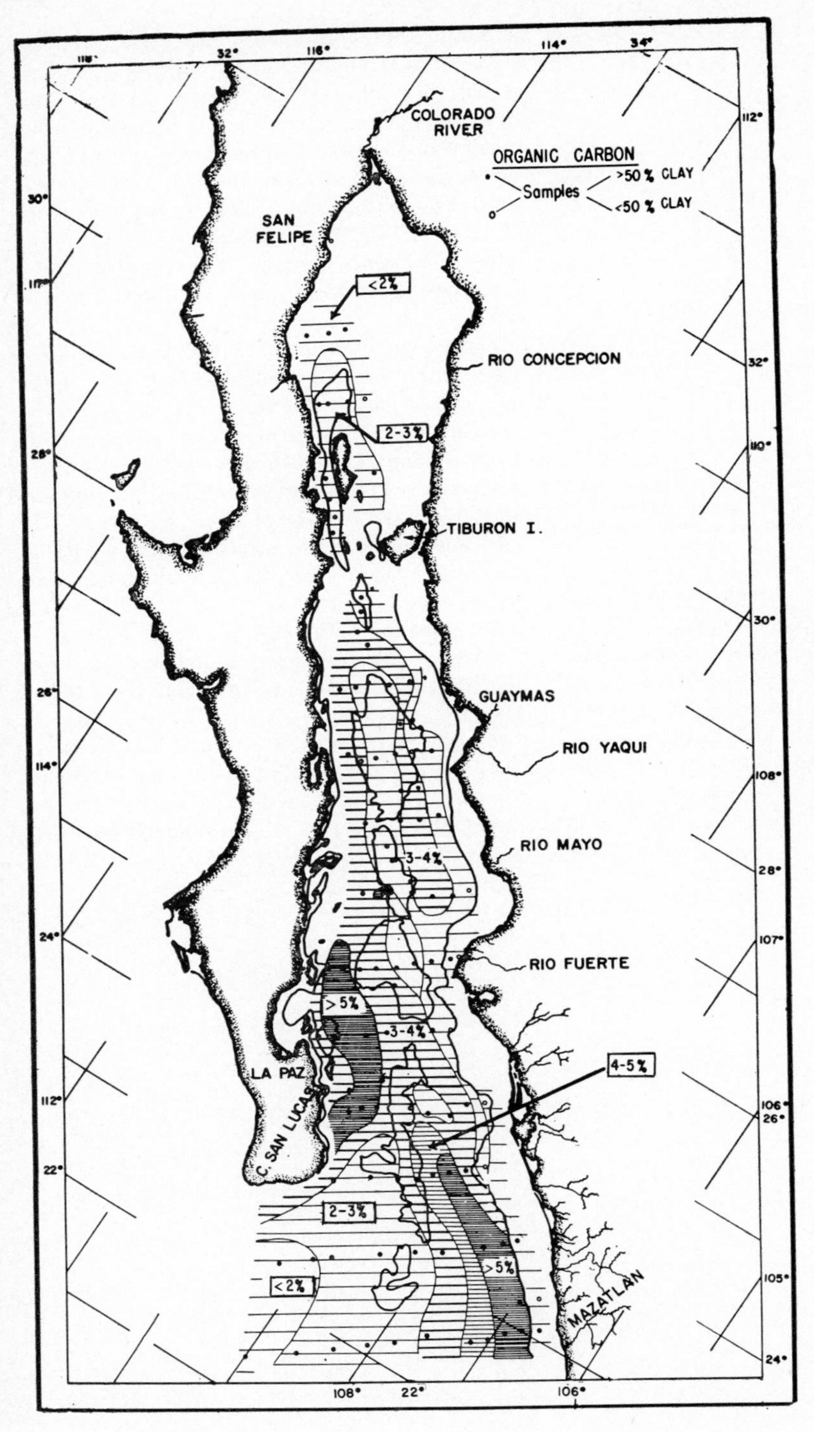

FIG. 33—Regional distribution of organic carbon in Gulf of California sediments in per cent by weight of dry sample. Samples with less than 50 per cent clay have low organic-carbon content and are shown with separate symbol. Organic carbon is concentrated on slopes.

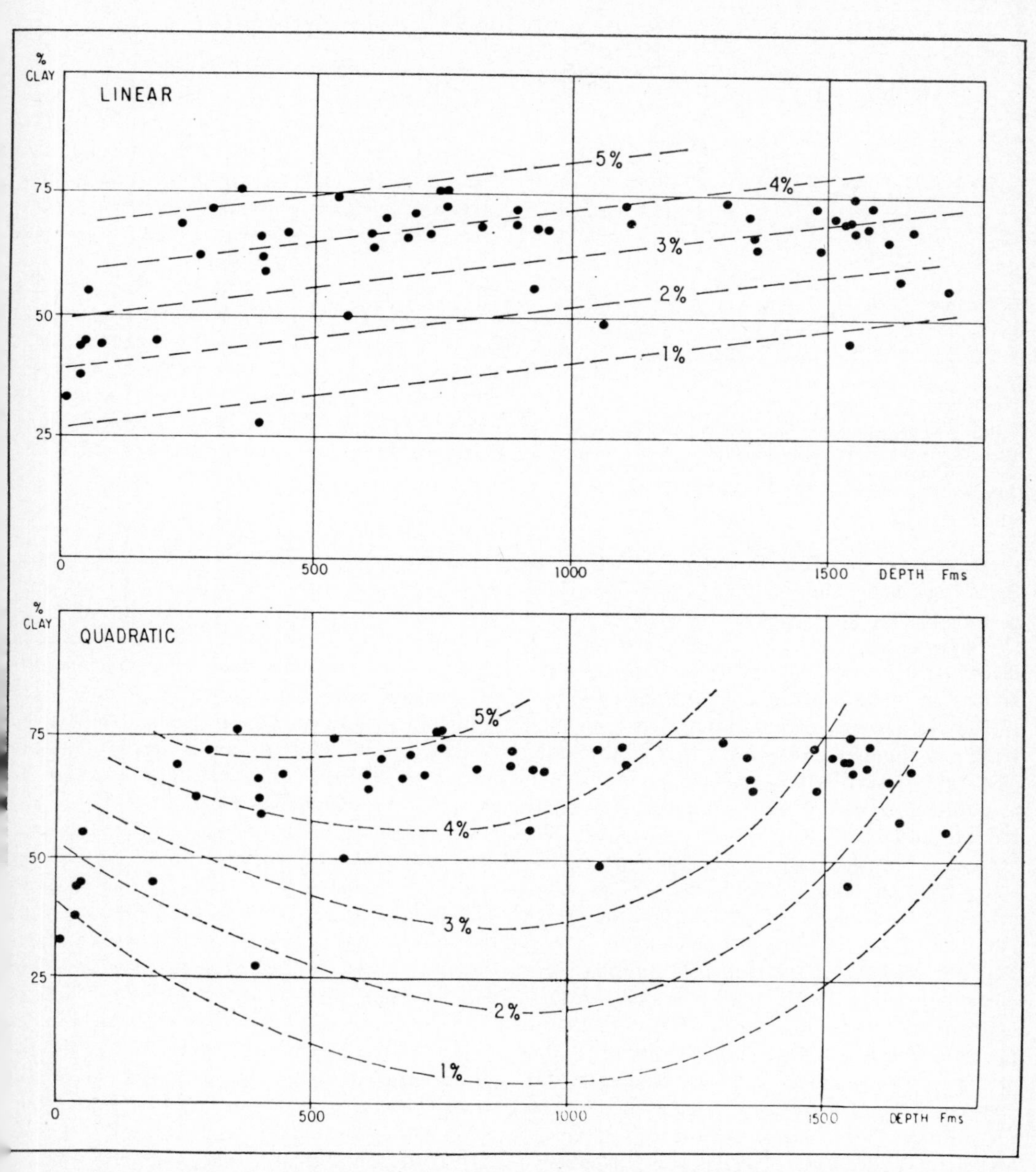

FIG. 34.—Linear and quadratic trend surfaces for organic carbon in dependence of clay content and water depth in the southern Gulf of California. Graph shows occurrence of maximum carbon content in intermediate water depths. For regression functions, see text.

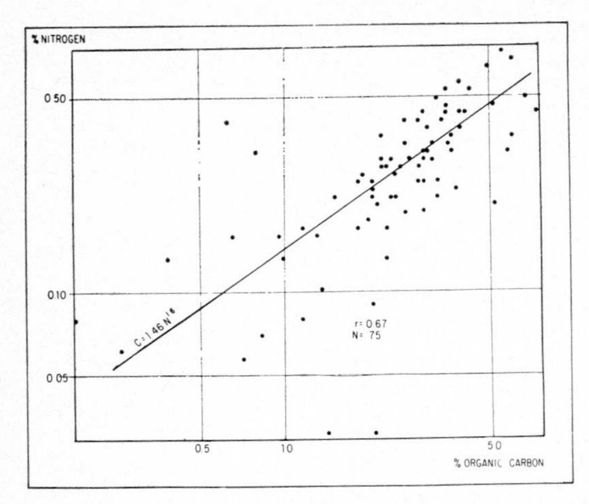

FIG. 35.—Correlation between organic carbon and nitrogen in per cent of dry weight of total sample in Gulf of California surface samples (9–10 cm). Correlation significant at one per cent level.

C/N ratios of recent sediments of the Gulf of Paria (van Andel and Postma, 1954, p. 103–107), two groups were distinguished with *C/N* ratios averaging 6.8 and 13.4, respectively. The regional distribution of these groups and microscopic examination of the organic matter suggested that the low values were derived from planktonic material and the higher ones from terrestrial plants. The regional distribution of high ratios in the Gulf of California does not suggest a terrestrial origin for this material.

Carbon/nitrogen ratios for planktonic organisms (Ketchum and Redfield, 1949) range from 6.7 to 8.3, and for diatomaceous plankton (Harvey, 1960), from 5.5 to 7.0. These values are lower than the median for the Gulf of California sediments. However, factors other than source of material control the *C/N* ratio (Debyser, 1961). Bacterial decomposition of organic matter results in a progressive loss of nitrogen leading to an increase of the *C/N* ratio with increasing depth in the sediment. This increase is most marked in the first few centimeters (Emery and Rittenberg, 1952; Trask, 1953; Bader, 1955). Consequently, the *C/N* ratios are also influenced by the relative rates of sedimentation and of organic matter production. The slightly higher *C/N* ratios of the Gulf of California sediments with respect to plankton may be due to partial decomposition at the 9–10 cm level of the cores.

SUMMARY AND DISCUSSION

In the previous sections, a substantial volume of observations has been presented to demonstrate the significant differences between slope and basin deposits in the Gulf of California. These differences are illustrated once more by the cross sections of Figure 36. The concentration of biogenous components on opposite slopes (*K-K′*), on one slope opposite a major sediment source (Fuerte River delta, *L-L′*, *M-M′*), or on the basin floor of the northern Gulf (*C-C′*, in the northern Sal si Puedes Basin) is clearly shown. The high glauconite content of sediments on submarine hills (*M-M′*, *O-O′*) and the occurrence of mica around Cape San Lucas (*O-O′*) are noteworthy. The sections show what was already evident from the distribution maps of this chapter, that although biogenous components appear generally concentrated on slopes, a high rate of terrigenous supply, such as around Cape San Lucas or off the Fuerte and Yaqui River deltas, will interrupt the systematic pattern. Conversely, a very low rate, as on the western slope, will result in very high amounts of biogenous material. However, although the distribution patterns appear strongly influenced by relative rates of supply of terrigenous and biogenous material, the zonal pattern cannot be explained by this factor alone.

An irregular and widely spaced sampling pattern, as used in the present study, and a free choice of categories for mapping sediment parameters may easily produce biased distribution maps that distort reality. The hypothesis that a major difference exists between the deposits of slopes and basins in the southern and central Gulf of California can be tested objectively. All samples from this area have been divided into two groups, a slope group limited by the shelf-edge and the sill depths of the basins (Table I), and a basin group below sill depth. A rank test (Mann-Whitney *U* test; Tate and Clelland, 1959, p. 89–91) was applied to test the null hypothesis that no difference exists between these groups. The results (Table XI) convincingly demonstrate that, at a high level of significance, the sediments of slopes and basins are indeed different, on the basis of all variables except the planktonic Foraminifera and the carbonate content. Thus, the biogenous components provide a useful tool to distinguish between slope and basin facies in the Gulf of California, and possibly in other modern and ancient basins of a similar type.

The explanation for this difference is not obvious and requires further discussion. Any hypothesis will have to account for the following facts.

1. The deposits on slopes contain higher amounts of organic matter and coarse biogenous silica than do the sediments in the basins.
2. The amounts of terrigenous sand in slope sediments are not greater than those in basin sediments, but the total coarse fraction is larger, reflecting the concentration of biogenous material on slopes.
3. The coarse fraction of slope samples is considerably and significantly richer in Radiolaria, diatoms, and benthonic Foraminifera than is the coarse fraction of the basin sediments. This is not true for the planktonic Foraminifera.
4. Slope sediments in the central Gulf do not appear to contain more biogenous opal in all fractions combined than do basin sediments.
5. If approximately 1 to 3 per cent of coarse biogenous components and organic carbon were removed from slope samples, they would be indistinguishable from basin deposits.

Plankton blooms can be observed abundantly in many localities in the Gulf of California (Fig. 37) throughout the year, especially in the winter and spring. The organic productivity can be so great that it leads to local over-saturation with oxygen (Roden and Groves, 1959), but direct measurements are not available. The high productivity is caused by upwelling in the central and southern Gulf. During the winter and spring, the predominant, strong, northwesterly winds produce a surface current which drives water out of the Gulf toward the Pacific and causes extensive upwelling in many places along the eastern side (Fig. 37). The areas of upwelling occur mainly near steep slopes and in lee of islands and promontories. The upwelling water is cooler, lower in salinity, and higher in nutrients than is the surface water, which throughout the summer has been depleted by organic productivity and subjected to evaporation (Roden, this volume; Roden and Groves, 1959). The surface outflow is compensated below the thermocline by inflow of Pacific water, which forms the ultimate source of the upwelling water.

During the summer and fall, wind patterns are reversed, and southeasterly winds, usually of less strength, cause moderate upwelling along the western margin of the Gulf. Upwelling is at a maximum in the winter and spring and gradually

TABLE XI. RESULTS OF RANK TESTS FOR DIFFERENCES BETWEEN SLOPE AND BASIN SEDIMENTS IN THE GULF OF CALIFORNIA

Sediment Property	*Mean*		N_1[4]	N_2[5]	T[6]	z[7]	P[8]
	Basin	*Slope*					
Organic carbon[1]	2.6	3.6	27	44	685	−3.396	0.002
Fine-grained carbonate[1]	6.6	9.4	30	44	875	−2.747	0.016
Coarse biogenous silica[1]	0.3	0.7	20	27	312	−3.613	0.002
Radiolaria[2]	10	20	21	35	389	−3.551	0.001
Diatoms[2]	15	36	14	18	166	−3.048	0.003
Planktonic Foraminifera[2]	6	6	45	47	1,910	−1.426	**0.152**
Benthonic Foraminifera[2]	2	14	45	48	1,410	−5.578	0.001
Total coarse fraction[3]	1.1	2.4	37	46	1,240	−2.932	0.003
Terrigenous in coarse fr.[3]	0.7	1.4	36	45	1,362	−1.101	0.138

[1] In per cent by weight of total sample.
[2] In per cent by number of 0.06–0.25 mm fraction.
[3] In per cent by weight of total sample.
[4] Number of samples from basin floors.
[5] Number of samples from slopes.
[6] Sum of ranks, basin floor samples.
[7] $z = \frac{2T - N_1(N_1 + N_2 + 1)}{N_1N_2(N_1 + N_2 + 1)/3}$
[8] Probability that slope and basin samples are drawn from same population.

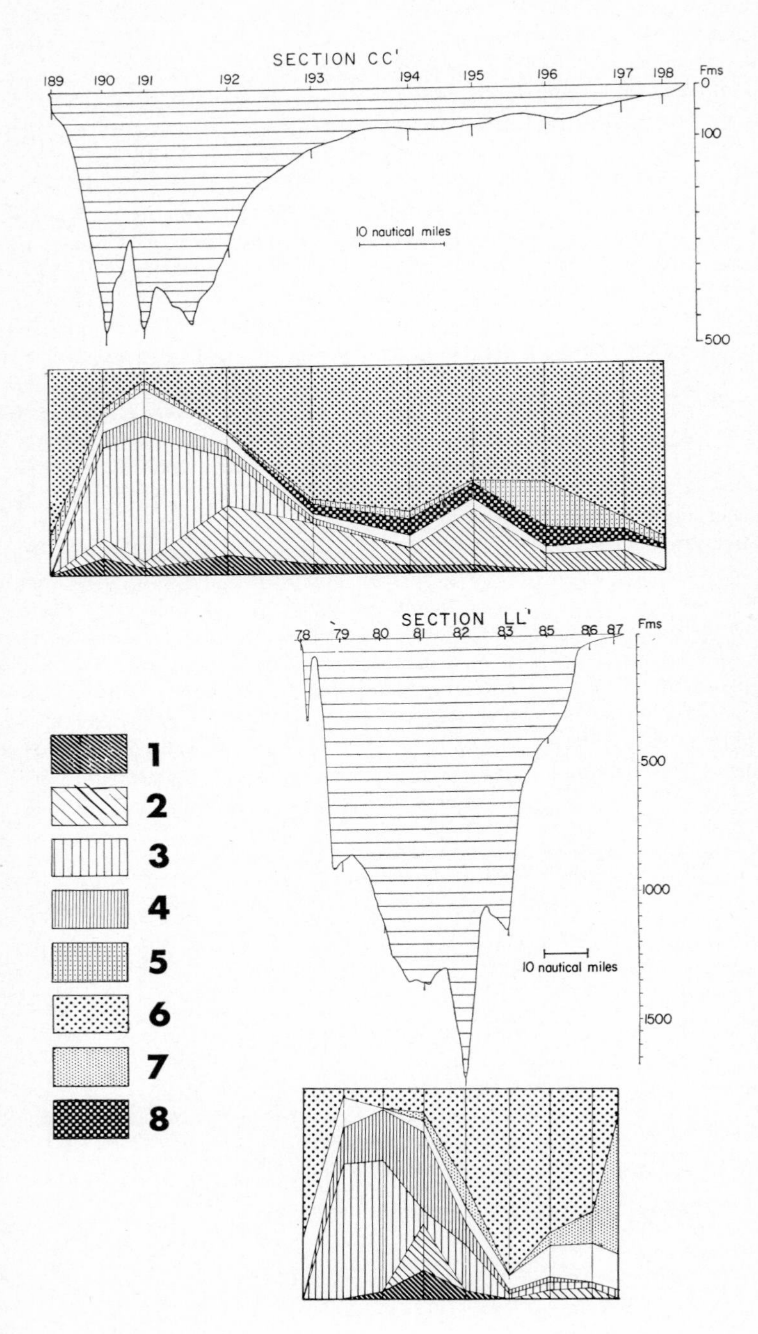

FIG. 36.—Variation of composition of the 0.06–0.25 mm fraction in several Gulf of California cross sections. Locations of stations in Fig. 1. Ordinate indicates cumulative per cent of composition, abscissa shows sample location. *Explanation*—(1) Planktonic Foraminifera, (2) benthonic Foraminifera, (3) diatoms, (4) Radiolaria, (5) skeletal carbonate, (6) terrigenous grains, (7) mica, (8) glauconite. For description, see text.

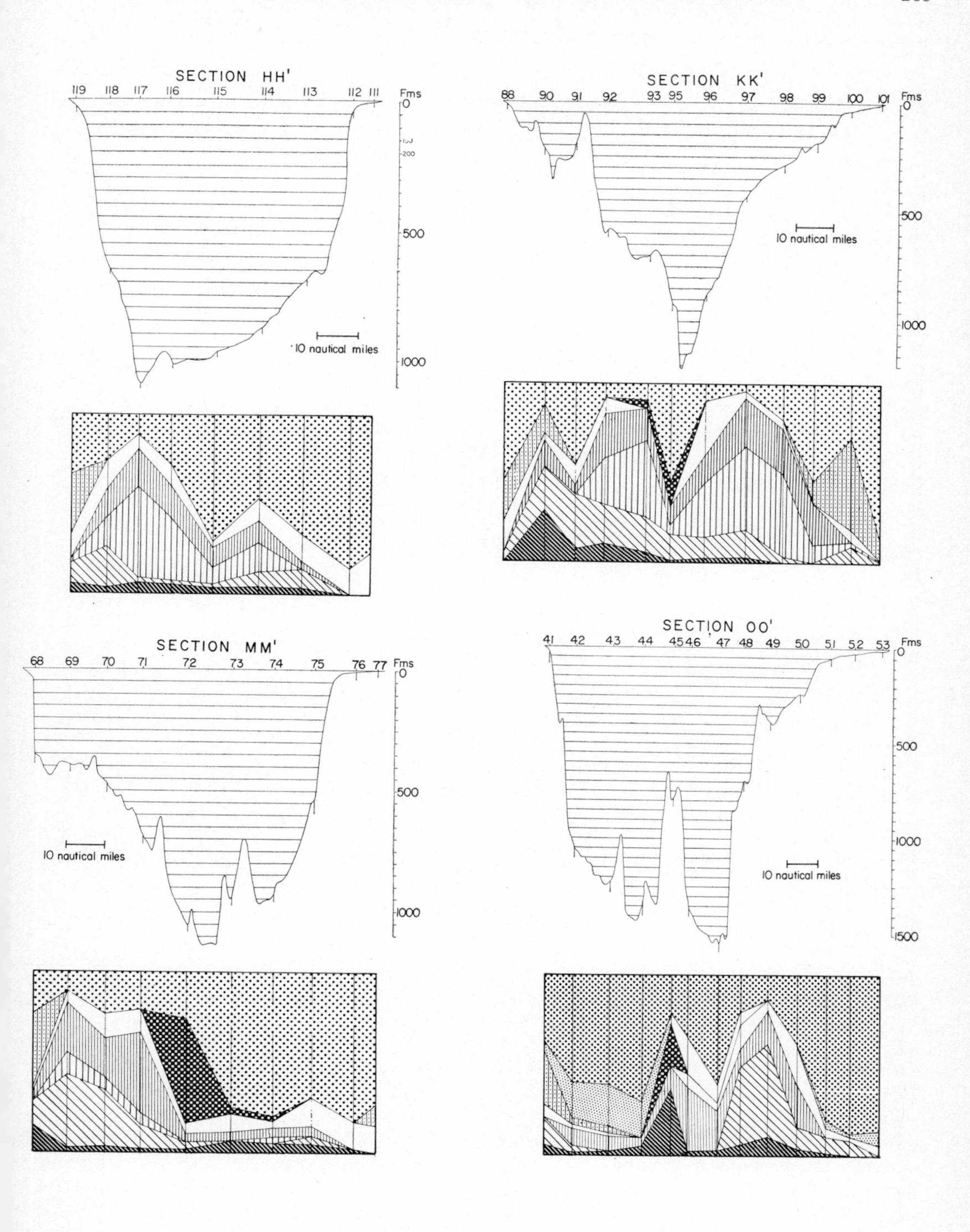
SECTION HH'
119 118 117 116 115 114 113 112 111
Fms
0
500
1000
10 nautical miles
SECTION KK'
88 90 91 92 93 95 96 97 98 99 100 101
Fms
0
500
1000
10 nautical miles
SECTION MM'
68 69 70 71 72 73 74 75 76 77
Fms
0
500
1000
10 nautical miles
SECTION OO'
41 42 43 44 45 46 47 48 49 50 51 52 53
Fms
0
500
1000
1500
10 nautical miles

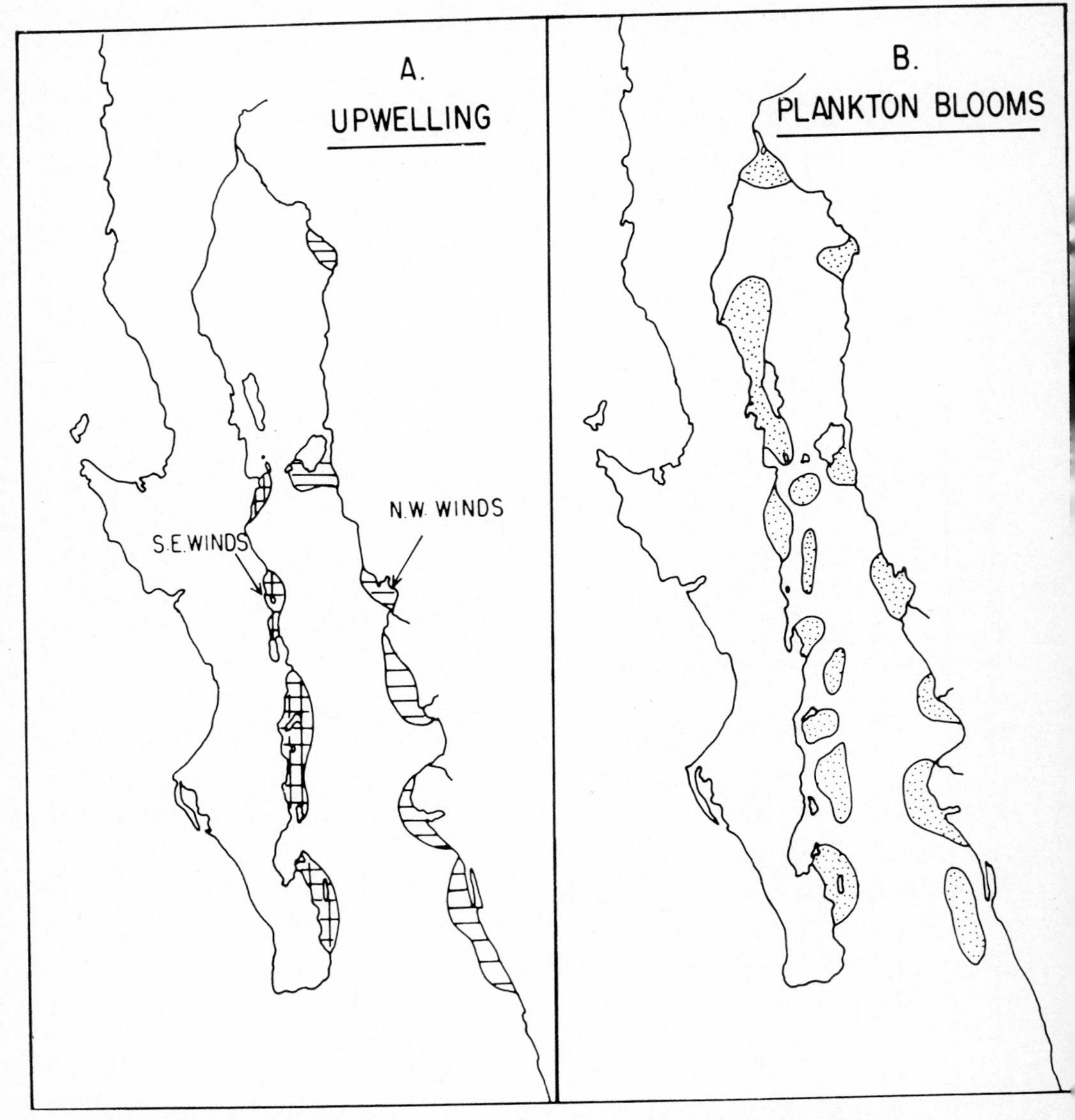

FIG. 37.—Areas of upwelling (*A*), after Roden and Groves (1959), and plankton blooms (*B*), after Byrne (1957) in the Gulf of California. Information is limited and patterns are certainly incomplete.

decreases in the course of the summer (Revelle, 1950). The extensive blooms result in almost complete depletion of the surface waters with respect to nutrients and silica. Only with the onset of the next upwelling season do these components return to values which are normal for open ocean water. Then they are again capable of sustaining prolific plankton growth.

Thus, silica-rich Pacific water enters the Gulf at moderate depth, replaces depleted surface water and in turn is depleted by diatom blooms, leading to a continuous accumulation of silica on the Gulf floor (Revelle, 1950) so that the Gulf acts as a sink for Pacific silica. Similar silica accumulation

:akes place in the Santa Barbara Basin, Southern California (Emery, 1960).

It has often been assumed (for example, Talia-'erro, 1933; Bramlette, 1946; Goldstein, 1959) :hat volcanic activity supplied the silica for an-:ient siliceous shales formed in deep basins. It nay be suggested that in at least some ancient basins, processes similar to those operating in the Gulf of California today have led to the formation of siliceous shales. Volcanism may have been a phenomenon accompanying the tectonic stage of uch a deep basin, but was not necessarily re-quired for the accumulation of siliceous shale. In he Gulf of California, volcanic rocks are abun-lantly available. However, on the basis of reason-ble assumptions, it can be calculated that the upply of silica through the annual water ex-hange between the Gulf and the Pacific Ocean is nore than sufficient to account for all the bioge-ous opal formed. The contribution by rivers is otally insignificant in proportion.

The incomplete data available at this time how that plankton blooms, and therefore organic roductivity, occur primarily along the Gulf nargins and in part over shelf areas. Locally, in heltered places, diatoms are being deposited in lace in the bloom area, but in general the high urbulence of the shallow zone prevents deposi-on, and the products of the blooms are dispersed oward deeper water.

At intermediate depths, the waters of the Gulf now a pronounced oxygen minimum (Roden, this olume). The precise depth of the oxygen mini-um zone varies with season and area, but be-ween 100 and 700 fathoms, oxygen values of elow 0.5 ml/L are found almost universally. A onsiderable part of the Gulf floor is situated etween these depth limits (Fig. 38). In this area, reduced decomposition of organic matter and a inimum of reworking by burrowing organisms ust be expected. Parker (this volume) has shown at macro-invertebrates are extremely rare in is zone. The zones of high concentration of biog-ous components coincide almost exactly with is oxygen minimum. Trask (1953) has observed similar relationship between high organic con-nt and an oxygen minimum near the bottom in e Gulf of Mexico. It is noteworthy that the nall amount of oxygen available does not seem

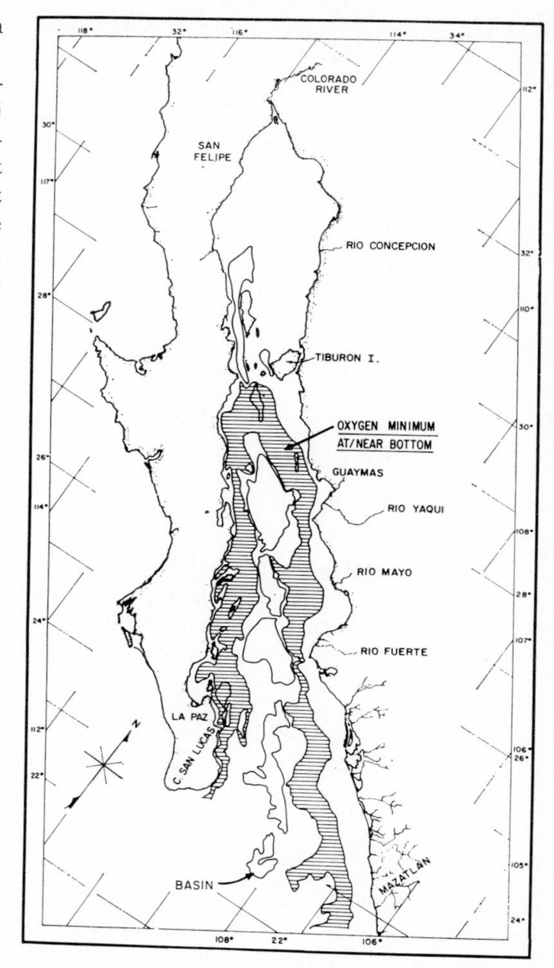

FIG. 38.—Approximate regions in the Gulf of California where bottom waters are low in oxygen (less than 0.05 ml/L).

to completely inhibit the development of a fauna of benthonic Foraminifera.

Together, these observations suggest that biogenous material is produced in greatest abundance near the Gulf margins, and that preservation of the more perishable products is most likely in the slope region. Only where terrigenous deposition is rapid are slope deposits poor in biogenous material. The assumption that the concentration of biogenous material on slopes can be accounted for simply by a higher relative rate of biogenous deposition near the sources of productivity implies that the dispersal of organic material does not extend far beyond the slopes.

However, although this may be true for the southern part of the Gulf, preliminary data (Calvert, in preparation) indicate that in the central Gulf biogenous opal is no less common in the basin than on the slopes, and that the difference between the two rests mainly in the coarse fraction. This suggests that sorting processes are operative to concentrate coarse biogenous material on the slopes, whereas the fine particles, including organic matter, are uniformly distributed. The organic matter is then secondarily concentrated by destruction in the basins and preservation on the slopes. Further studies will be required to solve this problem fully.

GRAIN-SIZE DISTRIBUTION OF GULF OF CALIFORNIA SEDIMENTS

In the present chapter, the texture of the Gulf of California sediments will be discussed in more detail and with different methods than was possible in the discussion of regional lithology, particularly with regard to changes in size distribution with increasing distance from shore and water depth. Textural properties of deep-water sands will be discussed in the next chapter.

METHODS OF ANALYSIS

Grain-size analyses have been made of the 9–10 cm section of all cores and most of the surface samples. Additional analyses were made of some deeper levels in cores and of all deep-water sands of sufficient thickness. After treatment with 10 per cent hydrogen peroxide to remove organic matter, and after dispersion in the presence of Ca^{++} ion by 0.005 molal sodium oxalate and 0.001 molal sodium carbonate, the sample was sieved wet on a 0.062 mm sieve, and a standard pipette analysis was made of the fine fraction. The fractions 0.062–0.031, 0.031–0.016, 0.016–0.008, 0.008–0.004, 0.004–0.002 mm, and finer than 0.002 mm were determined. Carbonate was not removed because a large part, if not all, of this component is detrital and forms an integral part of the size distribution.

The sand fraction was reduced to a subsample of a few grams by means of an Otto microsplit, and the size distribution was determined by a continuous-recording sedimentation balance developed at Scripps Institution of Oceanograph This instrument is a modification of the Doegl (1946) sedimentation balance, in which the weig increase caused by sand settling on a pan su pended in a water column is recorded contin ously against time by a strain gage and an amp fier-recorder system (Fig. 39). This system pr vides a continuous cumulative size-distributi curve from 2.000–0.062 mm, as a function of se tling velocity, with a reproducibility of better tha 2 per cent.

The raw data of the pipette analysis and pe centages read at 0.25 *phi* intervals from the sed mentation balance curve were processed by ele tronic computer. The program yields standa sample statistics for the entire size distributi curve, and a tabulation and graph of the cumul tive distribution in 0.25 *phi* intervals. For t fine-grained portion of the curve, where observ tions are obtained in 1.0 *phi* intervals, a five-poi interpolation method is used. In addition, t cumulative curve is differentiated by a method first differences between 0.25 *phi* intervals (Cu ray, 1961a); a graph and tabulation of the siz frequency distribution are provided. For the sa fraction, the size-frequency distribution is ve reliable. For the fine fraction, differentiation wi a wide spacing of observational points results curve irregularities, and a spurious mode at 4 *phi* is commonly created as a result of a poor between the coarse and fine sections of the curv Due to the fact that no minimum size can determined, the frequency curve is artificial terminated at 10.0 *phi*.

SIZE AND SORTING

Following Inman and Chamberlain (1955), t relation between average size and sorting of Gulf of California samples is presented in Figu 40. Computed mean and standard deviations a used instead of the graphic median and *phi* stan ard deviation (Inman, 1952). Although the scatt of points is large, the non-monotonic relation b tween mean size and standard deviation is e dent. Fine to very fine sands (1.0–4.0 *phi*) and t very fine, silty clays (finer than 6.5 *phi*) are t best sorted. Most very fine sands and all clay silts in the range of 3.0–6.0 *phi* are very poor sorted.

All samples can be divided into five groups

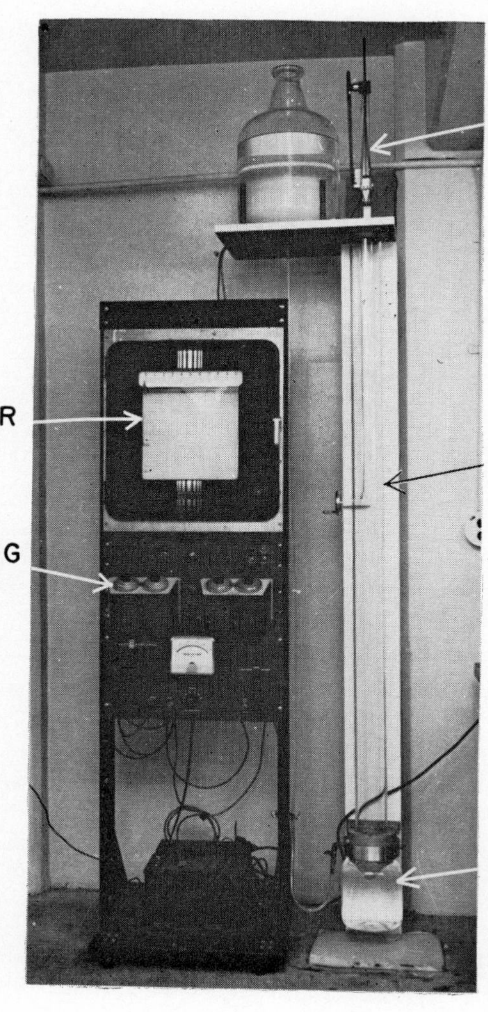

FIG. 39.—Recording sedimentation balance used for grain-size analyses of sand fraction (2.000–0.062 mm). ube is 182.5 cm long and has internal diameter of 7.8 cm. Adjustment for grain density and sample size can be ade with calibrating resistors.

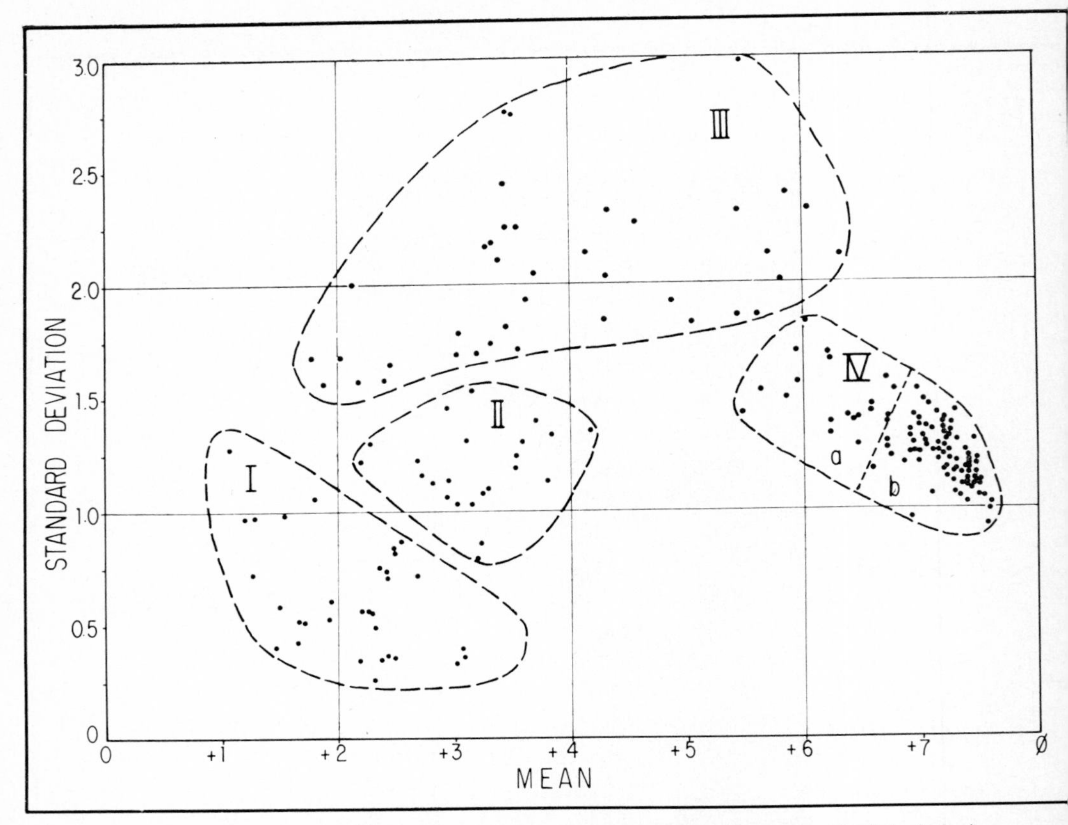

FIG. 40.—Relation between grain size and sorting (computed mean and standard deviation) of Gulf of California sediments. (Size in *phi* = $-\log_2$ of size in mm.)

the basis of the size-sorting relationship. The samples in groups I and II are generally unimodal, and the differences in sorting between the two groups are due to differences in spread of the individual modes, rather than to the inclusion of more than one mode. Some group II samples, however, owe their poor sorting to small modes of coarse calcarenite or fine silt and clay. Both types are generally found in nearshore areas and they fringe the Gulf almost everywhere except off some large deltas. Although type I is found most frequently between 5 and 20 fathoms and type II between 10 and 50 fathoms, the distinction between the types does not appear to be geologically very significant.

Group IV*b* samples are essentially unimodal, and those of group IV*a* bimodal or trimodal; with decreasing mean size, the modes in the 5.0–7.0 *phi* range tend to disappear and sorting improve[s]. Nearly all deep-water sediments belong to typ[e] IV*b;* shelfward, they generally grade into a zon[e] of more silty sediments of type IV*a*, which sepa[-]rate the deep-water deposits from the coarse she[lf] sands on the outer shelf and upper slope. Typ[e] IV*a* sediments fringe the coast near main delt[a] areas, and their distribution seems to be a func[-]tion of supply rather than of water depth alone.

Type IV*a* sediments are uncommon along th[e] western margin of the Gulf. The shelf here is nar[-]row and the upper slope is steep, so that possibl[y] the sampling pattern may have overstepped [a] narrow zone of this type. However, it is perhap[s] significant that the silt-clay ratio of sedimen[ts] with a western origin is only 0.52, whereas it [is] 0.67 for sediments derived from the east. T[he] rugged western hinterland, with its arid clima[te] and absence of rivers, possibly may account for a primary deficiency of silt-size particles.

Type III samples are predominantly polymo-dal, generally with one or more small modes above 4.0 *phi* and prominent modes in the 4.0–7.0 *phi* range. Such sediments locally occur in deep water, on banks, around Cape San Lucas, and on the flanks of steep basins in the northern and north-central Gulf. They are common on the shelves and generally are associated with irregular bedding and mottling. The poor sorting appears to be, in many cases, the result of mixing of alternating layers of coarse and fine sediments by burrowing organisms. Consequently, type III sediments are commonly associated with the deposits of the post-Pleistocene transgression.

On the upper slope, in the central part of the western Gulf margin, there are type III sediments in which the coarse fraction consists largely of foraminiferal and skeletal carbonate and glauconite. Without this biogenous fraction, these deposits would be very similar to the type IV*b* sediments which fringe the western margin elsewhere in this area.

REGIONAL DISTRIBUTION OF GRAIN-SIZE MODES

Most Gulf sediments (68 per cent) are bimodal or polymodal. In such samples, parameters as the mean and standard deviation lose their statistical rigor and have meaning only as broad indicators of average size and degree of sorting. Frequency modes, introduced by Curray (1960, 1961a), have evident advantages over conventional sampling statistics for tracing distribution patterns of such sediments.

Northern Gulf of California.—In the sediments of this region, well-defined modes which produce an apparently significant regional distribution pattern can be recognized. Most samples are polymodal, but generally the individual modes closely approximate a normal distribution (Fig. 41). Sorting of the individual modes is generally good (standard deviations of 0.2–0.6 for sand modes). Within the available set of samples, a complete spectrum of modes is absent; modes of approximately 0.75 *phi*, 2.25 *phi*, and 3.25 *phi* are predominant in the sand fraction; and intermediate positions are essentially vacant. Even over very large areas, principal modes cluster very closely around single values (Fig. 41*B*). Regional changes in mean size seem to be the result of changes in proportionality of fixed modes, rather than of gradual shifts of modal position (Fig. 41*A*). The absence of a spectrum of modal positions and of modal shifts is surprising, and its implications are of considerable interest. Further improvements in technique are required, however, to establish the reality of this phenomenon.

The regional distribution pattern (Fig. 42) is characterized by a progressive, stepwise shift from coarse to fine modes, from the shore to the deep Sal si Puedes Basin. The coarsest modes (0.50–1.00 *phi*) occur only in nearshore sediments close to mountainous sections of the coast, south of San Felipe, around Angel de la Guarda Island, and north of Tiburón Island. Their distribution appears to be controlled primarily by source (compare Fig. 10).

The distribution of the other modes appears to be influenced in part by the topography of the basin, with the exception of the area close to the Colorado River delta. In shallow water from 0–80 fathoms, the 2.25-*phi* mode, with only minor subsidiaries, is predominant, followed by a sequence of smaller modes in the zone of maximum depth change. The deepest portion of the Sal si Puedes Basin contains only 7.00–8.50-*phi* modes and clay (finer than 0.002 mm). This stepwise change in main modal position with change in depth is best developed along the northeastern side, as illustrated in Figure 41*A*. A similar change from coarse to fine modes is shown in a small and much shallower area just off the Concepción River delta bulge.

Although this decrease of modal size with depth can be observed everywhere in the northern Gulf, the depth range and distance vary, and south of the Colorado River delta the entire modal sequence is compressed within a very small interval. Along the western margin a similar sequence occurs, but it begins with a finer mode (3.25 *phi*) and is less complete.

At first sight, this distribution pattern suggests an equilibrium between present topography and sediment texture, with dispersal patterns originating from the Colorado River and essentially fol-

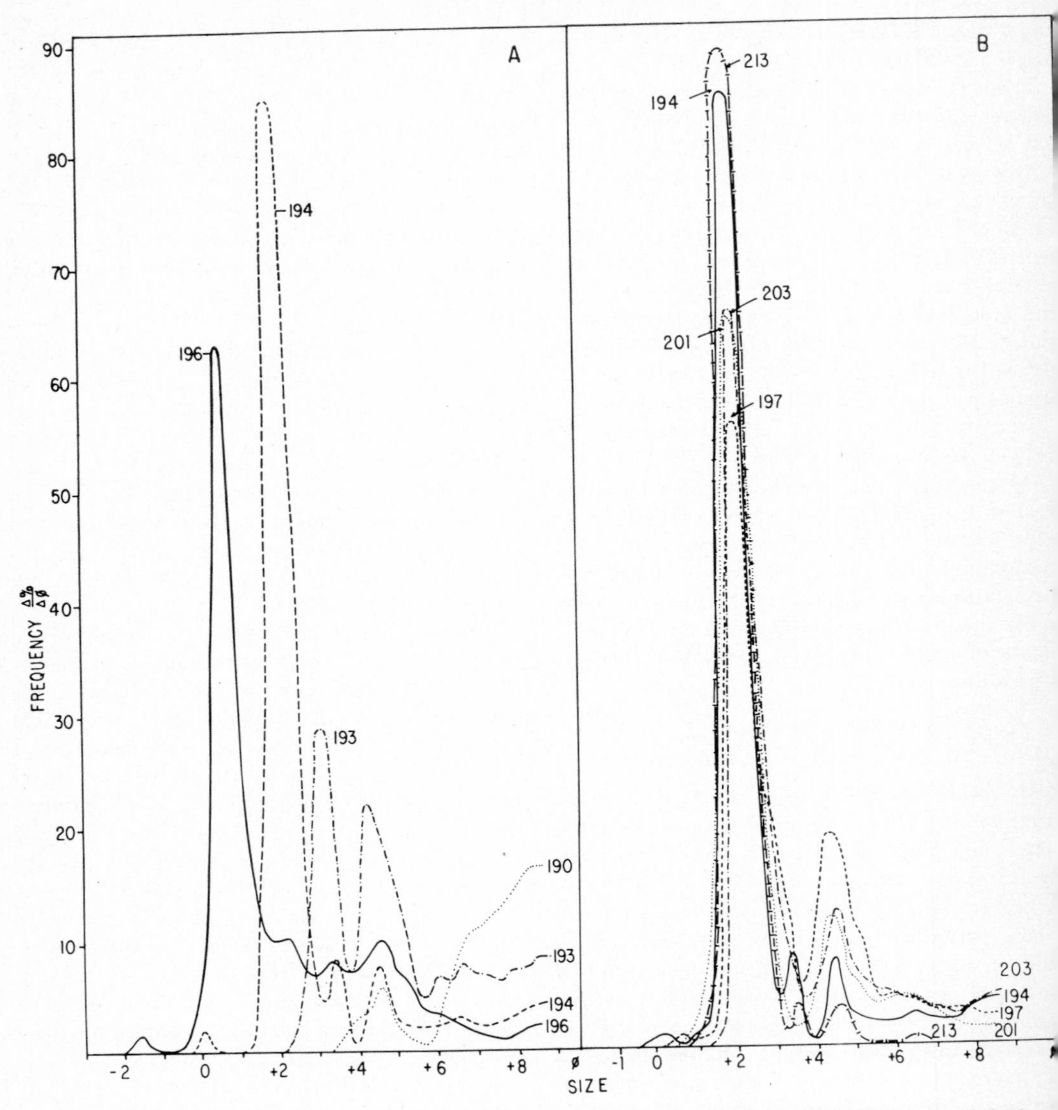

FIG. 41.—Typical size-frequency distributions of sediments in the northern Gulf of California—(*A*) chan in frequency distribution between nearshore zone off the Concepción River delta and the Sal si Puedes Bas (locations shown by large black dots in Fig. 42, upper left), (*B*) variation in frequency distribution within sing modal zone (2.00–2.25 *phi*; locations shown by black dots in Fig. 42, left center).

lowing the depth contours. For the area directly off the Colorado River mouth and for very fine fractions (finer than 5.50 *phi*), this appears reasonable. For other areas, however, and for coarser modes, this assumption is in direct contradiction with an assumption made elsewhere in this paper —that large portions of the northern Gulf a covered with relict sediments related to the pos Pleistocene rise of sea level. Moreover, an equili rium between present-day conditions and textu would require transportation of sand of 2.25 *phi* a depth of 75 fathoms, and of 3.25 *phi* to 125 fat

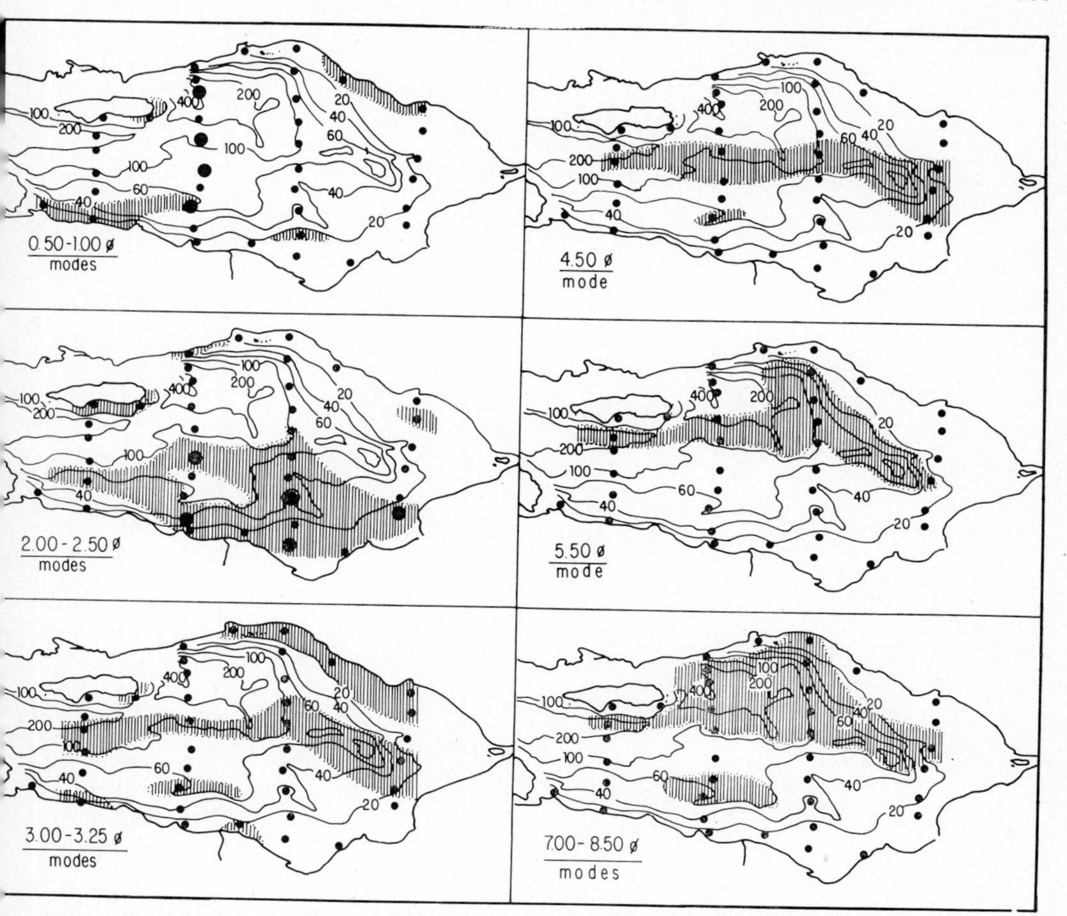

FIG. 42.—Regional distribution of grain-size modes in the northern Gulf of California. Depth contours in fathoms. Large black dots indicate positions of samples shown in Fig. 41.

ns in areas of very low relief. The necessary ottom velocities of at least 30–40 cm/sec, even ough they might be oscillatory, appear impossible in a basin with short fetch and no restrictions -as is the northern Gulf. Moreover, fine silt and ay are being deposited in much shallower depths f the Concepción River delta, in the same basin.

If we assume that a large portion of the sediments was deposited during the post-Pleistocene a-level rise, the 3.25-*phi* mode would be found at me distance beyond the minimum sea-level and, whereas nearshore sediments of that period d all transgressive deposits would be characterzed by the 2.25-*phi* mode. The distribution parallel to depth contours agrees well with littoral drift as a principal transporting agent.

Minor, finer modes are associated with the 2.25-*phi* mode (Fig. 41). Such secondary modes also have been observed by Curray (1960) in post-Pleistocene transgressive sediments of the Gulf of Mexico. Probably they are the result of the mixing of originally layered sediments or of a coarse relict sand with a top layer of fine-grained sediment deposited today.

Thus, the textural pattern of sediments of the northern Gulf of California appears to be the composite result of several sets of conditions (Fig. 43)—(1) a sand-to-clay series deposited during

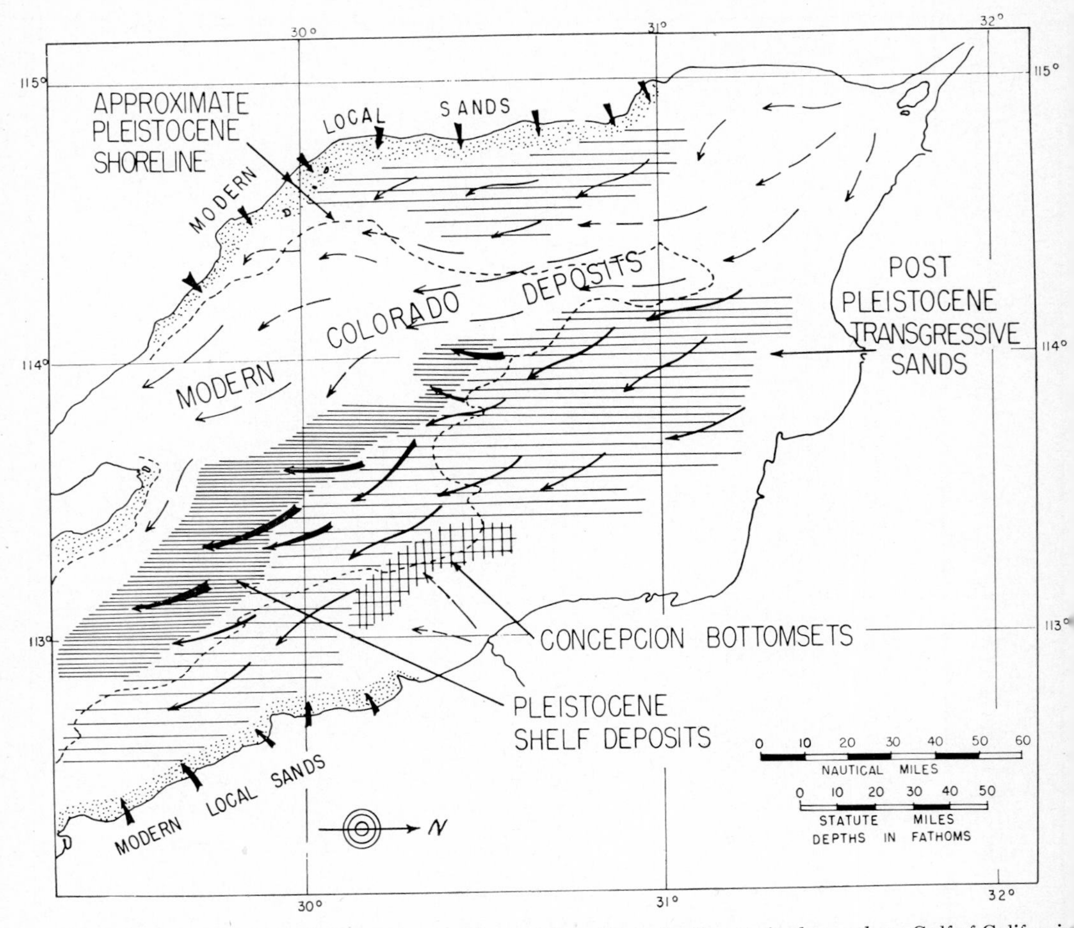

FIG. 43.—Hypothetical conditions of transportation and deposition of sediments in the northern Gulf of California based on texture and composition. Pleistocene shoreline placed at 65-fathom contour (Curray, 1961b).

the Pleistocene low stand, (2) a transgressive sand associated with the sea-level rise and now receiving minor admixture of fine material, (3) modern Colorado River deposition in the far northern part and in deep water, (4) modern prodelta deposition off the Concepción River delta, and (5) littoral sands near mountainous coasts.

Central and southern Gulf of California.—The sediments of the central and southern Gulf of California are predominantly fine grained. Sands are found on narrow shelves with a wide variety of sources and depositional conditions, and the number of samples is small with respect to the variability. Nevertheless, the regional distribution of modes (Fig. 44) shows a systematic and somewha unexpected pattern. It may be noted that Figur 44 merely shows the presence or absence of certai modes, not their frequency.

On the shelves, 2.25–2.75 *phi* modes and 3.00 3.25 *phi* modes are predominant. They fringe bot the eastern and western margins, are well define and are of relatively fixed position. Many of th sands are polymodal. Very coarse modes (0.50 *ph* 0.75–1.00 *phi*, 1.50–1.75 *phi*) are more spottil distributed but are prominent in many place along the west coast and in the northern part the area. Their distribution appears to be relate to the occurrence of a mountainous coast lin

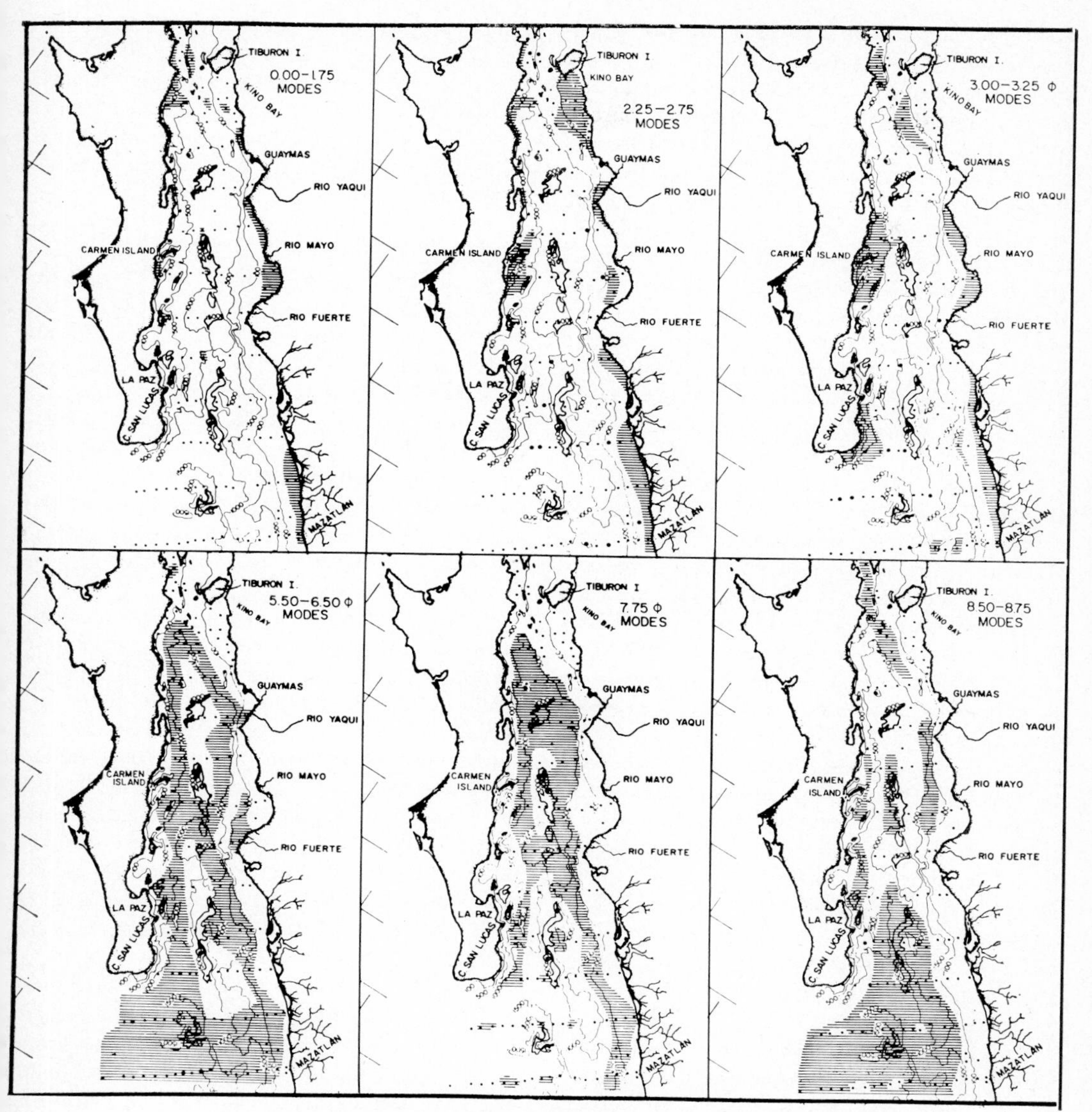

FIG. 44.—Regional distribution of grain-size modes in the central and southern Gulf of California. Depth contours in fathoms.

They also occur as secondary components of minor significance between the Yaqui and Fuerte River deltas and north of Mazatlán. In these areas they are largely composed of calcarenite (shell debris). Similarly, the prominent 2.25–2.50 *phi* mode of the foraminiferal deposits near Carmen Island mainly consists of calcareous material.

The coarsest modes extend appreciably beyond the shelf edge only in the north-central Gulf. The very fine sand mode (3.25 *phi*), on the other hand, has a much wider distribution in deep water, for example off Kino Bay, in the Sal si Puedes Basin, and around Cape San Lucas.

Silt and clay modes are systematically distributed in deep water beyond the shelf edge (clay fraction, finer than 9 *phi*, not shown). Inside the

Gulf, silt modes (5.50 and 6.50) are found primarily on slopes. Outside the Gulf, they are widely distributed in nearly all samples and at all depths. The presence of prolific sediment sources, such as the Fuerte River, is reflected by anomalies of the modal distribution. The 7.75 *phi* mode is clearly related to slope (or near-shelf) areas and does not occur in deep water except in the Guaymas Basin, on banks, and off the Yaqui River. This mode also is prominent in outer-shelf muds along the entire eastern margin. The 8.50–8.75 *phi* mode occurs in deep water farther from shore and is generally absent from shelves, upper slopes, and banks. The upper slope off the main eastern deltas and a few localities along the western side are exceptions.

In general, there appears to be a systematic change of predominant modes with increasing depth and distance from shore. Coarse modes occur on narrow shelves off rocky coasts; fine sand and silt modes are found on the outer shelf and upper slope and on banks; and fine silt and clay modes are restricted to deep water. Anomalies are found in regions of high sediment supply, where coarser modes may extend much farther seaward (Cape San Lucas, north-central Gulf), or where clay and silt modes may extend as far inward as the coastline (Fuerte River delta). The local occurrences of important, very fine modes on shelves and in the foraminiferal deposits around Carmen Island, and the wide distribution of 5.50 and 6.50 *phi* modes in the open Pacific are anomalous and unexplained. In the Sal si Puedes Basin and in the north-central Gulf, intermediate silt modes are absent, and the sediments consist of sand and clay only.

Seaward changes in modes are illustrated for a number of characteristic Gulf traverses (Fig. 45). These graphs again show the relation between water depth and/or distance from source and grain-size modes. The shifts caused by zones of high sediment supply are illustrated by a profile located off the Fuerte River delta.

The regional distribution of grain-size modes and the graphs of Figure 45 indicate a marked progressive sorting, reaching far into the silt and clay range where it is not normally assumed to exist. The processes associated with this sorting are not understood. Even when very low current velocities (10 cm/sec) and total absence of turbulence are assumed, modes finer than 5.50 *phi* could be distributed from the shelf edge over the entire deep Gulf before reaching the bottom (Kuenen, 1950, Table 15). Similarly, turbidity-current transportation should not produce the observed sorting effects.

TEXTURE AND INTERNAL WAVES

On the basis of oceanographic observations, Sverdrup (1939) postulated the existence of a standing internal wave in the Gulf of California, with three nodes inside the Gulf and one node outside. The theoretical plausibility of such a wave was later demonstrated by Munk (1941), who also calculated that the maximum horizontal velocity component at the nodes would be on the order of 20 cm/sec. In 1939, Revelle stated that the effect of the nodes of the standing internal wave could be observed in variations of the median size of Gulf sediments.

At the velocities computed by Munk, only the silt and clay fractions would be affected, and, in shallow water, the influence of such velocities would be entirely obscured by other high-energy agents. Therefore, ratios have been calculated for the various size fractions between 0.062 mm and 0.002 mm and for the fraction below 0.002 mm, for all fine-grained samples beyond the edge of the continental shelf. For each transverse series of samples, the mean and range of each ratio have been computed. Although the ranges are large, major fluctuations in the ratios appear to be significant.

The mean ratios of all traverses have been plotted on a longitudinal section from the open Pacific to Tiburón Island (Fig. 46). This graph shows that zones of coarser and finer sediment alternate in the axial portion of the Gulf. The effect is pronounced in the 0.032–0.016/<0.002 mm and in the 0.016–0.008/<0.002 mm fractions, but does not appear in the coarsest fraction. The 0.008–0.004/<0.002 mm ratio is not affected and merely shows a gradual increase toward the central Gulf. The finest fraction fluctuates in compensation of variations in the coarser sizes.

Therefore, although the size variation mentioned by Revelle appears to exist, the position of the coarse zones does not agree well with the

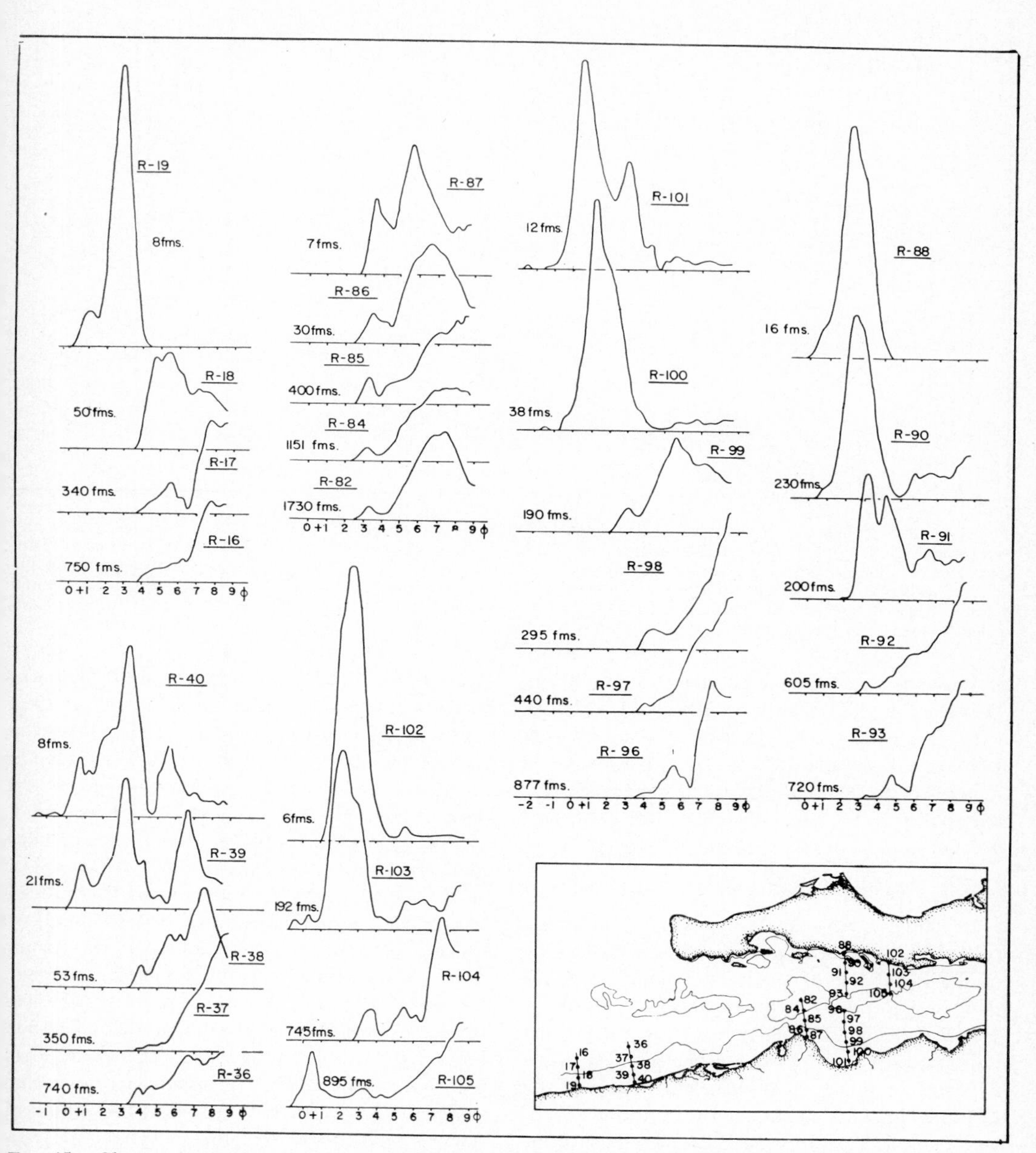

FIG. 45.—Changes in size-frequency distribution along profiles extending from the inner shelf (top) to the lower slope and deep basin (bottom) of the Gulf of California. For discussion, see text.

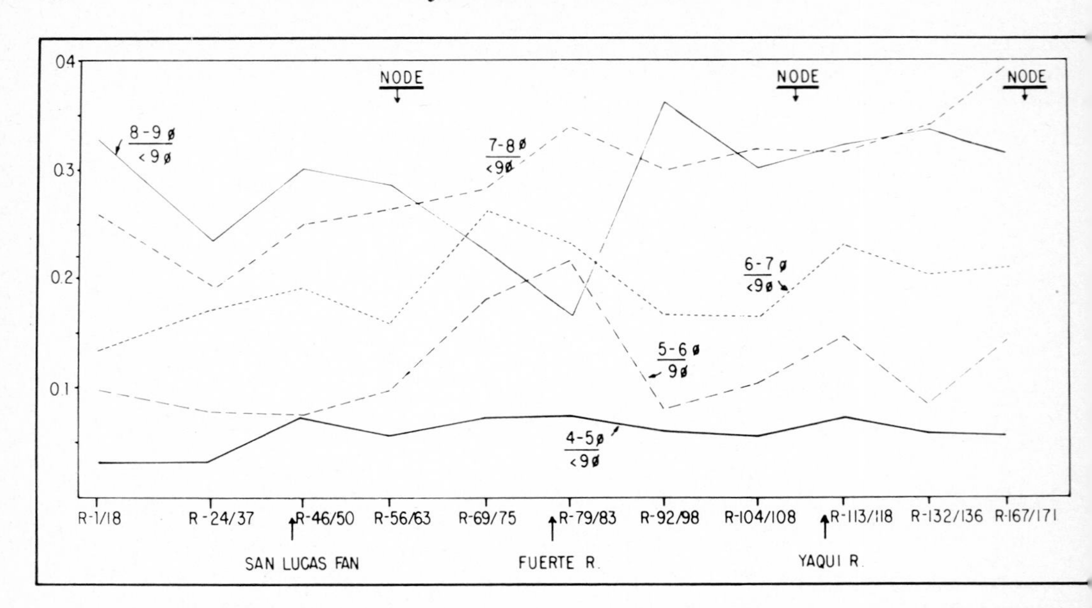

FIG. 46.—Longitudinal variation of grain size in the Gulf of California between Tiburón Island (right) and the open Pacific (left). *Horizontal*—positions of traverses (sample locations, see Fig. 1); *vertical*—mean ratios between various silt and clay fractions and the fraction finer than 9.0 *phi* (0.002 mm) for all deep-water sediments in each traverse. Approximate positions of nodes of standing internal wave (after Sverdrup, 1939) and of main areas of sediment supply are indicated. *Size classes*—4 *phi*=0.062 mm, 5 *phi*=0.031 mm, 6 *phi*=0.016 mm, 7 *phi* =0.008 mm, 9 *phi*=0.002 mm.

estimated locations of the internal wave nodes. On the other hand, the coarser zones clearly coincide with the locations of major sediment supply (San Lucas fan, Fuerte and Yaqui River deltas). Even if an effect of the internal wave system exists, it is apparently obscured by the much more important influence of variations in sediment supply.

DEEP-WATER SANDS AND BANK DEPOSITS

Beyond the edge of the continental shelf, less than 2 per cent of the surface deposits of the Gulf of California have median diameters of 4 *phi* (0.062) or larger, or can be classified as sands. However, even though they are quantitatively unimportant, the coarse-grained, deep-water deposits merit further discussion. All cores to be discussed are located outside the immediate vicinity of submarine canyons. Data have been tabulated in Appendix C.

Four principal types of coarse-grained, deep-water sediments can be distinguished—(1) thin sandy layers interbedded within thick, silty clay and clay sections (Fig. 47, R-108, R-68), (2) sandy mottles or disturbed layers in a silty clay or silt matrix (Fig. 47, R-45), (3) macroscopically homogeneous sand-silt-clay or, more rarely, silty sand and sandy silt deposits, and (4) layered or mottled sands with few intercalated fine-grained layers or little matrix (Fig. 47, R-150). Between types (1), (2), and (3), a continuous series of transition exists, and it may be assumed that they represent different intensities of secondary disturbance of originally layered deposits by burrowing organisms. As Arrhenius (1952, p. 86) has pointed out, burrowing by organisms in marine sediments is so universal that it is the preservation of depositional structures that requires explanation, not their destruction. The chance of

→

FIG. 47.—Photographs of cores of deep-water sand layers and mottles. R-45 is from a cut surface, the others from glue peels. Sample locations are shown in Fig. 1. Sand mottles in R-45, sand layers in R-68 (graded) and R-108, bedded sand in R-150.

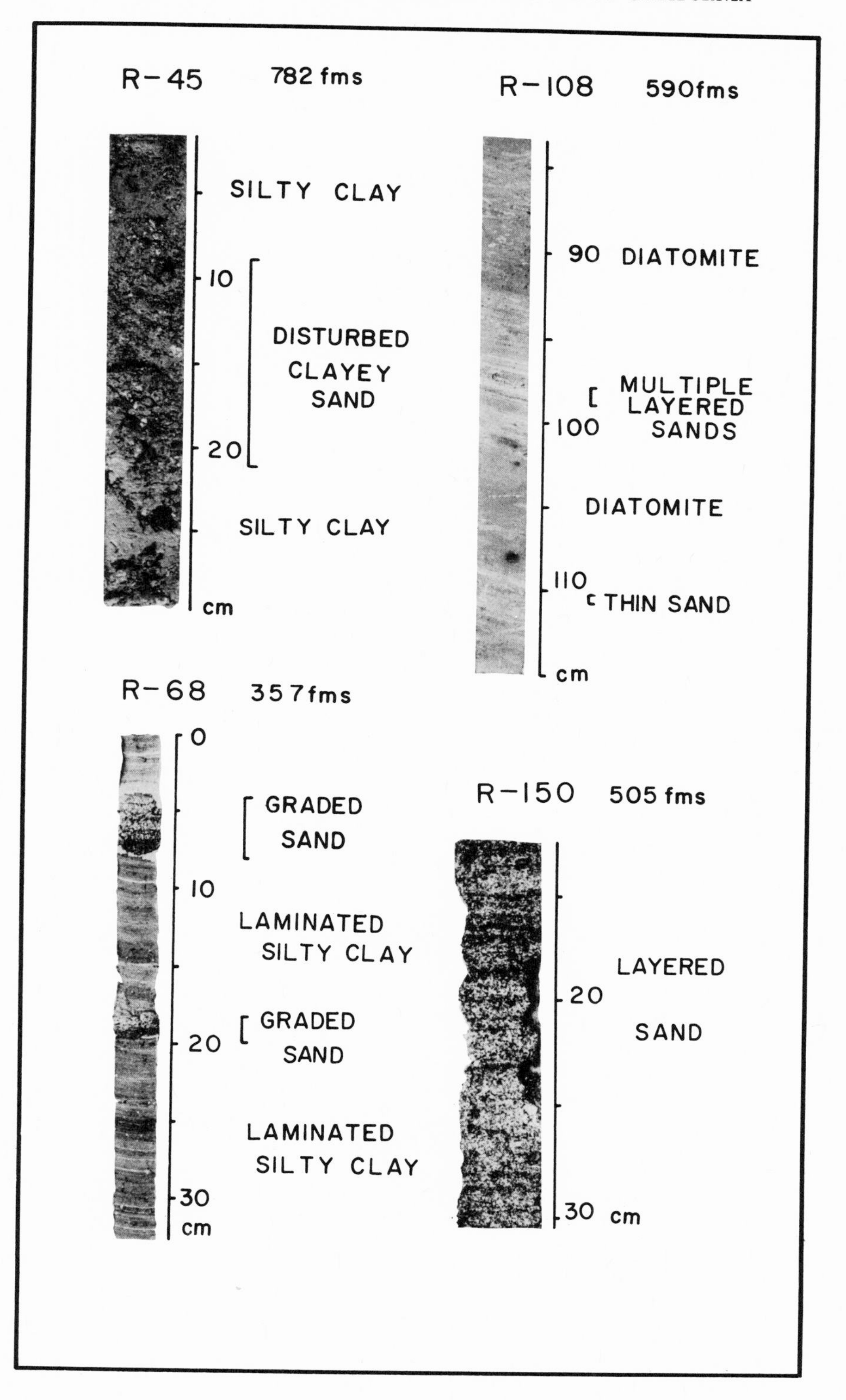
R-45
782 fms
SILTY CLAY
10
DISTURBED
CLAYEY
SAND
20
SILTY CLAY
cm
R-108
590fms
90
DIATOMITE
MULTIPLE
LAYERED
SANDS
100
DIATOMITE
110
THIN SAND
cm
R-68
357fms
0
GRADED
SAND
10
LAMINATED
SILTY CLAY
GRADED
SAND
20
LAMINATED
SILTY CLAY
30
cm
R-150
505 fms
LAYERED
20
SAND
30
cm

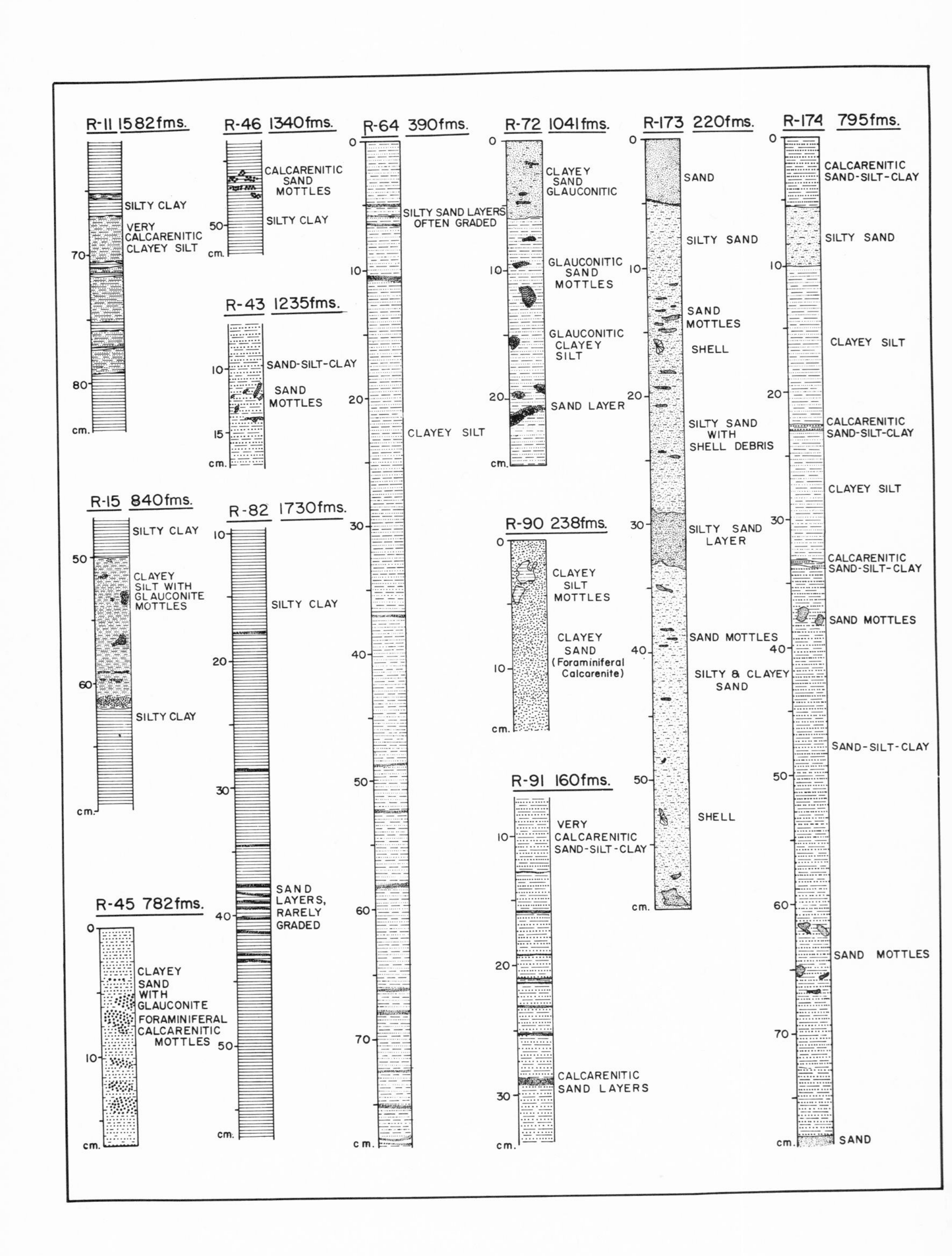
R-11 1582 fms.
SILTY CLAY
VERY CALCARENITIC CLAYEY SILT
R-46 1340 fms.
CALCARENITIC SAND MOTTLES
SILTY CLAY
R-64 390 fms.
SILTY SAND LAYERS OFTEN GRADED
CLAYEY SILT
R-72 1041 fms.
CLAYEY SAND GLAUCONITIC
GLAUCONITIC SAND MOTTLES
GLAUCONITIC CLAYEY SILT
SAND LAYER
R-173 220 fms.
SAND
SILTY SAND
SAND MOTTLES
SHELL
SILTY SAND WITH SHELL DEBRIS
SILTY SAND LAYER
SAND MOTTLES
SILTY & CLAYEY SAND
SHELL
R-174 795 fms.
CALCARENITIC SAND-SILT-CLAY
SILTY SAND
CLAYEY SILT
CALCARENITIC SAND-SILT-CLAY
CLAYEY SILT
CALCARENITIC SAND-SILT-CLAY
SAND MOTTLES
SAND-SILT-CLAY
SAND MOTTLES
SAND
R-43 1235 fms.
SAND-SILT-CLAY
SAND MOTTLES
R-15 840 fms.
SILTY CLAY
CLAYEY SILT WITH GLAUCONITE MOTTLES
SILTY CLAY
R-82 1730 fms.
SILTY CLAY
SAND LAYERS, RARELY GRADED
R-90 238 fms.
CLAYEY SILT MOTTLES
CLAYEY SAND (Foraminiferal Calcarenite)
R-91 160 fms.
VERY CALCARENITIC SAND-SILT-CLAY
CALCARENITIC SAND LAYERS
R-45 782 fms.
CLAYEY SAND WITH GLAUCONITE
FORAMINIFERAL CALCARENITIC MOTTLES
cm.

preservation is very small, especially where the original sand layers are thin. Consequently, in the Gulf of California considerable disturbance generally is in evidence in the form of mottling or even complete mixing. In areas of very slow sedimentation, as on isolated hills and banks, layering is rarely preserved.

Disturbance of primary structures by the coring process is common (Erickson and others, 1961; Shepard and Einsele, 1962). In the Gulf of California, the presence of undistorted layering in many cores (*see* Figs. 27 and 47) demonstrates that, provided caution is used in the interpretation, considerable reliance can be placed on core observations. It is believed that the minor structures shown in Figures 27, 47, and 48 and plotted on the map of Figure 49, are real and not artifacts.

The individual sand layers observed in Gulf of California cores are generally internally homogeneous; a few show lamination (Fig. 27, R-11; Fig. 47, R-150) or are clearly graded (Fig. 47, R-68, R-150; Fig. 48, R-64). The grading appears to be independent of layer thickness or texture; some of the thinnest and finest (R-64) and some of the coarsest and thickest layers (R-68) are well graded. Top and bottom contacts with the fine-grained sections are sharp. No other minor structures which are commonly associated with deep-water sands, such as current ripples and load casts, have been observed. In thin sections of laminated cores (R-17; R-68 between coarse graded sands), the sandy layers consist of silt and sand particles in a fine matrix. The well-defined upper and lower boundaries of the layers show that the mixing of sand and clay is primary and depositional in origin.

Individual sand layers are between 2 and 4 mm thick, and only a few exceed 10 mm. The mottles are small and few, indicating derivation from sparse thin layers. The distribution of sand layers and mottles in a number of typical cores is shown in Figure 48. This figure clearly shows the small thickness of individual sands in the southern and central Gulf (cores R-11 to R-91), as contrasted

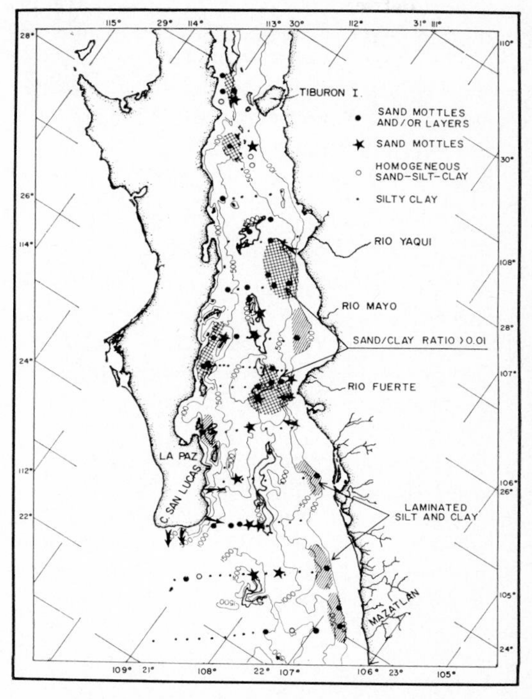

FIG. 49.—Regional distribution of deep-water sand layers and mottles in the Gulf of California. Locations of principal submarine canyons shown by heavy arrows. Depth contours in fathoms.

with thicker and more frequent sand beds in the north-central Gulf and in the Sal si Puedes and Tiburón Basins (cores R-173 and R-174 in Fig. 48, R-150 in Fig. 47).

The thin sand layers in the Gulf of California contrast markedly with the much thicker layers reported from the Atlantic (Ericson and others, 1961) and from offshore California basins (Gorsline and Emery, 1959; Shepard and Einsele, 1962), but the thin layers are similar to sands of the Gulf of Mexico, as reported by Ewing, Ericson, and Heezen (1958).

Generally, the sand layers are widely spaced vertically, and only a few occur in each core. The cores range from 15 to 134 cm in length, with a

←

FIG. 48.—Scale drawings of Gulf of California cores containing sand layers and mottles. Patterns representing fine-grained matrix are symbolic and do not represent actual structures. Sample locations are shown in Fig. 1. R-43 and R-45 are bank deposits. Very calcarenitic, clayey silt in R-11 consists of very thin (1–2 mm) sands alternating with silty clay. The sand layers contain a displaced shallow-water fauna.

majority between 60 and 90 cm. The average number of layers is one per 30 cm, but in a few cores (for example, R-64, R-91, Fig. 48) the layers are evenly distributed. Generally, the layers occur in closely spaced groups separated by thick intervals of silty clay (for example, R-82, Fig. 48).

A ratio of the total thickness of sand layers to total thickness of fine-grained sediment can be calculated for 34 cores, ranging in length from 60 to 110 cm. This ratio, which is comparable to a sandstone/shale ratio, is less than 0.02 in 18 cores, between 0.02 and 0.05 in 8 cores, between 0.05 and 0.10 in 4 cores, and larger than 0.10 in 5 cores. The higher ratios generally are due to a few thick sand layers (Fig. 48, R-72; Fig. 47, R-68), rather than to a large number of thin beds.

The regional distribution of sand layers and sand mottles and of the sand/clay ratio is shown in Figure 49 (*see also* Shepard, this volume). Deep-water sands are most common in the vicinity of Cape San Lucas, along the central western slope, in the north-central Gulf and southern Sal si Puedes Basin, and off the Yaqui and Fuerte River deltas. Even in the areas of highest sand-layer frequency, homogeneous silty clay cores are still common or even predominant. Low sand/clay ratios are widespread. Intermediate values (0.01–0.05) characterize the areas off the Yaqui and Fuerte River deltas, and very high ratios are found in a few cores in the north-central Gulf. The areas of highest incidence of deep-water sands appear to be closely related to the principal sediment sources and are associated with the occurrence of submarine canyons (Cape San Lucas, San Ignacio Canyon off the Fuerte River delta). Along the western margin, no submarine canyons are known, but a number of slope valleys appear to exist. However, deep-water sands also occur in places far from known submarine canyons, and the deep-water sands of the north-central Gulf are certainly not related to these features.

The available data do not suggest a systematic change of sand-layer thickness, sand-layer frequency, or sand/clay ratio with increasing distance from the source, as observed by Gorsline and Emery (1959) in the Santa Monica and San Pedro Basins off Southern California. Sand layers cannot be correlated between cores; numerous homogeneous silty clay cores alternate with cores containing sand layers (Fig. 50). This may be due to the relatively large spacing of cores, but it certainly precludes the possibility of extensive blanket-type sands as reported by Ewing, Ericson, and Heezen (1958, p. 1039–1041) for the Sigsbee Deep. Rapid lateral lithological variation and discontinuity of sand layers also have been observed by Shepard and Einsele (1962) in the San Diego Trough, California.

The source of many deep-water sands can be determined with reasonable certainty by their heavy-mineral assemblages, which, in composition (Table XII) and regional distribution, agree with the surface suites shown in Figure 11 and Table VII. Only one deep-water sand (R-15, 50–60 cm) has a mineral suite that is very different from the Sinaloa-Nayarit province in which it occurs, and that closely resembles the volcanic Santiago augite association. In nearly all cases, the deep-water sands can be related unambiguously to source areas by means of their heavy-mineral assemblages (Fig. 51). This allows the determination of minimum distances of transportation (in nautical miles) from the nearest shelf edge or head of a submarine canyon in the source area, as shown below. Compared to the enormous distances of turbidity-current transportation postulated in the literature, these distances are very modest, but they are well established.

	Nautical miles		*Nautical miles*		*Nautical miles*
R-25/26	50	R-72	40	L-36	20
R-15	30	R-82	30	L-66	30
R-31	65	R-116	25	L-90	40
R-34	50	R-121	55		
R-43/44	30	R-150	20		

The shallow-water origin of several deep-water sand layers is indicated by the presence of displaced shallow-water Foraminifera (by courtesy of F.B Phleger). At a depth of 1,582 fathoms and 75 nautical miles from the nearest shallow area, core R-11 contains, in a 2-cm-thick graded sand layer, abundant *Bolivina seminuda* and *Cassidulina delicata*. Core R-68, at a depth of 368 fathoms, contains a graded sand layer of 35 mm thickness at 37–40 cm with a rich shallow-water fauna of *Rosalina columbiensis*, *Hanzawaia nitidula*, *Cancris panamensis*, *Cibicides serialis*, *Textularia*

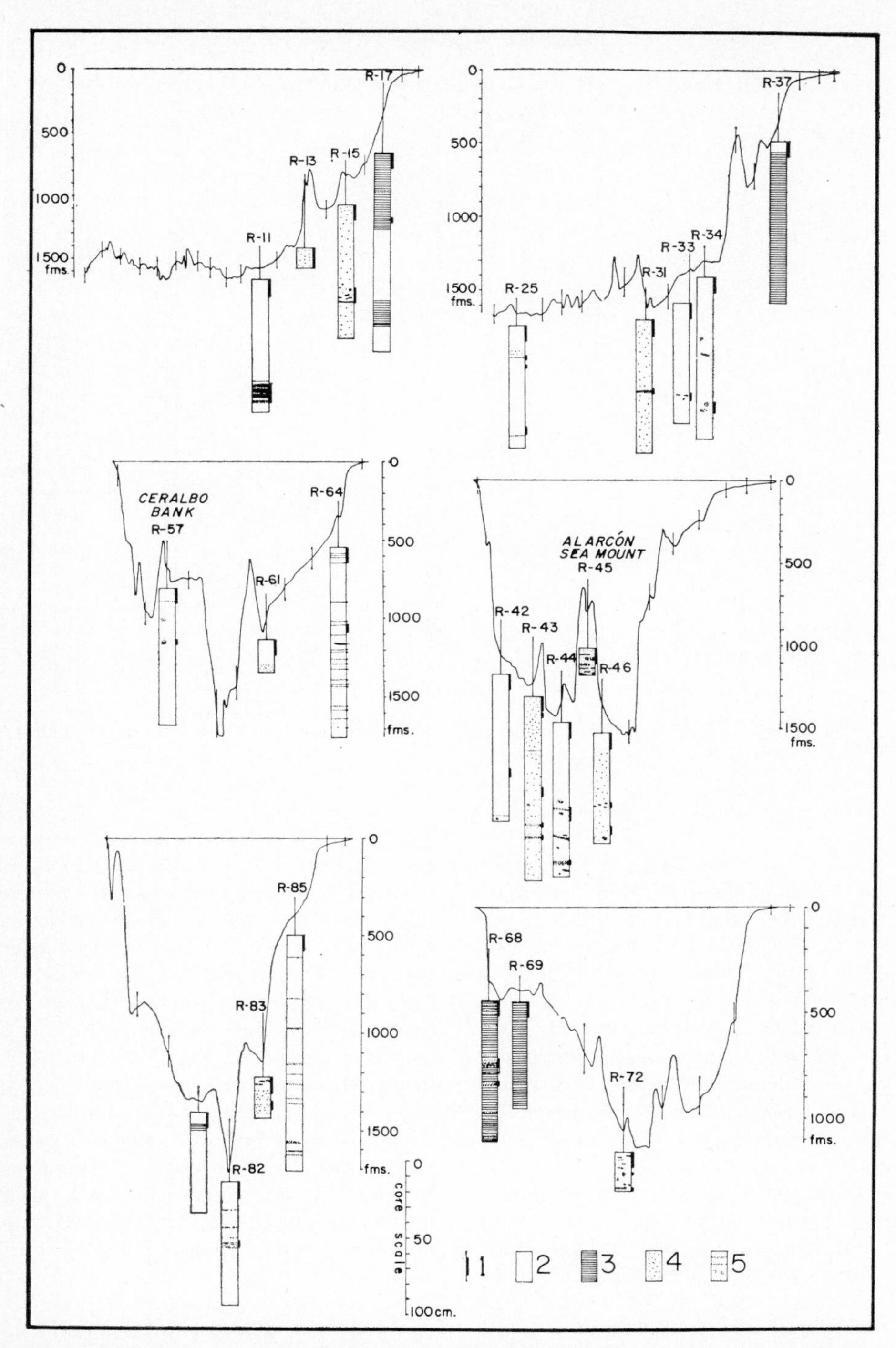

FIG. 50.—Bathymetric cross sections and lithologic variation in cores in the southern Gulf of California. Cores with mottles or sand layers shown in full; cores with homogeneous silty clay or clay shown by vertical line at core location. *Explanation*—(1) subsample, (2) silty clay or clay, (3) laminated silt and clayey silt, (4) homogeneous sand-silt-clay, (5) sand layers and mottles. Locations of samples in Fig. 1.

TABLE XII. HEAVY-MINERAL ANALYSES OF DEEP-WATER SAND LAYERS AND MOTTLES
(In per cent by number of the transparent fraction. For station locations *see* Figs. 1 and 51.)

Station Number	*Depth of sample (in cm)*	*Tourmaline*	*Zircon*	*Apatite*	*Garnet*	*Epidote*	*Amphibole*	*Basaltic Hornblende*	*Augite*	*Hypersthene*	*Titanite*	*Others*	*Lithology*
R- 15	50–60	2	—	—	—	9	29	2	46	12	—	—	mottles
R- 25	19–22	—	1	—	—	3	90	—	2	1	1	2	sand layer
R- 26	12–17	—	—	—	—	3	94	1	—	—	2	—	sand layer
R- 31	68–72	—	1	2	—	20	52	3	18	4	—	—	sand layer
R- 34	95–97	—	—	3	1	20	54	2	18	1	1	—	mottles
R- 43	90–92	—	2	3	—	12	74	—	3	1	5	—	sand layer
R- 44	93–95	—	4	1	1	5	85	1	—	—	3	—	sand layer
R- 72	27–35	1	2	2	—	15	41	5	24	6	4	—	sand mottles
R- 82	38–42	—	—	—	1	15	67	3	12	1	1	—	sand layer
R-108	75–76	—	2	2	2	13	26	5	45	2	2	1	sand layer
R-116	51–53	—	—	2	—	2	13	17	54	12	—	—	sand layers
R-121	35–42	—	1	1	2	22	36	6	26	4	2	—	sand mottles
R-129	140–150	2	—	1	2	25	25	6	28	7	4	—	sandy mud
R-150	30–40	—	1	2	4	16	38	5	20	8	4	2	sand layers
R-165	25–35	—	—	—	2	13	26	7	29	20	3	—	sand layer
L- 36	22–24	—	1	2	—	17	62	4	12	—	1	1	sand layer
L- 66	387–389	—	2	1	—	24	39	5	23	3	3	—	sand layer
L-190	267–271	—	—	—	—	8	20	8	62	—	2	—	sand layer
L-190	327–329	—	—	—	—	11	24	6	52	3	4	—	sand layer

schencki, and miliolids. R-174, at 807 fathoms in the Sal si Puedes Basin, has a sand layer at 22–25 cm with *Elphidium gunneri*, *Elphidium granulosum*, *Hanzawaia nitidula*, and *Bulimina marginata*.

The composition of the deep-water sands commonly is strikingly different from that of the coarse fraction of the silty clays in which they are intercalated (*see* Appendix C). Planktonic Foraminifera, Radiolaria, and diatoms, which are normally predominant in the silty clays, are scarce or absent in the deep-water sands, where they are replaced by large amounts of terrigenous material, foraminiferal and skeletal carbonate, and glauconite. Mica, where present, generally is reduced in the sand layers with respect to the silty clay.

Three main sand types can be distinguished on the basis of coarse-fraction composition—terrigenous sands, calcarenites or very calcarenitic sands, and glauconitic sands (Fig. 52). Calcarenitic deep-water sands fringe the western margin, where the shelf deposits also are very calcarenitic. The composition of the calcareous fraction of the deep-water sands is very similar to that of the shelf deposits. Elsewhere, where the shelf deposits are predominantly terrigenous, the deep-water sands also are terrigenous in composition.

In a few cores, the coarse fraction is predominantly or entirely glauconitic. Some of these cores come from the top or the flanks of banks or sea mounts (R-45, R-57), but some also are found on the basin slopes. The glauconite occurs in sand mottles or layers, but not in the fine-grained matrix. The proportions of glauconite, ranging from 20 to 80 per cent, are much higher than any encountered in shelf sediments. Similar highly glauconitic sediments have been described from banks off Southern California (Emery, 1960, p. 212–214). They generally are associated with abundant phosphorite, not recognized in the Gulf of California. It is difficult to conceive of a process by which the sparse glauconite of the shelf sediments could have been concentrated to such a high degree, and it is assumed that the deep-water glauconites have formed in place. It may be noted that, with the exception of core R-103 (192 fathoms), all highly glauconitic cores occur below the oxygen minimum zone, in agreement with Emery's observation (1960, p. 212–213) that the

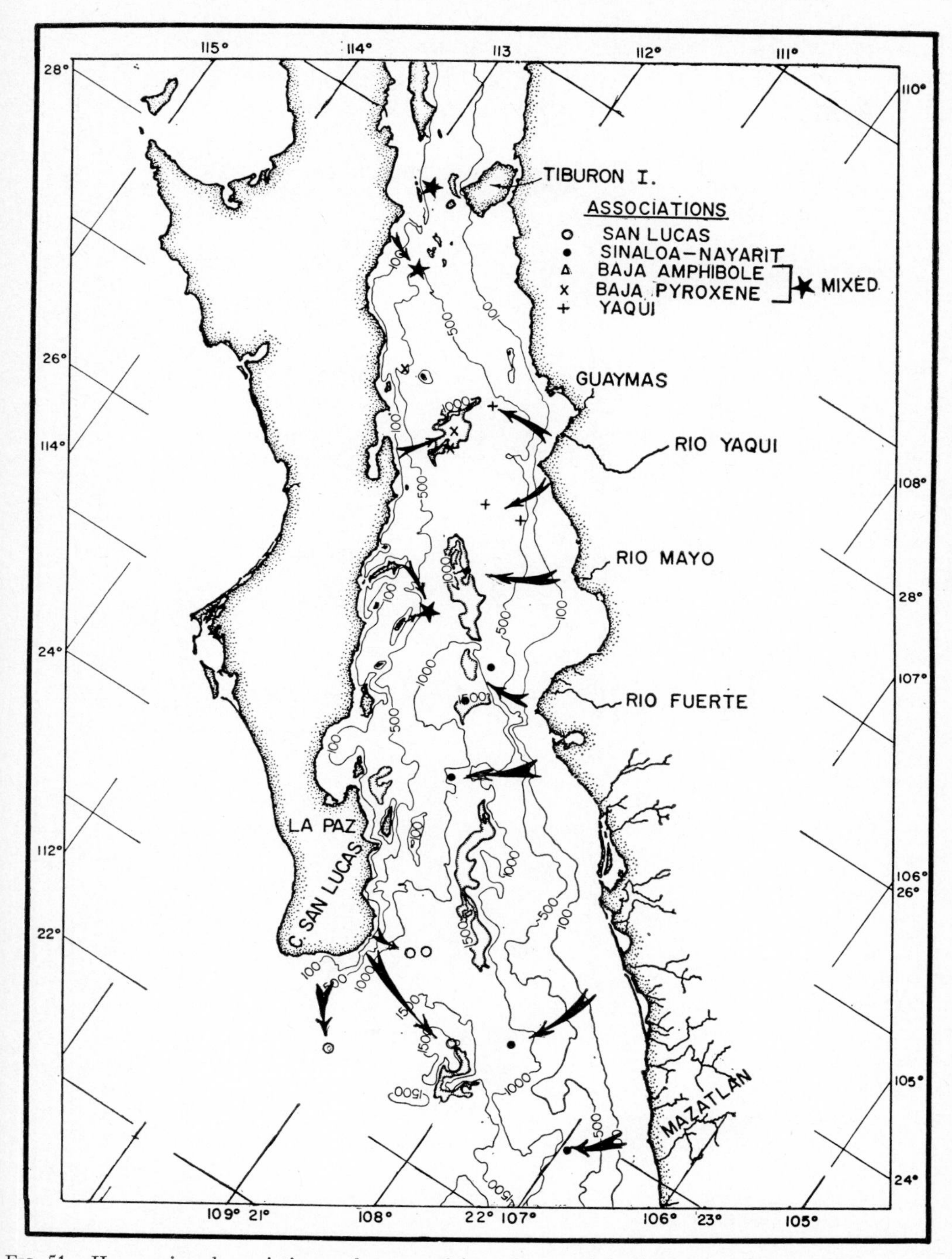

FIG. 51.—Heavy-mineral associations and sources of deep-water sands in the Gulf of California. For definition of associations, see Table VII. Depth contours in fathoms.

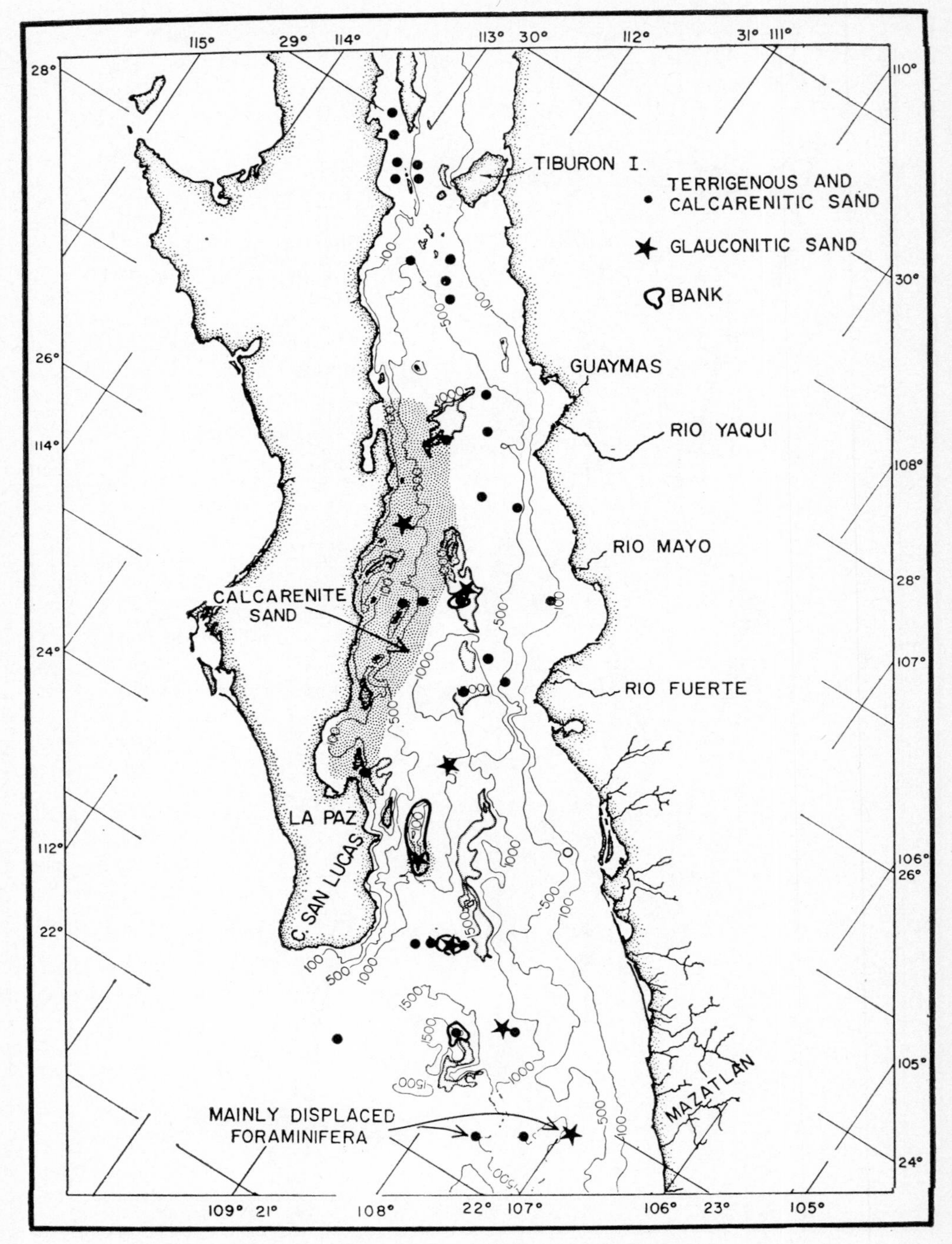

FIG. 52.—Distribution of terrigenous, calcarenitic, and glauconitic deep-water sands in the Gulf of California. Data from Appendix C.

glauconite environment is oxygenated.

A few highly calcareous samples (R-11, R-15, R-33, R-45, R-57) are found in areas where the deep-water sands generally are predominantly terrigenous. In all of these samples, the calcareous material is foraminiferal. Two of the samples (R-45, R-57) are from bank tops in depths of 700–800 fathoms. The high concentration of Foraminifera, here almost entirely planktonic, appears to be due to a low degree of dilution with terrigenous material. Such concentrates of Foraminifera in isolated, exposed locations from the tops of seamounts in the Pacific have been described by Hamilton (1956, p. 33) and are thought to be due to winnowing. The other samples contain mainly benthonic Foraminifera, which in R-11 (the only sample investigated for this purpose) are largely of shallow-water origin (Phleger, oral communication). These samples probably consist of displaced shallow-water calcarenites.

Grain-size analyses have been made of a fairly large number of deep-water sands, mottles, and homogeneous sand-silt-clays. In only a few cases was it possible to take the samples without any contamination by surrounding fine-grained material. Consequently, most size distributions contain varying amounts of silt and clay that are due largely to contamination. In those cases where it can be assumed that no such contamination exists, the sands either are clean or consist of a sand and a clay fraction, with a relatively small amount of silt.

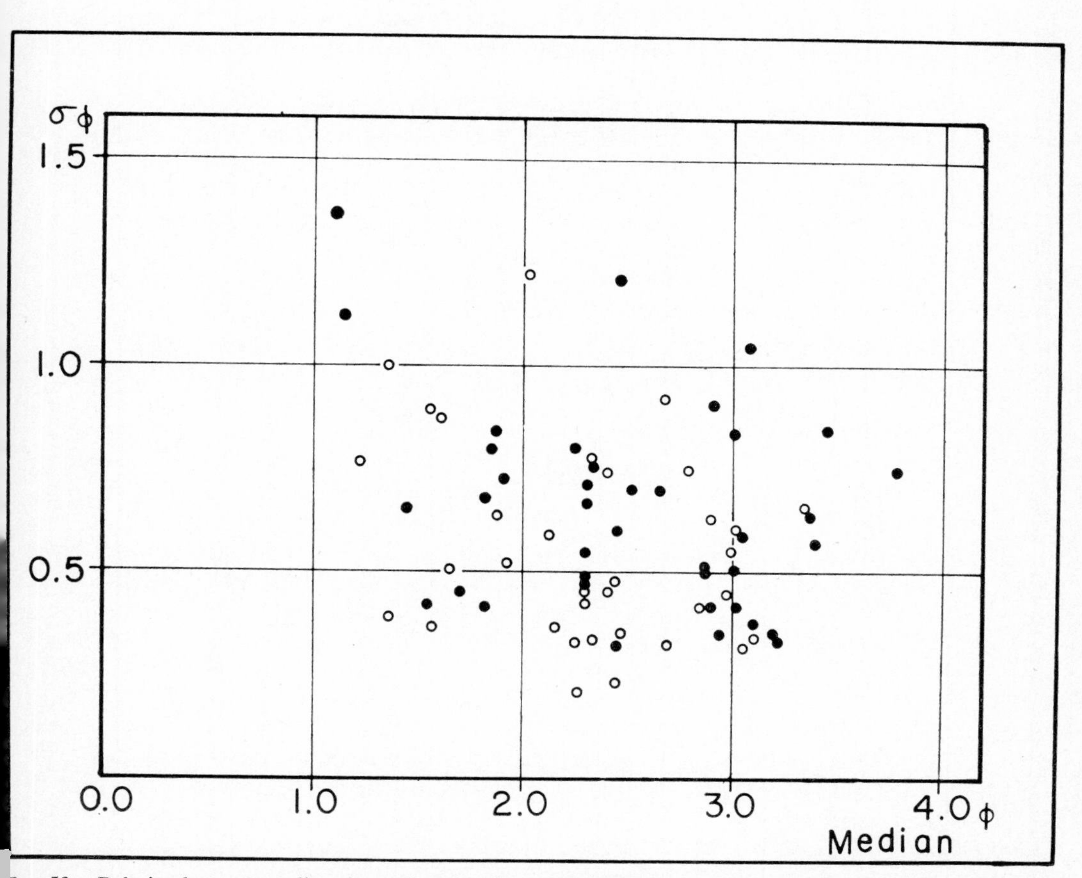

Fig. 53.—Relation between median size and sorting (*phi* standard deviation, Inman, 1952) of sand modes of Gulf of California deep-water (black dots) and shelf (open circles) sands.

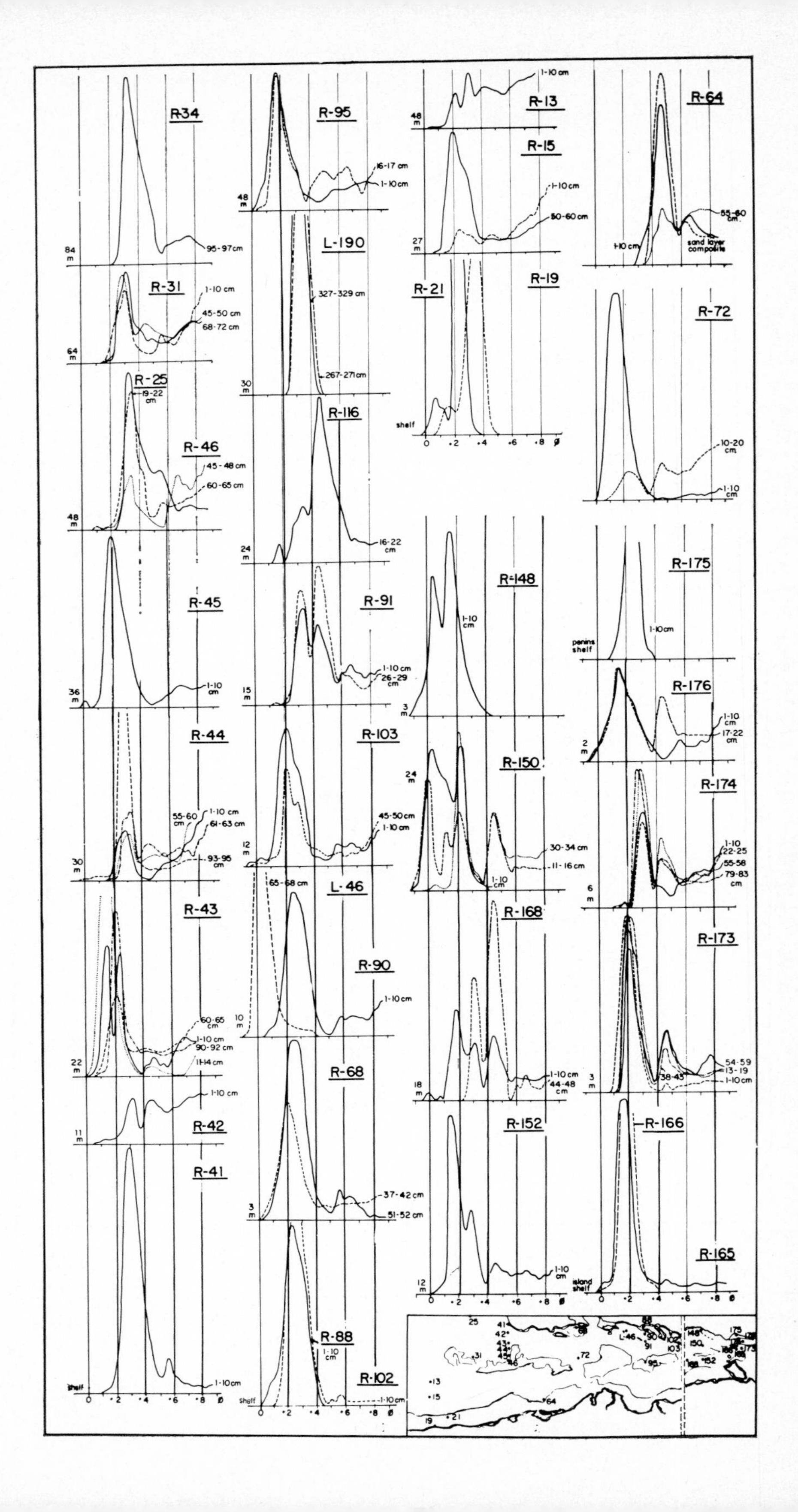

R-34
95-97 cm
84 m
R-31
1-10 cm
45-50 cm
68-72 cm
64 m
R-25
19-22 cm
R-46
45-48 cm
60-65 cm
48 m
R-45
1-10 cm
36 m
R-44
55-60 cm
1-10 cm
61-63 cm
93-95 cm
30 m
R-43
60-65 cm
1-10 cm
90-92 cm
11-14 cm
22 m
R-42
1-10 cm
11 m
R-41
1-10 cm
shelf
R-95
16-17 cm
1-10 cm
48 m
L-190
327-329 cm
267-271 cm
30 m
R-116
16-22 cm
24 m
R-91
1-10 cm
26-29 cm
15 m
R-103
45-50 cm
1-10 cm
12 m
L-46
65-68 cm
R-90
1-10 cm
10 m
R-68
37-42 cm
51-52 cm
3 m
R-88
1-10 cm
R-102
1-10 cm
shelf
R-13
1-10 cm
48 m
R-15
1-10 cm
50-60 cm
27 m
R-21
R-19
shelf
R-148
1-10 cm
3 m
R-150
30-34 cm
11-16 cm
1-10 cm
24 m
R-168
1-10 cm
44-48 cm
18 m
R-152
1-10 cm
12 m
R-64
55-60 cm
sand layer composite
1-10 cm
R-72
10-20 cm
1-10 cm
R-175
1-10 cm
penins shelf
R-176
1-10 cm
17-22 cm
2 m
R-174
1-10
22-25
55-58
79-83 cm
6 m
R-173
54-59
13-19
38-43
1-10 cm
3 m
R-166
R-165
island shelf
0
•2
•4
•6
•8
ø

The sands generally are fine to very fine grained, with a mode between 2.0 and 3.5 *phi*. Sorting, expressed as the graphic *phi* standard deviation (Inman, 1952) of the sand mode to eliminate the effect of contamination with matrix material, generally is fairly good and not significantly different from the sorting of adjacent shelf sands (Fig. 53). Mean size and sorting are similar to that of the California deep-water sands, described by Shepard and Einsele (1962), and of the canyons of the Atlantic coast of the United States (Shepard, 1961b), but are significantly different from the much coarser sand of the deep Atlantic (Ericson and others, 1961).

Representative size-frequency distributions of deep-water sands are shown in Figure 54, grouped by areas and arranged, from bottom to top, in order of increasing distance from the nearest shelf edge. Size distributions of shelf sands have been added for comparison. The extreme left-hand column shows a series of samples from the San Lucas area. Most analyses are unimodal in the sand range with closely similar modes. If allowance is made for variations in peak height due to differences in the admixture of fine-grained material, the similarity of size distributions at different depths in single cores is striking. This phenomenon, also observed in most other areas, suggests a remarkable constancy of depositional conditions at each locality. There is no systematic change in curve shape or modal position with increasing distance from the source, and, with the exception of R-43 and R-45, all curves, including the shelf sand, are very similar. The two exceptions are bank sediments—one highly glauconitic, the other containing much mica and foraminiferal calcarenite.

Considerable uniformity also is exhibited in a set of samples from the Mazatlán region (second column from the right, top), where a mode of approximately 2.0 *phi* can be followed from the shelf edge (R-21) to a distance of 48 miles. The inner shelf sand (R-19) is much coarser. A second mode at 3.25 *phi* occurs in both deep-water sands.

The calcarenitic sands of the central western margin (second column from the left) are much more variable. Many distributions are polymodal. Individual modes are relatively persistent—a 1.50 *phi*, a 2.50–2.75 *phi*, and a 3.25 *phi* mode can be found in many samples. The individual modes are not systematically dependent on composition. Again, the analyses within a single core or at any specific locality are very similar, and there appears to be no relationship between size distribution and distance of transportation. Very coarse sands are found both near the shelf edge (L-46) and at the outer limit of distribution of Peninsular material (R-116).

Sediments in the north-central Gulf are supplied from both sides. The distribution areas are separated by the San Pedro Martir Basin and a high ridge to the west of this basin. In the third column from the left, lower part, cores R-148 and R-150 belong to the western supply zone, whereas R-168 and R-152 are derived from the east. Again, remarkable similarities can be observed within each group, and there is no indication of a systematic change in size distribution with increasing distance from the source.

The best examples of constant texture at any individual depositional locality are provided by cores from the Sal si Puedes Basin (lower right column). Three sets of samples show an apparent shift of the principal mode toward finer sizes, with increasing distance from shallow water. However, the complex topography and the resulting difficulty in adequately determining the transportation distance of the sediments render this shift uncertain, as differences in individual core sources cannot be ruled out.

In summary, the principal features of the size distribution of deep-water sands of the Gulf of

←

FIG. 54.—Size-frequency distributions of Gulf of California deep-water sands. Curves grouped by area, and, wherever possible, from bottom to top in order of increasing distance from shelf edge. Shelf sands from source area are shown at bottom. Approximate distance from shelf is listed at left in nautical miles. Analyses from single core or from samples at same distance are shown in single graph. Column 1 from left, San Lucas area; column 2, central western margin; column 3, lower part, north-central Gulf, upper part, Mazatlán area; column 4, lower part, Sal si Puedes Basin, upper part, Fuerte River region.

California appear to be unimodality, good sorting, absence of systematic changes with increased distance of transportation, and a high degree of constancy of depositional conditions at each locality. This last characteristic suggests a surprising lack of variability of the energy of depositional agents over a reasonably long period of time and a considerable distance.

Some of the sediments discussed in this chapter are bank deposits. Although a few of them exhibit a distinct character of their own (coarse texture, abundant glauconite, large foraminiferal component, strong secondary disturbance), others are fine grained and indistinguishable from slope and basin deposits. Moreover, the special characteristics mentioned appear in several samples that do not occur on banks or seamounts. The variability of the small collection of randomly collected bank samples is not surprising in view of the complexity of bank sedimentation shown by the detailed studies of Emery, Butcher, Gould, and Shepard (1952); Holzman (1952); and Emery (1948).

It is customary to attribute the deposition of deep-water sands of terrigenous origin to turbidity currents. The observations from the Gulf of California neither reject nor support such a mechanism. If turbidity currents were responsible for deposition of most deep-water sands, they appear to have been of minor size and low frequency and to have formed a minor mechanism of sedimentation in the deep southern and central Gulf. It must be remembered that deposition in the deep Gulf still is influenced by the post-Pleistocene transgression, and that modern sediment supply is generally distant from the edge of the shelf. Under the present transgressive conditions, well-sorted littoral basal transgressive sands on the shelf are the main source of supply.

One observation cannot be satisfactorily explained by the turbidity-current theory. Core R-45, from the top of Alarcón Seamount (Fig. 50), contains a highly glauconitic sand in thin, irregular layers and small mottles. The small terrigenous fraction of these layers and mottles has a heavy-mineral assemblage (Appendix A) that leaves little doubt that the sand was derived from the Cape San Lucas area. The mean size of the sand fraction is approximately 3.0 *phi*, and except for its high glauconite content, it is in no way different from adjacent deep-water sands. However, the sample was taken at 782 fathoms on an isolated hill, far above the surrounding Gulf floor at approximately 1,350 fathoms. Similarly, R-43, which has the same heavy-mineral assemblage, is located on another, smaller hill, approximately 100 fathoms above the surrounding sea floor. It is difficult to conceive of a turbidity current that could deposit these very thin sand deposits (2–4 mm) at such a high level above the Gulf floor. The coarse size of the sands appears to exclude suspension transport.

DEPOSITIONAL FACIES AND GEOLOGIC SETTING

The introduction to this paper states as a principal objective the description of depositional facies, their characteristics and regional distribusion, and their control by the geologic setting. The evaluation of the role of the geologic setting requires a comparison between the facies of the Gulf of California and those of other depositional basins. At the present stage of our knowledge of modern marine sedimentation in general, such a synthesis and comparison must be qualitative. Further studies, some of which already are in progress, will have to prove or disprove the validity of the generalizations and conclusions. In this chapter, some broadly generalized inferences will be presented with regard to the objectives stated above, with emphasis on regional trends and large-scale systematic patterns, rather than on local details and anomalies. Consequently, the generalizations presented below must be considered with caution.

DEPOSITIONAL FACIES OF THE GULF OF CALIFORNIA

The numerous sedimentological observations discussed in previous chapters can be summarized in the form of a relatively small number of depositional facies units, in a manner similar to van Andel and Curray's (1960) synthesis of sedimentation in the Gulf of Mexico and on the Orinoco shelf. In this respect, the term *facies* will be considered to denote the sedimentary record of an environment or group of related environments (Ruchin, 1958, p. 339). The term is comparable to Moore's (1949) *lithofacies*.

Facies types of the Gulf of California can be defined on the basis of a combination of textural, compositional, structural, paleontological, and topographic characteristics. The geologic complexity of the Gulf region, the small number of samples, the lack of extensive paleontologic information for many samples, and the virtual absence of adequate studies in the nearshore and coastal environments result in an incomplete list of facies types and a sketchy areal distribution (Fig. 55). For example, very little is known about the Colorado River delta and estuary, the many alluvial fans that border the Gulf, the arid delta of the intermittent Concepción River, the topset and foreset facies of the Fuerte, Mayo, and Yaqui Rivers, the region of coalescing deltas and lagoons between the Fuerte River and Mazatlán, and the numerous lagoons and associated littoral deposits. Other facies form the subject of special studies not yet completed, such as the alluvial and fan-lagoon area of Kino Bay and the Costa de Hermosillo (Curray, in preparation), the extensive tidal flats south of the Colorado River delta (Thompson, in preparation), and the strand plain south of Mazatlán (Curray, in preparation).

Consequently, the facies units used here are less well defined and less complete than those used by van Andel and Curray (1960) in the Gulf of Mexico. Nevertheless, they serve a useful purpose as a summary of sedimentation in the Gulf of California and as a comparison with modern basins elsewhere. The petrographic characteristics of the facies units of the Gulf of California are presented in Table XIII.

In shallow water on the continental shelf, five different facies can be recognized, three of which are sandy. They are well defined in their extreme development, but commonly they appear to grade into each other, so that the boundaries shown in Figure 55 are highly arbitrary.

The rocky, cliff-bound shelves of the entire western margin of most islands and of the mountainous portions of the eastern margin are covered with a *calcarenite shelf facies*, characterized by coarse, fairly well-sorted calcarenite or very calcarenitic sand containing a large variety of skeletal debris. Although the sample pattern is inadequate to supply details, fine-grained deposits appear to be rare, and exposed rock surfaces seem common. The facies is restricted to areas with a very low terrigenous supply.

Terrigenous sands containing little carbonate, which generally are well sorted and medium grained, fringe all other coasts. The actively building bars, spits, and beaches common to Gulf shores belong to this facies. The seaward limit of this facies cannot be determined, because nearly everywhere these sands grade into nondepositional areas, where sands that belong to the post-Pleistocene transgression occur at the surface. These *basal transgressive sands*, first described in detail for the Gulf of Mexico by Curray (1960),

TABLE XIII. AVERAGE PETROGRAPHIC COMPOSITION OF GULF OF CALIFORNIA FACIES

(Number of samples used for each average indicated in parentheses. Values that significantly [rank test, 0.05 level of significance] distinguish a facies from another similar one are shown in bold-face type.)

Facies type	*Median in phi*	*Weight per cent*			*Number per cent*						
		Carbonate	*Organic Carbon*	*Glauconite*	[1]	*Terrigenous*	*Benthonic Foram.*	*Planktonic Foram.*	*Skeletal Carbonate*	*Radiolaria*	*Diatoms*
Calcarenite shelf	2.53 (17)	**30.3 (17)**		0.2 (16)	(18)	51.0	6.3	2.5	**22.4**	0.0	0.2
Littoral	2.76 (18)	**1.2 (15)**		**0.4 (13)**	(13)	87.5	**0.8**	0.5	**3.6**	0.0	0.0
Basal transgressive	2.96 (16)	**8.5 (16)**		**2.0 (23)**	(14)	73.6	**9.0**	5.2	**4.7**	0.0	0.0
Deltaic foreset-bottomset	7.48 (8)	1.9 (2)	**0.97 (3)**	0.0 (8)	(8)	74.6	**2.0**	**1.0**	2.5	0.0	0.7
Shelf silt-clay	7.00 (12)	7.4 (11)	**1.63 (11)**	0.0 (11)	(12)	64.0	**10.0**	**6.5**	2.0	3.0	1.5
Deep-sea fan[2]	7.89 (16)	5.8 (12)	**2.24 (12)**	0.0 (15)	(15)	83.2	0.8	2.0	0.7	6.5	3.6
Terrigenous slope	>9.00 (20)	**10.7 (17)**	**4.60 (17)**	0.0 (20)	(20)	48.7	17.6	**8.1**	**2.1**	14.4	1.2
Calcareous slope	3.81 (4)	**45.2 (4)**		1.3 (10)	(10)	47.6	17.2	**14.5**	**16.7**	7.1	1.0
Diatomite slope	8.83 (8)	**7.5 (8)**	**3.14 (8)**	0.0 (8)	(8)	20.6	10.5	**3.4**	**0.0**	21.7	48.6
Diatomite basin	**8.85** (12)	4.2 (12)	**2.60 (12)**	0.0 (12)	(12)	32.0	6.1	3.5	1.0	10.1	**43.1**
Terrigenous basin	**>9.00** (8)	6.9 (5)	**2.93 (5)**	0.0 (8)	(8)	**63.1**	1.5	**4.5**	0.3	**16.3**	**6.5**
Oceanic	**>9.00** (13)	5.3 (7)	**1.71 (7)**	0.0 (13)	(7)	**41.1**	2.0	**14.3**	0.9	**28.0**	0.0

[1] Number of samples used for all following averages.
[2] Median greatly variable, depending on inclusion of sand layers in samples.

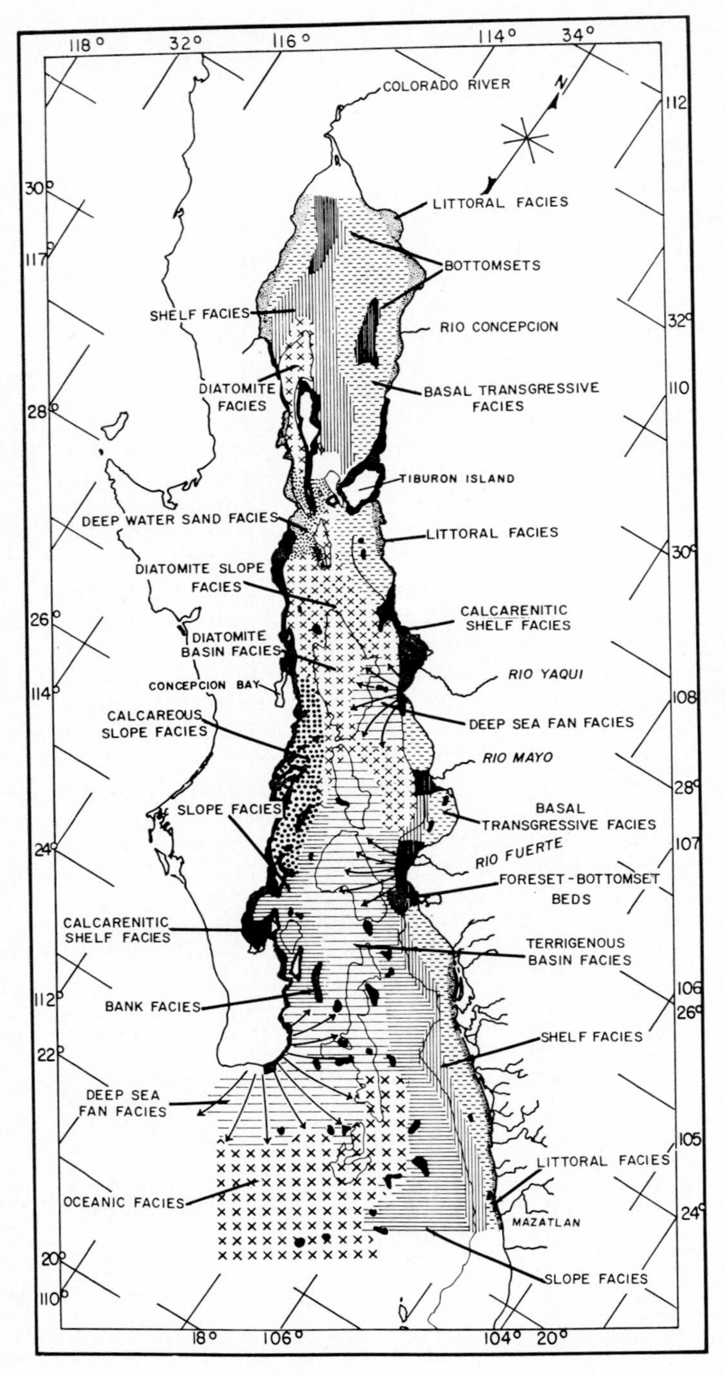

Fig. 55.—Regional distribution of depositional facies in the Gulf of California.

appear to be widespread in the northern Gulf of California and on the eastern shelf. In many places, they are typically developed as mottled or homogeneous, muddy sands with fairly large amounts of Foraminifera, skeletal carbonate, and glauconite. Patchy deposits of highly calcarenitic shelly and foraminiferal sands occur locally within this facies (for example, Stations R-19, R-39, R-100, R-124, R-126). The nearshore origin of at least some of the sands is shown by the occasional occurrence of locally abundant shallow-water Foraminifera, as shown in Table XIV. The early Holocene age of these sands has not been definitely established. However, the striking similarity to early Holocene basal transgressive deposits in the Gulf of Mexico, the occurrence of nearshore Foraminifera and macro-invertebrates (Parker, this volume), and evidence of nondeposition at the present time (formation of glauconite, mottling, extensive distribution of sand) justify the tentative conclusion that they represent predominantly littoral deposits formed during the post-Pleistocene rise in sea level. At present, they are being superficially modified by deposition of Foraminifera and small amounts of modern clay and silt, by reworking by waves and burrowing by organisms, and by the formation of authigenic glauconite.

Not all sands included in the nondepositional facies of Figure 55 are developed in the typical form. Southeast of Tiburón Island and on the shelf north of Mazatlán, purely terrigenous, well-sorted sand, which is indistinguishable from the littoral deposits forming at present, occurs over wide areas. The early Holocene, transgressive nature of these sediments is a mere assumption.

The deltaic sediments of the Gulf of California have not yet been studied in any detail, although a great variety of delta types offers a fertile field of investigation. *Foreset and bottomset beds* occur off the Yaqui and Fuerte River deltas, and probably off the Mayo River delta. The sediments are clayey silts, locally micaceous, with a very low carbonate content and an almost purely terrigenous sand fraction. They contain only small amounts of organic matter, mostly in the form of wood fragments. Commonly they are well laminated, similar to Mississippi (Scruton, 1960; Shepard, 1956) and Orinoco (van Andel and

TABLE XIV. NEARSHORE FORAMINIFERA IN BASAL TRANSGRESSIVE SANDS OF THE NORTHERN GULF OF CALIFORNIA
(Determinations by Jean Peirson Hosmer.)

Station number	*Present depth*	*Nearshore faunal elements (see Phleger, this volume)*
R-194	75 fms	*Bolivina acutula*
R-203	41 fms	*Elphidium* sp.
R-206	98 fms	*Ammonia beccarii*
R-207	97 fms	*Elphidium* sp., *Ammonia beccarii*
R-208	72 fms	*Elphidium* sp., *Ammonia beccarii*

Postma, 1954; Nota, 1958) delta front and prodelta deposits. In the northern Gulf, deposits of clayey silt off the Colorado and Concepción River deltas also have been interpreted as the equivalents of bottomset beds.

The *shelf facies* is fine grained and texturally indistinguishable from the foreset-bottomset facies. This facies, however, is characterized by appreciable numbers of Foraminifera in the sand fraction and fairly high carbon and carbonate contents, indicating a low rate of deposition. Shelf-facies deposits are found on the outer shelf between Mazatlán and the Fuerte River delta in depths ranging from 30 to 150 fathoms, separated by a wide, sandy shelf zone from the streams that supply the silt and clay. They also occur around the deepest part of the northern Gulf in depths between 70 and 200 fathoms.

A large number of facies types can be defined for the deep-water region of the Gulf.

The *deep-sea fan facies* is characterized by the occurrence of thin sand layers interbedded with thick, silty clays and clays. The sands are derived from the adjacent continental shelf, and probably were deposited by turbidity currents, with transportation distances of up to 90 miles. Three deep-sea fan areas have been found, two located off major sediment sources (Fuerte and Yaqui River deltas), and the third at the ends of the numerous submarine canyons cutting the Cape San Lucas shelf. Elsewhere, extensive deep-water sands are uncommon. The deep-sea fans cover both the continental slopes and the basin floor, and there is no well-developed slope facies within their area.

Several *slope facies* can be distinguished. In the southern Gulf and on the Pacific slope off Mazatlán, the slope facies is characterized by silty clays with a very high organic-matter content, a fairly high carbonate content, and large percentages of Radiolaria and benthonic Foraminifera in the coarse fraction. With detailed analysis, a slight decrease in grain size from the slope to the basin floor can be observed (Fig. 44). On the upper slope, the deposits are locally finely laminated.

Along the central western margin, the slope deposits are more coarse grained (silty sands, sand-silt-clay, and clayey silt) and contain from 25 to 40 per cent skeletal carbonate and Foraminifera (largely benthonic). The source of most of the carbonate is the adjacent shelf. Sediments of the entire western slope, even where not coarse grained, are characterized by relatively high carbonate percentages. Although turbidity currents may be the agent of displacement of the coarse calcarenite, it is noteworthy that in comparison with the turbidites of the deep-sea fans, the transportation distances are short. Only rarely do the calcarenites extend to the lower slopes or the basin floors.

Coarse slope sands of graywacke composition and locally graded also cover extensive portions of the north-central Gulf floor and the southern part of the Sal si Puedes and Tiburón Basins.

North of the Fuerte River delta and north of Concepción Bay, the slope facies is fine grained and highly diatomaceous, with only rare sand intercalations. This slope facies differs from the adjacent basin facies by its higher carbonate content along the western side, a higher proportion of coarse biogenous silica, and the occasional occurrence of fine laminations.

The *bank facies* is little known. Studies by Emery and co-workers (Emery, 1960) report a high degree of complexity of bank sediments off Southern California. The few bank samples available from the Gulf of California similarly vary from coarse, mottled, glauconitic, and foraminiferal sands to calcareous silty clays.

Three types of *basin facies* can be distinguished. In the central Gulf, the high organic productivity caused by the Gulf circulation pattern results in the deposition of highly diatomaceous sediments, which contain up to 50 per cent biogenous opal. In the southern Gulf, biogenous components are much less prominent, and terrigenous silty clays, homogeneous in structure and relatively poor in organic carbon, carbonate, and biogenous coarse fraction components, are found. Outside the Gulf, the *oceanic facies* is similar to the southern Gulf basin facies, except for an even lower organic-carbon content and a marked predominance of Radiolaria and planktonic Foraminifera in the entire coarse fraction.

The borderland off Southern California contains a series of basins which generally increase in depth and sill depth from the continent outward. Emery (1960, Table 14) has demonstrated that the properties of the sediments in these basins change systematically with distance from land and decreasing terrigenous influence. The Gulf of California possesses a similar series of basins increasing in depth from northwest to southeast (Table I). The basin sequence, however, is parallel, not perpendicular, to the continental margins. Consequently, no such systematic change in sediment properties is to be expected. Table XV shows that the basins can be divided into two groups—a diatomaceous group in the north-central Gulf, where productivity is highest and terrigenous dilution lowest, and a radiolarian-terrigenous group in the southern Gulf. The basin deposits are not markedly different from those of intervening sills and adjacent lower slopes, because none of the basins is stagnant below sill depth.

CONTROL BY GEOLOGIC SETTING

In a comparative study of the marginal-marine and shelf facies of the Gulf of Mexico and the Orinoco region, van Andel and Curray (1960) have demonstrated the importance of the relative rates of sediment supply, of marine reworking and transportation, and of sea-level change as principal factors that control the characteristics and distribution of depositional facies. In those regions the source areas are distant, the influence of structure on relief, and of relief on facies, is minor, and climate appears to be a factor of local and secondary importance. Oceanographic conditions are similar to those prevailing in the adjacent open ocean. The marine factor is represented primarily by wave and current action, and it varies with the degree of exposure, fetch of waves, and current patterns. The effect of all factors of the geologic setting is clearly discernible in the texture and composition of the sediments, the

TABLE XV. COMPARISON OF PETROGRAPHIC CHARACTERISTICS OF INDIVIDUAL GULF OF CALIFORNIA BASINS[1]

Basin	*Depth (fathoms)*	*Number of Samples*	*Median phi*	*Mean in phi*	*Standard deviation*	*Carbonate (per cent)*	*Organic carbon (per cent)*	*In per cent by number 0.25–0.06 mm fraction*					
								Terrigenous	*Benthonic Foraminifera*	*Planktonic Foraminifera*	*Skeletal carbonate*	*Diatoms*	*Radiolaria*
Sal si Puedes	830	(5)	9.00	7.36	1.38	10.9	2.32	31	10	6	6	39	6
San Pedro Martir	540	(4)	8.74	7.08	1.38	7.5	2.84	25	1	2	1	66	8
Guaymas	1,090	(5)	8.73	7.16	1.23	7.0	2.75	44	3	4	1	39	17
Carmen	1,480	(4)	9.00	7.37	1.18	9.5	2.97	41	7	5	1	45	29
Farallón	1,740	(7)	8.88	7.23	1.24	6.7	2.54	46	5	9	0	6	26
Pescadero	2,030	(3)	9.00	7.33	1.29	5.2	3.57	49	1	1	1	9	38
Pacific Ocean	1,700	(7)	9.00	7.41	1.25	5.3	1.71	41	2	14	1	0	28
La Paz	440	(1)	9.00	6.90	0.95	18.6	6.03	13	41	3	0	11	27

[1] Numbers given are averages.

dispersal patterns, and the regional facies distributions.

In the following pages the term *depositional basin* will be used loosely to denote depositional areas that can be considered homogeneous with respect to the geologic setting. The term does not carry the connotation of a closed, bowl-shaped depression.

The Gulf of California has a geologic setting which in many respects differs markedly from those of the basins mentioned above. Both the shape and the internal relief of the basin are primarily modeled by tectonic activity (Rusnak and others, this volume; Phillips, this volume). Most source areas are close to the depositional basin and possess rugged topography. With the exception of the Colorado River region, the rate of sediment supply is strongly influenced by climatic variations. The basin is sufficiently enclosed and separate from the Pacific Ocean to produce a well-defined circulation system that results in high organic productivity. Marine reworking and redistribution of sediments vary greatly with relief and with a whole spectrum of exposure to waves.

The following hierarchy of control, although entirely theoretical, is useful in discussing the influence of the various factors of the geologic setting on the distribution of depositional facies.

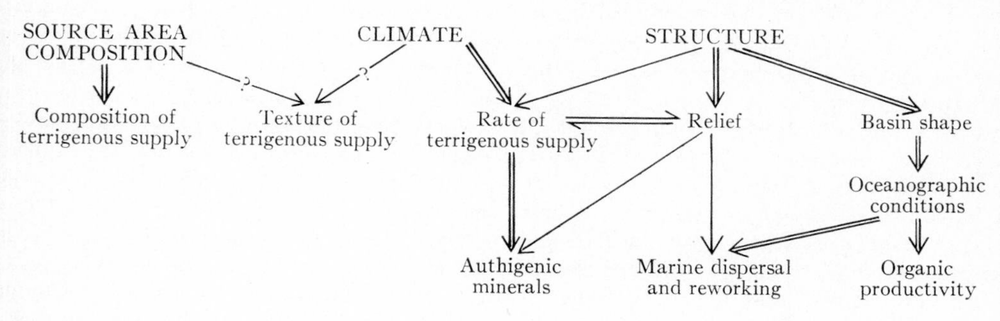

The influence of this system of factors is clearly reflected in the Gulf facies. It has been discussed in previous pages with respect to individual sediment properties, but it will be briefly summarized here.

The influence of source-area composition on the composition and rate of sediment supply has been discussed in the section on sediment sources. The unstable volcanic and batholithic source areas, all located close to the Gulf basin, provide a highly immature arkosic or graywacke sediment that is modified very little before deposition. In general, the composition of the sand fraction closely agrees with existing concepts of tectonic control of sedimentation, but, in detail, the rapid variation of source-area composition is clearly reflected in the Gulf sediments. The dispersal of sediments in the central and southern Gulf is predominantly at right angles to the basin strike. In the northern Gulf, on the other hand, the sediments are derived from a distant, regional source; their composition reflects source area composition less directly; and they are of greater maturity.

Climate, through control of the rate of supply, has a strong influence on the facies pattern. Much of the Gulf hinterland is extremely arid. Where rainfall is very low, such as on the Peninsula of Baja California, on most islands, and in the mountainous stretches of the eastern margin north and south of Tiburón Island, sediment supply is primarily a result of erosion of cliffs and alluvial fans. As a result of the very low and largely intermittent sediment supply, the shelf deposits in these areas are coarse and highly calcareous. Prograding of shorelines is very limited. The influence of the zones of low sediment supply extends to the slope deposits, which, in this area, are very calcareous (Fig. 52). This influence also is reflected in the position of the boundary between eastern and western supply, which is located well west of the Gulf axis (Fig. 19).

Along the eastern side of the Gulf, the rainfall gradually increases from northwest to southeast. North of Guaymas, streams are few and seasonal, and in many areas coastal erosion provides most of the sediment. In this zone of intermediate and intermittent sediment supply, there is sufficient time for very complete reworking of the sediment by waves, even though the fetch is fairly short and wave action is moderate. The littoral sediments are coarse grained, and fine-grained products of winnowing are deposited far offshore (*see* the Concepción bottomsets, Fig. 55). Deposition is mainly restricted to the nearshore zone, but extensive coastal prograding occurs, for example, in the Concepción River delta and in the lagoon region southeast of Tiburón Island.

South of Guaymas, rainfall in the mountains of the hinterland is adequate to maintain sizable, permanent streams. Three large rivers provide local areas of moderately large sediment supply (Table IV). Farther south, the number of streams per unit length of the coast is greatly increased and sediment supply is fairly high and uniform along the entire coastline.

As a result, south of Guaymas coastal prograding in the form of deltas, lagoon-bar complexes, and strand-plain sections is active. Fine-grained sediments are widespread. Where the local rate of supply is high, as off the Yaqui and Fuerte Rivers, even the slope and adjacent basin-floor facies clearly reflect the presence of the streams. These facies are characterized by a strong predominance of terrigenous components, compared with the more biogenous slope sediments elsewhere.

In the control of the facies distribution, the influence of the rate of sediment supply is counteracted by the rate of marine reworking and dispersal. The wave regime in the southern and central Gulf is strongly influenced by the shape and orientation of the basin. South of the Fuerte River delta, the east coast is exposed to the Pacific swell, modified only by a narrow shelf. In this zone, the coast progrades slowly by sand-bar accretion, forming a broad, sandy strand plain and sandy littoral and offshore deposits (Curray and Moore, this volume). North of Mazatlán, in a zone of slightly higher sediment supply, fine-grained lagoonal and deltaic deposits become more common, but the coast still progrades by marine processes, essentially as a straight line. The fine products of wave-winnowing are deposited fairly far offshore as a narrow zone of silty shelf sediments, slowly accreting on the outer shelf and upper slope and in the deep basin beyond.

Farther north, the rate of supply is higher than the rapidly decreasing rate with which waves can rework the sediment, and major delta complexes form, which extend nearly to the edge of the shelf. The shelf deposits in the vicinity of these deltas are fine grained. Between major delta complexes, little sediment is supplied, and the shelf is again sandy, even though wave action is moderate.

The northern Gulf is essentially a separate basin with its own sediment supply, wave regime and current pattern, and it is only partially understood. Nowadays, the Colorado River supplies a very fine-grained sediment which is deflected to the west and which settles predominantly in the deepest portions of the Gulf below 100 fathoms. In the much larger shallow portion of the basin, the sediment supply is low enough and wave turbulence is high enough to cause essentially nondepositional conditions everywhere except in the immediate nearshore zone.

The shape of the Gulf controls the main circulation system, which results in a high rate of organic productivity along the margins and in the north-central portions. The high productivity is directly reflected in large accumulations of biogenous opal wherever dilution by terrigenous material is low. The silica for these deposits probably is derived very largely from the Pacific Ocean. Similarly, the high productivity is the cause of a high organic-matter content in all deep-water sediments.

The organic matter, when settling through a water column, maintains a pronounced oxygen minimum approximately between 100 and 700 fathoms. Where the Gulf bottom intersects this zone, slope facies are formed that are locally laminated and preserve, in the absence of burrowing organisms, a high organic-matter content.

Evidence of the influence of the Gulf floor relief can be found in the development of coarse, glauconitic and foraminiferal facies on isolated banks, with a low supply of terrigenous sediment. This influence also is found in the existence of an extensive fan facies with thin turbidite layers of a minor sediment source, where submarine canyons provide channeling of the sediment stream (Cape San Lucas). Other examples no doubt exist, but they have not been detected with the very open sampling grid available.

COMPARISON WITH OTHER MODERN BASINS

In recent years, the study of modern sediments has made considerable progress. In particular, a large body of information on shallow-water sediments in areas of high terrigenous supply is now available. For deep-water environments, the situation is as yet less favorable, although a considerable number of studies exist in the Russian literature (*see*, for example, Strakhov and others, 1961) which, unfortunately, are inaccessible to the present author.

Counterparts of the calcarenite shelf facies of the Gulf of California have been described from several areas. An interesting case is given by Koldewijn (1958) for the shelf north and east of the island of Trinidad, northeastern South America. In this region, which is well supplied with large sediment-carrying rivers, the reduction of terrigenous supply needed to form this facies is provided by very large, shallow banks at some distance offshore. The resulting calcarenites and very calcarenitic sands are very similar to those of the Gulf of California.

The Gulf of California facies found in shallow water in areas of medium-to-high rates of sediment supply closely compare with the description of facies from the Gulf of Mexico (van Andel and Curray, 1960), the Orinoco Shelf (Nota, 1958; van Andel and Postma, 1954), and the Rhone Shelf in the Mediterranean (Kruit, 1955; van Straaten, 1959b). The marine deltaic, shelf, and basal transgressive facies all find their counterparts in these basins. On a regional basis, however, the Gulf of California shelf sediments are considerably more sandy, and nondepositional conditions are more widespread, than in the other basins mentioned. In the Gulf of California, approximately 70 per cent of the total shelf area is covered with sand, whereas in the Gulf of Mexico between the Mississippi and the Rio Grande Rivers, the figure is closer to 50 per cent. In the Orinoco region, less than 45 per cent of the shelf surface is sand. Even though a somewhat more coarse-grained supply from the nearby and arid source areas of the Gulf of California may be part of the cause, it is probable that the high degree of sandiness is due largely to a low rate of sediment supply as compared to the rate of marine reworking.

In the Orinoco region and in the Gulf of Mexico, the rate of supply and the rate of marine reworking were found to be the principal factors controlling sediment distribution. The supply rate in these basins is essentially independent of basin climate because of the large and distant source areas. In the Gulf of California, the same factors control shallow-water sedimentation, but the supply rate is strongly dependent on climate.

Knowledge of deep-water facies and sediment petrography is much more limited. Extensive studies of the basins of the borderland of Southern California have been made by Shepard, Emery and co-workers (*see* Emery, 1960), but elsewhere only limited investigations have been published, such as of the Atlantic continental slope (Stetson, 1949), the Gulf of Mexico slope and Sigsbee Deep (Stetson, 1953; Trask, 1953), and the Peru-Chile Trench (Trask, 1961; E-an Zen, 1959). Available pertinent information has been summarized in Table XVI. Because of the large difference in terrigenous supply, the eastern and western slope deposits of the Gulf of California are listed separately.

Although the Gulf of California sediments are being deposited closer to land than in any other area, except for a few California basins, these sediments and those of the Gulf of Mexico are the finest. As a result of their foraminiferal calcarenite content, only the deposits from the western slope fall in the same range as do the others. The figures suggest that grain size is a complex function of the proportion between terrigenous and marine components (foraminiferal carbonate), the geologic setting of the region, and the distance from land, rather than of the latter alone.

The carbonate content of all Gulf of California deep-water sediments is low. Only the Peru-Chile Trench has lower values, which are attributed (Trask, 1961) to solution during settling in this very deep trench. The low carbonate content of the Gulf of California is certainly due to a very high degree of dilution with fine terrigenous material. On the other hand, the organic carbon content is very high, comparable only to the values found in the California borderland. Even the Peru-Chile Trench, a region of known high organic productivity, has considerably lower values. If the low carbonate content is due to terrigenous dilution, then the high carbon values of the Gulf sediments indicate an exceedingly high productivity.

Information on biogenous opal in the literature is scarce. E-an Zen (1959) reports abundant diatoms and Radiolaria from the Peru-Chile Trench; Hülsemann and Emery (1961) describe laminated diatomites from the Santa Barbara Basin in the California borderland which form and are preserved at the bottom of an essentially stagnant basin, whereas the laminated diatomites of the Gulf of California are preserved on the slopes of a ventilated basin. For the California borderland as a whole, diatomites are a very minor lithological constituent (Emery, 1960, p. 247) in an association predominated by terrigenous muds and marine foraminiferal carbonate.

Deep-water sands have been reported in many of the areas listed in Table XVI. In nearly all cases they are described as common and prominent (Sigsbee Deep—Ewing, Ericson, and Heezen, 1958; Atlantic Slope—Stetson, 1949; Peru-Chile Trench—E-an Zen, 1959; Santa Monica and San Pedro Basins—Gorsline and Emery, 1959). Although quantitative information is available for only the latter region, the impression is that the very subordinate importance of such deep-water sands in the Gulf of California is exceptional.

Consequently, by virtue of low carbonate content, abundant organic matter and biogenous opal, and the minor role of turbidites, the Gulf of California deep-water facies differ significantly from the deposits of other modern deep basins near the continental margin. Sediment sources are close to the basin, and effective winnowing takes place on a relatively wide shelf, so that only very fine differentiates reach the deeper portions of the basin. Further, organic productivity is high and concentrated, due to the shape of the basin. These are the factors that are, in large measure, responsible for this difference.

RATES OF SEDIMENTATION

The sediments of the Gulf of California are composed of several major constituents which are derived from fundamentally different sources. In the central Gulf, biogenous opal, derived from plankton, forms probably more than 50 per cent of the total sediment accumulation. Biogenous carbonate, probably partially generated on the shelf, contributes between 10 and 40 per cent of the deposits along the western margin of the central Gulf. Elsewhere, sediments are predominantly composed of terrigenous material which is supplied at markedly different rates in different areas. From the total body of circumstantial evidence presented in previous chapters, the highest sedimentation rates can be inferred for the Guaymas Basin and the north-central Gulf, where a high rate of diatom production combines with an ample terrigenous supply from the Yaqui River. Slightly lower rates can be expected for the northern Sal si Puedes Basin, where most of the fine-grained sediment of the Colorado River settles, and for the Farallón and Carmen Basins and the adjacent eastern slope off the Fuerte and Mayo

TABLE XVI. COMPARISON OF PETROGRAPHIC CHARACTERISTICS OF BASIN AND SLOPE SEDIMENTS OF THE GULF OF CALIFORNIA AND OTHER MODERN DEEP-WATER BASINS[1]
(Averages of available data; number of samples indicated in parentheses.)

Basin	*Median microns*	*Trask sorting (So)*	*%CaCO₃*	*% Organic carbon*	*Distance from Continent (nautical miles)*
GULF OF CALIFORNIA					
Eastern slope	<2–3 (33)		6.1 (27)	3.62 (29)	15–70
Basin	<2–3 (47)		4.6 (30)	2.54 (30)	20–70
Western slope	4 (22)		12.7 (17)	4.22 (15)	5–25
ATLANTIC COAST, U.S.A. (Stetson, 1949)					
Slope	64 (29)	3.25			60–120
GULF OF MEXICO (Stetson, 1953; Trask, 1953)					
Slope	2 (170)	3.42 (166)	21.3 (750)	1.02 (750)	35–300
Sigsbee Deep	2 (33)	3.82 (33)	28.0 (750)	0.63 (750)	300
PERU-CHILE TRENCH (Trask, 1961)					
Upper slope	} 4 (81)	4.4 (17)	} 0.5 (21)	2.43 (31)	30–60
Lower slope and basin		2.6 (7)		0.63 (51)	60–120
CALIFORNIA OFFSHORE BASINS (Emery, 1960)					
Slope	4 (107)	2.7 (71)	19.0 (63)	1.6 (30)	
Basin (summary)	5 (549)	3.9 (384)	20.0 (420)	3.9 (80)	
Santa Barbara Basin	5 (36)	3.4 (33)	11.6 (43)	3.2 (10)	5–20
Santa Monica Basin	9 (165)	3.2 (54)	8.6 (42)	3.2 (13)	5–25
San Pedro Basin	8 (95)	3.6 (63)	10.2 (30)	3.6 (14)	2–17
San Diego Basin	6 (30)	4.6 (30)	10.8 (17)	4.0 (2)	15–30
Santa Cruz Basin	4 (24)	3.6 (24)	15.5 (34)	4.7 (11)	20–45
Santa Catalina Basin	4 (37)	3.7 (35)	18.0 (48)	4.8 (8)	30–55
San Clemente Basin	4 (56)	4.2 (54)	14.4 (57)	3.2 (4)	40–60
San Nicolas Basin	4 (35)	3.9 (33)	26.1 (29)	4.5 (4)	60–95
East Cortes Basin	4 (14)	3.2 (14)	26.1 (27)	3.6 (3)	80–100
No Name Basin	5 (1)	2.1 (1)	12.4 (10)	2.6 (1)	75–85
Tanner Basin	5 (27)	3.4 (24)	34.4 (21)	6.5 (4)	100–115
West Cortes Basin	6 (13)	3.7 (13)	38.8 (32)	3.6 (4)	110–125
Long Basin	3 (16)	3.2 (16)	30.6 (30)	2.7 (2)	120–150

[1] Carbon percentages for California offshore basins obtained from Emery's (1960, Table 12) organic matter values by division by 1.8. Distances are very approximate.

River deltas. Low rates should occur along the central western slope and in the entire southern Gulf, which are far removed from major sources of sediment.

These conclusions are partially supported by bathymetric evidence. As Figure 5 shows, extensive flat bottom and subsurface echoes, indicating the presence of 10–25 feet of very poorly consolidated sediment, are found in the Guaymas Basin and in the north-central Gulf. Very soft sediment also seems to occur in the northern Sal si Puedes Basin. Elsewhere, subsurface echoes are absent, and flat bottom is restricted to very small portions of the basin floors.

A few measurements of radiocarbon ages of sediments are available to evaluate these deductions. The radiocarbon ages, provided by G.S. Bien of the La Jolla Natural Radiocarbon Laboratory, Scripps Institution of Oceanography, are based on measurements of total carbon, both organic and carbonate, extracted by combustion from 20–40 cm sections from the top and bottom of six gravity cores and one piston core. The results are listed in Table XVII. Because fairly long core sections were needed to supply sufficient carbon, composite ages were obtained which, for the purpose of this discussion, are assumed to be centered at the midpoints of the samples.

The use of total carbon was dictated by the need for short sample sections of the small-diame-

TABLE XVII. RADIOCARBON DATES AND SEDIMENTATION RATES OF CORES IN THE GULF OF CALIFORNIA

Area	*Core Number*	*Depth (fathoms)*	*Sample depth in core (cm)*	*Radiocarbon age (years)*	*Extrapolated surface age (years)*	*Calculated rate of deposition in cm per 1,000 years*	*Corrected rate in cm per 1,000 years*	*Per cent carbonate*	*Per cent organic carbon*
Sal si Puedes Basin	R-190	465	0–20 84–104	2,730±150 3,260±200	2,650	158	316		2.01
Guaymas Basin	L-190	1,035	0–40 297–350	3,560±200 4,670±250	3,500	273	273	2.9	2.91
Farallón Basin	R- 82	1,730	0–25 65–85	2,250±200 3,530±170	1,975	50	100	2.7	1.79
Pescadero Basin	R- 47	1,542	0–25 75–100	2,590±125 5,850±250	2,025	23	46	4.0	4.05
Western slope	R- 79	885	0–30 61–86	2,200±150 4,080±200	1,700	30	60	11.6	6.55
Eastern slope, Fuerte R.	R- 85	400	0–25 145–170	1,600±100 5,040±250	1,300	42	84	5.7	2.83
Eastern slope, Mazatlán	R- 16	750	0–30 64–89	6,270±300 17,250±700	4,000	6	12	6.0	7.44

SEDIMENTATION RATES IN OTHER AREAS IN CENTIMETERS PER 1,000 YEARS

Area	Rate	Area	Rate
North Pacific (Goldberg and Koide, 1962)	0.1–0.4	Santa Barbara Basin (Emery and Bray, 1962)	114
Mississippi bottomsets (Shepard, 1956)	1,000	San Pedro Basin (do.)	54
Gulf of Paria (van Andel and Postma, 1954)	500	Santa Catalina Basin (do.)	29
Orinoco Delta (do.)	1,000	Continental slope, California (do.)	19
		Deep-sea floor, California (do.)	8

ter cores. Emery and Bray (1962) have shown that in the California borderland, coarse foraminiferal carbonate ages, with few exceptions, are higher by several hundred years than the corresponding organic-carbon ages. For fine-grained carbonate, the observed differences are small. The Gulf of California samples contain mainly fine-grained carbonate, and the ages obtained do not appear to be systematically related to the carbonate percentage.

A sedimentation rate in centimeters per thousand years and a surface age have been calculated by extrapolation, assuming a constant rate of sedimentation for the time intervals concerned. For most samples, this assumption is reasonable, as only a 3,000- to 5,000-year interval is considered. However, Broecker and others (1958) have shown that in the Atlantic, around 11,000 years B.P., a marked decrease in sedimentation rate took place. Similar changes in sedimentation rate prior to 5,000 years B.P. have been observed in the basins of the California borderland (Emery and Bray, 1962). As a result, the sedimentation rate and surface age of core R-16 may be significantly too high.

The extrapolated surface ages are high. The significance of such high surface ages, also observed in the sediments of the California borderland and the Atlantic Ocean, and of their apparent relation to topography, is not clear. Emery and Bray (1962) have extensively discussed possible explanations, but did not reach a satisfactory conclusion; the Gulf of California data do not shed further light on the problem except to confirm its existence. In order to obtain sedimentation rates from the age measurements, it is necessary to assume that the discrepancy between real age and surface age has been the same throughout the period of sedimentation considered.

Except for L-190, a piston core, all cores have

been shortened considerably by the coring process. No measurements of the amount of compression were made during sampling, but from published data (Emery and Dietz, 1941; Emery and Bray, 1962), a shortening of at least 50 per cent must be expected, which is in agreement with non-systematic observations of Gulf of California cores. Thus, sedimentation rates for these cores have to be approximately doubled to render them comparable to the rate of core L-190.

Insufficient information is available to correct for the effect of natural compaction. However, for the upper 100 cm used for most dates, this effect would be on the order of only 10 per cent—well within the margin of error of the data; nearly the same results are obtained in terms of uncorrected thickness, as in terms of weight deposited per unit area. In the highly diatomaceous core L-190 (probably more than 50 per cent opal—S.E. Calvert, oral communication), the effect of compaction may be more significant and different from that in the other cores, resulting in a disproportionally high apparent sedimentation rate.

The data of Table XVII show that, in accordance with expectation, the highest rates of deposition occur in the Guaymas and northern Sal si uedes Basins. If we assume that at least 60 per cent of the sediment accumulating in the Guaymas Basin is diatomaceous, and that initial compaction is somewhat lower than that in purely terrigenous cores, then the residual terrigenous deposition rate is approximately the same as in the Farallón Basin to the south. The terrigenous sedimentation rates show a clear relationship to the presence or absence of abundant supply of sediment, and the expected decrease on the western slope and in the southern Gulf does occur. Murray and Moore (this volume) have estimated that, as a result of the post-Pleistocene transgression, sedimentation on the slope south of Mazatlan should be very slow at present. On the other hand, it must have been rapid during the Pleistocene low stand and after a prolonged high stand when coastal progradation has reached the edge of the shelf. Comparison of the rates of R-16 and 85 supports this assumption.

The sedimentation rates observed are generally high and compare with rates in nearshore basins of the California borderland. They are several orders of magnitude higher than deposition in the open Pacific.

If we assume that no further subsidence will take place in the Gulf of California and that present sedimentation rates are typical for long time intervals, some approximate estimates concerning the ultimate filling of the basin can be made. Assuming a final gravity compaction of the deposits to 30 per cent of their original thickness (Hamilton, 1959; Emery and Bray, 1962), the northern Gulf will fill to present sea level in approximately 1.6×10^6 years. During this interval, the north-central Gulf and Guaymas Basin will fill with diatomite to a level of approximately 200 fathoms below present sea level, and the area off the Mayo and Fuerte River deltas will fill with terrigenous sediment to 1,000 fathoms. It appears probable that, as the central Gulf shoals, the main area of diatom deposition will shift southward with a resulting increase of the sedimentation rate in the Carmen and Farallón Basins. Also, present-day terrigenous sedimentation rates are probably low, because of the effect of the post-Pleistocene transgression, so that calculated levels of fill can be considered minima.

From these admittedly very speculative considerations, a facies model (Potter, 1959) can be constructed with the following characteristics. In the axial portion of the central and southern Gulf, the lowermost portion of the sedimentary fill will consist of terrigenous silty clays, locally interbedded with thin turbidites, and thickening southward. They will be overlain by a much thicker section of diatomite, which is laminated in the laterally thinning slope parts of the basin. The facies pattern will be characterized by a westward progradation of fine-grained slope deposits covered with a relatively thin section of coarser-grained shelf and deltaic sediments. Of the total thickness finally deposited, more than 75 per cent should consist of deep-water facies. As far as the sediment supply is concerned, it should be predominantly from the east, with a dispersal pattern perpendicular to the basin axis. Only in the very last phase of fill is longitudinal supply from the Colorado River probable.

REFERENCES

Anderson, C.A., 1950, Geology of islands and neighboring land areas, part 1 *of* The 1940 E.W. Scripps Cruise to the Gulf of California: Geol. Soc. America Mem. 43, 53 p.

——— Durham, J.W., Shepard, F.P., Natland, M.L., and Revelle, R.R., 1950, The 1940 E.W. Scripps Cruise to the Gulf of California: Geol. Soc. America Mem. 43, 362 p.

Arrhenius, G., 1950, Carbon and nitrogen in subaquatic sediments: Geochim. et Cosmochim. Acta, v. 1, p. 15–22.

——— 1952, Sediment cores from the east Pacific: Swedish Deep-Sea Exped. Repts., v. 5, pt. 1, p. 85.

Bader, R.G., 1955, Carbon and nitrogen relations in surface and subsurface marine sediments: Geochim. et Cosmochim. Acta, v. 7, p. 205–211.

Bandy, Orville L., 1961, Distribution of Foraminifera, Radiolaria, and diatoms in sediments of the Gulf of California: Micropaleontology, v. 7, no. 1, p. 1–26.

Beal, Carl H., 1948, Reconnaissance of the geology and oil possibilities of Baja California, Mexico: Geol. Soc. America Mem. 31.

Bramlette, M.N., 1946, Monterey Formation of California and origin of its siliceous rocks: U.S. Geol. Survey Prof. Paper 212.

Broecker, W.S., Turekian, K.K., and Heezen, B.C., 1958, The relation of deep-sea sedimentation to variations in climate: Am. Jour. Sci., v. 256, p. 503–517.

Byrne, J.V., 1957, The marine geology of the Gulf of California: Unpub. Ph.D. thesis, Univ. Southern Calif.

——— and Emery, K.O., 1960, Sediments of the Gulf of California: Geol. Soc. America Bull., v. 71, no. 7, p. 983–1010.

Chayes, F., 1949, A simple point counter for thin-section analysis: Am. Mineralogist, v. 34, nos. 1–2, p. 1–11.

Cloud, P.E., 1955, Physical limits of glauconite formation: Am. Assoc. Petroleum Geologists Bull., v. 39, no. 4, p. 484–492.

Crow, E.L., Davis, F.A., and Maxfield, M.W., 1960, Statistics manual: Dover Publications, New York, 288 p.

Curray, J.R., 1960, Sediments and history of Holocene transgression, continental shelf, northwest Gulf of Mexico, *in* Recent Sediments, Northwest Gulf of Mexico: Am. Assoc. Petroleum Geologists, p. 221–266.

——— 1961a, Tracing sediment masses by grain-size modes: Internat. Geol. Cong., 21st, Copenhagen, Denmark, Repts., v. 23, p. 119–130.

——— 1961b, Late Quaternary sea level—a discussion: Geol. Soc. America Bull., v. 72, no. 11, p. 1707–1712.

Dapples, E.C., Krumbein, W.C., and Sloss, L.L., 1953, Petrographic and lithologic attributes of sandstones: Jour. Geology, v. 61, no. 4, p. 291–317.

Debyser, J., 1961, Contribution á l'étude géochimique des vases marines: Soc. Éditions Technip, Paris, 249 p.

de Czerna, Z., 1961, Tectonic map of Mexico: Geol. Soc. America.

Doeglas, D.J., 1946, Interpretation of the results of mechanical analysis: Jour. Sed. Petrology, v. 16, no. 1, p. 19–40.

Dryden, L., 1931, Accuracy in percentage representation of heavy mineral frequencies: Nat. Acad. Sci. Proc., v. 17, p. 233–238.

Durham, J. Wyatt, and Allison, E.C., 1960, The geologic history of Baja California and its marine faunas: Systematic Zoology, v. 9, no. 2, p. 47–91.

Eisenhart, C., 1935, A test for the significance of lithological variations: Jour. Sed. Petrology, v. 5, p. 137–145.

Emery, K.O., 1948, Submarine geology of Ranger Bank Mexico: Am. Assoc. Petroleum Geologists Bull., v. 32, no. 5, p. 790–805.

——— 1960, The sea off Southern California: Joh Wiley & Sons, New York, 366 p.

——— and Bray, E.E., 1962, Radiocarbon dating o California basin sediments: Am. Assoc. Petroleum Geologists Bull., v. 46, no. 10, p. 1839–1856.

——— Butcher, W.S., Gould, H.R., and Shepard, F.P. 1952, Submarine geology off San Diego, California Jour. Geology, v. 60, no. 6, p. 511–548.

——— and Dietz, R.S., 1941, Gravity coring instru ment and mechanics of sediment coring: Geol. Soc America Bull., v. 52, p. 1685–1714.

——— and Hülsemann, Jobst, 1963, The relationship of sediments, life, and water in a marine basin: Deep Sea Research, v. 8, p. 165–180.

——— and Rittenberg, S.C., 1952, Early diagenesis o California basin sediments in relation to origin of oil Am. Assoc. Petroleum Geologists Bull., v. 36, no. 5 p. 735–806.

Ericson, D.B., Ewing, M., Wollin, G., and Heezen B.C., 1961, Atlantic deep-sea sediment cores: Geol Soc. America Bull., v. 72, no. 2, p. 193–286.

Ewing, M., Ericson, D.B., and Heezen, B.C., 1958 Sediments and topography of the Gulf of Mexico, *in* Habitat of oil: Am. Assoc. Petroleum Geologists p. 995–1053.

Fisk, H.N., and McFarlan, E., Jr., 1955, Late Quater nary deltaic deposits of the Mississippi River, *in* Crust of the earth: Geol. Soc. America Spec. Pape 62, p. 279–302.

Folk, R.L., 1954, The distinction between grain siz and mineral composition in sedimentary-rock nomen clature: Jour. Geology, v. 62, no. 4, p. 344–359.

——— 1956, The role of texture and composition i sandstone classification: Jour. Sed. Petrology, v. 26 no. 2, p. 166–171.

Geological Society of America, 1951, Rock-color chart reprint of National Research Council chart, 1948.

Goldberg, E.D., 1958, Determination of opal in marin sediments: Jour. Marine Research, v. 17, p. 178–182

——— and Koide, Minoru, 1962, Geochronologica studies of deep-sea sediments by the ionium/thoriur method: Geochim. et Cosmochim. Acta, v. 26, p. 417 450.

Goldstein, August, Jr., 1959, Cherts and novaculites c Ouachita facies, *in* Silica in sediments: Soc. Ecor Paleontologists and Mineralogists Spec. Pub. 7, p 135–149.

Gorsline, D.S., and Emery, K.O., 1959, Turbidity current deposits in San Pedro and Santa Monic Basins off Southern California: Geol. Soc. Americ Bull., v. 70, no. 3, p. 279–290.

Hamilton, E.L., 1956, Sunken islands of the mid-Pacif mountains: Geol. Soc. America Mem. 64, 97 p.

——— 1959, Thickness and consolidation of deep-se sediments: Geol. Soc. America Bull., v. 70, p. 1399 1424.

Harvey, H.W., 1960, The chemistry and fertility of se waters: Cambridge Univ. Press, 240 p.

Hayes, J.R., and Klugman, M.A., 1959, Feldspar stai ing methods: Jour. Sed. Petrology, v. 29, no. 2, p 227–232.

Holzman, J.E., 1952, Submarine geology of Cortes an Tanner banks: Jour. Sed. Petrology, v. 22, no. p. 97–118.

ülsemann, Jobst, and Emery, K.O., 1961, Stratification in recent sediments of Santa Barbara Basin as controlled by organisms and water character: Jour. Geology, v. 69, no. 3, p. 279–290.
ıman, D.L., 1952, Measures for describing the size distribution of sediments: Jour. Sed. Petrology, v. 22, no. 3, p. 125–145.
—— and Chamberlain, T.K., 1955, Particle-size distribution in nearshore sediments, *in* Finding ancient shorelines: Soc. Econ. Paleontologists and Mineralogists Spec. Pub. 3, p. 106–129 [Jan. 1956].
'es, R.L., 1962, Dating of the 1746 eruption of Tres Virgenes volcano, Baja California del Sur, Mexico: Geol. Soc. America Bull., v. 73, no. 5, p. 647–648.
etchum, B., and Redfield, A.C., 1949, Some physical and chemical characteristics of algae growth in mass cultures: Cellul. Compar. Physiol. Jour., v. 33, p. 281.
lein, G.D., 1963, Analysis and review of sandstone classifications in the North American geological literature, 1940–1960: Geol. Soc. America Bull., v. 74, no. 5, p. 555–576.
nill, J.L., 1959, Axial and marginal sedimentation in geosynclinal basins: Jour. Sed. Petrology, v. 29, no. 3, p. 317–325.
oldewijn, B.W., 1955, An examination of the light fraction, part 2 *of* Provenance, transport, and deposition of Rhine sediments: Geologie en Mijnbouw, v. 17, no. 2, p. 37–45.
—— 1958, Sediments of the Paria-Trinidad shelf, *in* Reports of the Orinoco shelf expedition: Mouton & Co., The Hague, v. 3, p. 1–109.
ruit, C., 1955, Grain size and microfauna, part 1 *of* Sediments of the Rhone Delta: Kon. Ned. Geol. Mijnbouwk Gen. Verhand., v. 15, no. 3, p. 357–499.
rumbein, W.C., 1959, Trend surface analysis of contour-type maps with irregular control-point spacing: Jour. Geophys. Research, v. 64, no. 7, p. 823–834.
rynine, P.D., 1948, The megascopic study and field classification of sedimentary rocks: Jour. Geology, v. 56, no. 2, p. 130–165.
uenen, P.H., 1950, Marine geology: John Wiley, New York, 568 p.
—— 1957, Longitudinal filling of oblong sedimentary basins: Kon. Ned. Geol. Mijnbouwk Gen. Verhand. v. 18, p. 189–196.
ejorado, S.H.S., compiler, 1956, Carta geologica de la Republica Mexicana; escala 1:2,000,000: Internat. Geol. Cong., 20th, Mexico, D.F., 1956.
iller, R.L., 1956, The relation of sediment-size parameters to current-wave systems and physiography, part 1 *of* Trend surfaces—their application to analysis and description of environments of sedimentation: Jour. Geology, v. 64, no. 5, p. 425–446.
oore, D.G., and Scruton, P.C., 1957, Minor internal structure of some recent unconsolidated sediments: Am. Assoc. Petroleum Geologists Bull., v. 41, no. 12, p. 2723–2751.
oore, R.C., 1949, Meaning of facies, *in* Sedimentary facies in geologic history: Geol. Soc. America Mem. 39, p. 2–34.
unk, W.H., 1941, Internal waves in the Gulf of California: Jour. Marine Research, v. 4, no. 1, p. 81–91.
ɔta, D.J.G., 1958, Sediments of the western Guiana shelf: Meded Landbouw. te Wageningen, v. 58, no. 2, p. 1–98.
.ckham, G.H., 1954, Sedimentary structures as an important factor in the classification of sandstones: Am. Jour. Sci., v. 252, no. 8, p. 466–476.
Pettijohn, F.J., 1957, Sedimentary rocks: Harper & Bros., New York, 718 p.
Phleger, F.B, 1960, Ecology and distribution of recent Foraminifera: The Johns Hopkins Press, Baltimore, Md., 297 p.
Poole, D.M., 1958, Heavy mineral variation in San Antonio and Mesquite bays of the central Texas coast: Jour. Sed. Petrology, v. 28, no. 1, p. 65–74.
Potter, P.E., 1959, Facies model conference: Science, v. 129, p. 1292–1294.
Pratt, W.L., 1962, The origin and distribution of glauconite from the sea floor off California and Baja California: Unpub. Ph.D. thesis, Univ. Southern Calif.
Rao, M. Subba, 1960, Organic matter in marine sediments off east coast of India: Am. Assoc. Petroleum Geologists Bull., v. 44, no. 10, p. 1705–1713.
Raupach, F. von, 1952, Die Rezente Sedimentation in Schwarzen Meer, in Kaspi und im Aral und ihre Gesetzmässigkeiten: Geologie, v. 1, no. 1, p. 78–132.
Revelle, R.R., 1939, Sediments of the Gulf of California [abs.]: Geol. Soc. America Bull., v. 50, no. 12, p. 1929.
——— 1950, Sedimentation and oceanography—survey of field observations, part 5, *of* The 1940 E.W. Scripps cruise to the Gulf of California: Geol. Soc. America Mem. 43, 6 p.
Roden, G.I., 1958, Oceanographic and meteorological aspects of the Gulf of California: Pacific Sci., v. 12, no. 1, p. 21–45.
——— and Groves, G.W., 1959, Recent oceanographic investigations in the Gulf of California: Jour. Marine Research, v. 18, no. 1, p. 10–35.
Ruchin, L.B., 1958, Grundzüge der Lithologie: Akademie-Verlag, Berlin, 806 p.
Russell, R. Dana, 1937, Mineral composition of Mississippi River sands: Geol. Soc. America Bull., v. 48, no. 9, p. 1307–1348.
Scruton, P.C., 1960, Delta building and the deltaic sequence, *in* Recent Sediments, Northwest Gulf of Mexico: Am. Assoc. Petroleum Geologists, p. 82–102.
Shepard, F.P., 1950, Submarine topography of the Gulf of California, part 3 *of* The 1940 E.W. Scripps Cruise to the Gulf of California: Geol. Soc. America Mem. 43.
——— 1954, Nomenclature based on sand-silt-clay ratios: Jour. Sed. Petrology, v. 24, no. 3, p. 151–158.
——— 1956, Marginal sediments of Mississippi Delta: Am. Assoc. Petroleum Geologists Bull., v. 40, no. 11, p. 2537–2623.
——— 1961a, Submarine canyons of the Gulf of California: Internat. Geol. Cong., 21st, Copenhagen, Denmark, Repts. v. 26, p. 11–23.
——— 1961b, Deep-sea sands: Internat. Geol. Cong., 21st, Copenhagen, Denmark, Repts. v. 23, p. 26–42.
——— 1963, Submarine geology: Harper & Row, New York, 2d ed.
——— and Einsele, G., 1962, Sedimentation in San Diego trough and contributing submarine canyons: Sedimentology, v. 1, no. 2, p. 81–133.
——— Phleger, F.B, and van Andel, Tj.H., editors, 1960, Recent sediments, northwest Gulf of Mexico: Am. Assoc. Petroleum Geologists.
Stetson, H.C., 1949, The sediments and stratigraphy of the east coast continental margin, Georges Bank to Norfolk Canyon: Papers in Phys. Oceanog. and

Meteor., Mass. Inst. Tech. and Woods Hole Oceanog. Inst., v. 9, no. 2, p. 1–60.

——— 1953, The continental terrace of the western Gulf of Mexico—its surface sediments, origin, and development, part 1 *of* The sediments of the western Gulf of Mexico: Papers in Phys. Oceanog. and Meteor., Mass. Inst. Tech. and Woods Hole Oceanog. Inst., v. 12, no. 4, p. 1–45.

Strakhov, N.M., Bezrukov, P.L., and Yablokov, V.S., 1961, Proc. Conf. on recent sediments of seas and oceans, May 24–27, 1960: Acad. Sci. U.S.S.R., Comm. Sed. Rocks, 1961.

Strøm, K.M., 1939, Land-locked waters and the deposition of black mud, *in* Recent marine sediments: Am. Assoc. Petroleum Geologists, p. 356–372; reprinted by Soc. Econ. Paleontologists and Mineralogists *as* Spec. Pub. 4, 1955.

Sverdrup, H.U., 1939, The Gulf of California—preliminary discussion on the cruise of the E.W. Scripps in February and March, 1939: 6th Pacific Sci. Cong. Proc., v. 3, p. 161–166.

Taliaferro, N.L., 1933, The relation of volcanism to diatomaceous and associated siliceous sediments: Univ. Calif. Dept. Geol. Sci. Bull., v. 23, p. 1–56.

Tate, Merle W., and Clelland, R.C., 1959, Nonparametric and shortcut statistics: Interstate Printers and Publishers, Illinois, 171 p.

Trask, P.D., 1953, Chemical studies of sediments of the western Gulf of Mexico, part 2 *of* The sediments of the western Gulf of Mexico: Papers in Phys. Oceanog. and Meteor., Mass. Inst. Tech. and Woods Hole Oceanog. Inst., v. 12, no. 4, p. 49–120.

——— 1961, Sedimentation in a modern geosyncline off the arid coast of Peru and northern Chile: Internat. Geol. Cong., 21st, Copenhagen, Denmark, Repts., v. 23, p. 103–118.

van Andel, Tj. H., 1959, Reflections on the interpreta-tion of heavy mineral analyses: Jour. Sed. Petrology, v. 29, no. 2, p. 153–163.

——— 1960, Sources and dispersion of Holocene sedi-ments, northern Gulf of Mexico, *in* Recent sediment northwest Gulf of Mexico: Am. Assoc. Petroleum Geologists, p. 34–55.

——— and Curray, J.R., 1960, Regional aspects c modern sedimentation in northern Gulf of Mexic and similar basins, and paleogeographic significanc *in* Recent sediments, northwest Gulf of Mexico: Am Assoc. Petroleum Geologists, p. 345–364.

——— and Poole, D.M., 1960, Source of recent sed-ments in the northern Gulf of Mexico: Jour. Se Petrology, v. 30, no. 2, p. 91–122.

——— and Postma, H., 1954, Recent sediments of th Gulf of Paria, *in* Reports of the Orinoco shelf exped-tion, v. 1: Kon. Nederl. Akad. Wetensch. Verh., v 20, no. 5, 245 p.

van Straaten, L.M.J.U., 1959a, Minor structures of some recent littoral and neritic sediments: Geologi en Mijnbouw, v. 21, no. 7, p. 197–216.

——— 1959b, Littoral and submarine morphology o the Rhone Delta: Proc., 2d Coastal Geomorph. Conf La. State Univ., Coastal Studies Inst., p. 233–264.

Weyl, R., 1952, Zur Frage der Schwermineralverwi-terung in Sedimenten, I, Erscheinungsbild un Vorkommen: Erdohl und Kohle, v. 5, p. 29–33.

Williams, H., Turner, F.J., and Gilbert, C.M., 195 Petrography—an introduction to the study of rock in thin sections: W.H. Freeman & Co., San Francisc 406 p.

Zen, E-An, 1959, Mineralogy and petrography of marin bottom sediments off the coast of Chile and Peru Jour. Sed. Petrology, v. 29, no. 4, p. 513–539.

APPENDIX A

Analyses of Gulf of California Heavy-Mineral Provinces

(Percentages by number; surface samples.[1] For locations *see* Fig. 1.)

Station	*Tourmaline*	*Zircon*	*Apatite*	*Garnet*	*Epidote*	*Amphiboles*	*Basaltic Hornblende*	*Augite*	*Hypersthene*	*Titanite*	*Other*
1. Colorado River Provinces											
R-184	2	1	2	3	14	47	13	10	6	2	
R-185	1	4	4	2	18	42	3	11	7	8	
R-186	3	7	1	2	12	48	4	8	9	5	1
R-192	2		6		24	45	8	7	6	1	1
R-193	2		6	1	19	54	5	10	3		
R-194		4	1	10	13	38	5	14	11	1	3
R-203				5	20	35	2	25	8	2	3
R-204	3	2		8	15	37		27	6		2
R-205	2	2	1	5	21	40	3	18	4	1	3
R-206	3	1	3	2	16	47	5	16	4	1	2
R-209	5	2	4	1	19	39	2	21	4	3	
R-213	2	3	5	6	19	42	3	15	4	1	
R-214	3	3	4	4	23	47	1	9	1	3	2
R-215	5	2		3	19	47	5	10	1	1	7
R-216	4	1	4	2	21	43	3	15	4	2	1
R-217	6	1	3	3	17	35	5	24	2	1	3

[1] For subsurface samples, see Table XII.

APPENDIX A—(*continued*)

Station	*Tourmaline*	*Zircon*	*Apatite*	*Garnet*	*Epidote*	*Amphiboles*	*Basaltic Hornblende*	*Augite*	*Hypersthene*	*Titanite*	*Others*
2. Concepción River Province											
R-197	4	5	4	7	40	23	4	5	3	3	2
R-198	5		1	5	39	35	2	8		4	1
R-200	2	2	2	3	44	31	3	6	3	3	1
R-201	4	4	3	4	51	20	1	9	1	2	1
R-202	2	2	4	8	43	30	3	6	1	1	
R-212	1	2	4	4	48	24	1	5	4	5	2
3. Kino Bay Province											
R-138		3	2	1	21	44	5	22	1	1	
R-141	1	3	2	3	17	50	10	8	3	2	1
R-142	1	4	1	2	29	43	3	11		6	
R-145	1	1	1	6	18	35	3	21	7	7	
R-146	1	2	2	6	22	42	3	17	3	2	
R-152	1	2	1	11	20	39	6	14	2	3	1
R-153	1	4	1	6	39	30	3	12	2	1	1
R-154	1	4	2	4	35	33	6	8	1	6	
R-155	1	7	1	4	29	38	5	10	2	3	
R-158		6	2	7	15	33	7	14	10	5	1
R-161	14	1	7	6	18	37	5	6	4	2	
R-169	1	2	1	4	20	47	5	15	2	3	
R-171	1	5	2	5	18	35	4	13	4	12	1
C-422		4	2	2	25	41	1	19	1	5	
C-438			1	6	22	33	5	24	1	7	1
C-450		2	2	1	22	56	4	7	2	3	1
C-452		3	1	5	28	34	6	16	2	4	1
C-457		4		5	29	40	6	13		3	
C-464		4		3	22	53	7	7	1	3	
4. Yaqui Province											
R-105	3	2	11	1	13	34	11	17	5	3	
R-109	1	1	2	1	16	35	4	33	2	3	2
R-111	1	3	1	1	11	27	5	41	3	6	1
R-114	2		2	4	26	26	4	30	3	2	1
R-115	1	2	1		14	34	5	38	3	2	
5. Sinaloa-Nayarit Complex											
R- 21		2	1	5	27	43		16	4	2	
R- 23	1	8			27	40	1	12	6	2	3
R- 39	1			5	21	30	8	19	12	2	2
R- 40		3	5	6	23	39	1	18	2	1	2
R- 52	2	3	1	2	33	40	1	8	8	2	
R- 59	1		1	3	26	39	1	25	2	2	
R- 65	1		2	1	22	46	1	22	2	1	2
R- 74			2	8	20	41	3	20	4	1	1
R- 75	1	1	3		23	45	3	20	3		1
R- 76		1	1	6	34	33		17	3	2	3
R- 77	1	1	3	4	29	29		22	5	2	4
R- 87			1	6	17	49	3	14	4	4	2
R- 95	1		2	4	19	44	2	20	2	3	3
R- 97			5	2	15	52	2	17	3	3	1
R-100		1	1	1	18	38	6	28	4	1	2
R-101	1	2	2		31	36	2	17	3	4	2
C-137		1		2	22	40	3	26	3	3	

APPENDIX A—(*continued*)

Station	*Tourmaline*	*Zircon*	*Apatite*	*Garnet*	*Epidote*	*Amphiboles*	*Basaltic Hornblende*	*Augite*	*Hypersthene*	*Titanite*	*Others*
AMPHIBOLE GROUP IN SINALOA-NAYARIT COMPLEX											
R- 18			1		30	51	4	11	1	2	
R- 19		2	1		23	54		14	3	3	
R- 53	3	1	2	3	26	52	2	6	3	2	
R- 61	1		2	3	20	63	1	9	1		
R- 63		1	1	1	19	54	2	17	2		3
R- 82			1		10	64	2	17	3	2	1
R-123					17	64	6	10	2		1
R-124		1		3	26	42	2	17	2	4	3
C-137			1		22	63	8	4	1	1	
6. ACAPONETA EPIDOTE PROVINCE											
C- 60			1		48	8	1	35	7		
C-323			2	1	47	21	1	22	6		
C-325	7	1			42	17	15	14	2	1	1
C-338		2	1	1	42	21	2	27	2	1	1
C-341	1	4	1	1	40	30	4	16	2	1	
C-355		2		1	39	40	4	12	2		
C-361			1		32	27	5	25	9	1	
C-368		1	3	3	35	29	3	18	5	2	1
C-372		5		2	34	22	4	27	2	3	1
C-376	1	10			43	24	5	14		2	1
7. SANTIAGO AUGITE PROVINCE											
C- 31				1	20	13		54	11		1
C- 32			1		15	5		65	13	1	
C- 33					8	7		71	12		2
C- 34		3	1		8	9	2	66	9		2
C- 53	1				14	20	3	52	9		1
C- 57		2	2		14	5	1	61	15		
C- 85		2			15	10		63	10		
C-109					6	3	1	76	14		
C-292		2			16	6	4	50	20	1	1
C-295		2			18	11	6	51	11	1	
C-298		1			20	21	2	42	14		
C-305			1		20	15	4	43	17		

(*Continued on facing page*)

APPENDIX C

Composition of Deep-Water Sands and Bank Sediments in the Gulf of California
(Composition of associated fine-grained deposits shown for comparison.)

Station	*Sample depth in cm*	*% 0.06–0.25 mm in sand fraction*	*In per cent by number of 0.06–0.25 mm fraction*							*Texture*[2]	*Lithology*
			Terrigenous	*Mica*	*Glauconite*	*Foraminifera*	*Skeletal carbonate*	*Radiolaria*	*Diatoms*		
R- 11	1–10	—	32	8	1	6	—	38	—	silty clay	homogeneous
	67–69	—	17	2	1	73	—	2	—	clayey silt	3–30 mm layers
R- 13[1]	1–10	91	84	7	—	—	—	4	—	sand-silt-clay	homogeneous
R- 15	1–10	91	2	1	1	80	—	5	—	silty clay	homogeneous
	50–60	67	8	—	79	—	—	7	—	sand-silt-clay	mottled, 10 mm layer
R- 25	1–10	—	13	75	—	1	—	9	—	silty clay	homogeneous
	19–22	99	74	19	—	5	—	2	—	sand-silt-clay	2 mm layers
R- 31[1]	1–10	97	50	4	1	1	—	39	2	sand-silt-clay	homogeneous
	45–50	99	61	1	16	13	1	3	—	sand-silt-clay	15 mm layer
	68–72	99	48	5	25	2	—	10	—	sand-silt-clay	homogeneous
R- 33	1–10	—	31	6	1	5	—	—	—	clay	homogeneous
	58–62	—	24	1	—	65	4	5	—	silty clay	mottled
R- 34	1–10	—	48	4	1	1	—	39	2	silty clay	homogeneous
	95–97	100	85	5	4	6	—	—	—	silty sand	mottled
R- 43[1]	1–10	90	61	23	—	2	4	9	—	sand-silt-clay	mottled
	11–14	72	83	14	—	1	—	2	—	sand	mottled
	60–65	97	60	15	—	19	2	4	—	sand-silt-clay	homogeneous
	82–85	—	81	7	—	9	1	1	—	sand-silt-clay	1–3 mm layers
	90–93	99	74	4	—	15	3	2	—	sand-silt-clay	3 mm layer
R- 44	1–10	97	70	20	11	2	—	2	—	silty clay	homogeneous
	55–60	96	83	1	11	4	—	—	—	silty clay	homogeneous
	61–63	99	72	11	3	—	—	4	—	sandy silt	2 mm layer, mottled
	93–95	97	85	6	—	1	—	38	—	sand-silt-clay	18 mm layer
R- 45[1]	1–10	67	26	—	23	50	—	—	—	clayey sand	mottled, layered
R- 46	1–10	—	35	21	2	1	—	38	—	silty clay	homogeneous
	45–48	98	71	1	2	18	—	4	—	silty clay	mottled
	60–65	98	75	2	3	17	—	2	—	sand-silt-clay	homogeneous
	65–71	—	54	4	—	26	—	14	—	clayey silt	mottled
R- 57[1]	1–10	—	20	5	8	50	1	12	—	silty clay	homogeneous
	78–85	73	18	—	60	18	—	—	—	sand-silt-clay	homogeneous
R- 61[1]	1–10	—	83	2	1	7	—	7	—	silty clay	homogeneous
R- 64	1–10	100	88	6	—	2	—	2	—	clayey silt	2 mm layers
	55–60	—	94	2	—	—	—	1	—	clayey silt	homogeneous
	—[3]	100	99	—	—	—	—	—	—	sandy silt	2 mm layers
R- 68	1–10	100	24	1	—	28	42	5	—	clayey silt	laminated
	37–40	45	11	—	—	27	59	1	—	silty sand	32 mm graded layer
	41–51	100	51	1	—	12	31	2	—	clayey silt	laminated
	51–52	77	12	1	—	27	57	—	—	sand	11 mm graded layer
R- 72	1–10	24	26	3	61	2	1	4	1	sand	mottled
	11–20	69	63	—	28	1	7	—	—	silty clay	mottled
R- 82	1–10	—	53	9	—	3	1	9	23	silty clay	homogeneous
	38–42	—	89	2	—	1	7	—	—	sand-silt-clay	2 mm layers
R- 91	1–10	99	48	4	—	37	1	5	1	sand-silt-clay	layered, mottled
	26–29	98	76	—	—	23	1	—	—	sandy silt	layered
R- 92	1–10	—	8	1	—	32	2	25	27	silty clay	homogeneous
	50–51	—	16	—	—	50	13	15	—	silty clay	4 mm layer
R- 95[1]	1–10	24	57	4	12	16	3	2	2	clayey sand	homogeneous
	16–17	45	79	—	14	5	—	—	—	sandy silt	mottled
	29–30	—	78	—	9	12	—	—	—	sand-silt-clay	layer
	55–57	—	52	—	10	26	8	2	—	sand-silt-clay	mottled
R- 99	1–10	—	57	6	—	—	—	23	10	clayey silt	homogeneous
	107–109	99	99	1	—	—	—	—	—	sand-silt-clay	mottled
R-103	1–10	70	23	4	23	44	5	—	—	clayey sand	homogeneous
	45–50	82	55	1	40	—	—	—	—	sand-silt-clay	homogeneous
R-108	1–10	—	59	1	—	6	—	—	21	silty clay	homogeneous
	75–76	—	88	6	—	2	—	—	2	silty sand	3–4 mm layers
R-108	94–96	—	19	1	—	—	—	—	77	clayey silt	3–4 mm layers
R-116	1–10	—	29	2	—	7	1	17	34	clayey silt	homogeneous
	16–22	88	98	1	—	1	—	—	—	sandy silt	2 cm layer
	31–34	—	37	—	2	12	3	7	39	silty clay	homogeneous
	51–53	—	92	—	—	4	2	1	—	clayey silt	3 mm layers
	60–65	—	59	2	1	25	3	1	4	silty clay	homogeneous
R-120	1–10	—	6	—	—	5	1	21	66	silty clay	homogeneous
	18–20	—	57	—	—	25	1	11	6	silty clay	5 mm layer
	95–100	—	49	—	—	6	34	6	3	silty clay	homogeneous
R-121	1–10	—	47	1	4	19	2	8	12	clayey silt	homogeneous
	35–42	—	92	—	4	2	—	—	—	silty clay	mottled
R-150	1–10	25	69	1	10	12	8	—	—	sand	layered
	11–16	30	66	1	8	14	7	—	—	silty sand	layered
R-150	30–34	94	78	—	5	9	4	1	—	sandy silt	layered
R-152	1–10	47	89	—	3	1	1	1	2	silty sand	mottled
R-160	1–10	97	44	5	2	14	11	2	16	sand-silt-clay	mottled
R-165	1–10	23	72	4	7	3	13	—	—	sand	mottled

[1] Bank samples.
[2] Texture of sample as collected. Many samples are contaminated with material outside sand layer or mottle. To provide criteria for evaluation of composition data, percentage of 0.06–0.25 mm fraction in total sand fraction is presented in column 3.
[3] Composite of eleven 1–2 mm sand layers.

APPENDIX C—(*continued*)

Station	*Sample depth in cm*	*% 0.06–0.25 mm in sand fraction*	*In per cent by number of 0.06–0.25 mm fraction*							*Texture*[2]	*Lithology*
			Terrigenous	*Mica*	*Glauconite*	*Foraminifera*	*Skeletal carbonate*	*Radiolaria*	*Diatoms*		
R-168	1–10	63	89	—	8	—	1	—	—	sand-silt-clay	homogeneous
	44–48	97	92	—	—	—	3	—	—	sandy silt	homogeneous
R-169	1–10	100	91	1	—	4	3	—	1	sand	homogeneous
R-173	1–10	36	71	3	—	6	6	—	—	sand	mottled
	13–19	70	85	1	—	6	5	—	—	silty sand	mottled
	38–43	71	94	1	—	—	2	—	—	silty sand	layered
	54–59	73	82	1	—	9	8	—	—	sand-silt-clay	mottled
R-174	1–10	97	56	5	—	17	10	2	—	sand-silt-clay	mottled
	22–25	100	67	3	—	15	11	1	—	sand-silt-clay	layered
	33–34	99	87	1	—	5	5	1	—	clayey silt	layered
	55–56	—	82	1	1	10	2	—	—	sand-silt-clay	homogeneous
	78–83	97	78	2	—	8	7	—	—	sand-silt-clay	layered
	90–92	—	75	8	1	4	8	—	—	silty clay	layered
R-176	1–10	37	45	6	—	16	21	1	1	clayey sand	homogeneous
	17–22	22	75	—	4	3	10	1	—	sand-silt-clay	homogeneous
R-177	1–10	—	10	3	—	6	11	8	60	silty clay	mottled
	58–63	—	75	—	—	12	8	2	—	silty clay	homogeneous
	63–78	—	72	—	2	8	7	—	—	clayey silt	3 mm layer
	90–95	—	64	2	—	11	11	6	—	silty clay	homogeneous
R-179	1–10	—	49	6	1	18	10	5	3	silty clay	homogeneous
	88–93	94	78	—	—	9	5	1	—	silty clay	layered
L- 46	1–10	—	52	8	—	19	4	14	1	clayey silt	homogeneous
	65–68	6	40	7	—	30	22	4	—	sand	5 mm layers

FACTORS AFFECTING DISTRIBUTION OF LAMINATED DIATOMACEOUS SEDIMENTS IN GULF OF CALIFORNIA[1]

S.E. CALVERT[2]
La Jolla, California

ABSTRACT

Laminated, richly diatomaceous sediments in the central Gulf of California are confined to the slopes of the basins. An investigation has been made of the water, organisms, and sediments in the Guaymas and San Pedro Martir Basins, which are the sites of most abundant diatom accumulation. The laminated sediments in these basins occur where the basin floor intersects the oxygen minimum in the water column. Burrowing organisms do not occur in this poorly oxygenated zone, and the laminations remain undisturbed. Such organisms are present in deeper parts of the basin where oxygen concentrations are higher, and, through their digging activities, the sediments are homogenized. In contrast to previously described occurrences of laminated sediments, the laminated diatomaceous sediments of the Gulf of California occur on the slopes of a basin which has free communication at all depths with the open ocean.

INTRODUCTION

The Gulf of California is a structural trough, approximately 1,500 km long and on the average 150 km wide, bounded on the west by the mountainous Peninsula of Baja California and on the east by the sedimentary plain of Sonora, Sinaloa, and Nayarit. The floor of the Gulf is characterized by a series of basins deepening to the south (Rusnak and others, this volume). The Guaymas Basin is northernmost of the major basins of the central and southern Gulf, having a maximum water depth of 2,000 m and an area of approximately 30,000 sq km.

During cruises VII and XVI of the research vessel *E.W. Scripps* in 1939 and 1940, and during the *Vermilion Sea Expedition* in 1959 (all of the Scripps Institution of Oceanography), richly diatomaceous, laminated sediments were collected from the central Gulf of California (Revelle, 1950; van Andel, this volume). The laminated sediments occurred on the slopes of the central basins —in particular, the Guaymas and Carmen Basins (Fig. 1). The purpose of this investigation was to study in more detail the distribution, petrography, and genesis of the laminated sediments. The Guaymas Basin, including the subsidiary San Pedro Martir Basin, was selected for investigation. This is the site of abundant diatom accumulation, containing the best developed laminated sediments. Aspects of the distribution of the laminated sediments are discussed here; the petrography and genesis of the laminations will be discussed more fully elsewhere (Calvert, in preparation).

The composition of the basin sediments of the Gulf of California is described by van Andel (this volume). They are dominated by silty muds, containing large amounts of diatomaceous and radiolarian opal. North of the 26th parallel, diatoms constitute the major source of biogenous opal, which in some cores exceeds 50 per cent by dry weight (Calvert, in preparation).

The sediment cores from the Guaymas Basin consist of homogenous and laminated types. The homogenous silty muds are drab, grayish olive in

[1] Manuscript received, August 25, 1963. Contribution from Scripps Institution of Oceanography, University of California.

The operation of the R/V *Hugh M. Smith* in the Gulf of California during October and November 1961, was supported by the Office of Naval Research. Ship-board laboratory equipment was financed by the American Petroleum Institute.

H. Klein provided necessary equipment for the hydrographic sampling. C.J. Shipek (U.S. Navy Electronics Laboratory) loaned the NEL Mark VI underwater camera. Grateful thanks are extended to Captain M. Hopkins, officers, and crew of the *Hugh M. Smith* for their cooperation in carrying out the sampling program. N.E. Anderson made the determinations of dissolved oxygen on the vessel. N.E. Anderson, D.J. Corrigan, D.G. Davis, J. Hart, G.W. Hohnhaus, R.W. Thompson, R. Wertheimer, and Ing. A. Yañez assisted with the sampling throughout the cruise. The figures were drafted by J.R. Moriarty.

Tj.H. van Andel, J.R. Curray, F.B Phleger, and R.W. Thompson kindly read and criticized the manuscript.

[2] Scripps Institution of Oceanography, University of California.

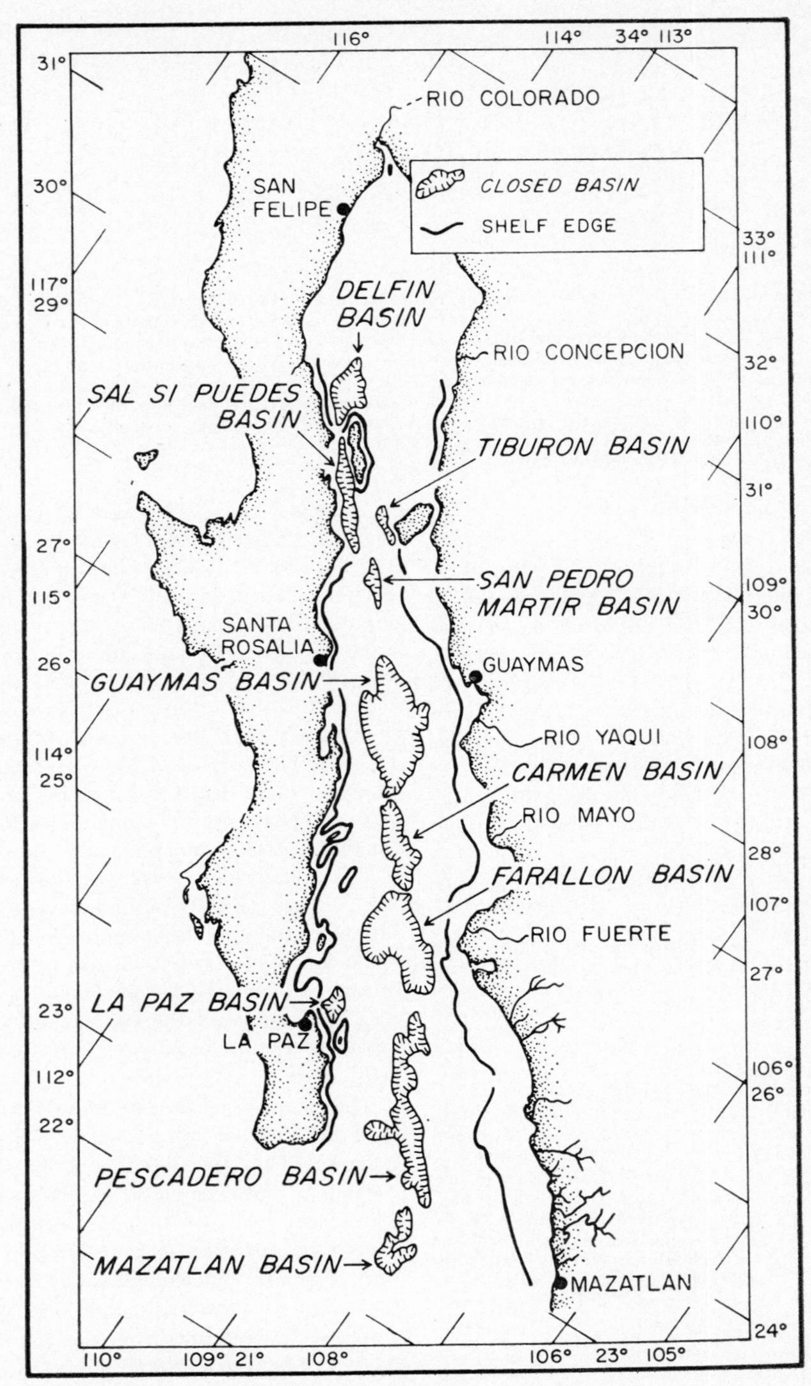

FIG. 1.—The basins of the Gulf of California. This is slightly modified from van Andel, this volume, Fig. 4.

color when wet (color code 10Y4/2, from the Rock-Color Chart, Geol. Soc. America, 1951). In the laminated cores (Fig. 2), alternate laminae are greenish yellow (10Y7/4) and diatom-rich, and grayish olive (10Y4/2) and clay-rich. The thickness of individual laminae is approximately 2 mm. Byrne and Emery (1960, p. 1004) suggest that the laminations reflect variations in the supply of diatoms from the plankton and terrigenous material from the rivers.

In October and November 1961, during an expedition to the central Gulf of California on the R/V *Hugh M. Smith*, the following collections and observations were made in an attempt to explain the distribution of laminated sediments previously described.

A. Closely spaced sediment cores were collected on traverses across the Guaymas and San Pedro Martir Basins. These cores provided a close network of samples with which to delineate the laminated sediment distribution, and provided material for comparisons between slope and basin-floor sediments. The majority of the cores were obtained with a tube gravity corer which is forced into the bottom by a 70-kg weight. They were recovered in $4\frac{1}{2}$-cm inside-diameter plastic tubes, which could then be sectioned longitudinally to reveal the internal megascopic structure and lithology. These cores average 1 m in length. A few piston cores (Kullenberg, 1947) were also collected; these were recovered in 6-cm inside-diameter plastic tubes, and range in length from 1.4 to 5.3 m.

B. Hydrographic casts were made to all depths along selected traverses across the Guaymas Basin, and dissolved oxygen concentrations were determined by the method of Winkler (1888). In addition, where it was not possible to take a full hydrographic cast (usually 15 Nansen bottles), water samples 1 m from the bottom were obtained with a modified van Dorn water sampler (van Dorn, 1956) that closed on impact.

C. Photographs of the basin floor were taken at various slope and floor stations, in order to determine the nature of the faunal populations and the minor features of the sediment surface.

DISTRIBUTION OF LAMINATED SEDIMENTS

The distribution of laminated sediments collected during the three previous expeditions to the Guaymas and San Pedro Martir Basins is shown in Figure 3. Data for the *E.W. Scripps* cruises were kindly made available by F.P. Shepard, in the form of ship-board core logs. From these core descriptions it is not possible to determine whether the laminated cores were in fact laminated to the core surface, or only partially so. Data for the *Vermilion Sea Expedition* were kindly furnished by Tj.H. van Andel; in this case more detailed core descriptions are available, and those cores plotted as laminated are laminated to the core surface. The remaining cores, plotted as homogeneous, are homogeneous, mottled, or partially laminated (homogeneous or mottled at the surface, but laminated at some variable depth).

This latter classification applies to the cores collected during the *Hugh M. Smith Expedition* in 1961, as shown in Figure 4. From this more detailed coring, the distribution of laminated sediments on the basin slopes, suggested by Figure 3, is confirmed. The distribution appears discontinuous on the steep eastern and western slopes of the Guaymas Basin owing to lack of stations on the steeper slopes through systematic bypassing on the sampling lines, or poor core recovery.

There appear to be two alternative explanations for the slope distribution of laminated sediments shown in Figure 4.

A. A variable supply of diatomaceous and terrigenous material reaches only the slopes of the basins, and produces laminated sediments. The deeper basin floors receive these materials continuously, the variations being damped out and the materials homogenized in their descent through the 2,000-meter water column.

B. A variable supply of diatomaceous and terrigenous material prevails over the basin slopes and floors, and produces laminated sediments. On the deep basin floors, the laminations are disturbed through the activities of burrowing and/or mud-ingesting benthic organisms. On the slopes, such organisms are absent owing to the low ambient oxygen concentrations close to the bottom. The distribution of laminated

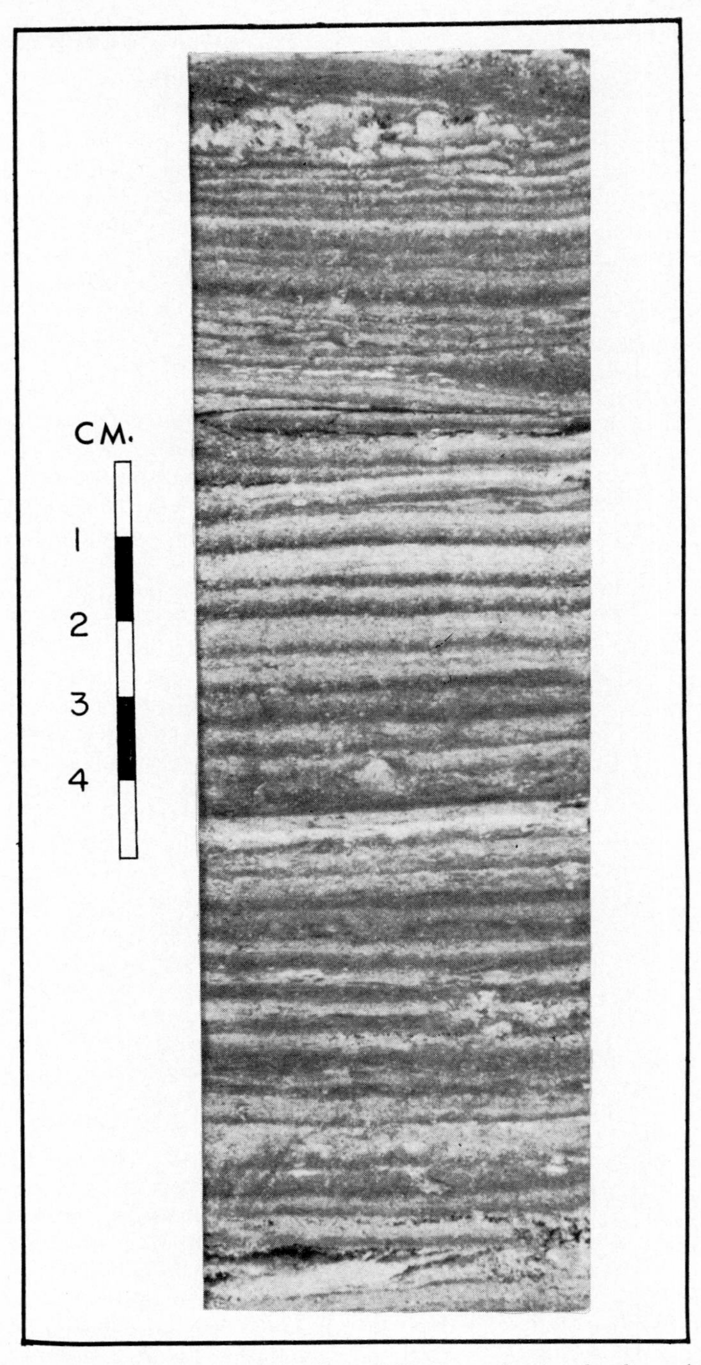

FIG. 2.—Partially dried section of core L-178, interval 28–44 cm, showing the alternating diatom-rich (light) and clay-rich (dark) laminae.

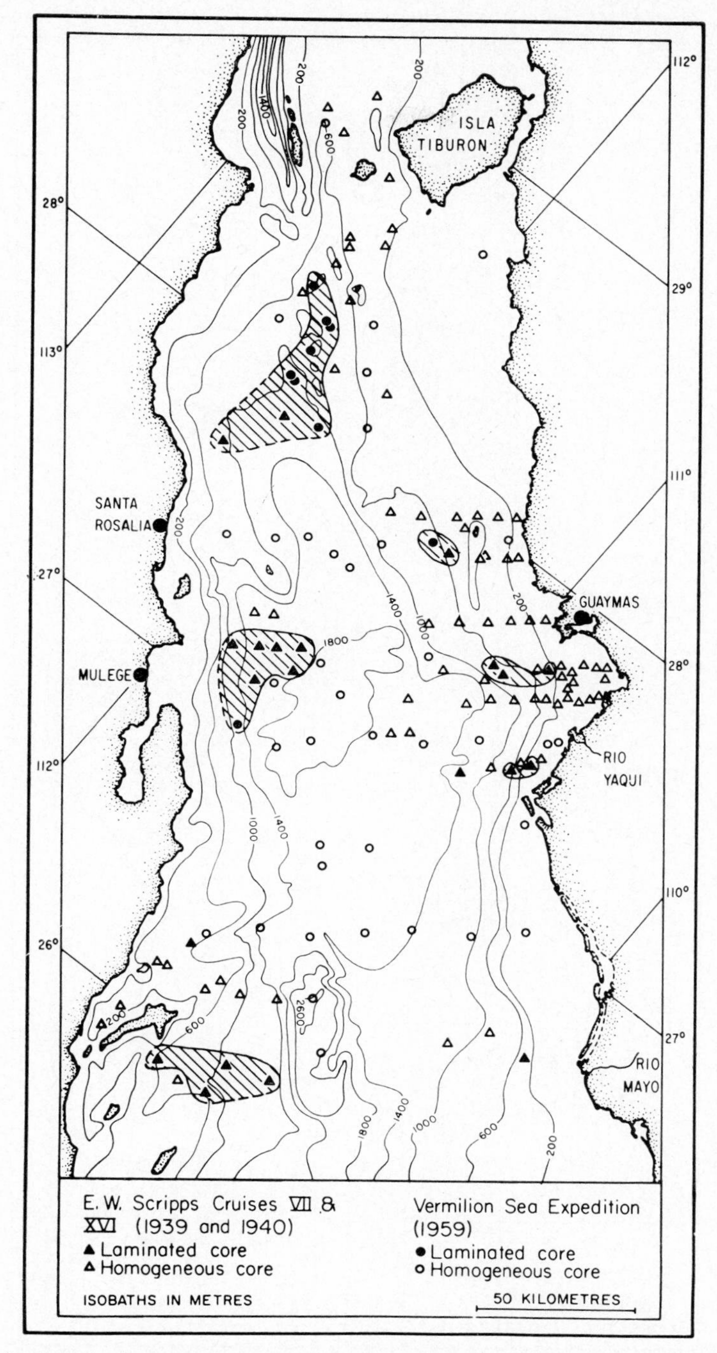

FIG. 3.—Distribution of sediment cores collected during the *E.W. Scripps* cruises in 1939 and 1940, and on the *Vermilion Sea Expedition*, 1959, in the Guaymas and San Pedro Martir Basins. Areas of laminated sediments are indicated by the shading.

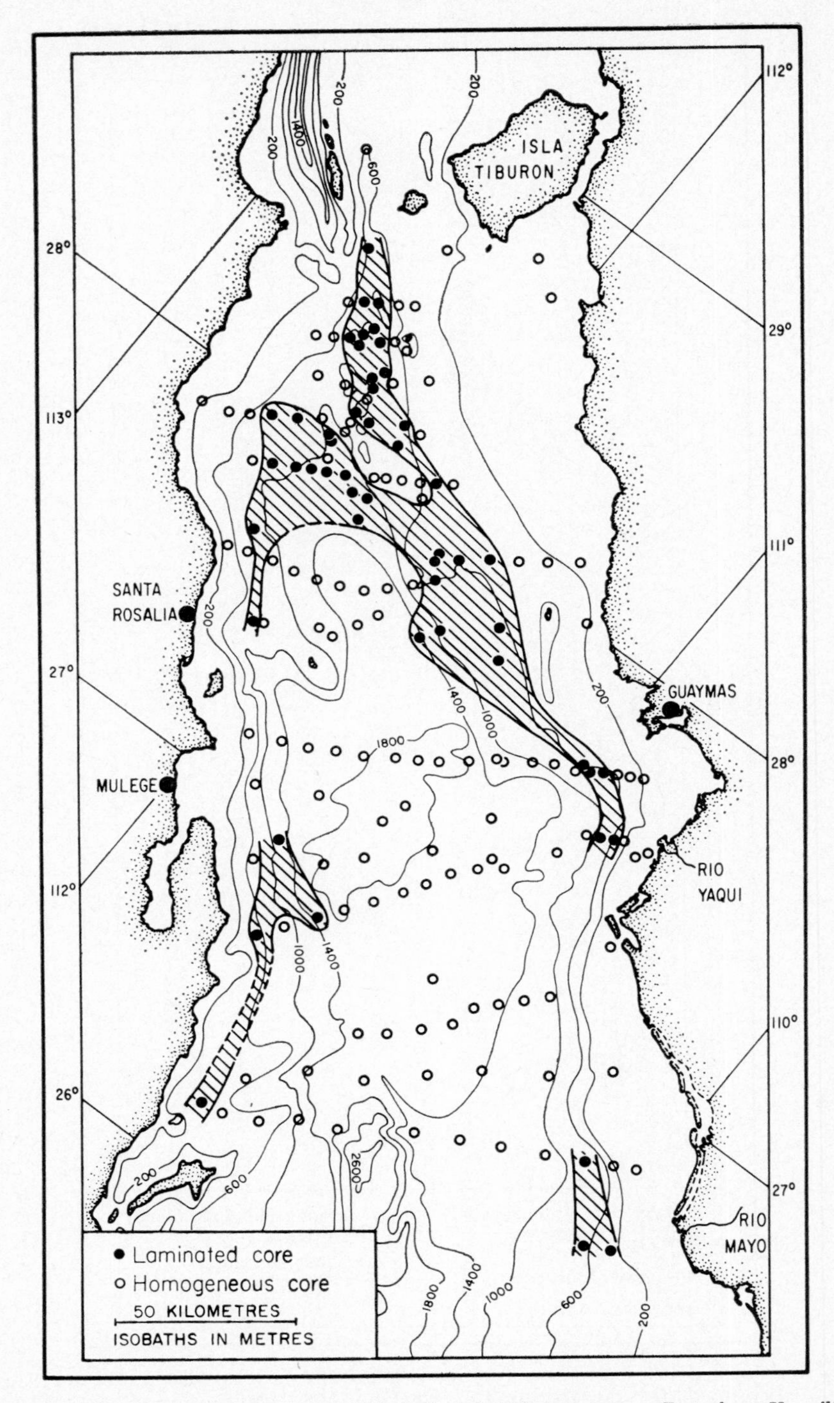

FIG. 4.—Distribution of sediment cores and their distinguishing structures. Data from *Vermilion Sea Expedition*, 1959, and the *Hugh M. Smith* expedition, 1961.

sediments would therefore correspond to the zone in which the basin floor intersects the oxygen minimum within the water column (Parker, 1960b; also *see* below).

DISTRIBUTION OF DISSOLVED OXYGEN IN GULF OF CALIFORNIA WATERS

A zone of minimum concentration of dissolved oxygen at intermediate depths is a characteristic feature of the vertical distribution of oxygen in the oceans (Richards, 1957). Concentrations of oxygen at the surface are controlled by exchange with the atmosphere; disequilibrium may temporarily occur through increased photosynthetic activity, upwelling, and vertical mixing. The existence of the oxygen minimum is considered to be biologically controlled (Richards, 1957, p. 207); that is, oxygen is consumed by organisms and settling organic detritus, while its position in the water column is determined by the circulation of the region concerned (Wyrtki, 1962).

The eastern tropical Pacific has a pronounced oxygen minimum at intermediate depths (Fig. 5*A*). A vertical section off the Central and North American coasts (lat 8° to 22° N.) shows a layer between approximately 100- and 1,000-m water depth with oxygen concentrations less than 0.1 ml/L (Sverdrup and others, 1942, Fig. 207).

The water in the Gulf of California is essentially Equatorial Pacific (Roden, 1958, p. 33), in open exchange with the Pacific Ocean. Vertical distributions of dissolved oxygen for the central Gulf are shown in Figures 5*B* and 5*C*. Concentrations at the surface range between 3.6 and 5.2 ml/L. At depths of 300 to 1,000 m, oxygen concentrations range between 0.1 and 0.5 ml/L. Stations on the basin slopes have an interrupted oxygen profile, so that oxygen concentrations at the bottom are those of the oxygen minimum (Fig. 5*C*). A cross section through the water mass of the Guaymas Basin (Fig. 6) shows an oxygen minimum at intermediate depths which meets the slopes on both sides. The values of oxygen concentrations close to the bottom, measured during two recent expeditions to the Gulf, are contoured in Figure 7. A zone of low oxygen at the bottom exists on the slopes of the Guaymas Basin and within the San Pedro Martir Basin.

The area of laminated sediments (Fig. 4) corresponds very closely to the zone of low oxygen close to the bottom (Fig. 7). This correspondence is interrupted in the northern part of the Guaymas Basin, owing to the presence of a submarine ridge trending from northwest to southeast, which is probably affected by tidal currents sweeping between the islands to the north.

The depth distribution of the 164 sediment cores from the Guaymas Basin is shown in Figure 8*A*. Of these cores, 50 are laminated to the core surface. The remaining 114 cores are homogeneous, mottled, or partially laminated. This depth distribution may be compared with the vertical distribution of dissolved oxygen from 20 hydrographic stations in the Guaymas Basin, which were occupied during the autumn of 1961 (Fig. 8*B*). The laminated sediments occur only between 300- and 1,400-m depth. The concentrations of dissolved oxygen at these depths are less than 1 ml/L, and most of the cores occur in areas where oxygen values are less than 0.5 ml/L.

The data in Table I may be used objectively to test the supposed correlation between core structure and oxygen concentrations close to the bottom. The null hypothesis states that there is no such correlation. A 2×2 contingency table (Dixon and Massey, 1957, p. 225) was constructed (Table II); this type of table is a simple and convenient method for testing independence of, or association between, two sets of data that contain dichotomies. In this case, the two dichotomies used were laminated and homogeneous sediments and oxygen concentrations above and below 0.5 ml/L. For this oxygen threshold, the null hypothesis is discredited at the $2\frac{1}{2}$ per cent level. Consequently, within the Guaymas Basin, the laminated sediments occur in those areas where the basin floor intersects the oxygen minimum.

THE BENTHIC FAUNA OF OXYGEN-POOR MARINE BASINS

The benthic fauna of the Gulf of California is described by Parker (1960a, 1960b, this volume). Of particular interest here is the observation that the oxygen minimum, where it impinges upon the bottom, appears to be an impoverished area. Several trawls in this zone produced no living organisms, but did produce large amounts of undecomposed wood and organic detritus (Parker, 1960b, p. 22). The list of living molluscs from the Gulf (Parker, 1960b, Fig. 8), containing a total of

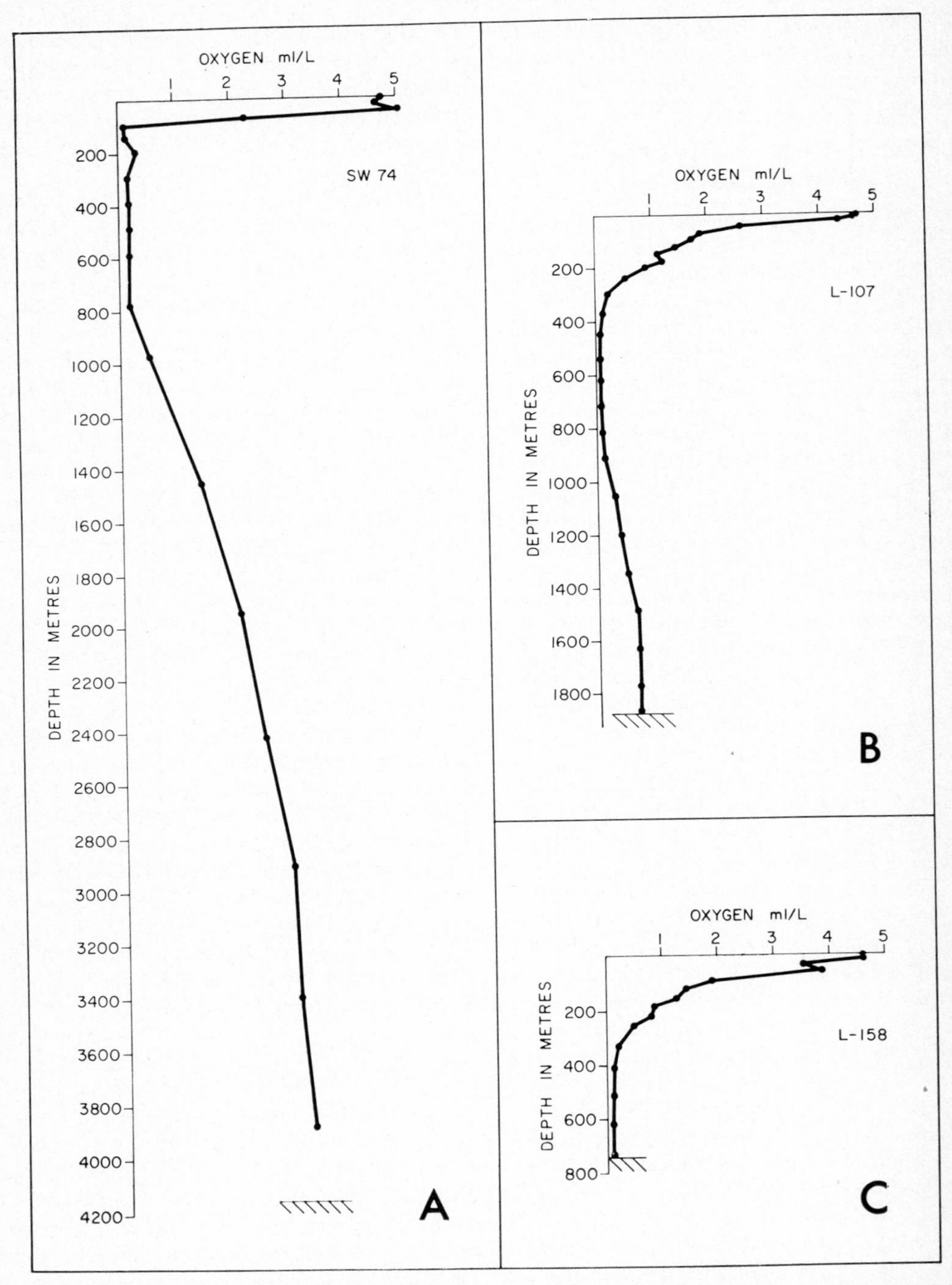

FIG. 5.—*A*. Vertical distribution of dissolved oxygen at Sta. 74, in the eastern tropical Pacific, *Swedish Deep Sea Expedition*, at 11°30′N., 114°15′W. Data from Bruneau and others, 1953. *B*. Vertical distribution of dissolved oxygen in the center of the Guaymas Basin, Sta. L-107, at lat 27°15′N., long 111°22′W. *C*. Vertical distribution of dissolved oxygen on the northeastern slope of the Guaymas Basin, Sta. L-158, at lat 27°47′N., long 111°25′W.

TABLE I. BOTTOM OXYGEN CONCENTRATIONS AND CORE STRUCTURES FROM THE 25 HYDROGRAPHIC STATIONS OCCUPIED DURING THE HUGH M. SMITH EXPEDITION TO THE GULF OF CALIFORNIA, 1961

Station	*Water Depth (meters)*	*Oxygen (ml/L)*	*Core Structure*
L-51	46	2.52	Homogeneous
L-52	187	1.11	Homogeneous
L-54	1,149	0.35	Homogeneous
L-56	1,368	0.59	Homogeneous
L-58	1,800	1.28	Homogeneous
L-60	447	0.10	Laminated
L-62	475	0.18	Laminated
L-104	657	0.08	Laminated
L-106	1,700	0.68	Homogeneous
L-107	1,875	0.67	Homogeneous
L-108	1,757	0.64	Homogeneous
L-109	900	0.20	Homogeneous
L-131	1,033	0.54	Homogeneous
L-132	948	0.46	Homogeneous
L-133	632	0.10	Laminated
L-134	250	0.52	Homogeneous
L-135	20	4.11	Homogeneous
L-155	642	0.10	Laminated
L-156	1,344	0.38	Homogeneous
L-157	1,105	0.26	Laminated
L-158	739	0.12	Laminated
L-161	335	0.16	Homogeneous
L-166	930	0.17	Homogeneous
L-172	403	0.16	Homogeneous
L-173	906	0.10	Laminated

35 species, has only 3 species that were collected from the oxygen minimum. Parker concluded from the trawling and hydrographic data from the *Vermilion Sea Expedition* that the Guaymas Basin bottom waters are stagnant, as no large invertebrates were collected on the basin floor.

The present description of the oxygen distributions demonstrates that the Guaymas Basin is not truly stagnant, but that oxygen concentrations reach low values on the basin slopes. In a later paper, Parker (this volume) lists three genera of organisms that commonly occur in the oxygen minimum zone—the stomatopod shrimp *Squilla*, and the galatheid shrimps *Pleuroncodes* and *Munida*. *Pleuroncodes* is known to disturb sediments in its search for food, but according to Boyd (1962), the distribution of *P. planipes* in the Pacific off Baja California is confined to the depth range of 75 to 300 meters. There is no comparable information on the depth range of *Pleuroncodes* in the Gulf of California.

The benthic fauna of some basins off Southern California has been extensively sampled and is described by Hartman (1955) and Hartman and Barnard (1958; 1960). Some of the oxygen-poor basins, notably Santa Barbara, San Pedro, and Santa Monica Basins, have few living animals in the deepest parts (Hartman, 1955, p. 7; Hartman and Barnard, 1958, p. 10). In the San Pedro and Santa Monica Basins, nearly all samples contain many dead tubes of the polychaetes *Phyllochaetopterus* and *Protis*, and fragments of *Cyclopecten*. This impoverished area coincides with the zone of low oxygen concentrations below sill depth (Emery and Hülsemann, 1962, p. 168). Moreover, the polychaetes are the most abundant and diversified group in the basins, being approximately six times more abundant than the molluscs, the next most abundant group (Hartman and Barnard, 1960, p. 220). The basins therefore appear to be habitats favoring worm-like associations. The polychaetous annelids may well be adapted to low-oxygen environments, owing to sedentary habits and reduced metabolic activities.

A series of bottom photographs was taken in the Guaymas Basin during October and November 1961, to examine the appearance of the faunal assemblages and the minor features of the basin floor (Fig. 9). From the preliminary data on the fauna by Parker (1960a, b), it was expected that the slopes of the basin would be azoic. The results of the photographic investigation are summarized in Table III, and representative photographs are shown in Figures 10–13.

A total of 12 camera stations were occupied, distributed to cover the basin floor and slopes of the Guaymas and San Pedro Martir Basins. Nine of these stations gave satisfactory results. The photographs obtained at stations within the oxygen minimum show populations of worm-like

TABLE II. SEDIMENT STRUCTURE AND OXYGEN LEVEL CORRELATION

		Sediment Structure		*Total*
		Laminated	*Homogeneous*	
Oxygen Concentration (ml/L)	>0.50	0	10	10
	<0.50	8	7	15
	Total	8	17	25

X^2(ldf) = 5.58 p. <0.025.

TABLE III. BOTTOM PHOTOGRAPHIC STATIONS IN THE GULF OF CALIFORNIA, 1961

Station	Location		Water Depth m.	Organisms[1]		Bottom Character	Bottom Sediment Structure	Oxygen ml/L[2]
	N. Lat	W. Long		Type	Abundance			
L- 66	26°50′	110°48′	1,588	Hydroids	Low	Burrows, mounds	Homogeneous	>0.50
L-115	27°52′	111°47′	603	Worms	Moderate	Smooth	Laminated	0.20–0.50
L-160	27°51′	111°47′	607	Worms	Moderate	Smooth	Laminated	0.20–0.50
L-173	28°16′	112°27′	890	?	Low	Small mounds	Laminated	**0.10**
L-178	28°12′	112°19′	831	?	Low	Small mounds	Laminated	**0.10**
L-181	28°06′	112°08′	780	Worms, fish, crustaceans, asteroid	High	Smooth	Laminated	**0.34**
L-184	27°03′	112°18′	894	Hydroids, asteroid	Moderate	Mounds	Homogeneous	**0.21**
L-190	27°11′	111°24′	1,910	Crustacean	Low	Burrows, mounds	Homogeneous	>0.50
L-191	26°52′	111°39′	911	Asteroid, hydroid, ophiuroid, crustacean	Low	Burrows, mounds	Disturbed, slumped?	0.10

[1] This summary is based on more than one photograph at each station, whereas single representatives are shown in Figs. 10–13.
[2] Oxygen concentrations shown in bold-face type are direct determinations close to the bottom on the same station. Others are estimated from Fig. 7.

organisms and relatively smooth floors (Figs. 10–11). On the remaining stations, located both within and outside of the oxygen minimum and wherever the sediments are not laminated at the surface, the photographs show hydroids, asteroids, ophiuroids, and crustaceans, and burrowed and uneven floors (Figs. 12–13).

The oxygen minimum is therefore by no means azoic; rather, it is populated by a distinctive assemblage of worm-like organisms, one very different from that of the deeper basin. The oxygen minimum in the Guaymas Basin appears to be populated by an assemblage of organisms similar to the assemblages of the oxygen-poor basins off Southern California. In spite of the relatively high concentrations of worm tubes at some stations, there is no evidence of worm tubes in the sediment cores collected from these stations. Where the sediment is not too fluid, undisturbed laminations continue to the core surface. The worms, owing to their sedentary habits, apparently do not disturb the sediment surface. In fact, high concentrations of worms may act as a sediment stabilizer, restricting down-slope movement of fine sediment, and thus may aid in the preservation of the laminations.

Minor Sediment Structures

If incipient laminations are destroyed in the deep basin sediments by the activities of burrowing organisms, evidence for this disturbance should be present in the sediments. Destruction of original structures by organisms to produce mottled and eventually homogeneous sediments is a well-documented mechanism (Moore and Scruton, 1957). In the Guaymas Basin, the deeper water sediments are silty muds with occasional sand layers. Homogenization by organisms would be difficult to observe, as the textural and mineralogical components are not well contrasted.

Sections from visibly homogeneous or vaguely mottled cores have been examined for latent structures by X-radiography (Hamblin, 1962; Calvert and Veevers, 1962). Representative sections are shown in Figure 14. The radiographs show a variety of mottling structures which are interpreted as disturbances produced by organisms. In addition, the sections show fine regular laminations (Fig. 14*B*) and indistinct, disturbed laminations (Fig. 14*A* and *D*) within these mottled cores. Laminations are indeed produced in the deep basin, but are destroyed soon after their formation.

Discussion

The processes leading to the distribution of laminated, diatomaceous sediments in the Gulf of California may be summarized as follows. Variations in the supply of diatomaceous and terrigenous materials to the floor of the Guaymas Basin produce regularly laminated sediments. The laminations are destroyed on the deep basin floor by the activities of burrowing and/or mud-ingesting benthic organisms. In this manner, homogeneous and mottled sediments are produced. The real structures present in these sediments, which are revealed by X-radiography, point convincingly to this mechanism. No burrowing organisms occur on the slopes of the Guaymas Basin wherever the basin floor intersects the oxygen minimum in the

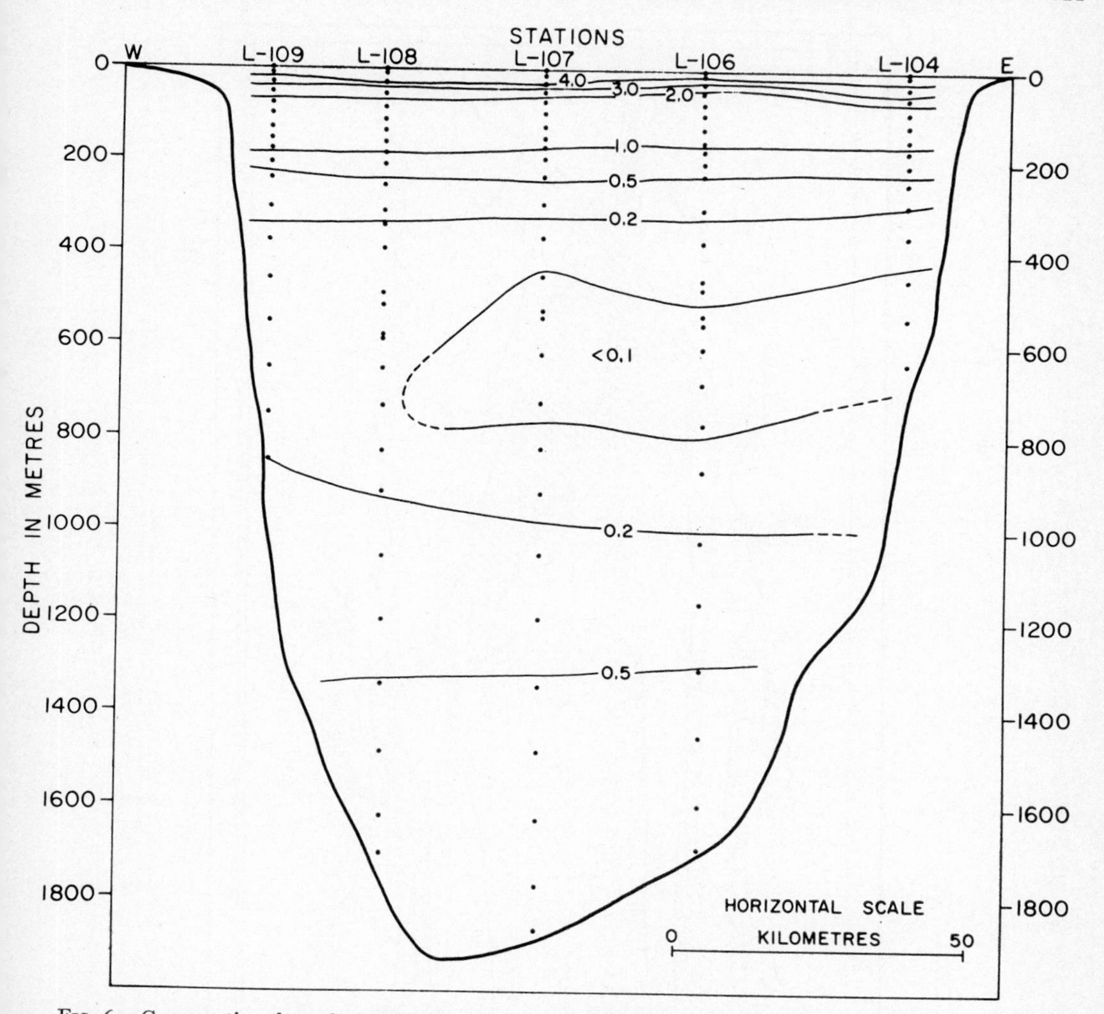

FIG. 6.—Cross section through the water mass of the central Guaymas Basin to show the distribution of dissolved oxygen. The section extends from Mulege to the mouth of the Rio Yaqui (*see* Fig. 7). Isoplethes of oxygen concentration in ml/L.

water column. In these poorly oxygenated areas the populations are dominated by sessile, wormlike organisms that do not disturb the sediment surface. Therefore, the laminations are preserved.

Van Andel (this volume) has demonstrated significant differences between slope and basin deposits in the Gulf of California. The slopes are characterized by high concentrations of organic carbon and coarse skeletal remains (diatoms, Radiolaria, and benthonic Foraminifera). This is explained by a combination of (1) greater rates of production of biogenous material near the margins of the Gulf, (2) sorting processes which concentrate coarse materials on the slopes, and (3) preservation of the perishable components on the slopes owing to the low oxygen concentrations at the bottom. The restriction of laminated sediments to the slopes of the basins further emphasizes the effect of the oxygen minimum on the composition and structure of the sediments.

The absence of burrowing organisms in the oxygen minimum of the Guaymas Basin is ex-

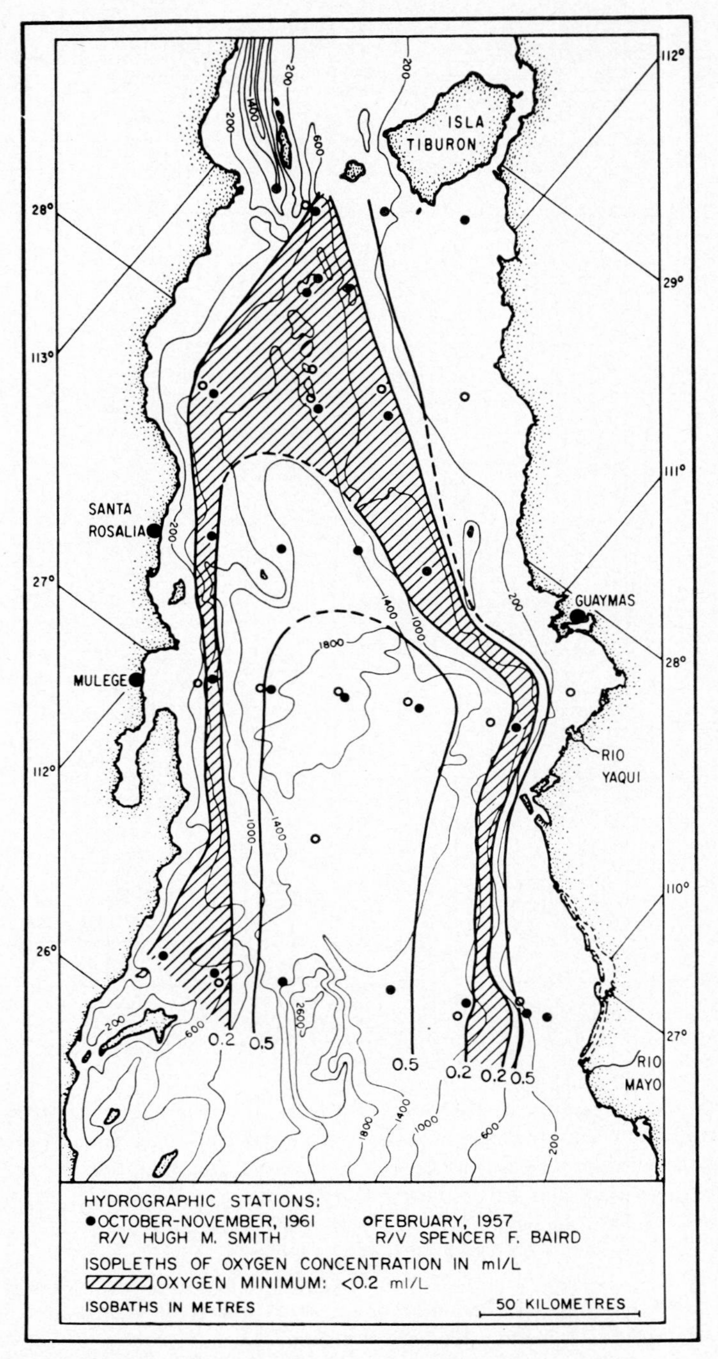

FIG. 7.—Distribution of dissolved oyxgen at, or close to, the bottom of the Guaymas and San Pedro Martir Basins. Data from February 1957, is from the California Cooperative Oceanic Fisheries Investigation Cruise 5702. Data from October–November 1961, is from the *Hugh M. Smith* expedition to the central Gulf. The points represent oxygen determinations within 200 m of the bottom.

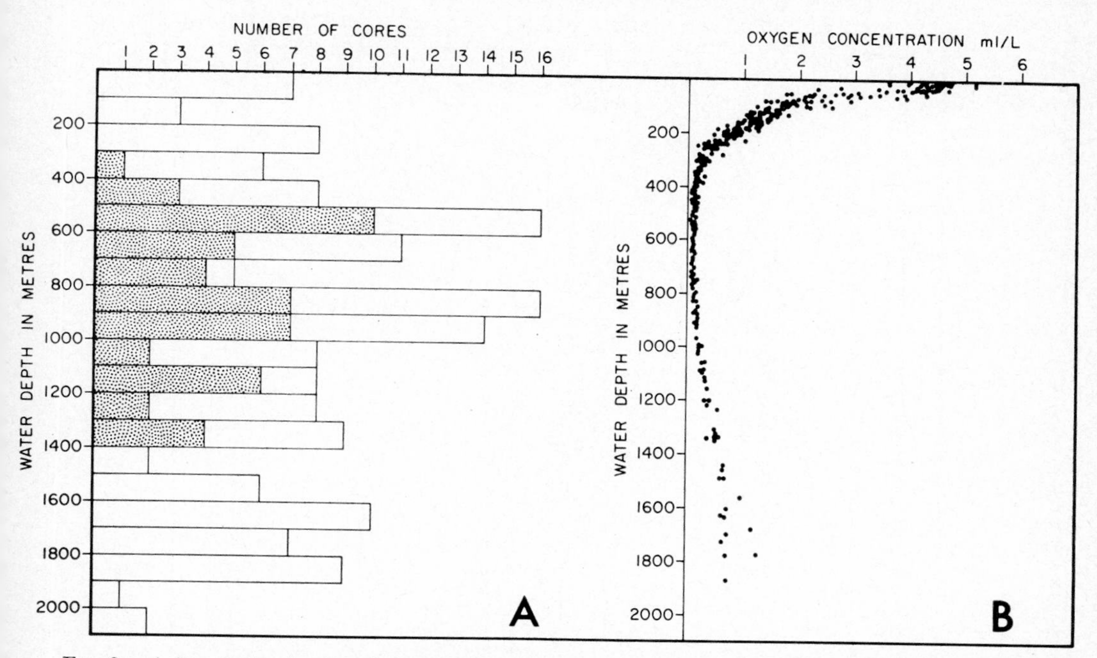

FIG. 8.—*A*. Depth distribution of the 164 sediment cores from the Guaymas and San Pedro Martir Basins. Those cores showing laminations to the core surface are indicated by the shaded area on the histogram. The remaining cores are homogeneous, mottled or partially laminated (homogeneous at the surface, but laminated at some variable depth in the core). *B*. Vertical distribution of dissolved oxygen from 20 hydrographic stations occupied in the Guaymas and San Pedro Martir Basins during October-November 1961. Each point represents a single determination from a Nansen bottle sample at the depth indicated.

plained by the low oxygen concentrations close to the bottom; that is, such animals are unable to withstand low oxygen tensions. Byrne and Emery (1960, p. 1004) attribute the absence of organisms from areas of laminated sediments to the presence of hydrogen sulfide in the interstitial waters. However, the production of H_2S in the sediments depends on an originally low-oxygen environment and therefore an absence of burrowing organisms which would normally ventilate the sediments and oxidize any sulfide produced by anaerobic bacteria. The lack of disturbance in the oxygen minimum may subsequently allow the production and accumulation of H_2S in the interstitial waters (Berner, 1964; personal communication).

Correlations between stagnant waters and laminated sediments have been described previously from several localities. Perhaps the best known marine occurrences are in the Black Sea (Archangelsky, 1927), Drammens Fjord (Strøm, 1936), Malo Jezero Bay on the island of Mljet in the Adriatic (Seibold, 1958), and in the Santa Barbara Basin (Hülsemann and Emery, 1961). In these localities, the laminated sediments occur in an enclosed basin or bay that either is completely stagnant or has very low oxygen concentrations.

The sediments of the Santa Barbara Basin resemble those of the Guaymas Basin. Sections of some cores show alternating diatom-rich and clay-rich laminae that are considered to be annual (Hülsemann and Emery, 1961, Plate 2). The cores showing laminations occur in the deepest part of the basin, where oxygen contents close to the bottom are less than 0.1 ml/L.

The situation in the Guaymas Basin is much different. All of the deep basins of the Gulf of California are in open communication with the Pacific Ocean, and none is stagnant. The laminated sediments occur on the slopes of the basins, not on the floors. The distribution of laminations is controlled by the depth of the oxygen minimum layer in the overlying water. The occurrence of

(*Text continued on page 330*)

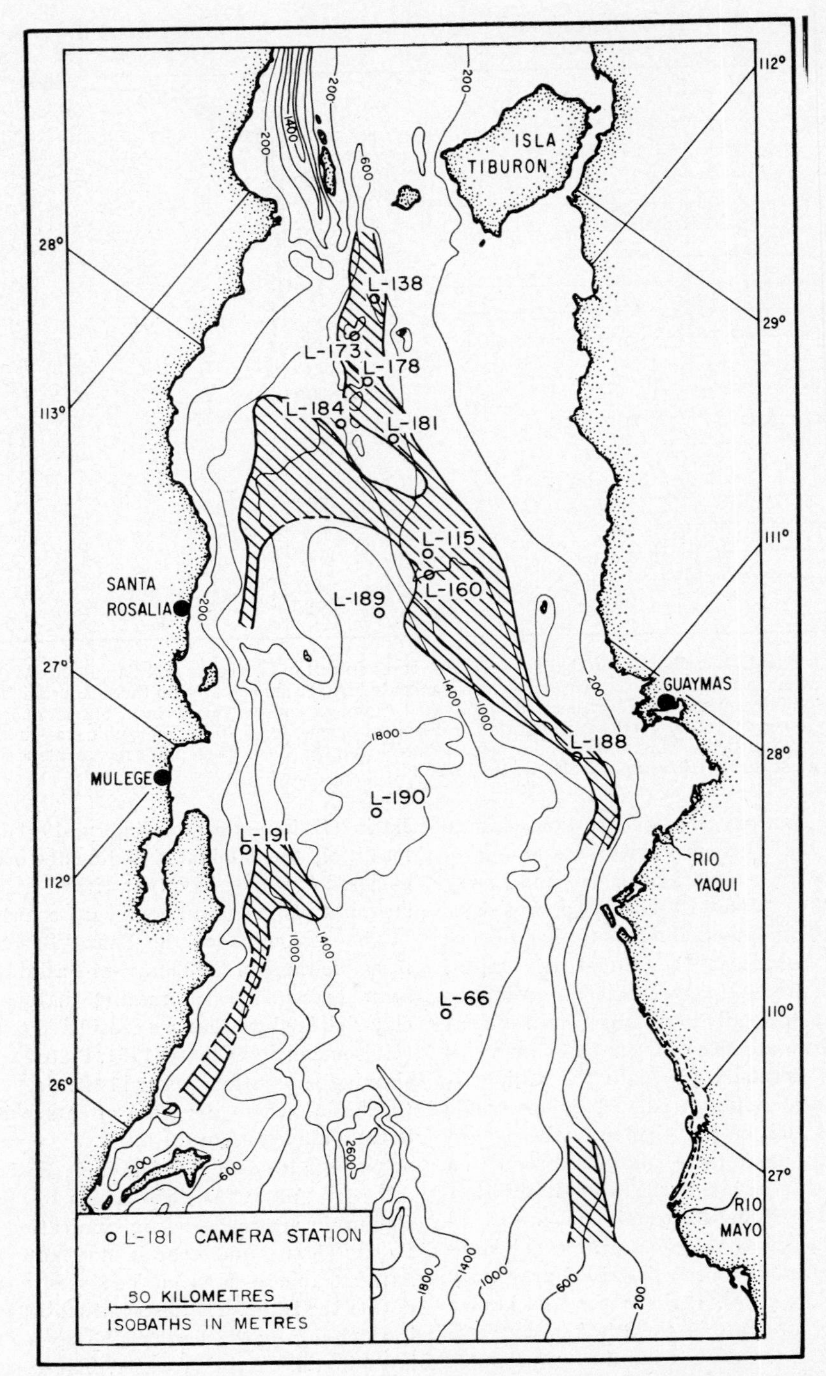

FIG. 9.—Distribution of the 12 camera stations occupied in the Guaymas and San Pedro Martir Basins during October–November 1961. The area of laminated sediments from Fig. 4 is indicated by the shading.

FIG. 10.—Bottom photograph from Sta. L-181, depth 780 m, from the northern slope of the Guaymas Basin. Note the smooth floor and the low density of worms. Distance across the center of the photograph is approximately 2 m. Official photograph, U.S. Navy.

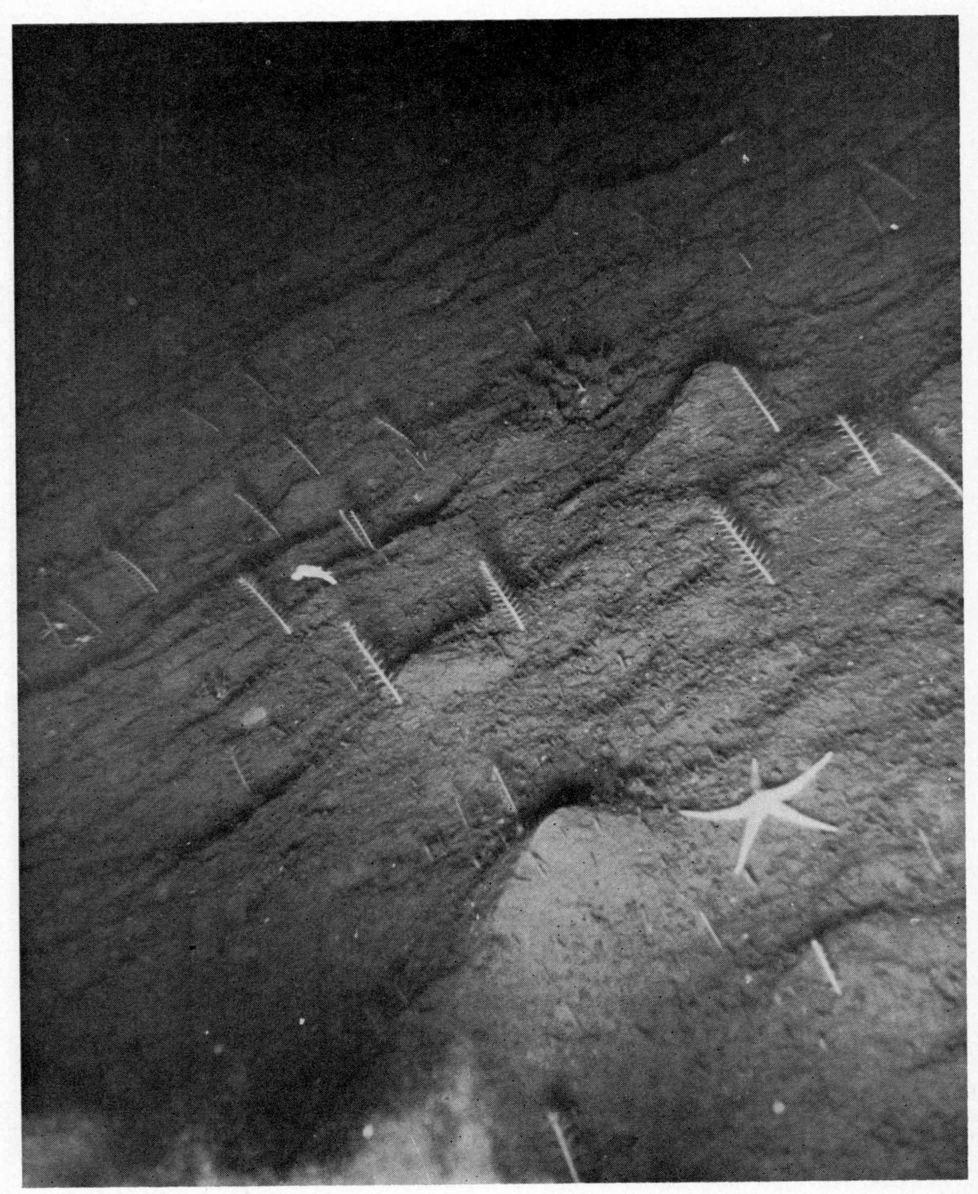

FIG. 13.—Bottom photograph from Sta. L-184, depth 894 m, from the northern Guaymas Basin. Note the uneven floor and the presence of hydroids and an asteroid. Distance across the center of the photograph is approximately 1 m. Official photograph, U.S. Navy.

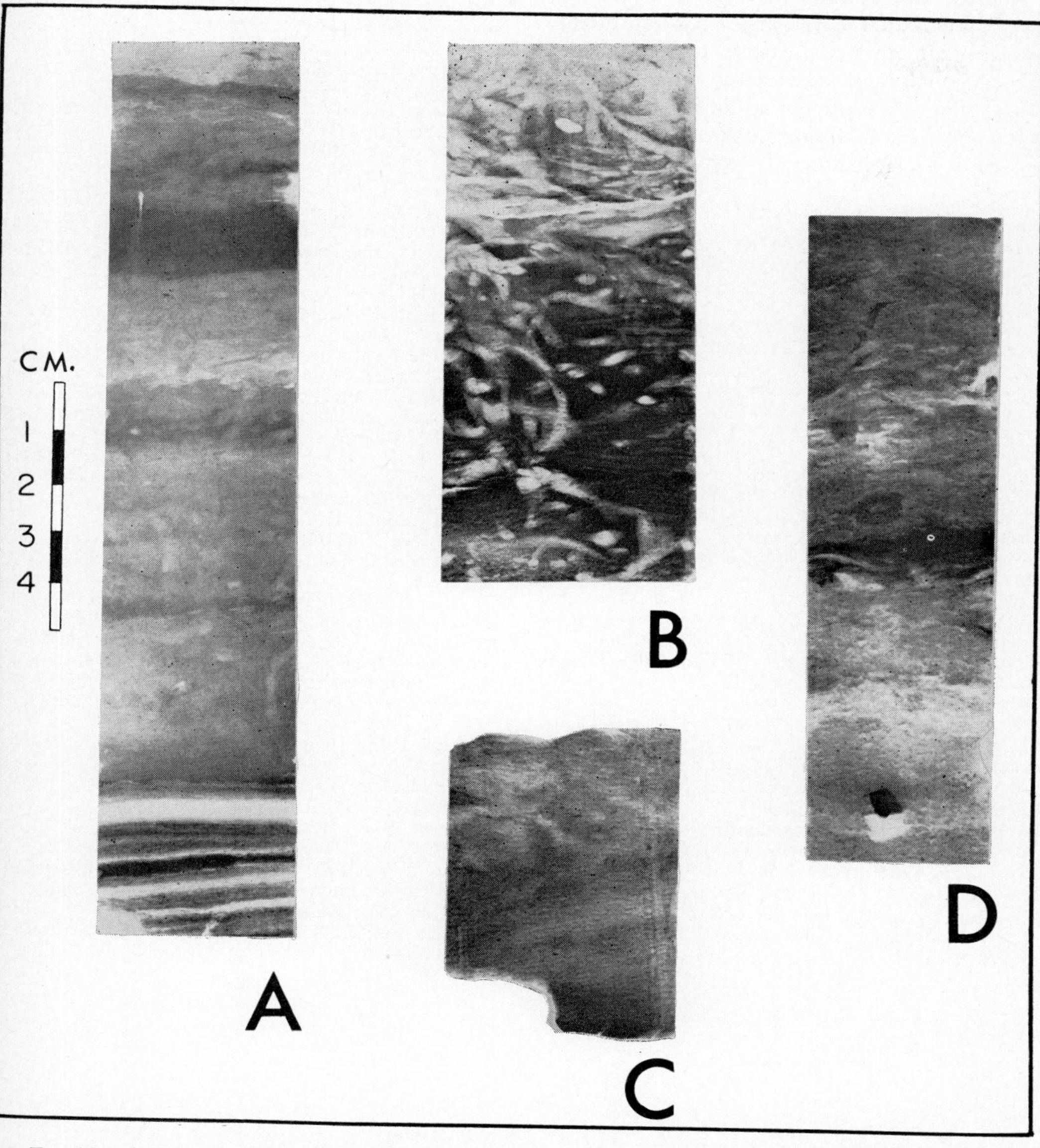

FIG. 14.—*A*. X-radiograph of core L-105, interval 13-31 cm, from the eastern slope of the Guaymas Basin, off he delta of the Rio Yaqui. This is a partially laminated core, showing visibly distinct, regular laminations with omogeneous sediment above. The radiograph shows the regular laminations at the bottom, passing up into mottling vith vague laminations. *B*. X-radiograph of core L-190, interval 302–316 cm, from the deep Guaymas Basin. Disinct mottles are evident with fine regular laminations between the mottles. *C*. X-radiograph of core L-66, interval 54–260 cm, from the deep Guaymas Basin. Vague mottling is evident in an otherwise visibly homogeneous core.). X-radiograph of core L-80, interval 40–56 cm, from the deep Guaymas Basin, showing disruption of regular lamnations, and mottling.

laminated sediments under these circumstances may be attributed to the presence of an intense oxygen minimum in the eastern tropical Pacific. The commonly accepted interpretation of laminated sediments representing an enclosed, completely stagnant environment should therefore be broadened accordingly.

REFERENCES

Archangelsky, A., 1927, On the Black Sea sediments and their importance for the study of sedimentary rocks: Soc. Nat. Moscou. Bull., Sec. Geol., n.s., v. 35, p. 264–289.

Berner, R.A., 1964, Distribution of sulfur in some sediments from the Gulf of California: Marine Geology, v. 1, no. 2.

Boyd, C.M., Jr., 1962, The biology of a marine decapod crustacean, *Pleuroncodes planipes* Stimpson, 1860: Unpub. Ph.D. thesis, Univ. of Calif., San Diego, 123 p.

Bruneau, L., Jerlov, N.G., and Koczy, F.F., 1953, Physical and chemical methods: 3d Swed. Deep-Sea Exped. Repts., f. 2, pt. 4, p. 99–113.

Byrne, J.V., and Emery, K.O., 1960, Sediments of the Gulf of California: Geol. Soc. America Bull., v. 71, p. 983–1010.

Calvert, S.E., and Veevers, J.J., 1962, Minor structures of unconsolidated marine sediments revealed by X-radiography: Sedimentology, v. 1, p. 287–295.

Dixon, W.J., and Massey, F.J., 1957, Introduction to statistical analysis: McGraw-Hill, New York, 488 p.

Emery, K.O., and Hülsemann, J., 1962, The relationships of sediments, life, and water in a marine basin: Deep-Sea Research, v. 8, p. 165–180.

Geological Society of America, 1951, Rock-color chart; reprinted from National Research Council Chart, 1948.

Hamblin, W. K., 1962, X-radiography in the study of structures in homogeneous sediments: Jour. Sed. Petrology, v. 32, p. 201–210.

Hartman, 1955, Preliminary results, pt. 1 *of* Quantitative survey of the benthos of San Pedro Basin, Southern California: Allan Hancock Pacific Expeds., v. 19, no. 1, 185 p.

——— and Barnard, J.L., 1958, The benthic fauna of the deep basins off Southern California: Allan Hancock Pacific Expeds., v. 22, no. 1, 67 p.

——— 1960, The benthic fauna of the deep basins off Southern California, pt. 2: Allan Hancock Pacific Expeds., v. 22, no. 2, p. 69–297.

Hülsemann, J., and Emery, K.O., 1961, Stratification in recent sediments of Santa Barbara Basin as controlled by organisms and water character: Jour. Geology, v. 69, p. 279–290.

Kullenberg, B., 1947, The piston core sampler: Svenska Hydrog. Biol. Komm. Skr., ser. 3, v. 1, no. 2.

Moore, D.G., and Scruton, P.C., 1957, Minor internal structures of some recent unconsolidated sediments: Am. Assoc. Petroleum Geologists Bull., v. 41, p. 2723–2751.

Parker, R.H., 1960a, Macro-invertebrate studies: A.P.I. Project 51 Quart. Rept., Jan. 1960, p. 2–3.

——— 1960b, Macro-invertebrates, Gulf of California: A.P.I. Project 51 Quart. Rept., July 1960, p. 13–23.

Richards, F.A., 1957, Oxygen in the Ocean, *in* Treatise on marine ecology and paleoecology: Geol. Soc. America Mem. 67, v. 1, p. 185–238.

Revelle, R.R., 1950, Sedimentation and oceanography—survey of field observations, pt. 5 *of* The 1940 E.W. Scripps cruise to the Gulf of California: Geol. Soc. America Mem. 43, 6 p.

Roden, G.I., 1958, Oceanographic and meteorological aspects of the Gulf of California: Pacific Sci., v. 12, p. 21–45.

Seibold, E., 1958, Jahreslagen in Sedimenten der Mittleren Adria: Geol. Rundschau, v. 47, p. 100–117.

Strøm, K.M., 1936, Landlocked waters; hydrography and bottom deposits in badly ventilated Norwegian fjords with remarks upon sedimentation under anaerobic conditions: Skifter Norske Viden. Akad. Oslo, v. 1, p. 1–85.

Sverdrup, H.U., Johnson, M.W., and Fleming, R.H., 1942, The oceans—their physics, chemistry, and general biology: Prentice-Hall Inc., Englewood Cliffs, New Jersey, 1087 p.

van Dorn, W.G., 1956, Large-volume water samplers: Am. Geophys. Union Trans., v. 37, p. 682–684.

Winkler, L.W., 1888, Die Bestimmung des in Wasser Gelösten Sauerstoffes: Ber. der Deut. Chem. Gesell., v. 21, p. 2843–2854.

Wyrtki, K., 1962, The oxygen minimum in relation to ocean circulation: Deep-Sea Research, v. 9, p. 11–23.

ZOOGEOGRAPHY AND ECOLOGY OF MACRO-INVERTEBRATES OF GULF OF CALIFORNIA AND CONTINENTAL SLOPE OF WESTERN MEXICO[1]

ROBERT H. PARKER[2]
Woods Hole, Massachusetts

ABSTRACT

Based on a reconnaissance study of the zoogeography and ecology of benthic invertebrates in the Gulf of California, 11 faunal assemblages have been established which characterize various environments—(I) intertidal rocky shores; (II) intertidal beaches and sand flats to 10 m; (III) low-salinity lagoons and mangrove mud flats; (IV) nearshore shelf, sand bottom, 11–26 m; (V) intermediate shelf, clayey sand and sandy clay bottom, 27–65 m; (VI) outer shelf, clay bottom, southern Gulf, 66–120 m; (VII) outer shelf, sand bottom, northern Gulf, 66–120 m; (VIII) northern Gulf basins and troughs, 230–1,500 m; (IX) upper slope, central and southern Gulf, 121–730 m; (X) middle slope, 731–1,799 m; (XI) abyssal southern borderland basins and lower slope, 1,800–4,122 m.

Compared with benthic communities elsewhere in the world, the diversity of shallow-water species in the Gulf of California is striking. No single species is dominant. The distribution of shell remains with depth provides indications for former low stands of sea level. Shells of shallow-water species at 110–115 m were dated by radiocarbon method at 17,000 to 19,000 years B.P. Shells belonging to the California shelf province are found in abundance in deposits of the northern Gulf basins and in deep water in the southern end of the Gulf. The occurrence of these cold-water species implies that during the Pleistocene, migration southward of more than 700 miles was possible.

Comparisons between the macro-invertebrate assemblages of the Gulf of California and those of the Gulf of Mexico and other parts of the world demonstrate that great similarities, generally at the subgeneric level, exist in similar environments throughout the subtropical and tropical regions of the world.

INTRODUCTION

Previous studies of the ecology and environ-nental distribution of macro-invertebrates by the uthor (Parker, 1956, 1959, 1960; Parker and Curray, 1956) were concerned with lagoons, bays, deltas, and, in part, with the continental shelf. In contrast, the investigation of the Gulf of California primarily deals with the continental shelf between 18 and 64 m, and with the continental slope and adjacent basins to a depth of more than 4,000 m. The present study, based on approximately 270 stations, is a reconnaissance intended to provide the basis for more detailed investigations in the future. It is the purpose of this paper to delineate the faunal assemblages of the Gulf of California, define in general terms their environments, and examine similarities and differences between the Gulf of California and other tropical and subtropical marine environments.

Sample stations are shown in Figures 1 (Gulf of

[1] Manuscript received, May 1, 1963. Support for this :udy has been received from the National Science oundation (Grants G-5419, G-13163, G-20060) and the ffice of Naval Research, Contract Nonr-2216(01), ith the University of California, San Diego.
Marine Biological Laboratory Contribution No. 17.
Numerous staff members of the Scripps Institution of ceanography have contributed material to this study. he assistance of F.P. Shepard, Tj.H. van Andel, and R. Curray has been especially valuable. R.W. Rownd assisted in the processing of the samples and in field ork. Jerry Cook, Gail Cook, and Linda Lightbowen, mmer students in a National Science Foundation ogram, helped in the compilation of the data. The atistical analysis used in the paper was programmed r the C.D.C. 1604 computer by E. Ferguson, Mrs. nna Devore, R. Mitchell, and Mrs. Eileen Mitchell the Computer Facility of the University of California San Diego. C.L. Hubbs, R. Rosenblatt, R.L. Fisher, d G.I. Roden, all of Scripps Institution of Oceanogphy, supplied information and counsel.
A considerable portion of the biological work was cared out by the author at the Zoological Museum of the niversity of Copenhagen. The author is grateful for e permission to use its facilities and collections, and is pecially indebted to H. Lemche, J. Knudsen, and . Bjarnov for their criticism and assistance. Valuable eas and information were also obtained from G. Thorson, W.K. Ockelmann and A. Møller-Christiensen of the University of Copenhagen Marine Biological Laboratory in Helsingør, Denmark. A large number of specialists in many institutions assisted in the identification of the specimens collected. To them, the author acknowledges his debt collectively. Most of the illustrations were prepared by N. Bjarnov; J. Freitas, of Denmark; and J.R. Moriarty, of Scripps Institution of Oceanography; the drawings of Plate 10 were executed by P. Winther.

[2] Systematics-Ecology Program, Marine Biological Laboratory.

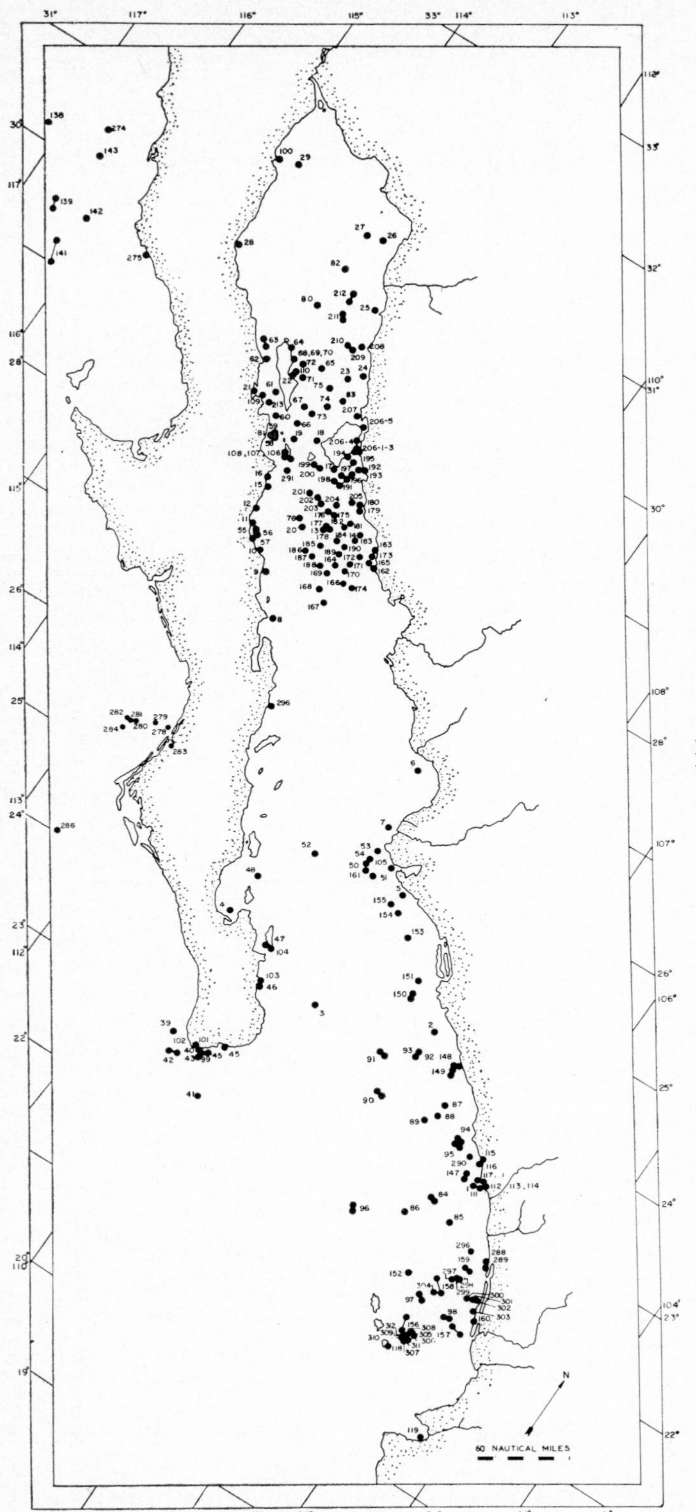

FIG. 1.—Station locations of biological samples, Gulf of California and west coast of Baja California.

California) and 2 (continental slope of western Mexico and California). Samples at the majority of the shallow-water stations were taken with a small shell dredge towed for 5 to 10 minutes, or with otter trawls; at all the deeper stations, with large beam and otter trawls or with a high-speed, deep-diving dredge (Isaacs and Kidd, 1953). A series of quantitative samples was obtained with Petersen and Van Veen grab samplers.

A fairly large set of physical and chemical data for the Gulf of California exists in the literature. In addition, numerous measurements were made in connection with the present program of Gulf of California studies. Sediment analyses are available for nearly all biological stations, and sediment maps are presented in papers by van Andel and by Curray and Moore (both, this volume).

The principal factors considered in explaining the distribution of invertebrates in the Gulf of California are depth, sediment composition, bottom-water temperature, salinity, turbulence, upwelling and oxygen content, and various biological processes.

METHODS OF COLLECTION AND DATA PROCESSING

Collections of biological material were made on he following expeditions—*Tuna Oceanographic Cruise II*, November 1958; *Vermilion Sea Expedition*, March-June 1959; *Southern Borderland Cruise III*, February 1960; *Orca Cruise, Gulf of California*, March–April 1960; *Holt Expedition*, December 1960; *Baja Slope Expedition*, May 1961; *Gulf of California Cruise*, November 1961—ll under the sponsorship of the Scripps Institution of Oceanography (Figs. 1, 2). In all programs, biological sampling was part of a larger undertaking, so that sampling patterns were, in some instances, incidental. Few quantitative and standing-crop samples could be taken. After thorough orting, all material that could not be identified y the author was sent to specialists. Sets of the mollusk material are stored at the Scripps Institution of Oceanography and at the Zoological Museum in Copenhagen; most of the other material as retained by the specialists who identified it. A omplete list of these is included in Parker (1964).

DATA PROCESSING

Following methods partly developed by Tj.H. an Andel and J.R. Curray for geological data, all information obtained on the approximately 270 stations and 1,150 identified species has been recorded on I.B.M. cards. The system is discussed in detail in a comprehensive paper on the macro-invertebrate studies of the Gulf of California (Parker, 1964), which contains all data. By inspection, the ranges of various environmental parameters (depth, oxygen, sediment types, geographic locality) were subdivided into classes. A computer was used to list all species occurring in each of the environmental categories so established.

In another analysis, species were grouped on the basis of affinity calculated for all possible pairs of species. The index used was the geometric mean of the proportion of co-occurrences of each pair of species, minus a term that corrects for sample size (modified after Fager, 1957). Two sets of data, one for 136 species occurring in more than 8 stations each, and another 114 species with only 5 to 7 station occurrences, were used. For the first set, pairs of species were judged to show affinity if the index had a value of 0.495 or over; a cutoff value of 0.295 was used for a rerun of the first set and for the second set. A total of 55 groups with more than 5 affiliated species was formed from the first set of species; 22 groups with more than 3 affiliated species were formed from the second set. For each group, all stations that had large numbers of associated species were examined as to location and common environmental factors. Most of the significant species-groups produced station groupings with distinct geographic location and a well-defined range of environmental parameters. Details of the analysis are given in Parker (1964), and a program description can be obtained from the author. A similar analysis is feasible for ancient sediments if adequate paleontological data are available, and a direct comparison of the results with modern assemblages established in the same manner can be carried out rigorously.

Several other methods were used to determine the faunal assemblages of the Gulf of California. About 350 areal distribution maps of common species were prepared and compared with the distribution of ecological factors. Graphs of the depth ranges of living and dead specimens of the 1,150 species identified in the area were used to determine the depth concentration of each (Parker, 1964), and were checked against known

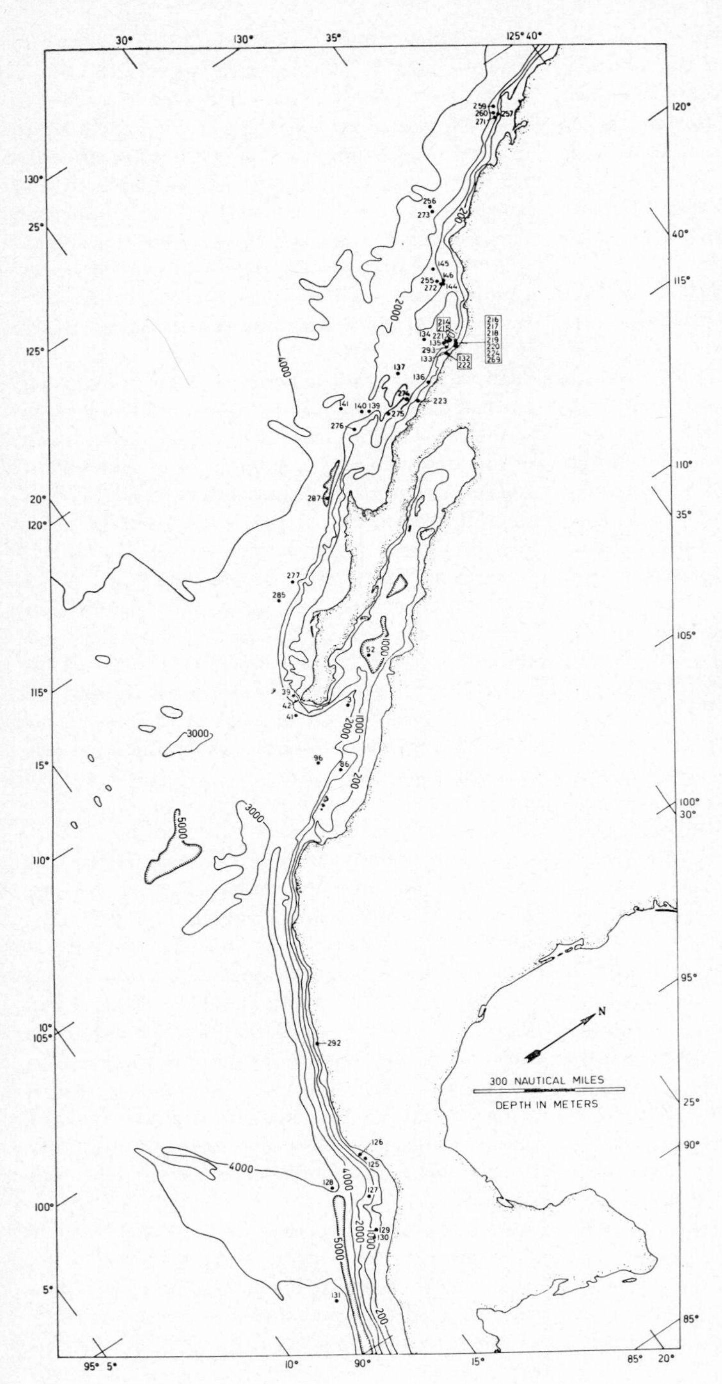

FIG. 2.—Station locations of bic logical samples, continental slope fror San Francisco, California, to Guate mala.

ranges in the literature (Keen, 1958; Olsson, 1961; and various papers in the *Albatross Expedition* Reports). Complete taxonomic data have been listed by Parker (1964).

DESCRIPTION OF THE REGION INVESTIGATED

Most of the samples were collected in the Gulf of California and the adjacent southern area extending to Banderas Bay and the Tres Marías Islands (Fig. 3). The geology and morphology of this region have been discussed by Allison (this volume); Rusnak, Fisher, and Shepard (this volume); Anderson (1950); and Byrne and Emery (1960). Much of the Gulf, in particular along the western side, is bordered by high-cliff coasts with an abundance of rocky shores and numerous pocket beaches. The eastern side, on the other hand, is bordered by broad sandy beaches and mud flats in the area of the Colorado Delta, along the Costa de Hermosillo north of Guaymas, and south from the Yaqui River. Coastal lagoons are rare over most of the Gulf coastal region, which receives little rainfall, but they become important south of Mazatlán, where the rainfall increases to more than 50 inches near Puerto Vallarta. Information concerning these lagoons was obtained from J.R. Curray and F.B Phleger (oral communication), and from Keen (1958). A number of semi-enclosed bays in open contact with Gulf water occur along the west side, and a few tidal lagoons, some with hypersaline conditions, are found north of Guaymas. A few large lagoons occur on the Fuerte River delta, but little is known about their fauna. The continental shelf was sampled in detail in only two areas, the Costa de Hermosillo north of Guaymas, and the Costa de Nayarit south of Mazatlán. The shelf in this area is broad and gently sloping, and faunal assemblages are found that parallel those of the Gulf of Mexico. The western shelf is very narrow and absent locally. Little level bottom is present, and the rocky bottom is mainly inhabited by epifaunal species. The northern Gulf, north of Angel de Guarda and Tiburón Islands, contains a large, gently sloping shelf, very similar to the shelf of the Gulf of Mexico.

The largest part of the central and southern Gulf is occupied by deep basins, ranging from 1,000 to 3,600 m in depth, and bordered by relatively steep slopes. The basin floors are relatively flat, but the area available for level-bottom communities is small compared to the total area of the Gulf (Fig. 4).

The sediments of the Gulf of California (Figs. 5, 6) are discussed in detail by van Andel (this volume).

The northern Gulf, from the shoreline to depths exceeding 400 meters, is predominantly sandy. The only exceptions are the deep basin between Angel de la Guarda Island and the Peninsula, and its northern extension, a zone directly off the Colorado and Concepción River deltas, and some deeper deposits just east of Angel de la Guarda. In the central and southern Gulf, the sediments predominantly consist of silty clay, except for the shelf on the western side and the inner portions of the eastern shelf. The deeper basins and adjacent slopes north of the Fuerte River are covered with diatomaceous sediments. The eastern shelf generally shows a gradation from sands on the inner and middle portions to clayey silts on the outer margin and upper slope. Studies by Curray (oral communication; also *see* Fig. 6) show that, in detail, the pattern is complex and the deposits are commonly patchy, resulting in patchiness of the faunal assemblages.

OCEANOGRAPHIC CONDITIONS

Roden (this volume; also *see* Roden, 1958; Roden and Groves, 1959) has presented a summary of the physical oceanography of the Gulf of California. In addition, a substantial volume of information is available in the files of Scripps Institution of Oceanography. The following discussion is based on material from both sources.

Oxygen concentration data for bottom waters have been compiled for a depth range from about 40 to 3,000 m (Fig. 7). The northern Gulf is characterized by a normal decrease of oxygen content with increasing depth. South of Tiburón Island, a pronounced oxygen minimum is present at intermediate depth. Between approximately 100–200 and 1,200 m, the oxygen values are below 0.5 ml/L. Below 1,200 m, the values rise again to 1 ml/L in the southern basins and even higher at the entrance to the Gulf. An exception to this pattern is the basin off Guaymas, which has oxygen values of less than 0.5 ml/L at the bottom,

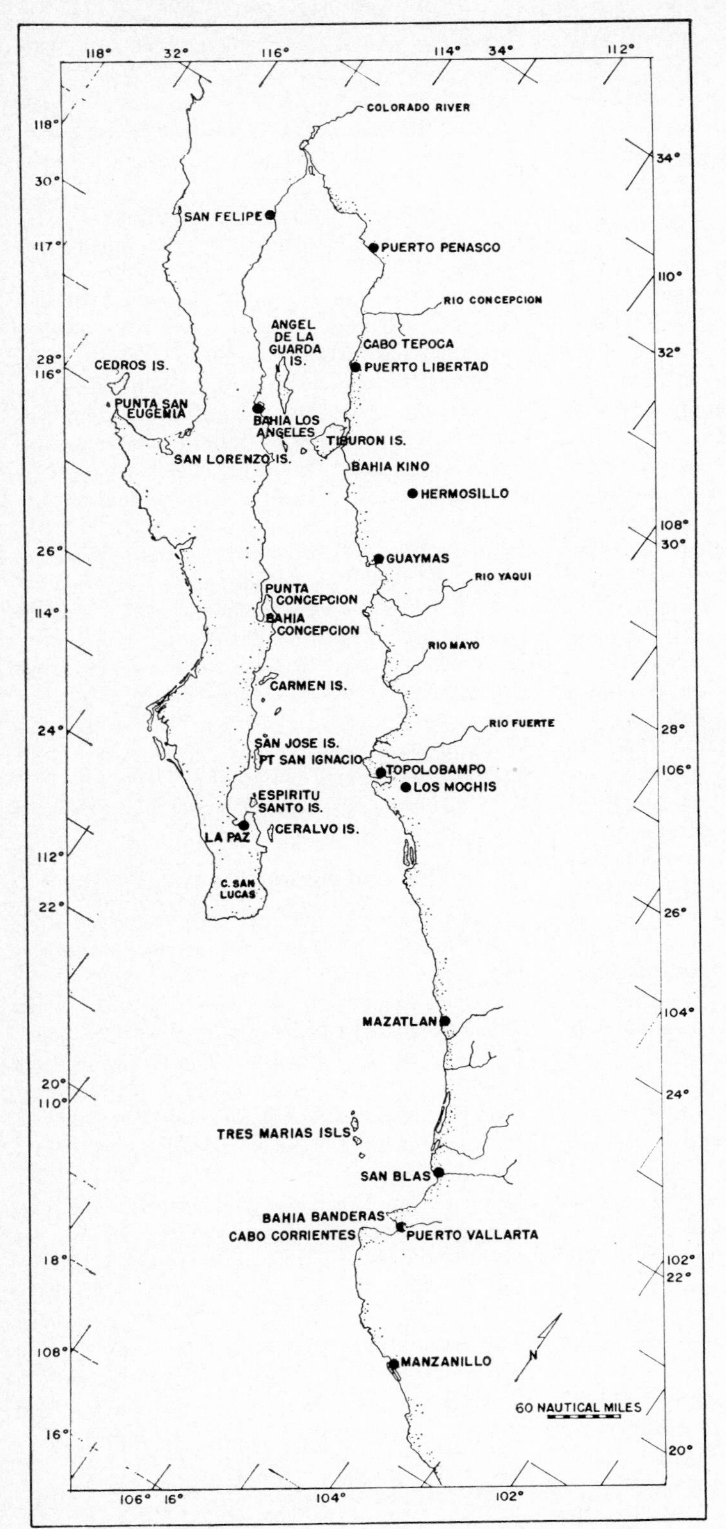

FIG. 3.—Place names of the Gulf of California region.

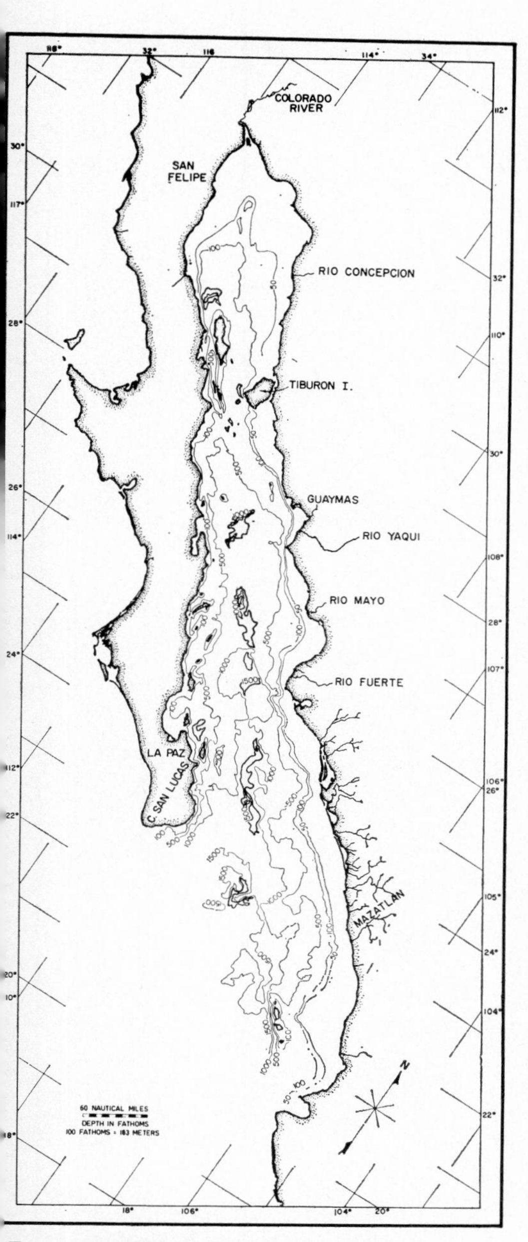

FIG. 4.—Bathymetry of the Gulf of California. Depth fathoms. Simplified after Rusnak, Fisher, and Shep- d (this volume).

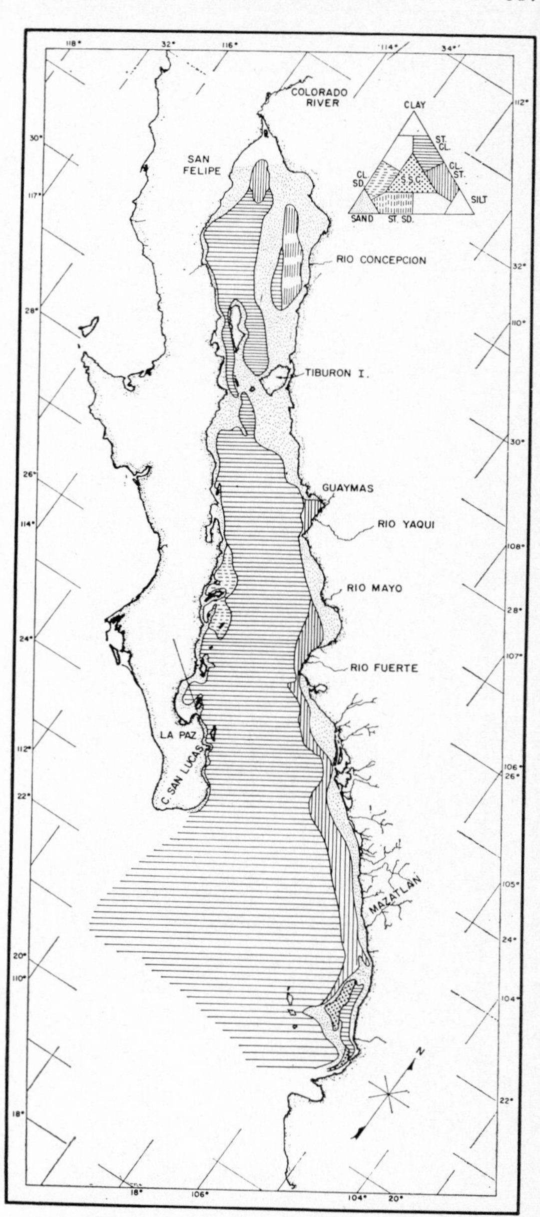

FIG. 5.—Sediments of the Gulf of California, based on data from van Andel (this volume, Fig. 21) and J.R. Curray (personal communication). Classification according to Shepard (1954).

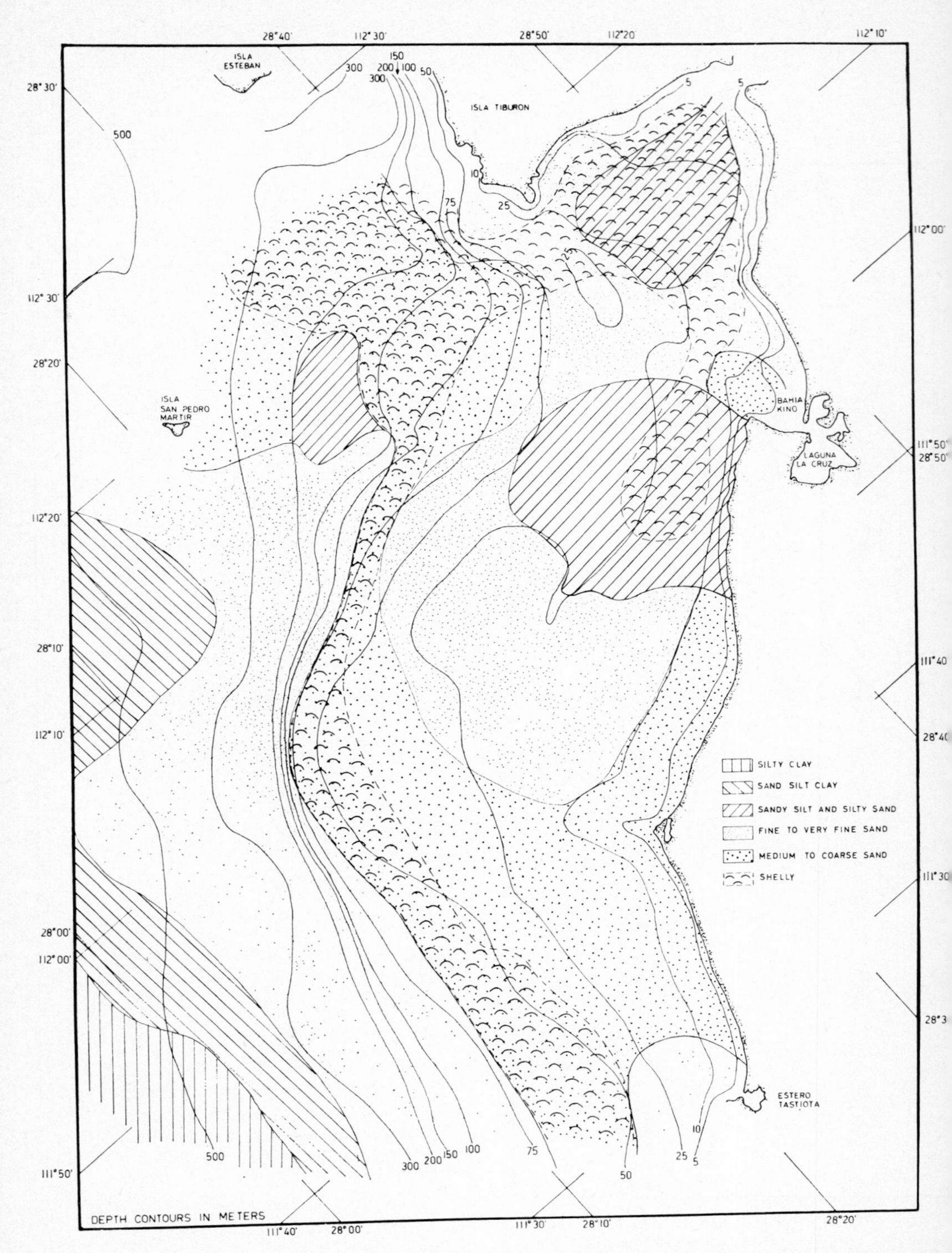

FIG. 6.—Sediment distribution in the Costa de Hermosillo region, southeast of Tiburón Island. Depth and sediment contours after J.R. Curray (personal communication). Shell zone added by this author.

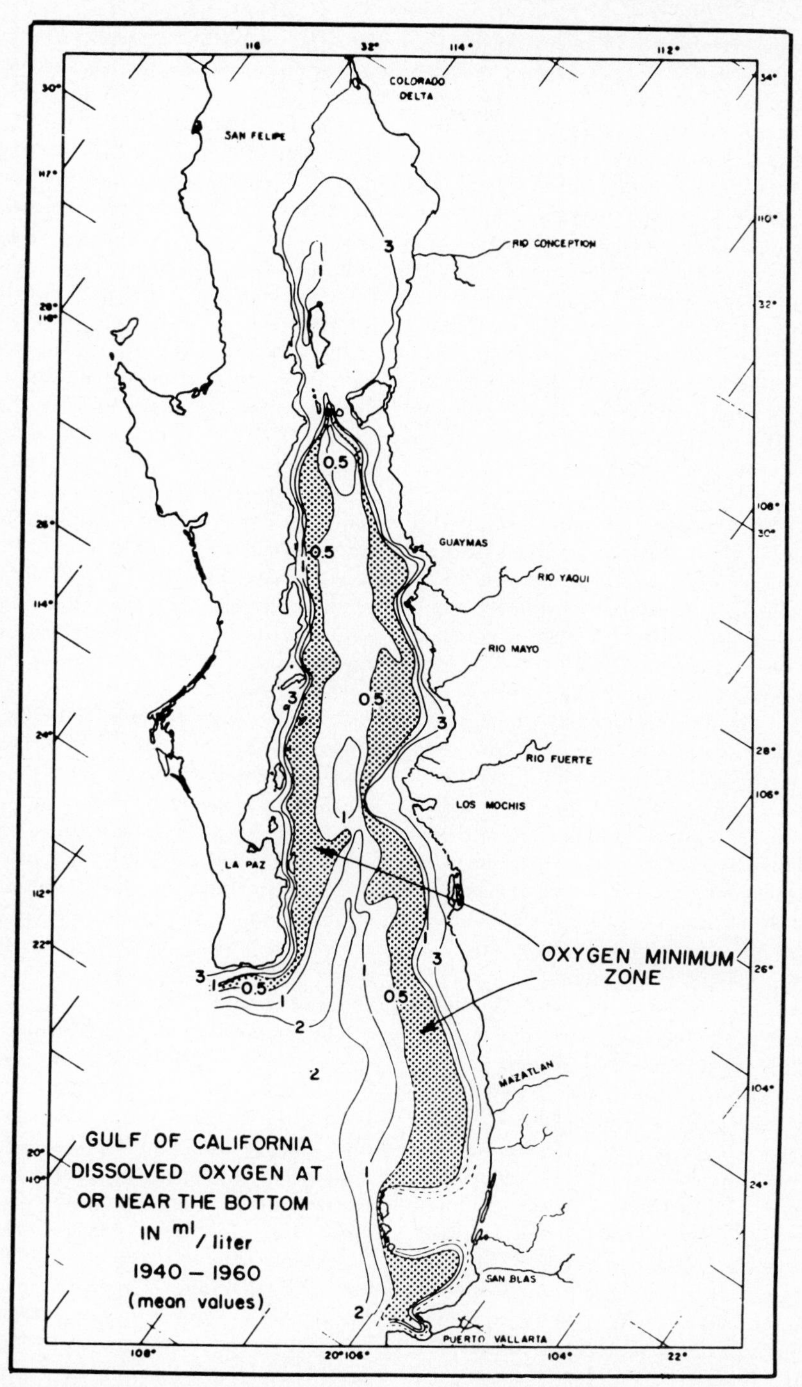

FIG. 7.—Dissolved oxygen in bottom waters of the Gulf of California, based on published (Roden, 1958; Roden and Groves, 1959) and unpublished data, taken in various seasons over a 20-year period.

and shows little disturbance of its sediments by burrowing organisms. The apparent lack of benthonic life may be attributed to the oxygen deficiency. Similar conditions on a seasonal basis have been described by Emery and Hülsemann (1962) for the Santa Barbara Basin in the California borderland. The areas of lowest oxygen concentration on the slopes coincide with zones of maximum upwelling and abundant plankton blooms (Fig. 8).

In the channel between the Peninsula and the San Lorenzo and Angel de la Guarda Islands, waters are well oxygenated over the entire column, notwithstanding the great depth (1,000–1,500 m). The high, uniform oxygen values of between 1 and 3 ml/L in this area result from mixing by tidal currents, and give rise to abundant animal life.

The faunas at the southern end of the Gulf also reflect the presence of abundant oxygen in deep water. Trawls taken in this region were very rich and comparable to slope samples elsewhere along the coast of Central America, in striking contrast to deep stations in the central Gulf.

On the continental shelf, oxygen values are normally high, except in some areas where depletion by prolific organic productivity locally may occur close to shore. This is especially true north of Mazatlán, where the oxygen minimum occurs close to the land, despite the appreciable width of the shelf. This condition seems to influence the faunal assemblage, which has an abnormal character in depths between 65 and 120 m. However, the somewhat different sediments of this area may contribute to the change in faunas.

The *temperature of the water near the bottom* (Fig. 9) decreases systematically from a mean of 14°C in shelf depths to 2°C in the deepest portions of the Gulf. Between Tiburón Island and Puerto Vallarta, the edge of the continental shelf is fairly well marked by bottom temperatures between 14° and 10°. In the central Gulf, the basin floors have temperatures of 4°; farther south the minimum temperature is 2°, similar to the bottom-water temperature of the equatorial Pacific.

Between Angel de la Guarda and the Peninsula, and east of the island, temperatures are nearly uniform from surface to bottom as a result of tidal mixing. Roden and Groves (1959) have shown that in April the surface temperature is about 15°, while the bottom value is 12°. During the warmest month, August, surface waters may be as high as 28°; at 200 m, the temperature is still 15°, and at 1,000 m it is 12°. These high values found at such great depths have a marked effect on the composition of the fauna on the slopes and floors of the depressions. Vertical stratification, which is normal elsewhere in the Gulf, is lacking, and many species generally found in 150 to 200 m occur here at the bottom in depths of 1,500 m.

The water temperatures of the nearshore shel are subject to a pronounced seasonal variation which is most extreme in the northern Gulf. In the vicinity of San Felipe, the annual range of wate temperature is from 16° in January to more than 31° in August. This variation possibly exclude many species; the Tiburón region is, in fact, th northern end of the geographic range for many invertebrates (Fig. 10). The summer temperatures are high enough for many Panamic or tropica forms, but the winter minima probably are limiting for many species with a small temperature tolerance.

Between Guaymas and Tiburón, the annual range of shallow-water temperature is 13.8° which still is limiting to many tropical forms. A Mazatlán, however, temperatures range from only 20° to 30°. This area is the northern limit fo a few southern species and the southern boundary for many northern forms. The geographic range of 253 common living species show that many geographic breaks in species distribution corre spond well with temperature changes and othe physical barriers (Fig. 10).

The temperature distribution along the wester side of the Gulf is less well known. At Los Angele Bay on the Peninsula, west of Angel de la Guarda Island, the range is about 15°, whereas betwee Los Angeles Bay and the southern end of th Peninsula the temperature ranges from 19° to 29° Records at La Paz, which is sheltered from th open Gulf, are approximately the same as a Mazatlán, with a range of 9.3°. The narrowes temperature range is reported from Cape San Lucas (8.5°). Cape San Lucas temperatures ar comparable to oceanic equatorial Pacific tempera tures, which may explain why a number of Indo Pacific invertebrates and fish are found only in

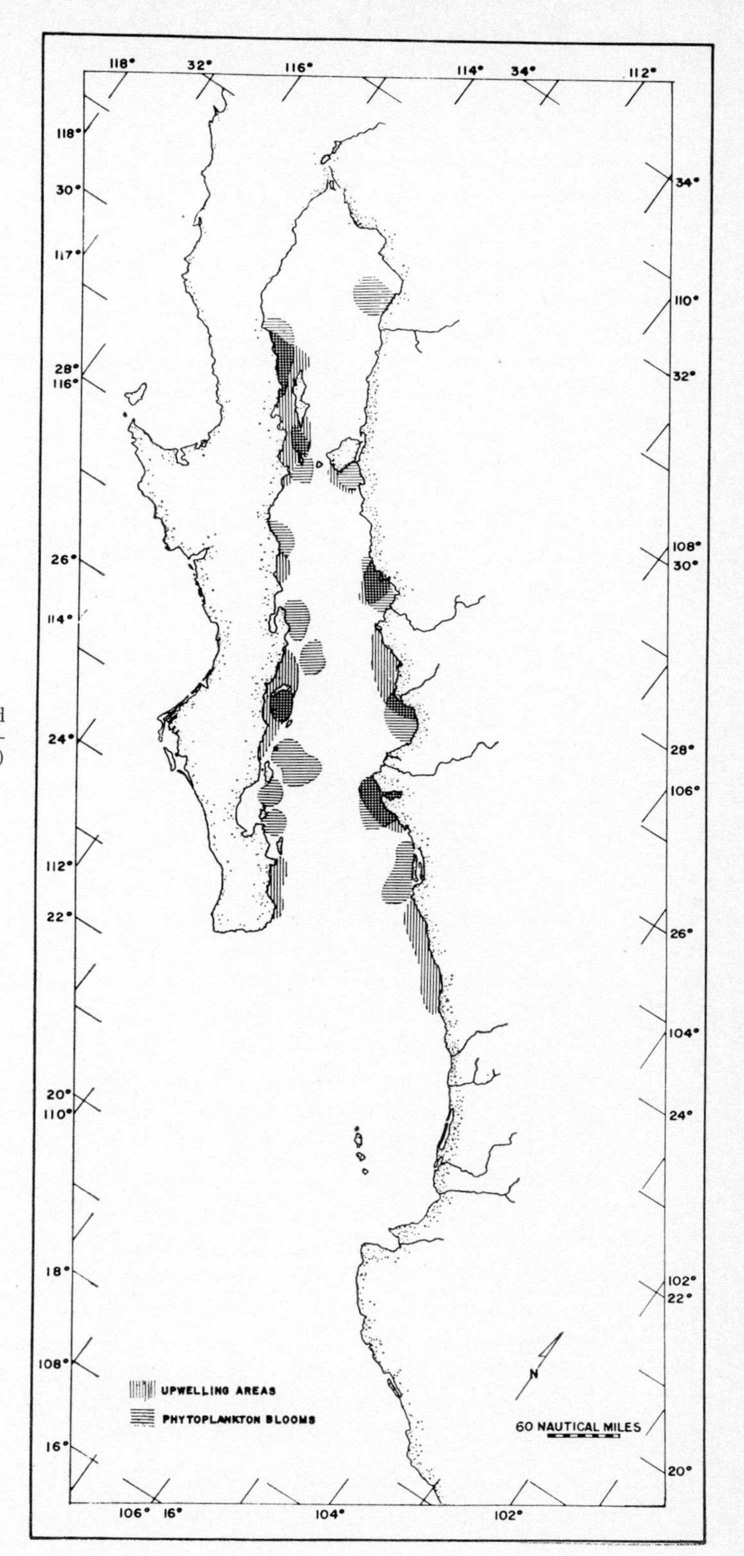

FIG. 8.—Areas of upwelling and plankton blooms in the Gulf of California. After Byrne and Emery (1960) and Roden and Groves (1959).

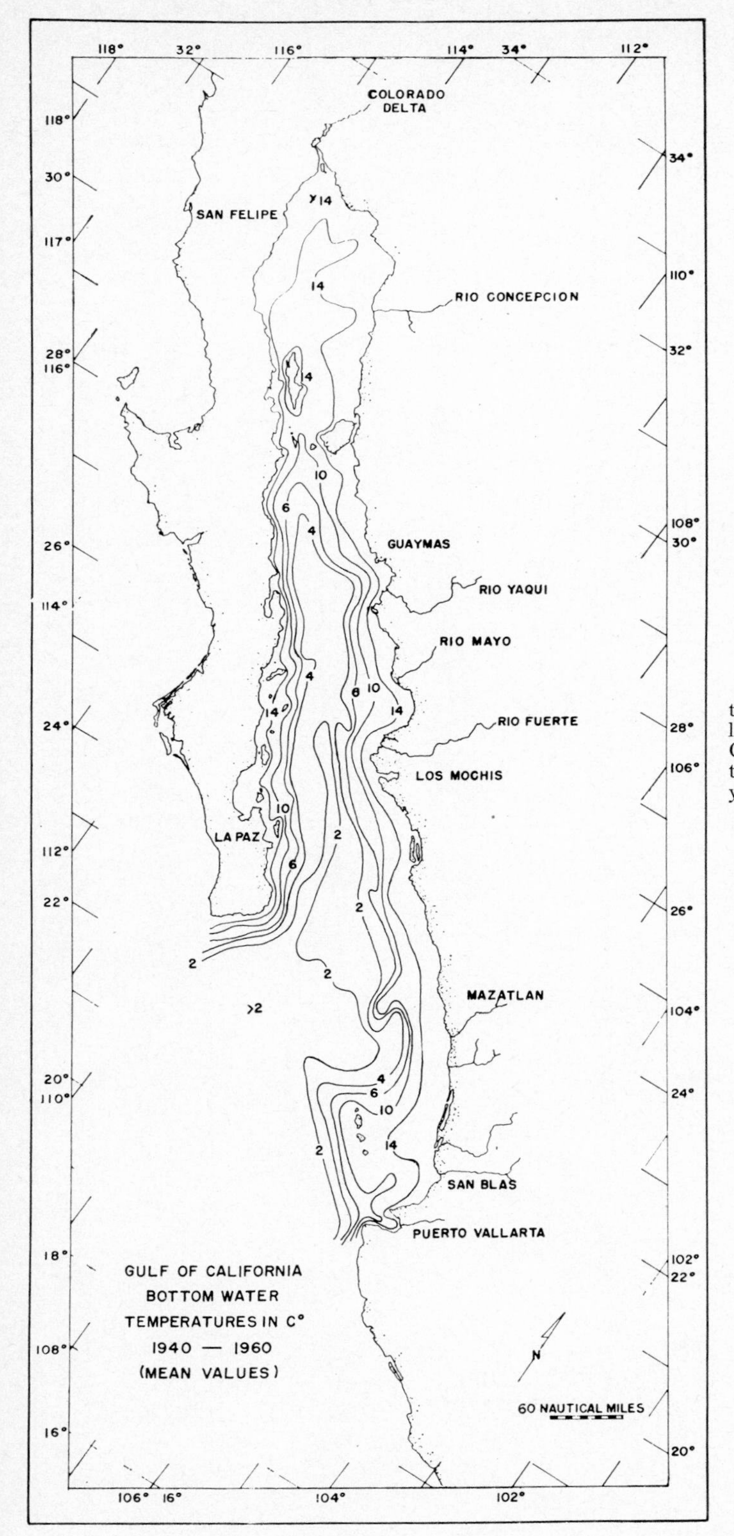

FIG. 9.—Bottom-water isotherms of the Gulf of California, based on published (Roden, 1958; Roden and Groves, 1959) and unpublished data, taken in various seasons during a 20-year period.

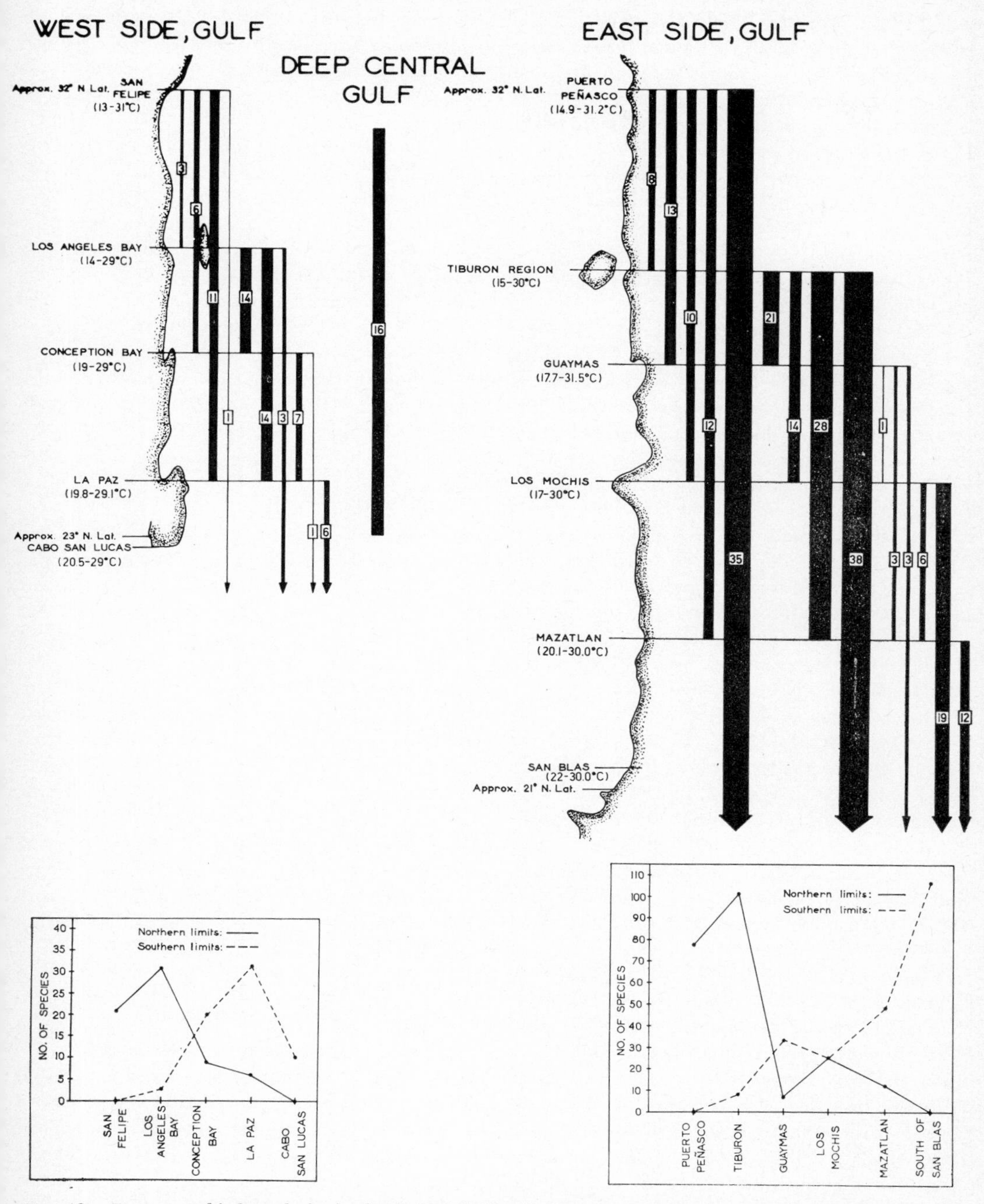

FIG. 10.—Zoogeographic boundaries in the Gulf of California, based on ranges of common invertebrates. Thickness of bars is related to number of species. Small graphs represent geographic variation of number of species with principal northern and southern distribution in dependence of geographic position.

this locality (Walker, 1960; Rosenblatt, 1959; Keen, 1958). In general, the faunal breaks along the western side of the Gulf also can be correlated with various temperature regimes.

Salinity differences in the open Gulf from north to south and from surface to bottom are small (Roden, this volume; Roden and Groves, 1959) and relatively unimportant in the distribution of benthic animals. The range from north to south is about 1°/₀₀, and from the surface to 1,800 meters it is approximately 1.4°/₀₀. The seasonal variation is equally small.

Certain inshore regions of the Gulf of California, however, are characterized by salinity changes large enough to affect animal distribution. Such areas are the lagoons and bays of the east coast between Tiburón Island and San Blas. North of the Yaqui River, the lagoons seldom receive much fresh water runoff, and long-period hypersaline conditions prevail (Nichols, 1962). Few benthic animals can live permanently in these lagoons, but observations on Indian middens indicate that brackish-water and lagoonal species have been present at some time in the past. South of the Fuerte River and as far as Mazatlán, the lagoons receive more fresh water, and seasonal populations of shrimp and permanent populations of oysters are known to exist there. South of Mazatlán, the numerous large lagoons are frequently almost fresh, although higher salinities may occur in the summer. A permanent population of shrimp, *Corbula*, oysters, and *Anadara* clams which are used as food, occur there. Rainfall and river discharge are sufficient permanently to maintain a low-salinity regime which renders these lagoons similar to those of the Texas-Louisiana coast (Parker, 1959).

Circulation in the Gulf of California is complex and not completely understood (Roden, 1958; this volume). In the winter months, strong, steady, northerly winds produce a surface current which drives surface water out to the Pacific. This water is replaced by inflow of Pacific water at moderate depths. At the same time, the high-salinity water of the northern Gulf is cooled and fills the deeper basins, moving southward along the coast of the Peninsula. Together with the high tidal currents existing in the narrow channels between islands, this water movement causes complete mixing in the basin between Angel de la Guarda and the mainland. In the summer, coastal surface currents move northwestward along the eastern side of the Gulf with average velocities of between 5 and 20 cm/sec.

The surface currents probably have little affect on the adult benthic populations. They are important, however, in the transport of the larval stages of many benthic animals. The termination of northward currents near Tiburón Island may account for the northern limit of most Panamic species with planktonic larvae in this area. The fact that many mollusk and crustacean species occurring on the eastern side of the Gulf are not found on the western side, and vice-versa, also may be due to the fact that the currents on both sides flow in opposite directions.

DESCRIPTION OF MACRO-INVERTEBRATE ASSEMBLAGES AND ENVIRONMENTS

The present sample coverage is inadequate to establish all faunal assemblages that may exist in the Gulf of California, but probably it is sufficient to discuss the most common and important groups. The number of ecological niches is very great for such a relatively small region, particularly along the rocky, dissected coast of the Peninsula. With the exception of fine-grained carbonate environments, nearly all possible environments that have occurred during the Tertiary history of the Americas are found in the Gulf of California, although reef environments are small and insignificant (Squires, 1959). Polychaetes, ophiuroids, asteroids, anthozoans, sponges, and bryozoans are not included in the following discussion, although some of them are very characteristic of certain environments.

I. THE INTERTIDAL ROCKY SHORES ASSEMBLAGES

The fauna of the intertidal rocky shores is widespread along the Gulf of California (Fig. 11) and the coast of Central America. Although the literature on this fauna is extensive (*see* review by Doty, 1957), few papers deal with this assemblage in the Gulf of California (Steinbeck and Ricketts, 1941; Keen, 1958; McLean, 1961; Dushane, 1962). A selection of the most important species is given in the Appendix (Table I); a more complete

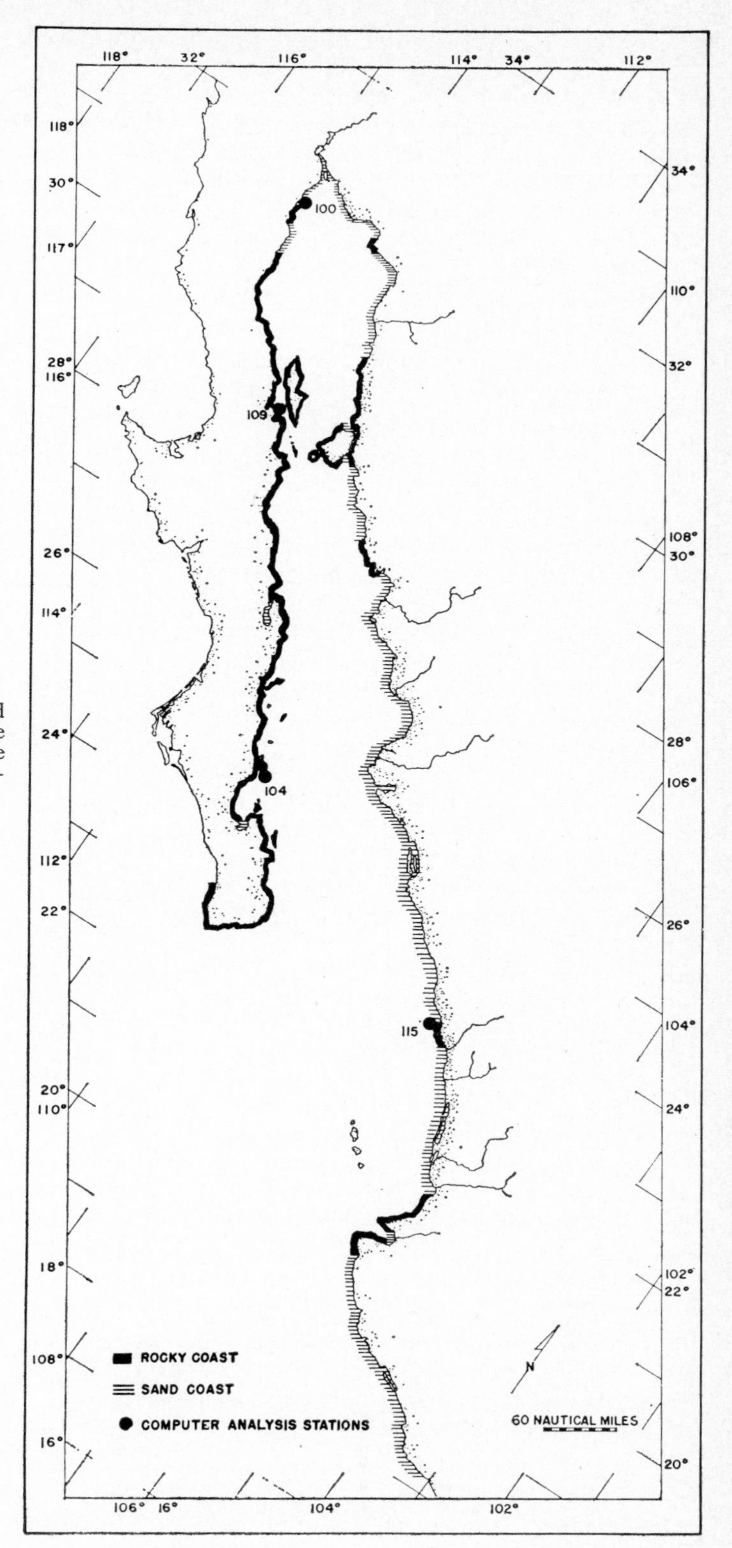

FIG. 11.—Distribution of sandy and rocky areas along the coasts of the Gulf of California. Numbers indicate stations highly correlated by contingency matrix.

list can be found in Parker (1964). Most of the species occur only in one or a few stations; the following appear to be highly correlated in this environment.

GASTROPODS
Nerita scabricosta Lamarck, 1822
Purpura patula pansa Gould, 1852
Turbo fluctuosus Wood, 1828
Pyrene fuscata (Sowerby, 1832)
LAMELLIBRANCHS
Barbatia reeveana (d'Orbigny, 1846)
Isognomon chemnitziana (d'Orbigny, 1853)
Ostrea conchophila Carpenter, 1856
Anomia adamas Gray, 1830
Cardita affinis californica Deshayes, 1854

Inspection of the total number of stations assigned to this group shows that these species represent only a minor portion of the assemblage. A total of 53 living species has been identified in this environment; another 18 species, known to live in it, were taken as dead shell. A few of the typical mollusks are shown on Plate 1. Much more extensive lists of species than are found in the present study are reported by the authors mentioned above, but the same predominant species are found by both.

II. INTERTIDAL SAND BEACH AND SAND FLATS TO 10 METERS

The faunal assemblages found in this environment resemble those of the sand beaches and flats of the Gulf of Mexico (Parker, 1956, 1960). In the Gulf of California, this environment is almost as widespread as that of the intertidal rocky shores. One-third to one-half of all known mollusk species from the Gulf of California have been found in this environment, but it is difficult to ascertain from the literature which species were found alive. The species list of the present paper is mainly based on the author's own collections.

Relatively few species are found in more than a single station, and only a few are closely correlated statistically.

Cardita megastropha (Gray, 1825)
Tivela byronensis (Gray, 1838)
Heterodonax bimaculatus (Linné, 1758)

All species had between three and five station occurrences in common and were taken alive. Other common invertebrates from this environment are listed in the Appendix (Table I). Most species range from the head of the Gulf to the Gulf of Panama, but a few are restricted to the southern Gulf of California.

Many other invertebrates are reported in the literature as abundant on sand beaches. Dushane lists 112 living species for sand and sand-mud bottoms near Puertocitos (1962). McLean (1961) found two living sand dollars, *Encope grandis* L. Agassiz and *E. californica* Verrill, and the following list of living mollusks on sand flats near Los Angeles Bay.

PROSOBRANCHS
Calliostoma eximium (Reeve)
Neritina luteofasciata Miller*
Balcis cf. *rutila* (Carpenter)
Cerithium sculptum Sowerby
Cerithidea albonodosa Gould and Carpenter*
C. mazatlanica Carpenter
Natica chemnitzii Pfeiffer
Polinices bifasciatus (Gray)
P. uber (Valenciennes)
P. reclusianus (Deshayes)
Strombus gracilior (Sowerby)
S. granulatus Swainson*
Hexaplex erythrostomus (Swainson)

→

EXPLANATION OF PLATE 1

INTERTIDAL ROCKY SHORES ASSEMBLAGE

FIGS. 1.—*Littorina aspersa* Philippi, 1846. Aperture; size 20×13 mm.
2.—*Nerita scabricosta* Lamarck, 1822. Aperture; size 43×40 mm.
3.—*Turbo fluctuosus* Wood, 1828. Aperture; size 31×30 mm.
4.—*Turbo saxosus* Wood, 1828. Aperture; size 16×15 mm.
5.—*Cerithium stercusmuscarum* Valenciennes, 1833. Aperture; size 26×11mm.
6.—*Vermicularia pellucida* (Broderip and Sowerby, 1829). Aperture; size 16×9 mm.
7.—*Pyrene fuscata* (Sowerby, 1832). Aperture; size 18×11 mm.
8.—*Purpura patula pansa* Gould, 1852. Aperture; size 37×24 mm.
9.—*Jenneria pustulata* (Solander, 1786). *a.* dorsal; *b.* aperture; size 16×10 mm.
10.—*Siphonaria maura* Sowerby, 1835. *a.* dorsal; *b.* interior and animal; size 7×8 mm.
11.—*Arcopsis solida* Sowerby 1833. *a.* exterior; *b.* interior; size 12×7 mm.
12.—*Isognomon chemnitzianus* (d'Orbigny, 1853). *a.* exterior; *b.* interior; size 33×23 mm.
13.—*Cardita affinis californica* Deshayes, 1854. *a.* exterior; *b.* interior; size 65×28 mm.
14.—*Anomia adamas* Gray, 1850. *a.* exterior; *b.* interior; size 32×27 mm.

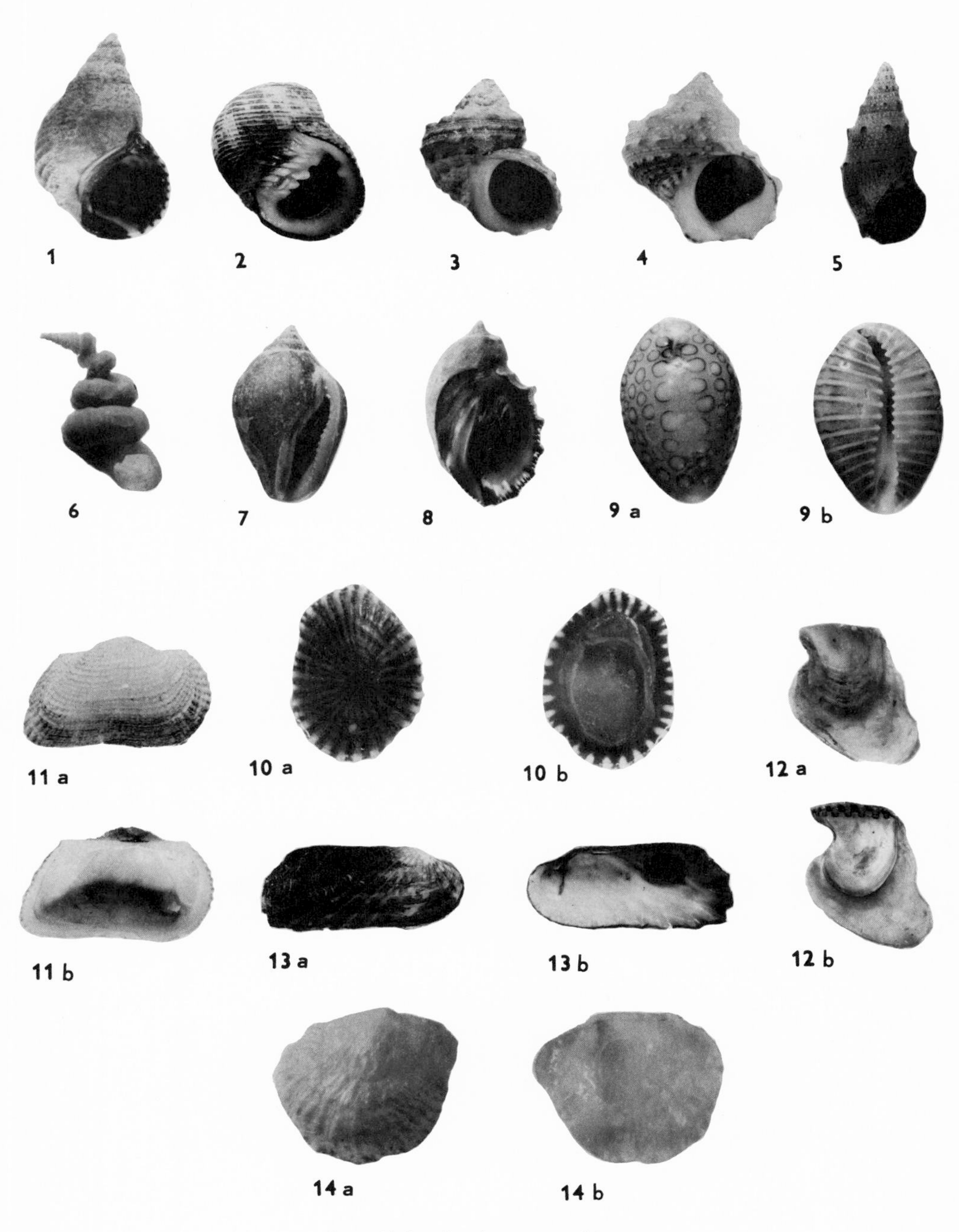

Intertidal rocky shores assemblage

Explanation of Plate 2

SAND BEACHES AND SAND FLATS TO 10 METERS

Figs. 1.—*Cerithium maculosum* Kiener, 1841. Aperture; size 45×27 mm.
2.—*Turritella leucostoma* Valenciennes, 1832. Aperture; size 69×16 mm.
3.—*Strombus granulatus* Swainson, 1822. Aperture; size 81×40 mm.
4.—*Oliva incrassata* (Solander, 1786). Aperture; size 60×33 mm.
5.—*Olivella fletcherae* Berry, 1958. Aperture; size 11×4 mm.
6.—*Bulla gouldiana* Pilsbry, 1895. Aperture; size 40×28 mm.
7.—*Anadara multicostata* (Sowerby, 1833). *a*. exterior; *b*. interior; size 53×46 mm.
8.—*Anadara labiosa* (Sowerby, 1833). *a*. exterior; *b*. interior; size 20×14 mm.
9.—*Diplodonta sericata* (Reeve, 1850). *a*. exterior; *b*. interior; size 10×10 mm.
10.—*Tivela byronensis* (Gray, 1838). *a*. exterior; *b*. interior; size 39×33 mm.
11.—*Megapitaria squalida* (Sowerby, 1835). *a*. exterior; *b*. interior; size 67×54 mm.
12.—*Dosinia dunkeri* (Philippi, 1844). *a*. exterior; *b*. interior; size 61×63 mm.
13.—*Dosinia ponderosa* (Gray, 1838). *a*. exterior; *b*. interior; size 123×114 mm.
14.—*Anomalocardia subimbricata tumens* (Verrill, 1870). *a*. exterior; *b*. interior; size 29×25 mm.
15.—*Pitar lupanaria* (Lesson, 1830). Exterior; size 26×20 mm.
16.—*Heterodonax bimaculatus* (Linné, 1758). *a*. exterior; *b*. interior; size 26×15 mm.
17.—*Mulinia pallida* (Broderip and Sowerby, 1829). *a*. exterior; *b*. interior; size 49×36 mm.
18.—*Tellina felix* Hanley, 1844. Interior; size 10×5 mm.
19.—*Donax carinatus* Hanley, 1843. Exterior; size 26×15 mm.
20.—*Donax punctatostriatus* Hanley, 1843. *a*. exterior; *b*. interior; size 32×21 mm.
21.—*Tagelus affinis* (C.B. Adams, 1852). *a*. exterior; *b*. interior; size 48×18 mm.

Sand beaches and sand flats to 10 meters

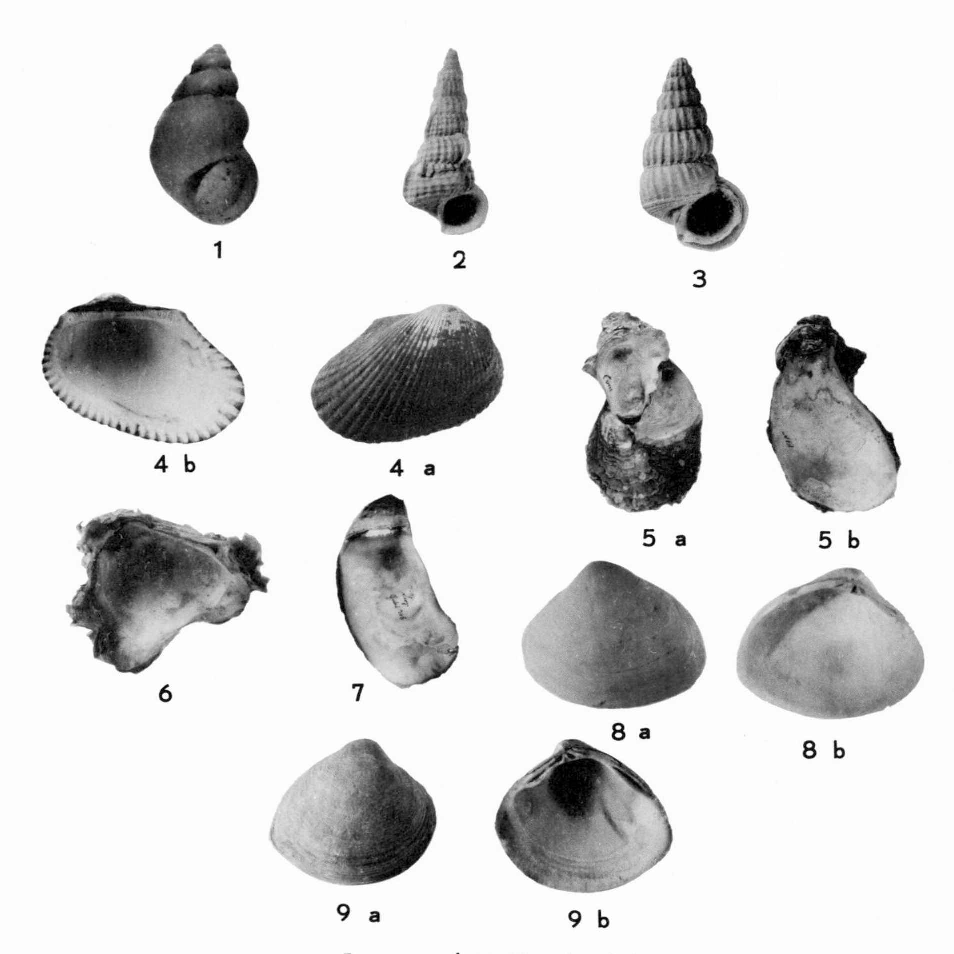

Lagoons and mangrove swamps

EXPLANATION OF PLATE 3

LAGOONS AND MANGROVE MUD FLATS

FIGS. 1.—*Littoridina* sp. Aperture; size 3×2 mm.
2.—*Cerithidea mazatlanica* Carpenter, 1856. Aperture; size 26×11 mm.
3.—*Cerithidea montagnei* (d'Orbigny, 1837). Aperture; size 30×17 mm.
4.—*Anadara tuberculosa* (Sowerby, 1833). *a.* exterior; *b.* interior; size 65×45 mm.
5.—*Crassostrea corteziensis* Hertlein, 1951. *a.* exterior; *b.* interior; size 80×45 mm.
6.—*Crassostrea columbiensis* Hanley, 1846. Interior; size 45×50 mm.
7.—*Crassostrea corteziensis* Hertlein, 1951. Interior; size 126×60 mm (large specimen).
8.—*Polymesoda olivacea* (Carpenter, 1855). *a.* exterior; *b.* interior; size 21×18 mm.
9.—*Polymesoda mexicana* (Broderip and Sowerby, 1829). *a.* exterior; *b.* interior; size 42×43 mm.

Nearshore shelf, 11 to 26 meters

Explanation of Plate 4

NEARSHORE SHELF, 11 TO 26 METERS

Figs. 1.—*Architectonica nobilis* Röding, 1798. Aperture; size 10×21 mm.
2.—*Crucibulum spinosum* (Sowerby, 1824). Exterior; size 17×14 mm.
3.—*Natica broderipiana* Recluz, 1844. Aperture; size 24×23 mm.
4.—*Polinices reclusianus* (Deshayes, 1839). Aperture; size 24×25 mm.
5.—*Polinices otis* (Broderip and Sowerby, 1829). Aperture; size 10×10 mm.
6.—*Sinum debile* (Gould, 1853). Aperture; size 8×2 mm.
7.—*Hexaplex erythrostomus* (Swainson, 1831). Aperture; size 95×71 mm.
8.—*Hexaplex brassica* (Lamarck, 1822). Aperture; size 79×58 mm.
9.—*Strombus gracilior* Sowerby, 1825. Aperture; size 67×47 mm.
10.—*Nassarius versicolor* (C.B. Adams, 1852). Aperture; size 9×5 mm.
11.—*Oliva spicata* (Röding, 1798). Aperture; size 32×17 mm.
12.—*Mitra erythrogramma* Tomlin, 1931. Aperture; size 17×6 mm.
13.—*Hormospira maculosa* (Sowerby, 1834). Aperture; size 45×14 mm.
14.—*Anadara obesa* (Sowerby, 1833). *a.* exterior; *b.* interior; size 22×16 mm.
15.—*Anadara nux* (Sowerby, 1833). *a.* exterior; *b.* interior; size 19×17 mm.
16.—*Adrana penascoensis* (Lowe, 1935). Exterior; size 16×5 mm.
17.—*Lioberus salvadoricus* (Hertlein and Strong, 1946). Exterior; size 17×12 mm.
18.—*Crassatella gibbosa* Sowerby, 1832. *a.* exterior; *b.* interior; size 30×18 mm.
19.—*Trigoniocardia granifera* (Broderip and Sowerby, 1829). Exterior; size 8×7 mm.
20.—*Trachycardium panamense* (Sowerby, 1833). Exterior; size 18×18 mm.
21.—*Chlamys tumbezensis* (d'Orbigny, 1846). *a.* exterior; *b.* interior; size 15×14 mm.
22.—*Chlamys circularis* (Carpenter, 1864). *a.* exterior; *b.* interior; size 33×30 mm.
23.—*Laevicardium elenense* (Sowerby, 1840). Exterior; size 13×12 mm.
24.—*Mactra californica* Conrad, 1837. Exterior; size 33×23 mm.
25.—*Pitar concinnus* (Sowerby, 1835). *a.* exterior; *b.* interior; size 24×17 mm.
26.—*Chione mariae* (d'Orbigny, 1846). Exterior; size 30×20 mm.
27.—*Pandora claviculata* Carpenter, 1856. *a.* exterior; *b.* interior; size 30×12 mm.
28.—*Tellina arenica* Hertlein and Strong, 1949. Exterior; size 13×8 mm.
29.—*Donax gracilis* Hanley, 1845. *a.* exterior; *b.* interior; size 18×7 mm.
30.—*Lyonsia gouldii* Dall, 1915. Exterior; size 13×6 mm.

Explanation of Plate 5

INTERMEDIATE SHELF, 27 TO 65 METERS

Figs. 1.—*Calliostoma bonita* Strong, Hanna and Hertlein, 1933. Aperture; size 20×21.
2.—*Astele rema* (Strong, Hertlein and Hanna, 1933). Aperture; size 9×12 mm.
3.—*Solariella triplostephanus* Dall, 1910. Aperture; size 6×7 mm.
4.—*Architectonica placentalis* (Hinds, 1844). Aperture; size 8×19 mm.
5.—*Polinices uber* (Valenciennes, 1832). Aperture; size 16×12 mm.
6.—*Cassis centiquadrata* (Valenciennes, 1832). Aperture; size 42×32 mm.
7.—*Distorsio decussatus* (Valenciennes, 1832). Aperture; size 47×25 mm.
8.—*Bursa californica sonorana* Berry, 1960. Aperture; size 51×36 mm.
9.—*Bursa nana* (Broderip and Sowerby, 1829). Aperture; size 50×30 mm.
10.—*Murex recurvirostris* Broderip, 1833. Aperture; size 43×23 mm.
11.—*Eupleura muriciformis* (Broderip, 1833). Aperture; size 26×16 mm.
12.—*Cantharus* n. sp. Aperture; size 37×24 mm.
13.—*Fusinus dupetitthouarsi* (Kiener, 1846). Aperture; size 79×25 mm.
14.—*Mitra hindsii* Reeve, 1844. Aperture; size 24×8 mm.
15.—*Harpa crenata* Swainson, 1822. Aperture; size 34×21 mm.
16.—*Clavus roseolus* (Hertlein and Strong, 1955). Aperture; size 17×7 mm.
17.—*Pleuroliria picta* (Reeve, 1843). Aperture; size 36×11 mm.
18.—*Anodontia edentuloides* (Verrill, 1870). *a.* exterior; *b.* interior; size 40×37 mm.
19.—*Trachycardium belcheri* (Broderip and Sowerby, 1829). *a.* exterior; *b.* interior; size 29×30 mm.
20.—*Eucrassatella gibbosa* forma *rudis* Sowerby, 1832. *a.* exterior; *b.* interior; size 45×28 mm.
21.—*Tellina pristiphora* Dall, 1900. *a.* exterior; *b.* interior; size 38×28 mm.
22.—*Semele paziana* Hertlein and Strong, 1949. *a.* exterior; *b.* interior; size 27×21 mm.
23.—*Nemocardium pazianum* (Dall, 1916). Exterior; size 11×10 mm.

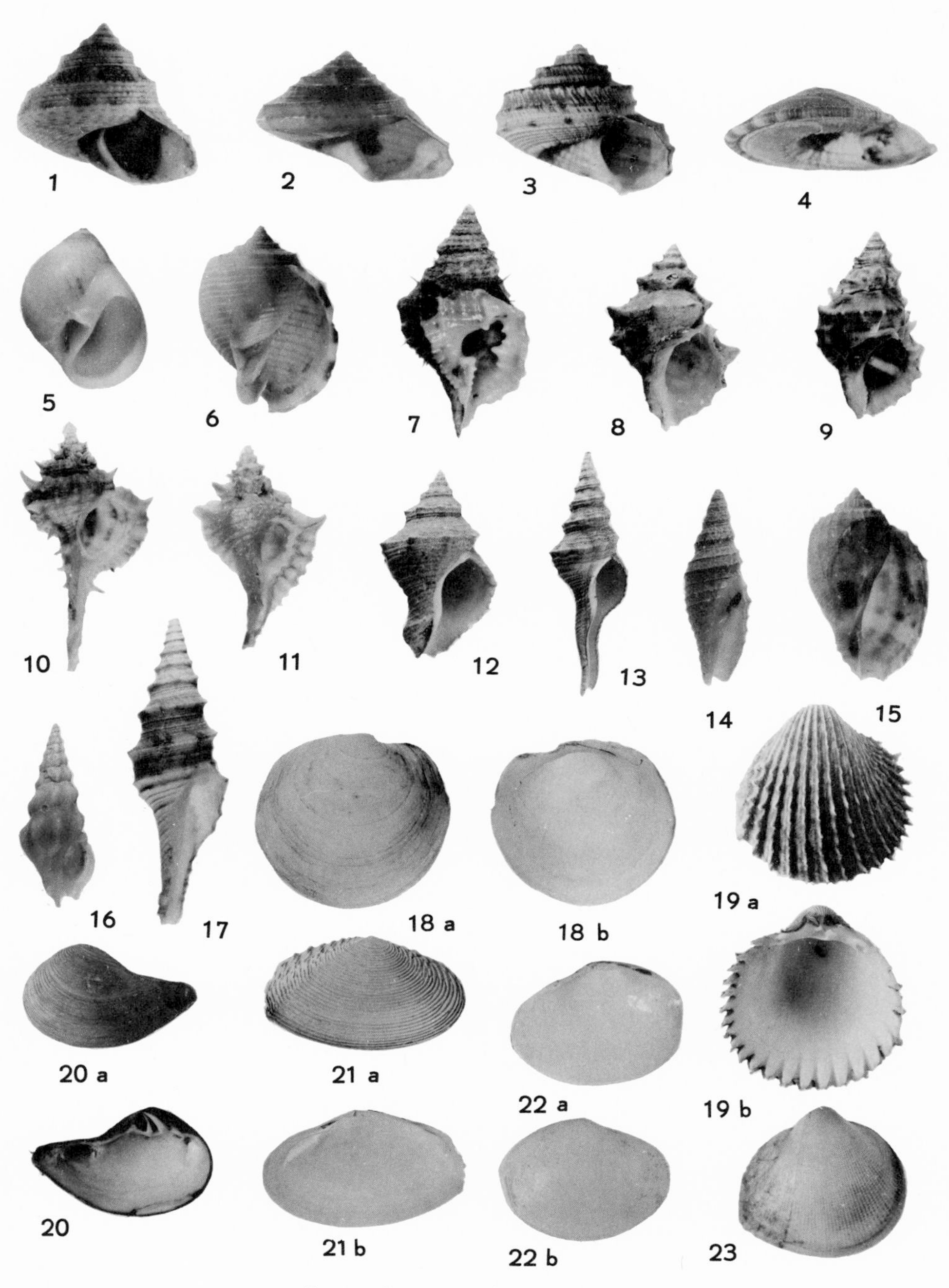

Intermediate shelf, 27 to 65 meters

Explanation of Plate 6

OUTER SHELF, SOUTHERN GULF, CLAY BOTTOM, 66 TO 120 METERS

Figs. 1.—*Crucibulum* n. sp. *a.* exterior; *b.* interior; size 31×27 mm.
2.—*Nassarius catallus* Dall, 1908. Aperture; size 17×10 mm.
3.—*Conus arcuatus* Broderip and Sowerby, 1829. Aperture; size 40×20 mm.
4.—*Anadara mazatlanica* (Hertlein and Strong, 1943). *a.* exterior; *b.* interior; size 42×27 mm.
5.—*Chione kellettii* (Hinds, 1845). *a.* exterior; *b.* interior; size 53×43 mm.
6.—*Pitar mexicanus* Hertlein and Strong, 1948. *a.* exterior; *b.* interior; size 50×40 mm.
7.—*Periploma carpenteri* Dall, 1896. *a.* exterior; *b.* interior; size 30×42 mm.

OUTER SHELF, NORTHERN GULF, SAND BOTTOM, 66 TO 120 METERS

8.—*Polinices intemeratus* (Philippi, 1853). Aperture; size 9×9 mm.
9.—*Strombus granulatus* Swainson, 1822. Pliocene? Aperture; size 69×43 mm.
10.—*Cymatium amictum* (Reeve, 1844). Aperture; size 34×18 mm.
11.—*Pleuroliria nobilis* (young) (Hinds, 1843). Aperture; size 32×17 mm.
12.—*Pleuroliria oxytropis* (Sowerby, 1834). Aperture; size 19×6 mm.
13.—*Glycymeris tessellata* (deep form) (Sowerby, 1833). Exterior; size 25×25 mm.
14.—*Lucinoma annulata* (Reeve, 1850). *a.* exterior; *b.* interior; size 43×38 mm.
15.—*Nemocardium centifilosum* (Carpenter, 1864). *a.* exterior; *b.* interior; size 10×9.5 mm.
16.—*Macoma lamproleuca* (Pilsbry and Lowe, 1932). *a.* exterior; *b.* interior; size 36×21 mm.
17.—*Corbula ventricosa* Adams and Reeve, 1850. Exterior (whole); size 11×7 mm.

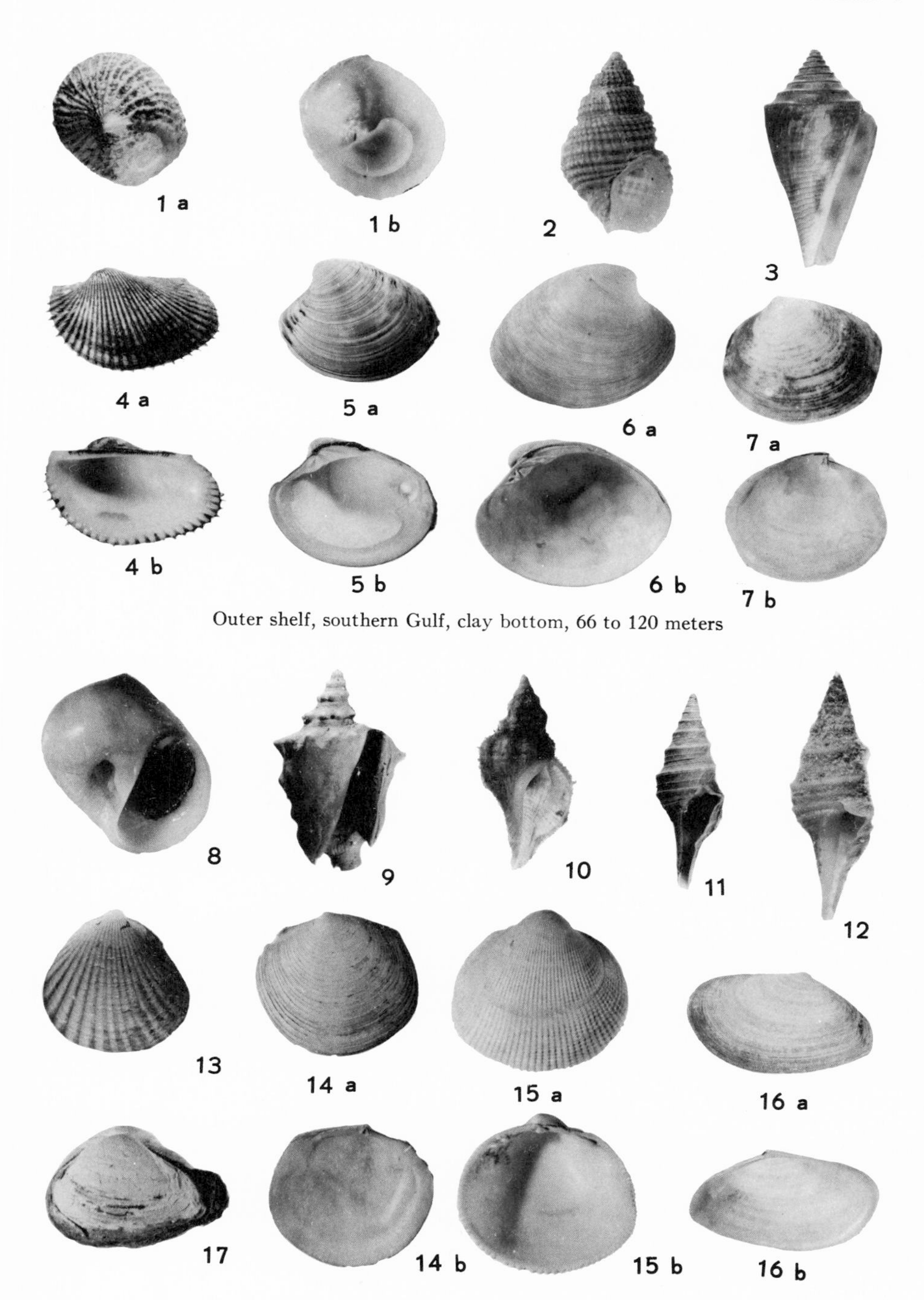

Outer shelf, southern Gulf, clay bottom, 66 to 120 meters

Outer shelf, northern Gulf, sand bottom, 66 to 120 meters

Explanation of Plate 7

DEEP NORTHERN BASINS AND TROUGHS, 230 TO 1,500 METERS

Figs. 1.—*Turritella* sp. Aperture; size 37×10 mm.
2.—*Boreotrophon* n. sp. Aperture; size 40×19 mm.
3.—*Fusinus traski* Dall, 1915. Aperture; size 43×15 mm.
4.—*Acila castrensis* Hinds, 1843. Exterior; size 11×10 mm.
5.—*Nuculana taphria* (Dall, 1897). Exterior; size 13×8 mm.
6.—*Nuculana hamata* Carpenter, 1864. *a.* exterior; *b.* interior; size 11×6 mm.
7.—*Glycymeris corteziana* Dall, 1901. *a.* exterior; *b.* interior; size 19×8 mm.
8.—*Cardita barbarensis* (Stearns, 1890). *a.* exterior; *b.* interior; size 17×15 mm.
9.—*Lucina tenuisculpta* (Carpenter, 1864). *a.* exterior; *b.* interior; size 8.7×5 mm.
10.—*Hiatella arctica* (Linné, 1767). *a.* exterior; *b.* interior; size 11×6 mm.

UPPER SLOPE, CENTRAL AND SOUTHERN GULF, 121 TO 730 METERS

11.—*Puncturella expansa* Dall, 1896. *a.* exterior; *b.* interior (animal); size 23×20 mm.
12.—*Solariella permabilis* Carpenter, 1864. Aperture; size 7×9 mm.
13.—*Nassarius insculptus gordanus* Hertlein and Strong, 1951. Aperture; size 22×12 mm.
14.—*Nassarius miser* (Dall, 1908). Aperture; size 12×7 mm.
15.—*Clathurella thalassoma* (Dall, 1908). Aperture; size 22×8 mm.
16.—*Nucula cardara* Dall, 1917. Exterior; size 10×7 mm.
17.—*Cyclopecten zacae* (Hertlein, 1935). Exterior; size 8×7 mm.

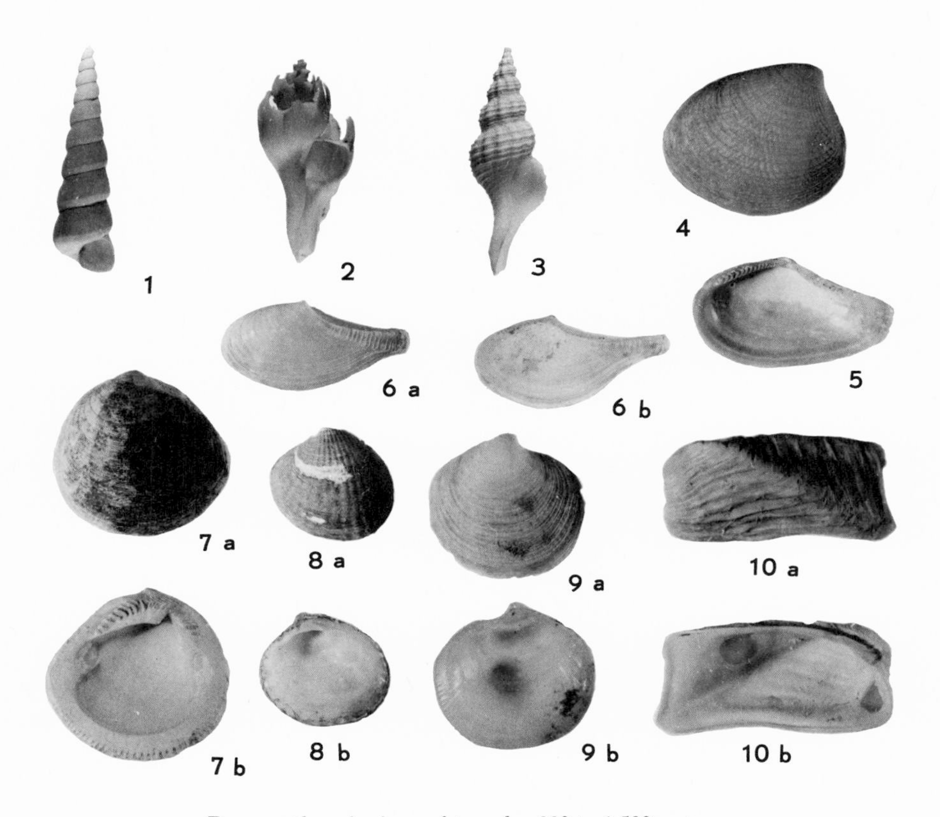

Deep northern basins and troughs, 230 to 1,500 meters

Upper slope, central and southern Gulf, 121–730 meters

Explanation of Plate 8

MIDDLE SLOPE, 731 TO 1,799 METERS

FIGS. 1.—*Cocculina diomedea* Dall, 1908? Exterior; size 9×6 mm.
2.—*Turcicula bairdii* Dall, 1889. Aperture; size 44×41 mm.
3.—*Solariella nuda* Dall, 1896. Aperture; size 10×13 mm.
4.—*Solemya agassizi* Dall, 1908. *a*. exterior; *b*. interior; size 42×18 mm.
5.—*Vesicomya lepta* Dall, 1896. *a*. exterior; *b*. interior; size 45×33 mm.

CALIFORNIA BORDERLAND BASINS, 1,641 TO 2,358 METERS[1]

6.—*Colus halidonus* Dall, 1919. Aperture; size 34×20 mm.
7.—*Colus* cf. *halli* Dall, 1873. Aperture; size 34×20 mm.
8.—*Colus trophius* Dall, 1919. Aperture; size 29×16 mm.
9.—*Ancistrolepis magnus* Dall, 1894. Aperture; size 60×46 mm.
10.—*Buccinum diplodetum* Dall, 1907, Aperture; size 16×11 mm.
11.—*Chrysodomus liratus* Martyn, 1784. Aperture; size 67×37 mm.
12.—*Antiplanes vinosa* Dall, 1874. Aperture; size 27×13 mm.
13.—*Solemya* cf. *johnsoni* Dall, 1891. *a*. exterior; *b*. interior; size 65×30 mm.
14.—*Malletia faba* Dall, 1897. *a*. exterior; *b*. interior; size 18×11 mm.
15.—*Cyclopecten randolphi tillamookensis* (Arnold, 1906). Exterior; size 23×23 mm.
16.—*Chlamys latiaurata monotimeris* (Conrad, 1837). Exterior; size 23×23 mm.
17.—*Vesicomya stearnsi* Dall, 1895. *a*. exterior; *b*. interior; size 45×33 mm.

[1] Not discussed in text. (*See* Parker, 1964).

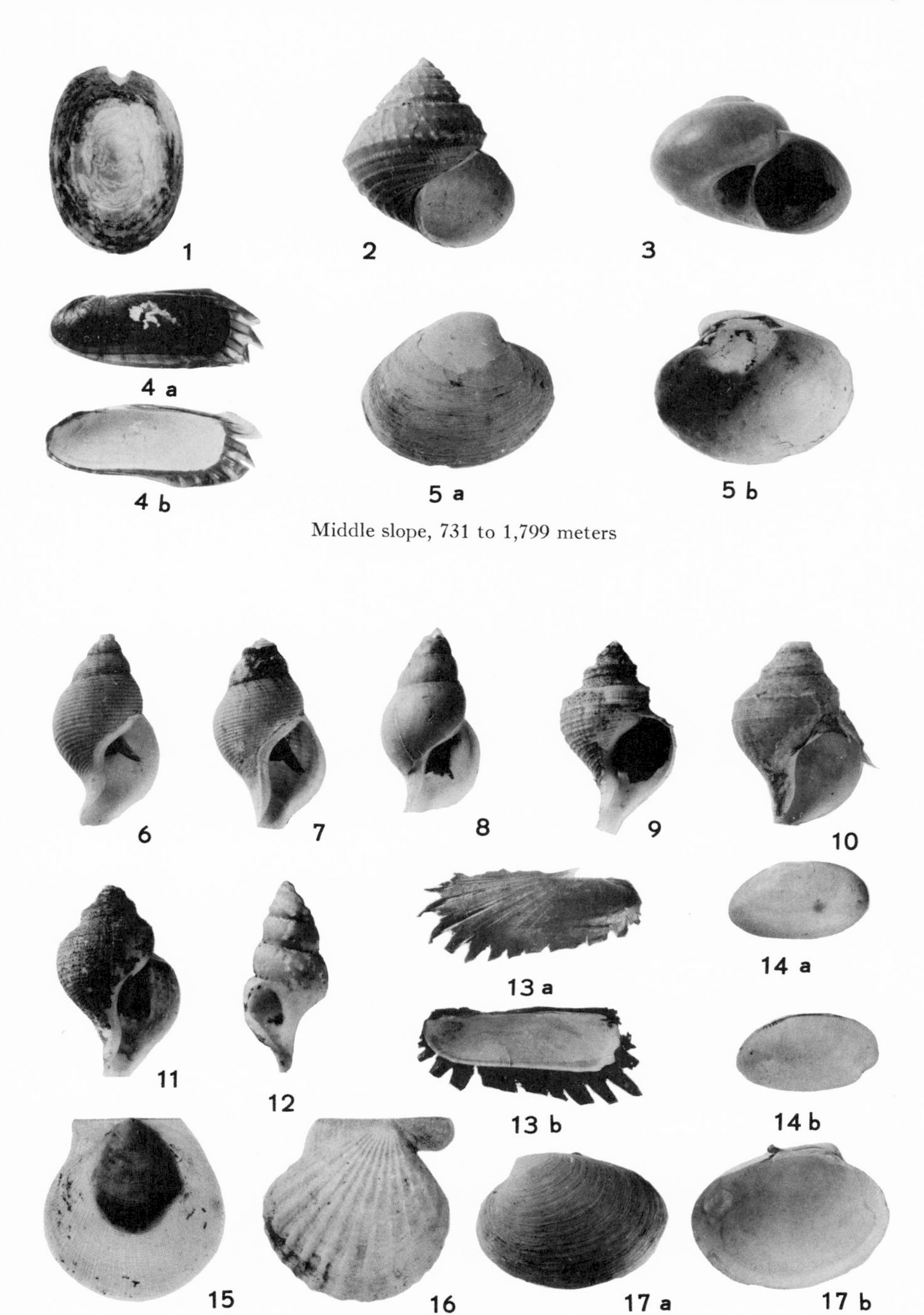

Middle slope, 731 to 1,799 meters

California borderland basins and lower slope, 1,800 to 4,122 meters

Explanation of Plate 9

ABYSSAL SOUTHERN BORDERLAND BASINS AND LOWER SLOPE, 1,800 TO 4,122 METERS

Figs. 1.—Chitinous gastropod? *a*. aperture; *b*. back; size 50×35 mm.
2.—*Solariella ceratophora* Dall, 1896. Aperture; size 21×19 mm.
3.—*Solariella equatorialis* Dall, 1908. Aperture; size 23×20 mm.
4.—*Fusinus rufocaudatus* Dall, 1896. Aperture; size 40×11 mm.
5.—*Tractolira sparta* Dall, 1896. Aperture; size 19×9 mm.
6.—*Pleurotomella clarinda* Dall, 1908. Aperture and animal; size 67×29 mm.
7.—*Steiraxis aulaca* Dall, 1896. Aperture; size 52×21 mm.
8.—*Turris* (*Gemmula*) sp. (see Dall, 1889). Aperture; size 42×29 mm.
9.—*Solemya agassizi* Dall, 1908. *a*. exterior; *b*. interior; size 42×18 mm.
10.—*Nucula panamina* Dall, 1908. *a*. exterior; *b*. interior; size 15×10 mm.
11.—*Nuculana agapea* (Dall, 1908). *a*. exterior; *b*. interior; size 21×12 mm.
12.—*Tindaria compressa* Dall, 1908. *a*. exterior; *b*. interior; size 10×8 mm.
13.—*Limopsis compressus* Dall, 1908. *a*. exterior; *b*. interior; size 29×20 mm.
14.—*Arca corpulenta pompholynx* Dall, 1908. *a*. exterior; *b*. interior; size 25×29 mm.
15.—*Arca* cf. *nucleator* Dall, 1908. *a*. exterior; *b*. interior; size 14×15 mm.
16.—*Abra profundorum* E.A. Smith, 1885. Exterior (broken, whole); size 20×13 mm.
17.—*Cuspidaria panamensis* Dall, 1908. Exterior; size 42×25 mm.
18.—*Myonera garretti* Dall, 1908. Exterior; size 21×15 mm.
19.—*Poromya perla* Dall, 1908. Exterior (whole); size 18×17 mm.

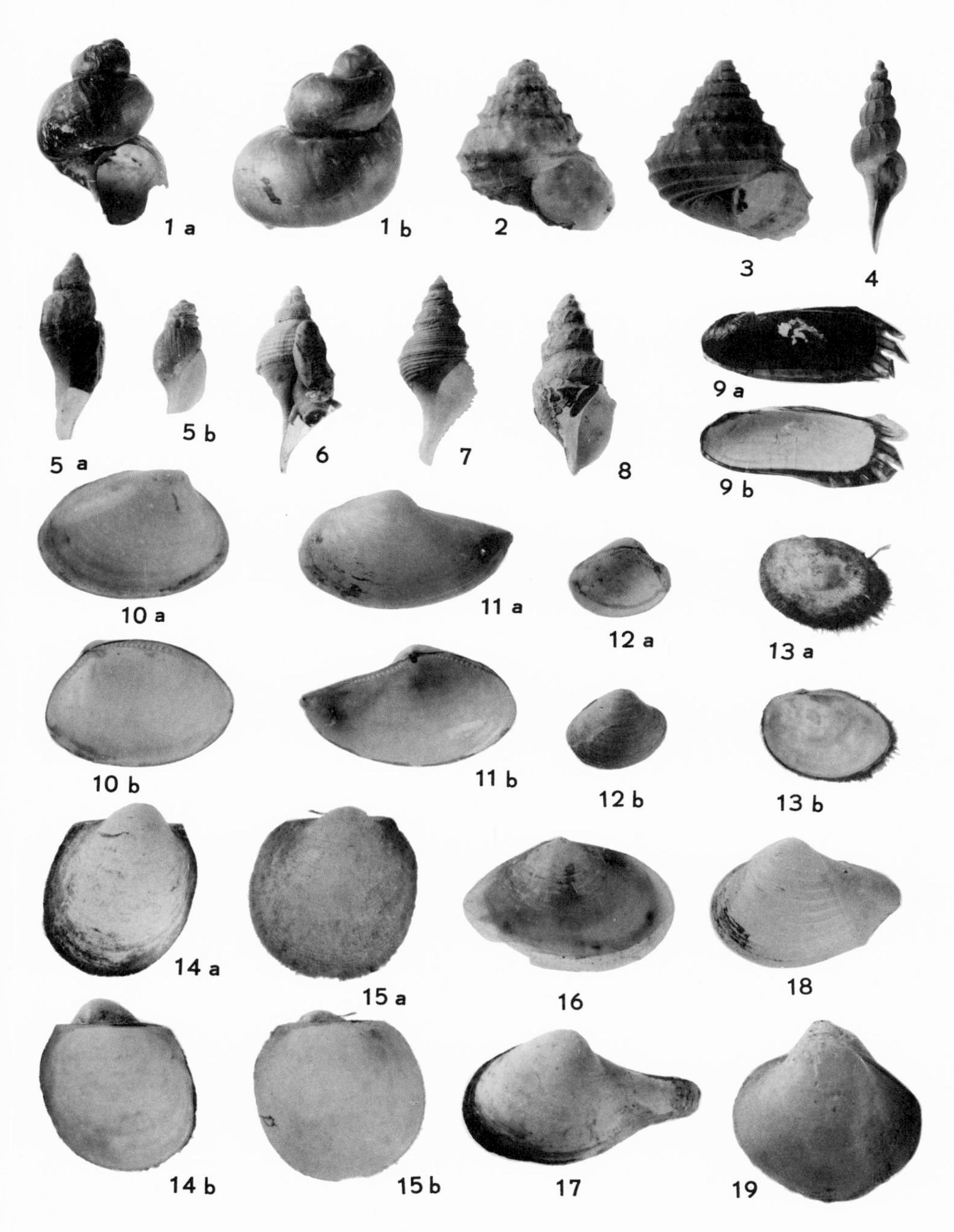

Abyssal southern borderland basins and lower slope, 1,800 to 4,122 meters

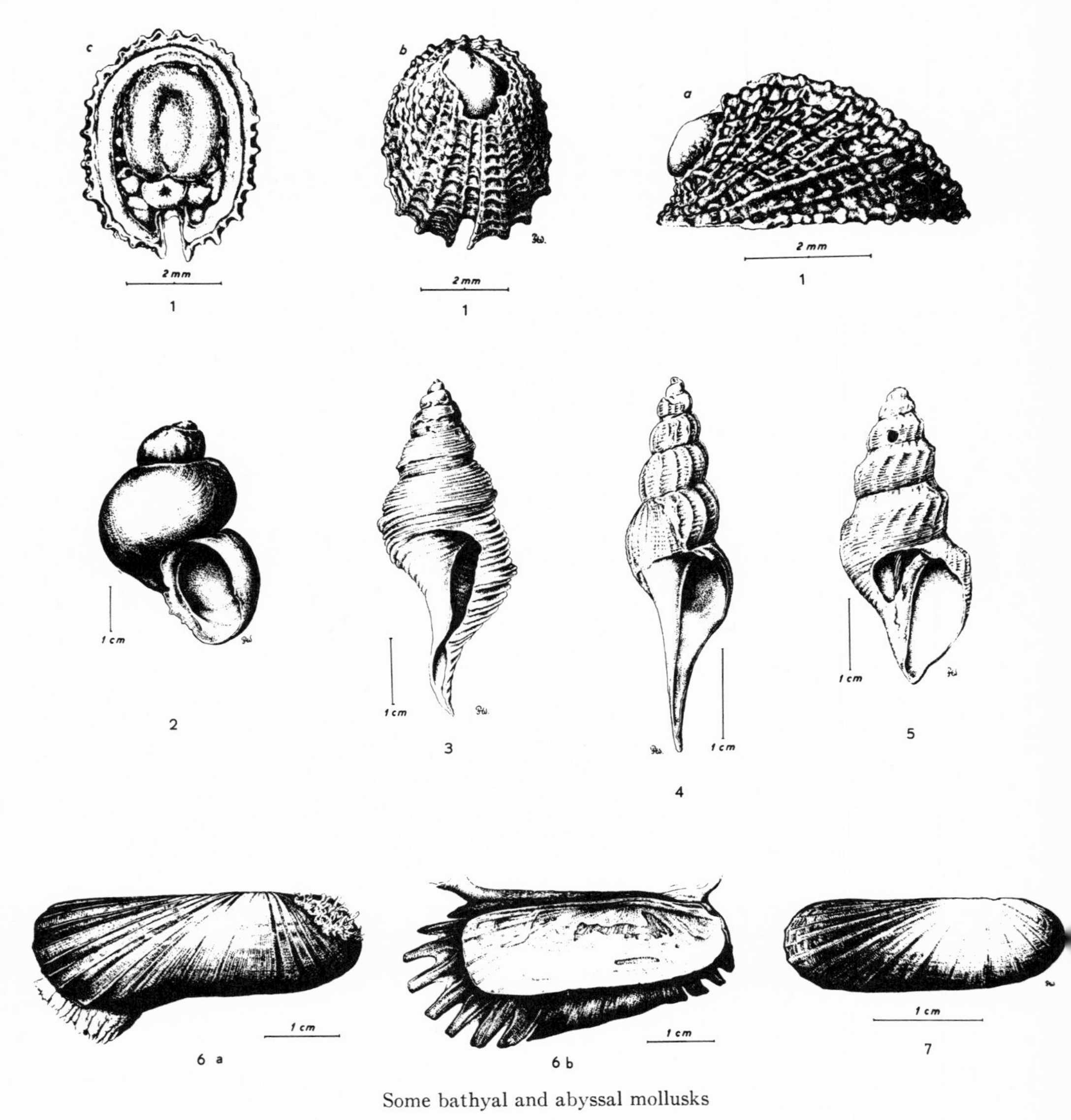

Some bathyal and abyssal mollusks

EXPLANATION OF PLATE 10

SOME BATHYAL AND ABYSSAL MOLLUSKS

Drawings by Poul Winther

FIGS. 1.—*Emarginula velascoensis* Shasky, 1961. Upper slope. *a.* side view; *b.* top; *c.* interior with animal.

2.—Chitonous gastropod? Abyssal southern borderland. Aperture (see Plate 9).

3.—*Steiraxis aulaca* Dall, 1896. Abyssal southern borderland. Aperture (Plate 9).

4.—*Fusinus rufocaudatus* Dall, 1896. Abyssal southern borderland (see Plate 9).

5.—*Turris* (*Gemmula*) sp. Abyssal southern borderland. Aperture (see Plate 9).

6.—*Solemya agassizi* Dall, 1908. Abyssal southern borderland. a. whole live specimen with undescribed hydroid attached. b. interior (see Plate 9).

7.—*Solemya valvulus* Carpenter, 1864. Upper slope. Whole live specimen.

Nassarius iodes (Dall)
N. moestus (Hinds)
N. tiarula (Kiener)*
Oliva spicata (Röding)*
Olivella dama (Wood)
Cancellaria cassidiformis (Sowerby)
Conus ximines Gray
Terebra variegata Gray

TECTIBRANCHS
Bulla gouldiana Pilsbry*
Haminoea angelinsis Baker and Hanna
H. strongi Baker and Hanna

PULMONATES
Melampus olivaceus Carpenter

LAMELLIBRANCHS
Anadara multicostata (Sowerby)
A. cepoides (Reeve)
Glycymeris gigantea (Reeve)
G. maculata (Broderip)
G. multicostata (Sowerby)
Atrina tuberculosa (Sowerby)
Trachycardium consors (Sowerby)
T. panamense (Sowerby)
Trigoniocardia granulifera (Broderip and Sowerby)
Laevicardium elenense (Sowerby)
Pitar newcombianus (Gabb)
Megapitaria squalida (Sowerby)
Dosinia ponderosa (Gray)
Protothaca grata (Say)
Heterodonax bimaculatus (Linne)*
Lyonsia gouldii Dall
Pinna rugosa Sowerby

* Species also taken alive on sand beach and flat area during present study.

Many of these species also were collected by the present author, but they were not found to be living. Many others were found alive at greater depth, where they form an important part of other living assemblages. Typical species are illustrated on Plate 2.

III. LOW-SALINITY LAGOON AND MANGROVE MUD FLATS

Only small collections were made in this environment by the author and various other members of Scripps' expeditions. The discussion is confined to the mollusks, but several species of shrimp and crabs occur in large numbers in the lagoons between Mazatlán and Panamá. The lagoon inlets south of Mazatlán generally are restricted and commonly are entirely closed. For this reason, salinities are rarely high enough to support a wholly marine fauna, and few strictly marine species are able to survive in the lagoons. A list of the typical mollusks found in this environment, selected from Keen (1958), is presented below. Species marked with an asterisk also have been taken in the present investigation. A few of the low-salinity species are shown on Plate 3.

PROSOBRANCHS
Neritina luteofasciata Miller, 1879
N. latissima Broderip, 1833
Cerithidea mazatlanica Carpenter, 1856*
C. montagnei (d'Orbigny, 1837)*
Ellobium stagnalis (d'Orbigny, 1835)
Littoridina, sp.*

TECTIBRANCHS
Bulla gouldiana Pilsbry, 1895*

PULMONATES
Melampus olivaceus Carpenter, 1856*

LAMELLIBRANCHS
Anadara tuberculosa (Sowerby, 1833)*
Mytella falcata (d'Orbigny, 1846)
Ostrea columbiensis Hanley, 1846
O. corteziensis Hertlein, 1951*
Polymesoda mexicana (Broderip and Sowerby, 1829)*
Polymesoda (7 other species)
Cyrenoides panamensis Pilsbry and Zetek, 1931
Mytilopsis adamsi Morrison, 1946
Rangia mendica (Gould, 1851)
Corbula inflata (C.B. Adams, 1852)

* Species also taken alive in low-salinity lagoons during present study.

IV. NEARSHORE SAND AND SAND-MUD ASSEMBLAGE, 11–26 METERS

This is by far the most prolific assemblage in species and numbers of individuals in the Gulf of California, because conditions in this environment are optimal for most marine species. Salinities are constant at normal oceanic values, and the temperature has a much smaller annual range than in the inshore environments. The water is relatively quiet near the bottom, and sediments are silty sands, clayey sands, and sand-silt-clay, containing relatively large quantities of organic matter. This permits a large population of deposit-feeding and burrowing animals. Under these optimal conditions, a total of 258 species of identified invertebrates were taken at 17 stations—an average per station significantly higher than in any other environment in the Gulf of California.

The separation between northern and southern Gulf is very distinct in this assemblage. The association matrix shows two assemblages, both on sand bottom and in depths from 11 to 26 m; one is in the Tiburón region and the other is south of Mazatlán. Ecological differences between the two regions are the higher water-temperature extremes and higher primary productivity of the Tiburón area. The greater annual range (16°C) in the Tiburón area as compared with Mazatlán (10°C) probably is the main limiting factor.

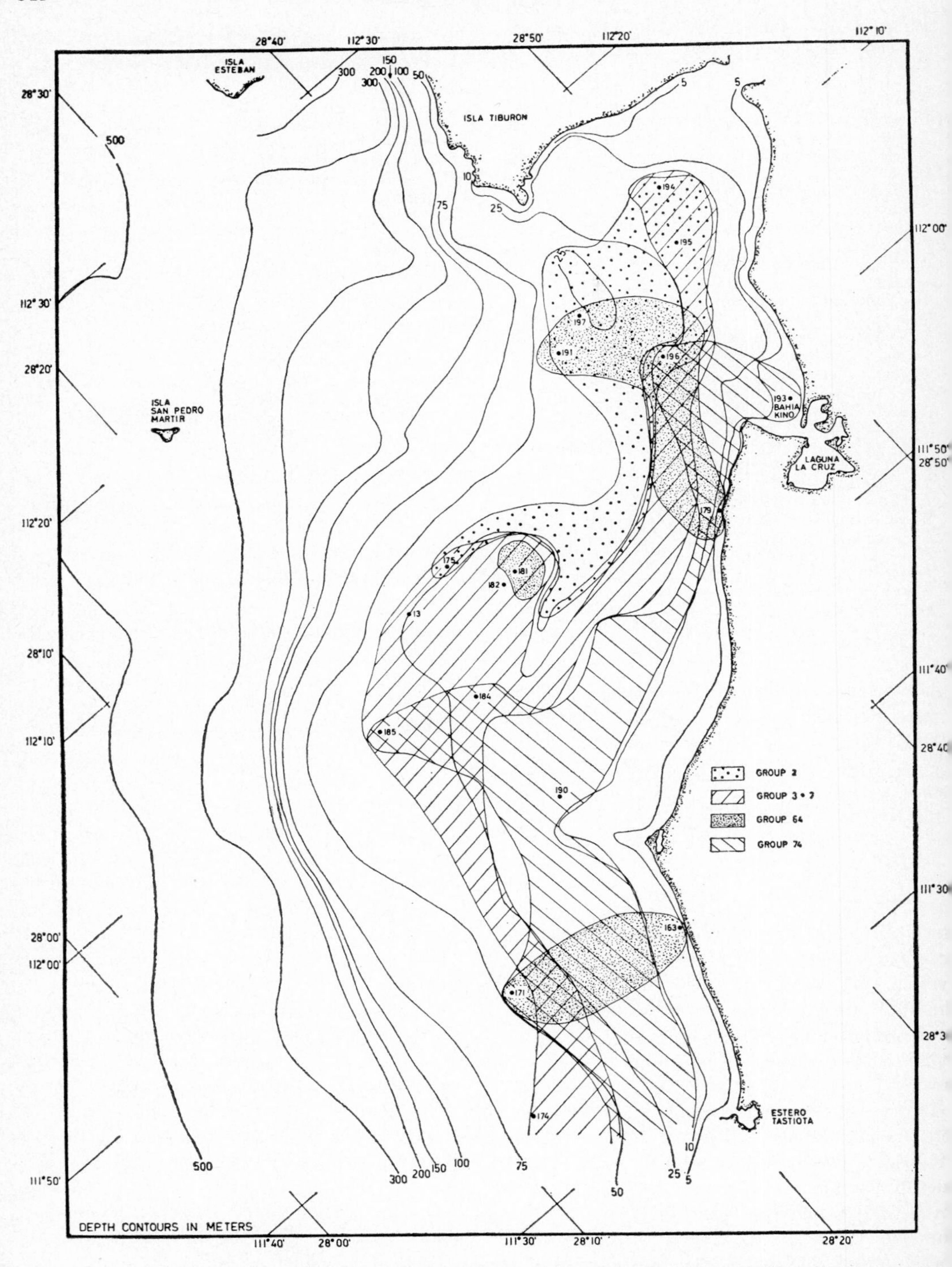

FIG. 12.—Areal distribution of index groups of assemblages in the northern nearshore shelf environment of the Costa de Hermosillo. Species and station composition of each index group are listed in the Appendix, Table II.

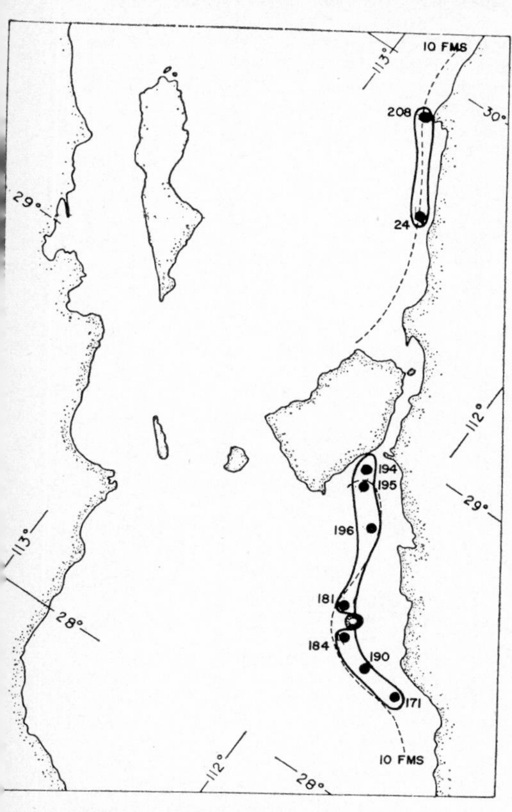

FIG. 13.—Areal distribution of stations characteristic r the nearshore shelf environment in the northeastern ulf of California. These stations have the largest num- r of common occurrences of species belonging to all dex groups.

Many invertebrate species are common to both gions. The Tiburón area between 4 and 30 m ows a very complex pattern of invertebrate semblages. Five different associations, each cupying different areas but with considerable erlap, can be recognized (Fig. 12). Table II of e Appendix lists the species for each association d the environmental factors. Only stations with ing faunas were used in establishing the faunal oups.

In order to describe the general faunal charac- ristics of the shallow-water environment of the burón region, all species which were most fre- ently found together alive were listed, and all ations in which this group had the greatest undance were selected (Fig. 13). The index ecies for this supergroup are given in Table III, with the percentage of occurrence in nine typical stations and the percentage of occurrence over the entire Gulf. For example, *Laevicardium elatum* was found living or dead in eight of the nine samples, but five of the seven living occurrences in the Gulf as a whole are in the Tiburón area. These two percentages were averaged to form an index of "uniqueness" for this species in this environment. The species in Table III are listed in order of decreasing importance; the last four were found only dead. Although they are statistically important components of the assemblage, they may be subfossil.

The 21 species of mollusks of Table III are only part of the important invertebrates in the nearshore sand environment. Others are listed in Table I in the Appendix. Many species taken in the 9 stations typical of this environment also occur in other environments and in similar depths in the southern Gulf. The fact that 3 species of corals, 14 crustaceans, 7 echinoids, 1 ophiuroid, 1 asteroid, 35 pelecypods, 3 scaphopods, and 54 species of gastropods so far have been identified from the 9 type stations demonstrates the diversity of life in this small area.

Although some of the important species are ubiquitous throughout the Gulf in this environment, a large number disappear south of the Fuerte River and are replaced by closely related types of the same genus or subgenus. Consequently, a separate station group with a well-defined assemblage can be recognized south of the Fuerte River (Fig. 14). A few of the more abundant invertebrates that are restricted to the southern area are listed below. A complete list can be found in Parker (1964); a few characteristic types are illustrated on Plate 4.

HEXACORALS
Astrangia conferta Verrill
GASTROPODS
Architectonica placentalis Hinds, 1944
Natica chemnitzii Pfeiffer, 1840
N. othello Dall, 1908
Sinum debile (Gould, 1853)
S. sanctijohannis (Pilsbry and Lowe, 1932)
Distorsio decussatus (Valenciennes, 1832)
Bursa nana (Broderip and Sowerby, 1829)
Typhis cummingii Broderip, 1833
Cominella subrostrata (Wood, 1828)
Olivella anazora (Duclos, 1835)
Cancellaria exopleura Dall, 1908
LAMELLIBRANCHS
Anadara nux (Sowerby, 1832)
Chlamys tumbezenzis (d'Orbigny, 1846)
Pitar frizzeli (Hertlein and Strong, 1948)

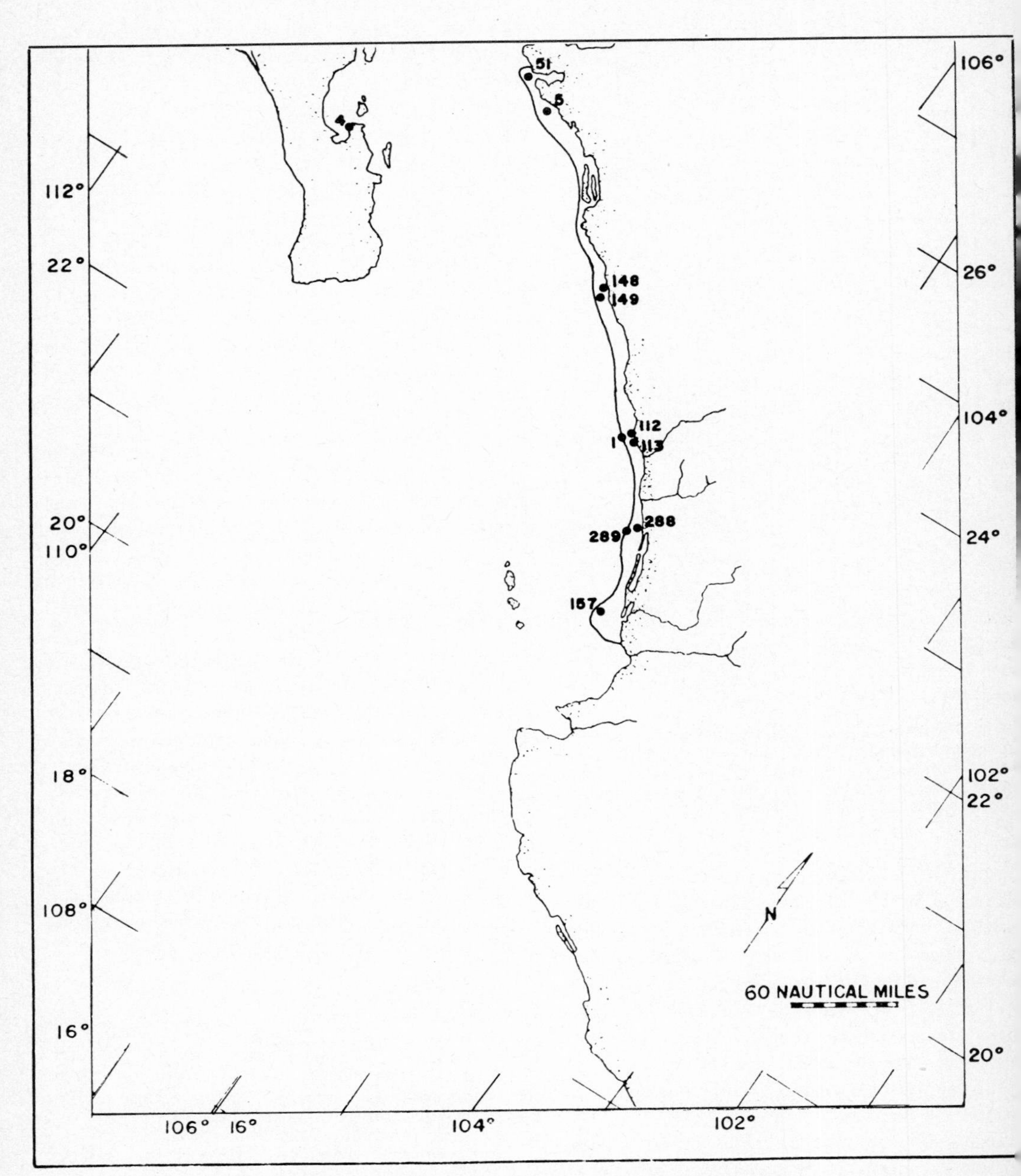

FIG. 14.—Location of stations characteristic for the nearshore shelf assemblage in the southern Gulf of California

Mulinia bradleyi Dall, 1894
Tellina cognata C.B. Adams, 1854
Abra palmeri Dall, 1915

CRUSTACEANS
Euceramus panatelus Glassell
Pagurus smithi (Benedict)

ASTEROIDS
Astropecten californicus Fisher

OPHIUROIDS
Amphiura seminuda Lütken and Mortensen?

V. INTERMEDIATE SHELF, 27 TO 65 METERS

This environment also is very distinct and is second only to the nearshore shelf in the diversity and number of organisms. Differences occur between the northern and southern Gulf, both in the richness of the fauna and in the species compositions. The contingency matrix indicates a close association between a group of animals at 6 stations in the Tiburón region, ranging in depth from 66 to 74 m, and between those of 4 others from 25 to 74 m (Fig. 15). Few mollusks were taken alive in these stations, but a large number of dead specimens, representing many species, was collected. The crustaceans appear to be the best indicators for this assemblage. A list of species, proving to be closely associated by the contingency matrix, is given below, including both living and dead species. Most of the pelecypods are more abundant as dead shells.

Species	*Degree of Association*
GASTROPODS	
Polinices uber (Valenciennes, 1837)	11
Fusinus dupettithouarsi (Kiener, 1846)	12
Natica grayi Philippi, 1852	15
LAMELLIBRANCHS	
Nemocardium pazianum (Dall, 1916)	6
Chione mariae (d'Orbigny, 1846)	8
Diplodonta subquadrata (Carpenter, 1846)	9
Macoma siliqua (C.B. Adams, 1852)	13
Cyclopecten pernomus (Hertlein, 1935)	14
Solecurtus guaymasensis (Lowe, 1935)	16
Plicatula inezana Durham, 1950	18
CRUSTACEANS	
Euprognatha bifida Rathbun	1
Mesorhea belli (A. Milne-Edwards)	2
Randallia americana (Rathbun)	3
Collodes tenuirostris Rathbun	4
Pagurus gladius (Benedict)	5
Cancer amphioetus Rathbun	7
Paradasygius depressus (Bell)	10
Cymopolia zonata Crane	14

Most of the characteristic living species of this assemblage are listed in Table I of the Appendix (also *see* Parker, 1964). All stations in the northern portion of this environment were taken on

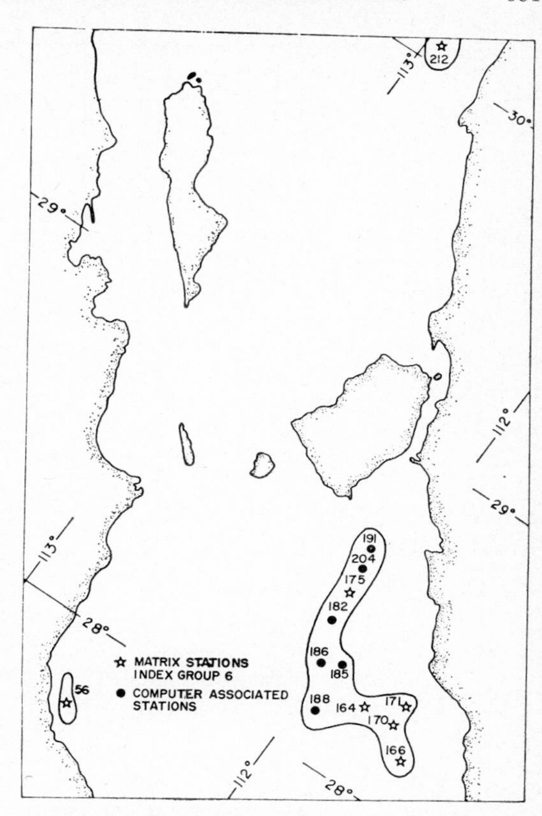

FIG. 15.—Location of stations highly correlated with the intermediate shelf assemblage of the northern Gulf of California. These stations are characterized primarily by *Euprognatha bifida* (index group 6).

sand bottom in well-oxygenated water with a temperature range from 13° to approximately 20° C.

A distinct assemblage exists in this environment in the southern portion of the Gulf. Species occurring at seven closely related stations are listed in Table IV of the Appendix and are shown in Figure 16. Selected species are illustrated on Plate 5. All stations occur on silty clay and range in depth from 36 to 75 m. As in the northern shelf region, crustaceans outnumber all other important components. Several other stations, although they contain the animals listed in Table IV, have a more heterogeneous composition and form a peripheral group. Of the 128 live species of invertebrates in 11 southern stations, 40 species occur both on sand and on silty clay. Sixteen of

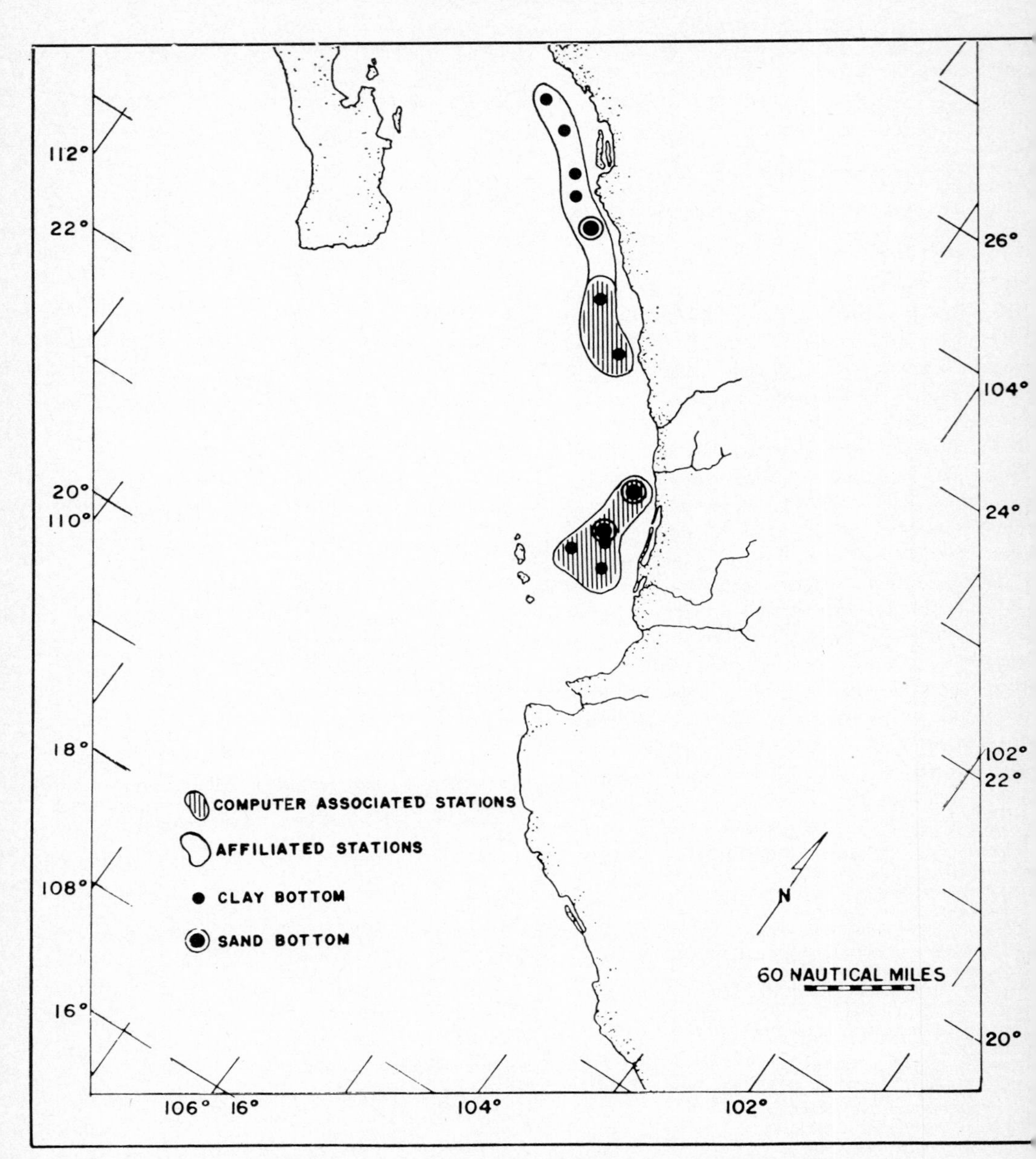

FIG. 16. Location of characteristic and related stations of the intermediate shelf assemblage on sand and clay in the southern Gulf of California.

these also occur on both sediment types in the northern area. In the southern area, only 28 species are restricted to silty clay, 3 of which occur on sand in the north. On the other hand, 57 species in 2 stations were found only on sand, of which only 8 also were taken in the north.

VI. OUTER SHELF, 66 TO 120 METERS, CLAY BOTTOM, SOUTHERN GULF

A distinct faunal region can be recognized on the outer shelf from the Fuerte River to just south of Mazatlán. Six stations are closely associated on the basis of five common species, sufficient in number to characterize the environment (Fig. 17). All six stations were taken on silty clay. The five common species are—

POLYCHAETA
- *Protula superba*

GASTROPODS
- *Crucibulum* n. sp. (allied to *C. striatum* of the Atlantic)
- *Conus arcuatus* Broderip and Sowerby, 1829

LAMELLIBRANCHS
- *Anadara mazatlanica* (Hertlein and Strong, 1943)
- *Chione kelletti* (Hinds, 1845)

Most of the important species are listed in Table I of the Appendix and are illustrated on Plate 6. A complete list can be found in Parker (1964). Two other outer-shelf stations in the southern Gulf were taken on sandy bottom, but only two of the species from these stations also were found on clay bottom, both epifaunal in nature.

VII. OUTER SHELF, 66 TO 120 METERS, SAND BOTTOM, NORTHERN GULF

All faunas collected between Tiburón Island and the Colorado Delta in the northern Gulf, in depths between 66 and 120 m, occur on sand bottoms. They are completely different from the assemblage occurring at the same depths on clay bottom in the southern Gulf. The substrate of these stations (Fig. 17) probably is the relict littoral transgressive sand deposited by the post-Pleistocene rise in sea level (van Andel, this volume), a conclusion borne out by the abundance of dead shell belonging to nearshore assemblages in each sample. A total of 91 living invertebrate species was found at 18 stations, but the number of dead species was many times greater. The composition of the 18 stations is heterogeneous and no statistically significant assemblage can be established. Only two species occur at enough stations to be considered diagnostic—the echinoid *Clypeaster europacificus* H.L. Clark, 1914, and the pelecypod *Lucinoma annulata* (Reeve, 1850). The latter also is common in the deeper waters of the northern Gulf and on the outer shelf off California. The most interesting aspect of the assemblage is the large number of living gastropods and crustaceans. Most of these belong to species which occur also on inshore sand bottom to depths of less than 20 m. Apparently, the nature of the bottom is more important than depth or temperature in limiting the distribution of more motile invertebrates in the northern Gulf of California. Most of the important invertebrates from this environment are listed in Table I of the Appendix and in Parker (1964); some common mollusks are illustrated on Plate 6.

VIII. NORTHERN GULF BASINS, 230 TO 1,500 METERS

Owing to the peculiar temperature conditions in this deep portion of the northern Gulf, this environment may well be unique in the world today. Virtually uniform conditions of temperature, salinity, and oxygen exist throughout the water column, and the bottom consists of a complex pattern of gravels, sand, and mud. There is almost no vertical stratification of faunas on the slopes.

Only 34 living species were taken on 16 stations (Fig. 18). Those unique to the northern basins are (number of stations in parentheses)—

OCTOCORALS
- *Acanthogorgia* n. sp. (2)
- *Callogorgia flabellum* (Ehrenberg) (1)
- *Eumuricea horrida* (Mobius) (1)
- *Eumuricea* n. sp. (1)

HEXACORALS
- *Balanophyllia* sp. (2)
- *Caenocyathus bowersi* Vaughn (1)
- *Desmophyllum crista-galli* Milne-Edwards and Haime (3)
- *Dendrophyllia cortezi* Durham and Barnard (1)

BRACHIOPODS
- *Laqueus californianus* (1)
- *Morrisia horneii* (2)
- *Terebratulina kiiensis* (1)

GASTROPODS
- *Fusinus traski* Dall, 1915 (1)

SCAPHOPODS
- *Dentalium pretiosum berryi* Smith and Gordon, 1958 (1)
- *Cadulus austinclarki* Emerson (1)

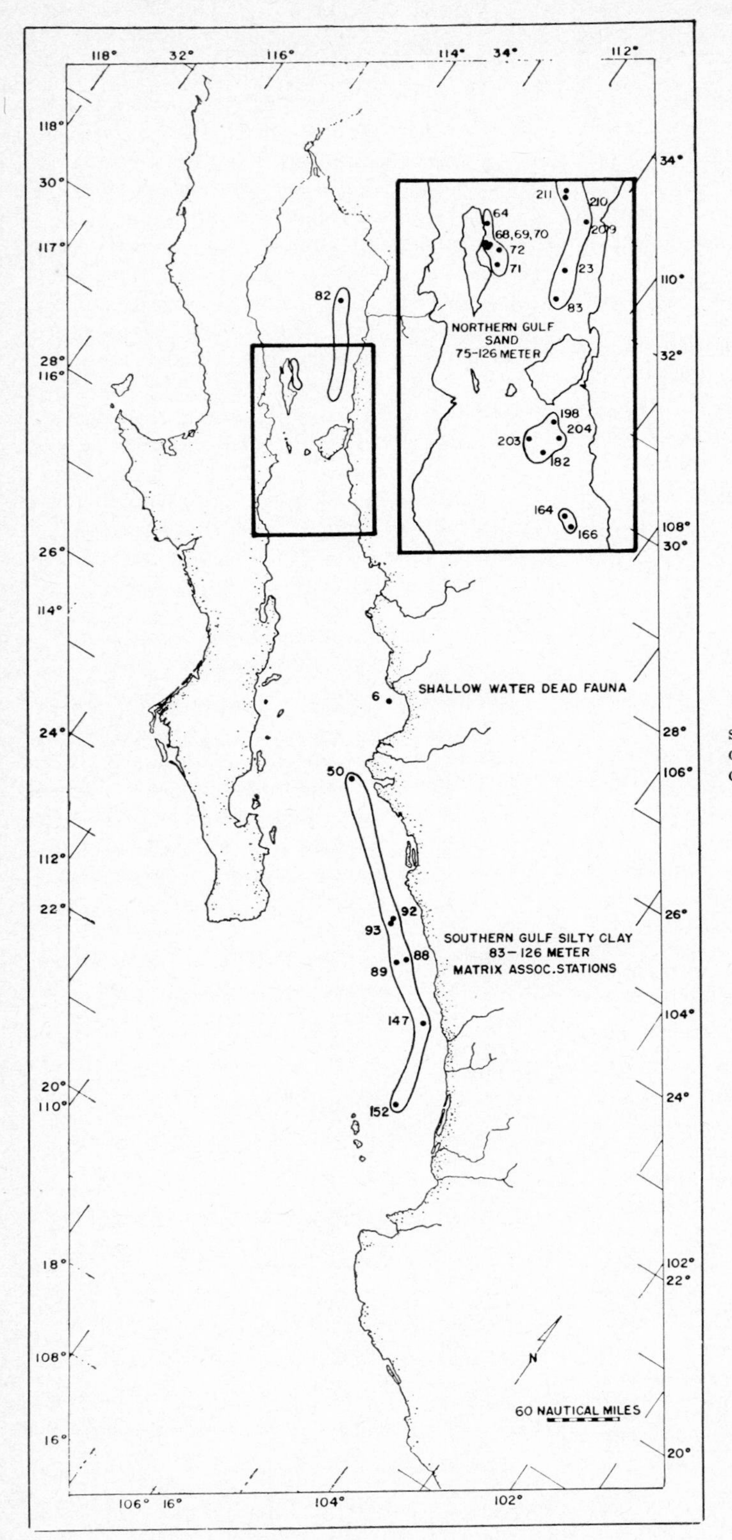

FIG. 17.—Location of characteristic stations of the outer shelf environment on sand bottom (northern Gulf) and clay bottom (southern Gulf).

Siphonodentalium quadrifisatum (Pilsbry and Sharp, 1898) (1)
LAMELLIBRANCHS
Macoma siliqua spectri Hertlein and Strong, 1949 (2)
Nuculana taphria (Dall, 1897) (1)
CRUSTACEANS
Salmoneus sp. (1)
ECHINOIDS
Brissaster townsendi (A. Agassiz) (1)
Hesperocidaris perplexa (H.L. Clark) (1)
ASTEROIDS
Astropecten californicus Fisher

Another 14 species are common both to this area and to the same depth zone in the southern and central Gulf (Appendix, Table I). A complete species list is given by Parker (1964); a few typical species are illustrated on Plate 7.

The dead shells collected from the northern Gulf basins can be divided into two groups. The first group consists of a large number of local shallow-water rock-bottom and shallow-water sand species, which either have been transported into deeper water by slumps or turbidity currents, or actually may live there as a result of high bottom-water temperatures. Some of these species are listed below (station occurrences in parentheses).

GASTROPODS
Acmaea sp. (2)
Fissurella sp. (1)
Diodora alta (C.B. Adams, 1852) (1)
D. aspera Escholtz (1)
Turbo sp. (1)
Crucibulum scuttelatum (Wood, 1828) (1)
Crepidula onyx Sowerby, 1824 (1)
Natica chemnitzi Pfeiffer, 1840 (1)
Polinices otis (Broderip and Sowerby, 1829) (2)
Cypraea annettae Dall, 1909 (1)
Ficus ventricosa (Sowerby, 1825) (1)
Olivella sp. (1)
Pyrene fuscata (Sowerby, 1832) (2)
Mitra crenata Broderip, 1836 (1)
Hindsiclava andromeda (Dall, 1919) (1)
Pleuroliria oxytropis (Sowerby, 1834) (1)
SCAPHOPODS
Dentalium oerstedii Mörch, 1861 (2)
D. vallicolens Raymond, 1901 (2)
Cadulus perpusillus Sowerby, 1832 (4)
LAMELLIBRANCHS
Barbatia alternata Sowerby, 1833 (1)
B. baileyi Bartsch, 1931 (1)
B. gradata (Broderip and Sowerby, 1839) (1)
Anadara cepoides (Reeve, 1834) (2)
Glycymeris multicostata (Sowerby, 1833) (1)
Pecten vogdesi Arnold, 1906 (1)
Cyclopecten pernomus (Hertlein, 1935) (1)
Pododesmus cepio (Gray, 1850) (1)
Crassinella varians (Carpenter, 1855) (1)
Cardita megastropha (Gray, 1825) (1)
Trigoniocardia guanacastense (Hertlein and Strong, 1947) (2)
Ventricolaria isocardia (Verrill, 1870) (2)
Semele sp. (1)
Corbula marmorata Hinds, 1843 (1)

Most of these species were found below 300 m—far below their normal habitat of the intertidal rocky shore.

The other group of dead shells is far more interesting. This assemblage of shells is very distinct and forms one of the most clear-cut associations of species. Of the nine species involved, only one was collected alive, and that only once, in the northern basins, although three more were taken alive on the upper slope of the central Gulf. The nine species of this group are (station occurrences in parentheses)—

GASTROPODS
Turritella sp. (cf. *T. cooperi* Carpenter, 1864) (6)
Nassarius miser Dall, 1908 (8)
LAMELLIBRANCHS
Nuculana hamata (Carpenter, 1864) (8)
N. taphria (Dall, 1897) (5)
Cardita barbarensis Stearns, 1890 (13)
Lucina tenuisculpta (Carpenter, 1864) (10)
Lucinoma annulata (Reeve, 1850) (14)
Nemocardium centifilosum (Carpenter, 1845) (20)
Hiatella arctica (Linné, 1767) (6)

Without exception, all of these species are found off the California coast; all are continental-shelf species not living in depths beyond 180 m, and most have not been recorded south of San Diego on the outer Pacific coast.

IX. UPPER SLOPE, CENTRAL AND SOUTHERN GULF, 121 TO 730 METERS

A slightly different fauna occurs between 121 and 730 m in the area separating the northern and central Gulf, south of the large islands. Twenty-four species were found to be common to the northern and southern Gulf, and 31 species were taken alive on 14 stations (Fig. 18). A considerable number of dead shallow-water mollusks were found on sand bottoms, probably as a result of slumping and a Pleistocene low stand of sea level. Some characteristic species from this region are shown in Plates 7 and 10; a complete list is given by Parker (1964). The living species taken at the 14 stations on the upper slope are listed below (number of stations in parentheses).

SPONGES
Poecillastra tricornis Wilson (1)
OCTOCORALS
Anthomuricea sp. (1)

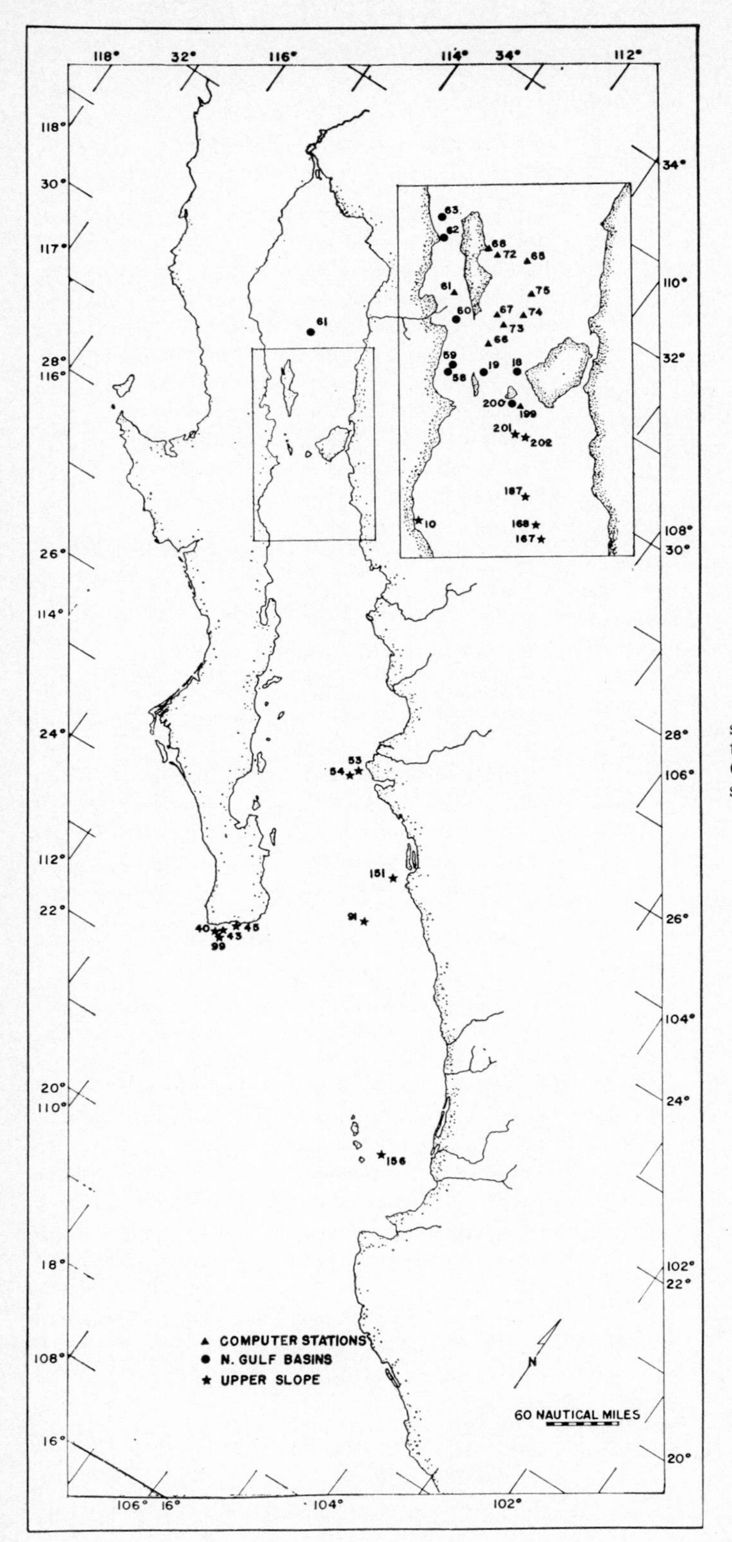

FIG. 18.—Location of characteristic stations (triangles) and all others of the basin environment of the northern Gulf of California, and of the upper slope environment.

BRACHIOPODS
Terebratula obsoleta Dall (1)
Argyrotheca lowei (1)
AMPHINEURA
Lepidopleurus? (1)
SCAPHOPODS
Dentalium spendidulum Sowerby, 1832 (1)
Cadulus californicus Pilsbry and Sharp, 1898 (1)
GASTROPODS
Emarginula velascoensis Shasky, 1961 (2)
Solariella permabilis Carpenter, 1864 (1)
Calliostoma sp. (1)
Polinices intemeratus (Philippi, 1853) (1)
Nassarius insculptus gordanus (Hertlein and Strong, 1951) (1)
N. miser Dall, 1908 (1)
Fusinus colpoicus Dall, 1915 (1)
Cancellaria? sp. (1)
Clathurella thalassoma (Dall, 1908) (2)
LAMELLIBRANCHS
Solemya valvulus Carpenter, 1864 (1)
Nucula cardara Dall, 1917 (2)
Amygdalum pallidulum (Dall, 1916) (1)
Cyclopecten zacae (Hertlein, 1935) (1)
Corbula ventricosa Adams and Reeve, 1850 (1)
Pandora convexa Dall, 1915 (1)
PYCNOGONIDS
Collosendeis bicincta Schimkewitsch (1)
CRUSTACEANS
Sicyonia ingentis (Burkenroad) (1)
Heterocarpus vicarius Faxon (2)
Pleuroncodes planipes Stimpson (3)
Paguristes holmesi Glassell (1)
Cancer porteri Rathbun (1)
Stenocionops beebei Glassell (1)
Ethusa ciliafrons Faxon (1)
Squilla sp. (3)
HOLOTHURIANS
Pseudostichopus mollis Theel, 1886 (1)
ASTEROIDS
Astropecten californicus Fisher
OPHIUROIDS
Schizoderma diplax Nielsen
Amenichondrius granulosus Fisher

This list shows that the number of living species on the upper slope is sharply reduced with respect to the continental shelf. A partial explanation may be that, in the Gulf of California, this depth zone falls within the oxygen minimum area (Fig. 7). Moreover, sampling difficulties on steep slopes also may have contributed to the deficiency in species of this assemblage.

X. MIDDLE CONTINENTAL SLOPE, 731–1,799 METERS

The middle continental slope with its steep, dissected topography is possibly the most difficult environment in the Gulf to sample. Of the 12 stations occupied at this depth, only 4 were occupied in the Gulf of California. Two more were taken in the deep basins of the northern Gulf, but belong to a different environment. All others are from elsewhere along the Pacific coast south of San Diego and off Central America, where the conditions are nearly uniform (Stations 39, 84, 90, 127, 135, 138, 214, 215, 216, 221, 273; Figs. 1 and 2). Bottom-water temperatures in this lower bathyal zone range from 3° to 6°C, and much of the middle slope falls in the oxygen minimum zone (0.5 to 0.9 ml/L oxygen). Only 32 species have been identified in this environment; 6 of them were found only as dead shell. Only 3 species were taken twice—the crustaceans *Acanthephyra curtirostris* and *Paralomis multispina*, and the pelecypod *Solemya agassizi*. Low oxygen and inadequate sampling probably account for the poverty of the species list. A complete list is given below; some important mollusks are shown on Plate 8. Some of the mollusks taken in continental borderland basins off California (discussed in Parker, 1964) also are shown on Plate 8.

HEXACORALS
Cyathocerus sp. (dead)
OCTOCORALS
Distichoptilum n. sp.
Pennatula phosphorea californica Kukenthal
Stachyptilum superbum Studer
Swiftia sp. (aff. *S. pacifica* [Nutting])
MONOPLACOPHORANS
Neopilina galatheae Lemche, 1957 (dead)
GASTROPODS
Solariella nuda Dall, 1896
Turcicula bairdii Dall, 1889
Cocculina diomedae Dall, 1908 (dead)
LAMELLIBRANCHS
Solemya agassizi Dall, 1908
Lucinoma n. sp.
Vesicomya lepta (Dall, 1896)
CEPHALOPODS
Argonauta pacifica Dall, 1896 (dead)
SOLENOGASTERS
Prochaetoderma n. sp.
CRUSTACEANS
Benthesicymus tanneri Faxon
Heterocarpus affinus Faxon
Heterocarpus n. sp.
Paracrangon areolata Faxon
Glyphocrangon spinalosa Faxon
Acanthephyra curtirostris Faxon
Axiopsis (*Calocarides*) n. sp.
Munidopsis sp.
Parapagurus pilasimanus Smith
Neolithodes diomedae (Benedict)
Paralomis multispina (Benedict)
Paralithodes rathbuni (Benedict)
Gnathaphausia zoea Sars
HOLOTHURIANS
Molpadia musculus Risso (*violaceum* type)
M. musculus (*musculus* type) Risso
Synallactes ishikawa forma?

XI. ABYSSAL SOUTHERN BORDERLAND BASINS AND OUTER CONTINENTAL SLOPE, 1,800 TO 4,122 METERS

The abyssal region is markedly different from the previously discussed slope environments, because of the great diversity of its fauna and the large number of individuals. Although only 15 stations were occupied in abyssal depths, 77 species of benthonic invertebrates have been identified, and many more are still in the hands of specialists. Whereas in most of the shallower Gulf of California stations a species is generally represented by only a few individuals, the species in the abyssal stations generally were present with numerous individuals per station. The richness of the fauna is comparable to that of the inner portions of the continental shelf.

Bottom-water temperatures of this environment range from 1.2° to 2.6°C, and oxygen from 1 to 2.8 ml/L—high enough to support most forms of marine life. All stations except one have a silty clay bottom; the one exception at the mouth of the Gulf of California contains a substantial amount of manganese crust. The majority of the stations is less than 100 nautical miles from land, as the continental shelf is generally narrow along the Pacific coast of Central America. Upwelling and high primary surface productivity are common in the areas where sampling was carried out. As a result, organic matter accumulates in large quantities in the borderland basins, the continental slope, and the adjacent ocean floor (Parker, 1961; van Andel, this volume).

A complete list of the invertebrates identified so far in the 15 stations of this environment is given below (station occurrences in parentheses). Of the 77 species, only 5 also are found on the middle slope. Many typical mollusks are illustrated on Plates 9 and 10.

Octocorals
- *Anthomastus ritteri* Nutting
- *Thouarella* sp.
- *Scleroptilum* cf. *durissimum* Studer

Hexacorals
- *Caryophillia diomedaea* Von Marenzeller

Polychaetes
- *Maldane* sp.

Brachiopods
- *Macandrevia americana diegenesis* (2)

Pogonophora
- *Galathealinum bruuni* Kirkegaard?

Monoplacophora
- *Neopilina galathaea* Lemche, 1957

Gastropods
- *Puncturella* cf. *expansa* Dall, 1896
- *Solariella ceratophora* Dall, 1896 (dead)
- *S. equatorialis* Dall, 1908 (2)
- Chitinous trochids?
- *Fusinus rufocaudatus* Dall, 1896
- *Tractolira sparta* Dall, 1896
- *Gemmula* n. sp. (aff. *G. exulans*)
- *Pleurotomella clarinda* Dall, 1908
- *Steiraxis aulaca* Dall, 1896

Nudibranchs
- *Bathydoris aioca* E. and E. Marcus, 1962

Scaphopods
- *Dentalium megathyris* Dall, 1889 (5)

Lamellibranchs
- *Solemya agassizi* Dall, 1908
- *Nucula panamina* Dall, 1908
- *N. agapea* (Dall, 1908)
- *Malletia truncata* Dall, 1908
- *Tindaria compressa* Dall, 1908
- *Arca corpulenta pompholynx* Dall, 1908
- *A. nucleator* Dall, 1908 (2)
- *Limopsis compressus* Dall, 1908 (6)
- *Chlamys latiaurata monotimeris* (Conrad, 1837) (2)
- *Cyclopecten* n. sp.
- *Vesicomya* sp. (dead)
- *Abra profundorum* E.A. Smith, 1885
- *Cuspidaria panamensis* Dall, 1908 (2)
- *Myonera garretti* Dall, 1908 (2)
- *Poromya perla* Dall, 1908

Crustaceans
- *Storthyngura* aff. *pulchra* (Hansen, 1897)
- *Paropsurus giganteus* Wolff, 1962
- *Benthesicymus altus* Bate (2)
- *Hymenopenaeus doris* Faxon (2)
- *Sergestes phorcus* Faxon
- *Pandalopsis ampla* Bate
- *Pontophilus occidentalis* Faxon
- *Glyphocrangon* n. sp. (aff. *G. longirostris*)
- *Lebbeus* sp. (2)
- *Nematocarcinus cf. ensifer* Smith
- *Acanthephyra curtirostris* Faxon (2)
- *A. brevirostris* Smith
- *A.* n. sp. (aff. *sibogae*)
- *Munidopsis* sp.
- *M. bairdii* (Smith) (2)
- *Parapagurus pilosimanus* Smith (3)
- *Parolomis verrilli* (Benedict)
- *Ethusina faxonii* Rathbun

Pycnogonids
- *Collosendeis angusta* Sars (2)
- *C. bicincta* Schimkewitsch
- *C. collossea* Wilson
- *C. macerrima* Wilson
- *Pallenopsis californica* Schimkewitsch
- *Ascorhynchus agassizi* Schimkewitsch

Holothurians
- *Bathyplotes* sp.
- *Pseudostichopus mollis* Theel, 1886
- *Oneirophonta mutabilis* Theel, 1886
- *Peniagone* sp.
- *Benthodytes sanguinolenta* Theel, 1886 (4)
- *Psychropotes raripes* Ludwig, 1894
- *P. dubiosa* Ludwig, 1894
- *Abyssicucumis abyssorum* (Theel, 1886) (3)

Sphaerothuria bitentaculata Ludwig, 1894
Molpadia granulosa Ludwig, 1875
M. musculus Risso, 1826 forma *musculus*
M. musculus Risso, 1826 forma *violaceum*
M. musculus Risso, 1826 forma *spinosum*

ECHINOIDS
Aporocidaris milleri (A. Agassiz) (3)
Kamptosoma asterias (A. Agassiz)
Tromikosoma panamense (A. Agassiz) (2)
T. hispidum (A. Agassiz)
Urechinus loveni (A. Agassiz)
Brisaster latifrons (A. Agassiz)

ASTEROIDS
Eremicaster pacificus (Ludwig)

OPHIUROIDS
Ophiura irrorata Lyman
Ophiomusium glabrum Lütken and Mortensen
O. lymani W. Thomsen
Ophiocantha setosa Lyman
Amphiura seminuda Lütken and Mortensen
Amphiodia digitata Nielsen
Amphilepis patens Lyman
Amphioplus hexacanthus H.L. Clark

DISCUSSION

The presence of distinct faunas in the 11 environments described above (Fig. 19) is a function not only of the physical characteristics of the environments themselves, but also of the geological history of the region and of the biology of the principal species. An evident correlation exists between simple physical and chemical factors such as temperature, depth, sediment distribution, turbulence, salinity, and dissolved oxygen, and the distribution of macro-invertebrate assemblages. However, the presence of some species, or even of entire assemblages, may not be determined by the environmental parameters alone, but also by biological factors such as food preferences and feeding mechanisms, food competition, predator-prey relationships, reproductive capacity and larval development, and commensal or parasitic relationships. The basic organization of animal communities results from interdependence of biological factors and an over-all dependence upon the physical and chemical environment. Thorson (1957) has stated that parallel bottom communities, characterized by the same or closely related genera of dominants, exist wherever environmental conditions are similar. It has also been proposed that perhaps these communities are not so much similar in generic composition as they are comparable in biological organization. Communities found in all waters with similar environmental conditions may be characterized by similar feeding types and dominated by animals with characteristic kinds of reproduction or larval development. It is not necessary that the genera, or even families, be the same for the dominants in two communities in the same environment, so long as the dominants perform the same function within the commmunity. For this reason, a preliminary analysis of the feeding types to which the characteristic animals of each environment belong was made (Fig. 20). In the following pages both biological and environmental aspects of the faunal assemblages will be discussed; a more detailed treatment can be found in Parker (1964).

I. THE INTERTIDAL ROCKY SHORES

The rocky-shore assemblage is entirely an epifaunal group, dominated by algal and suspension feeders (Fig. 20), accompanied by a number of predatory species. Because little sediment normally accumulates, deposit feeders are absent. The same composition of feeding types was observed in the Okhotsk Sea by Savilov (1961). The majority of the gastropods are adapted to living in a rigorous environment, and nearly all lamellibranchs possess byssal threads which attach them to the rocks. Most forms have rather long, planktonic larval stages. Many of the characteristic genera are widespread in this environment (*Littorina*, *Ostrea*, *Mytilus*, *Fissurella*, *Balanus*, and *Bugula*, a bryozoan), although tropical shores commonly are characterized by more genera and species and fewer individuals than temperate or boreal regions. The principal environmental factors influencing this assemblage are the rocky substrate, great turbulence, extreme temperature range, high oxygen, and normal oceanic salinity.

The fossil assemblages known from the Baja California and Gulf of California regions, largely of Pleistocene to Pliocene age, generally consist of a mixture of the rocky shore and nearshore shelf assemblages (Emerson, 1960; Hertlein and Emerson, 1959; Durham, 1950). Of the 34 species from the Pleistocene of Ceralvo Island described by Emerson, 12 belong to the rocky-shore assemblage; the others are from the nearshore shelf group. The entire fauna is, as Emerson states, a reworked suite. The Pleistocene fauna

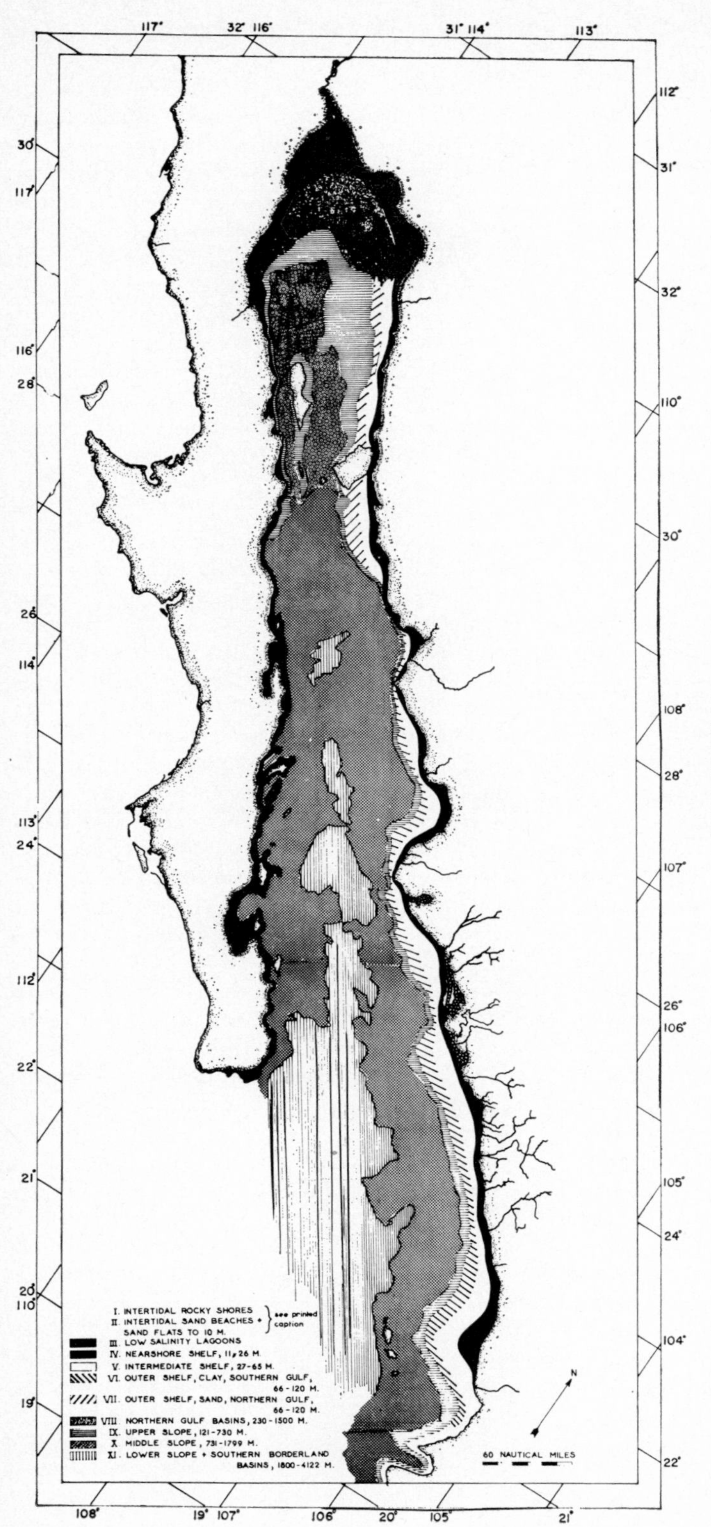

FIG. 19.—Regional distribution of Gulf of California faunal assemblages and environments. The distribution of the intertidal environments is shown in Fig. 12. Stippled area at the head of the Gulf has been sampled inadequately and does not represent a specific environment.

from María Cleofas Island, in the Tres Marías group, is primarily a level-bottom fauna (Hertlein and Emerson, 1959). Of the 28 species, 8 are attaching forms generally found in intertidal rocks. Few of the members of the rocky-shore community living at present in the Gulf are found as fossils in Pleistocene outcrops along the northwestern Baja California coast; the majority of the fossils are rock-living species normally found on the Californian coast (Emerson, 1956; Addicott and Emerson, 1959; Emerson and Addicott, 1958).

II. INTERTIDAL SAND BEACH AND SAND FLATS TO 10 METERS

The assemblage of sand flats and sand beaches is similar throughout the warm-temperate and tropical regions of the world (Pearse, Humm, and Wharton, 1942; Gauld and Buchanan, 1956). A great many similarities exist, for example, between the surf-zone and inner-shelf assemblage of the Gulf of Mexico (Parker, 1960, p. 320–321) and that of the Gulf of California, especially at the subgeneric level of mollusks and crustaceans. Many of the species of the two regions are nearly identical and have common ancestors in the Miocene and Pliocene of Panamá and Colombia (Olsson, 1961). However, the Gulf of California fauna is richer, possibly because of the more restricted air temperature range (15° to 30°C), as compared with the Gulf of Mexico (−5° to 40+° C).

The dominant feeding type among the lamellibranchs is suspension feeding (Fig. 20), because an abundant supply of suspended organic matter and living organisms is provided by the high turbulence and longshore-current transport. Predators are predominant among the gastropods and probably are dependent upon the lamellibranch population. The relative absence of deposit-feeding mollusks and the lack of selective deposit feeders among the echinoids can be attributed to the lack of organic detritus, which is not easily deposited in the agitated bottom water. Most of the inhabitants of this environment have long, pelagic larval stages, with the exception of the very large prosobranch gastropods, whose large larvae contained in egg capsules can withstand the turbulence. The long pelagic development and the mobility of most of the inhabitants of the sand flat environment may explain the uniformity of this assemblage over long stretches of coastline, even where interrupted by considerable portions of rocky shore.

This assemblage has been important in the interpretation of the late Quaternary history of the continental shelf. Fossil assemblages, indicative of lower sea-level positions than the present one, have been found at various depths on the continental shelf, and dating of the shells by radiocarbon has aided in the understanding of history of the post-Pleistocene trangression. This assemblage, composed of sturdy and commonly large specimens, is resistant to destruction and common in Pleistocene deposits of the Gulf of California (Emerson, 1960; Hertlein and Emerson, 1959).

III. LOW SALINITY LAGOONS AND MANGROVE MUD FLATS

This assemblage, with its abundant populations of oysters, *Rangia*, mytilids, corbiculids, and penaeid shrimp, closely resembles the low-salinity, river-influenced assemblage of the northwestern Gulf of Mexico, discussed in detail by Parker (1956, 1959, 1960). Of the 19 species listed for the Gulf of California, 11 have their counterparts in the Gulf of Mexico lagoons, although the large *Anadara tuberculosa* and the large corbiculids are typical for the Gulf of California alone. Many of the genera and subgenera also are known from similar environments in South America, Africa, and tropical, subhumid Asia.

Little is known about the feeding types and larval stages of this assemblage. Suspension feeders predominate even in these turbid waters and on fluid mud bottoms (Fig. 20). Virtually all of the large lamellibranchs from this environment have planktonic larvae which settle to the bottom comparatively rapidly.

This assemblage is rare in the older deposits of the Gulf of California region, but is very common in the prehistoric shell middens of the southern part of the Gulf. Occasional specimens of some of the characteristic species were found in outer-shelf sand deposits. The species characteristic of this environment also are excellent climatic indicators.

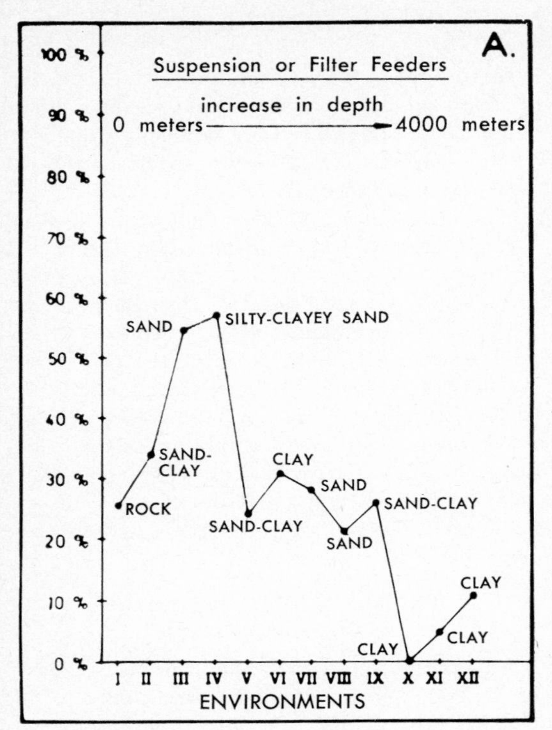
A.
Suspension or Filter Feeders
increase in depth
0 meters → 4000 meters
100 %
90 %
80 %
70 %
60 %
50 %
40 %
30 %
20 %
10 %
0 %
ROCK
SAND-CLAY
SAND
SILTY-CLAYEY SAND
SAND-CLAY
CLAY
SAND
SAND
SAND-CLAY
CLAY
CLAY
CLAY
I II III IV V VI VII VIII IX X XI XII
ENVIRONMENTS

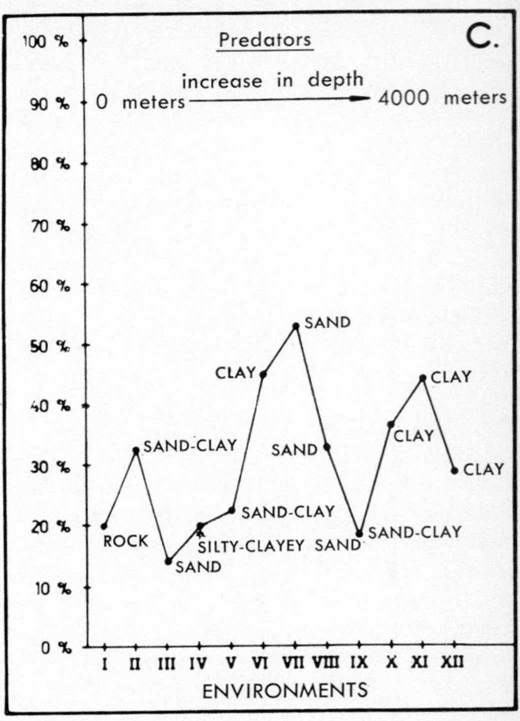
C.
Predators
increase in depth
0 meters → 4000 meters
100 %
90 %
80 %
70 %
60 %
50 %
40 %
30 %
20 %
10 %
0 %
ROCK
SAND-CLAY
SAND
SILTY-CLAYEY SAND
SAND-CLAY
CLAY
SAND
SAND
SAND-CLAY
CLAY
CLAY
CLAY
I II III IV V VI VII VIII IX X XI XII
ENVIRONMENTS

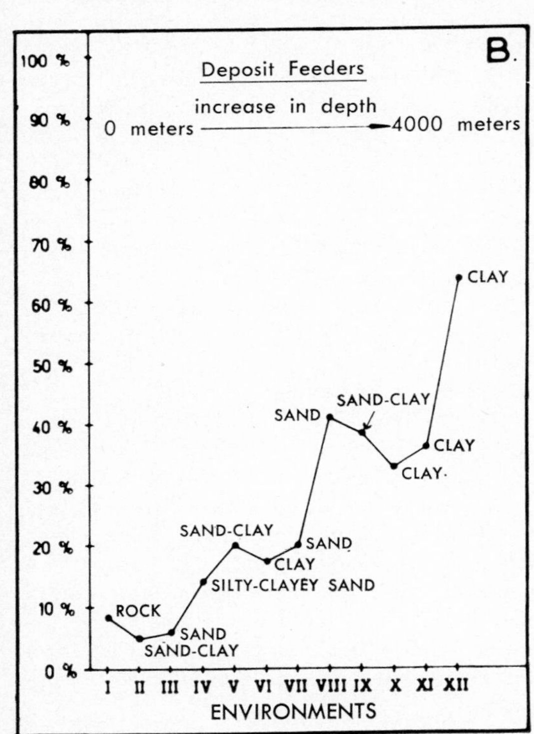
B.
Deposit Feeders
increase in depth
0 meters → 4000 meters
100 %
90 %
80 %
70 %
60 %
50 %
40 %
30 %
20 %
10 %
0 %
ROCK
SAND-CLAY
SAND
SILTY-CLAYEY SAND
SAND-CLAY
CLAY
SAND
SAND
SAND-CLAY
CLAY
CLAY
CLAY
I II III IV V VI VII VIII IX X XI XII
ENVIRONMENTS

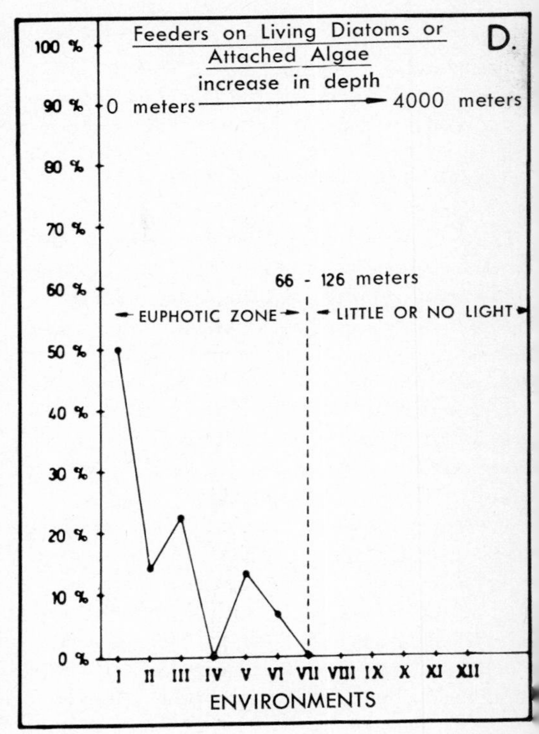
D.
Feeders on Living Diatoms or Attached Algae
increase in depth
0 meters → 4000 meters
100 %
90 %
80 %
70 %
60 %
50 %
40 %
30 %
20 %
10 %
0 %
66 - 126 meters
EUPHOTIC ZONE
LITTLE OR NO LIGHT
I II III IV V VI VII VIII IX X XI XII
ENVIRONMENTS

IV. NEARSHORE SAND TO SAND-MUD, 11 TO 26 METERS

This environment corresponds closely to the hallow and nearshore shelf off the Mississippi Delta (Parker, 1956) and to portions of the near-hore and intermediate shelf off Texas (Parker, 960). Of the assemblage off the Mississippi Delta, 8 of the 11 gastropod species, 15 of the 25 'elecypoda, all echinoderms, and a large number f the crustaceans have counterparts on the sub-eneric level in the equivalent environment of the ulf of California. Most of these species also ere found off Texas in similar depths. On the ther hand, similar environments in India (Sam-el, 1944), the Persian Gulf (Thorson, 1957), and hana, West Africa (Buchanan, 1958), show much ss faunal diversity for similarly sized samples for comparable areas, and do not have the same dominant species (Parker, 1964).

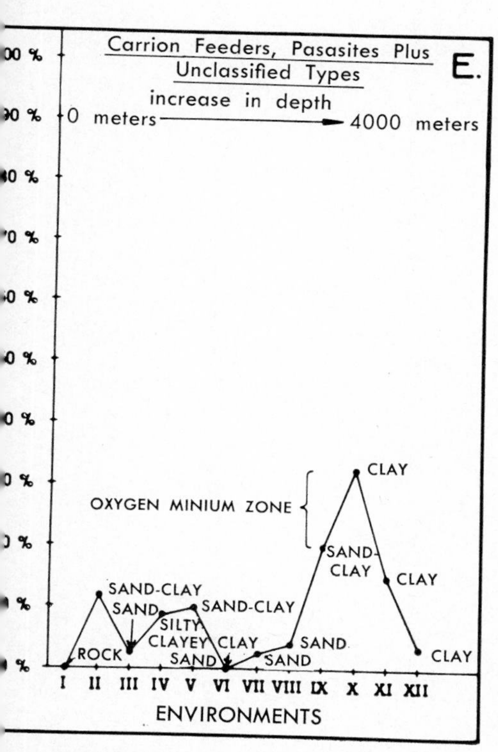

IG. 20.—Distribution of feeding types of inverte-es in all environments discussed in this paper. Ro-numerals refer to sections of the discussion.

The diversity of animal life in this environment in the Gulf of California is great. Each new grab sample or dredge haul produced an almost completely new set of species (Fig. 21-A, B). Five 0.1 m^2 Petersen grab samples were taken at a single locality (Fig. 21-C), four of which produced 2 to 5 new species (of a total 11) for each new sample taken. On the other hand, consecutive samples from Danish (Petersen and Boysen Jensen, 1911) and English (Holme, 1953) waters proved to be fairly uniform (Fig. 21-D). Complete data on these samples can be found in Parker (1964). This lack of species dominance, due to both geological and biological causes, is not confined to the recent assemblage. A similar variety can be found in the Pliocene of Florida (Dall, 1890b–1903), in a thin horizon of the Miocene of Florida (Dall, 1915), and in large lists of mollusks from the older Tertiary of North and South America (Gardner, 1926 to 1947; Woodring, 1925, 1928, 1957, 1959; Olsson, 1922). Apparently there was as much diversity in the molluscan fauna during the middle and late Tertiary as there is today in the warmer waters of the Americas. On the other hand, the warm-temperate to boreal faunas of the middle Atlantic Miocene (Dall, 1904) and Danish Miocene (Sorgenfrei, 1958) possess only a comparatively small number of species.

One explanation for the great variety of mollusks in the Gulf of California may be found in its geological history. In middle Tertiary time, the relatively deep marine connections between the Caribbean and the Pacific permitted mixing of the two faunas, the principal migration taking place from east to west (Ekman, 1953) and adding a large number of species to the already rich and continually evolving eastern Pacific fauna. In addition, there has been a continuous renewal of species from the Indo-Pacific area. During the Pleistocene, a southward migration of some species from the California province also took place. With the high productivity of the Gulf, the availability of a great variety of ecological niches, and the comparative stability of the physio-chemical environment, virtually all species from these various zoogeographic regions have successfully maintained themselves.

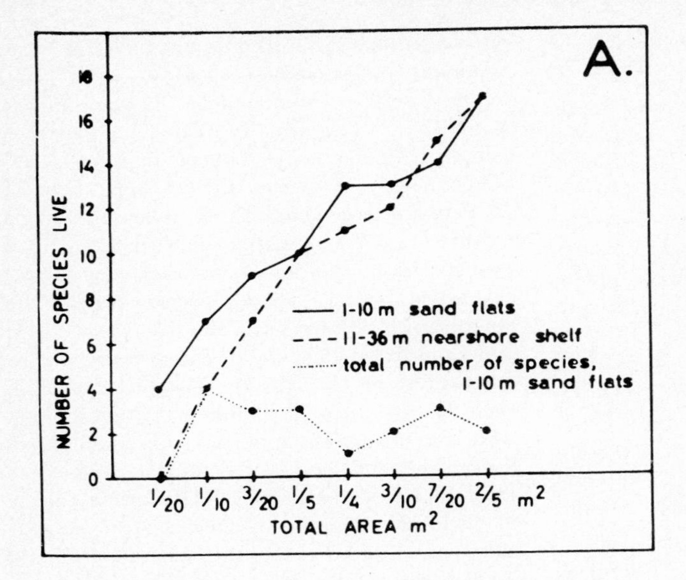

A. Curves of 1/20 m² Van Veen samples in two shallow environments in the southern Gulf of California region.

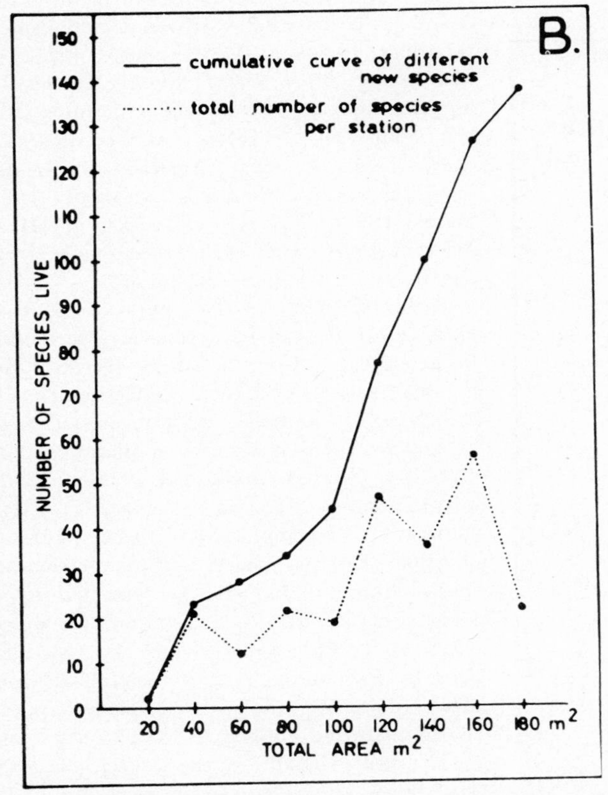

B. Curve of 9 successive samples from the northern shelf region, taken with a small shell dredge, covering roughly 20 m² per sample.

FIG. 21.—Cumulative curves of appearances of new species in successive samples from various localities in the Gulf of California and northwestern Europe.

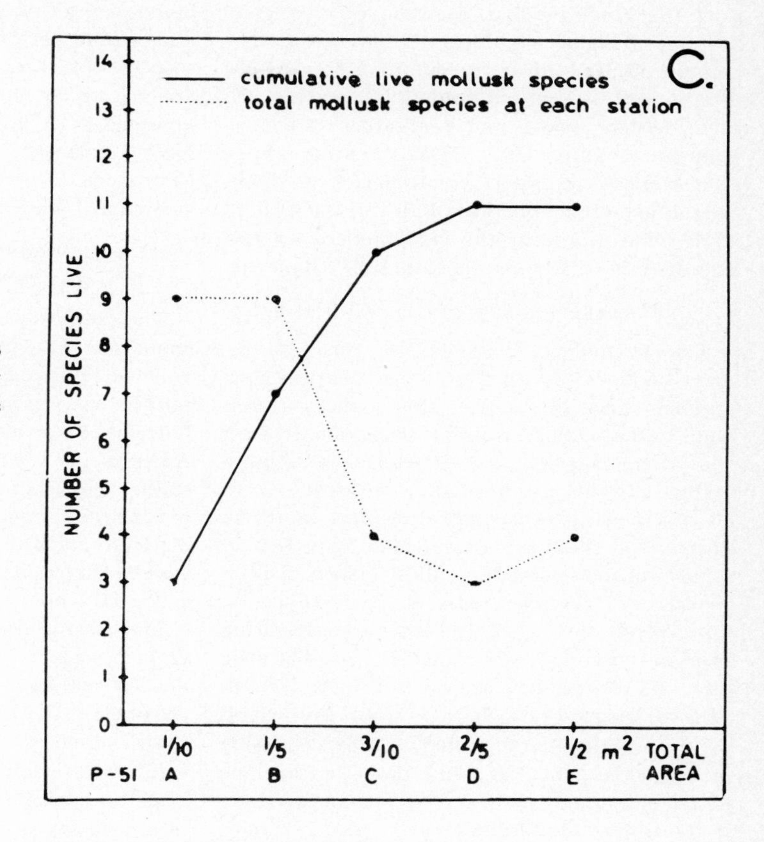

C. Curve of mollusk species nly, from 5 equal-sized samples in ne spot off Topalabompo, Mexico, 1 a depth of 17 m, using a 1/10 m^2 'etersen Grab.

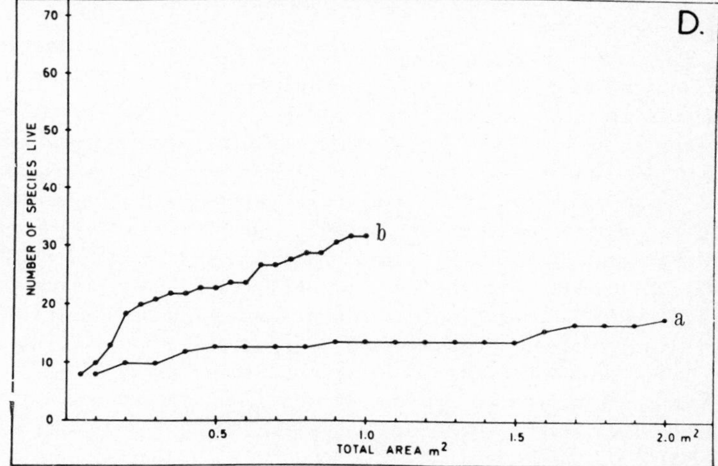

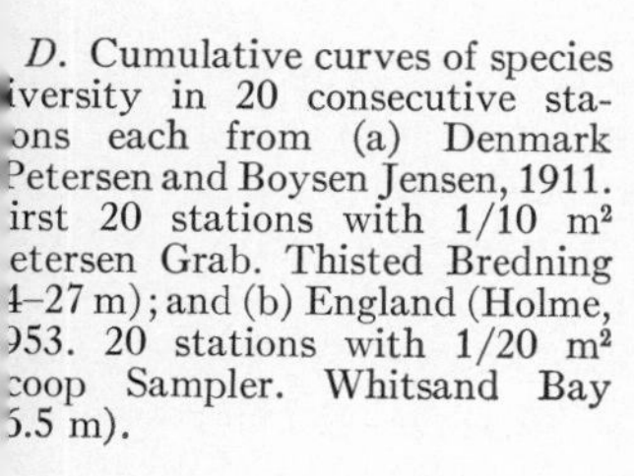

D. Cumulative curves of species iversity in 20 consecutive sta- ons each from (a) Denmark Petersen and Boysen Jensen, 1911. irst 20 stations with 1/10 m^2 etersen Grab. Thisted Bredning 4–27 m); and (b) England (Holme, 953. 20 stations with 1/20 m^2 coop Sampler. Whitsand Bay 5.5 m).

Of the living species at the 9 closely associated stations of Figure 13, 45 per cent are suspension feeders, 30 per cent are predators or scavengers, 19 per cent are deposit feeders, 4 per cent are algae feeders, and 2 per cent are parasitic or commensal (Fig. 20). Similar feeding types characterize the same environment in Long Island Sound and Buzzards Bay (Sanders, 1958, 1960). Two-thirds of the characteristic species appear to have a planktonic larval development.

V. INTERMEDIATE SHELF, 27 TO 65 METERS

The assemblage characterizing this environment becomes a distinct entity at depths below approximately 40 m, especially in the southern Gulf. In the northern Gulf, the transition between this assemblage and the previous one is more gradual. In the intermediate zone, from 27 to 40 m, there is considerable overlap in depth ranges, and there is a considerable reduction in number of species and individuals. The transition zone is well developed only on finer sediments, especially on those inshore of relict sands resulting from the post-Pleistocene transgression. The zone also was observed in the northwestern Gulf of Mexico (Curray, 1960; Parker, 1960). In the Gulf of Mexico, the standing crop, mainly consisting of deposit feeders, was much lower (an average of 2.2 individuals per 0.2 m^2 grab sample) than in the Gulf of California (an average of 25.2 individuals per 0.2 m^2), where the primary productivity is much higher.

The sand-bottom assemblage between 39 and 65 m is the most distinct of the intermediate shelf faunas. It occurs, in part, on reworked relict nearshore sediments and in this respect is similar to faunas off the Texas coast in waters from 36 to 63 m (Parker, 1960, p. 322–323). Closely related or twin species are found in the Gulf of Mexico and in the Gulf of California, which have common origins in the Miocene and Pliocene shallow seas of Central America. A large number of these species, or their precursors, also can be found in the middle Tertiary of Central and South America (Olsson, 1961) and of Florida (Dall, 1890b–1903) and the Caribbean (Woodring, 1925, 1928).

Suspension and detritus feeders and predators are almost equally represented in the modern fauna of the Gulf of California (Fig. 20). Generally, a sand bottom is inhabited by an excess of suspension feeders, but the sands in deeper water are relatively quiet and organic detritus can accumulate. A high percentage of the mollusks have nonplanktonic larvae, but most of them are gastropods. The majority of the intermediate shelf lamellibranchs have planktonic larvae.

VI. OUTER SHELF, 66 TO 120 METERS, CLAY BOTTOM, SOUTHERN GULF

The fauna found in this environment is very similar to that of the same environment in the Gulf of Mexico. The large number of closely related species indicates a persistence of clay bottoms to 100 m depth across Central and South America in Tertiary time. Of the 21 typica species taken between 70 and 120 m in the Gul of Mexico, 13 have exact counterparts in the Gul of California, and an additional 6 were taken a slightly different depths. These closely relate species also are predominant in both areas.

Most of the lamellibranchs are deposit feeder or suspension feeders, feeding nonselectively o detrital material; the majority of the gastropod are predators (Fig. 20). Savilov (1961) also foun that nonselective deposit feeders reach thei greatest development in zones of rapid depositio of fine sediment on the upper slope. The majorit of the mollusks have pelagic larvae which ar well adapted to the rather uniform environmen

VII. OUTER SHELF, 66 TO 120 METERS, SAND BOTTOM, NORTHERN GULF

No exact counterpart of this assemblage known from any other part of the world, becau deep, uniform, terrigenous sand deposits are rel tively uncommon. The composition of the faun in this environment is very patchy, in contrast the uniform distribution of the assemblage d scribed above, and few mollusk species were take more than twice in 18 stations. The crustacea were by far the most abundant, and many we taken at four or five stations, but they also a distributed rather uniformly in this region fro shore to shelf edge. This environment is a trans tion zone rather than a distinct entity. Th majority of the lamellibranchs probably are su pension feeders, whereas 20 of the 24 living gastr pods are predators (Fig. 20). An abundant supply of organic matter is available, because primary production in the region is high. The breakdown of the thermocline in this region, as a result of intense tidal turbulence, may contribute to the transitional nature of the assemblage. A number of lamellibranch species proved to have a direct or lecithitrophic larval development, differing from those of previous environments.

VIII. NORTHERN GULF BASINS AND TROUGHS, 230 TO 1,500 METERS

This environment is characterized by its vertical uniformity and resulting high bottom-water temperatures and oxygen values. Vertical stratification of the benthic fauna is lacking. Similar environments may exist elsewhere, but the only possible case studied—the Red Sea (Fuchs, 1901)—seems to possess a normal faunal sequence somewhat similar to that of the southern Gulf of California. A similar ancient environment has been assumed by Baldi (1961) for parts of the Miocene in Hungary; others may occur in Southern California and Venezuela.

A striking feature of the fauna in this environment is the occurrence of numerous shells of species now extending no farther south than the California province on the Pacific coast. The present bottom-water temperature in the northern Gulf basins ranges from 11° to 14°C, which is comparable to the temperature range of the California shelf. Many of the cold, shallow-water species were taken in the Gulf from sand layers in piston cores and may have been displaced from an original shelf position. Others have been collected as dead shell from the region around Cape San Lucas in depths of 200 to 800 m. It may be assumed that during the late Pleistocene, when sea level stood approximately 100 m lower than at present (substantiated by the dating of near-shore mollusk shells found in 110–115 m off San Blas, Mexico, which were 17,000–19,000 years old), the California-province species invaded the Gulf along the upper slope, and the basin floors in the northern Gulf now are in the only environment in which survival is possible.

All of the pelecypod species occurring in this environment are deposit feeders; the gastropod is a predator, and the echinoids and scaphopods are deposit feeders, feeding on the abundance of organic matter resulting from high surface productivity. The dead shallow-water species found in the bottom of the deep troughs are suspension and algae feeders, which agree with the feeding types of the nearby rocky-shore assemblage. The California-province species found as dead shell are predominantly deposit feeders, indicating an environment rich in organic detritus similar to the present one. Most of the species have a pelagic larval stage, although a few lamellibranchs prove to have brood-protection for their larvae.

IX. UPPER SLOPE, CENTRAL AND SOUTHERN GULF, 121 TO 730 METERS

Few living organisms were taken on the upper slope, much of which lies in the oxygen minimum zone. Several parts of the region appear devoid of life. The only animals that were at all common were several species of stomatopod shrimp (*Squilla*) and occasionally large numbers of *Munida* and *Pleuroncodes planipes*, both galatheid shrimp, all carrion feeders and well adapted to this environment of great accumulation of organic detritus.

Assemblage studies of this environment elsewhere in the world do not exist, although taxonomic monographs are abundant (Dall, 1886, 1889, 1890a, 1908; *Albatross*, *Challenger*, and *Galathea* Reports; Ekman, 1953). The majority of the animals are deposit feeders or scavengers, but a rather high percentage (27 per cent) can be classified as suspension feeders, probably subsisting on the rain of planktonic material. W.K. Ocklemann of the Marine Biological Laboratory, Helsingør, Denmark, and this author, indicate that the majority of species have lecithitrophic or direct (nonpelagic) development. In general, the number of mollusk species with nonpelagic larval development increases with increasing depth below the shelf edge.

X. MIDDLE CONTINENTAL SLOPE, 731 TO 1,799 METERS

The mid-slope assemblage is a typical deep-sea fauna, composed of lower bathyal and upper abyssal components. Three of the eight species of mollusks taken in this environment are listed as abyssal by Clarke (1962), and all genera are primarily abyssal in distribution. Bottom-water temperatures are between 3°C and 6°C, but there are no definite depth or temperature criteria on which the boundary between abyssal and bathyal can be based. Monographs of a taxonomic nature on slope animals are common in the literature, but community and ecological studies concerned with the bathyal-abyssal environment are very rare.

All but five of the mollusks collected alive are deposit feeders, but the corals can be considered suspension-feeding predators. The shrimp and large decapod crabs are most probably scavengers, but nothing certain is known of their feeding habits. The suspension feeders probably live off the rain of plankton from the high surface productivity along the Pacific Coast. A few of the mollusk species related to those occurring in this assemblage have been found in the Miocene and Pliocene of the west coast of North America (Grant and Gale, 1931), and in Tertiary sediments of Panamá, Costa Rica, and Ecuador (Olsson, 1942).

XI. ABYSSAL SOUTHERN BORDERLAND BASINS AND OUTER CONTINENTAL SLOPE, 1,800 TO 4,122 METERS

Notwithstanding the great depth and low temperature (1°–2.5°C) of this environment, the richness and complexity of the fauna are not equalled elsewhere in the deep sea, and not commonly even on the continental shelf. Similar rich development on the outer slope region has been observed elsewhere (Wolff, 1961; Sanders, personal communication). In Wolff's paper, 54 species of invertebrates are listed from one station in the Gulf of Panama, and some material is not yet identified. Similarly, incomplete determinations from the 15 stations off Mexico and Guatemala show 86 species. Only 11 species of invertebrates were taken in common by the two programs. Elements of this fauna have been found in Tertiary sediments of Panamá, Costa Rica, and Ecuador (Olsson, 1942).

The majority of the animals living in this environment are deposit feeders, whereas most of the others probably are scavengers and predators. Many of the species, however, have no shallow-water relatives, and it is almost impossible to deduce their feeding habits or larval development from the present material. More sophisticated sampling techniques and emphasis on the biology rather than on the taxonomy of deep-sea animals are urgently needed.

SUMMARY AND CONCLUSIONS

The data obtained in this study have contributed to the knowledge of shallow-water faunas in a somewhat unusual subtropical and tropical region and have provided considerable information on the composition of deep-sea assemblages. Many of the environments and assemblages of the Gulf of California have counterparts elsewhere in the world, but some, especially those of outer-shelf to bathyal depth in the northern Gulf, appear to be almost unique.

The density of animals in the tropical and subtropical region studied appears to be smaller than in boreal and temperate regions. Moreover, the density decreases with increasing depth, with the exception of the lower slope. On the other hand, the diversity of animals in level-bottom communities seems to be greater in the tropics than in more northerly climates. Thorson (1957) disagrees with this statement, but he does admit that the diversity of epifaunal habitats is greater in the tropics because many more niches are available, particularly on coral reefs. Neither this study nor other studies of the tropical region provides enough quantitative data, however, for a significant comparison between warm- and cold-water faunas.

The study has provided additional information for the interpretation of ancient environments, particularly those of deeper water, and many similarities have been noted between the living faunas of the area studied and the Tertiary assemblages of Central America and the Caribbean region.

REFERENCES

Addicott, W.O., and Emerson, W.K., 1959, Late Pleistocene invertebrates from Punta Cabras, Baja California, Mexico: Am. Mus. Novitates, no. 1925, p. 1–33.

Anderson, C.A., 1950, Geology of the islands and neighboring land areas, pt. 1 *of* The 1940 E.W. Scripps cruise to the Gulf of California: Geol. Soc. America Mem. 43, 53 p.

——— Durham, J.W., Shepard, F.P., Natland, M.L. and Revelle, R.R., 1950, The 1940 E.W. Scripps cruise to the Gulf of California: Geol. Soc. America Mem. 43, 216 p., 48 pls.

Baldi, T., 1961, Geobiology of the middle Miocene fauna from Szokolya (Börzsöny Mountains): Ann. Universit. Scient. Budapestinensis de Rolando Eötvös Nomin. Sectio Geol., v. 4, p. 3–28.

Buchanan, J.B., 1958, The bottom fauna communities across the continental shelf off Accra, Ghana (Gold Coast): Zool. Soc. London Proc., v. 130, p. 1–56.

Byrne, J.V., and Emery, K.O., 1960, Sediments of the Gulf of California: Geol. Soc. America Bull., v. 71, p. 983–1010.

Clarke, A.H., Jr., 1962, Annotated list and bibliography of the abyssal marine molluscs of the world: Natl. Mus. Canada Bull., no. 181, biol. ser. no. 67, 114 p.

Curray, J.R., 1960, Sediments and history of Holocene transgression, continental shelf, northwest Gulf of Mexico, *in* Recent sediments, northwest Gulf of Mexico: Am. Assoc. Petroleum Geologists, p. 221–266.

Dall, W.H., 1886, Brachiopoda and Pelecypoda, pt. 1 *of* Report on the Mollusca (29)—Reports on the results of dredging, under the supervision of Alexander Agassiz, in the Gulf of Mexico (1877–'78), and in the Caribbean Sea (1879–'80), by the U.S. Coast Survey Steamer *Blake:* Mus. Comp. Zool. Harv. Bull., v. 12, no. 6, p. 171–318, pl. i–ix.

——— 1889, Gastropoda and Scaphopoda, pt. 2 *of* Report on the Mollusca (29) . . . : Mus. Comp. Zool. Harv. Bull., v. 18, p. 1–492, 42 pls.

——— 1890a, Preliminary report on the collection of Mollusca and Brachiopoda obtained in 1887–88, no. 7 *of* Scientific results of exploration by the U.S. Fish Commission Steamer *Albatross:* U.S. Nat. Mus. Proc., v. 12, no. 773, p. 219–362, pls. 5–14.

——— 1890b–1903, Pulmonate, opisthobranchiate and orthodont gastropods, pt. 1 *of* Contributions to the Tertiary fauna of Florida: Wagner Free Inst. Sci. Trans., v. 3, p. 1–200, pls. 1–12; Streptodont and other gastropods, pt. 2, *ibid.*, p. 201–473, pls. 13–22; Pelecypods, pt. 3, *ibid.*, p. 474–600.

——— 1904, Miocene deposits of Maryland; relations of the Miocene of Maryland to that of other regions and to the recent fauna: Md. Geol. Survey, Miocene, p. cxxix–clv.

——— 1908, The Mollusca and Brachiopoda, pt. 14 *of* Reports on the dredging operations off the west coast of Central America to the Galapagos, to the west coast of Mexico, and in the Gulf of California: Mus. Comp. Zool. Harv. Bull., v. 43, no. 6, p. 205–487, pls. 1–22.

——— 1915, A monograph of the molluscan fauna of the *Orthaulax pugnax* zone of the Oligocene of Tampa, Florida: U.S. Natl. Mus. Bull. 90, 173 p., 26 pls.

Doty, M.S., 1957, Rocky intertidal surfaces, *in* Treatise on marine ecology and paleoecology, v. 1: Geol. Soc. America Mem. 67, p. 535–585, 18 figs., 1 pl.

Durham, J.W., 1950, Megascopic paleontology and marine stratigraphy, pt. 2 *of* The 1940 E.W. Scripps cruise to the Gulf of California: Geol. Soc. America Mem. 43, 216 p., 48 pls.

Dushane, Helen, 1962, A checklist of mollusks for Puertocitos, Baja California, Mexico: The Veliger, v. 5, no. 1, p. 39–50.

Ekman, Sven, 1953, Zoogeography of the sea: Sidgwick and Jackson, Ltd., London, 417 p.

Emerson, W.K., 1956, Pleistocene invertebrates from Punta China, Baja California, Mexico, with remarks on the composition of the Pacific Coast Quaternary faunas: Am. Mus. Nat. History Bull., v. 111, art. 4, p. 319–342.

——— 1960, Pleistocene invertebrates from Ceralvo Island, pt. 2 *of* Results of the *Puritan*-American Museum of Natural History expedition to western Mexico: Am. Mus. Novitates, no. 1995, 6 p.

——— and Addicott, W.O., 1958, Pleistocene invertebrates from Punta Baja, Baja California: Am. Mus. Novitates, no. 1909, p. 1–11.

Emery, K.O., and Hülsemann, J., 1962, The relationships of sediment, life, and water in a marine basin: Deep-Sea Research, v. 8, p. 165–180.

Fager, E.W., 1957, Determination and analysis of recurrent groups: Ecology, v. 38, no. 4, p. 586–595.

Fuchs, Theodor, 1901, Über den Charakter der Tiefseefauna des Rothen Meeres auf Grund der von Östereichschen Tiefsee-Expeditionen Gewonnen Ausbeute: Sitzungsber. der Kais. Akad. Wissens.-Mathemat.-Naturwissens, v. 110, Abt. 1, p. 249–258.

Gardner, Julia, 1926–47, The molluscan fauna of the Alum Bluff group of Florida: U.S. Geol. Survey Prof. Paper 142, 656 p., 62 pls. [issued in 8 separate parts].

Gauld, D.T., and Buchanan, J.B., 1956, The fauna of the sandbeaches of the Gold Coast: Oikos, v. 7, no. 2, p. 293–301.

Grant, U.S., IV, and Gale, H.R., 1931, Catalogue of the marine Pliocene and Pleistocene Mollusca of California: San Diego Soc. Nat. Hist. Mem., v. 1, 1036 p., 32 pls.

Hertlein, L.G., and Emerson, W.K., 1959, Pliocene and Pleistocene megafossils from the Tres Marías Islands, pt. 5 *of* Results of the *Puritan*-American Museum of Natural History expedition to western Mexico: Am. Mus. Novitates, no. 1940, 15 p.

Holme, N.E., 1953, The biomass of the bottom fauna in the English Channel off Plymouth: Marine Biol. Assoc., U.K., Jour., v. 32, p. 1–49, 7 figs.

Isaacs, J.D., and Kidd, L.W., 1953, Final report—high-speed deep diving dredge: mimeo., Oceanogr. Equip. Rept. no. 4, Univ. of Calif., Scripps Inst. of Oceanography, SIO Ref. 53–37, p. 1–11 (unpub. ms.)

Keen, A.M., 1958, Sea shells of tropical west America: Stanford Univ. Press, Stanford, Calif., 624 p.

McLean, J.H., 1961, Marine mollusks from Los Angeles Bay, Gulf of California: San Diego Soc. Nat. Hist. Trans., v. 12, no. 28, p. 449–476.

Nichols, M.M., 1962, Hydrology and sedimentology of Sonoran lagoons, Mexico, *in* Abstracts for 1962: Geol. Soc. America Special Paper 73, p. 210.

Olsson, Axel A., 1922, The Miocene of northern Costa Rica: Bull. Am. Paleontology, v. 9, no. 39, 309 p., 32 pls.

——— 1942, Tertiary and Quaternary fossils from the Burica Peninsula of Panama and Costa Rica: Bull. Am. Paleontology, v. 27, no. 106, 82 p.

——— 1961, Mollusks of the tropical eastern Pacific; particularly from the southern half of the Panamic-Pacific faunal province (Panama to Peru): Panama-Pacific Pelecypoda, Paleont. Res. Inst., Ithaca, N.Y., 574 p., 86 pls.

Parker, R.H., 1956, Macro-invertebrate assemblages as indicators of sedimentary environments in east Mississippi Delta region: Am. Assoc. Petroleum Geologists Bull., v. 40, no. 2, p. 295–376, 8 pls.

——— 1959, Macro-invertebrate assemblages of central

Texas coastal bays and Laguna Madre: Am. Assoc. Petroleum Geologists Bull., v. 43, no. 9, p. 2100–2166, 6 pls.

——— 1960, Ecology and distributional patterns of marine macro-invertebrates, northern Gulf of Mexico, *in* Recent sediments, northwest Gulf of Mexico: Am. Assoc. Petroleum Geologists, p. 302–337, 17 figs., 6 pls.

——— 1961, Speculations on the origin of the invertebrate fauna of the lower continental slope: Deep-Sea Research, v. 8, nos. 3, 4, p. 286–293.

——— 1964, Zoogeography and ecology of macro-invertebrates, particularly mollusks, in the Gulf of California and the continental slope off Mexico: Vid. Medd. fra Dansk Naturhist. Foren., bd. 126, p. 1–178, 15 pls.

——— and Curray, J.R., 1956, Fauna and bathymetry of banks on continental shelf, northwest Gulf of Mexico: Am. Assoc. Petroleum Geologists Bull., v. 40, no. 10, p. 2428–2439, 1 pl.

Pearse, A.S., Humm, H.J., and Wharton, G.W., 1942, Ecology of the sand beaches of Beaufort, N.C.: Ecol. Mon. v. 12, p. 135–190.

Petersen, C.G. Joh., and Boysen Jensen, P., 1911, Animal life of the sea bottom—its food and quantity, pt. 1 *of* Valuation of the sea: Danish Biol. Stat. Repts. v. 20, 81 p.

Roden, G.I., 1958, Oceanographic and meteorological aspects of the Gulf of California: Pacific Science, v. 12, no. 1, p. 21–45.

——— and Groves, G.W., 1959, Recent oceanographic investigations in the Gulf of California (Sears. Found.): Jour. Marine Resch., v. 18, no. 1, p. 10–35.

Rosenblatt, R.H., 1959, A revisionary study of the blennoid fish family Tripterygiidae: Unpub. thesis, Univ. Calif., L.A., 376 p.

Samuel, Mary, 1944, Preliminary observations on the animal communities of the level sea-bottom of the Madras coast: Madras Univ. Jour., v. 15, no. 2, p. 45–71.

Sanders, H. L., 1958, Animal-sediment relationships, pt. 1 *of* Benthic studies in Buzzards Bay: Limnology and Oceanography, v. 3, p. 245–258.

——— 1960, The structure of the soft-bottom community, pt. 2 *of* Benthic studies in Buzzards Bay: Limnology and Oceanography, v. 5, p. 138–153.

Savilov, A.I., 1961, Ecologic characteristics of invertebrate bottom communities in the Sea of Okhotsk: Trudy Inst. of Okeanol, Akad. Nauk, S.S.S.R., v. 46, p. 3–84 [in Russian].

Shepard, F.P., 1954, Nomenclature based on sand-silt-clay ratios: Jour. Sed. Petrology, v. 24, p. 151–158.

Sorgenfrei, Theodor, 1958, Molluscan assemblages from the marine middle Miocene of south Jutland and their environments: Geol. Surv. Denmark, 2d ser., no. 79, v. 1, 2, 503 p., 76 pls.

Squires, D.F., 1959, Results of the *Puritian*-American Museum . . . 7. Corals and coral reefs in the Gulf of California: Am. Mus. Nat. Hist. Bull., v. 118, art. 7, p. 367–432.

Steinbeck, John, and Ricketts, Edward, 1941, Sea of Cortez, a leisurely journal of travel and research: Viking Press, New York, 598 p., 40 pls.

Thorson, Gunnar, 1957, Bottom communities (sublittoral or shallow shelf), *in* Treatise on marine ecology and paleoecology, v. 1: Geol. Soc. America Mem. 67, p. 461–534.

Walker, B.W., 1960, The distribution and affinities of the marine fish fauna of the Gulf of California: Syst. Zool., v. 9, nos. 3–4, p. 123–133.

Wolff, Torben, 1961, The animal life from a single abyssal trawling: Galathea Rept., v. 5, p. 129–162, pls. 7–10.

Woodring, W.P., 1925, Pelecypods and scaphopods, pt. 1 *of* Miocene mollusks from Bowden, Jamaica: Carnegie Inst. Wash. Pub. 366, 222 p., 28 pls.

——— 1928, Gastropods and discussion of results, pt. 2 *of* Miocene mollusks from Bowden, Jamaica: Carnegie Inst. Wash. Pub. 385, 564 p., 40 pls.

——— 1957, Geology and paleontology of Canal Zone and adjoining parts of Panamá; description of Tertiary mollusks (Gastropoda: Trochidae to Turritellidae): U. S. Geol. Survey Prof. Paper 306-A, p. 1–145, pls. 1–23.

——— 1959, Geology and paleontology of Canal Zone and adjoining parts of Panamá; descriptions of Tertiary mollusks (Gastropoda: Vermetidae to Thaididae): U. S. Geol. Survey Prof. Paper 306-B, iii, p. 147–239, pls. 24–38.

APPENDIX

TABLE I. CHECK-LIST OF CHARACTERISTIC INVERTEBRATE SPECIES IN GULF OF CALIFORNIA ENVIRONMENTS
(Key to class symbols at bottom of page)

Species	*Class*[1]	I	II	III	IV	V	VI	VII	VIII	IX	X	XI[2]
		Environments										
Acmaea discors	G	X										
Tegula ligulata	G	X										
Turbo fluctuosus	G	X										
T. squamiger	G	X										
Nerita scabricosta	G	X										
Littorina aspersa	G	X										
L. conspersa	G	X										
Vermicularia pellucida	G	X										
Diodora alta	G	X										
Cerithium stercusmuscarum	G	X										
C. sculptum	G	X										
Jenneria pustulata	G	X										
Acanthina lugubris	G	X										
Morula ferruginosa	G	X										
Purpura patula pansa	G	X										
Pyrene fuscata	G	X										
Nassarius tiarula	G	X										
Marginella californica	G	X										
Onchidiella binneyi	PUL	X										
Siphonaria maura	PUL	X										
Arca pacifica	P	X										
Barbatia reeveana	P	X										
Arcopsis solida	P	X										
Brachidontes multiformis	P	X										
Isognomon chemnitzianus	P	X										
Ostrea conchophila	P	X										
Anomia adamas	P	X										
A. peruviana	P	X										
Cardita affinus californica	P	X										
Grapsus grapsus	CR	X										
Tetraclita stalactifera	CR	X										
Diadenum mexicanum	E	X										
Heliaster kubiniji	AS	X										
Athyone glanelli	HO	X										
Brandtothuria impatians	HO	X										
Cerithium maculosum	G		X									
Cerithidea albonodosus	G	X	X									
Neritina luteofasciata	G		X	X								
Turritella gonostoma	G		X									
T. leucostoma	G		X									
Natica chemnitzii	G		X		X							
Cypraea arabicula	G		X									
Strombus granulatus	G		X									
S. gracilior	G		X		X							
Oliva spicata	G		X									
Olivella anazora	G		X									
Nassarius angulicostus	G		X									
Bulla gouldiana	G		X	X								
Cadulus austinclarki	SC		X									
Anadara labiosa	P		X									
A. multicostata	P		X									
Glycymeris delessertii	P		X									
G. gigantea	P		X									
Cardita grayi	P		X									
C. megastropha	P		X									
Codakia distinguenda	P		X									
Trachycardium procerum	P		X									
Papyridea aspersa	P		X									
Diplodonta subquadrata	P		X			X						
Tivela byronensis	P		X									
Transanella puella	P		X									
Pitar concinna	P		X									
P. lupanaria	P		X									
Megapitaria squalida	P		X		X							
Dosinia dunkeri	P		X									
D. ponderosa	P		X									

[1] Key for letter symbols under *Class* column
AN—Anthozoa
BR—Brachiopoda
MON—Monoplacophora
G—Gastropoda
PUL—Pulmonata
SC—Scaphopoda
P—Pelecypoda
PO—Polychaeta
CR—Crustacea
PYC—Pycnogonida
POG—Pogonophora
HO—Holothuroidea
E—Echinoidea
AS—Asteroidea

[2] Roman numeral headings under the environments correspond to the same numbers used for the environments throughout the text.

Table I—(*continued*)

Species	Class[1]	I	II	III	IV	V	VI	VII	VIII	IX	X	XI[2]
		Environments										
Chione californiensis	P		X									
C. picta	P		X									
Anomalocardia subimbricata	P		X									
A. subimbricata tumens	P		X									
Protothaca metadon	P		X									
Mulinia pallida	P		X									
Tellina felix	P		X		X							
Macoma pacis	P		X									
Donax assimilis	P		X									
D. californiensis	P		X									
D. carinatus	P		X									
D. punctostriatus	P		X									
Heterodonax bimaculatus	P		X									
Tagelus affinus	P		X									
Semele guaymasensis	P		X		X							
Pholas chiloensis	P		X									
Uca crenulata	CR		X									
Clibanarius diguetii	CR		X									
Ocypode occidentalis	CR		X									
Neopanope petersenii	CR		X									
Encope grandis	E		X									
E. californica	E		X									
Echinometra vanbruntii	E		X									
Brissus latecarinatus	E		X									
Selenkothuria lubrica	HO		X									
Thyone parafusus	HO		X									
Neothyone gibbosa	HO		X									
Cerithidea mazatlanica	G			X								
C. montagnii	G			X								
Littoridina sp.	G			X								
Melampus olivaceous	PUL			X								
Anadara tuberculosa	P			X								
Mytella falcata	P			X								
Ostrea columbiensis	P			X								
O. corteziensis	P			X								
Polymesoda mexicana	P			X								
P. olivacea	P			X								
Rangia mendica	P			X								
Architectonica placentalis	G				X							
Calyptraea conica	G				X							
Crepidula arenata	G				X							
C. excavata	G				X							
C. perforans	G				X							
Crucibulum serratum	G				X		X					
C. spinosum	G				X	X						
Polinices reclusianus	G				X							
Sinum debile	G				X							
Hexaplex erythrostomus	G				X							
Nassarius versicolor	G				X							
Oliva incrassata	G				X							
O. spicata polposta	G				X							
Olivella fletcherae	G				X							
Mitra hindsii	G				X							
Cancellaria balboae	G				X							
Clathrodrillia pilsbryi	G				X							
Hormospira maculosa	G				X	X						
Conus perplexus	G				X							
Terebra specillata	G				X							
T. variegata	G				X							
Dentalium oerstedii oerstedii	SC				X		X					
Nuculana impar	P				X							
Adrana penascoensis	P				X							
Barbatia alternata	P				X							
Anadara nux	P				X							
A. obesa	P				X							
Lioberus salvadoricus	P				X							
Chlamys circularis	P				X	X						
C. tumbezensis	P				X							
Crassatella gibbosa	P				X	X						
Lucina prolongata	P				X							
Trachycardium panamense	P				X							
Trigoniocardia granifera	P				X							
Laevicardium elatum	P				X	X						
L. elenense	P				X							
Pitar newcombianus	P				X							
Chione mariae	P				X	X						
Mactra californica	P				X							
Tellina tabogensis	P				X							
Donax gracilis	P				X							
Ensis californicus	P				X							
Pandora claviculata	P				X							

TABLE I—(*continued*)

Species	*Class*[1]	I	II	III	IV	V	VI	VII	VIII	IX	X	XI[2]
		Environments										
Lyonsia gouldii	P				X							
Balanus concavus mexicanus	CR				X	X	X					
Dardanus sinistripes	CR				X	X						
Petrochirus californicus	CR				X	X						
Pylopagurus varians	CR				X							
Encope micropora	E				X							
Lovenia cordiformis	E				X	X						
Moira clotho	E				X							
Heterocyathus aequicostatus	AN					X						
Calliostoma bonita	G					X						
C. nepheloide	G					X						
Astele rema	G					X						
Solariella triplostephanus	G					X						
Architectonica nobilis	G					X						
Natica broderipiana	G					X						
N. grayi	G					X						
Polinices uber	G					X						
Cassis centiquadrata	G					X						
Distorsio decussatus	G					X						
Bursa nana	G					X						
Murex recurvirostris	G					X						
Hexaplex brassica	G					X						
Eupleura muriciformis	G					X						
Coralliophila hindsii	G					X						
Strombina fusinoidea	G					X						
Cantharus capitaneus	G					X						
Hindsia acapulcana	G					X						
Nassarius pagodus	G					X						
Mitra erythrogramma	G					X						
Fusinus dupettithouarsi	G					X						
Harpa crenata	G					X						
Clavus roseolus	G					X						
Pleuroliria oxytropis albicarinata	G					X		X				
P. picta	G					X						
Glycymeris tessellata	P					X						
Cyclopecten pernomus	P					X						
Plicatula inezana	P					X						
Anodontia edentuloides	P					X						
Trachycardium belcheri	P					X						
Nemocardium pazianum	P					X						
Cyclinella kroyeri	P					X						
C. saccata	P					X						
Macoma siliqua	P					X						
Solecurtus guaymasensis	P					X						
Semele paziana	P					X						
Clypeaster europacificus	P					X		X				
Munida tenella	CR					X		X		X		
Porcellana cancrisocialis	CR					X						
Clibanarius panamensis	CR					X						
Paguristes bakeri	CR					X						
P. praedator	CR					X		X				
Pagurus gladius	CR					X						
Hypoconcha loweii	CR					X						
Calappa sausserei	CR					X		X				
Cyclöes bairdii	CR					X						
Hepatus kossmanni	CR					X						
Iliacantha hancocki	CR					X						
Persephone townsendi	CR					X						
Randallia americana	CR					X		X				
R. buligera	CR					X						
Euphylax robustus	CR					X						
Portunus acuminatus	CR					X						
P. affinus	CR					X						
P. pichilinquei	CR					X						
Cancer amphioetus	CR					X						
Medaeus lobipes	CR					X						
Leiolambrus punctatissimus	CR					X						
Mesorhea belli	CR					X						
Collodes gibbosus	CR					X						
C. tenuirostris	CR					X		X				
Euprognatha bifida	CR					X		X				
Paradasygius depressus	CR					X		X				
Pyromaia tuberculata	CR					X		X				
Stenorhynchus debilis	CR					X						
Cymopolia zonata	CR					X						
Protula superba	PO						X					
Crepidula incurva	G						X					
Crucibulum n. sp.	G						X					
Polinices intemerata	G						X					
Nassarius cattalus	G						X			X		
Conus arcuatus	G						X					

TABLE I—(*continued*)

Species	*Class*[1]	I	II	III	IV	V	VI	VII	VIII	IX	X	XI
		Environments										
Anadara mazatlanica	P						X					
Chione kellettii	P						X					
Corbula luteola	P						X					
Periploma carpenteri	P					X	X					
Pleuroncodes planipes	CR						X			X		
Ceratotrochus franciscana	AN							X				
Polinices otis	G							X				
Cymatium amictum	G							X				
Pleuroliria nobilis	G							X	X			
P. oxytropis oxytropis	G							X				
Lucinoma annulata	P							X	X	X		
Nemocardium centrifilosum	P							X	X			
Corbula ventricosa	P							X				
Stenocionops beebei	CR							X				
S. ovata	CR							X				
Libinia mexicana	CR							X				
Cymopolia zacae	CR							X				
Ethusa lata	CR							X				
Parastichopus californicus	HO							X				
Vaneyothuria zacae	HO							X				
Balanophyllia sp.	AN								X			
Desmophyllum crista-galli	AN								X			
Acanthogorgia n. sp.	AN								X			
Terebratalia obsoleta	BR								X	X		
Morrisia hornei	BR								X			
Calliostoma variegatum (dead)	G								X			
Turritella cf. *cooperi* (dead)	G								X			
Boreotrophon n. sp. (dead)	G								X	X		
Nassarius insculptus gordanus	G								X	X		
Fusinus traski	G								X			
Pleuroliria artia	G								X			
Acila castrensis	P								X			
Nuculana hamata (dead)	P								X			
N. taphria	P								X			
Glycymeris corteziana (dead)	P								X			
Cyclopecten vancouverensis (dead)	P								X			
Cardita barbarensis (dead)	P								X	X		
Lucina tenuisculpta (dead)	P								X	X		
Trigoniocardia guanacastense (dead)	P								X			
Tellina carpenteri (dead)	P								X			
T. tabogensis (dead)	P								X			
Macoma siliqua spectri	P								X			
Hiatella arctica (dead)	P								X			
Dentalium vallicolens (dead)	SC								X			
Cadulus perpusillus (dead)	SC								X			
Hesperocidaris perplexa	E								X			
Brisaster townsendi	E								X			
Emarginula velascoensis	G									X		
Solariella permabilis	G									X		
Nassarius miser	G									X		
Fusinus colpoicus	G									X		
Daphnella imparella	G									X		
Clathurella thalassoma	G									X		
Solemya valvulus	P								X	X		
Nucula cardara	P									X		
Nuculana callimene	P									X		
Amygdalum pallidulum	P								X	X		
Cyclopecten zacae	P									X		
Pandora convexa	P									X		
Pseudostichopus mollis	HO									X		
Pennatula phosphorea californica	AN										X	
Stachyptilum superbum	AN										X	
Solariella nuda	G										X	
Turcicula bairdii	G										X	
Solemya agassizi	P										X	X
Lucinoma n. sp.	P										X	
Vesicomya lepta	P										X	
Collosendeis bicincta	PYC										X	X
Paracrangon areolata	CR										X	
Heterocarpus affinus	CR										X	
Acanthophyra curtirostris	CR										X	X
Parapagurus pilosimanus	CR										X	X
Neolithodes diomedaea	CR										X	
Paralomis multispina	CR										X	
Paralithodes rathbuni	CR										X	
Synallactes ishikawa	HO										X	

TABLE I—(*continued*)

Species	Class[1]	I	II	III	IV	V	VI	VII	VIII	IX	X	XI[2]
		Environments										
Molpadia musculus	HO										X	X
Caryophillia diomedaea	AN											X
Anthomastus ritteri	AN											X
Galathealinum bruunei	POG											X
Macandravia americana diegensis	BR											X
Neopilina galathaea	MON											X
Puncturella expansa	G											X
Solariella equatorialis	G											X
Tractolira sparta	G											X
Pleurotomella clarinda	G											X
Steiraxis aulaca	G											X
Dentalium megathyris	SC											X
Nucula panamina	P											X
Malletia truncata	P											X
Tindaria compressa	P											X
Arca corpulenta pompholynx	P											X
A. nucleator	P											X
Limopsis compressus	P											X
Abra profundorum	P											X
Cuspidaria panamensis	P											X
Myonera garretti	P											X
Poromya perla	P											X
Colossendeis angusta	PYC											X
Pallenopsis californica	PYC											X
Benthesicymus altus	CR											X
Hymenopenaeus doris	CR											X
Pandalopsis ampla	CR											X
Munidopsis bairdii	CR											X
Paralomis verrilli	CR											X
Aporocidaris milleri	E											X
Tromikosoma hispidum	E											X
T. panamense	E											X
Urechinus loveni	E											X
Brisaster latifrons	E											X
Abyssicucumis abyssorum	HO											X
Benthydotes sanguinolenta	HO											X
Psychropotes dubiosa	HO											X
P. raripes	HO											X

(*For Table II, please turn the page.*)

TABLE III. FAUNAL CHARACTERISTICS OF THE TIBURÓN SUBGROUP OF THE NEARSHORE SAND-MUD ASSEMBLAGE

	Per cent of Occurrences in Stations Alive	Per cent of Total Live Occurrences in Whole Gulf	Index
Leavicardium elatum	88	71	80
Hexaplex erythrostomus	44	100	72
Donax gracilis	44	100	72
Ensis californicus	44	100	72
Strombus gracilior	33	100	66
Tellina tabogensis	33	100	66
Polinices reclusianus	66	60	63
Trachycardium panamense	66	50	58
Olivella fletcherae	55	60	58
Crepidula excavata	55	57	56
Terebra specillata	44	66	55
Lioberus salvadoricus	33	75	54
Anadara obesa	33	75	54
Laevicardium elenense	60	40	50
LESSER IMPORTANCE, LIVING			
Trigoniocardia granifera	44	50	47
Crepidula arenata	20	60	43
Nassarius versicolor	44	40	42
LESSER IMPORTANCE, DEAD			
Barbatia alternata	55	55	55
Semele guaymasensis	55	36	45
Lucina prolongata	33	43	38
Mactra californica	33	33	33

TABLE IV. FAUNAL CHARACTERISTICS OF THE SOUTHERN GULF SUBGROUP OF THE INTERMEDIATE SHELF ASSEMBLAGE

	Per cent of Occurrences in Stations	Per cent of Total Occurrences In Whole Gulf	Index
CRUSTACEANS			
Iliacantha hancocki Rathbun	86	66	76
Portunus acuminatus Stimpson	71	71	71
Persephone townsendi (Rathbun)	71	71	71
Stenorhynchus debilis Smith	71	62	66
Medaeus lobipes Rathbun	71	62	66
Dardanus sinistripes (Stimpson)	86	38	62
Pyromaia tuberculata (Lockington)	86	27	57
Paradysygius depressus (Bell)	57	44	51
Randallia bulligera Rathbun	43	60	51
Leilolambrus punctatissimus (Owen)	43	60	51
Hepatus kossmanni Newman	43	43	43
GASTROPODS			
Distorsio decussatus (Broderip, 1833)	100	86	93
Cantharus capitaneus (Berry, 1957)	100	53	76
Calliostoma bonita Strong, Hanna, and Hertlein, 1933	57	66	61
Architectonica nobilis Röding, 1789	57	50	53
Crucibulum spinosum (Sowerby, 1824)	86	17	51
Hexaplex brassica (Lamarck, 1822)	43	60	51
Strombina fusinoidea Dall, 1916	57	44	50
Hormospira maculosa (Sowerby, 1834)	71	26	48

TABLE II. SPECIES AND ENVIRONMENTAL CONDITIONS OF THE NEARSHORE SAND AND SAND-MUD ASSEMBLAGES

Species	*Index Group Numbers*				
	2	*3*	*7*	*64*	*74*
GASTROPODS					
Crepidula arenata			×		
C. excavata				×	
Polinices intemerata				×	
P. reclusianus			×		
Strombus gracilior (Index species grp. 64)				×	
Hexaplex erythrostomus				×	
Distorsio decussatus	×				
Nassarius versicolor			×		
Strombina gibberula		×			
Olivella fletcherae			×		
Terebra specillata		×			
Acteocina angustior			×		
PELECYPODS					
Nuculana elenensis					×
Barbatia alternata				×	
Anadara obesa	×				
Lioberus salvadoricus		×			
Chlamys circularis (Index species grp. 2)	×				
Lucina prolongata		×			
Ctena mexicana	×				
Laevicardium elatum				×	
L. elenense (Index species grp. 7)			×		
Trachycardium panamense			×		
Trigoniocardia biangulata			×		
Megapitaria squalida			×		
Dosinia dunkeri			×		
Chione mariae			×		
Tellina amianta			×		
T. inaequistriata		×			
Macoma siliqua	×				
Semele guaymasensis			×		
Donax gracilis (Index species grp. 74)					×
Ensis californica (Index species grp. 3)		×			
CRUSTACEANS					
Portunus pichelinqui		×			

Physical Factors

Station Numbers	*Depth in Fathoms*	*Temp. in °C*	*Oxygen in ml/L*	*Sediment Type*	*2*	*3*	*7*	*64*	*74*
24	13	16	2.5	sand			×		
114	4	30	4.0	sand	×				
163	1	20	4.0	sand				×	
172	7	20	3.0	shell sand	×				
175	14	13	1.2	mud sand	×				
179	1	14	3.0	sand			×		×
181	9	18	3.0	sand		×		×	
184	9	14	3.0	sand		×	×		×
185	31	13	2.4	sand			×		×
190	7	20	3.0	sand					×
191	14	15	3.0	mud sand				×	
194	7	20	3.0	mud sand	×	×	×		
195	12	18	3.0	mud sand	×		×		
196	13	16	3.0	sand	×	×	×	×	×
208	7	19	2.6	sand	×			×	
212	31	13	2.4	sand		×	×		
Average environmental conditions			Depth in fathoms		10.6	19.0	16.6	7.4	9.4
			Temperature in °C		17.0	14.3	14.0	19.2	18.0
			Oxygen in ml/L		2.6	2.8	2.7	3.2	3.2
			Sediment type		mud 3/5	sand 6/7	sand 3/4	sand 6/7	sand 8/8

PATTERNS OF LIVING BENTHONIC FORAMINIFERA, GULF OF CALIFORNIA[1]

FRED B PHLEGER[2]
La Jolla, California

ABSTRACT

Distributions of living Foraminifera were analyzed from 76 stations in the Gulf of California. Approximately 220 living species were identified.

Standing crops of living Foraminifera at depths greater than 1,000 fm average 26.5 specimens/10 ml of wet surface sediment. Standing crops are larger in shallow water. Areas of unusually large living populations at the head of the Gulf may be due to river influence, hypersalinity, or the effect of the silty substrate. Large living populations at three locations on the border of the Gulf may be due to high organic production caused by upwelling.

The following boundaries between depth biofacies are indicated by ranges of 66 common species—15–20 fm, 30–35 fm, 40–50 fm, 70 fm, 90 fm, 200 fm, 400–500 fm, 600–800 fm, 1,000 fm, 1,300 fm, and 1,500 fm. Ecological explanations for these 12 depth assemblages must await further understanding of the physical and chemical environments of the area.

Relative rates of deposition based on living-total ratios of Foraminifera suggest a very slow overall present rate of deposition in the Gulf, with small areas of faster deposition around the borders. The deposition rates south of the entrance to the Gulf, in depths greater than 1,000 fm, appear to be much faster than those within the Gulf.

INTRODUCTION

It is necessary to know the distribution of living marine organisms for a valid understanding of the ecology of any group such as the Foraminifera. Knowledge of distribution of empty tests is not sufficient because of contamination of faunas which may occur naturally and which recent studies have shown to be very common. Natural contamination of faunas (and sediments) may be from older marine rocks, such as from Tertiary and Cretaceous submarine exposures, and from sediment deposited during earlier cycles, such as during lowered sea level of the last glacial stage. In deep water, contamination may occur with faunas which are displaced from shallow water. Such faunal mixing may be from different geological ages and different marine environments.

Quantitative studies of living faunas are of value for at least two additional purposes. They can be useful as a measure of the rates of accumulation of inorganic and organic detritus composing the marine sediment. The standing crop of any abundant and diverse group, such as the Foraminifera, also can give a clue to the relative amounts of organic production in different environments.

Little is known of the Gulf of California Foraminifera with the exception of Bandy's (1961) and Brenner's (1962) studies of some distributions of empty tests. The purpose of this paper is to decribe quantitatively the distributions of the more common living benthonic Foraminifera in the Gulf of California, and to attempt to relate the distributions to what is known of the environments.

The samples were collected in 1959 by members of the *Vermilion Sea Expedition* using R/V *Horizon* of the Scripps Institution of Oceanography. The top centimeter of sediment from short gravity cores was taken for study of Foraminifera and was preserved in buffered formalin and sea water to which a small amount of sodium carbonate was added. In the laboratory the samples were stained with Rose Bengal (Walton, 1952) to identify specimens containing protoplasm and which were alive at the time of collection. Fine

[1] Manuscript received, April 1, 1963. Contribution from Scripps Institution of Oceanography, University of California; Marine Foraminifera Laboratory, Contribution No. 42.

Identifications of the Foraminifera were made by Jean P. Hosmer. Photographs of the illustrated specimens were by Joseph W. Cobarrubias. The figures were drafted by Jean P. Hosmer and James R. Moriarty. The laboratory work was supported by a contract of the Office of Naval Research with the University of California, by the National Science Foundation, and by the American Petroleum Institute.

[2] Scripps Institution of Oceanography, University of California.

sediment was removed by washing over a screen having openings of 0.062 mm. Samples were examined wet to identify specimens containing stained protoplasm.

The living populations listed on Figures 4 and 5 are those in 10 ml of wet surface sediment. Total populations (living and dead specimens) were estimated in each sample, but the dead specimens were not identified in this study.

Living faunas were analyzed in 76 samples having a wide geographic and bathymetric distribution in the area. Locations of stations are on Figure 2 and Table I.

THE GULF OF CALIFORNIA

There is little definitive information on the environments represented in the Gulf of California which may apply to understanding the ecology of the organisms living there. Shepard (1950) and Rusnak, Fisher, and Shepard (this volume) have given a good description of the bathymetry. Roden (1958; this volume) and Roden and Groves (1959) have recorded a generalized description of the temperature, salinity, tides, and currents based on relatively few observations. Over-all aspects of the sediments are described and discussed by van Andel (this volume). A few general features of the area are believed to be of possible ecologic importance.

The Gulf is a long and narrow marine basin which is open to the Pacific Ocean at the southeast end, and is closed at the northwest end. It is approximately 600 mi long and the width is about 100 mi at the southern entrance; the average width is about 60 mi. Owing to the presence of large islands, the basin is constricted somewhat north of the mid-section to an effective width of only about 30 mi.

There is little runoff into the Gulf and evaporation exceeds precipitation. The only permanent streams are on the east side in the southern half of the Gulf. Little water from the Colorado River drainage now flows into the Gulf. As a result, the salinities of the inner Gulf are somewhat higher than the typical Pacific salinities at the entrance (*see* Roden, this volume). Surface water temperatures in the northern Gulf range from approximately 15° to 30°C, and in the southern Gulf they range from about 21° to 30°C. There is considerable upwelling of water owing to winter northwesterly winds and summer southeasterly winds.

→

EXPLANATION OF PLATE 1

FIGS. 1.—*Reophax dentaliniformis* Brady. ×34. Sta. 4.
2.—*Lagenammina longicollis* (Wiesner). ×42. Sta. 13.
3.—*Adercotryma glomeratus* (Brady). ×62. Sta. 4.
4.—*Reophax hispidulus* Cushman. ×38. Sta. 25.
5.—*Reophax subfusiformis* Earland. ×45. Sta. 24.
6.—*Reophax scorpiurus* Montfort. ×24. Sta. 109.
7.—*Reophax nanus* Rhumbler. ×77. Sta. 145.
8,14.—*Textularia schencki* Cushman and Valentine group. ×42. Sta. 94.
9.—*Eggerella advena* (Cushman). ×68. Sta. 214.
10,11.—*Ammoscalaria pseudospiralis* (Williamson). Fig. 10, ×49; Fig. 11, ×55. Sta. 138.
12.—*Bigenerina* sp. ×48. Sta. 1.
13.—*Eggerella* sp. ×36. Sta. 36.
15.—*Quinqueloculina costata* Terquem. ×52. Sta. 94.
16.—*Quinqueloculina laevigata* d'Orbigny. ×52. Sta. 94.
17.—*Quinqueloculina compta* Cushman. ×38. Sta. 127.
18.—*Triloculina inflata* d'Orbigny. ×50. Sta. 65.
19,20.—*Trochammina vesicularis* Goes. Fig. 19, ×63; Fig. 20, ×71. Sta. 27.
21.—*Trochammina globigeriniformis* (Parker and Jones). ×63. Sta. 5.
22,23.—*Trochammina pacifica* Cushman. Fig. 22, ×64; Fig. 23, ×62. Sta. 214.
24,25.—*Trochammina* sp. Fig. 24, ×50; Fig. 25, ×57. Sta. 82.
26,27.—*Trochammina kellettae* Thalmann. Fig. 26, ×98; Fig. 27, ×95. Sta. 211.
28,29.—*Nouria polymorphinoides* Heron-Allen and Earland. ×45. Sta. 214.
30.—*Nonionella basispinata* (Cushman and Moyer) var. ×54. Sta. 21.
31.—*Nonion parkerae* Uchio. ×47. Sta. 36.
32.—*Nonion pompilioides* (Fichtel and Moll). ×68. Sta. 9.
33,34.—*Nonionella stella* Cushman and Moyer. ×60. Sta. 210.
35,36.—*Nonionella basispinata* (Cushman and Moyer). ×72. Sta. 94.

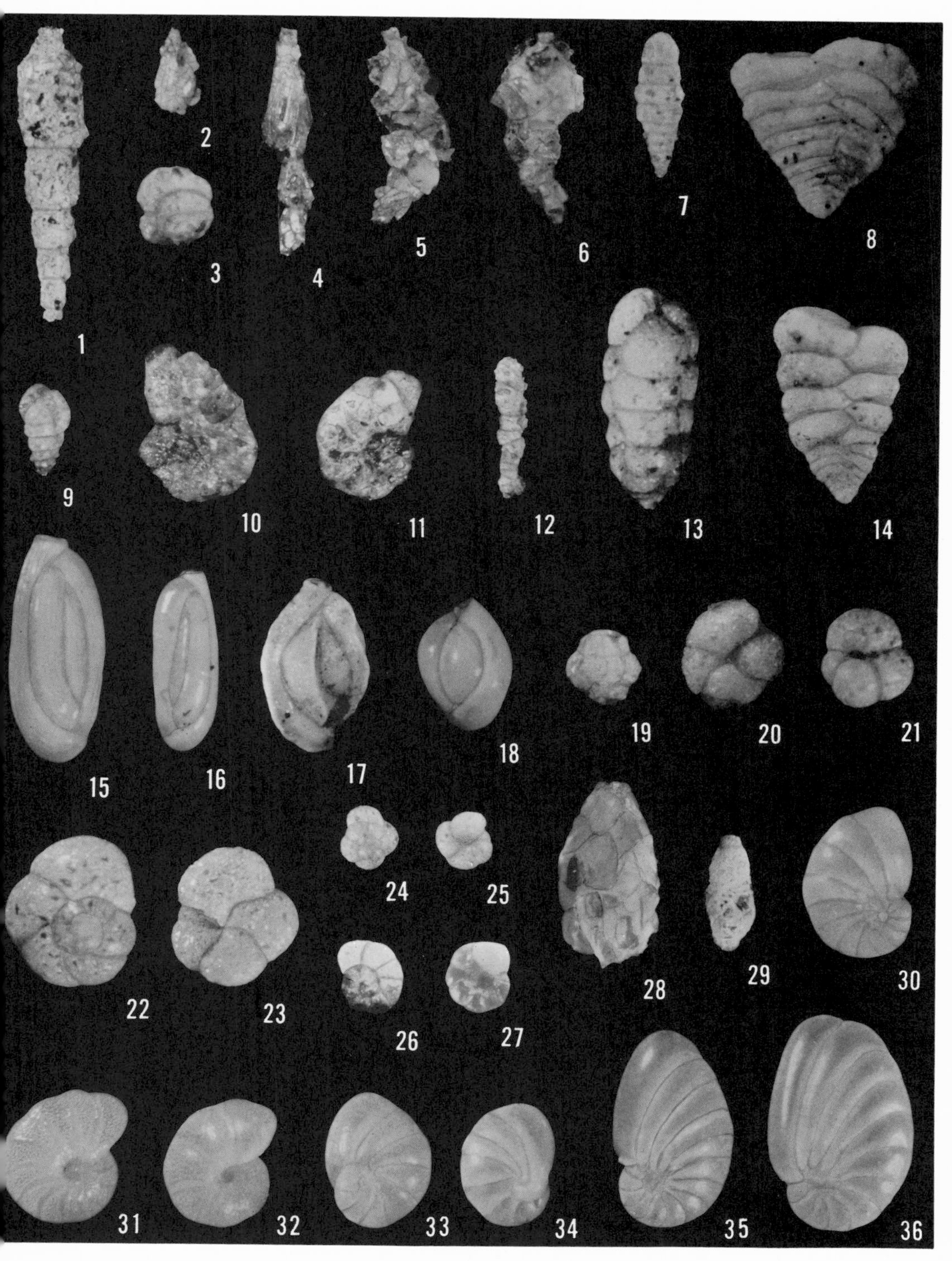

Common living benthonic Foraminifera from Gulf of California

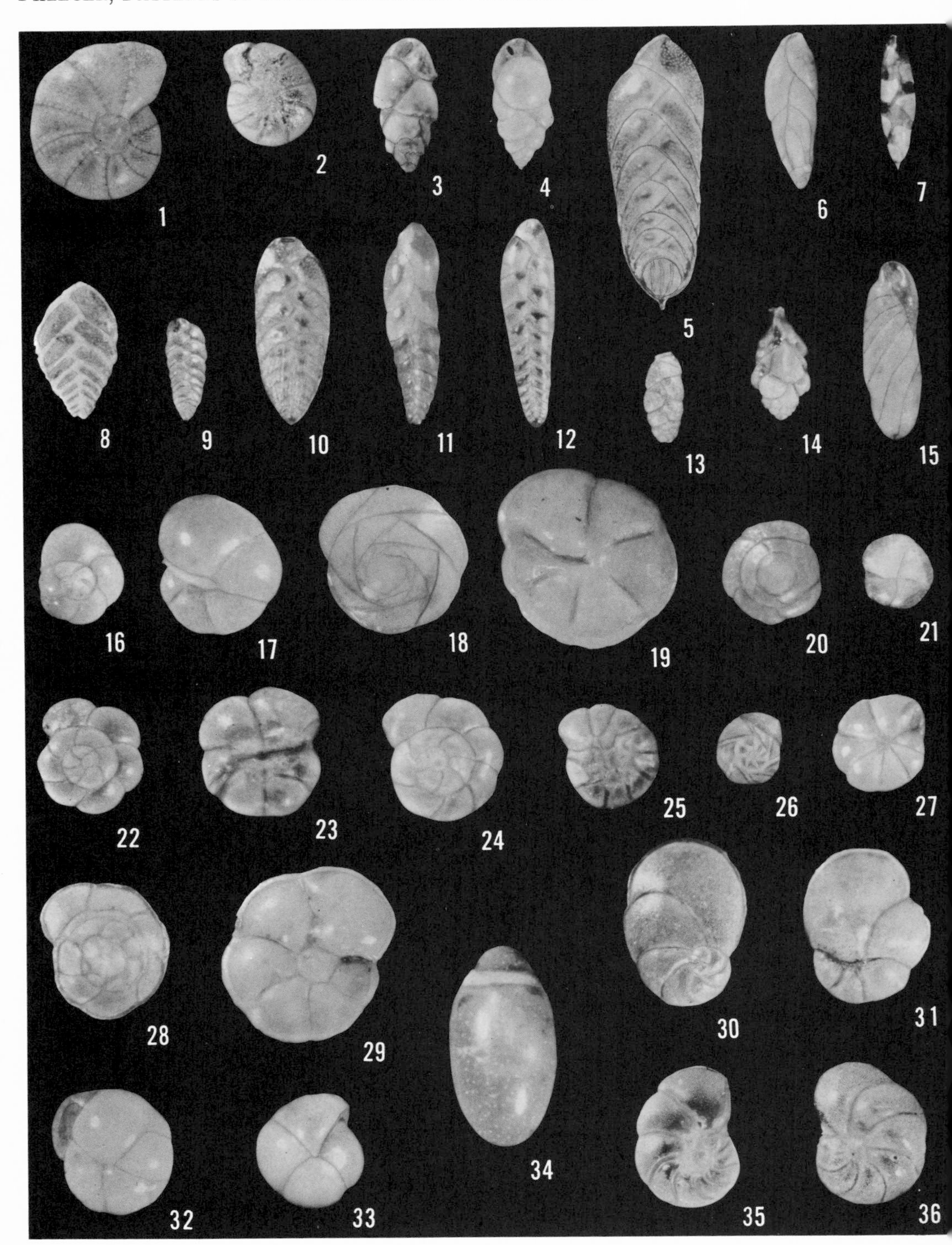

Common living benthonic Foraminifera from Gulf of California

Explanation of Plate 2

FIGS.

1.—*Elphidium translucens* Natland. ×62. Sta. 211.
2.—*Elphidium incertum* (Williamson) var. ×47. Sta. 209.
3.—*Bulimina marginata* d'Orbigny. ×57. Sta. 21.
4.—*Bulimina denudata* Cushman and Parker. ×65. Sta. 209.
5.—*Bolivina spissa* Cushman. ×57. Sta. 75.
6.—*Fursenkoina pontoni* (Cushman) ×54. Sta. 21.
7.—*Fursenkoina seminuda* (Natland). ×53. Sta. 69.
8.—*Bolivina minuta* Natland. ×75. Sta. 13.
9.—*Bolivina vaughani* Natland. ×79. Sta. 21.
10.—*Bolivina acutula* Bandy. ×76. Sta. 100.
11,12.—*Bolivina pacifica* Cushman and McCulloch. Fig. 11, ×78, Sta. 82; Fig. 12, ×69, Sta. 207.
13.—*Bolivinopsis* sp. ×82. Sta. 21.
14.—*Angulogerina* sp. cf. *A. jamaicensis* Cushman and Todd. ×57. Sta. 138.
15.—*Buliminella elegantissima* (d'Orbigny). ×89. Sta. 65.
16,17.—*Valvulineria glabra* Cushman. Fig. 16, ×58; Fig. 17, ×80. Sta. 80.
18,19.—*Eponides antillarum* (d'Orbigny). ×42. Sta. 100.
20,21.—*Eponides leviculus* (Resig). Fig. 20, ×98; Fig. 21, ×83. Sta. 13.
22-25.—*Ammonia beccarii* (Linné) vars. Fig. 22, ×51; Fig. 23, ×75; Fig. 24, ×65; Fig. 25, ×73. Sta. 214.
26,27.—*Epistominella obesa* Bandy and Arnal. Fig. 26, ×84; Fig. 27, ×105. Sta. 80.
28,29.—*Rotorbinella? campanulata* (Galloway and Wissler). Fig. 28, ×63; Fig. 29, ×73. Sta. 206.
30,31.—*Cancris auriculus* (Fichtel and Moll). ×47. Sta. 21.
32.—*Cassidulina* sp. 1. ×94. Sta. 208.
33.—*Pullenia bulloides* (d'Orbigny). ×62. Sta. 73.
34.—*Chilostomella ovoidea* Reuss. ×50. Sta. 80.
35,36.—*Hanzawaia nitidula* (Bandy). ×48. Sta. 127.

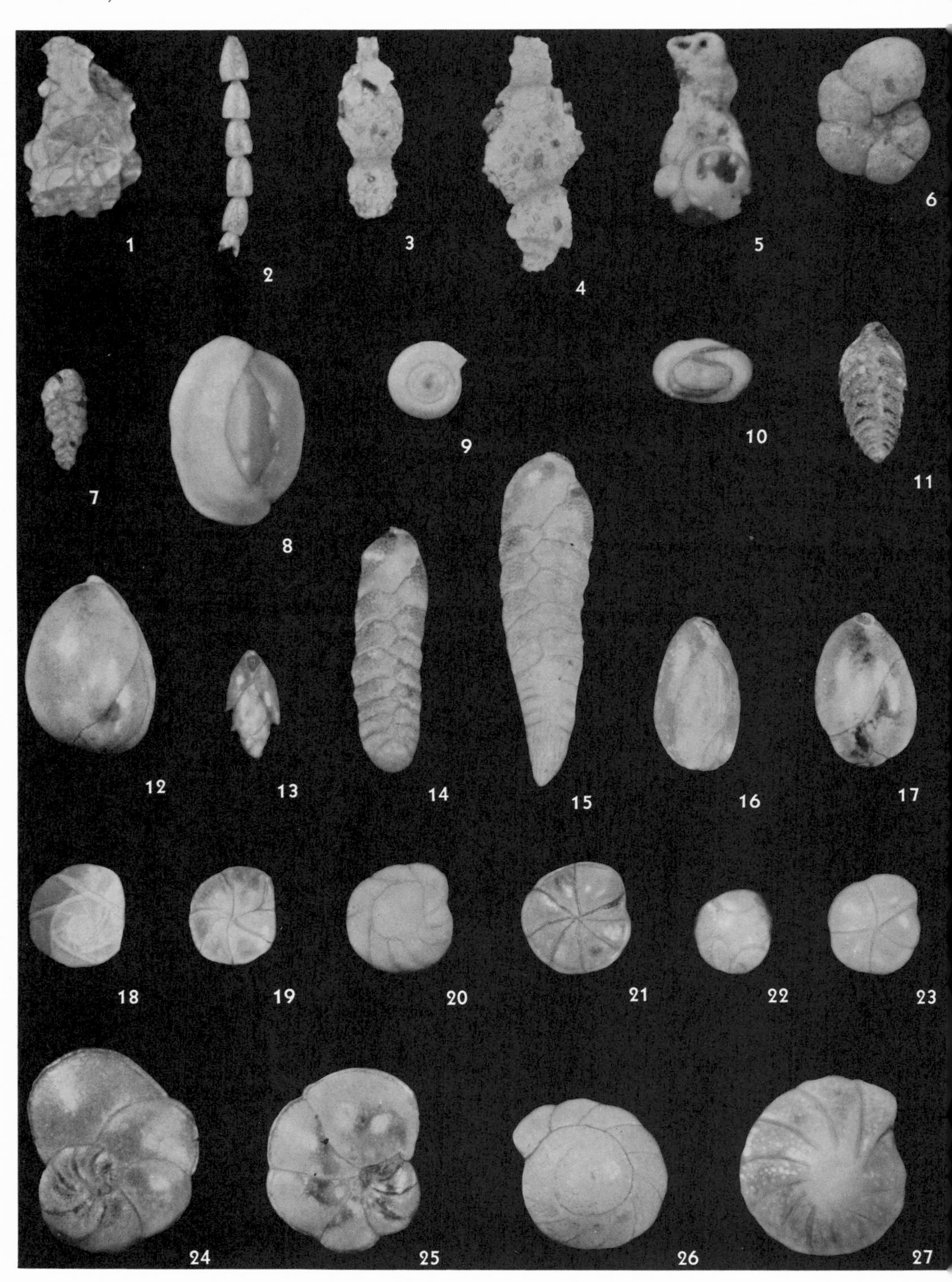

Common living benthonic Foraminifera from Gulf of California

The Gulf generally is deep for its size and there are several enclosed basins, one of which is more than 1,500 fm deep. (*See* Fig. 1.) Most submarine slopes are relatively steep for marine areas, averaging 3–6° and locally attaining as much as 8°. Continental shelf depths, less than about 50–60 fm, occupy only a small percentage of the area on the eastern side. The largest area of relatively shallow water is in the northern end where the inner 30–40 mi of the Gulf is less than 50 fm deep. There is no continental shelf on the western side.

The mean tidal range varies from about 3 ft at the entrance to about 23 ft at the inner end and there is a spring tidal range at the inner end of more than 30 ft. There is a tidal delay of about 5–6 hrs from the mouth to the northern end. Tidal currents are strong in many places in the inner Gulf, such as where the width is restricted by islands and in the Hardy River (Lower Colorado). Thin salt pans border the inner Gulf in many high tidal-flat areas which are flooded only at spring tides.

Oceanic water entering the Gulf is entirely from the tropical Pacific. This water contains the equatorial West Central planktonic Foraminifera (Bradshaw, 1959), and the living planktonic Foraminifera in the Gulf are exclusively of this fauna. The benthonic fauna, based mainly on the study of molluscs, belongs to the Panamic-Pacific zoogeographic province (Ekman, 1953, p. 38). The Gulf is the northernmost extension of this province because of the separation of the northern end from the Pacific at the same latitudes.

LIVING BENTHONIC FORAMINIFERA

SPECIES

Approximately 220 living species were identified and it is estimated that there are at least 50 additional living forms which were not identified. Most of the species are rare and only 66 were sufficiently common to warrant their use for the present ecological study. The common species are illustrated on Plates 1–3 and references to the original descriptions are listed below.

Adercotryma glomeratus (Brady)
=*Lituola glomerata* Brady, 1878, Ann. Mag. Nat. History, ser. 5, v. 1, p. 433, pl. 20, fig. 1.

Alveolophragmium columbiense (Cushman)
=*Haplophgragmoides columbiense* Cushman, 1925, Cushman Lab. Foram. Research, Contr., v. 1, p. 39, pl. 6, fig. 2.

Ammonia beccarii (Linné) variants
=*Nautilus beccarii* Linné, 1758, Syst. Nat., ed. 10, p. 710.

Ammoscalaria psuedospiralis (Williamson)
=*Proteonina pseudospirale* Williamson, 1858, Recent Foram. Great Britain, p. 2, pl. 1, figs. 2, 3.

Ammotium planissimum (Cushman)
=*Haplophragmoides planissima* Cushman, 1927, Scripps Inst. Oceanography, Bull., tech. ser., v. 1, no. 10, p. 135, pl. 1, fig. 6.

Angulogerina cf. *A. jamaicensis* Cushman and Todd,

←

EXPLANATION OF PLATE 3

FIGS. 1.—*Lagenammina atlantica* (Cushman). ×54. Sta. 207.
2.—*Reophax gracilis* (Kiaer). ×66. Sta. 215.
3,4.—*Reophax excentricus* Cushman. Fig. 3, ×54; Fig. 4, ×45. Sta. 7.
5,10.—*Tolypammina* sp. ×75. Fig. 5, Sta. 114; Fig. 10, Sta. 24.
6.—*Alveolophragmium columbiense* (Cushman). ×45. Sta. 77.
7.—*Textularia* sp. ×70. Sta. 12.
8.—*Quinqueloculina lamarckiana* d'Orbigny. ×45. Sta. 65.
9.—*Cyclogyra* sp. ×70. Sta. 94.
11.—*Bolivina acuminata* Natland. ×48. Sta. 207.
12,16,17.—*Globobulimina pacifica* Cushman. Figs. 12, 17, ×36; Fig. 16, ×68. Fig. 12, Sta. 83-B; Figs. 16, 17, Sta. 121.
13.—*Fursenkoina spinosa* (Heron-Allen & Earland). ×78. Sta. 115.
14,15.—*Bolivina subadvena* Cushman. ×48. Sta. 37.
18,19.—*Epistominella* cf. *E. sandiegoensis* Uchio. Fig. 18, ×72; Fig. 19, ×70. Sta. 209.
20,21.—*Buccella tenerrima* (Bandy) var. ×68. Sta. 218-B.
22.—*Cassidulina* sp. 2. ×80. Sta. 94.
23.—*Pullenia quinqueloba* (Reuss). ×68. Sta. 5.
24,25.—*Cancris panamensis* Natland. ×48. Sta. 21.
26,27.—*Cibicides mckannai* Galloway & Wissler. Fig. 26, ×48; Fig. 27, ×54. Sta. 73.

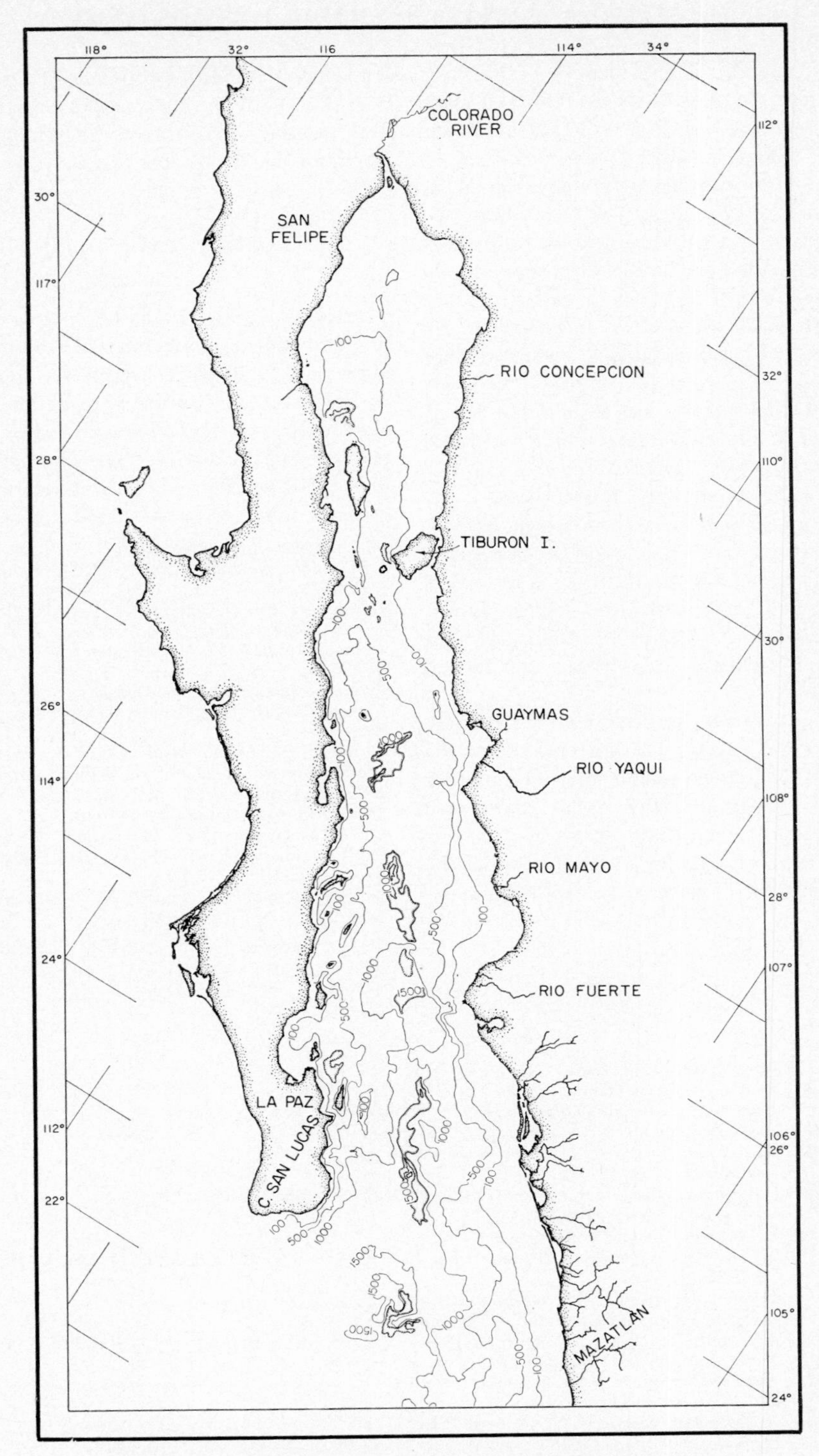

FIG. 1.—Generalized submarine topography of the Gulf of California.

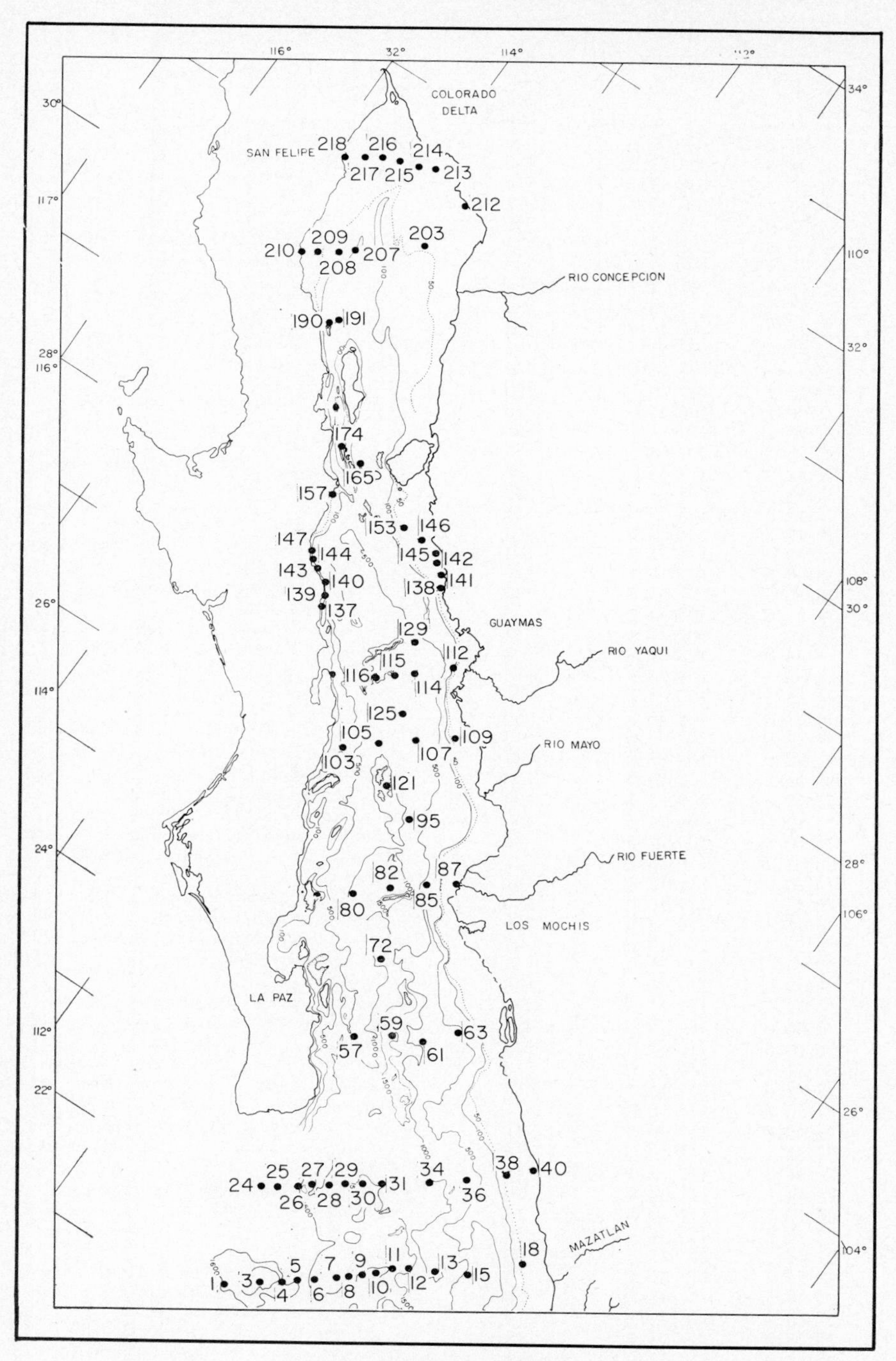

FIG. 2.—Locations of stations.

TABLE I. LOCATIONS OF STATIONS

Sta.	N. Lat ° ′	W. Long ° ′	Depth (fathoms)
1	21 02.0	109 00.0	1,620
3	21 34.6	108 43.3	1,480
4	21 39.2	108 33.1	1,543
5	21 45.2	108 25.7	1,572
6	21 52.0	108 16.8	1,530
7	21 59.0	108 06.1	1,533
8	22 03.9	108 00.0	1,580
9	22 09.6	107 54.1	1,667
10	22 14.8	107 48.3	1,638
11	22 21.7	107 40.6	1,582
12	22 28.7	107 33.1	1,513
13	22 34.2	107 18.0	877
15	22 43.5	106 59.5	840
18	23 06.5	106 35.7	50
24	22 20.4	109 17.7	1,665
25	22 25.5	109 08.0	1,655
26	22 31.9	108 58.0	1,658
27	22 38.4	108 51.5	1,580
28	22 43.8	108 43.0	1,577
29	22 49.2	108 34.5	1,564
30	22 55.0	108 25.8	1,473
31	23 00.8	108 16.7	1,610
34	23 16.0	107 53.5	1,295
36	23 31.5	107 34.7	740
38	23 45.0	107 17.1	53
40	23 55.0	107 04.5	8
57	24 03.4	109 23.8	675
59	24 15.1	109 05.2	1,590
61	24 24.0	108 46.2	1,050
63	24 38.8	108 32.0	610
72	24 50.0	109 38.0	1,041
80	25 13.5	110 15.9	1,100
82	25 26.6	109 58.5	1,730
85	25 40.0	109 41.0	400
87	25 50.0	109 27.5	7
95	26 02.3	110 23.2	927
103	26 20.0	111 13.4	192
105	26 33.0	110 56.0	895
107	26 46.3	110 38.0	750
109	26 59.0	110 19.0	44
112	27 32.5	110 45.0	34
114	27 18.0	111 03.1	888
115	27 12.2	111 13.5	973
116	27 04.0	111 22.4	1,020
121	26 16.0	110 37.0	1,245
125	26 54.5	110 57.0	918
129	27 32.6	111 14.1	655
137	27 20.5	112 16.0	7
138	28 08.0	111 20.3	17
139	27 27.2	112 19.0	18
140	27 34.2	112 23.3	15
141	28 14.1	111 24.9	10
142	28 17.7	111 33.0	15
143	27 37.5	112 32.0	10
144	27 42.0	112 37.5	90
145	28 22.2	111 37.7	6
146	28 24.5	111 48.5	6
147	27 46.4	113 42.1	6
153	28 25.0	112 03.1	18
157	28 18.0	112 52.0	12
165	28 44.2	112 48.5	230
174	28 45.0	113 03.4	795
190	29 39.0	113 56.0	465
191	29 42.6	113 52.3	440
203	30 44.9	113 34.0	41
207	30 22.7	114 09.2	95
208	30 16.2	114 17.1	70
209	30 10.0	114 27.7	35
210	30 05.2	114 36.0	14
212	31 14.4	113 29.0	10
213	31 22.8	113 57.4	8
214	31 19.2	114 17.1	17
215	31 15.3	114 18.4	22
216	31 11.1	114 28.2	18
217	31 07.1	114 38.2	15
218	31 02.0	114 49.5	10

1945, Cushman Lab. Foram. Research, Spec. Pub. 15, p. 53, pl. 8, fig. 3.

Bigenerina sp.

Bolivina acuminata Natland
=*Bolivina subadvena* Cuhsman var. *acuminata* Natland, 1946, *in* Cushman and Gray, Cushman Lab. Foram. Research, Spec. Pub. 19, p. 34, pl. 5, fig. 46.

Bolivina acutula Bandy
=*Bolivina advena* Cushman var. *acutula* Bandy, 1953, Jour. Paleontology, v. 27, no. 3, p. 180, pl. 24, fig. 7.

Bolivina minuta Natland, 1938, Scripps Inst. Oceanography, Bull. tech. ser., v. 4, no. 5, p. 146, pl. 5, fig. 10.

Bolivina pacifica Cushman and McCulloch
=*Bolivina acerosa* Cushman var. *pacifica* Cushman and McCulloch, 1942, Allan Hancock Pacific Expeds., v. 6, no. 4, p. 185, pl. 21, figs. 2–3.

Bolivina spissa Cushman
=*Bolivina subadvena* Cushman var. *spissa* Cushman, 1926, Cushman Lab. Foram. Research, Contr., v. 2, pt. 2, p. 45, pl. 6, fig. 8.

Bolivina subadvena Cushman, 1926, Cushman Lab. Foram. Research, Contr., v. 2, pt. 2, p. 44, pl. 6, fig. 6.

Bolivina vaughani Natland, 1938, Scripps Inst. Oceanography, Bull., tech. ser., v. 4, no. 5, p. 146, pl. 5, fig. 11.

Bolivinopsis sp.

Buccella tenerrima (Bandy) var.
=*Rotalia tenerrima* Bandy, 1950, Jour. Paleontology, v. 24, no. 3, p. 278, pl. 42, fig. 3.

Bulimina denudata Cushman and Parker, 1938, Cushman Lab. Foram. Research, Contr., v. 14, p. 57, pl. 10, figs. 1, 2.

Bulimina marginata d'Orbigny, 1826, Ann. Sci. Nat., Foraminifères, ser. 1, v. 7, p. 269, no. 4, pl. 12, figs. 10–12.

Buliminella elegantissima (d'Orbigny)
=*Bulimina elegantissima* d'Orbigny, 1839, Voy. Amér. Mérid., v. 5, pt. 5, Foraminifères, p. 51, pl. 7, figs. 13–14.

Cancris auriculus (Fichtel and Moll)
=*Nautilus auriculus* Fichtel and Moll, 1798, Test Micr., var. α, p. 108, pl. 20, figs. a–c; var. β, p. 110, pl. 20, figs. d–f.

Cancris panamensis Natland, 1938, Scripps Inst. Oceanography, Bull., tech. ser., v. 4, no. 5, p. 148, pl. 6, fig. 1.

Cassidulina sp. 1
Cassidulina sp. 2
Chilostomella ovoidea Reuss, 1850, K. Akad. Wiss. Wien, Denkschr., v. 1, p. 380, pl. 48, fig. 12.
Cibicides mckannai Galloway and Wissler, 1927, Jour. Paleontology, v. 1, no. 1, p. 65, pl. 10, figs. 5, 6.
Cyclogyra sp.
Eggerella advena (Cushman)
=*Verneuilina advena* Cushman, 1922, Contr. Canadian Biology, no. 9, p. 141.
Eggerella sp.
Elphidium incertum (Williamson) var.
=*Polystomella umbilicatula* Walker and Boys var. *incerta* Williamson, 1858, Recent Foram. Great Britain, p. 44, pl. 3, fig. 82a.
Elphidium translucens Natland, 1938, Scripps Inst. Oceanography, Bull., tech. ser., v. 4, no. 5, p. 144, pl. 5, figs. 3–4.
Epistominella obesa Bandy and Arnal, 1957, Cushman Found. Foram. Research, Contr., v. 8, pt. 2, p. 56, pl. 7, fig. 8.
Epistominella cf. *E. sandiegoensis* Uchio, 1960, Cushman Found. Foram. Research, Spec. Pub. 5, p. 68, pl. 9, figs. 6, 7.
Eponides antillarum (d'Orbigny)
=*Rotalina antillarum* d'Orbigny, 1839, in De la Sagra, Hist. Phys. Pol. Nat. Cuba, "Foraminifères," p. 75, pl. 5, figs. 4–6.
Eponides leviculus (Resig)
=*Epistominella levicula* Resig, 1958, Micropaleontology, v. 4, no. 3. p. 304, text-fig. 16.
Fursenkoina pontoni (Cushman)
=*Virgulina pontoni* Cushman, 1932, Cushman Lab. Foram. Research, Contr., v. 8, pt. 1, p. 17, pl. 3, fig. 7.
Fursenkoina seminuda (Natland)
=*Virgulina seminuda* Natland, 1938, Scripps Inst. Oceanography, Bull., tech. ser., v. 4, p. 145, pl. 5, fig. 12.
Fursenkoina spinosa (Heron-Allen and Earland)
=*Virgulina schreibersiana* Czjzek var. *spinosa* Heron-Allen and Earland, 1932, Discovery Repts., v. 4, p. 352, pl. 9, figs. 3, 4.
Globobulimina pacifica Cushman, 1927, Cushman Lab. Foram. Research, Contr., v. 3, p. 67, pl. 14, fig. 12.
Hanzawaia nitidula (Bandy)
=*Cibicidina basiloba* (Cushman) var. *nitidula* Bandy, 1953, Jour. Paleontology, v. 27, no. 2, p. 178, pl. 22, fig. 3.
Lagenammina atlantica (Cushman)
=*Proteonina atlantica* Cushman, 1944, Cushman Lab. Foram. Research, Spec. Pub. 12, p. 5, pl. 1, fig. 4.
Lagenammina longicollis (Wiesner)
=*Proteonina longicollis* Wiesner, 1929, Deutsche Süd-Polar-Exped., v. 20, Zool., p. 82, pl. 6, fig. 55.
Nonion parkerae Uchio, 1960, Cushman Found. Foram. Research, Spec. Pub. 5, p. 60, pl. 4, figs. 9, 10.
Nonion pompilioides (Fichtel and Moll)
=*Nautilus pompilioides* Fichtel and Moll, 1798, Test. Micr., p. 31, pl. 2, figs. a–c.
Nonionella basispinata (Cushman and Moyer)
=*Nonion pizarrensis* Berry var. *basispinata* Cushman and Moyer, 1930, Cushman Lab. Foram. Research, Contr., v. 6, p. 54, pl. 7, fig. 18.
Nonionella stella Cushman and Moyer
=*Nonionella miocenica* Cushman var. *stella* Cushman and Moyer, 1930, Cushman Lab. Foram. Research, Contr., v. 6, p. 56, pl. 7, fig. 17.
Nouria polymorphinoides Heron-Allen and Earland, 1914, Zool. Soc. London, Trans., v. 20, pt. 12, p. 376, pl. 37, figs. 1–15.
Pullenia bulloides (d'Orbigny)
=*Nonionina bulloides* d'Orbigny, 1826, Ann. Sci. Nat., Foraminifères, ser. 1, v. 7, p. 293, no. 2.
Pullenia quinqueloba (Reuss)
=*Nonionina quinqueloba* Reuss, 1851, Zeitschrift deut. Geol. Ges., v. 3, p. 71, pl. 5, fig. 31.
Quinqueloculina compta Cushman, 1947, Cushman Lab. Foram. Research, Contr., v. 23, pt. 4, p. 87, pl. 19, fig. 2.
Quinqueloculina costata Terquem (1826) (*nom. nud.*), Tabl. Méth., p. 135 (301), no. 3, planches inédites, pl. 1, figs. 11–13. Terquem, 1878, Soc. Géol. France, Mém., Sér. 3, tome 1, no. 3, p. 63, pl. 6, figs. 3–5.
Quinqueloculina laevigata d'Orbigny, 1826, Ann. Sci. Nat., p. 301, no. 6; *in* Barker Webb and Berthelot, 1839, Hist. Nat. Iles Canaries, v. 2, pt. 2, Foraminifères, p. 143, pl. 3, figs. 31–33.
Quinqueloculina lamarckiana d'Orbigny, 1839, *in* De la Sagra, Hist. Phys. Pol. Nat. Cuba, Foraminifères, p. 189, pl. 11, figs. 14, 15.
Reophax dentaliniformis Brady, 1881, Micr. Sci. Quart. Jour., v. 19, p. 49.
Reophax excentricus Cushman, 1910, U.S. Natl. Mus., Bull. 71, pt. 1, p. 92, text fig. 134.
Reophax gracilis (Kiaer)
=*Nodulina gracilis* Kiaer, 1900, Norwegian Fish Mar. Invest., Rept., v. 1, no. 7, p. 24, text figs. 1, 2.
Reophax hispidulus Cushman, 1920, U.S. Natl. Mus., Bull., v. 104, pt. 2 p. 24, pl. 5, fig. 7.
Reophax micaceous Earland, 1934, Discovery Repts., v. 10 (1935), p. 82, pl. 2, figs. 37–40.
Reophax nanus Rhumbler, 1911, Plankton-Exped. Humboldt Stiftung, Ergeb., v. 3, pt. 2, p. 471, pl. 8, figs. 6–12.
Reophax scorpiurus Montfort, 1808, Conch. Syst. Class. Meth. Coqu., p. 331, text fig. (p. 330).
Reophax subfusiformis Earland, 1933, Discovery Repts., v. 7, p. 74, pl. 2, figs. 16–19.
Reussella pacifica Cushman and McCulloch, 1948, Allan Hancock Pacific Exped., v. 6, no. 5, p. 251, pl. 31, fig. 6.
Rotorbinella? campanulata (Galloway and Wissler)
=*Globorotalia campanulata* Galloway and Wissler, 1927, Jour. Paleontology, v. 1, p. 58, pl. 9, fig. 14.
Saccammina spp.
Textularia schencki Cushman and Valentine group, 1930, Dept. Geol. Stanford Univ., Contr., v. 1, no. 1, p. 8, pl. 1, fig. 3.
Textularia sp.
Tolypammina sp.
Triloculina inflata d'Orbigny, 1826, Ann. Sci. Nat., ser. 1, tome 7, p. 300, no. 10.
Trochammina globigeriniformis (Parker and Jones)
=*Lituola nautiloidea* Lamarck var. *globigeriniformis* Parker and Jones, 1865, Roy Soc. London, Philos. Trans., v. 155, p. 407, pl. 15, figs. 46–47.
Trochammina kellettae Thalmann
=*Trochammina peruviana* Cushman and Kellett (not W. Berry, 1928), 1929, U.S. Natl. Mus., Proc., no. 2796, v. 75, art. 25, p. 4, pl. 1, fig. 8. *Trochammina kellettae* Thalmann, 1932, Eclog. Geol. Helv., vol. 25, no. 2, p. 313.
Trochammina pacifica Cushman, 1925, Cushman Lab Foram. Research, Contr., v. 1, pt. 2, p. 39, pl. 6, fig. 3.

Trochammina vesicularis Goes, 1894, K. Sven. Vet. -Akad. Handl., N. F., Bd. 25, no. 9, p. 31, pl. 6, figs. 235–237.
Trochammina sp.
Valvulineria glabra Cushman
= *Valvulineria vilardeboana* (d'Orbigny) var. *glabra* Cushman, 1927, Scripps Inst. Oceanography, Bull., tech. ser., v. 1, p. 161, pl. 4, figs. 5, 6.

SIZE OF THE LIVING POPULATION

The size of the living population is reported as number of living specimens in the surface centimeter of sediment from an area of 10 sq cm (Figs. 3–5). These data may be compared to populations reported in several previous studies (Walton, 1955; Uchio, 1960; Phleger, 1956, 1960b; Phleger and Ewing, 1962; Lankford, 1959). The size of the population ranges from 2 to 702 specimens per sample in the samples studied. A few interesting population trends are noted.

There are no previous data on the standing crop of benthonic Foraminifera at depths greater than 1,000 fm. At 25 stations in depths greater than 1,000 fm the population range is 2–62 specimens /sample with a mean population of 26.5 specimens/sample. In 12 samples at 500–1,000 fm the mean standing crop is about 26 specimens/sample. These populations are much smaller than those reported by Uchio (1960, p. 42) from depths of 500–650 fm in the San Diego, California, area. The present data are comparable to those reported from the Todos Santos Bay area, Baja California, where the average living populations are about 20 specimens/sample at 400–600 fm (Walton, 1955, p. 983).

Standing crops are larger in more shallow water, and there are two areas of very large living populations. One area is off the Fuerte River where there are 702 specimens in the sample collected at Station 85 in 400 fm and 492 specimens at Station 87 in 7 fm. Both stations are less than 20 mi off the mouth of the river. Unusually large standing crops off the mouths of rivers have been reported by Lankford (1959, p. 2086) off Main Pass in the Mississippi Delta and by Phleger and Lankford (1957) off the mouth of the Guadalupe River in San Antonio Bay, Texas.

The other striking area of large standing crops is at the northern margin of the Gulf where at four stations populations range from 372 to 632 specimens/sample. These relatively large populations may be related to the Hardy River or may be related to the presence of marginal salt flats. Large standing crops are reported from Laguna Madre, Texas (Phleger, 1960b, p. 84) and from Laguna Ojo de Liebre, Baja California (Phleger and Ewing, 1962, p. 163), both hypersaline lagoons.

DEPTH DISTRIBUTIONS

The samples studied were collected from depths of 5.5 to 1,730 fm. Eleven boundaries between faunal depth assemblages are suggested from the depth range data in Figures 4–6 based both on deep limits and shallow limits of the living specimens.

A faunal boundary at 15–20 fm can be recognized by the deep limits of

Ammonia beccarii in abundance
Buliminella elegantissima in abundance
Triloculina inflata
Quinqueloculina laevigata
Elphidium translucens
Reussella pacifica
Quinqueloculina lamarckiana
Nonionella basispinata in abundance
Trochammina kellettae in abundance

The 15–20 fm boundary also is marked by the shallow limits of

Fursenkoina pontoni in abundance
Epistominella cf. *E. sandiegoensis*
Bolivina acuminata
Reophax gracilis

A faunal boundary at 30–35 fm can be recognized by the deep limits of

Elphidium incertum var.
Quinqueloculina compta
Eponides antillarum
Angulogerina cf. *A. jamaicensis*
Hanzawaia nitidula in abundance
Miliolidae commonly

The 30–35 fm boundary is marked by the shallow limits of

Bolivina subadvena
Cibicides mckannai
Cancris panamensis

A 40–50 fm faunal boundary is defined by the deep limits of

Buccella tenerrima var.
Bolivina acutula
Textularia schencki
Ammoscalaria pseudospiralis

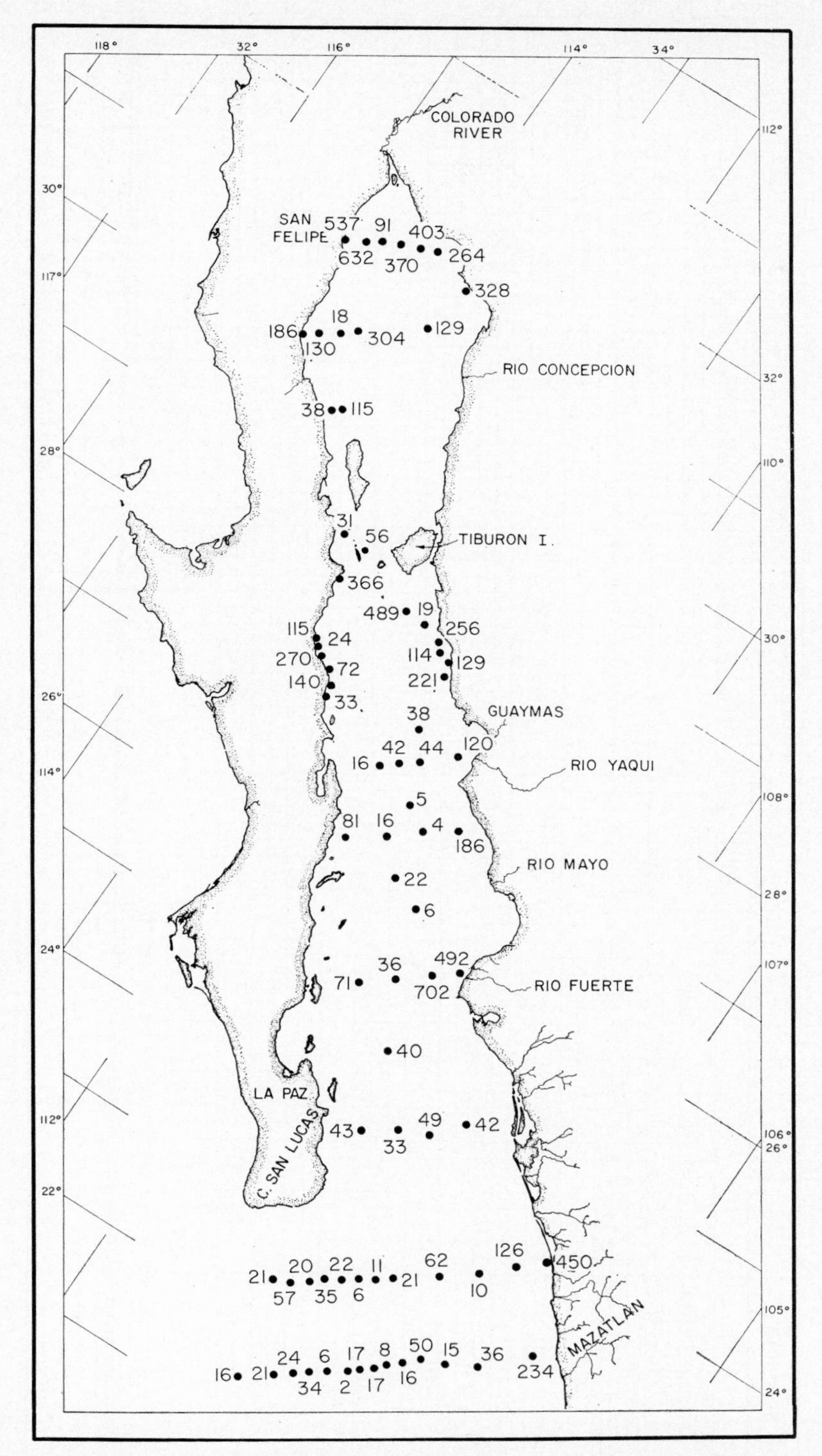

FIG. 3.—Numbers of specimens of living benthonic Foraminifera in 10 ml of wet sediment at each station.

STATION	145	146	147	87	137	40	213	141	218	212	143	157	210	217	140	142	138	214	216
DEPTH IN FATHOMS	6	6	6	7	7	8	8	10	10	10	10	12	14	15	15	15	17	17	18
LIVING POPULATION	256	19	115	492	33	450	264	129	537	328	270	366	186	632	72	114	221	403	91
Adercotryma glomeratum																			
Alveolophragmium columbiense				.1		.2	2		2			1		.5			4		
Ammonia beccarii vars.				2			.4		45	.6			16	30					3
Ammoscalaria pseudospiralis				4		2	.4		14	14			4	18		.9	4	4	5
Ammotium planissimum																			
Angulogerina jamaicensis					9						2	2					3		
Bigenerina sp.																			
Bolivina acuminata														.2				1	
B. acutula				3	6			.8	.9	.6			1	2			4	.3	3
B. minuta																			
B. pacifica																			
B. spissa																			
B. subadvena																			
B. vaughani			2	3			.4	8	3	.6	7	5	.5	1		6		2	2
B., other spp.	1		2				.8		.6		4	1		.8	1			.7	
Bolivinopsis sp.				1				2	2	.6				2				.3	
Buccella tenerrima var.				1			.4		3				.5	.8		8			1
Bulimina denudata				.2				2					9	1		6	4		10
B. marginata				.7		.2			1	.3			18	1				2	4
Buliminella elegantissima	.8			26		1	.8	10	9	7	.4	.3	15	.3		3			2
Cancris auricula					9			.8								3	32	2	
C. panamensis																			
Cassidulina sp. 1			2				.4				10			.2	1		.9		
C. sp. 2				.2					.2		2	21						.4	
C., other spp.				.5	22						5	3					1		
Chilostomella ovoidea																			
Cibicides mckannai																			
Cyclogyra sp.							.8	.8			4						3	.1	
Eggerella advena	14			1	18		.8	5		.3	8	11						6	2
E. sp.																			
Elphidium incertum var.				6		.7	2		2				23	2					4
E. translucens	8	5		4		3	.4		2	3			.5	7		2	.4		
E., other spp.	1		2	12		.4	5		2	.6		.8	1	5	11	.9			
Epistominella obesa																			
E. cf. E. sandiegoensis																.9		.4	.6
Eponides antillarum								.8			.4	.3				3	4	.7	
E. leviculus																			
Fursenkoina pontoni								2	.2	.9	1			.6		3	12	9	7
F. seminuda																			
F. spinosa																			

STATION	153	139	215	112	209	203	109	18	38	208	144	207	103	165	85	191	190	63	129
DEPTH IN FATHOMS	18	18	22	34	35	41	44	50	53	70	90	95	192	230	400	446	465	610	655
LIVING POPULATION	489	140	370	120	130	129	186	234	126	18	24	304	81	56	702	115	38	42	38
Adercotryma glomeratum																			
Alveolophragmium columbiense					.4								1	5					
Ammonia beccarii vars.			1	.4															
Ammoscalaria pseudospiralis			2	8	.4	4	2												
Ammotium planissimum																			
Angulogerina jamaicensis	3	7		13															
Bigenerina sp.																			
Bolivina acuminata								2	7			3			1	2			
B. acutula	2	3	1	12	.8	13	7												
B. minuta									.8						.8			1	4
B. pacifica		.7	.1								38	29		5	.2	13	69	19	6
B. spissa									2						.8			6	6
B. subadvena													23		15				
B. vaughani	9	3	16	2	7	2	17	9	8	3					.1		3		
B., other spp.	.6				.8	.4		5	47			3	21	15	25				
Bolivinopsis sp.	.2		.3	1			1												
Buccella tenerrima var.	.2			1	.4		.3												
Bulimina denudata		.7	.4		31	.4		1	.8	3									
B. marginata			4	5	6	38	4	2	.8			.2							
Buliminella elegantissima	.2		.3	.4	.8			6				.5		1	.1	17			
Cancris auricula	1	5	2	.9	.4	1	.9	.7	2			.4							
C. panamensis				11				40	2			10							
Cassidulina sp. 1	4	4	.1					.5	3			2				.5			
C. sp. 2	4		.7	2		.4	4	.5	2			15							
C., other spp.		1			.4			.2			8	1	1		3	2			
Chilostomella ovoidea																		1	4
Cibicides mckannai				3			1				13			2					
Cyclogyra sp.	.2			.4							4			1		.5			
Eggerella advena	18	4	1	1		12	.9	.5											
E. sp.									.8									3	
Elphidium incertum var.			2		7														
E. translucens			.6																
E., other spp.			.1		.4						4		1						
Epistominella obesa																			
E. cf. E. sandiegoensis	1		.4		6	5		.2	3	9		5		3	1	5	1	5	16
Eponides antillarum	.2		.6	.9															
E. leviculus																		3	7
Fursenkoina pontoni	.6	7	33	4	2	6	5					.2							
F. seminuda													1	5	2			8	
F. spinosa												.9			3	41	1	27	11

STATION	57	36	107	174	15	13	114	105	125	95	115	116	72	61	80	121	34	30	3
DEPTH IN FATHOMS	675	740	750	795	840	877	888	895	918	945	973	1020	1041	1050	1100	1245	1295	1473	1480
LIVING POPULATION	43	10	4	31	36	15	44	16	5	6	42	16	40	49	71	22	62	11	21
Adercotryma glomeratum																			5
Alveolophragmium columbiense																			
Ammonia beccarii vars.																			
Ammoscalaria pseudospiralis																			
Ammotium planissimum					2		1	7									7		2
Angulogerina jamaicensis																			
Bigenerina sp.	2				2								7						2
Bolivina acuminata																			
B. acutula																			
B. minuta	13				2	4													
B. pacifica	12	58	58	3	2	4	21	3	11		28	35	8	41	5	2	12	10	
B. spissa	1	5																	
B. subadvena																			
B. vaughani						4													
B., other spp.	2									9									
Bolivinopsis sp.																			
Buccella tenerrima var.																			
Bulimina denudata																			
B. marginata																			
Buliminella elegantissima									11										
Cancris auricula																			
C. panamensis																			
Cassidulina sp. 1																			
C. sp. 2				2									1						
C., other spp.	4			3	13		12						1		2	2			
Chilostomella ovoidea	4	11						3			1				12		3		
Cibicides mckannai	1				2														
Cyclogyra sp.																			
Eggerella advena																			
E. sp.	34	11				11		11		18									
Elphidium incertum var.																			
E. translucens																			
E., other spp.																			
Epistominella obesa		5			7			3	11		1				2	9			
E. cf. E. sandiegoensis																			
Eponides antillarum																			
E. leviculus	6				3	6	10	19	22		1	10	34	10	12	5	2	5	2
Fursenkoina pontoni																			
F. seminuda	5		14		2	6		11					13	19	7	2	5		
F. spinosa				40		6	3				22	24	1		2	5			

STATION	12	6	7	4	29	5	28	27	8	11	59	31	1	10	25	26	24	9	82
DEPTH IN FATHOMS	1513	1530	1533	1543	1564	1572	1577	1580	1580	1582	1590	1610	1620	1638	1655	1658	1665	1667	1730
LIVING POPULATION	50	6	2	24	6	34	22	35	17	16	33	21	16	8	57	20	21	17	36
Adercotryma glomeratum	7					8		5							4	3	5		
Alveolophragmium columbiense																			
Ammonia beccarii vars.																			
Ammoscalaria pseudospiralis																			
Ammotium planissimum	1									7									
Angulogerina jamaicensis																			
Bigenerina sp.	4			9		3	10	3	14	7	3		3	7	9	3	11	3	
Bolivina acuminata																			
B. acutula																			
B. minuta																			
B. pacifica					17		2	6			2	10			4	3			14
B. spissa																			
B. subadvena																			
B. vaughani																			
B., other spp.																			
Bolivinopsis sp.																			
Buccella tenerrima var.																			
Bulimina denudata																			
B. marginata																			
Buliminella elegantissima											3								
Cancris auricula																			
C. panamensis																			
Cassidulina sp. 1																			
C. sp. 2																			
C., other spp.	2					2			3	3	3								3
Chilostomella ovoidea							2	3							7	3		3	
Cibicides mckannai																			
Cyclogyra sp.																			
Eggerella advena																			
E. sp.																			
Elphidium incertum var.																			
E. translucens																			
E., other spp.													3						
Epistominella obesa											2								
E. cf. E. sandiegoensis																			
Eponides antillarum																			
E. leviculus	7			5		3	2	3	6	13	12		3	14	.9		3		3
Fursenkoina pontoni																			
F. seminuda	1	9		5		8	2				3							3	
F. spinosa																			

FIG. 4.—Occurrences of common species of living benthonic Foraminifera in per cent of total living population.

STATION	145	146	147	87	137	40	213	141	218	212	143	157	210	217	140	142	138	214	216
DEPTH IN FATHOMS	6	6	6	7	7	8	8	10	10	10	10	12	14	15	15	15	17	17	18
LIVING POPULATION	256	19	115	492	33	450	264	129	537	328	270	366	186	632	72	114	221	403	91
Globobulimina pacifica																			
Hanzawaia nitidula				3	3	11	2	13				10		.5		26	3	15	2
Lagenammina atlantica						.4													3
L. longicollis																			
Lagenidae				.3	3	.2	3		.6					.3				.9	
Miliolidae	3	16	46	1			20	2	5	2	6	3		3	57	5	9	2	.6
Nonion parkerae																			
N. pompilioides																			
Nonionella basispinata				10		15		5		52		.3		12		2		13	7
N. stella				4		57				5			5	.8		2		4	22
Nouria polymorphinoides				.1	3	1	2	8		4				.3		3		1	
Pullenia bulloides																			
P. quinqueloba																			
Quinqueloculina compta	3			.4	6	2	15	2	2	.3				2	5				
Q. costata	14		4	.7			8						2	.3	1				
Q. laevigata	2			.2			2		.6	.6	4	.8				6	4		
Q. lamarckiana				4		.2	.8	3		.3					14			1	2
Reophax dentaliniformis																			
R. excentricus																			
R. gracilis													.5	.2		.9		1	2
R. hispidulus																			
R. micaceous																			
R. nanus	26	5		.3	3	.2	2	.8	.6		.7	2	3	.2				.4	
R. scorpiurus																			
R. subfusiformis																			
Reussella pacifica	5		13	6			.4	.8		.6		.8			1				
Rotorbinella (?) campanulata	2			.9			11				3	3			1			3	
Saccammina spp.							.4		.2	2	2			2			7	.9	4
Textularia schencki group	18	16	4		3		3	2		.3	17	8				3	.4	14	
T. sp																			
Tolypammina sp.																			
Triloculina inflata			8					4			1					3	.9		
Trochammina globigeriniformis																		.1	
T. kellettae	2	11		.2	9		3	20	.7		4	5		.5					
T. pacifica		5			3	.2	3				15			.8		10	2	9	
T. vesicularis																			
T. sp.																			
T., other spp.				.9			8		3	3		7		1				.1	3
Valvulineria glabra																			
Miscellaneous spp.	.2	42	17	3	3	5	2	5	.4	1	4	15	1	4	8	2	1	6	11
% arenaceous	60	37	4	7	39	6	25	36	21	24	47	34	8	25		18	19	40	20

STATION	153	139	215	112	209	203	109	18	38	208	144	207	103	165	85	191	190	63	129
DEPTH IN FATHOMS	18	18	22	34	35	41	44	50	53	70	90	95	192	230	400	446	465	610	655
LIVING POPULATION	489	140	370	120	130	129	186	234	126	18	24	304	81	56	702	115	38	42	38
Globobulimina pacifica										3					.2				7
Hanzawaia nitidula	15	5	.3	11			3		2		13		1	1					
Lagenammina atlantica			.3									.5							
L. longicollis								.5					1			.5			
Lagenidae		.7	.9			2	.9	.5		6		.4							
Miliolidae	.4	9	.1	.9		1						.2		1					
Nonion parkerae																			
N. pompilioides																			
Nonionella basispinata	4	3	8		.8		1			9		2		1					
N. stella			12	3	12	3	4	24	5	15		8			19	1	1	19	6
Nouria polymorphinoides	10		3			.4				3		5							
Pullenia bulloides																			
P. quinqueloba																			
Quinqueloculina compta		5		.4															
Q. costata																			
Q. laevigata	2	8																	
Q. lamarckiana		4	.4																
Reophax dentaliniformis																			
R. excentricus																			
R. gracilis	.4	.7	3	2	18	2	7						1	1		.9			3
R. hispidulus																			
R. micaceous																			
R. nanus	2	1					.6									3			
R. scorpiurus												1							
R. subfusiformis													3		.1				
Reussella pacifica	.2	.7	.3																
Rotorbinella (?) campanulata	2			2			.3												
Saccammina spp.			.4			2	.9												
Textularia schencki group	3	10	2	.9	.4	3	.3							6					
T. sp				5															
Tolypammina sp.													1		.2				
Triloculina inflata		1																	
Trochammina globigeriniformis															.1	.9			
T. kellettae	5	7		.4			.3	1			8			6			7		
T. pacifica	.6			2							4	.2		11					3
T. vesicularis														2			3		
T. sp.																			3
T., other spp.	1	7		.4	.4	2	.3	4	.8			.2		11	1	2			
Valvulineria glabra																			
Miscellaneous spp.	10	2	4	6	5	2	38	2	13	49	8	12	45	23	27	10	15	8	24
% arenaceous	40	30	13	20	20	27	35	6	4	34	16	8	20	46	5	11	11	5	14

STATION	57	36	107	174	15	13	114	105	125	95	115	116	72	61	80	121	34	30	3
DEPTH IN FATHOMS	675	740	750	795	840	877	888	895	918	945	973	1020	1041	1050	1100	1245	1295	1473	1480
LIVING POPULATION	43	10	4	31	36	15	44	16	5	6	42	16	40	49	71	22	62	11	21
Globobulimina pacifica							1	3		9	8	17			13		6		
Hanzawaia nitidula																			
Lagenammina atlantica																			
L. longicollis					3										7	5	20	55	19
Lagenidae								7					1			5			
Miliolidae							4									2			
Nonion parkerae	2				2			3					5	2	4	2			2
N. pompilioides																	.9		
Nonionella basispinata																			
N. stella														4	.8	9			
Nouria polymorphinoides																			
Pullenia bulloides	2																.9		
P. quinqueloba										9					.8		.9		
Quinqueloculina compta																			
Q. costata																			
Q. laevigata																			
Q. lamarckiana																			
Reophax dentaliniformis											13	7	3				2		5
R. excentricus															8	10	.9	15	14
R. gracilis			14																
R. hispidulus																	2		2
R. micaceous																			
R. nanus																			
R. scorpiurus																			8
R. subfusiformis																	9		16
Reussella pacifica																			
Rotorbinella (?) campanulata																			
Saccammina spp.																			
Textularia schencki group																			
T. sp					2												6		
Tolypammina sp.	1	5			3		4	3					3	2	2		2		
Triloculina inflata																			
Trochammina globigeriniformis											1		5	4					
T. kellettae			14	2							1								
T. pacifica						11													
T. vesicularis				26	29	4													
T. sp.				3				11						13	9	13	6		
T., other spp.				3	4	8	1	3	34			3	4	4	.8	10	5		2
Valvulineria glabra	6				2		4			28					2	2			
Miscellaneous spp.	5	5		18	20	36	39	13	11	27	24	4	14	1	11	17	9	15	21
% arenaceous	38	21	28	43	45	42	4	45	34	18	17	10	28	23	31	42	63	85	94

STATION	12	6	7	4	29	5	28	27	8	11	59	31	1	10	25	26	24	9	82
DEPTH IN FATHOMS	1513	1530	1533	1543	1564	1572	1577	1580	1580	1582	1590	1610	1620	1638	1655	1658	1665	1667	1730
LIVING POPULATION	50	6	2	24	6	34	22	35	17	16	33	21	16	8	57	20	21	17	36
Globobulimina pacifica	1							1			2				.9		3		
Hanzawaia nitidula																			
Lagenammina atlantica																			
L. longicollis	27		100	27	67	27	46	20	27	18	3	20	28	30	17	41	28	39	7
Lagenidae											2		3						
Miliolidae									3						.9				
Nonion parkerae													3			3			
N. pompilioides				2	8		5	6		3	17					9		3	
Nonionella basispinata																			
N. stella											2								3
Nouria polymorphinoides																			
Pullenia bulloides	1					2		1			5			7	.9		3		
P. quinqueloba	2							5		3	2	8		7	4			3	
Quinqueloculina compta																			
Q. costata																			
Q. laevigata																			
Q. lamarckiana																			
Reophax dentaliniformis	1			11															
R. excentricus	3	27		5		3	5	1	6	13	8	10		7	7	12		11	
R. gracilis																			
R. hispidulus	1			2		6		6	3						2			3	
R. micaceous	2			7				3		7				7				11	
R. nanus																			
R. scorpiurus						5	2		6	7		5	3		2	3		3	
R. subfusiformis	4			9		5			3				3		.9	3	14	3	
Reussella pacifica																			
Rotorbinella (?) campanulata																			
Saccammina spp.																			
Textularia schencki group																			
T. sp	17						5			3		2			2				
Tolypammina sp.								18							2			3	
Triloculina inflata																			
Trochammina globigeriniformis	4	9		2			8	3	3	10	6	13		7		5	5	3	
T. kellettae						2									.9	3		3	3
T. pacifica				2		9		1		3					6		3	6	1
T. vesicularis	1				8	3	2	1	11		6	8			16				
T. sp.																			10
T., other spp.	5			2		4	5	6	6		17	5	3		2	3	3		
Valvulineria glabra																			
Miscellaneous spp.	9	55		12		10	4	8	9	3	2	19	48	14	11	6	22		56
% arenaceous	84	91	100	84	75	80	87	29	88	78	45	73	75	72	80	82	85	88	38

FIG. 5.—Occurrences of common species of living benthonic Foraminifera in per cent of total living population.

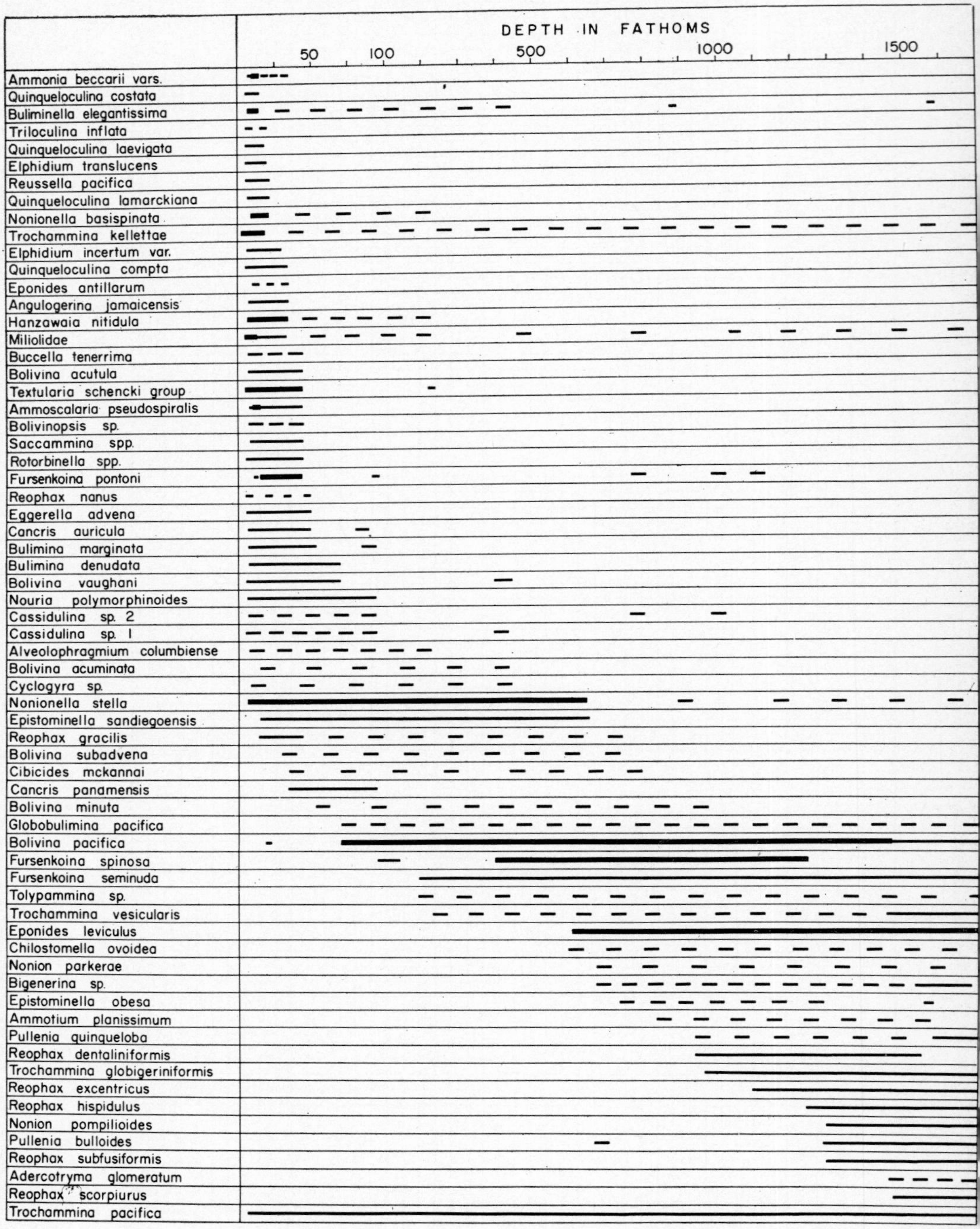

DEPTH IN FATHOMS
50 100 500 1000 1500

Ammonia beccarii vars.
Quinqueloculina costata
Buliminella elegantissima
Triloculina inflata
Quinqueloculina laevigata
Elphidium translucens
Reussella pacifica
Quinqueloculina lamarckiana
Nonionella basispinata
Trochammina kellettae
Elphidium incertum var.
Quinqueloculina compta
Eponides antillarum
Angulogerina jamaicensis
Hanzawaia nitidula
Miliolidae
Buccella tenerrima
Bolivina acutula
Textularia schencki group
Ammoscalaria pseudospiralis
Bolivinopsis sp.
Saccammina spp.
Rotorbinella spp.
Fursenkoina pontoni
Reophax nanus
Eggerella advena
Cancris auricula
Bulimina marginata
Bulimina denudata
Bolivina vaughani
Nouria polymorphinoides
Cassidulina sp. 2
Cassidulina sp. 1
Alveolophragmium columbiense
Bolivina acuminata
Cyclogyra sp.
Nonionella stella
Epistominella sandiegoensis
Reophax gracilis
Bolivina subadvena
Cibicides mckannai
Cancris panamensis
Bolivina minuta
Globobulimina pacifica
Bolivina pacifica
Fursenkoina spinosa
Fursenkoina seminuda
Tolypammina sp.
Trochammina vesicularis
Eponides leviculus
Chilostomella ovoidea
Nonion parkerae
Bigenerina sp.
Epistominella obesa
Ammotium planissimum
Pullenia quinqueloba
Reophax dentaliniformis
Trochammina globigeriniformis
Reophax excentricus
Reophax hispidulus
Nonion pompilioides
Pullenia bulloides
Reophax subfusiformis
Adercotryma glomeratum
Reophax scorpiurus
Trochammina pacifica

FIG. 6.—Generalized depth ranges of common species. Relative abundance shown by heaviness of lines.

Bolivinopsis sp.
Sacammina spp.
Rotorbinella? campanulata
Fursenkoina pontoni in abundance
Reophax nanus
Cancris auriculus commonly
Bulimina marginata commonly
Eggerella advena commonly

The 40–50 fm boundary is marked by the shallow limit of

Bolivina minuta

A faunal boundary at approximately 70 fm is defined by the deep limits of

Bulimina denudata
Bolivina vaughani

The 70 fm boundary is marked by the shallow limits of

Bolivina pacifica
Globobulimina pacifica

A faunal boundary at approximately 90 fm is defined by the deep limits of

Cassidulina sp. 1
Cassidulina sp. 2
(Occasional specimens of these two species occur deeper)

The 90 fm boundary is defined by the shallow limit of

Fursenkoina spinosa

A faunal boundary at approximately 200 fm is marked by the deep limit of

Alveolophragmium columbiense

and the shallow limit of

Fursenkoina seminuda
Tolypammina sp.
Trochammina vesicularis

A faunal boundary at 400–450 fm is defined by the deep limit of

Cyclogyra sp.
Bolivina acuminata

and the shallow limit of

Fursenkoina spinosa in abundance

A 600–800 fm boundary is defined by the deep limit of

Nonionella stella in abundance
Epistominella cf. *E. sandiegoensis*
Reophax gracilis
Bolivina subadvena
Cibicides mckannai

The 600–800 fm faunal boundary marks the shallow limit of

Eponides leviculus
Chilostomella ovoidea
Nonion parkerae
Bigenerina sp.
Epistominella obesa

A faunal boundary at approximately 1,000 fm is defined by the deep limit of

Bolivina minuta

and the shallow limit of

Pullenia quinqueloba
Reophax dentaliniformis
Trochammina globigeriniformis

A faunal boundary at approximately 1,300 fm is marked by the deep limit of

Fursenkoina spinosa

and the shallow limit of

Reophax hispidulus
Nonion pompilioides
Pullenia bulloides
Reophax subfusiformis

A faunal boundary at approximately 1,500 fm is marked by the deep limit of

Bolivina pacifica in abundance

and the shallow limit of

Adercotryma glomeratus
Reophax scorpiurus

GEOGRAPHIC DISTRIBUTIONS

There is an apparent geographic restriction of a few species in the Gulf, at least within the samples studied. *Ammonia beccarii* has been found only in the northern shallow basin. *Textularia schencki* and *Bolivina acutula* seem to be confined to the inner two-thirds of the Gulf. *Triloculina inflata* occurs only in the shallow-water samples of the middle Gulf. *Textularia* sp. and *Bigenerina* sp., both restricted to depths greater than 500–1,000 fm, occur south of the entrance and not at equivalent depths in the Gulf. All species which occur at depths greater than 1,000 fm are restricted to the lower half of the Gulf because those depths are essentially restricted to this area. The highest percentage of arenaceous specimens occurs at depths greater than approximately 1,500 fm where they average 85 per cent of the population;

such depths occur mainly south of the Gulf entrance.

The following species in the present fauna are previously reported only from off Central America in the eastern Pacific (Bandy and Arnal, 1957) and are not recorded off California and northern Baja California—*Cancris panamensis*, *Epistominella obesa*, and *Eponides antillarum*. Presence of these species indicates an affinity of the Gulf fauna with that of the Panamic zoogeographic province. Most of the remaining species, however, also are living in the California areas.

DISCUSSION OF RESULTS

STANDING CROPS OF FORAMINIFERA

It seems reasonable to assume that the standing crops of benthonic Foraminifera are at least partial measures of relative rates of organic production. The areas of unusually large standing crops of benthonic Foraminifera in the Gulf of California are of considerable interest. The reasons for these high production areas are not presently known.

It has been suggested that large standing crops observed near the mouths of the Mississippi River (Lankford, 1959) and the Guadalupe River, Texas, (Phleger and Lankford, 1957) may be due to river influence. It is well known that soil extract provides nutrients and trace materials which are desirable in laboratory cultures of various marine algae. A river introduces abundant soil extract into the marine environment and this would be most concentrated near the river mouth. It is also known that organic production rates, in terms of rate of organic-carbon fixation, are very high off the mouth of the Mississippi River in the area of large standing crops of benthonic Foraminifera (Thomas and Simmons, 1960). It may also be suggested that rivers provide food materials directly to Foraminifera of the nearshore zone.

The large standing crops at Stations 85 and 87 near the mouth of the Fuerte River may be attributed to such river influence. No similar large populations are found in a sample off the Yaqui River which also has a significant flow. Another possible explanation is that these large living populations are related to high organic production rates caused by upwelling of nutrient-rich water. Roden (this volume) reports that north westerly winds cause extensive upwelling alon the east coast of the Gulf of California in winte It is also known that there are extensive bloom of plankton along this southeast coast of the Gul in winter—evidenced as "red tide." This has bee observed by the writer from an airplane in winte during several successive years. A large standin crop of benthonic Foraminifera also is recorde from Station 40 near the coast a few miles nort of Mazatlán. There is no significant river near thi station, but it is in an area where the writer ha consistently observed intense plankton bloom during the winter season.

Two other stations having unusually larg living populations are 153 south of Tiburón Islan and 157 which is very near the Baja Californi coast south of San Lorenzo Island. Both of thes stations are in areas where abundant "red tide is frequently observed and are not near runo areas.

The other area of large standing crops is in th inner Gulf, and is represented by four sample collected from the northernmost line of stations Presently available evidence indicates that hig production rates are characteristic of hypersalin lagoons (Phleger, 1960b; Phleger and Ewing 1962). The reasons for this are not known, bu such high production may be related to constan re-supply of nutrients from water entering t replace that lost by evaporation. This explanatio may also be applied to the Gulf because it is a evaporation basin, as reflected by the relativel high salinities in the area of these northern stations; the data available indicate an increase fro about 34.6‰ at the entrance, to about 36.0‰ at the head of the Gulf, in summer. This increas in salinity is not comparable to that in the hypersaline lagoons studied, where the increase usuall is about 20 per cent more than normal oceani salinity and frequently is much more.

There are moderately large areas of intertida flats bordering the northern end of the Gulf, an these have some deposits of salt. Drainage fro these salt pans may locally increase salinities an thus affect production. The salt pans, howeve are flooded only at spring tides and thus thei influence, if any, probably is limited.

There is some flow of water from the lowe

Colorado River basin into the Gulf through the Hardy River. It is probable that most, or all, of this is seepage from the irrigation district except under unusual conditions. It is possible that this soil seepage has an effect on production of organic materials off the mouth of the Hardy River.

Another possible explanation of high production may be the composition and depth of the substrate. The bottom in this area is composed largely of silt and clay which were deposited by the Colorado River. This material is soil from the drainage basin of the river. The depths at the stations having high living populations are shallow, with the deepest at 22 fm. The bottom sediment may act as a submarine soil supporting a large growth of algae and other plants which provide food for Foraminifera. It is observed that the silty substrate at the shallow heads of many coastal lagoons supports an abundant growth of *Zostera*, filamentous algae, and diatoms.

GEOGRAPHIC DISTRIBUTIONS

The fauna of the upper Gulf differs somewhat from that of the lower section. This is also confirmed by the study of Brenner (1962) on Foraminifera from littoral samples. This difference in assemblages suggests that in the upper Gulf a water mass develops which is ecologically distinctive and which differs from that in the lower part of the basin.

It seems likely that in this respect the Gulf of California is similar to a coastal lagoon which extends several miles from its inlet. The best known lagoon for comparison is Laguna Ojo de Liebre on the Pacific coast of Baja California (Phleger and Ewing, 1962). This lagoon extends approximately 35 miles inland from its inlet and is hypersaline in the inner reaches. There is a tidal delay of 3 hrs or more from the inlet to the head of the lagoon. An ecologically distinctive water mass in the inner section is evidenced by the distinctive assemblage of benthonic Foraminifera. It can also be shown that the tidal current excursion cannot effect a complete exchange of water between the open ocean and the inner lagoon, and it appears that the main exchange is by diffusion and replacement of water lost by evaporation.

The Gulf of California is several hundred miles long, but is wider and deeper than Laguna Ojo de Liebre. The tidal delay is 5 to 6 hrs and its inner section is an evaporation basin. The water north of the constriction formed by the islands may be confined to the inner section and may not return in any appreciable quantity to the open Pacific. The development of an ecologically distinctive water mass under such conditions probably is inevitable.

DEPTH BIOFACIES

Bandy (1961) studied the dead populations of Foraminifera in numerous core and snapper samples from the Gulf of California collected mostly by members of the Scripps Institution of Oceanography in 1939 and 1940. He suggested 15 depth biofacies on the basis of these materials. The following list is a comparison of Bandy's depth biofacies boundaries with those identified in the present study.

Bandy (1962) (fathoms)	*Present study (fathoms)*
10, 20	15–20
40	30–35, 40–50
83	70, 90
133	
200	200
330	
500	400–500
660, 830	600–800
1,000	1,000
1,170	
1,330	1,300
1,500	1,500

Bandy's interpretation of depth assemblages is remarkably similar to the present interpretation. Both were made independently on different types of material, and are based on sampling that may be considered inadequate. Conclusions in both instances are based on inspection of quantitative data.

Comparison with other, selected areas shows that in the Todos Santos Bay area of Baja California (Walton, 1955) there are boundaries at 30 fm, 50 fm, 100 fm, and 350–400 fm. In the San Diego, California area the boundaries are at 13 fm, 45 fm, 100 fm, 250 fm, 350 fm, and 450 fm (Uchio, 1960). In the northwest Gulf of Mexico biofacies boundaries reported are at 10 fm, 30 fm,

50 fm, 100 fm, 350 fm, 600 fm, and 1,000 fm (Phleger, 1960a).

The number of apparently distinct depth biofacies in the Gulf of California is larger than that reported from other areas which have been studied. The choice of a boundary is largely a matter of opinion, especially with the methods of analysis which have been widely used. The distribution of each species differs somewhat from that of all other species. When enough is known about these distributions it may be possible further to define depth zonation in the modern ocean. Verification of depth assemblages will require more data analyzed by more reliable methods.

Possible reasons for depth distributions of foraminiferal assemblages have been discussed previously (Phleger, 1960a, p. 102–24). Explanations for depth biofacies in the Gulf of California will require much additional information and understanding of the environments in the area.

RATES OF DEPOSITION

Relative rates of deposition may be suggested by the ratio of living to dead populations of benthonic Foraminifera. (*See* Phleger, 1960a, p. 189–191.) A small ratio suggests slow deposition and a large ratio suggests fast deposition. Living-total ratios of Foraminifera are plotted on Figure 7. These ratios are very low at the stations within the Gulf of California except for a few stations near the coasts. These data indicate very slow over-all deposition rates within the Gulf at the present time, with a few local high rates near the coasts.

South of the entrance to the Gulf the relative deposition rates indicated near the coast are very low. Offshore, however, in water deeper than 1,000 fm the rates are much higher than either nearshore in the same area or than the general deposition rates in the Gulf of California. The explanation for these relatively high rates offshore in deep water is not apparent to the writer.

EVALUATION OF RESULTS

The study of only 76 samples from an area as large as the Gulf of California is obviously not sufficient to give a complete description of the distribution of foraminiferal assemblages. In addition to the large size, there is a varied topography including several deep basins and many areas of shallow water of various sizes and in different locations. Great variation in tide ranges and resultant strong currents in the inner Gulf must have an important influence on local distributions. Many, or perhaps most, of these large and small but possibly distinctive environments were not sampled or were sampled inadequately. Even the environments covering a larger area are each represented by only a few samples, and thus the assemblage distributions are only approximately defined. The results presented are therefore somewhat general and subject to considerable modification when more material is studied. Additional data may also define new environmental assemblages not indicated in the present study.

This study may be considered a preliminary report of progress and definition of problems for future study. The next stage will be study of numerous samples forming a more or less random collection over a large-scale grid pattern. The data thus obtained will be analyzed by more sophisticated methods than the present data. Stage three will consist of collections and analyses which apply to specific problems. Examples of such problems are a possible fauna characterizing the oxygen-minimum water, the causes for unusually large standing crops in some areas, and the further refinement and validation of depth distributions. A reliable understanding of the ecology of Foraminifera in the Gulf of California will depend, also, on much additional information and understanding of the distribution of physical and chemical conditions in the region.

REFERENCES

Bandy, O.L., 1961, Distribution of Foraminifera, Radiolaria, and diatoms in sediments of the Gulf of California: Micropaleontology, v. 7, no. 1, p. 1–26.

——— and Arnal, R.E., 1957, Distribution of Recent Foraminifera off west coast of Central America: Am. Assoc. Petroleum Geologists Bull., v. 41, no. 9, p. 2037–2053.

Bradshaw, J.S., 1959, Ecology of living planktonic Foraminifera in the north and equatorial Pacific Ocean: Cushman Found. Foram. Research, Contr., v. 10, pt. 2, p. 25–64.

Brenner, G.L., 1962, A zoogeographic analysis of some shallow-water Foraminifera in the Gulf of California: Am. Mus. Nat. History Bull., v. 123, art. 5, p. 253–297.

Ekman, Sven, 1953, Zoogeography of the sea: Sidgwick and Jackson, Ltd., London.

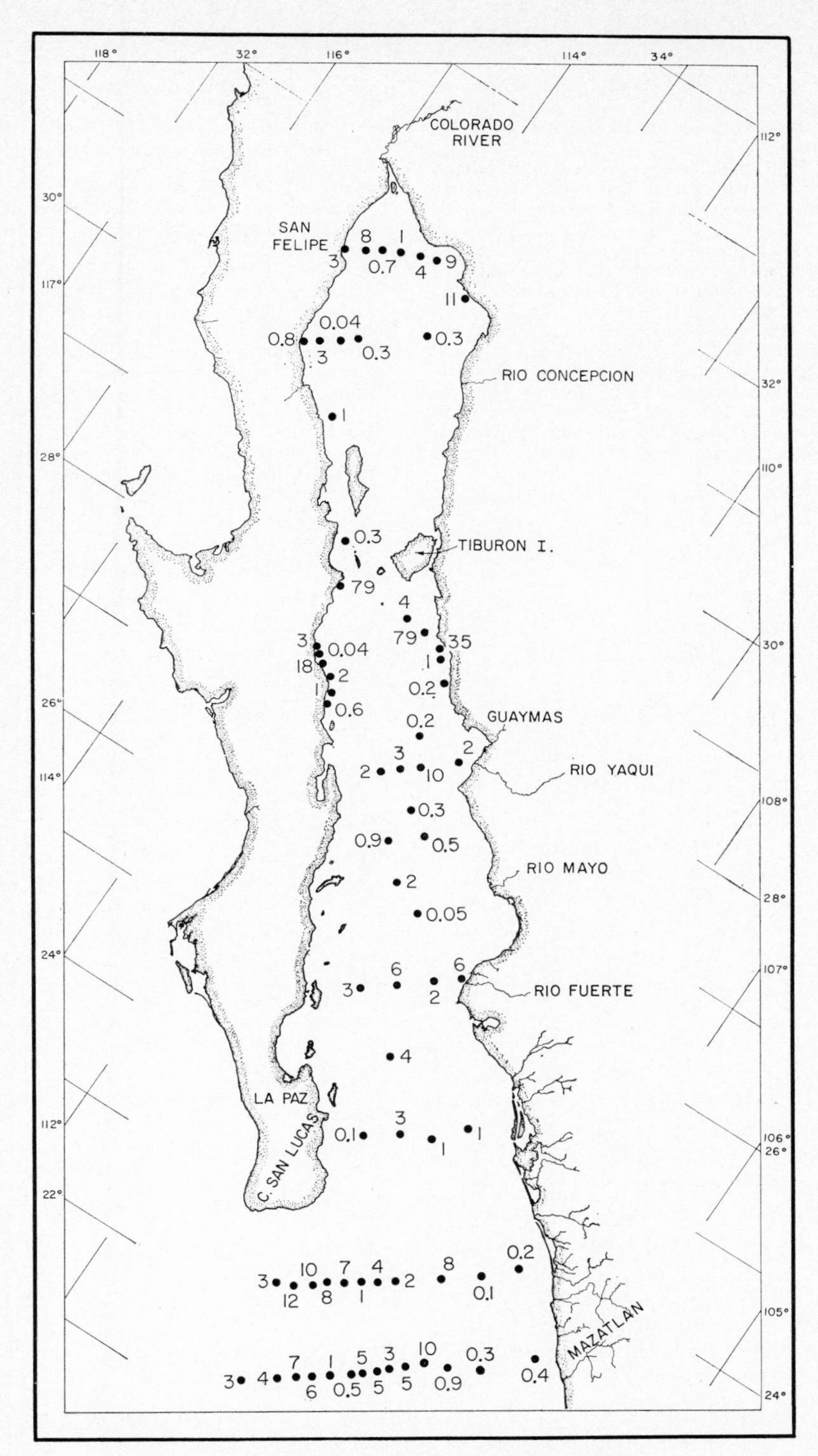

FIG. 7.—Living-total population ratios ×100.

Lankford, R.R., 1959, Distribution and ecology of Foraminifera from east Mississippi delta margin: Am. Assoc. Petroleum Geologists Bull., v. 43, no. 9, p. 2068–2099.

Phleger, F.B, 1956, Significance of living foraminiferal populations along the central Texas coast: Cushman Found. Foram. Research, Contr., v. 7, pt. 4, p. 106–151.

——— 1960a, Ecology and distribution of Recent Foraminifera: Johns Hopkins Press, Baltimore, Md.

——— 1960b, Foraminiferal populations in Laguna Madre, Texas: Sci. Repts., Tohoku Univ., Sendai, Japan, v. 4 (Hanzawa Memorial Volume), p. 83–91.

——— and Ewing, G.C., 1962, Sedimentology and oceanography of coastal lagoons in Baja California, Mexico: Geol. Soc. America Bull., v. 73, p. 145–182.

——— and Lankford, R.R., 1957, Seasonal occurrences of living benthonic Foraminifera in some Texas bays: Cushman Found. Foram. Research, Contr., v. 8, pt. 3, p. 93–105.

Roden, G. I., 1958, Oceanographic and meteorological aspects of the Gulf of California: Pacific Science, v. 12, no. 1, p. 21–45.

——— and Groves, G.W., 1959, Recent oceanographic investigations in the Gulf of California: Jour. Marine Research, v. 18, no. 1, p. 10–35.

Shepard, F.P., 1950, Submarine topography of the Gulf of California, Pt. 3 *of* The E.W. Scripps cruise to the Gulf of California: Geol. Soc. America Mem. 43, 32 p.

Thomas, W. H., and Simmons, E.G., 1960, Phytoplankton production in the Mississippi Delta, *in* Recent sediments, northwest Gulf of Mexico: Am. Assoc. Petroleum Geologists, p. 103–116.

Uchio, Takayasu, 1960, Ecology of living benthonic Foraminifera from the San Diego, California, area: Cushman Found. Foram. Research, Spec. Pub. 5.

Walton, W. R., 1952, Techniques for the recognition of living Foraminifera: Cushman Found. Foram. Research, Contr., v. 3, pt. 2, p. 56–60.

——— 1955, Ecology of living benthonic Foraminifera, Todos Santos Bay, Baja California: Jour. Paleontology, v. 29, no. 6, p. 952–1018.

OSTRACODA FROM GULF OF CALIFORNIA[1]

F.M. SWAIN, P.L. MILLER, AND E.C. MANDELBAUM[2]
Minneapolis, Minnesota

The Ostracoda of the upper 1 cm of sediment of the Gulf of California have been studied in a preliminary way. About 100 species have been recognized, only 40 of which have been tentatively identified with described species. The majority of the ostracode specimens were obtained in the shallower parts of the Gulf at depths of 100 fathoms or less.

A detailed study of the taxonomy and, so far as possible, the environmental distribution of the species is being made. The following data are of a preliminary nature and are subject to later revision. Species marked with an asterisk were found living in the collections studied.

Forty-nine of the species are characteristic of nearshore, relatively shallow waters of the Gulf margin.

1. Restricted to eastern margin in collections studied.

Bythocypris sp.
Bythocythere? sp.
**Cytherella* sp. *a*
Cytherelloidea, n. sp.
Cytherelloidea cf. *umbonata* Edwards
Cytherura sp. *d*
Hemicythere sp. *a*
Hemicythere sp. *c*
Kangarina quellita Coryell and Fields
Loxoconcha lenticulata LeRoy
Microcythere cf. *gibba* Müller
Microcythere, n. sp.
Paracytheropteron, n. sp.
**Paradoxostoma* cf. *rarum* Müller
Paradoxostoma sp. *b*
Paradoxostoma sp. *c*
Perissocytheridea sp.
Psammocythere, n. sp.
Trachyleberis sp.
Xiphichilus tenuissimum (Norman)

2. Found on western margin in collections studied.

Ambostracon sp.
**Cushmanidea* sp. *a*
**Cytherelloidea*, n. sp. *a*
Cytherelloidea, n. sp. *b*
Cytheropteron sp. *a*
Cytheropteron sp. *d*
Cytherura, n. sp.
Cytherura sp. *c*
Hemicythere?, n. sp. *b*
Trachyleberida? sp. *b*
Trachyleberida? sp. *c*
Trachyleberida? sp. *d*

3. Found in prodeltaic area off mouth of Colorado River.

Cytherissa, n. sp.
Krithe sp.

4. Found on both eastern and western margins of Gulf in collections studied.

Aurila sp.
New genus and species resembling *Cythereis* Jones
Cytherella sp. *a*
Cushmanidea aff. *C. elongata* (Brady)
**Basslerites*, n. sp.
Cytheropteron aff. *C. alatum* Sars
Cytheropteron sp. *c*
Hemicythere californiensis LeRoy
**Pellucistoma scrippsi* Benson
Pterygocythereis sp. *b*
Quadracythere? cf. *regalia* Benson
Quadracythere?, n. sp.
Stenocypris? sp.
Trachyleberida?, n. sp.
Trachyleberis sp.

Six species of the collection are restricted to fresh or brackish water deltaic areas along the eastern side of the Gulf—*Limnocythere sanctipatricii* Brady and Robertson, *Cyprideis*, n. sp., *Perissocytheridea*, n. sp., *Potamocypris*, n. sp., *Stenocypris*, n. sp., and *Cyprinotus unispinifera* Furtos.

Two species have been found only in offshore deeper water stations in the present collection—*Krithe* cf. *bartonensis* (Jones) and *Leptocythere* sp.

The other species in the collection are more or less generally distributed in the Gulf in both shallow and deep waters, but are considerably more common in the nearshore than in offshore areas.

Argilloecia conoidea Sars
Bairdia fortificata Brady
Bairdia, n. sp.
Bairdia verdesensis LeRoy
Basslerites delrayensis Le Roy
Basslerites delrayensis Le Roy
Basslerites, n. sp.?
Bradleya diegoensis (LeRoy)
Bythocypris cf. *elongata* LeRoy
Bythocythere, n. sp.

[1] Manuscript received, April 1, 1963.

[2] Department of Geology, University of Minnesota.

Bythoceratina, n. sp.
Cativella, n. sp.
?*Caudites fragilis* Le Roy
Cletocythereis, n. sp.
Costa cf. *seminuda* Bold
Cushmanidea, n. sp.
Cytherois cf. *fischeri* (Sars)
Cytheropteron sp. *b*
Cytheropteron, n. sp.
Cytherura, n. sp. *b*
Hermanites? sp.
Kangarina aff. *chipolensis* Puri
**Loxoconcha*, n. sp.
Loxocorniculum sp.
Monoceratina cf. *bifurcata* Puri
New genus and species resembling *Platyrhomboides* Harris
**Occultocythereis kewi* (LeRoy)
**Orionina vaughani* (Ulrich and Bassler)
Paracypris pacifica LeRoy
Paracypris sp.
**Paracytheridea granti* LeRoy
Paradoxostoma sp. *a*
**Perissocytheridea* sp.
Procythereis confragosa (Edwards)
Pterygocythereis sp. *a*
Pterygocythereis sp. *c.*
Pterygocythereis sp. *d*

Explanation of Plate 1

INDEX MAP SHOWS STATIONS FROM WHICH OSTRACODA WERE OBTAINED

Figs. 1.—*Cytherella* sp. Exterior of left valve, ×31. Sta. 123.
2.—*Cytherelloidea*, n. sp. *a*. Left side of shell, ×31. Sta. 111.
3a,b.—*Hemicythere californiensis* LeRoy. Exterior views of right and left valves, ×21. Sta. 123.
4.—*Basslerites*, n. sp. Exterior of right valve, ×31. Sta. 194.
5.—*Cytherura*, n. sp. Exterior of left valve, ×31. Sta. 67.
5a,b.—*Cushmanidea* sp. Left valve exterior and dorsal views, ×31. Sta. 129.
6.—*Trachyleberis* sp. Exterior of left valve, ×31. Sta. 67.
7.—*Cytherelloidea*, n. sp. *b*. Exterior of immature right valve, ×31. Sta. 67.
8.—*Pellucistoma scrippsi* Benson. Right side of shell, ×31. Sta. 123.
9.—*Perissocytheridea*, n. sp. Exterior of right valve, ×31. Curray's Sta. 80 "at edge of lagoon near road from Escuinapa and Las Cabras; salinity 42.0; at Km 13 from Escuinapa."
10a,b.—*Aurila* spp. Exterior views of right and left valves, ×31. Sta. 143.
11.—*Trachyleberida*?, n. sp. Exterior of left valve, ×31. Sta. 143.
12.—*Stenocypris*, n. sp. Interior of left valve, ×31. Same locality as Fig. 9.
13a,b.—*Potamocypris*, n. sp. Exterior of right valve and dorsal view, ×31. Same locality as Fig. 9.
14.—*Limnocythere sancti-patricii* Brady and Robertson. Exterior of right valve, ×31. Same locality as Fig. 9
15.—*Cyprinotus unispinifera* Furtos. Exterior of left valve, ×31. Curray's Sta. 83 "at Km 11½ along same road [from Escuinapa] in narrow lagoon between well developed cheniers; surface of water covered with algal slime; salinity 91.7."
16a,b.—*Bairdia verdesensis* LeRoy. Right side of shell and interior of right valve, ×31. Sta. 67.
17.—*Bythocythere* sp. Exterior of left valve, ×31. Sta. 194.
18.—*Xiphichilus tenuissimum* (Norman). Exterior of left valve, ×31. Sta. 143.
19.—*Xestoleberis* cf. *setigera* Brady. Exterior of left valve, ×31. Sta. 102.
20.—*Paracypris pacifica* LeRoy. Exterior of right valve, ×21. Sta. 143.
21.—*Loxoconcha lenticulata* LeRoy. Exterior of left valve, ×31. Sta. 143.
22.—*Cytherois fischeri* Sars. Exterior of right valve, ×31. Sta. 143.
23.—*Pterygocythereis*?, n. sp. Exterior of right valve, ×31. Sta. 67.
24.—*Bradleya diegoensis* (LeRoy). Exterior of right valve, ×31. Sta. 102.
25a,b.—*Xestoleberis* cf. *aurantia* Baird. Exterior of left valve and interior of right valve, ×31. Sta. 67.
26.—*Xestoleberis* cf. *aurantia* Baird. Exterior of right valve, ×31. Sta. 143.
27.—*Loxocorniculum* sp. Exterior of left valve, ×31. Sta. 143.
28.—*Kangarina* aff. *K. chipolensis* Puri. Exterior of left valve, ×31. Sta. 143.
30.—*Bradleya diegoensis* (LeRoy). Exterior of right valve, ×21. Sta. 102.
31a,b.—*Puriana pacifica* Benson. Exterior of right valve and left valve, ×31. Sta. 67.
32.—*Bythocypris* sp., Exterior of right valve, ×31. Sta. 111.
33.—*Perissocytheridea*? sp. Exterior of left valve, ×31. Sta. 123.
34a,b.—*Cativella*, n. sp. *a*. Exterior of right valve, Sta. 102; *b*. exterior of intermediate instar right valve, ×31 Sta. 123
35.—*Cytheropteron*, n. sp. Exterior of right valve, ×31. Sta. 143.
36.—*Paracytheridea granti* LeRoy. Exterior of left valve, ×31. Sta. 119.
37.—*Orionina vaughani* (Ulrich and Bassler). Exterior of right valve, ×31. Sta. 119.
38.—*Costa* cf. *seminuda* Bold, n. sp. Exterior of right valve, ×21. Sta. 194.
39.—*Hermanites*? sp. Exterior of left valve, ×62. Sta. 67.
40.—*Cytherura*, n. sp. Exterior of left valve, ×31. Sta. 67.
41.—*Pterygocythereis* sp. Exterior of early instar right valve, ×31. Sta. 123.

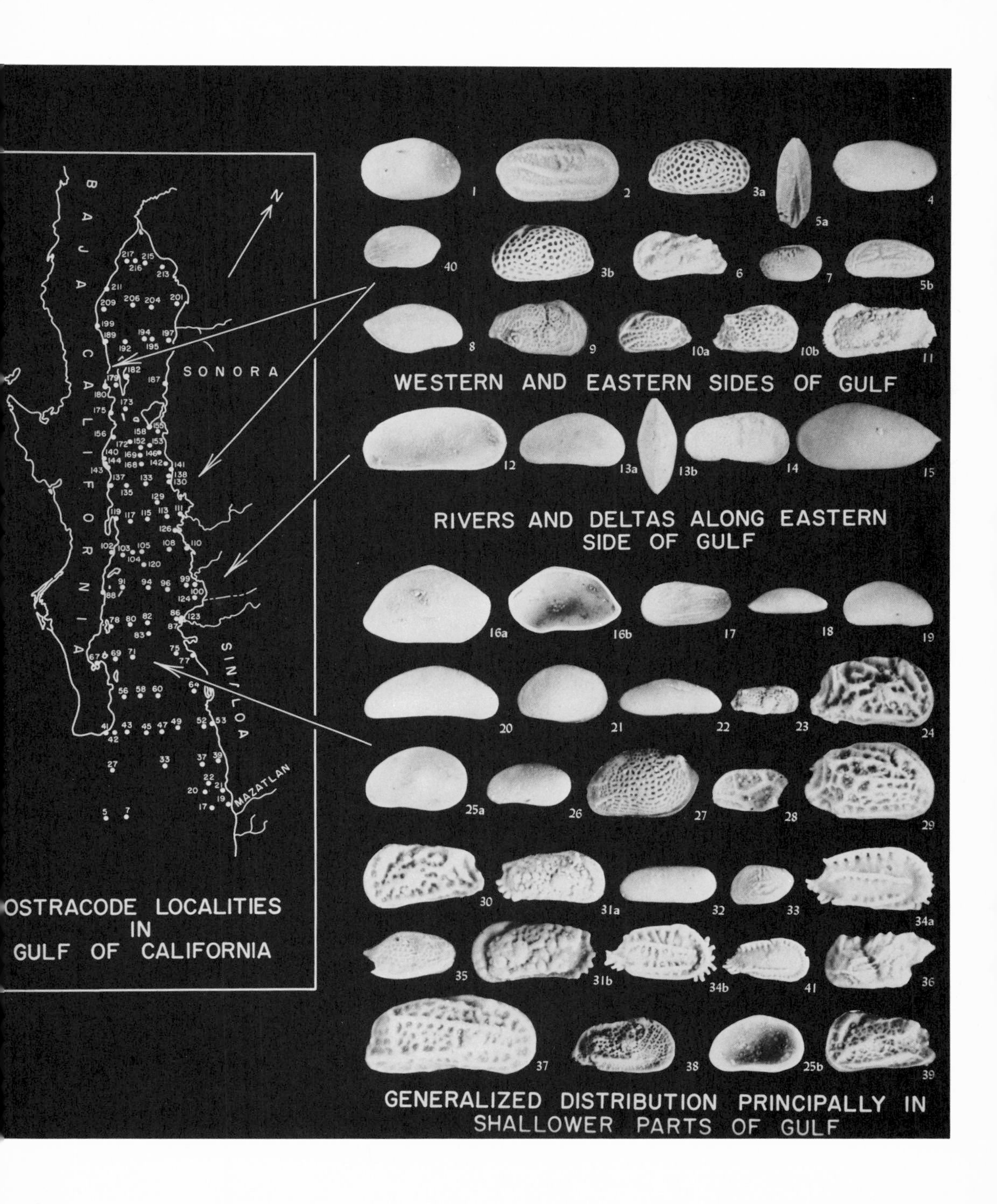

BAJA CALIFORNIA
SONORA
SINALOA
MAZATLAN
N
OSTRACODE LOCALITIES IN GULF OF CALIFORNIA
WESTERN AND EASTERN SIDES OF GULF
RIVERS AND DELTAS ALONG EASTERN SIDE OF GULF
GENERALIZED DISTRIBUTION PRINCIPALLY IN SHALLOWER PARTS OF GULF

**Puriana pacifica* Benson
Sclerochilus cf. *contortus* Norman
**Sclerochilus nasus* Benson
Trachyleberida?, n. sp.
**Xestoleberis* cf. *aurantia* Baird

Plate 1 shows some of the ostracodes of the Gulf of California. Published references on the Ostracoda of this general area include the following—Benson, 1959; Benson and Kaesler, 1963; Baker, 1912; Crouch, 1949; Herrick, 1887; Juday, 1906; LeRoy, 1943, 1945; Rothwell, 1944, 1948; Skogsberg, 1928, 1950.

REFERENCES

Benson, R. H., 1959, Ecology of Recent ostracodes of the Todos Santos Bay region, Baja California, Mexico, art. 1 *of* Univ. Kansas Paleont. Contr., Arthropoda: p. 1–80, pls. 1–11, figs. 1–20.

——— and Kaesler, R.L., 1963, Recent marine and lagoonal ostracodes from the Estero de Tastiota region, Sonora, Mexico (northeastern Gulf of California), art. 3 *of* Univ. Kansas Paleont. Contr., Arthropoda: p. 1–34, pls. 1–4, text figs. 1–20.

Baker, C.F., 1912, Notes on the Crustacea of Laguna Beach: Laguna Marine Lab., 1st Ann. Rept., Claremont, Calif.

Crouch, R. W., 1949, Pliocene Ostracoda from southern California: Jour. Paleontology, v. 23, p. 594–599.

Herrick, C. L., 1887, Contribution to the fauna of the Gulf of Mexico and the south: Denison Sci. Assoc. Mem., v. 1, p. 1–46.

Juday, C., 1906, Littoral forms, part 2 *of* Ostracoda of the San Diego region: Calif. Univ. Pub. Zool., v. 3, no. 9, p. 135–156.

LeRoy, L. W., 1943, Pleistocene and Pliocene Ostracoda of the coastal region of southern California: Jour. Paleontology, v. 17, p. 354–373.

——— 1945, A contribution to ostracodal ontogeny: Jour. Paleontology, v. 19, p. 81–86.

Rothwell, W.T., Jr., 1949, Preliminary ecological study of some Recent Pacific Ostracoda: Geol. Soc. America Bull., v. 55, p. 1470.

——— 1948, Distribution of living ostracodes, Newport Bay, California: Geol. Soc. America Bull., v. 59, p. 1380–1381.

Skogsberg, T., 1928, External morphology of the genus *Cythereis* with descriptions of twenty-one new species, part 2 *of* Studies of marine ostracoda: Calif. Acad. Sci. Proc., v. 15, p. 3–154.

——— 1950, Two new species of marine Ostracoda (Podocopa) from California: Calif. Acad. Sci. Proc., v. 26, p. 483–505.

PRELIMINARY REPORT ON RADIOLARIA IN RECENT SEDIMENTS OF THE GULF OF CALIFORNIA[1]

RICHARD N. BENSON[2]
Minneapolis, Minnesota

The Radiolaria of the Gulf of California have not been studied in detail although reference to their occurrence and abundance has been made by Bandy (1961), who included the Foraminifera in his analysis.

The writer, as part of a more comprehensive study, has analyzed the clay-free, HCl-insoluble residues of 28 sediment samples from the Gulf for their radiolarian content (Fig. 1). The results show an abundance of species, perhaps 200 or more, in the samples examined from the southern part of the Gulf which are, furthermore, particularly rich in individuals. The number of species is somewhat diminished in the middle and northern parts of the Gulf. Other noncalcareous components of the microfauna exclusive of diatoms and Radiolaria include silicoflagellates, a few microforaminifera, and sponge spicules, the last of which increase in abundance in nearshore areas.

The more than 100 species illustrated (Plates 1 and 2) are characteristic of the southern part of the Gulf. They, furthermore, are representative of many samples from the middle and northern parts of the Gulf where there are several species not yet found in the southern Gulf.

In stations studied from the southern Gulf—specifically Stations 27, 34, 46, 56, 60, 64, and 71—the spumelline Radiolaria predominate markedly over the nasselline forms in numbers of individuals. In the middle and northern parts of the Gulf the number of Radiolaria relative to other components of the sediment decreases and nasselline forms generally predominate over spumellines (Fig. 1). Such results, although at present only semiquantitative, are perhaps an indication of the more truly oceanic nature of the Spumellina relative to the Nassellina.

The nearshore parts of the Gulf are characterized not only by low total numbers of Radiolaria but also by a reduction in number of species. This may be due to ecological factors as well as to masking of the pelagic microfaunas by terrigenous sediments.

West of mid-Gulf many diatoms occur in the bottom sediments. The Radiolaria in that area, although diverse and more spinose in some individuals, seem to be represented by fewer species than in the southern Gulf.

A complete taxonomic and environmental analysis of the Gulf of California Radiolaria is

[1] Manuscript received, May 1, 1963.
Appreciation is expressed to W. Riedel, Tj.H. van Andel, and other staff members of the Scripps Institution of Oceanography for their assistance.

[2] Department of Geology, University of Minnesota.

EXPLANATION OF PLATE 1

FIGS. 10,16,21,28,29,34,36,45–47, ×95; FIGS. 20,52,55, ×140; FIGS. 30,31,42, ×65; other figures, ×130.

SUBORDER SPUMELLINA

FIGS. 1–4; 6–16 .... Superfamily Liosphaericae
5; 17–25 .... Superfamily Ellipsidiicae
26–47 .... Superfamily Cenodiscicae
48–61 .... Superfamily Laracariicae

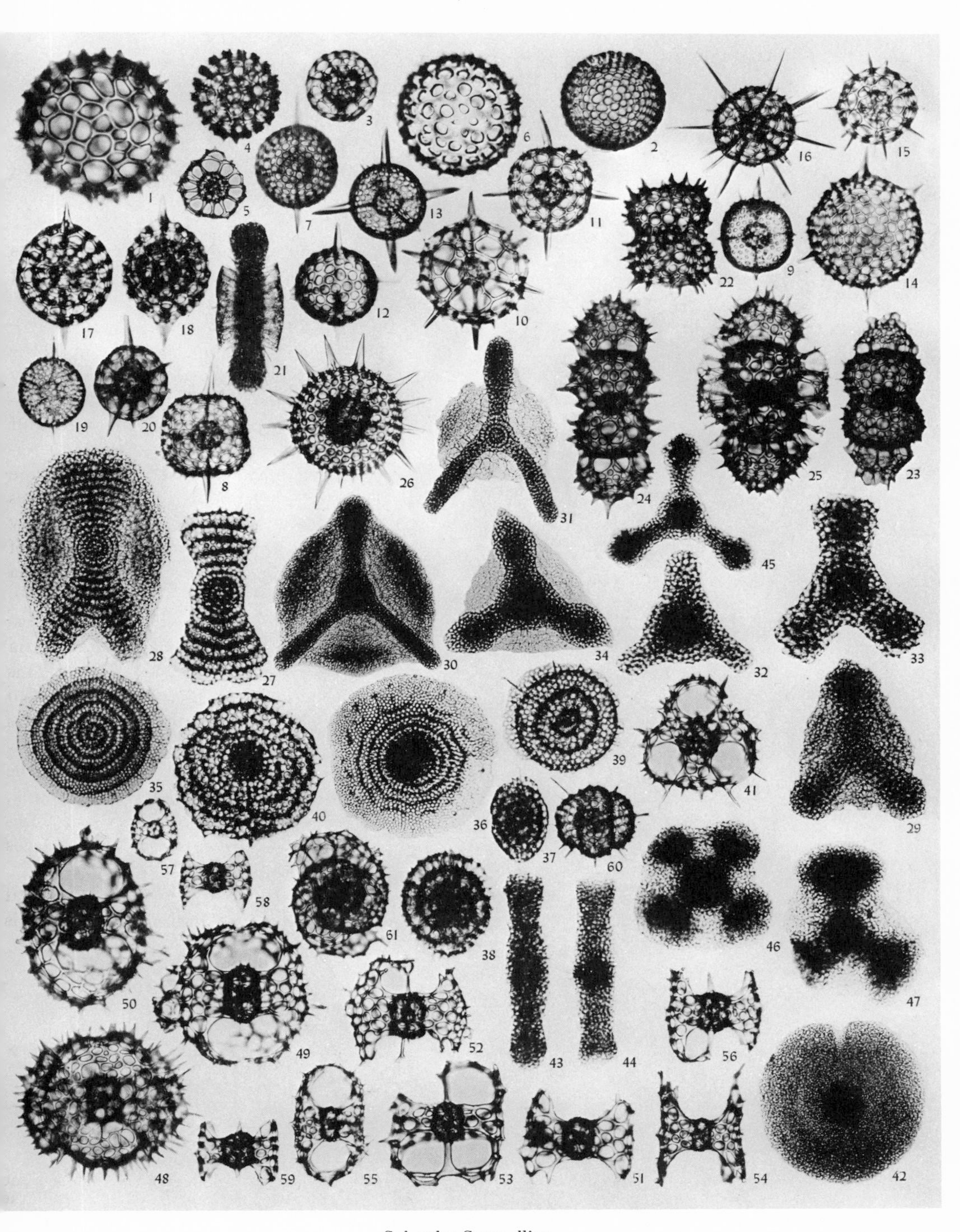

Suborder Spumellina

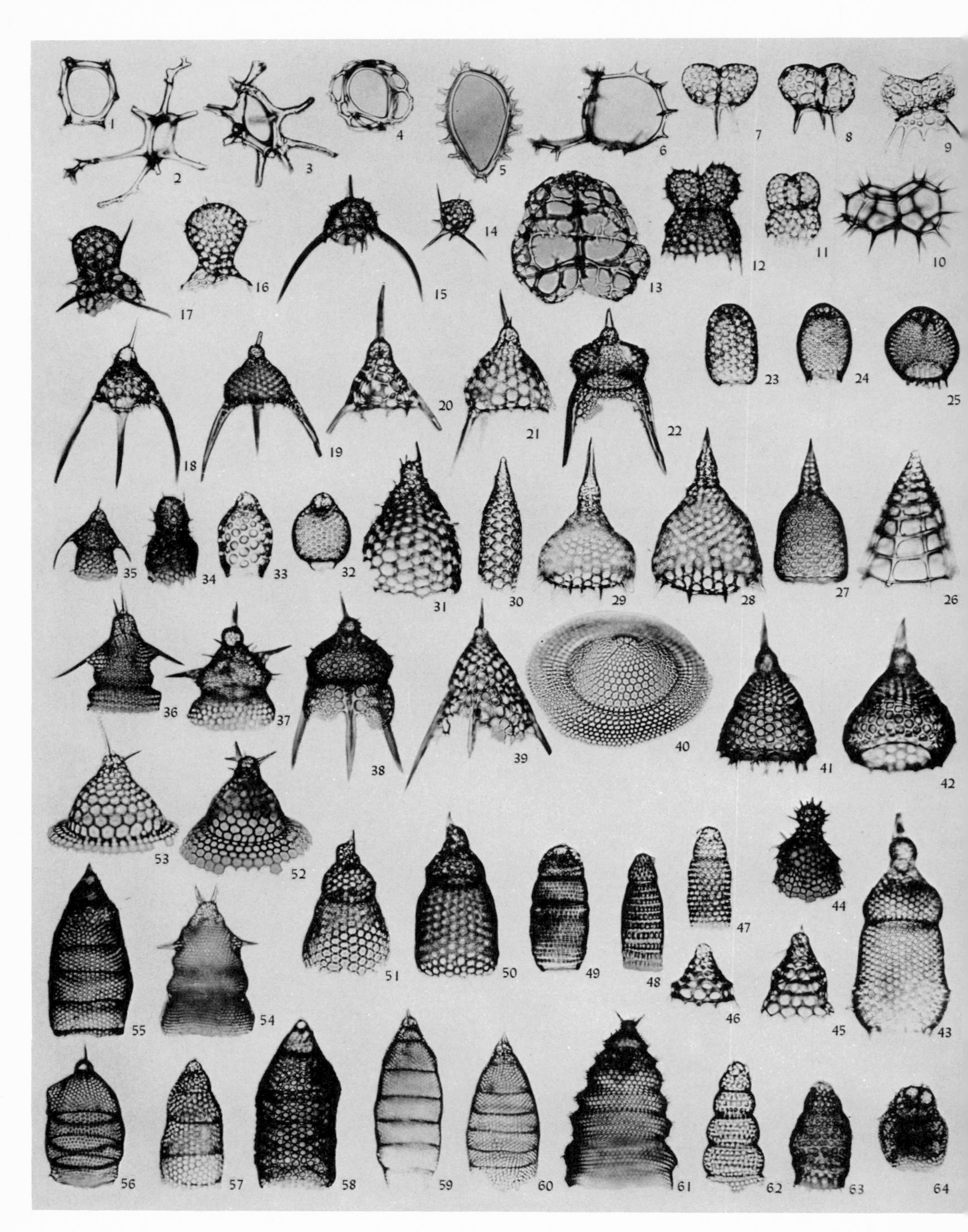

Suborder Nassellina

being made and will be presented later. For this reason only superfamily designation (Campbell, 1954) of the specimens has been made.

REFERENCES

Bandy, O.L., 1961, Distribution of Foraminifera, Radiolaria, and diatoms in sediments from the Gulf of California: Micropaleontology, v. 7, no. 1, p. 1–26, pls. 1–5.

Campbell, A.S., 1954, Protista 3, Protozoa (chiefly Radiolaria and Tintinnina), Pt. D *of* Treatise on invertebrate paleontology, Moore, R.C., ed.: Geol. Soc. America and Univ. Kans. Press, p. 11–163, text figs. 6–86.

(*Please turn the page for Figure 1.*)

←

EXPLANATION OF PLATE 2

FIGS. 19,39,41,42,61, ×95; other figures ×130.

SUBORDER NASSELLINA

FIGS. 1–6 . . . . Superfamily Stephaniicae
7–13 . . . . Superfamily Triospyridicae
14–63 . . . . Superfamily Archipiliicae
64 . . . . Superfamily Cannobotrydicae

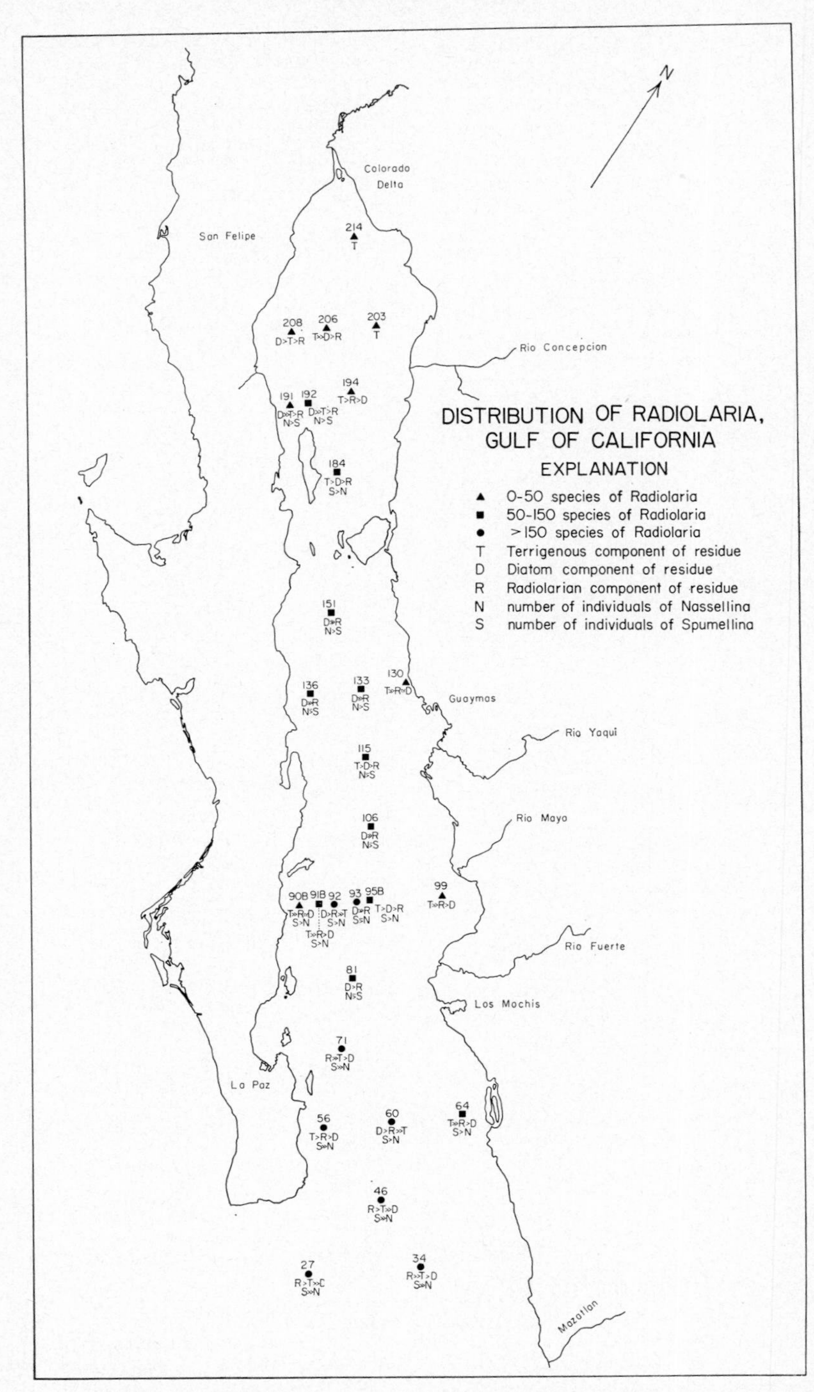

FIG. 1.—Distribution of Radiolaria in the Gulf of California.

INDEX[1]

A

abyssal assemblages, 358
  fauna, richness of, 368
Acaponeta Epidote province, 230, 234, 304
acoustic reflection profiling, 198
adiabatic temperature increase, 56, 57
age, lead-alpha, of Baja California batholith, 147
  radiometric, 12, 24
Agua Blanca fault, 15, 72, 127
Alarcon Seamount, 281, 288
Alegria Formation, 5, 9
Alisitos Formation, 5, 13, 14, 15
Allen, Clarence R., Biehler, S., and Kovach, R.L., 126–43
Allison, Edwin C., 3–29
Amphineura, 357
analyses, grain-size, 268, 269
  heavy-mineral, in deep-water Gulf sands, 282
  of heavy-mineral provinces, 302–305
Anita Formation, 5, 9
anomalies of Gulf sea level, 40
  gravity, 76, 132, 135, 138
Apache Formation, 5
Arcer (Sonic Profiler), 198, 200
  records, continental terrace, 205–207
  station locations, 201
Arena Canyon, 187
assemblages, faunal, in Gulf continental slope, 331–76
    determining factors, 359
    differences, northern and southern Gulf, 347
    of Pleistocene to Pliocene age, 359
    regional distribution map, 360
  heavy-mineral, 224, 226–30, 283
    grain-size, 231
    source areas, map, 227
asteroids, 351, 355, 357, 359

B

Bahía Sebastián Vizcaíno, sea floor adjacent to, 70
Baja California Amphibole association, 229, 230, 232, 233, 234, 305
  Augite association, 230, 233, 234, 305
  batholith, age of, 147
  Hypersthene association, 230, 232–34, 305
  hypothetical crustal structure, 153
  mineral associations, 230, 232–34, 305
  offset from mainland, 74, 88
  schematic diagram, 72
  Seamount province, 6, 11
  submarine topography of lower end, 157–92
  translation of, along strike-slip faults, 73
Ballenas Channel, 49, 86
bank deposits, in Gulf, 278
  composition of, table, 309–10

[1] Titles of papers are shown in capital and small capital letters.

Banning-Mission Creek fault, 21, 136
  aerial view of, 137
Barranca Group, 5, 23
basement complex, seismic velocity of, 97
basin and slope deposits, differences, 263
basin, northern and southern Gulf, faunal assemblages, 353, 358, 367, 368
basins of Gulf of California, location maps, 62, 221, 312
  other modern, comparisons, 295
  petrographic characteristics, 293
batholithic roots, 152, 154
BATHYMETRY AND FAULTS OF GULF OF CALIFORNIA, 59–75
  basins and shelves, map, 62
  chart, of Costa de Nayarit, 196
    of northern Gulf, 219
  features, general, 61
  rift, 72
  topographic profiles, 63
    provinces, map, 61
beach-dune ridges, Costa de Nayarit, 197
Bedford Canyon Formation, 5, 13
Benson, Richard N., 398–400
benthic fauna of oxygen-poor basins, 317
Biehler, Shawn, Kovach, R.L., and Allen, C.R., 126–43
biofacies, depth, 391
biogenous deposits of Gulf, 254, 267
biological samples, locations, 332, 334
  methods of collection and data processing, 333–35
Black Mountain Volcanics, 5, 14
Black Sea, stagnant waters and laminated sediments in, 323
BORDERING AREAS, GULF OF CALIFORNIA, GEOLOGY OF, 3–29—*see* GEOLOGY OF. . . .
Borrego Formation, 132
bottom oxygen concentrations and core structures, 319
  photographs of Gulf, 325–28
    location of stations, 320
  waters of Gulf, dissolved oxygen in, 339
    isotherms of, map, 342
    temperatures, abyssal stations, 358
Bouguer anomaly map, central Gulf, 85
boundaries, zoogeographic in Gulf, 343, 384, 389, 391
brachiopods, 357, 358
brackish water deltaic areas, ostracodes restricted to, 395
burrows on bottom, photo, 327

C

Cabrillo Seamount, 63, 66, 177, 179
California, Southern, basins, compared to Gulf, 259, 297, 323
    oxygen-poor, 319
Calvert, S.E., 311–30
camera stations, distribution of, 324
Candalaria Canyon, 179, 181, 192
  core, photo, 175
canyon heads, submarine contours, 178, 184

Cape San Lucas area, 158, 262, 340
  samples from, descriptive table, 159–67
  submarine topography, 168
carbonate content, Gulf sediments, 246, 296
  regional distribution, 249
carbon-clay content correlation in Gulf sediments, 257, 259
  /nitrogen ratios, Gulf sediments, 262
Cardonal Canyon, 169, 180, 181
  laminated formation from, photo, 182
Carmen Basin, 62, 68, 71, 220, 221, 312
  diatomaceous sediments in, 311
Central Gulf, 50, 61
  gravity contour map, 85
  province, topography of, 64
cephalopods, 357
Ceralbo Island, northeast slope, 190
  Trough, 124
charts, in pocket
  Bouguer anomaly map, Salton trough
  submarine canyons and troughs, southern end of Baja California
  submarine topography of Gulf of California
chubascos, 35
Clarion fracture zone, 11, 72, 152
clay- and diatom-rich laminae alternating in core, 314
  /carbon ratio, Gulf sediments, 257, 279
  organic carbon, relation to, 261
  /sand ratio, 280
  /water ratio, 248
climate of Gulf, influence of facies pattern, 294
Coachella Valley area, faulting in, 136
color of recent sediments, 246
Colorado River, 37, 391
  heavy-mineral associations, 229, 230, 233
    provinces, 231, 232, 302
  prodeltaic area, Ostracode species in, 395
  sediment composition, 226
Comondú Formation, 5, 18, 20, 148
composition of Gulf beach and nearshore sands, 224
  of deep-water sands and bank sediments, 309–310
  of heavy-mineral associations, 226, 228, 230
  of surface samples, 306–310
  petrographic, of Gulf facies, 289
computational methods, seismic work, 92
Concepción River heavy-mineral province, 229, 232, 303
    associations, 230, 233
Consag Rock, 21, 63, 64, 154
Continental Borderland province, 6, 11
  crust pulled apart, 88, 154
  shelf assemblages, 351–53, 366
    Quaternary history, 361
  slope assemblages, 355, 357, 358, 367, 368
  terrace, facies type distribution, 210, 211
    PLEISTOCENE DELTAIC PROGRADATION OF, COSTA DE NAYARIT, MEXICO, 193–215—*see* Costa de Nayarit
  structure, 209
    cross section, 211
contour map, bathymetry, northern Gulf, 219, 232
  gravity, 80, 85, 87
  sea-floor valleys, southern Gulf, 169, 170, 177, 178, 180, 181, 183, 184, 186, 187, 189, 190
cores, distribution of, in Gulf, 315, 316
  in Mohole test site, Baja California, 11
  in Sal Si Puedes Basin, 287
  in Tinaja Trough and San Lucas Canyon, 174–75
  laminated, 313
  lithologic variation in, 281
  lower peninsula, descriptions, 159–67
  structure and bottom oxygen concentrations, 319
  x-radiograph, Guaymas Basin, 329
correlation chart, outcrop stratigraphy, 147
  of events, continental terrace, Costa de Nayarit, 203
Costa de Hermosillo region, nearshore shelf environment, 348
  sediment distribution in, map, 338
COSTA DE NAYARIT, MEXICO, PLEISTOCENE DELTAIC PROGRADATION OF CONTINENTAL TERRACE, 193–215
  Arcer records, with facies interpretations, 205–207
  charts, 194, 196
  chronology, 207
  continental terrace structure, 209
  facies types, 210
  former position of shorelines, 204, 205–207
  regional geology and physiography, 195
  structural cross section, 211
cruises, hydrographic, of Gulf, chronological list, 31
crustaceans, 351, 355, 357, 358, 375, 376
crust, oceanic, southern Gulf, 87
  thickness in Gulf, 104, 112, 116, 120, 135
crustal columns in Gulf, compared to other areas, table, 84
  movement, regional uplift, 152
  schematic diagram, hypothetical, 153
  structure, 120, 150–51
Cucapa fault, 127
  aerial view, 140
Curray, Joseph R., and Moore, D.G., 193–215
Current, California, 55
currents, surface, 42, 344
  hydrodynamic aspects of, 42
  ship drift, 44–45
  speed and direction of, 43
  tidal, 38, 50, 64

D

dates, lead-alpha, 147, 298
  radiocarbon, 208, 298
  radiometric, 12, 24
Dead Sea rift, compared with Salton trough, 141
deep-water sands in Gulf, 278
  composition of, 309–310
  cores from, 278, 279
  deposition discussed, 288
  heavy-mineral associations in, 282, 283
  regional distribution, 279, 284
  size-frequency distribution, 286
  sources of, 283
Delfin Basin, 62, 64, 71, 220, 312
deposition of benthonic Foraminifera, rates of, 392
depositional facies in Gulf, 288
  control of, by geologic setting, 292
  petrographic composition of, 289
  regional distribution, 290
depositional terraces, 209
depth biofacies, 391
  distributions of Foraminifera, 384, 388, 391
Depth Recorder, Precision, 60
depths, great, hydrographic conditions at, 56

diatom- and clay-rich laminae, alternating, in core, 314
Diatomaceous Sediments in Gulf of California, Factors Affecting Distribution of, 311–30
diatomite, 9, 182, 251
diatoms, 311, 335, 362
  distribution in Gulf, 256
dike swarms, 10, 72
dispersal of Gulf sediments, 223, 244
displacement along faults, 73
dissolved oxygen, distribution in Gulf, 47–58, 318, 321–23, 339
distribution, depth, of Foraminifera, 384, 388, 391
  of Laminated Diatomaceous Sediments in Gulf of California, Factors Affecting, 311–30
  of sediment cores from Guaymas and San Pedro Martir Basins, 315
Drammens Fjord, stagnant waters and laminated sediments in, 323

E

earthquakes, 128, 129, 138, 155
East Pacific Rise, 88, 112, 142, 146, 149, 152, 153
Eastern Cordillera, transverse features of, 10
echinoids, 355, 359
Ecology and Zoogeography of Macro-Invertebrates of Gulf of California and Continental Slope of Western Mexico, 331–76—*see* Zoogeography. . . .
Elsinore fault, 21, 68, 72, 127, 139
environment, abyssal, 358
environment, basin, northern Gulf, 356
  intermediate shelf, 352
  nearshore shelf, Costa de Hermosillo, 348–50
  outer shelf on sand bottom, 354
  regional distribution, map, 360
  species characteristic of, 371–75
environmental parameters, 333, 359
Erben Guyot, 7, 11
escarpments—*see* scarps
Espada Formation, 5, 8
Eugenia Formation, 5, 14
evaporation from Gulf, 31
Evolution and Structural History of Gulf of California, 144–56

F

facies control by geologic setting, 292
  depositional, in Gulf, 288
Factors Affecting Distribution of Laminated Diatomaceous Sediments in Gulf of California, 311–30
Farallón Basin, 62, 68, 71, 125, 220, 221, 312
  Canyon, 192
Faults and Bathymetry of Gulf of California, 59–75—*see* Bathymetry. . .
  and faulting, 25, 68–74, 88, 139, 191
  Baja California, schematic diagram, 72
  displacement along, 73
  of Little San Bernardino Mtns., 139
  parallel to coast line, 88
  translation of Baja California along, 73
  valleys, sea floor, 191
fauna, benthic, of oxygen-poor basins, 317
faunal assemblages—*see* assemblages, faunal
  boundaries, foraminiferal, 384, 389, 391
  lists, 346–59, 375–78, 382–84, 395–97
  mixing, Caribbean and Pacific, 363
feeding types, macro-invertebrates, 359, 362, 363
Fisher, Robert L., and Rusnak, G.A., 144–56
  Rusnak, G.A., and Shepard, F.P., 59–75
flowing sand, submarine, 171, 172
fluctuations, sea-level, 16, 207–209
Foraminifera, dead populations of, 391
  living benthonic, depth distributions, 384, 388, 391
  Living Benthonic, Patterns of, Gulf of California, 377–94
    faunal boundaries, 384, 389, 391
    geographic distributions, 389, 391
    occurrences of, 386, 387
    sampling stations, locations, 381, 382
    size of living population, 384
    species of, 379, 382–84
    /total population ratios, 393
  nearshore, in basal transgressive sands, 291
  regional distribution map, 258
  standing crops of, 390
Franciscan Formation, 5, 8
fresh-water deltaic areas, ostracodes restricted to, 395
Fuerte Canyon, 188, 189, 192
  River, 390

G

Garlock fault, 7, 10
gastropods, 346–57, 375, 376
geographic restriction of Foraminifera, 389
geologic map of Gulf region, 225
Geology of Areas Bordering Gulf of California, 3–29
  formation names, correlation, 5
  physiographic provinces, map, 6
  setting, 5
Geophysical Framework of Northern End of Gulf of California Structural Province, 126–43
  en-echelon fault pattern, Salton trough, 141, 142
  gravity interpretations, 135
  regional comparisons and problems, 140
  rocks of, 128
  seismic refraction profiles, 130
    cross sections, 133, 134
  tectonic framework, 127
glauconite, in recent sediments, 250, 253, 262
Glen Canyon Group, 23
Gorda Canyon, 177, 178
graben, 25, 149, 154
  en-echelon, 68, 70
grain size and sorting, relation between, 270
  distribution in Gulf sediments, 268
  longitudinal variation of, 278
  regional distribution, 271
gravity and topographic profiles across Gulf, 81, 83, 133, 134
  Anomalies in Gulf of California, 76–89
    contour maps, 80, 85, 87
    data interpretation, 79, 135
    maximum, 82, 138
    measurements, positions of, 77, 78
    minimum, 132, 141
Guadalupe River, Texas, 390
Guaymas Basin, 62, 65, 67, 72, 220, 221, 312, 315
  bottom photographs, 325–28
  camera station locations in, 324

diatomaceous sediments in, 311
dissolved oxygen in, 317, 318, 320–23
X-radiograph of cores from, 329
Gulf of 'Aqaba, 141
Gulf of California, Bathymetry and Faults of, 59–75—*see* Bathymetry...
Diatomaceous Sediments in, Factors Affecting Distribution of, 311–30
Geology of Areas Bordering, 3–29—*see* Geology...
Gravity Anomalies in, 76–89—*see* Gravity....
Magnetic Profiles Across, 122–25
northern and southern, difference between, 117, 347
Oceanographic Aspects of, 30–58—*see* Oceanographic...
origin of, 25, 74
Ostracoda from, 395–97
Recent Marine Sediments of, 216–310—*see* Recent...
rift, 72
Sea-Floor Valleys of, 157–192—*see* Sea-Floor...
Seismic Refraction Studies in, 90–121—*see* Seismic...
Structural History and Evolution of, 144–56—*see* Structural...
Province, Northern End, Geophysical Framework of, 126–43—*see* Geophysical...
submarine topography of, map, 380
trough, 19
Zoogeography and Ecology of Macro-Invertebrates of Gulf of California and Continental Slope of Western Mexico, 331–76—*see* Zoogeography...
Gulf of Suez, 141

H

half-graben, 25
Hardy River, 391
Harrison, J.C., and Mathur, S.P., 76–89
heat-flow measurements, of Gulf, 112, 113, 128, 149
heavy-mineral associations in Gulf, 227
composition, average, and variability of, 230
of beach and nearshore sands, 224
of Colorado River sediments, 226
of deep-water sands, 282
of eastern Gulf, 228, 229
provinces in Gulf, analyses, 302–305
location map, central and southern Gulf, 234
regional distribution of, 229, 232
hexacorals, 349, 357, 358
Hilde, Thomas W.C., 122–25
holothurians, 357, 358
homogenization of sediments, 320
Honda Formation, 5, 8
Hugh M. Smith Expedition, 313, 316, 322
hurricanes, 33, 35, 36
hydrographic conditions in Gulf, at great depth, 56
hypersaline lagoons, 390

I

Imperial fault, 21, 68, 127, 129
Formation, 5, 19, 20, 21, 128
index groups of assemblages, nearshore environment, Costa de Hermosillo, 348
intertidal rocky shores faunal assemblage, 344, 345, 346
sand beach and sand flats faunal assemblage, 346, 361
Isidro Formation, 5, 17
isostatic equilibrium in Gulf, 149
isotherms, bottom-water, of Gulf, 342

J

Jalama Formation, 5, 8
Julian Schist, 12

K

Kino Bay province, 230, 233, 234, 303
Kovach, Robert L., Biehler, S., and Allen, C.R., 126–43

L

lagoon, low-salinity, faunal assemblages, 347, 361
lagoons, hypersaline, 390
Laguna Salada fault, 68, 139
lamellibranchs, 346–58
laminated sediments and stagnant waters, correlation between, 323
distribution of, 320
water depth of, 317
La Paz Basin, 62, 66, 220, 221, 312
fault, 74
layer thicknesses and seismic velocities, 93, 94, 106, 107, 109–11
light-mineral fraction, composition, 235
lineaments, graben-and-horst, 154
identified as faults, 69
lithofacies, recent sediments in Gulf, 245
distribution of, 253
Little San Bernardino Mtns., faults of, 139
Living Benthonic Foraminifera, Gulf of California, Patterns of, 377–94—*see* Foraminifera...
Los Frailes Canyon, 182, 183, 184

M

macro-invertebrates, assemblages and environments, 344
common, ranges of, 343
species, characteristic in Gulf, check-list, 371–75
Zoogeography and Ecology of Gulf of California and Continental Slope of Western Mexico, 331–76—*see* Zoogeography...
magnetic and topographic profiles across southern Gulf, 124
Profiles Across Gulf of California, 122–25
survey, ship track of, 123
Malo Jezero Bay, stagnant waters and laminated sediments of, 323
Mandelbaum, E.C., Swain, F.M., and Miller, P.L., 395–97
mangrove and mud flats assemblage, 347, 361
Maniobra Formation, 5, 20
Mar Bermejo, 1
Martinez Formation, 5, 8
Mathur, S.P., and Harrison, J.C., 76–89
Mazatlán Amphibole association, 230
Basin, 62, 71, 220, 221
meteorological aspects of Gulf, 31
mica, regional distribution, 240
mid-Atlantic ridge, 88
Middle America trench, 60, 91, 149, 152
Mid-Gulf, seismic studies in, 105
sediment fill in, 108
thickness of crust, 108

Miller, P.L., Swain, F.M., and Mandelbaum, E.C., 395–97
Mississippi River, 390
model, composite, structural framework of Gulf, 212
earthquake, 155
facies, depositional, 299
modes, grain-size, Gulf, regional distribution, 271
Moenkopi Formation, 23
Mohole test, cores from, 11
Mohorovičić discontinuity, 88
depth to, in Gulf, 120
monoplacophorans, 357, 358
Monterey Formation, 17
Moore, David G., and Curray, J.R., 193–215
morphology, of Gulf, 61, 218
Morrison Formation, 23
mottles, in Gulf, 278, 279, 288
regional distribution, 279
Murray fracture zone, 6, 7, 11, 152

N

nearshore sand and sand-mud faunal assemblage, 347, 363, 375, 376
nitrogen/carbon ratios, Gulf sediments, 262
Northern Gulf, 47, 61, 271, 335
basement of, 104
gravity data interpretation, 86
province, topography of, 64
stations, sediment fill in, 104
seismic refraction studies of, 94–105
velocity and layer thicknesses at, 93–94
nudibranchs, 358
nutrients, 390

O

Obsidian Buttes area, gravity anomaly over, 138
oceanic character, central and southern Gulf, 149
OCEANOGRAPHIC ASPECTS OF GULF OF CALIFORNIA, 30–58
hydrographic conditions at great depths, 56
cruises, chronological list, 31
stations occupied, 1956–61, map, 32
meteorological aspects, 31
surface currents, 42
tides and sea level in, 37
vertical distribution of properties in, 47
octocorals, 355, 357, 358
Okhotsk Sea, analogous to Gulf, 359
opal, 267, 295, 311
regional distribution of, 252
ophiuroids, 351, 357, 359
organic carbon content of recent marine sediments in Gulf and other basins, 259
carbon-nitrogen correlation, 262
matter, in recent sediments, 257
production rates, 390
organisms, burrowing, absent in oxygen-minimum zone, 321
Orinoco shelf sediments, 295
Ostracoda, faunal plates, 396
FROM GULF OF CALIFORNIA, 395–97
outbuilding terraces, 211
oxygen concentrations, bottom, 335
and core stuctures, table, 319
in deep water, southern Gulf, 340
on continental shelf, 340
oxygen, dissolved, distribution in Gulf, 47–58, 317
in bottom waters, 339
in Guaymas and San Pedro Martir Basins, 321–23
level and sediment structure, correlation, 319
minimum, 54, 267, 295, 323, 335, 339, 340, 363
absence of burrowing organisms in, 321
an impoverished area, 317
in eastern tropical Pacific, 317, 330
not azoic, 320

P

Pacific Coastal Plain province, 22, 145
Palm Springs Formation, 21
Palmas Bay Canyons, 186, 187
Panamic-Pacific zoogeographic province, 379, 390
Parker, Robert H., 331–76
PATTERNS OF LIVING BENTHONIC FORAMINIFERA, GULF OF CALIFORNIA, 377–94—*see* FORAMINIFERA. . .
Patton Escarpment, 7, 12
pelecypods, 376
Peninsular Range batholith, 12, 14, 15, 20
Peninsular Ranges province, 6, 12, 15
Pescadero Basin, 62, 68, 71, 108, 124, 220, 221, 312
Canyon, 186, 187
petrographic characteristics of individual basins, 293
compared to other basins, 297
Phillips, Richard P., 90–121
Phleger, Fred B, 377–94
photographs, bottom, of Gulf, 325–28
locations of stations, 320
physiographic provinces of Gulf area, 5–24
location map, 6
place names of Gulf area, map, 336
plankton blooms, 263, 266, 340, 341, 390
plastic flow, 88, 89
PLEISTOCENE DELTAIC PROGRADATION OF CONTINENTAL TERRACE, COSTA DE NAYARIT, MEXICO, 193–215 —*see* COSTA DE NAYARIT
Pleistocene-Pliocene faunal assemblages, described, 359–68
Pogonophora, 358
Point Arena, valleys off, 185, 186, 192
polychaetes, 353, 358
Poway Formation, 5, 16
precipitation in Gulf, 31, 33, 34
Precision Depth Recorder, 60
PREFACE, 1
prehistoric shell middens, 361
PRELIMINARY REPORT ON RADIOLARIA IN RECENT SEDIMENTS OF THE GULF OF CALIFORNIA, 398–400
profiles across Gulf, 81, 83, 124
prosobranchs, 346, 347
provinces, heavy-mineral, 229–35
morphological, 61–68
physiographic, 5–24
"pull apart" of rock plates, 154
Pulmo Canyon, 185
pulmonates, 347
pycnogonids, 357, 358

Q

"quartz diorite line," 147
Quaternary history, continental shelf, 361

R

radiocarbon dates, 208, 298
Radiolaria, figured, 398, 399

in Recent Sediments of Gulf of California, Preliminary Report on, 398–400
regional distribution, 255, 400
ranges of common macro-invertebrates, 343
rates of deposition, benthonic Foraminifera, 392
rates of Gulf sedimentation, 296
compared with other areas, 298
Recent Marine Sediments of Gulf of California, 216–310
biogenous deposits, 254, 267
comparison with other modern basins, 295
deep-water sands and bank deposits, 278
depositional facies, 288
control by geologic setting, 292
grain-size distribution, 268
heavy-mineral associations, 227
maps showing, 232, 234
provinces, distribution of, 229
light-mineral fraction, composition, 235
lithofacies, 245
morphology, 218
organic matter, 257
source and dispersal of sediments, 223
texture and internal waves in, 276
red detritals, regional distribution, 242
Red Sea, an analagous area, 88, 125, 141, 149
"red tide," 390
relief, degree of, Gulf floor, 222
rhombic basin origin, 66
rift, Gulf of California, 72
between continental blocks, 149
valleys, 140
Rincon Formation, 5, 9
ripple marks, at 1,000 fathoms, photograph, 173, 174
rivers, chemical composition of, 37
discharge of, 37
Roden, Gunnar I., 30–58
Rosario Formation, 5, 15
runoff for drainage areas, Gulf, table, 226
Rusnak, Gene A., and Fisher, R.L., 144–56
Fisher, R.L., and Shepard, F.P., 59–75

S

Salado Canyon, 183, 195
salinity of Gulf, 46, 47–58, 344
Sal si Puedes Basin, 62, 64, 65, 220, 221, 312
fault, 72
Saltito Canyon, 183, 185
Salton trough, 130–34, 140
compared with Dead Sea rift, 141
regional anomaly, 135
seismicity, 128, 129
thickness of sediments, 136
San Andreas fault system, 20, 68, 72, 88, 127, 136, 152
strike-slip movement of, 21, 73
San Clemente Rift valley, 191
San Diego Formation, 5, 19
San Fernando Formation, 5, 13
San Gregorio Formation, 5, 17
San Hipólito Formation, 5, 14
San Ignacio Canyon, 188, 189, 192
San Jacinto earthquake of 1918, 128
fault, 21, 68, 127, 128, 138
vertical air view, 130
San José Canyon, 177, 192
fan valley outside, 180
head of, 178
San Lucas Amphibole association, 230, 233, 234, 305
Canyon, 168, 169
cores from, 175
gradient of, 172
head of, 170
photo, angular granitic rocks, 176
ripple? marks in 1,000 fm, 173
San Pedro Martir Basin, 62, 220, 221, 312, 315
camera station localities in, 324
diatomaceous sediments in, 311
oxygen distribution in, 322
San Rafael Group, 23
uplift, 7
sand, flowing, 168
photo, 171, 172
sands, deep-water—*see* deep-water sands
types, regional distribution, 239
Santa Barbara Basin, 340
Santa Cruz Hypersthene association, 230
Santa Lucia Escarpment, 7
Santa María Canyon, 169, 173, 174, 177
Santa Monica Slate, 5, 8
Santa Rosalía fault, 72, 221
Santiago Augite province, 234, 304
Canyon, 187
Peak Volcanics, 5, 14
Santillán Formation, 14
scaphopods, 355, 357, 358
scarps, 61, 65, 71, 85, 122, 188, 190
Sea-Floor Valleys of Gulf of California, 157–92
cores from, 175
heads of canyons, contours, 170, 178, 184
origin of, 191
photographs, 171–73, 176, 182
sample locations and descriptions, 159
sea level, 37
anomalies, 40
at tide-gage stations, 41
past fluctuations, 16, 204, 207–209
Seamount province, Baja California, 6, 11
seamounts, 63, 66, 122
Sebastián Vizcaíno fault, 74
sediment fill, in Gulf, 104, 108, 112
sediment structure, distribution of, in Gulf, 316
and oxygen level, correlation, 319
minor, 251, 320
sediments, Gulf, distribution of, 247, 337
in Costa de Hermosillo area, 338
Sediments, Laminated Diatomaceous, in Gulf of California, Factors Affecting, 311–30
sedimentation, rates of, in Gulf, 296
compared with other areas, 298
seismic refraction profiles, Salton trough, 130
Refraction Studies in Gulf of California, 90–121
results, 92
sections, 118, 119, 133, 134
stations, 91
travel-time plots, 95–102
velocities and layer thicknesses, 93, 94, 106, 107, 109–11, 120
seismicity, Salton trough, 128, 129
Sespe Formation, 5, 9
shelf faunal assemblages, 351, 352, 353, 366

nearshore, environment, 348
shelf-break, 203, 204, 219
ancient, in Gulf, 206
origin and significance, 213
shell middens, prehistoric, 361
shelves and basins, locations, 221
Shepard, Francis P., 157–92
Rusnak, G.A., and Fisher, R.L., 59–75
ship drift currents, 44–45
Shor, George G., Jr., and van Andel, Tj.H., 1
shorelines, fluctuating, 16, 203, 207–209, 212
shrimps, found in oxygen minimum zones, 319
Sierra Blanca Formation, 5, 8
Sierra Madre Occidental province, 6, 22, 24
silica, biogenous, in recent Gulf sediments, 248
replinishment from Pacific, 266
Sinaloa Canyon, 188, 189
-Nayarit heavy-mineral province, 230, 233, 234, 304
size and sorting, Gulf sediments, 268, 285
-frequency sediment distribution in Gulf, 272, 277, 286
of arkose and graywacke, 237
slope and basin deposits in Gulf, major differences, 262, 263
soil extract, 390
solenogasters, 357
Sonoprobe records, 198, 200, 201, 202
station locations, 201
Sonoran Desert province, 6, 22, 145
sorting and grain size in Gulf, relation between, 270, 285
source and dispersion of Gulf sediments, 223, 228–45
map, 244
source areas, heavy-mineral assemblages, 227
Southern Gulf, 53, 61
gravity data, 79
contour map, 80
oceanic crust of, 87
province, submarine topography of, 66
Split Mountain Formation, 21
sponges, 355
standing crops of Foraminifera, 390
stations, foraminiferal sampling, 381, 382
stratigraphy, bordering areas of Gulf, 3–29
of Peninsular Range province, 12
strike-slip faults, 73, 153, 192
STRUCTURAL HISTORY AND EVOLUTION OF GULF OF CALIFORNIA, 144–56
correlation chart, outcrop stratigraphy, 147
evolution of, 152, 153
physiographic provinces, 145
cross sections, 146
regional setting, 144
structural map, central Gulf section, 85
model of Gulf, 149
sections across Gulf, showing gravity profiles, 83
structure, crustal, 150–51
schematic diagram, hypothetical, 153
sediment and oxygen level, correlation, 319
subcrustal welt, 154
submarine fans in Gulf, 223
sandfall, 171, 172
topography, Baja California Seamount province, 6
Cape San Lucas area, 168
surface currents, 42, 344
speed and direction of, 43
Swain, F.M., Miller, P.L., and Mandelbaum, E. C., 395–97

T

tectibranchs, 347
tectonic framework, Northern Gulf province, 127
terraces, 209
temperature, air, in Gulf, 31, 33, 34
bottom water, abyssal stations, 358
water, at 10 m depth, 46
at sea surface, 41, 47–58
near bottom, 340, 342
tension, over crests and flanks, subcrustal welt, 154
perpendicular to axis, 88
tensional stress, 72
textural diagram, showing sediments from different areas, 246
types, regional distribution in Gulf, 247
texture and internal waves in Gulf sediments, 276
of Gulf recent sediments, 245
of Gulf surface samples, 306–10
thrusting, large-scale, of continental crustal plates, 153–55
Tiburón Basin, 62, 64, 220, 312
tidal constants, table, 38
currents, 38, 50, 64
mixing, 46, 50, 340, 344
tides, 37, 39
tilting and drift, 154
Tinaja Trough, 174, 175, 179, 181
fault origin of, 191
Topanga Formation, 18
topographic profiles, Gulf shelf edge, 220
scarps, 88
topography and magnetic anomalies, relation, southern Gulf, 122–25
Tortugas Formation, 5, 17
trans-Mexico volcanic belt, 11
transportation and deposition of northern Gulf sediments, 274
transverse features, Eastern Cordillera, 10
pattern, sediment transportation, 223, 245
Transverse Ranges, Eastern, 9
structural trend, 6–11, 12, 18, 128, 142
Western, 7–9
travel-time plots, Northern Gulf stations, 95–102
Tres Virgenes volcano, 18
Trinidad Canyon, 187
Truckhaven Rhyolite, 5, 20
turbidites, minor role in Gulf, 296

U

upbuilding terraces, 211
uplift, regional, main crustal movement, 152
upwelling, 47, 51, 53, 263, 340
areas of, map, 341
of nutrient-rich water, 390

V

Valle Salitral Formation, 5, 14
valleys, landslide, 192
sea-floor, origin, of, 191
van Andel, Tj.H., 216–310
and Shor, George G., Jr., 1
Vaqueros Formation, 5, 9
variability, heavy-mineral associations in Gulf, 230
velocities and layer thicknesses in Gulf, tables, 93, 94, 106, 107, 109–11

Vermilion Sea Expedition, 1, 31, 76, 90, 311
Vigia Canyon, 169, 176, 181
Vinorama Canyon, 183, 185
volcanic glass, regional distribution of, 243
  islands, anomalies associated with, 122
volcanism, in Gulf, 9, 11, 18, 148

W

water and clay content, in Gulf, relation between, 248
waters, stagnant, and laminated sediments, 323
  temperature, at bottom abyssal stations, 358
    near bottom, 340, 342
wave-base, concept of, 214
waves, tidal, 38
western Gulf margin, Ostracoda species, 395
winds in Gulf, 33
  speed, 35
worms, 320, 325, 326

X

X-radiograph of cores, Guaymas Basin, 329

Y

Yaqui heavy-mineral province, 230, 233, 234, 303
  River, 390

Z

zoogeographic boundaries, 343, 384, 389, 391
ZOOGEOGRAPHY AND ECOLOGY OF MACRO-INVERTEBRATES OF GULF OF CALIFORNIA AND CONTINENTAL SLOPE OF WESTERN MEXICO, 331–76
  biological sample locations, 332, 334
  descriptions of assemblages and environments, 344
  faunal lists, 346–59, 371–76